AN INTRODUCTION TO *Modern Philosophy*

THE MACMILLAN COMPANY
NEW YORK · CHICAGO
DALLAS · ATLANTA · SAN FRANCISCO

THE MACMILLAN COMPANY
OF CANADA, LIMITED
TORONTO

AN INTRODUCTION TO *Modern Philosophy*

IN SIX PHILOSOPHICAL PROBLEMS

by ALBUREY CASTELL PROFESSOR OF PHILOSOPHY · UNIVERSITY OF OREGON

NEW YORK · *The Macmillan Company*

PRINTED IN THE UNITED STATES OF AMERICA
Published January, 1943
Fourteenth Printing 1953

To my friend and colleague,
Joseph Warren Beach

There is nothing more wholesome for us than to find problems that quite transcend our powers.

— Charles Peirce to William James, 1905

ACKNOWLEDGMENTS

A good portion of this book has been made possible only by the generosity of publishers who have graciously permitted the author to quote or paraphrase from works which they held in copyright. This debt of gratitude the author acknowledges to the following: Longmans Green, for permission to select from the writings of William James; The Macmillan Company, for permission to select from their translation of Kant; Harcourt Brace, for permission to select from Vaihinger's "Philosophy of the As If"; Charles Scribner's, for permission to select from the writings of George Santayana; and A. A. Knopf, for permission to select from Spengler's "Decline of the West." Only one who has wielded scissors and paste-pot can realize how co-operative and helpful publishers can be.

When this book was submitted for publication, it was reported on by persons unknown to the author. To the writers of these reports, especially the report which was so hard to take, the author wishes to acknowledge his gratitude. These "anonymous evaluators" are a marvellous institution, as anyone must realize, who has felt their praise or their censure.

To students who helped to make this book, by registering for "Phil I"; to colleagues who helped to make this book by patiently using it in mimeographed form; to its publishers who have put up with apparently endless delays, my sincere thanks!

ALBUREY CASTELL

MINNEAPOLIS, MINNESOTA
December, 1942

110

74 93
118

184

TABLE OF CONTENTS

AN INTRODUCTION TO *Modern Philosophy*

INTRODUCTION. AN ACCOUNT OF THIS BOOK

I

This book contains readings and comments on six philosophical problems. The problems, in the order presented here, are these: a problem in theology, a problem in metaphysics, a problem in epistemology, a problem in ethics, a problem in political theory, and a problem in philosophy of history. These somewhat academic expressions refer to very simple ideas.

1. *Theology* is the inquiry into the existence and nature of God. The term is derived from two Greek words meaning "God" and "discourse on." Within the general field of theology there are many problems. Of these, some are philosophical, some are not. Among those which are, attention is directed to the following: From our knowledge of the nature of things, is it possible to infer the existence of God? If not, why not? If so, can we go further and infer any of His attributes? If so, which? The attempt to answer these questions is called *natural* theology. It is to be distinguished from *revealed* theology on the one hand, and *mystical* theology on the other. With reference to the central problems of natural theology, we examine the views of Thomas Aquinas, Blaise Pascal, David Hume, John Stuart Mill, and William James.

2. *Metaphysics* is the inquiry into the nature of ultimate reality and the categories in terms of which it may be most fittingly described. The derivation of the word is curiously

accidental. Among the writings of the Greek philosopher, Aristotle, is a treatise in which he has analyzed the meanings of some terms in Greek physics. This treatise was lost after his death, and recovered by a later scholar. It bore no title. Seeing the intended connection between this nameless monograph and Aristotle's general account of physics, the discoverer bestowed upon it the rather laconic title, *ta-meta-ta-phusika*, which is simply the Greek for "placed after the physics," the word *meta* meaning "after." The treatise became Aristotle's *metaphysics*. The problems with which he dealt, together with associated problems added by subsequent philosophers, came gradually to form the field of metaphysics. Now, this field is large, and its problems exceedingly abstract. From among them, attention is directed to the following: If we admit the distinction between a "reality" and its "appearances," if we hold that things in *reality* are so-and-so, whereas they *appear* to be otherwise, then what is this reality? And what is the relation between this reality and its appearances? For instance, it is possible these days to read that everything is "really" energy. This, however, is not what things appear to be. And what of energy? Is it, in turn, "really" something else? If so, what? With reference to this particular metaphysical problem we examine the views of René Descartes, Thomas Hobbes, George Berkeley, Arthur Schopenhauer, and William James.

3. *Epistemology* is the inquiry into the nature of knowledge. The term is derived from two Greek words meaning "knowledge" and "discourse on." In epistemology there are many problems. How does knowledge originate? Has knowledge any definable limits? Wherein does it differ from error? Wherein from opinion? Wherein from speculation? Suppose a man turns from a page of natural theology or metaphysics with the belittling remark, "Such stuff is mere speculation." Clearly, he has a theory concerning the nature of knowledge,

in the light of which he discriminates between knowledge and speculation, and dismisses theology and metaphysics as speculation. What would his theory be? Many philosophers, both ancient and modern, have had views on the nature of knowledge. In some instances these views led them to repudiate theology and metaphysics as "mere speculation"; in some instances to include them within the scope of the term *knowledge*. With some representative studies in natural theology and metaphysics close at hand, attention is directed to the problem of knowledge in the writings of John Locke, David Hume, Immanuel Kant, Auguste Comte, and Hans Vaihinger. Each of these thinkers holds a theory concerning the nature of knowledge. Each of them uses it to discriminate between knowledge and speculation.

The first three topics — theology, metaphysics, epistemology — belong together. The transition from God and nature to appearance and reality, and then to knowledge and speculation is easily made. The second three topics form another loosely connected set. From God, reality, and knowledge, attention is directed to morals, politics, and history.

4. *Ethics* is the inquiry into the nature and conditions of the criticism we direct at action in such terms as *right-wrong*, *good-bad*, *ought-ought not*. We say an act was wrong, or that its results were bad. What is the principle upon which this right-wrong distinction rests? Can it be defended? With reference to this problem we examine the writings of five modern moralists: William Paley, Immanuel Kant, John Stuart Mill, Friedrich Nietzsche, and William James.

5. It is a short step from morals to *politics*. The great fact which is encountered here is the presence of an institution, the state, which dominates the field and generates most of the problems. The state differs from other institutions in the modern world. It alone issues absolute commands. It alone claims authority over life and death. It alone claims sover-

eign power. What is implied in this claim? Upon what grounds can it be shown to rest? Upon what grounds could it be challenged? Attention is here directed to James I of England, to Thomas Hobbes, to Jean Jacques Rousseau, to Edmund Burke, and to John Stuart Mill. A perusal of their writings as brought together here will lead us from the theory of the divine right of kings to the modern theory of government as resting eventually upon the consent of the governed.

6. Once in the field of politics, the transition to *history* is inevitable. Indeed, history has been described as "past politics." It may be more than that, but it is at least that. We deal here with what is usually described as "the philosophy of history." It arises thus: If one considers the enormous mass of details which constitute history, is there any pattern, any controlling regularity, any large movement within which the details find their place and significance? That there is, forms the first conviction of any thinker who professes to have a philosophy of history. One philosophy of history differs from another in respect to *what* the pattern is. Inasmuch as the pattern contains the meaning of the details, we can say that one differs from another in respect to the meaning of history. Attention is directed here to five great interpretations of history: the Augustinian, the rationalistic, the idealistic, the economic, and the cyclical. The first is drawn from the Middle Ages. It provides the best point of depature for considering the others. The remainder are from the writings of Immanuel Kant, Georg Wilhelm Friedrich Hegel, Karl Marx, and Oswald Spengler, respectively.

As far as feasible, I have quoted the actual words of each of the philosophers. But it should be clearly understood that this has not always been done. I have not hesitated to drop, or change the order of, words, phrases, clauses, sentences, where to do so seemed to make the meaning clearer. In extreme cases, I have resorted to paraphrases. It is therefore never safe to assume that any passage is, word for word, exactly as it would be found in the original. Literal textual accuracy has been subordinated wherever it seemed to me the author's *ipsissima verba* would get between him and the readers of this book. For this reason the citations are not enclosed in quotation marks, but merely printed in a smaller type.

II

There is little doubt that the first result of working through this large body of analyses and speculations will be profound confusion. The problems stand out clearly. The presence of rival alternative answers tends to unsettle one's mind. A sense of crosslights, of winding paths, not to say mazes, of claims and counterclaims, of assertion and denial, of proofs and disproofs, of principles and prejudices, and always the sense that finality may be apparent only is, to repeat, the first result of reading one's way through the authors brought together in this volume. Is *that*, then, the last word? Are persuasive alternatives the essentials of modern philosophy? Is suspended judgment its parting counsel? Four reflections present themselves at this point:

1. The first is this: Why not? If a survey of modern philosophical thought leaves a sense of bewilderment, not to say chaos, and if the survey has been made as representative as possible, what is gained by closing one's eyes to the fact? Modern philosophical thought appears to be chaotic, incoherent, confusing. Anyone who denies this is simply revealing his ignorance. I say it appears to be. This appearance may be deceptive, but it is at least the beginning of wisdom to allow for the possibility that this appearance may be a reality.

2. The second point is this: Past and present discord, no matter how deep and far-flung, are no grounds for asserting dogmatically that such must be the case in the future. How

old is the modern mind? Three or four centuries; younger, in point of time lived, than any of its predecessors. The only guarantee against further chaos and more "alternatives" is an invincible skepticism bred from a knowledge of past and present efforts and failures.

3. The third point is this: To turn over in one's mind the sequences of thoughts brought together in this book is an intellectual experience of the first order. It is permissible for the present writer to say this because his own part in the book has been largely that of wielding the scissors and paste pot. To read and meditate upon Hobbes, Pascal, Rousseau, Hume, Mill, James, Berkeley, Schopenhauer, Kant, Comte, Vaihinger Nietzsche, Burke, Marx, and Spengler is to encounter large minds at moments when they are concerned with great issues. If this does not loosen the soil around the roots of a man's soul, and enable it to grow in wisdom, then philosophy was indeed misnamed "the love of wisdom."

4. The fourth point is this: Despite the disagreement and inconclusiveness which characterize modern philosophy, no person who is reflectively inclined can foreswear it. The late Professor Schiller gave to one of his books the title, *Must Philosophers Disagree?* The question suggests that indeed they must, and that the more's the pity of it. It suggests that they need not, if only they will listen to Mr. Schiller. It suggests that in the matter of disagreements, philosophers are unlike historians, speculative scientists, statesmen, poets, educators, and other depositaries of the contemporary Zeitgeist. But, more important than these, it suggests a question, which is almost ruled out by the note of censure in the title of Schiller's book. The question is this: "Must men philosophize?" And to that, given the nature of man and the nature of philosophy, the answer would seem to be, "Yes." It would seem to be "Yes" even if the answer to Mr. Schiller's question were also "Yes."

By way of conclusion, I should like to emphasize two points The first is that an introduction to modern philosophy is not a modern introduction to philosophy. This book is intended to say, in effect: These analyses and speculations are typical of what philosophers have been doing during the last three or four centuries. The second is that a modern introduction to philosophy can be written and should be written. Its central problem would be an inquiry into the nature, the varieties, and the presuppositions of criticism. It would note that criticism is the fundamental activity of the human soul, but that the nature of this activity is far from clear. It would note that criticism occurs in different forms, e.g., logical, ethical, political, aesthetic, etc.; but that the rationale of these varieties of critical experience is far from clear. It would note that criticism has presuppositions, e.g., freedom, objectivity, communicability, etc., but that inquiry into these matters is difficult and obscure, once it attempts to go beyond the declaration of intuition.

These matters, however, call for another and quite different sort of book.

TOPIC ONE. A THEOLOGICAL PROBLEM

THE PROBLEM STATED

Men are religious. They do have beliefs about God. What is the rational foundation for these beliefs? It is customary to distinguish between *revealed* and *natural* or *rational* theology. Knowledge about God which rests upon revelations made directly to some man or group, and recorded in various sacred writings, constitutes *revealed* theology. Knowledge about God which is arrived at by a process of reasoning from the facts of nature constitutes *natural* or *rational* theology. It is named *natural* theology because it purports to be knowledge of God derived from our knowledge of nature. It is named *rational* theology because it purports to be knowledge of God derived by a process of reasoning from what we know about nature.

Our primary concern, in this topic, is with the central problem of natural or rational theology: Can a man, in an understanding of nature, find reasons for justifying a belief in the existence of God? With respect to revealed theology, it is possible to say very little. These limitations do not arise out of any inherent impossibility in the idea of God revealing His existence and nature to man. They arise out of the fact that a revelation, or the record of a revelation, is not open to the same kind of critical verification which we can make, for example, of the claim that the earth is round or that Napoleon was defeated at the battle of Waterloo. This impossibility of critical verification arises out of the fact that the revelation, or its record in sacred writings, has to be taken at its face value. We cannot go "back" of it, to see whether its claims are true.

One turns, then, to the possibility of there being a natural or rational theology, which shall not rest upon the claim to be revealed directly by God. Natural theology, so understood, is at least as old as the writings of Plato in the fourth century B.C. In examining this matter, therefore, we are breaking into a long and venerable tradition reaching down to our own day in the writings of contemporary philosophical theologians. The problem remains much the same throughout its history.

The citations which follow these introductory remarks present five sets of reflections upon the problem of natural theology. The first set, in which the competence of human reason to prove God's existence is unquestioned, has been drawn from the writings of St. Thomas Aquinas. The second set, in which the competence of human reason to prove God's existence is sharply questioned, and the argument advanced that man's helplessness without God is the surest proof of His existence, is from the writings of Blaise Pascal. The third set, in which the incompetence of human reason to prove God's existence is carefully argued for, is from the writings of David Hume. The fourth set, in which the hypothesis of a finite or limited God is advanced as the most that human reason can defend, is from the writings of John Stuart Mill. The fifth set, in which the whole notion of an "appeal to reason" is rejected in favor of an appeal to the emotions, is from the writings of William James. These five sets span the modern period and provide examples characteristic of the analyses and speculations which this problem has evoked. Aquinas, the greatest of late medieval theologians, is included, from the thirteenth century, in order to provide the necessary background for those who follow. Pascal is seventeenth century; Hume is eighteenth century; Mill is nineteenth century; James is twentieth century. A careful perusal of what these men have said about this one problem should do two things: indicate the many sides which this problem presents when different minds make it the object of reflective analysis, and indicate the continuity of the problem over a period of several centuries.

1. THE PRINCIPLES OF NATURAL THEOLOGY — FROM ST. THOMAS AQUINAS

Biographical Note. Thomas Aquinas was born in Italy in 1225 and died in 1274 at the age of forty-nine. The story of his life is soon told. (1) His father was a nobleman. At the age of five, Thomas was sent for his education to the Benedictine monastery of Monte Cassino, where his uncle ruled as abbot. He studied grammar, poetry, rhetoric, logic, and some elementary philosophy. From the monastery he attended the University of Naples. While there, or shortly after, he formed the design of becoming a monk in the order of St. Dominic. His mother objected, even going so far as to imprison him for two years. However, he escaped and entered the order in 1243. (2) During the next dozen years or so he pursued advanced studies in theology and philosophy at various European universities. In 1256 or 1257 he received the degree of "master of sacred sciences" and began a career of teaching and writing and controversy. (3) His writings are many. Among these the most important was his huge *Summa Theologica* in which he provided his generation with an extraordinarily systematic digest of Christian theology and much ancient philosophy. This great work, which was still unfinished at the time of his death, fills many volumes in its English translation. It begins with the question of God's existence, deals then with His attributes, traces the processes of things from God and the return of man to God through Christ by means of the sacraments which Christ instituted.

This *Summa* soon became, and still continues to be, the official presentation of Catholic theology and philosophy. (4) At the command of Pope Gregory X, Thomas undertook to be present at an ecclesiastical council to be held in Lyons. On the way he fell sick. He put up at a near-by monastery, but died after a few months' illness. In 1323, almost half a century after his death, Thomas was canonized by Pope John XXII. A recent translator remarks, "Whatever may be the proper statement of the grounds of his sainthood, his vast intellectual achievements are certainly events out of the natural order and appropriate to a miracle."

Why Theology? It may be well to ask ourselves why we begin the study of philosophy with a set of chapters on theology; and why, among theologians, we begin with Saint Thomas Aquinas. The answers to these questions are very simple.

There are few methods better suited to introduce a student to philosophy than to spend a little time with theology. The reason is that in most ages men have sought to answer philosophical questions in terms of theological beliefs. "What shall I believe?" has frequently been answered by "The word of God." "What shall I do?" has frequently been answered by "Obey the Will of God." "Where did the world come from?" has frequently been answered by "It was created by God." "What happens to me when I die?" has frequently been answered by "You return to God." In these and countless other ways, the notion of God has entered into the very texture of men's thinking; and wherever it has entered, it has always been to answer some ultimate and highly critical question. We can generalize all of this by saying that the idea of God has functioned as an ultimate principle of explanation and an ultimate principle of criticism. Now, inasmuch as philosophy (literally, "the love of wisdom") is the systematic inquiry into our ultimate principles of explanation and criticism, in every department of life and thought, there has always been a close connection between it and theology. If the answers to ultimate questions of explanation and evaluation are to be found in theology, it is a man's philosophical business to know this. If there is reasonable doubt about these matters, it is likewise a man's philosophical business to inform himself that such is the case.

It is for this reason that theology provides a good beginning in philosophy. The questions which *define* philosophy have frequently been answered by theology. From a slight familiarity with the latter, therefore, we may at least expect to discover what questions are philosophical in character.

Why Saint Thomas? The answer to this second question is that he is in many ways the prince among theologians. His two great works, *Summa Theologica* and *Summa Contra Gentiles* are, in many respects, the most elaborate and painstaking and influential of all theological writings. If we read Saint Thomas, we will confront ourselves with things which are among the best which theology has to offer. The full text of his *Summa* runs to about a score of volumes. We are concerned with the first part of the first volume. There Saint Thomas poses, and endeavors to answer the questions, Does God exist? How do we know that He exists? Can this knowledge be demonstrated?

A Matter of Inference. Thomas's first claim is that the existence of God is not something which we can know directly; it is not given as, e.g., the color of this page is given; it is not known by intuition; it is not known by direct insight. It is inferred or deduced. In other words, belief in the existence of God rests upon an argument, upon discourse having the form If-then, where the If-part is something directly given and the then-part is something inferred from what is directly given. Such being the case, we are naturally curious about the fact or facts, directly knowable, from which Thomas will infer the existence of God. He proposes five facts. Each gives rise to its proper argument. These are known as the argument from change; the argument from cause; the argument from contingency; the argument from degrees of excellence; and the argument from design. In considering these five theological arguments, we shall not quote Saint Thomas's own words, since his manner of stating them would be rather elusive and foreign. In place of direct quotation, we shall paraphrase and describe what he says.

THE ARGUMENT FROM CHANGE. Change is an undoubted fact in nature. Wherever we look, things are changing. A-changing-into-B is a phrase which has a very wide application. How are we to explain or account for the fact of change? Any particular instance of change we can refer to some previous change; but this will not help us to account for the presence of change, as such. There are three possibilities: (a) We may accept change as an ultimate fact, neither requiring or permitting any explanation. (b) We may refer every case of change to some prior case, extending our reference backward to infinity. (c) We may postulate what Saint Thomas calls an Unmoved Mover, or Prime Mover, itself unchanging but the source from which all particular instances of change proceed.

The first two alternatives Thomas rejects. His reasoning is not so clear as one could wish it. He rejects the notion of change as an ultimate fact neither requiring nor permitting any explanation, because such a position would seem to be needless skepticism. Why *should* the fact of change in nature be allowed to fall outside the range of explanation? If there are going to be ultimate mysteries, why should change be among them? Is there any necessity in the claim that change is an ultimate, inexplicable fact? For these and similar reasons Thomas rejects the "skeptical" solution in favor of a more "rationalist" solution; that is, in favor of the claim that there is a reason for the fact of change.

He rejects the notion of explaining changes by referring them to prior changes, and so on back to infinity. His reasoning here seems to be that such an explanation is wrong in principle, and would hence break down and leave one in the first position of accepting change as an ultimate fact. The point here seems to be two-fold. First, that referring change to prior change is always to be left with change; whereas to be left with change is precisely the thing we are seeking to avoid. Second, the notion of an infinite regression is itself a highly unsatisfactory one. It involves the mind in many different puzzles and paradoxes which leave matters no better off than the skeptical solution. For these and similar reasons, Saint Thomas rejects the notion of infinite regression as required by the attempt to explain change by referring it to prior change.

If there is no fourth alternative, then he has a strong case for the remaining third explanation. If there are just three possibilities, and you show cause for rejecting two of them, you do not require any further justification for accepting the third. This, at any rate, seems to be Thomas's reasoning in respect to his argument from the fact of change to the existence of an Unmoved Mover, or Prime Mover, or God.

THE ARGUMENT FROM CAUSATION. These arguments in natural theology, as their name suggests, are inferences *from* some fact about nature *to* the existence of God. From the fact of change, Thomas argued to the existence of God. His second argument, known as the argument from causation, is similar in form, but begins with a different fact. This time the fact selected is causation. Like change, causation is a large, obvious, ubiquitous fact. When we examine nature, our minds seem to detect the fact of causation almost everywhere. We have many different words and phrases for expressing this fact. This causes that. This is causally connected with that. The principle of causality is illustrated between this and that.

Granted this fact about nature, Thomas's procedure is the same as in the case of change. How are we to explain or account for the fact of causation? Any particular instance of causation we can refer to some previous instance. Suppose B is the cause of A. We can refer B itself back to C, as its cause; and C itself back to D, as its cause, and so on. But this will not help us to account for the fact of causation as such. The question is not, Does this cause that? It is, Why does this cause that? Why does anything cause anything? Why is there causation in nature? As in the case of change, there are three possibilities: (a) We may accept causation as an ultimate fact, neither requiring nor permitting any explanation. (b) We may refer every instance of causing to some prior instance, extending our reference back to infinity. (c) We may postulate what Saint Thomas calls a First Cause, itself uncaused.

There is no need to retrace his argument in any detail. He rejects the notion that causation is an ultimate fact neither requiring nor permitting any explanation. He rejects the notion of an infinite regression. He is left with the notion of a First Cause.

The Argument from Contingency. We have seen that Thomas's procedure is to select some obvious fact about nature, and to argue from the existence of this fact to the existence of God. From the fact of change, he argued the existence of God as unchanging First Mover. From the fact of causation, he argued the existence of God as uncaused First Cause. It will be noticed that these arguments begin with one sort of notion and conclude with the "opposite" notion. Thus from change, he argued an unchanging Being; from causation, he argued an uncaused Being. This inference from one sort of fact in nature, to God as an "opposite" sort of fact, characterizes Thomas's third argument.

The argument from contingency begins with the fact that in nature many things appear to be contingent, accidental, possible, dependent. A man is walking across a field. He encounters a stray bullet, fired by someone who was ignorant of his presence in that field. Death results. Speaking of this death, we say it was accidental. Among the things we mean when we say this is the notion that it did not *have* to happen. Matters might have been, could have been, otherwise. The man might have been elsewhere when the bullet came by. The shot might have been fired in some other direction. The compresence of the victim and the bullet, at just that time and place, was not necessary. The victim's presence, at just that time and place, did not necessitate the bullet's presence, at just that time and place. There were other possibilities. The way things actually happened did not exhaust all the possibilities. We have many different words and phrases which enable us to describe this sort of thing. We can say that his actual death was possible, but not necessary; that it was contingent or dependent upon the fact that he was there when the bullet came by; that it happened, but did not have to happen; that it was accidental, not necessary.

Like change and causation, contingency is an obvious fact about nature. Many things in nature exhibit this fact of contingency, or what Thomas sometimes calls "dependent being." It may be that *every* object and event in nature exhibits this fact of contingency. The question is, how are we to account for the fact of contingency in nature? The question is not, Was this contingent upon that? It is, Why are there contingent facts in nature? Why is anything contingent? We could put our question about contingency in the same form as our question about change and causation:

Why is there change in nature? Why is there causation in nature? Why is there contingency in nature?

Once the *sort* of fact is clear, the rest of the argument is easily grasped. We have again three possibilities: (a) We may accept contingency as an ultimate fact about nature, neither requiring nor permitting any explanation. (b) We may refer every instance of contingency to some prior instance, extending our reference back to infinity. (c) We may postulate what Thomas calls a Necessary Being, itself not contingent upon anything.

There is again no need to retrace his argument in detail. He rejects the notion that contingency is an ultimate fact neither requiring nor permitting any explanation. He rejects also the notion of an infinite regression. He is left with the notion of a Necessary Being.

The Argument from Degrees of Excellence. Thomas's fourth argument differs slightly in character from the first three. If we examine the nature of things, we notice the fact of degrees of excellence. This is more excellent than that. What sort of excellence is in question does not matter. Saint Thomas seems to suggest that there are kinds or sorts or classes of things, and that particular cases exhibit varying degrees of excellence, each according to its kind. Thus, one horse may be more excellent than another; one tree more excellent than another; one man more excellent than another. Thomas does not seem to suggest that this notion of degrees of excellence cuts across kinds or classes. Thus, his idea is not that a horse is more excellent than a tree, but rather that one horse is more excellent than another. However this may be, nature exhibits degrees of excellence. Degrees of excellence, like change and causation and contingency, is a fact about nature.

Granted this fact, he urges that the notion of degrees of excellence implies the notion of perfection. Unless we have the notion of perfection, we could not say that something was more or less excellent. Imperfect being, of no matter what sort, implies perfect being of that sort. Evaluation of the actual, in terms of degrees of excellence, implies a grasp of the ideal. Now the totality of actuals, exhibiting their degrees of excellence, make up nature. Nature is the whereabouts of degrees of excellence. But what can we say of perfection? Its whereabouts is obviously not nature; nothing in nature is perfect after its kind.

It is easier to state Thomas's position here than it is to understand exactly what the words mean. What he seems to say is that nature is the realm of imperfect being, and God is the realm of perfect being. In nature, nothing is perfect. In God, all things are perfect. God is the whereabouts of perfect being, just as nature is the whereabouts of imperfect being. And our power to detect imperfect being (degrees of excellence) in nature implies our knowledge of perfect being in God. If knowing imperfect being entails the existence of imperfect being — if it did not exist you could not know it — then knowing perfect being entails the existence of perfect being.

This argument can be given the same formulation as we gave to the others. We can say, The fact in nature this time is degrees of excellence, or imperfect being. We have three possibilities: (a) We may accept this as an ultimate fact, neither requiring nor permitting any explanation. (b) We may refer every instance of a degree of excellence to some other instance of greater excellence, extending our reference to infinity. (c) We may postulate what Thomas calls Perfect Being, in whom all sorts of perfections live and move and have their being, and through knowledge of whom we are able to recognize the fact of imperfect being, or degrees of excellence, in nature.

But this is to overlook the fact that the human artist did not create his materials. The second is that we must ascribe the imperfections in nature to the fact that they make possible some good things not otherwise possible, as we might say that trials are a necessary condition to the exercise and development of patience, and patience is a good thing. On the hypothesis that some good things require imperfections in order that they may come into being, Thomas argues that if all imperfections were excluded by divine providence, then the number of good things would be diminished. It does not seem necessary to criticize this argument. Thomas is in a dilemma, and there is no reason to prod him with the horns.

Problem of Free Will. Among the imperfections which are obvious to Saint Thomas is the fact of evil-doing, or sin, in the life of man. This sort of imperfection Thomas could dispose of by ascribing it to a man's free-will. However, if free-will is to be added to the facts of nature, we are obliged to ask how it is to be reconciled with the omnipotence of God. If God does *everything*, then in what sense does man do *anything*? If God's will governs all things, in what sense is man's will responsible for the evil acts which it performs? The argument would seem to require that Thomas sacrifice God's omnipotence to save man's freedom, if he proposes to use man's freedom to save God's righteousness. Thomas has three lines of defense, none of which are satisfactory. He says, in the first place, that the Scriptures tell us that God made man and left him in the hands of his own counsel, i.e., gave him free will to choose between good and evil. He says, in the second place, that man must have a free-will, since otherwise rewards and punishments would be inappropriate; i.e., if man's will is not free, then he is not responsible for his acts, and he should not be punished if those acts are evil, or rewarded if they are good. He says in the third place, that God made man rational, and that being rational includes having freedom of mind and will. These arguments are all irrelevant. The last two are good arguments in support of the thesis that man has a free will; but that was not Thomas's problem. That problem was how man's free-will is to be reconciled with God's omnipotence. The teaching of the Catholic Church is more forthright. It says that moral evil is a fact, explainable by reference to man's free-will, but that man's free-will, while a fact, is also a mystery.

Of Man's Last End. These snags and bucklings are, it would seem, essential ingredients in the argument of Saint Thomas's natural theology. However, once they have been noted one may pass on to further matters. Of these, in the voluminous *Summas*, there are many. One, selected here by way of conclusion, is the question of what Thomas calls man's last end. By that he means man's highest good, the term "end" being used in the sense of goal or object. Man's highest good, as set forth by Saint Thomas, is easily stated: it is the enjoyment of God. What this means is less easily stated. It is probably as follows: Man's last end is happiness. Wherein is true happiness to be found? It is to be found in those activities of the human psyche whereby man raises himself from a state of confusion and chaos about the world, to a grasp of the fact that the world's changeableness is rooted in God's unchangeableness; its causality rooted in God as first cause; its contingency rooted in God's necessity; its imperfection rooted in God's perfection; and its intelligibility rooted in God's intelligence. As the Spanish proverb has it, these are major words.

Thomas's writings exemplify one type of natural theology and one approach to the central problem. So long as the appeal to reason goes hand in hand with piety, his ideas are likely to be re-echoed in other men's minds, as in his mind they were echoes from classical Greek philosophy. The essentials are simple. God exists as the First Mover, the

First Cause, the Author of the order and harmony in nature. His attributes include perfection, omnipotence, omniscience, omnipresence, benevolence, justice, rationality, prevision, and so forth. How these are to be squared with man's free will and the world's great evils are nice theoretical problems. In God's ordering of things, man stands a little lower than the angels and exercises dominion over the animals and plant and inanimate orders. With his Creator he shares an intelligence and a power to know good from evil. In the knowledge and enjoyment of God man finds his only true and lasting happiness.

READING REFERENCES. Thomas's writings have been studied and written about almost continuously since their publication. In the year 1879 Leo XIII issued a papal encyclical in which he enjoined upon Catholics the wisdom of reading the writings of scholastics in general and Thomas in particular. It is a difficult task to point to two or three books and say, "Above all, do not fail to look into these." Much of the literature on Thomistic thought is in Latin or Italian or German or French. Of this, rather little has been translated. There are, however, two treatises, written by English scholars, which will repay any time spent on them: *The Conception of God in the Philosophy of Thomas Aquinas*, by R. L. Patterson, and *Thomas Aquinas* by M. C. D'Arcy. The same may be said for the translation of M. Gilson's *Le Thomisme*. Anyone who finds these books difficult should turn to the translation of M. Maritain's *Le docteur Angelique* or to G. K. Chesterton's charming little volume *Thomas Aquinas*.

READING QUESTIONS

1. Distinguish between revealed and natural theology.
2. Why is *rational* synonymous with *natural* in this connection?
3. Formulate the central problem of natural theology.
4. Why ignore the question of revealed theology?

5. How would you distinguish between theism and atheism?
6. How between atheism and skepticism?
7. What is the argument from change?
8. From causation?
9. From contingency?
10. From degrees of excellence?
11. From harmony?
12. Why does Thomas reject the idea of an infinite regression?
13. What qualities does Thomas ascribe to the Deity?
14. What is the problem of evil in natural theology?
15. Along what lines does Thomas seek to deal with it?
16. What criticism is his position open to?
17. What is the problem of free will in natural theology?
18. Do you see any connection between these two problems?
19. Why would Thomas hesitate to deny man's free will?
20. How does he seek to deal with this problem?
21. What two attributes of Deity raise these two problems?
22. What does Thomas mean by man's last end?
23. Wherein does he believe man will find it?
24. Formulate one or more problems you would put to Thomas.

2. *THE RELIGIOUS WAGER—FROM BLAISE PASCAL*

From Thomas to Pascal. Thomas Aquinas wrote in an age of Christian faith. His trust in reason to find out God was a trust shared by most of his contemporaries and readers. This, however, was in the thirteenth century. The Renaissance and the Reformation succeeded the Middle Ages. The new science of Copernicus, Kepler, Galileo, succeeded the old science of Aristotle, Ptolemy, and the medieval scholars. The new philosophy of Montaigne, Descartes, Hobbes, Bacon succeeded the old philosophy of Augustine, Anselm, Abélard, and Aquinas. It was only to be expected that the placid argumentation by which Thomas built up his *Summa* should be replaced by something more vibrant and uneasy. This change is seen most clearly in the religious writings of Blaise Pascal.

Biographical Note. Pascal was born in 1623 and died in 1662 at the age of thirty-nine. It is convenient to consider his life in three periods. (1) He was educated at home. His parents, especially his father, were devout Catholics, pious but stern. Blaise early displayed a remarkable precocity in physics and mathematics; at the age of fifteen he was producing monographs on conic sections which were thought important enough to be read to "the most learned and scientific men in Paris." He was counted one of the outstanding physicists and mathematicians of his time. His discoveries were made during the years when most scientists are still mastering the known facts of their field. (2) The elder Pascal died in 1650 leaving a patrimony to Blaise and his sister Jacqueline. Jacqueline entered a convent; Blaise went off to Paris. During the next four years he lived among scholars, scientists, wits, and the nobility. On November 23, 1654, he had what is termed a mystical experience. That he had this experience, there is no reason to doubt; that it meant what he interpreted it to mean is perhaps more open to debate. (3) That hour, described for posterity in a note which was found sewn into the coat he was wearing at the time of his death, wrought a complete change in Pascal's life. Austerity, self-denial, boundless almsgiving, and absolute obedience to his spiritual director replaced his previous routine of scientist and man-about-town. He threw himself into the defense of the Cistercian abbey of Port Royal des Champs, which was being persecuted by the hierarchy for a number of real or supposed heresies. The case for the Port Royalists was stated by Pascal in his celebrated *Letters to a Provincial*. The closing years of his life were given to planning and sketching in what was to have been, had he lived to complete it, an apologia for the Christian faith in an age of unbelief and indifference. The book was never finished. It consists of hundreds of loosely grouped fragments, aphorisms, jottings. It has always been known, in French, by the title *Pensées;* in English, by the title *Thoughts.* The citations which follow are drawn from this unfinished defense of Pascal's religious beliefs.

THE ARGUMENT OF THE CITATIONS. The citations given below do not trace the argument of Pascal's entire book. Much of that volume deals with special topics, for example, the relation of other religions to Christianity, the significance of miracles, prophecy, revelation, etc. With these we are not concerned. Our interest is limited to the question: Can a man, by the use of his reason, argue the existence of God from the existence of nature? To this question Thomas had answered in the affirmative. Pascal, an equally devout Christian and Catholic, answers in the negative. The movement of thought is as follows: Some persons are skeptical or indifferent in matters of religious belief. Such persons are to be pitied and scorned. But no appeal to reason, no natural theology in the manner of Thomas, will avail to dissolve their doubts, denials, indifference. This for two reasons: They are too hardened, and in any case, human reason is frankly unequal to the task of elaborating a rational theology. Pascal soliloquizes at some length on the littleness of man and the impotence of reason. If not through his rational powers, then through what can the doubting and indifferent soul be brought to a knowledge of God? Pascal's answer is this: through his emotions. In a famous line he remarks: "The heart hath its reasons, which the reason knows not of." The utmost that reason can do is to pose and defend what Pascal describes as a "wager," that is, a bet that God exists. Man must see for himself that his happiness lies in belief in and love of God. When he has seen this fact, his skepticism and indifference will be replaced by faith and happiness and true goodness.

He begins with those who have doubts about the existence of God and are not particularly worried over it:

Before entering on the proofs of the Christian religion, I find it necessary to set forth the unfairness of men who are indifferent to the search for truth in a matter which is so important to them and which touches them so nearly. Among all their errors, this most proves them to be fools and blind.

We know well enough how men of this temper behave. They believe they have made a great effort after their instruction when they have spent a few hours reading some book of Scripture and putting a few questions to some ecclesiastic. Whereupon they boast that they have "in vain consulted books and men." Such carelessness is intolerable.

Among unbelievers I make a vast distinction. I can have nothing but compassion for all who sincerely lament their doubt, who look upon it as the worst of evils, who spare no pains to escape it, who make these matters their chief and most serious occupation. But those who pass their lives without thinking of this ultimate end of existence, who neglect to examine whether these are matters which people receive through credulous simplicity or have a solid and impregnable basis, such persons I regard in a wholly different manner. Their negligence irritates me much more than it excites my pity. It astonishes and overwhelms me; it is for me something monstrous.

There are but three classes of persons: those who have found God and serve Him; those who have not found God, but do diligently seek Him; and those who have not found God, and live without seeking Him. The first are happy and wise. The second are unhappy, but wise. The third are unhappy and fools.

It is a sorry evil to be in doubt. It is an indispensable duty to seek when we are in doubt. Therefore he who doubts and neglects to seek to dispel these doubts, is at once in a sorry plight and guilty of great perversity. If he is calm and contented in his doubt, if he frankly avows it, if he boasts of it, if he makes it the subject of vanity and delight, I can find no terms with which to describe him.

How do men come by these sentiments? What delight is there

in such things? What is there to be proud of in beholding ourselves in the midst of impenetrable darkness? How can any rational man reason in this way: "I know not who has put me in the world, nor what the world is, nor what I am myself. I am in terrible ignorance of all these things. I view the awful spaces of the universe that surround me, I find myself fixed to a corner of this vast extent, I see nothing but infinities on every side enclosing me like an atom. All that I know is that I must soon die. Such is my state — full of misery, weakness, obscurity. And from this I conclude that I ought to pass all the days of my life without thinking of what is to happen to me hereafter. It may be that I could find some answers to my doubts; but I am unwilling to take the trouble."

Who would desire to have for a friend a man who discourses in such a fashion? Who would select such a person to be the confidant of his affairs? Who would have recourse to such a one in his afflictions? In fine, for what use in life could such a man be destined? It is the glory of religion to have such irrational men for its enemies. Such strange insensibility for the greatest things is something monstrous. It is an incomprehensible delusion.

There must be a strange revulsion in the nature of man, to make him glory in such a state. Most of those who are thus involved are people who have heard that fine worldly manners consist in what they call "throwing off the yoke." This they try to imitate. But, what good does it do us to hear a man say that he has "thrown off the yoke," that he does not believe there is a God, that he is answerable in his conduct to none but himself? Is this a thing to be said gaily? On the contrary, is it not a thing to be said with sadness, as of all things the saddest? It requires all the love of the religion which they despise, not to despise such persons and abandon them in their folly.

So much for perverse doubts and callous indifference. Pascal knows that there is a long tradition of rational theologizing which, in its heyday, triumphed easily over such skepticism and infidelity. But that day has passed. Since then, Montaigne had written. Doubt had taken too firm a hold to be dislodged by appeals to man's reason in support of religious belief. To what point, he seems to ask, to what point such intellectual circumgyrations as the argument from design, or the argument from first cause, when a man has really ceased to believe in God?

I wonder at the boldness of those who undertake to speak of God to the irreligious. Their first chapter is to prove the existence of God by reference to the works of nature. I should not be astonished if they addressed their argument to those who already believe; for those who have a lively faith in their heart see at once that all that exists is none other than the handiwork of God. But for those who are destitute of faith — to tell them that they need only look at nature around them in order to see God unveiled, to give them the course of the sun and the moon as the sole proof of this important matter, to imagine with such an argument we have proved anything, is only to give grounds for believing that the proofs of our religion are very feeble. Indeed, I see by reason and experience that nothing is more fitted to excite contempt.

This is what I see, and what troubles me. I look on all sides, and see nothing but obscurity; nature offers me nothing but matter for doubt. If I saw nothing in nature which marked a Divinity, I should decide not to believe in him. If I saw everywhere the marks of a Creator, I should rest peacefully in faith. But I see too much to deny, and too little to affirm; so my state is pitiful. A hundred times I have wished that God would mark His presence in nature unequivocally, if He upholds nature; or that nature would wholly suppress the signs which she gives of God, if those signs are fallacious; that she would either say all or say nothing, so I might see what part I should take. While in my present state, ignorant of what I am and of what I ought to do, I know neither my condition nor my duty.

The metaphysical proofs of God are so far apart from man's reason, and so complicated, that they are but little striking. If they are of use to any, it is only during the moment that the demonstration is before them. An hour afterwards they fear they have been mistaken. Therefore I do not here undertake to prove by natural reason the existence of God. I do not feel myself strong enough to find in nature proofs to convince hardened atheists. All who seek God in nature find no light to satisfy them. They fall either into atheism or into deism, two things which the Christian religion almost equally abhors.

What then? Revealed theology, as Pascal well knows, is a dead horse when one is chasing doubters and deniers. Rational theology, in the sense of a reasoned appeal from nature to God, he has himself rejected as barren and unconvincing if a man does not already feel God in his heart. His answer worked out bit by bit in the fragments of his unfinished *Thoughts*, comes to this: The strongest proof for the existence of God is the great need felt by the human soul for the sustaining presence of such a Being in an otherwise empty universe.

He begins by drawing attention to the immensity of the spatio-temporal universe in which man finds himself:

Let a man contemplate nature in her full majesty. Let him extend his view beyond the objects which surround him. Let him regard the sun. Let him consider the earth whereon he lives as a point in comparison with the vast orbit described by the sun. Let him learn that this vast orbit is but a point compared with that embraced by the stars which roll in the firmament. Let his imagination pass beyond. All this visible cosmos is but a point in the ample bosom of nature. In vain we extend our conceptions beyond imaginable spaces: We bring forth but atoms in comparison with the reality of things. For the universe is an infinite sphere whose center is everywhere and whose circumference is nowhere.

From the vastness of things, he passes to the other extreme. Compared to the whole of nature, man may be a mere speck. But compared to the infinitely small particles which compose the material world, he is a colossus.

There is another aspect, equally astonishing. Let a man seek things the most minute. Let him consider a mite, in the exceeding smallness of its body: parts incomparably smaller, limbs with joints, veins in those limbs, blood in those veins, humors in this blood, globules in these humors, gases in the globules. Let him divide these globules. Let him exhaust his powers of conception. He will think perhaps that he has arrived at the minutest atom of nature. I will show him therein a new abyss. I will picture to him the inconceivable immensity of nature in the compass of this abbreviation of an atom. Let him view therein an infinity of worlds, each with its own firmament, its planets, its earth, in the same proportion as the visible world. Let him lose himself in these wonders, as astonishing in their littleness as the others in their magnitude. His body, which just before was imperceptible in the universe, is now a colossus in comparison with the infinitely small at which it is possible to arrive.

With this contrast in mind, he pauses to ask: What is man, amid all this? If Pascal had completed his argument, he would doubtless have used the words of the Psalmist, "What is man that Thou art mindful of him?" But at this point, that would be a flagrant begging of the question: It is precisely that "Thou" that is in question.

What is man, in the midst of these two infinities? A nothing compared with the infinitely large, all compared with the infinitely small. A mean between all and nothing, infinitely far from comprehending the extremes. Let us, then, know our range. Such is our true state. This is what renders us incapable, alike of absolute knowledge and absolute ignorance.

Nature confounds the skeptics, and reason confounds the dogmatists. What will become of you, O man, who would search out your true condition by your natural reason? You can avoid neither skepticism nor dogmatism; but, alas, you can live with neither!

Our intelligence holds the same position as our body, in the vast extent of nature. This middle state between two extremes is common to all our weaknesses: Our senses can perceive no extreme; too much noise deafens us, too much light blinds us, too far or too near interferes with our vision, too much brevity or too much prolixity obscures our understanding, too much truth overwhelms us, too much pleasure cloys on us, too many benefits annoy us, we feel neither extreme heat nor extreme cold, too much and too little teaching hinder our minds — in a word, all extremes are for us as though they were not. They escape us or we escape them.

Man is a creature full of natural error. Nothing shows him the truth, everything deceives him. His reason and his senses deceive each other. The senses trick the reason by false appearances; reason in turn avenges herself and deceives the senses. His emotions trouble his senses and make false impressions on him. Reason, senses, emotions, lie and deceive, outdoing each other.

What a chimera is man! Strange and monstrous! A chaos, a contradiction, a prodigy. Judge of all things, yet a weak earthworm. Depository of truth, yet a cesspool of uncertainty and error; the glory and the scrapings of the universe.

Who will unravel such a tangle? It is beyond the power of dogmatism, of skepticism, of philosophy. Man is incomprehensible by man. We grant that to the skeptics. Truth is not within our reach, nor to our taste; her home is not on earth.

We sail on a vast expanse of being, ever uncertain, ever drifting, ever hurried from one goal to another. If we seek to attach ourselves to any one point, it totters and fails us; if we follow, it eludes our grasp, vanishing forever. Nothing stays for us. This is our natural condition. Yet, it is the condition most contrary to our inclination; for we burn with desire to find a steadfast place and a fixed basis whereon we may build. But our whole foundation breaks up, and the abysses open before us.

When I consider the short duration of my life, swallowed up in an eternity before and after, the small space I fill engulfed in the infinite immensity of spaces whereof I know nothing, and which know nothing of me, I am terrified. The eternal silence of these infinite spaces alarms me. I wonder why I am here, rather than there, now rather than then. Who has set me here? By whose order and design have this place and time been destined for me?

When I see the blindness and misery of man; when I survey the whole dumb universe; when I see man left to himself without a light unto his path, lost in this corner of the cosmos, ignorant of who placed him here, of what he has come here to do, of what will overtake him when he dies, I fall into terror. And my terror is like that of a man who should awake upon a terrible desert island with no means of escape. And I wonder why men do not fall into despair. I see others around me, of like nature. I ask if they are better informed than I am; and they say they are not.

We may not, then, look for certainty or stability. Our reason is always deceived by changing shows. It matters not that man should have a trifle more knowledge of the universe; if he has it, he but begins a little higher; but he is always infinitely distant from the end. In regard to the infinities, all finites are equal, and I see no reason why we should fix our imagination on one more than on another.

Who would not think, when we declare that man consists of mind and matter, that we really understood this combination? Yet — it is the one thing we least understand. Nothing is more obscure than just this mixture of spirit and clay. Man is, to himself, the most marvelous object in nature, for he cannot conceive what matter is, nor what mind is, nor how a material body should be united to an immaterial mind. This is the crown of all his difficulties; yet it is his very being.

These are some of the causes which render man so totally unable to know nature. For nature has a twofold infinity, while he is finite. Nature is permanent, while he is fleeting and mortal. All things change and fail; he sees them only as they pass. All things have their beginning and their end; he sees neither the one nor the other. Things are simple and homogeneous. He is complex and composed of two different elements.

Not from space must I seek my dignity. I should have no more if I possessed whole worlds. By space the universe encompasses and swallows me as an atom. Man is but a reed, weakest in nature, but a reed which thinks. A thinking reed. It needs not that the whole universe should arm to crush him. A vapor, a drop of water is enough to kill him. But were the universe to kill him, man would still be more noble than that which has slain him, because he knows that he dies, and that the universe has the better of him. The universe knows nothing of this.

Know then, proud Man, how great a paradox thou art to thyself. Bow down thyself, impotent reason; be silent, thou foolish human nature. Learn that man is altogether incomprehensible by man.

Let man now estimate his value. Let him love himself, because he has a nature capable of good. But let him not love the vileness which exists in that nature. He has in himself the capacity of knowledge and happiness, yet he finds no last truth or satisfaction. I would lead him to desire it; to be freed from passions, to know how his passions obscure his knowledge and his achievement of happiness. I would have him hate in himself the desires which bias his judgment, that they might neither blind him in choosing nor obstruct him when he has chosen.

The net result of all this is that man, of himself, is ignorant and helpless and alone. The blind forces of nature offer him no haven. The universe at large cares as little for his living as for his dying. In his quest for happiness and goodness, he is confronted by an alien, indifferent, even hostile world. Pascal might have let it go at that. Many have, for example, Schopenhauer and Thomas Hardy and Bertrand Russell. Not so Pascal. In such a plight, his soul could find no peace and rest. So he picks up the argument again, reminding man that the conquest of true happiness is at stake:

All men seek happiness. To this there is no exception. Our will makes no step, except toward this object. This is the motive of every action of every man. And yet, after so many years no one has arrived, without faith, at the point to which all eyes are turned. All complain, rulers and ruled, nobles and commons, old and young, strong and weak, learned and ignorant, sound and sick, of all countries, all times, all ages, and all conditions.

A trial so long, so constant, so uniform, should have convinced us of our inability to arrive at our complete happiness by our own strength. But example teaches us little. We expect that our efforts will not be foiled on this occasion, as before. Thus while the present never satisfies us, experience never teaches us; and from misfortune to misfortune we are led on to death, the eternal crown of our sorrows.

This desire, and this weakness, cry aloud to us that there is an empty space in man which he seeks vainly to fill from all that surrounds him, seeks vainly to find in things absent the happiness which he finds not in things present.

Peace of mind, happiness of soul, are nowhere within reach so long as these are sought for among the things of this world. Who can deny that? But who is prepared to let it go at that? Not Pascal, at any rate. It is at this point that his argument becomes a record of his personal findings:

Man finds his lasting happiness only in God. Without Him, there is nothing in nature which will take His place; neither the stars, nor heaven, nor earth, nor the elements; not plants, cabbages, animals, insects, calves, serpents, fever, pestilence, war, famine, vices, adultery, incest. Since man has lost track of his true happiness, all things appear equally good to him, even his own destruction, though so contrary to God, to right reason, and to the whole course of nature.

There is no good without knowledge of God. Only as we approach Him are we happy; and our ultimate good is to know Him certainly. We are unhappy, in proportion as we are removed from Him; and the greatest evil would be the certainty of being cut off from Him.

These reflections bring Pascal to the terms of his famous religious wager. It may be well to restate his position before proceeding: Some men doubt God's existence, and are indifferent to their doubts. For them Pascal has nothing to say. But others doubt, and are concerned. Like the man in the New Testament they cry, paradoxically: "Lord, I believe, help Thou my unbelief!" To those who feel this cry, Pascal addresses himself. They must recognize the futility of attempting a "rational" solution to their doubts; Renaissance skepticism, personified in Montaigne, has blown up that bridge. It remains to face squarely the utter loneliness and littleness of man. Left to himself, his hopes and joys and values and aspirations are doomed to extinction. In God alone, if there be a God, can he hope to find a friend and protector. But, good skeptic that he is, Pascal knows that there is a gap between the fact of our need for God and God's inferred existence to fill that need. Hence his genuine intellectual honesty. He is himself satisfied to argue from our need for God to the existence of God. But he does not ask his reader to follow him in that jump. He proposes a wager:

If there be a God, He is infinitely incomprehensible, since, having neither parts nor limits, He has no relation to us. We are, then, incapable of knowing either that He is or what He is.

Let us examine this point. "Either God is, or is not," we can say. But to which side shall we incline? Reason cannot help us. There is an infinite gulf fixed between creature and creator. What will you wager? It is like a game in which heads or tails may turn up. There is no reason for backing either the one possibility or the other. You cannot reasonably argue in favor of either.

If you know nothing either way, it might be urged, the true course is not to wager at all. But you must wager; that does not depend on your will. You are embarked in this business. Which will you choose?

Let us see. Since you must choose, your reason is no more affronted in choosing one way than the other. The point is clear. But what of your happiness? Let us weigh the gain and the loss in wagering that God does exist. If you wager that He does, and He does, you gain all; if you wager that He does, and He does not, you lose nothing. If you win, you take all; if you lose, you lose nothing. Wager then, unhesitatingly, that He does exist. This is demonstrable, and if men are capable of any truths, this is one.

If we ought to do nothing except on a certainty, we ought to do nothing for religion, because it is not a matter of certainty. But it is false to say, "We ought to do nothing except on a certainty." In a voyage at sea, in a battle, we act on uncertainties. If it be the case that we ought to do nothing except on a certainty, then we ought to do nothing at all, for nothing is certain.

You may object: "My hands are tied, my mouth is gagged. I am forced to wager, I am not free. But, despite this, I am so made that I cannot believe. What then would you have me do?"

I would have you understand your incapacity to believe. Labor to convince yourself, not by more "proofs" of God's existence, but by disciplining your passions and wayward emotions. You would arrive at faith, but know not the way. You would heal yourself of unbelief, yet know not the remedies. I answer: Learn of those who have been bound as you are. These are they who know the way you would follow, who have been cured of a disease you would be cured of. Follow the way by which they began, by making believe what they believed. Thus you will come to believe.

Now, what will happen to you if you take this side in the religious wager? You will be trustworthy, honorable, humble, grateful, generous, friendly, sincere, and true You will no longer have those poisoned pleasures, glory and luxury; but you will have other pleasures. I tell you that you will gain this life; at each step you will see so much certainty of gain, so much nothingness in what you stake, that you will know at last that you have wagered on a certainty, an infinity, for which you have risked nothing.

If my words please you, and seem to you cogent, know that they are the words of one who has thrown himself on his knees before and after to pray to that infinite Being to whom he submits all; know too that you also would submit to him your all for your own good and his glory, and that this strength may be in accord with this weakness.

Thus Pascal. Between the two of them, Thomas and this seventeenth-century religiously minded skeptic, they leave little more to be said on the question of natural theology. Hume, who follows in the eighteenth century only articulates more delicately the case against "reason" in these matters. Mill, in the nineteenth century, advances a startling hypothesis designed to save men like Thomas from the emotionalism of Pascal and the skepticism of Hume. James, in the twentieth century, comes full circle back to Pascal in a pragmatic approach to this perennial question.

Reading References. Aldous Huxley, the English novelist, has written what amounts to a small book on Pascal. It is to be found in his volume of essays, *Do What You Will*. In this study, Huxley attempts to "take Pascal to pieces" to see just precisely what it is that "makes the wheels go round." The result is catastrophic — for Huxley, if you agree with Pascal; for Pascal, if you agree with Huxley. Such highly seasoned and partisan treatment should be balanced by something more conventional and appreciative. Several first-rate monographs exist. Among these are *Pascal* by Jacques Chevalier and *Pascal — the Life of Genius* by Morris Bishop. Bishop's volume is more suited to those who come to the study of Pascal from Anglo-American traditions.

READING QUESTIONS

Pascal differs significantly from Thomas; in nothing, perhaps, more than in that elusive thing called *spirit* or *mood*. As one reads Thomas, one feels the presence of what is essentially a teacher, one who has the facts in hand and proposes to impart them in an orderly and dispassionate manner. One result is that it is comparatively easy to cross-question one's self on the points that are made and the general conclusions reached. It is otherwise with Pascal. The man is articulating a mood, rather than calmly arguing a case. To catch the point it is more important to get *en rapport* with the author than to bother much with the steps through which his thought proceeds. It is the difference, perhaps, between reading a page of Euclid and a page of Shelley.

1. What "unfairness," "foolishness," and "blindness" does Pascal begin by noting?
2. Why does he think such "carelessness" is "intolerable"?
3. Into what three classes would he divide mankind?
4. What is his attitude toward religious doubt?

5. What is the "chief glory of religion" so far as concerns indifferent skeptics?
6. What spectacle requires "all the love of the religion they despise"?
7. What is his attitude toward natural or rational theology?
8. Why does he describe his state as "pitiful"?
9. To what end does he contrast man with the atom and the cosmos?
10. Wherein is man a paradox to himself?
11. Why does Pascal wish to show this?
12. What kinds of facts strike terror into his (Pascal's) heart?
13. Why does Pascal introduce an appeal to happiness as a first step in his wager?
14. In what, according to Pascal, does man find his true happiness?
15. State the terms of his religious wager.
16. Why does he urge wagering for God?
17. What advice does he offer the congenital doubter?
18. What advantages does he foresee from belief?
19. Formulate one or more questions you would put to Pascal.

3. *A SKEPTICAL CRITIQUE OF NATURAL THEOLOGY — FROM DAVID HUME*

From Pascal to Hume. The problem of natural theology continued to command men's attention. We have examined what is perhaps the most typical orthodox presentation of these matters. We have seen their unargued repudiation by Pascal; a repudiation, however, which left no bitter taste in the devout reader's mouth, since Pascal strove earnestly to restore with one hand what he had swept aside with the other. By the middle of the eighteenth century times and tempers had changed. The "Age of Reason" had set in. The French Revolution was drawing nearer. The sciences, from their small beginnings with Galileo and Bacon and Harvey in the seventeenth century, had come to exercise an almost unquestioned dominion over the imaginations of the intellectual classes. It was in this somewhat more chilly climate of opinion that David Hume turned his critical attention to the central problem of natural theology.

Biographical Note. Hume was born in Scotland in 1711 and died in 1776 at the age of sixty-five. Although he was destined, along with Immanuel Kant, to mark the opening of an as yet unclosed chapter in the history of philosophy, his early life was passed in obscurity, and his fame, among his contemporaries, was based principally upon his writings in the field of political history. (1) He was intended by his father for the law, and to that end was educated in Edinburgh. Hume, however, abandoned the study of law and tried his hand in a Bristol counting-house. This, too, proved uncongenial. He went to France, where he proceeded to write one of the epoch-making books in modern philosophy, his *Treatise of Human Nature*. The theme of this philosophical masterpiece is simply stated in the form of a question: How much of human knowledge, human emotional preferences and aversions, human morality, is what it is for no better reason than the fact that human nature is what it is? The suggestion, that once you have taken the "human" out of these things there is nothing left over, was too much for his generation to entertain. It contained too many skeptical implications. The *Treatise* fell, as though stillborn, from the press. (2) Hume now set about to find some employment which would put him in a position of independence. He applied, without success, for the chair of moral philosophy in the University of Edinburgh. For two years he tutored an almost insane Scottish marquis. He accompanied a diplomatic expedition to France. He applied, again without success, for the chair of logic in the University of Glasgow. At last he secured the position of Keeper of the Advocates' Library in Edinburgh. The access to books and original authorities which this gave him, suggested the idea of writing a work on history. This he proceeded to do, and between the years 1754 and 1762, he produced his famous *History of England* which ranked, in that country, with Gibbon's *Decline and Fall of the Roman Empire*. (3) In the lean years before he became Keeper and turned historian, Hume continued reworking and expanding the ideas of his original philosophical treatise. These were published in a series of short monographs and collections of essays. In this form they gained a gradual acceptance. But it was still the historian who overshadowed the philosopher in the minds of his generation. He retired from active life in 1769, on a combined income and pension of £1,000 a year. He spent the remainder of his days, the recognized head of the intellectual and literary society in Edinburgh, admired by those who read his *History* and his miscellaneous essays, distrusted or misunderstood by those who tried their hand at his philosophy.

THE ARGUMENT OF THE CITATIONS. The selections which follow provide a skeptical examination of the principles of natural theology. They are, for the most part, from Hume's *Essay on Miracles* and *Dialogues Concerning Religion*. They presuppose, as a starting point, the general approach outlined in the chapter on Thomas Aquinas.

The position finally occupied by Hume is somewhat complex. It requires, therefore, a few words of introduction and summary. We may imagine Hume saying to himself: "Now, as to this matter of natural theology. Either we have knowledge of God's existence and nature, or we do not. If we do not possess such knowledge, there is no call for a skeptical examination of the beliefs which embody such knowledge. If, however, we do possess, or claim to possess, such knowledge, then it must rest on some sort of evidence. What is this evidence? It is formulated, usually, in three 'arguments.' There is the argument from miracles, the argument from design, and the argument from first cause.

A skeptical examination of the claims of natural theology will resolve itself finally into a skeptical examination of these three arguments. We shall advance two lines of criticism with respect to each: first, that the argument itself is very questionable; second, that even if it were accepted without question, it does not prove what it is claimed to prove." This outline of Hume's position is perhaps more systematic than the citations will at first suggest. But a careful study of what he says will, I think, leave some such general claim in one's mind. A word of caution: It is well to remember the limitations of the task which Hume sets himself to perform. He is not attempting to prove that God does not exist; that is, he is not stating the case for atheism. Nor is he seeking to discredit all belief in God. His claim is the more modest one, namely, that such belief, whether true or false is not susceptible of the traditional rational justification; that no appeal to reason, in the sense in which that appeal is made by Thomas, can be made in support of the claims of natural theology.

Belief in God has, in times past, been supported by what is called the *argument from miracles*. It is to this effect: Miracles, violations of natural laws, occur from time to time. An explanation of such events must therefore refer to something outside or beyond nature. That is, miracles point to a miracle-worker, namely, God. Hence Hume's interest in the question of miracles. His approach is indirect, as will be seen. He does not, as a well-known writer in the nineteenth century did, deny that miracles ever happen. He directs attention to the nature of the evidence upon which we believe that miracles happen and claims that the evidence in question is not strong enough to support any such belief. This rather oblique approach characterizes most of the man's writings and should, therefore, be watched carefully from the start.

I flatter myself I have discovered an argument which will be an everlasting check to all kinds of superstitious delusion, all accounts of miracles and prodigies sacred and profane.

A miracle is a violation of the laws of nature. Now, as a firm and unalterable experience has established our belief in those laws, the proof against miracles, from the very nature of the case, is as entire as any argument from experience can possibly be imagined. There must be a uniform experience against any miracle; otherwise it would not be so described. Now, as a uniform experience amounts to a proof, there is here a full proof against the occurrence of any miracle. Nor can such a proof against any miracle be weakened or destroyed, except by an opposite proof which would be superior to it.

The plain consequence is this: No testimony is sufficient to establish a miracle unless the testimony be of such a kind that its falsehood would be as miraculous as, or more miraculous than, the fact which it endeavors to establish. Even in that case there is a mutual destruction of arguments; and the superior only gives us an assurance suitable to that degree of evidential force which remains after deducting the inferior.

A man tells me he saw one dead restored to life. I ask myself: Is it more probable that he should deceive or be deceived, or that the fact which he relates should really have happened? I weigh one miracle against the other, and reject the greater. If the falsehood of his testimony would be more miraculous than the event which he relates, then (but not until then) can he command my belief.

There are two parts to Hume's criticism of the evidence for believing that miracles happen. The first, and most incisive, has been given already: Miracles purport to be violations of the laws of nature. Our evidence for believing in the uniformity of nature is very great; so great, in fact, that no evidence for doubting it could possibly be strong enough, since it would have to be stronger than the evidence for believing in nature's uniformity and this latter includes practically all our experience. Hume's point here is subtle, but important. He moves on to his second criticism:

We have supposed in the foregoing that the evidence for a miracle may be so strong that its falsehood would itself be a miracle. But it is easy to show that we have been a great deal too liberal in our concessions, and that no miracle has ever been established on so full an evidence.

First: There is not to be found in all history any miracle attested by a sufficient number of men of such unquestioned good sense, education, and learning, as to secure us against all delusion in themselves; of such undoubted integrity as to place them beyond all suspicion of any design to deceive others; of such credit and reputation as to have a great deal to lose in case of being detected in any falsehood; and, at the same time, attesting facts in such a manner and in so celebrated a place as to render that detection unavoidable.

Second: The many instances of mistaken or fraudulent miracles which have been detected show that mankind have a strong propensity to believe in the extraordinary and marvelous. This fact ought reasonably to beget a suspicion against all narratives concerning such matters.

Third: Reports of miracles abound chiefly among ignorant and barbarous peoples; or if such reports have been admitted by civilized and educated peoples they will be found to have received them from ignorant and barbarous peoples who transmitted them with that sanction and authority which, among such peoples, attends received opinions. This fact constitutes a strong presumption against all accounts of miracles.

Fourth: There is no *a priori* case in favor of the miracles peculiar to any one religion. The miracles of all religions stand on the same footing. If any such should be mutually incompatible, they simply cancel each other out. Nor is there any *a priori* case in favor of religious over secular miracles.

Fifth: The records of miracles in ancient times are not to be placed on an equal level with the records of nonmiraculous events in ancient times. Because some human testimony has the utmost force and authority in some cases, as when it relates to the battle of Philippi or Pharsalia, the assassination of Caesar or the execution of Socrates, it is not therefore reasonable that all kinds of testimony must, in all cases, have equal force and authority.

It appears, then, that no testimony for any kind of miracle has ever amounted to a probability, much less a proof. Experience only gives authority to human testimony, and it is experience which assures us of the laws of nature. When, therefore, these two kinds of experiences are contrary, we can only subtract the one from the other and embrace the opinion with that assurance which arises from the remainder. But, according to the measures of probability above established, this subtraction amounts to entire annihilation. Therefore no human testimony can have such force as to prove a miracle and make it a just foundation for any system of religion.

Mere reason is not sufficient to convince us of the miracles of the Christian religion. Whoever is moved by faith to assent to it, is conscious of a continued miracle in his own person, which subverts all the principles of his understanding and gives him a determination to believe what is most contrary to custom and experience.

The net result of what has been said thus far comes to this: Belief in God rests in part on belief in miracles. Belief in miracles rests on questionable grounds. Belief in God, therefore, insofar as it rests on belief in miracles, rests on questionable grounds. Hume's case against the argument from miracles ends at that point. He might have rounded out his argument with greater force. This was done by T. H. Huxley, Hume's biographer, in the next century. It amounts to this: Suppose the evidence for believing in miracles is left unquestioned. Suppose, that is, that we admit without argument, that miracles do take place. What follows? Belief in the Deity described by Thomas? It would seem not. For miracles are a very equivocal kind of evidence. They point frequently to a Deity who befriends some people at the expense of others. Consider, for example, the Old Testament miracle of the taking of Jericho. What kind of evidence would this be, in the eyes of a citizen of

Jericho? Or consider the miracle of the Gadarene swine recorded in the New Testament. What kind of evidence would this be, in the eyes of the unfortunate individual who owned those swine, or (to stretch a point) in the eyes of the still more unfortunate swine? These, and similar miracles, are not unequivocal testimony to Deity's universal benevolence. Moreover, if miracles are evidence of His benevolence, why do they fail to occur in so many cases where benevolence would seem to be very much in order, for example, when a vessel is sinking in a storm at sea? The point is a simple one and does not, perhaps, deserve elaboration. It is merely this: The fact of miracles, even if not disputed, does not provide us with decisive evidence one way or the other about the nature of God. And, when evidence points in opposite directions, it is wiser to omit it altogether.

Hume proceeds, in his examination of the principles of natural theology to a statement and refutation of the *argument from design*. This is one of his most famous pieces of destructive criticism. It demands, and repays, careful attention.

The chief argument for divine existence is derived from the order of nature. Where there appear marks of intelligence and design, you think it extravagant to assign for its cause either chance or the blind unguided force of matter. This is an argument from effects to causes. From the order of the work, you infer there must have been project and forethought in the workman.

Look around the world. Contemplate the whole and every part of it. You will find it to be nothing but one great machine, subdivided into an infinite number of lesser machines, which again admit of subdivisions to a degree beyond what human senses can trace and explain.

All these various machines, and even their most minute parts, are adjusted to each other with an accuracy which ravishes into admiration all men who have ever contemplated them. The curious adapting of means to ends, throughout all nature, resembles exactly, though it much exceeds, the productions of human contrivance, human design, human thought, wisdom, intelligence.

Anatomize the eye. Survey its structure and contrivance. Does not the idea of contriver immediately flow in upon you with the force like that of a sensation? Behold the male and female of each species, their instincts, their passions, the whole course of their life before and after generation. Millions of such instances present themselves through every part of the universe. Can language convey a more intelligible, more irresistible meaning than the curious adjustment of means to ends in nature?

Since the effects (natural productions and human productions) resemble each other, you are led to infer, by analogy, that the causes also resemble; that the author of nature is somewhat similar to the mind of man, though possessed of larger powers, proportioned to the grandeur of the work He has created.

You compare the universe to productions of human intelligence, to houses, ships, furniture, machines, and so forth. Since both terms of the comparison exhibit adaptation and design, you argue that the cause of the one must resemble the cause of the other.

The above citations give Hume's statement of the argument from design. It requires condensation, if we are to catch the point of his criticism. The argument from design, he says, is an argument from analogy. What he means is something like this: We examine a watch, a house, or a ship, and we conclude that such things were produced by beings possessing intelligence and controlled by purposes. We can, if we wish, verify this inference by acquainting ourselves with watchmakers, architects and shipwrights. We examine the universe, or parts of it, and conclude that it too must have been produced by a being possessing intelligence and controlled by purposes. Our reason for drawing this inference is that we do, as a matter of fact, find the universe, or parts of it, intelligible and answering to our needs and purposes. That is, we draw the analogy watch-watchmaker and universe-Deity. From the intelligibility and utility of a watch, we infer intelligence and purposiveness in the watchmaker. By analogy, from the intelligibility and utility of nature we infer intelligence and purposiveness in the author of nature. Hume's entire critique is directed toward undermining the strength of the proposed analogy between human-product-human-producer, on the one hand, and nature-author-of-nature on the other. "Is the analogy entire and perfect?" he asks and proceeds to show in what respects he thinks it is weak.

When two things (human intelligence and the products of human intelligence) have been observed to be conjoined, you can infer, by custom, from the one to the other. This I call an *argument from experience*. But how this argument can have place in the present case, may be difficult to explain. If you see a house, you can conclude it had an architect or builder because such effects, you have experienced, proceed from such causes.

But does the universe resemble a house so closely that we can with the same certainty infer a similar cause? Is the analogy entire and perfect? Can you pretend here to more than a guess, a conjecture, a presumption, concerning a similar cause? To ascertain such reasoning, it were necessary that you have had experience in the origin of the world. Have worlds ever been formed under your eye? Have you experienced the generation of the universe as you have experienced the building of a house?

If you survey a ship, you form an exalted idea of the ingenuity of the builder. You find him a stupid mechanic who imitated others, who copied an art which through a long succession of ages, after multiplied mistakes, corrections, deliberations, and controversies has been gradually improving. On your argument, then, many worlds might have been botched and bungled ere this one was arrived at; much labor lost; many fruitless trials made; a slow improvement during infinite ages in the art of world-making.

When you read a book, you enter into the mind and intention of the author, and have an immediate feeling and conception of those ideas which revolved in his imagination while employed in that composition. Is it thus when you read the book of nature?

By this argument from analogy, how prove the unity of Deity? Many men join in building a house or ship or city or commonwealth. Why may not several deities have combined in framing a world? This is only so much greater similarity to human affairs, to the operation of human intelligence. By dividing thus the work among several, you would get rid of that extensive power and knowledge which must be supposed in one deity.

Were one deity, who possessed every attribute necessary to the production of the universe, and not many deities, proved by this argument from analogy, it would be needless to suppose any other deity. But while it is still an open question whether all these attributes are united in one deity or dispersed among several independent deities, by what phenomena in nature can you pretend to decide the controversy? On this kind of argument from nature, polytheism and monotheism are on a like footing. Neither has any advantage over the other.

By this method of reasoning from analogy you renounce all claim to perfection in any of the attributes of the Deity. Imperfections in human productions you ascribe to imperfections in human producers. There are many inexplicable difficulties in the work of nature. Are you to ascribe these to the imperfections of the author of nature?

By representing Deity as so intelligible and comprehensible, so similar to a human mind, you make ourselves the model. Is this reasonable? The sentiments of the human mind include gratitude and resentment, love and hate, friendship and enmity, blame and approval, pity and scorn, admiration and envy. Do you propose to transfer such sentiments to a Supreme Being? Or suppose Him actuated by them? Do you propose to ascribe to Him only knowledge and power but no virtues?

The above citations bring out several difficulties in the proposed analogy which, Hume thinks, lie at the heart of the argument from design. The criticism continues, the point of attack being shifted slightly. From the nature of the product, you infer certain characteristics in the producer; from a man's handiwork you infer that the man is of such-

and-such character. Hume has no objection to this. His next point is merely that we should extend the same reasoning to the world and the maker of the world. What sort of place is this world, anyway? Is it such that we are obliged to argue that its author must have possessed the benevolent and providential attributes ascribed to him by traditional theology?

Can any man, by a simple denial, hope to bear down the united testimony of mankind? The whole earth is cursed and polluted. A perpetual war is kindled among all living creatures. Necessity, hunger, want, stimulate the strong and courageous; fear, anxiety, terror, agitate the weak and the infirm. The first entrance into life gives anguish to the newborn infant and to parent. Weakness, impotence, distress, attend each stage of many lives which are finished at last in agony and horror.

Is it not thus in nature? Observe the curious artifices of nature to embitter the life of living beings. The stronger prey upon the weaker, and keep them in perpetual terror and misery. The weaker, too, often prey upon the stronger. Consider these species of insects which are bred on the body of animals, or flying about, infix their stings into them. These insects have others, still more minute, which torment them. On every hand animals are surrounded with enemies which cause their misery and seek their destruction.

Why should man pretend to be exempted from the lot which befalls all other animals? Man is the greatest enemy of man. Oppression, injustice, contempt, slander, violence, sedition, war — by these men torment each other. The external ills of humanity, from the elements, from other animals, from men themselves, form a frightful catalogue of woes; but they are nothing compared with those that arise from conditions within. How many lie under the lingering torment of disease? How many suffer remorse, shame, anguish, rage, disappointment, fear, despair? How many suffer those deep disorders of mind, insanity, idiocy, madness? Who has passed through life without cruel inroads from these tormentors?

Were a stranger to drop into this world, I would show him, as a specimen of its ills, a hospital full of diseases, a prison crowded with malefactors, a battlefield strewn with carcasses, a fleet floundering in the ocean, a nation languishing under tyranny, famine, or pestilence. Labor and poverty are the certain lot of the far greater number, while the few who enjoy riches and ease never reach contentment or true felicity. All the good things of life taken together make a man very wretched indeed.

You ascribe an author to nature, and a purpose to the author of nature. What, I beseech you, is the object fulfilled by these matters to which attention has been drawn? Our sense of music, harmony, beauty, has some purpose. But what of gout, gravels, megrims, toothaches, rheumatisms? How does divine benevolence and purpose display itself here? Why argue for the power and knowledge of the Deity while His moral qualities are in doubt?

You say: But this world is only a point in comparison of the universe; this life is but a moment in comparison of eternity. Present evils are rectified in other regions and future times. And the eyes of men, being then opened to large views of things see the whole connection of general laws, and trace with adoration the benevolence and wisdom of the Deity through all the mazes and intricacies of his providence.

I answer: The only method of supporting divine benevolence is for you to deny outright the misery and wickedness of man; to say to me, "Your representations are exaggerated; your melancholy views are mostly fictitious; your inferences are contrary to fact and experience; health is more common than sickness; pleasure, than pain; happiness, than misery; for one vexation we meet, we attain a hundred enjoyments."

I add: Can such apologetics be admitted? Even allowing your claim that human happiness exceeds human misery, yet it proves nothing. For an excess of happiness over misery is not what we expect from infinite power coupled with infinite wisdom and infinite goodness.

The questions asked by Epicurus, of old, are yet unanswered. Is Deity willing to prevent evil, but not able? Then He is impotent. Is He able, but not willing? Then He is malevolent. Is He both able and willing? Then whence cometh evil? Is He neither able nor willing? Then why call Him Deity?

Evil and unhappiness are the rocks upon which all arguments for Deity must finally come to wreck. Why is there any misery and wickedness at all in the world? Not by chance, surely. From some purpose or cause then? Is it from the intention of the Deity? But He is perfectly benevolent. Is it contrary to his intention? But He is almighty. Nothing can shake the solidity of this reasoning, so short, so clear, so decisive; unless we agree that these matters lie beyond human capacity, that our human reason is not applicable to them. This is the counsel of skepticism that I have all along insisted on.

In the above citations Hume has been making capital out of the problem of evil which we meet with in Thomas' treatment of natural theology. He has, by this time, made his two principal criticisms of the argument from design: The analogy upon which it rests cannot be admitted; and even if it were admitted, it would come to grief over the problem of evil. However, he cannot let it go at that. The next seven citations give a different line of criticism. The point which they make is sufficiently self-evident to require little comment. From God as Designer, he turns to God as Soul, of the world.

You have argued, thus far, on the principle that like effects have like causes. But there is another you might try, based no less on experience: Where several known parts are observed to be similar, the unknown parts will also be found similar. Thus, if you see the limbs of a human body, you conclude that it is attended with a human head, though hid from you. If you see a small part of the sun, through a chink in the wall, you conclude that, were the wall removed, you should see the rest. Within the limits of experience, this method of reasoning is obvious and reliable.

Now I say, if you survey the universe, so far as it falls under your knowledge, it bears a great resemblance to an animal, or organized body, and seems actuated by a like principle of life and motion. A continual circulation of matter produces no disorder. A continual waste in every part is incessantly repaired. Each part, in performing its proper offices, operates both to its own preservation and that of the whole. From all this, why not infer that the world is an organism, an animal, and that Deity is the soul of the world, actuating it and being actuated by it?

If it be legitimate to argue thus by analogy from part to whole, I affirm that other parts of the world bear a greater resemblance to the structure of the world than do matters of human invention; and, therefore, should afford a better conjecture concerning the origin and nature of the whole. These parts are animals and vegetables. The world resembles more an organism than a clock or a knitting loom. Its cause, therefore, more probably resembles the cause of the former, namely, generation.

As a tree sheds its seed into neighboring fields, so the great system of the world produces certain seeds which, being scattered into the surrounding chaos, grow into new worlds. A comet, for instance, may be taken as such a seed. After it has been fully ripened, by passing from sun to sun and star to star, it is at last tossed into the unformed elements which surround this universe, and sprouts into a new system.

Or, for variety (for I see no other advantage), suppose this world to be an animal instead of a vegetable. A comet then would be an egg. And, in like manner as an ostrich lays its egg in the sand, which without any further care hatches the egg, so . . .

You protest: What wild, arbitrary suppositions are these? What data have I for such extraordinary conclusions? Is the slight resemblance of the world to a vegetable or animal sufficient basis for an argument as to further resemblances? You are right. This is what I have been insisting on, all along. We have no data, or insufficient data, for any such speculations. Our experience, from which alone we can argue safely, is so limited in extent and duration as to afford us no probable conjecture concerning the whole of things.

If you agree that our limited experience is an unequal standard by which to judge of the unlimited extent of nature, a too narrow stretch upon which to erect hypotheses concerning so vast a matter, you entirely abandon your case, and must admit of the absolute incomprehensibility of the author of nature.

The whole matter is summarized in the two following citations:

In a word, a man who follows this kind of argument from analogy, where one of the terms of the analogy lies beyond his experience, may perhaps be able to conjecture that the universe arose from something like design. But beyond that he cannot go, except by the utmost license of thought.

On this argument, for all you know to the contrary, this world may be a very faulty and imperfect copy compared to a superior standard; only the first rude essay of some infant deity who afterwards abandoned it, ashamed of his lame performance; only the work of some dependent, inferior deity, the object of derision to his superiors; only the product of old age and dotage in some superannuated deity, and ever since his death running on at adventures from the first impulse it received from him.

Thus far, the argument from miracles and the argument from design. It comes to this. The argument from the analogy of human producers led one to deny or left one unable to account for the facts of evil and misery, and led one to admit or left one unable to deny the absurd speculations which he suggested regarding the organic nature and origin of the world. If this *a posteriori* argument presented so many difficulties, would one fare better with the *a priori* argument from first Cause? By this argument could one prove the infinity, the unity, and the perfection, of the author of nature? Hume states this argument as follows:

The argument from first cause is this. Whatever exists must have a cause of its existence. Nothing can produce itself. In mounting up, therefore, from effects to causes, we must go on tracing an infinite regression without any ultimate cause, or must finally have recourse to an ultimate cause. Now, it is insisted, the conception of an infinite regression, of utterly no beginning cause to which all others can be traced, is absurd. We must, therefore, have recourse to a necessarily existent being, the first cause of all things, who carries the reason of His existence in Himself, and whom we cannot suppose not to exist without embracing an absurdity. Such a being is the Deity.

His criticism is brief and to the point:

> Wherein do we find the absurdity of an infinite regression? It leads us beyond our powers of conceiving? So also does the conception of an infinite deity.
>
> Let us admit its absurdity. Let us admit the necessity of a first cause. Shall we then ask for a cause of this cause? If not, then may we not argue a material first cause of this material universe? If not, may we ascribe to the spiritual first cause the origin of evil and misery and waste which we noted in our analysis of the argument from analogy? If not, to what cause then are they to be traced? If so, wherein do we fare better with the argument from the necessity of a first cause than from the probability of an intelligent designer?

His conclusion to the whole business is a frank plea for skepticism in natural theology:

> All religious systems are subject to insuperable difficulties. Each disputant triumphs in his turn, exposing the absurdities, barbarities, and pernicious tenets of his antagonist. But all of them prepare a complete triumph for the skeptic who tells them no system ought ever to be embraced with regard to such questions. A total suspense of judgment is here our only reasonable recourse.

The upshot of Hume's critique of natural theology is skepticism. Its historical importance is to be seen along several lines. In the first place, it was a nemesis visited upon the Age of Reason; for what Hume showed his rationalistic century was precisely the helplessness of reason to cope with the problems of natural theology. In some minds this work has never been undone. There is a sense in which Hume administered a deathblow to the speculations at which he directed his attention. Rational theology, in the grand manner of Thomas and the seventeenth- and eighteenth-century deists, has never been completely restored to its former intellectual respectability. In the second place, Hume's handling of these questions led to an interesting attempt, by John Stuart Mill in the following century, to introduce into theology the conception of a finite God; in the twentieth century, to the pragmatic approach to these matters in the writings of the American, William James.

READING REFERENCES. Hume's skeptical examination of the principles of natural theology forms only one part of his general philosophy. He cultivated comparable doubts in other fields. The reading from Hume given in the third chapter of this book, the chapter dealing with epistemology, provides the premises from which he approached all problems. These will be looked at at that point, and some references noted. There are, however, one or two pieces of philosophical commentary which deal with Hume as critic of natural theology. These are worth reading. The first of these is A. E. Taylor's lecture, *David Hume and the Miraculous*. This lecture is published in the form of a little book, and again in a volume of philosophical essays. The second is Chapter 6, of Volume 2, of Sir Leslie Stephen's *English Thought in the Eighteenth Century*.

READING QUESTIONS

1. Why is Hume interested in a critique of the belief in miracles?
2. Formulate the argument from miracles in support of theism.
3. Why, according to Hume, must the evidence for miracles be unusually strong?
4. How strong, precisely, must it be?
5. For what five reasons, according to Hume, can it never be strong enough?
6. Why are miracles an equivocal kind of evidence for theism?
7. To what analogy does Hume reduce the argument from design?
8. "On this argument, many worlds might have been botched . . ." How so?

9. "By this argument, how prove the unity of the Deity?" Why not?
10. "By this argument you renounce all claim to perfection in the Deity." Why so?
11. "By this argument you make ourselves the model." Why so?
12. Why does Hume describe nature in such gloomy terms?
13. "Present evils are rectified in other regions and future times." What is his comment?
14. What trilemma did Epicurus formulate?
15. What is the argument "by analogy from part to whole"?
16. What absurdities does Hume develop, granted this analogy?
17. Why does he do this?
18. What follows, "for all you know to the contrary," on this argument?
19. What two criticisms does he make of the argument from first cause?
20. Are these decisive? Wherein do they fail to meet Thomas' presentation of this argument?
21. Formulate one or more questions you would put to Hume.

4. AN ARGUMENT FOR LIMITED THEISM—FROM JOHN STUART MILL

From Hume to Mill. The student who has followed these readings thus far should find himself, by now, in possession of a considerable amount of natural theology. With Thomas, he examined the great tradition. With Pascal, he noted the appeal from reason to feeling and need. With Hume he reviewed skeptically the arguments from miracles, from design, and from first cause. This brings matters to the close of the eighteenth century. In the century which followed, several interesting variations were struck in philosophical theology. Not the least among these was John Stuart Mill's celebrated attempt to save natural theology from skepticism by advancing the challenging hypothesis that an appeal to reason might be made in support of belief in a finite or limited Deity.

Biographical Note. John Stuart Mill was born in England in 1806 and died in 1873 at the age of sixty-seven. The late Lord Morley, in a review of Mill's life and work, referred to him as "the saint of Victorian rationalism." He might well have added "and of Victorian liberalism." For a great portion of Mill's contribution to modern liberalism is summed up in two propositions: that human reason applied to the data of human experience is the only source of human knowledge; and that a maximum of individual liberty of thought and action is the surest means of extending knowledge and increasing happiness. In the elaboration and defense of these claims he wrote book after book which came, in time, to form the staples of British liberalism in the nineteenth century. That all knowledge comes from experience is the thesis of his *System of Logic*. That the distribution of wealth is the fundamental problem in economics is the thesis of his *Principles of Political Economy*. That freedom of thought and action is the safest guarantee of individual and social well-being is the thesis of his essay *On Liberty*. That an act is right if, and only if, it produces more happiness than any other act possible, is the thesis of his *Utilitarianism*. That government by elected representatives is preferable to either constitutional monarchy or an enlightened aristocracy is the thesis of his *Considerations on Representative Government*. That women have as much right to votes and careers as men, is the thesis of *The Subjection of Women*. That the evils of a capitalistic economy give some point to the doctrines of socialists is the thesis of his *Socialism*. And that only so much as can be grounded in experience should be retained in a living theology, is the thesis of *Three Essays on Religion*. For further biographical material, see page 321.

The Argument of the Citations. In this chapter Mill seeks to establish (1) that Deity is a Being of "great but limited power"; (2) that He is a Being of "great and perhaps unlimited knowledge and intelligence"; (3) that benevolence but not justice is one of His attributes; (4) and that a theology centering in this conception has several things to recommend it over the more traditional views. The citations are from his essay on theism. The argument opens as follows:

The most important quality of an opinion on any momentous subject is its truth or falsity. It is indispensable that the subject of religion should be reviewed from time to time, and that its questions should be tested by the same methods, and on the same principles as any of the speculative conclusions drawn by physical science.

From this introductory remark, Mill passes at once to a consideration of the argument from design. He prefers it because it "is grounded wholly on our experience of the appearances of the universe"; that is, we can see order and harmony and adaptation of some sort by merely observing the nature of things, whereas we have no experience whatever of such things as first causes and unmoved movers.

Whatever ground there is to believe in an author of nature is derived from the appearances of the universe. The argument from design is grounded wholly on our experience of the appearances of the universe. It is, therefore, a far more important argument for theism than any other.

Mill's formulation of the argument from design, given in the next six citations, is somewhat more elaborate than we have met hitherto. His words bear close attention:

The order of nature exhibits certain qualities that are found to be characteristic of such things as are made by an intelligent mind for a purpose. We are entitled from this great similarity in the effects to infer similarity in the cause, and to believe that things which it is beyond the power of man to make, but which resemble the works of man in all but power, must also have been made by intelligence armed with a power greater than human.

The argument from design is not drawn from mere resemblances in nature to the works of human intelligence, but from the special character of those resemblances. The circumstances in which it is alleged that the world resembles the works of man are not circumstances taken at random, but are particular instances of a circumstance which experience shows to have a real connection with an intelligent origin; the fact, namely, of conspiring to an end or purpose.

To show this, it will be convenient to handle, not the argument from design as a whole, but some one of the most impressive cases of it, such as the structure of the eye or the ear. It is maintained that the structure of the eye proves a designing mind. The argument may be analyzed as follows:

1. The parts of which the eye is composed, and the arrangement of these parts, resemble one another in this very remarkable respect, that they all conduce to enabling the animal to see. These parts and their arrangement being as they are, the animal sees. This is the only marked resemblance we can trace among the different parts of the eye; beyond the general likeness in composition which exists among all other parts of the animal.

2. Now, the combination of the parts of the eye had a beginning in time and must therefore have been brought together by a cause or causes. The number of instances (of such parts being brought together to enable organisms to see) is immensely greater than is required to exclude the possibility of a random or chance concurrence of independent causes. We are therefore warranted in concluding that what has brought all these parts together was some cause common to them all. And, since the parts agree in the single respect of combining to produce sight, there must be some connection between the cause which brought the parts together, and the fact of sight.

3. Now sight, being a fact which follows the putting together of the parts of the eye, can only be connected with the production of the eye as a final cause, not an efficient cause; since all efficient causes precede their effects. But a final cause is a purpose, and at once marks the origin of the eye as proceeding from an intelligent will.

At this point we should expect Mill to proceed with his evaluation of the design argument. But he proposes, instead, to develop an alternative explanation covering the type of facts which would be explained by the hypothesis of God's existence if that hypothesis were accepted. This alternative to "creative forethought," or "intelligent will," is the hypothesis of "natural selection" suggested by Mill's contemporary, Charles Darwin. The important point to notice is the way in which natural selection, if granted as an hypothesis, would account for the type of fact which seems to demand explanation in terms of intelligent will.

Of what value is this argument? Is intelligent will, or creative forethought, the only hypothesis that will account for the facts? I regret to say that it is not. Creative forethought is not the only link by which the origin of the mechanism of the eye may be connected with the fact of sight. There is another connecting link on which attention has been greatly fixed by recent speculation. This is the principle of natural selection, of "the survival of the fittest."

This principle of the survival of the fittest does not pretend to account for the origin of sensation, or of animal or vegetable life. It assumes the existence of some one or more very low forms of organic life, in which there are no complex adaptations. It next assumes, as experience warrants us in doing, that many small variations from those simple types would be thrown out, which would be transmissible by inheritance, some of which would be advantageous to the creature in its struggle for existence and others disadvantageous. The forms which are advantageous would always tend to survive; and those which are disadvantageous, to perish. Thus there would be a constant, though slow, general improvement of the type as it branched out into many different varieties, until it might attain to the most advanced examples which now exist.

It must be acknowledged that there is something very startling, and *prima facie* improbable in this hypothetical history of nature.

With reference to the eye, for example, it would require us to suppose that the primeval animal could not see, and had at most such slight preparation for seeing as might be constituted by some chemical action of light upon its cellular structure; that an accidental variation (mutation) would produce a variety that could see in some imperfect manner; that this peculiarity would be transmitted by inheritance while other variations continued to take place in other directions; that a number of races would thus be produced who, by the power of even imperfect sight, would have a great advantage over all other races which could not see and would in time extirpate them from all places except perhaps from a few very peculiar situations underground. Fresh variations would give rise to races with better and better seeing powers until we might at last reach as extraordinary a combination of structures and functions as are seen in the eye of man and of the more important animals.

Of this theory, when pushed to this extreme point, all that can now be said is that it is not so absurd as it looks; and that the analogies which have been discovered in experience, favorable to its possibility, far exceed what anyone could have supposed beforehand. Whether it will ever be possible to say more than this is at present uncertain.

Leaving this remarkable speculation to whatever fate the progress of discovery may have in store for it, I think it must be allowed that, in the present state of our knowledge, the adaptions in nature afford a large balance of probability in favor of creation by intelligence. It is equally certain that this is no more than a probability.

Having noted these two hypotheses, creative forethought and natural selection, and rejected the latter as less probable, Mill turns to the question of the nature of the being whose creative forethought is under consideration:

The question of the existence of a Deity standing thus, it is next to be considered what sort of Deity do the indications point to? What attributes are we warranted, by the evidence which nature accords of a creative mind, in assigning to that mind?

The first attribute is great but limited power:

It needs no showing that the power, if not the intelligence, must be so far superior to that of man as to surpass all human estimate.

but from this to omnipotence and omniscience there is a wide interval. And the distinction is of immense importance.

For I shall argue that the net result of natural theology, on the question of the divine attributes is this: a Being of great but limited power; how, or by what, limited we cannot even conjecture; of great, perhaps unlimited intelligence; who desires and pays some regard to the happiness of His creatures but who seems to have other motives of action for which He cares more, and who can hardly be supposed to have created the universe for that purpose alone.

Then follow the passages in which this claim is supported by a series of ingenious arguments:

Every indication of design in the cosmos is so much evidence against the omnipotence of the designer. For what is meant by *design*? Contrivance, the adaptation of means to end. But the necessity for contrivance, the need of employing "means" to achieve an "end," is a consequence of the limitation of power.

Who would have recourse to means, to attain his end, if his mere wish or word was enough? The very idea of *means* implies that the means have an efficacy which the direct action of the being who employs them has not. Otherwise, they are not means but an encumbrance.

A man does not use machinery to move his arms; unless he is paralyzed, i.e., has not the power to do so directly by his volition.

But, if the use of contrivance is a sign of limited power, how much more so is the careful and skillful choice of contrivance? Could we speak of "wisdom in the selection of means," if he who selects them could, by his mere will, have achieved the same results without them, or by any other means? Wisdom and contrivance are shown in overcoming difficulties, and there is no room for difficulties, and so no room for wisdom or contrivance, in an omnipotent being.

Any evidences of design in nature, therefore, distinctly imply that the author of nature worked under limitations; that he was obliged to adapt himself to conditions independent of his will, and to attain his ends by such arrangements as those conditions admitted of.

On this hypothesis, the Deity had to work out His ends by combining materials of given nature and properties. This did require skill and contrivance; and the means by which it is effected are often such as justly excite our wonder and admiration. But, exactly because it requires wisdom, skill, contrivance, it implies limitation of power.

It may be said: An omnipotent Creator, though under no necessity of employing contrivances such as man must use, thought fit to do so in order to leave traces by which man might recognize his Creator's hand.

The answer is: This equally supposes a limit to the Deity's omnipotence, for it is a contrivance to achieve an end. Moreover, if it was His will that man should know that they and the world are His work, He, being omnipotent, had only to will that they should be aware of it.

From the question of God's power, Mill turns to the question of His knowledge and wisdom. The claim here is that there are probably no grounds for ascribing infinite knowledge or intelligence to Deity:

Omnipotence, therefore, cannot be predicated of the Creator on the evidences of design in nature. But what of omniscience? If we suppose limitation of power, must we also suppose limitation of knowledge and wisdom?

To argue that Deity possesses only limited power does not preclude us from ascribing unlimited knowledge and wisdom to Him. But there is nothing to prove it. The knowledge and wisdom necessary to planning and arranging the cosmos are, no doubt, as much in excess of human knowledge as the power implied is in excess of human power. But nothing obliges us to suppose that either the knowledge or the skill is infinite.

We are not even obliged to suppose that the contrivances and arrangements were always the best possible. If we judge them as we judge the work of human artificers, we find abundant defects. The human body, for example, is one of the most striking instances of artful and ingenious contrivance which nature offers. But we may well ask whether so complicated a machine could not have been made to last longer, and not get out of order so easily and frequently.

We may ask why the human race should have been so constituted as to grovel in wretchedness and degradation for countless ages before a small portion of it was enabled to lift itself into the very imperfect state of intelligence, goodness, and happiness which we enjoy.

If, however, Deity, like human rule, had to adapt Himself to a set of conditions which He did not make, it is as unphilosophical, as presumptuous in us to call Him to account for any imperfections in His work; to complain that he left anything in it contrary to what (if indications of design prove anything) He must have intended.

Great but limited power. Great, perhaps unlimited, knowledge and intelligence. What moral attributes? To settle this question Mill suggests a consideration of the probable purposes of the author of nature. The idea here is that one's moral qualities will be embodied in, and therefore inferable from, whatever one devotes time and forethought to making or doing. The only conclusion Mill is able to reach is "some benevolence but no justice." The argument is as follows:

Assuming then, that while we confine ourselves to the evidences of design in nature, there is no ground for ascribing infinite power, and probably no grounds for ascribing infinite knowledge or intelligence to Deity, the question arises as to the same evidence afforded with regard to His moral attributes. What indications does nature give of the purposes of its author?

This question bears a very different aspect to us from what it bears to those who are encumbered with the doctrine of the omnipotence of Deity. We do not have to attempt the impossible problem of reconciling infinite benevolence and justice with infinite power and knowledge in such a world as this. The attempt to do so involves a contradiction, and exhibits to excess the revolting spectacle of a jesuitical defense of enormities.

To what purpose, then, do the expedients and contrivances in the construction of animals and vegetables appear to tend? These are the "adaptations" which most excite our admiration. If they afford evidence of design, of purpose, in nature, we can best hope to be enlightened by examining such parts of nature.

There is no blinking the fact that these animal and vegetable adaptations tend principally to no more exalted object than to make the structure remain in life and in working order for a certain time: the individual for a few years, the species for a longer but still limited period.

The greater part of the design or adaptation in nature, however wonderful its mechanism, is, therefore, no evidence of any moral attributes in the author of nature; because the end to which it is directed is not a moral end: it is not the good of any creature but the qualified permanence, for a limited period of the work itself.

The only inference that can be drawn from most of nature, respecting the character of the author of nature, is that He does not wish His work to perish as soon as created. He wills them to have a certain duration.

In addition to the great number of adaptations which have no apparent object but to keep the organism going, there are a certain number of provisions for giving pleasure and a certain number for giving pain. These, perhaps, should be included among the contrivances for keeping the creature or its species in existence; for both the pleasures and the pains are generally so disposed as to attract to the things which maintain existence and deter from the things which would destroy it.

When these matters are considered, a vast deduction must be made from the facts usually cited as evidence of the benevolence of the Creator; so vast, indeed, that some may doubt whether any remains.

Yet, viewing the matter impartially, it does appear that there is a preponderance of evidence that the Creator desired the pleasure of His creatures. This is indicated by the fact, which cannot itself be denied, that pleasure of one description or another, is afforded by almost all of the powers, mental and physical, possessed by the creature.

The author of these pleasure-giving and pain-preventing adaptations is no doubt accountable for having made the creature susceptible of pain. But this may have been a necessary condition of its susceptibility to pleasure: a supposition which avails nothing on the theory of an omnipotent creator, but is extremely probable in the case of a limited creator.

There is, therefore, much evidence that the creature's pleasure is agreeable to the Creator; while there is very little if any evidence that its pain is so. There is, then, justification for inferring that benevolence is one of the attributes of the Creator.

But to jump from this to the inference that his sole or chief purposes are those of benevolence, and that the single end and aim of creation was the happiness of his creatures, is not only not justified by any evidence but is a conclusion in opposition to such evidence as we have.

If the motive of the Deity for creating sentient beings was the happiness of those beings, His purpose, in our corner of the universe at least, must be pronounced to have been thus far an ignominious failure. If God had no purpose but our happiness, and that of other living creatures, it is incredible that He would have called them into existence with the prospect of being so completely baffled.

If man had not the power, by the exercise of his own energies, to improve himself and his circumstances, to do for himself and other creatures vastly more than God had in the first instance done, then He [God] would deserve something very different from thanks at his [man's] hands.

Of course, it may be said that this very capacity of improving himself was given to man by God, and that the changes which man will be able ultimately to effect will be worth purchasing by the sufferings and wasted lives.

This may be so; but to suppose that God could not have procured these blessings for man at a less frightful cost is to make a very strange supposition concerning the Deity. It is to suppose that God could not, in the first instance, create anything better than a primitive savage, and was yet able to endow this primitive savage with power of raising himself into a Newton or a Fénelon. We do not know the nature of the barriers which limit the divine omnipotence; but it is a very odd notion of them that they enable the Deity to confer on a primitive savage the power of producing what God Himself had no other means of creating.

Such are the indications respecting the divine benevolence. If we look for any other moral attribute, for example, justice, we find a total blank. There is no evidence whatever in nature of divine justice, whatever standard of justice we may hold. There is no shadow of justice in the general arrangements of nature. Whatever justice exists in human society is the work of man himself, struggling upwards against immense natural difficulties into civilization, and making to himself a second, and far better and more unselfish nature than he was created with.

Looking back, Mill summarizes his finding:

These, then, are the net results of natural theology on the question of the divine attributes. A Being of great but limited power, how or by what limited we cannot even conjecture; of great and perhaps unlimited intelligence; who desires, and pays some regard to the happiness of His creatures, but who seems to have other motives of action which He cares more for, and who can hardly be supposed to have created the universe for that purpose alone.

Such is the Deity whom natural religion points to; and any idea of God more captivating than this comes only from human wishes, or from the teaching of either real or imaginary revelation.

There are several considerations in favor of this hypothesis of a finite Deity. It eliminates the problem of evil and the problem of free will, as a moment's thought will show. These problems, it will be recalled, were raised by the claim that Deity combines in Himself the two attributes of omnipotence and complete benevolence. It keeps close to what experience actually tells us about the world we live in. And, by way of conclusion, it gives some semblance of meaning to the notion of helping or working with God:

This religious idea admits of one elevated feeling, which is not open to those who believe in the omnipotence of the good principle in the universe, the feeling of helping God — of requiting the good He has given by a voluntary cooperation which He, not being omnipotent, really needs, and by which a somewhat nearer approach may be made to the fulfillment of His purposes. This is the most invigorating thought which can inspire a human creature.

A contemporary of Mill had argued "that even if the investigation of the concept of God as the absolute, infinite, all-powerful, all-good Being, leads to self-contradiction, yet we must believe in such a Being, since neither human logic nor human ethics are applicable to such a being." To this Mill replied:

Convince me that the world is ruled by a being whose attributes are infinite, but what they are we cannot learn (except that the highest human morality which we are capable of conceiving does not sanction them) and I will bear my fate as I may. But when I am told that I must believe this, and at the same time call this being names that affirm the highest human morality, I say in plain terms that I will not. Whatever power such a being may have over me, there is one thing which he shall not do; he shall not compel me to worship him. I will call no being good who is not what I mean when I apply that epithet to my fellow creatures; and if such a being can sentence me to hell for not so calling him, to hell I will go.

Reading References. There are not many valuable commentaries on Mill's handling of this particular theological problem. The notion of a finite or limited deity did not originate with Mill; indeed, it is to be found as far back as Plato's *Republic* in the fourth century B.C. But Mill did set himself more deliberately to argue the case for the conception than any of his predecessors had done. Since his day, it has passed into the writings of William James and has been used by H. G. Wells as the theme of his little book, *God the Invisible King*.

When J. S. Mill was still exercising a great influence in England, his work was subjected to considerable critical overhauling by one of his fellow countrymen, F. H. Bradley. In the course of many years' study and writing Bradley declared himself upon most of the major themes in Mill's general philosophy. In a volume, *Essays on Truth and Reality*, he has a chapter "On God and the Absolute" which contains some suggestive remarks on the conception of a limited God. It is instructive to watch another philosopher at work on the idea. Moreover, in the concluding sentences, Bradley raises a point which forms, so to speak, the logical beginning of William James's pragmatic approach to this question. Says Bradley:

There is a fundamental inconsistency in religion. For, in any but an imperfect religion, God must be perfect. God must be at once the complete satisfaction of all finite aspiration, and yet on the other hand must stand in relation to my will. Religion (at least in my view) is practical, and on the other hand in the highest religion its object is supreme goodness and power. We have a perfect real will, and we have my will, and the practical relation of these wills is what we mean by religion. And yet, if perfection is actually realized, what becomes of my will which is set over against the complete good will? While, on the other hand, if there is no such will, what becomes of God? The inconsistency seems irremovable. . . .

An obvious method of escape is to reject the perfection of God. God will remain good, but in a limited sense. He will be reduced to a person who does the best that is in Him with limited knowledge and power. Sufficiently superior to ourselves to be worshipped, God will nevertheless be imperfect, and, with this admitted imperfection, it will be said, our religion is saved. . . .

Now certainly on such terms religion still can persist, for there is practical devotion to an object which is taken to be at a level far above our own. Such a religion even in one sense, with the lowering of the Deity, may be said to have been heightened. To help a God in His struggle, more or less doubtful and blind, with resisting evil, is no inferior task. And if the issue were taken as uncertain, or if even further the end were known to be God's indubitable defeat and our inevitable disaster, our religion would have risen thereby and would have attained to the extreme of heroism.

But on the other hand, if religion is considered as a whole and not simply from one side, it is not true that with the lowering of God religion tends to grow higher. A principal part of religion is the assured satisfaction of our good will, the joy and peace in that assurance, and the added strength which in the majority of men can come perhaps from no other source. To sacrifice altogether or in part this aspect means on the whole to set religion down to a lower level. And it is an illusion to suppose that imperfection, once admitted into the Deity, can be stopped precisely at that convenient limit which happens to suit our ideas. The assertor of an imperfect God is, whether he knows it or not, face to face with a desperate task or a forlorn alternative. He must try to show (how, I cannot tell) that the entire rest of the universe, outside his limited God, is known to be still weaker and more limited. Or he must appeal to us to follow our Leader blindly and, for all we know, to a common and overwhelming defeat. In either case, the prospect offered entails, I should say, to the religious mind, an unquestionable loss to religion.

And yet it will be urged that we have ourselves agreed that all other ways of escape are closed. For, if God is perfect, we saw that religion must contain inconsistency, and it was by seeking consistency that we were driven to a limited God. But our assumption here, I reply, is precisely that which we should have questioned from the first. Is there any need for our attempt to avoid self-contradiction? Has religion really got to be consistent theoretically? Is ultimate theoretical consistency a thing which is attainable anywhere? And, at all events, is it a thing attainable in life and in practice? That is the fundamental question upon which the whole issue depends. And I need not pause here to ask whether it is quite certain that, when God is limited, the universe becomes theoretically consistent. . . .

Viewed thus, the question as to what may be called religious ideas is seriously changed. To insist upon ultimate theoretical consistency, which in no case can we reach, becomes once for all ridiculous. The main question is as to the real nature and end of religion, and as to the respective importance of those aspects which belong to it. The ideas which best express our highest religious needs and their satisfaction, must certainly be true. Ultimate truth they do not possess, and exactly what in the end it would take to make them perfect we cannot know.

READING QUESTIONS

1. Why does Mill prefer the argument from design?
2. Restate concisely his version of the design argument.
3. What type of fact is the hypothesis of a creative designer used to account for?
4. Illustrate this point with reference to the human eye.
5. What is the distinction between a final and efficient cause?
6. How is the hypothesis of natural selection an alternative explanation for the type of fact noted in question 3?
7. Illustrate this point with reference to the eye.
8. What are Mill's own views on the tenability of this hypothesis?
9. By what lines of reasoning does Mill argue that God's power is "great but not infinite"?
10. What objection does he anticipate? How does he meet it?
11. On what grounds does he argue that God's knowledge may be limited?
12. "What indications does nature give of the purposes of its author?"
13. Why does he feel that he is in a better position to answer this than Thomas was?
14. Why does he deny complete benevolence to God?
15. Why does he nevertheless admit partial benevolence?
16. What bearing might Mill's hypothesis (limited theism) have on the problem of evil?
17. On the problem of free will?
18. What "elevated feeling" does he think his hypothesis admits of?
19. "There is a fundamental inconsistency in religion." State it.
20. What has he to say *for* the notion of a finite Deity?
21. What two things has he to say *against* it?

22. What "desperate task or forlorn alternative" does he note?
23. What is his final word on this question of God's finitude or infinitude?

5 THE PRAGMATIC APPROACH TO NATURAL THEOLOGY — FROM WILLIAM JAMES

From Mill to James. It will be recalled that Pascal, writing in the seventeenth century, repudiated the possibility of rational theology but clung to orthodox convictions. He rejected the appeal to reason in theology, but he retained the theology. John Stuart Mill, writing two centuries later, reversed the procedure. He clung to the idea of a rational theology, but repudiated the orthodox convictions. He rejected the orthodox theology, but he retained the appeal to reason. His hypothesis of a finite or limited Deity represented precisely that. The most man can rationally justify, he argued, is the belief in a finite God. Now, William James, writing toward the close of the nineteenth century and in the opening years of the twentieth century, combined Pascal's rejection of reason and Mill's hypothesis of a limited Deity. James must be envisaged as standing reflectively at the hither end of a long line of rational theologians stretching back to Thomas Aquinas and beyond. He knew his Thomas, his Pascal, his Hume, and his Mill. Dispassionate consideration convinced him that the appeal to reason in theology was bankrupt. No one had ever properly answered Hume on his own grounds. But James found himself believing wholeheartedly in the existence of God. That, he could not shake off. Accordingly, he sought to combine the two compromises offered by Pascal and Mill respectively: an appeal to emotional need in support of the belief in a finite God.

Biographical Note. William James was born in 1842 and died in 1910 at the age of sixty-eight. He was educated at Harvard and in Europe. He was appointed to the teaching staff in Harvard in the department of physiology. From physiology he moved later to psychology, writing his brilliant and epoch-making *Principles of Psychology* and *Varieties of Religious Experience*. From psychology he moved finally to philosophy. His best-known and most readable books were written during his years as professor of philosophy. He gathered about him, at Harvard, what was perhaps the most brilliant group of teachers and writers ever assembled at any one time in any university in this country. His philosophical colleagues included Josiah Royce, George Herbert Palmer, George Santayana, and (in psychology) Hugo Münsterberg.

Although James was trained as physiologist and psychologist, he was essentially a moralist and theologian. His robust assurance that the good life, in the long run, provides the deepest and most lasting satisfaction; his passionately felt need for a "Friend" sustaining the universe and reaching out to man in his struggle for righteousness and truth, are convictions which pervade almost every chapter he has written. His three books, *The Will To Believe and Other Essays*, *The Varieties of Religious Experience*, and *Pragmatism*, contain the most popular and persuasive presentation of these views. They can and ought to be read by everyone professing interest in the human significance of the problems canvassed in this and succeeding topics.

The Argument of the Citations. The citations quoted hereunder are, for the most part, from James's essay, "The Will to Believe." He states somewhere that it might better have been called "The Right to Believe." His aim is to point out that, in certain cases, where the evidence is insufficient to justify belief on "rational" grounds, there may nevertheless be other grounds. In a word, sufficient evidence is not the only thing which justifies belief, is not the only thing which gives us a "right to believe." Clearly, there is an issue being raised here. Upon what does our right to believe rest? Upon what, especially, does it rest in instances where the evidence is insufficient? That is the central problem of the essay. James begins by a few remarks on hypotheses in general. The purpose of these remarks is gradually to define what he means by a "genuine option" between rival hypotheses. Where we are faced with a genuine option between rival hypotheses, neither of which is backed by sufficient evidence, upon what principle may we legitimately exercise our right to believe one and not the other? James then formulates the principle which, he thinks, justifies belief under such circumstances. We shall call this the "pragmatic principle." The question now is: Are there any hypotheses which present themselves for acceptance on this pragmatic principle? James notes that moral judgments are of this nature. However, and more important, the "religious hypothesis" is of this nature. He then states the terms of this hypothesis, using considerable care and deliberateness. In what follows, he deals with two possible lines of criticism which, he knows, will be directed against his position. The first of these is the objection of the skeptic, namely, that where evidence is insufficient to justify belief, we have no right to believe. James is good on this point and deserves close attention. The second objection is to the effect that once you set up any principle designed to justify belief on insufficient grounds, you have (in principle) obliterated the distinction between intelligent belief and any but the wildest superstition. James is not so good on this point. The reader must judge for himself. My own feeling is that he is hard pressed, if not actually in full retreat. Finally, in a few citations, we note his acceptance of Mill's limited theism.

He begins:

Let us give the name of *hypothesis* to anything that may be proposed to our belief. And, just as electricians speak of live and dead wires, let us speak of an hypothesis as either live or dead. A live hypothesis is one which appeals as a real possibility to him to whom it is proposed.

Next, let us call the decision between hypotheses an *option*. Options may be of several kinds. They may be living or dead, forced or avoidable, momentous or trivial.

A living option is one in which both hypotheses are live ones. If I say to you: "Be a theosophist or be a Mohammedan," it is probably a dead option, because for you neither hypothesis is likely to be alive. But if I say: "Be an agnostic or be a Christian," it is otherwise. Trained as you are, each hypothesis makes some appeal, however small, to your belief.

A forced option is one which arises when there is no standing outside of the alternative hypotheses. If I say to you: "Choose between going out with your umbrella or without it," I do not offer you a forced option. You can easily avoid it by not going out at all. But if I say: "Either accept this truth or go without it," I put on you a forced option, for there is no third alternative and no standing outside of these two alternatives.

A momentous option is one that is presented when the opportunity is unique, when the stake is significant, or when the decision is irreversible if it later prove unwise. If I were Dr. Nansen and proposed to you to join my North Pole expedition, your option would be momentous; for this would probably be your only opportunity, and your choice now would either exclude you from the North Pole sort of immortality altogether, or put at least the chance of it into your hands. *Per contra*, the option is trivial when the opportunity is not unique, when the stake is insignificant, or when the decision is reversible if it later prove unwise.

An option is genuine when it is of the living, forced, momentous kind.

So much for hypotheses and options. Suppose, now, that a man is confronted by a pair of rival hypotheses, neither of which can be said to rest on sufficient evidence to justify belief. What is he to do? Upon what principle can he justify himself in believing one or the other of these hypotheses? It is the following:

The thesis I defend is this: Our passional [emotion] nature not only lawfully may, but must, decide an option between propositions, whenever it is a genuine option that cannot by its nature be decided on intellectual grounds.

The essence of the matter is contained in this principle. Its full meaning should become clearer as we proceed. Whether it can be defended against criticism is a further question that lies ahead. Just now, however, we are curious to know where, among our many beliefs, we shall find some which call for acceptance on this pragmatic principle. The eye is at once struck by our moral beliefs, for example, that it is better to do this than that, better to be this sort of man than that, etc.

The question arises: Are there any such forced options in our speculative opinions? Are there some options between opinions in which this passional influence must be regarded both as an inevitable and as a lawful determinant of our choice?

Moral questions immediately present themselves. A moral question is a question not of what exists, but of what is good, or would be good if it did exist.

Science can tell us what exists; but to compare the worths, both of what exists and what does not exist, we must consult not science, but what Pascal calls our "heart," i.e., our passional nature. Science, herself, consults her heart when she lays it down that the infinite ascertainment of fact and correction of false belief are the supreme goods for man. Challenge the statement, and science can only repeat it oracularly, or else prove it by showing that such ascertainment and correction bring man all sorts of other goods which man's heart in turn declares desirable.

Moral beliefs. Is that all? While James is, I think, more fundamentally a moralist than a theologian in the whole of his work, he is, for the immediate occasion, more interested in theology than morality. So:

Let us pass to the question of religious faith. What do we mean by the religious hypothesis? Broadly it is this: Science says things are: morality says some things are better than other things: religion says that the best things are the more eternal things, the things in the universe that throw the last stone, so to speak, and say the final word: and that we are better off, even now, if we believe her first affirmation to be true.

Now let us consider what the logical elements of this situation are in case the religious hypothesis in both its branches be really true. We must admit that possibility at the outset.

We see, first, that religion offers itself as a momentous option. We are supposed to gain, even now, by our belief, and to lose by our nonbelief, a certain vital good.

We see, second, that religion is a forced option so far as that vital good is concerned. We cannot escape the issue by remaining skeptical, because although we do avoid error in that way if religion be untrue, we lose the good, if it be true. Skepticism, then, is not an avoidance of the option.

In these matters, the skeptic's position is exactly this: Better risk the loss of truth than the chance of error. But in this he is actively playing his stake as much as the believer is. He is backing the field against the religious hypothesis, just as the believer is backing the religious hypothesis against the field.

Now, to most of us, religion comes in a still further way. What I mean is this. The more perfect and more eternal aspect of the universe is represented in our religions as having a personal form. The universe is no longer a mere It, but a Thou, if we are religious; and any relation that may be possible from person to person might be possible here. We feel, too, as if the appeal of religion were made to our own active good will, as if evidence for its truth might be forever withheld from us unless we met the hypothesis halfway.

This feeling, forced on us we know not whence, that by obstinately believing that there are gods we are doing the universe the deepest service we can, seems part of the living essence of the religious hypothesis.

God is the natural appellation, for us Christians at least, for the supreme reality, so I will call this higher part of the universe by the

the name of God. We and God have business with each other; and in opening ourselves to His influence our deepest destiny is fulfilled. The universe, at those parts of it which our personal being constitutes, takes a turn genuinely for the worse or for the better in proportion as each one of us fulfills or evades God's demands.

God's existence is the guarantee of an ideal order that shall be permanently preserved. This world may indeed some day burn up or freeze up; but if it is part of His order, the old ideals are sure to be brought elsewhere to fruition, so that where God is, tragedy is only provisional and partial, and shipwreck and dissolution are not the absolutely final things.

Only when this farther step of faith concerning God is taken, and remote objective consequences are predicted, does religion, as it seems to me, bring hypothesis into play.

What is this but to say that religion, in her fullest exercise of function, is a postulator of new facts? The world interpreted religiously is not the materialistic world over again, with an altered expression. It must have, over and above the altered expression, a natural constitution different at some point from that which a materialistic world would have. It must be such that different events can be expected in it, different conduct must be required.

All this on the supposition that our passional nature may be prophetic and right: and that the religious hypothesis is a live hypothesis which may be true.

We are now in possession of the essentials of James's position. We know what he means by a genuine option between rival hypotheses. We know the principle by which he would justify belief in such circumstances. We know that he considers the religious hypothesis a case in point. We know, finally, what he means by this religious hypothesis. His defense of the whole position is still to be made. He deals first with the skeptic. The point here is this: It may be all very well to talk about the demands of our "passional nature," but, as a matter of fact, why is it not just as legitimate to refuse to believe either hypothesis when neither is backed by sufficient evidence? Why may a skeptic not take the stand, in all conscience, that under the circumstances stipulated by James, the proper attitude is one of suspended judgment? Let us hear, through James, the skeptic's statement of the case:

It does seem preposterous on the very face of it, to talk of our opinions being modifiable at will. Can our will either help or hinder our intellect in its perceptions of truth? . . . Indeed, the talk of believing by our volition seems from one point of view, simply silly. From another point of view it is worse than silly, it is vile. When one turns to the magnificent edifice of the physical sciences, and sees how it was reared, what thousands of disinterested moral lives of men lie buried in its mere foundations; what patience and postponement, what choking down of preference, what submission to icy laws of outer fact are wrought into its very stones and mortar; how absolutely impersonal it stands in its vast augustness — then how besotted and contemptible seems every little sentimentalist who comes blowing his voluntary smoke wreaths! Can we wonder if those bred in the rugged and manly school of science should feel like spewing such subjectivism out of their mouths? The whole system of loyalties which grow up in the schools of science go dead against its toleration; so that it is only natural that those who have caught the scientific fever should pass over to the opposite extreme and write sometimes as if the incorruptibly truthful intellect ought positively to prefer bitterness and unacceptableness to the heart in its cup.

Clough sings:

"It fortifies my soul to know
That, though I perish, Truth is so"

while Huxley exclaims: "My only consolation lies in the reflection that, however bad our posterity may become, so far as they hold by the plain rule of not pretending to believe what they have no reason to believe, because it may be to their advantage so to pretend, they will not have reached the lowest depth of immortality."

And that delicious *enfant terrible*, Clifford, writes: "Belief is desecrated when given to unproved and unquestioned statements for the solace and private pleasure of the believer. Whoso would deserve well of his fellows in this matter will guard the purity of his belief with a very fanaticism of jealous care, lest at any time it should rest on an unworthy object, and catch a stain which can never be wiped away. If a belief has been accepted on insufficient evidence, even though the belief be true, the pleasure is a stolen one. It is sinful because it is stolen in defiance of our duty to mankind. That duty is to guard ourselves from such beliefs as from a pestilence which may shortly master our body and then spread to the rest of the town. It is wrong, always, everywhere, and for everyone, to believe anything upon insufficient evidence."

Now, all of this strikes one as healthy, even when expressed by Clifford with somewhat too much of robustious pathos in the voice. Willing and wishing do seem, in the matter of our beliefs, to be only fifth wheels to the coach.

How shall this indictment be answered? It will be noticed that James has been scrupulously fair to the skeptic in admitting the genuine possibility here of an ethical issue. The skeptic's claim is not, at its best, that we are merely foolish to believe on insufficient evidence. It is the more serious claim that we *ought* not to believe on insufficient evidence; that belief, in such cases, is positively immoral. That is the charge with which James is faced. The first move in his defense is to note that in this unique case of the religious hypothesis doubt is the equivalent of denial; and, the point is, denial is not suspended judgment. (It may be necessary to reread James's wording of the religious hypothesis, especially its *second* part, to follow his argument here.)

To preach skepticism in these matters is tantamount to telling us, when in the presence of the religious hypothesis, that to yield to our fear of its being false is wiser and better than to yield to our hope that it may be true.

As James points out, this puts a slightly different face on matters. Why is it "wiser and better" to refrain from belief on all occasions where the evidence is insufficient? It should be noted that, by developing the ethical case for skepticism, James is cleverly jockeying the skeptic into a "moral" question. He has already explained that moral questions must be decided on "emotional" grounds.

> This is not a case of "intellect" against "passion." It is only intellect, with one passion — the dread or horror of believing what may be false — laying down its law — never to believe what may be false when there is no evidence that it may be true.
>
> And by what, forsooth, is the supreme wisdom of this passion warranted? Dupery for dupery, what proof is there that dupery through hope is so much worse than dupery through fear? I, for one, can see no proof; and I simply refuse to imitate the skeptic's option in a case where my own stake is important enough to give me the right to choose my own form of risk.

And what it comes down to is this:

> We may regard the case for truth as paramount, and the avoidance of error as secondary; or we may treat the avoidance of error as more imperative, and let truth take its chance. Clifford exhorts us to the latter course. Believe nothing, he tells us, keep your mind in suspense forever, rather than, by closing on insufficient evidence, incur the awful risk of believing lies. You, on the other hand, may think that the risk of being in error is a very small matter when compared with the blessings of real knowledge, and be ready to be duped many times rather than postpone indefinitely the chance of guessing true.

This being so, he knows where he stands:

> For my own part, I have also a horror of being duped. But I can believe that worse things than being duped may happen to a man in this world. So Clifford's exhortation has to my ears a thoroughly fantastic sound. Our errors are surely not such awfully solemn things. In a world where we are so sure to incur them, a certain lightness of heart seems healthier than this excessive nervousness on their behalf.

If the religious hypothesis be true, and the evidence for it still insufficient, I do not wish, by putting a skeptical extinguisher upon my nature, to forfeit my sole chance of getting upon the winning side; that chance depending, of course, on my willingness to run the risk of acting as if my passional need of taking the world religiously might be prophetic and right.

When I look at the religious hypothesis, as it really puts itself to men, and when I think of all the possibilities which it involves, then the skeptical command to put a stopper on our heart and wait — acting meanwhile more or less as if religion were not true — wait till doomsday, or till such time as our intellect and senses may have raked in enough evidence — this command, I say, seems to me the queerest idol ever manufactured in the philosophic cave.

If the religious hypothesis were true, then pure intellectualism, with its veto on our willingness to make advances, would be an absurdity; and some participation of our sympathetic nature would be logically required. I, therefore, for one, cannot see my way to accepting the agnostic rules for truth seeking (never to believe any hypothesis when there is no evidence or insufficient evidence) or to willfully agree to keep my willing nature out of the game.

I cannot do so for this plain reason: A rule of thinking which would prevent me from acknowledging certain kinds of truth if those kinds of truths were really there, would be an irrational rule. That, for me, is the long and short of the logic of the situation.

The great empiricists are only empiricists on reflection; left to their instincts, they dogmatize like infallible popes. When the Cliffords tell us how sinful it is to be Christians on such "insufficient evidence," insufficiency is really the last thing they have in mind. For them the evidence is absolutely sufficient, only it makes the other way. They believe so completely in an anti-Christian order of the universe that there is no living option: Christianity, for them, is a dead hypothesis from the start.

As a kind of Parthian shot, James throws a question at the skeptics themselves:

Our belief in truth itself, for instance, that there is a truth and that our minds and it are made for each other — what is it but a passionate affirmation of desire in which our social system backs us up? We want to have a truth; we want to believe that our experiments and studies and discussions must put us in a continually better and better position toward it; and on this line we agree to fight out our thinking lives.

But if a skeptic asks us how we know all this, can our logic find a reply? It cannot. It is just one volition against another; we are willing to go in for life upon a trust or assumption which he, for his part, does not care to make. As a rule we disbelieve all facts and theories for which we have no use. Clifford's cosmic emotions find no use for Christian feelings. Huxley belabors the bishops because there is no use for sacerdotalism in his scheme of life. But Newman goes over to Romanism, and finds all sorts of reasons good for staying there, because a priestly system is for him an organic need for delight.

So Clifford notwithstanding, our nonintellectual nature evidently does influence our convictions. The state of things is far from simple, and pure insight and pure logic, whatever they may do ideally, are not the only things that really do produce our creeds.

If we had an infallible intellect, with its objective certitudes, we might feel ourselves disloyal to such a perfect organ of knowledge in not trusting to it exclusively, in not waiting for its releasing word. But if we believe that no bell in us tolls to let us know for certain when truth is in our grasp, then it seems a piece of idle fantasticality to preach so solemnly of our duty of waiting for the bell.

James has still to deal with another sort of critic, no less hostile in his way than the skeptic. The charge this time is not that where evidence is lacking it is wiser and better to suspend judgment. It is, rather, to this effect: If you start justifying belief (for example, in Christian convictions) on this pragmatic basis, where and how are you going to draw the line? The pragmatic justification is not, by its nature, the peculiar property of the man who desires to believe in God. It would seem to be equally available, as a principle of justification, for other beliefs as well, some of which (no doubt) might be incompatible with those beliefs which James used it to defend. A man who advances a principle which would justify belief in incompatible hypotheses has, to say the least, some explaining to do. James knew this. Although convinced that his argument was sound, he knew that others would not be. Thus:

> I confess I do not see how this logic can be escaped. But sad experience makes me fear that some of you may still shrink from saying with me that we have the right to believe at our own risk any hypothesis that is live enough to tempt our will.
>
> If this is so, however, I suspect it is because you have got away from the logical point of view altogether, and are thinking of some particular religious hypothesis which for you is dead. The freedom to "believe what we will" you apply to the case of some patent superstition; and the faith you think of is the faith defined by the schoolboy when he said: "Faith is when you believe something that you know ain't true."
>
> I can only repeat that this is a misapprehension of my position. The freedom to "believe what we will," for which I have been arguing, can only cover living options which the intellect by itself cannot resolve; and living options never seem absurd or superstitious to him who has them to consider.
>
> Where there is no such forced option, the dispassionately judicial intellect with no pet hypothesis, saving us, as it does, from dupery, at any rate, ought to be our ideal.

It would appear that James has only restated his difficulty. It is still open to anyone to point out: "Yes, what you have said, you have said. The point is, however, that what you have not said, you have not said. What about the man whose passional nature inclines him to embrace, as true, a proposition which is incompatible with one which your passional nature has inclined you to embrace? As between two passional natures having divergent inclinations, how do you decide?" A glance through the published letters of William James shows that he was mightily bothered by this point. Writing to his brother Henry, the novelist, he protests:

When *I say* that, *other things being equal*, the view of things that seems more satisfactory morally will legitimately be treated by men as truer than the view that seems less so, *they quote me as saying* that anything morally satisfactory can be treated as true, no matter how unsatisfactory it may be from the point of view of its consistency with what we already know or believe to be true about physical or natural facts, which is rot!!

Of course this is rot. But the rot is on the side of James. So vague and ambiguous a phrase as "the view of things that seems more satisfactory morally" is in no better case than the phrase "demands of our passional nature." It is a pinch of objectivity which his critics have been demanding. They could find none in "passional nature." I suspect they found no more in "the view of things that seems satisfactory morally." James has drawn a two-edged sword. To vary the metaphor, his principle may be used to reinforce either theism or atheism, or for the matter of that, some third alternative equally removed from either, say skepticism or polytheism. In the last analysis pragmatism merely reinforces the most deeply congenial belief; it does not state which belief is or ought to be the most congenial. However, he is not done protesting. Writing to an English philosopher, L. T. Hobhouse, he has much the same sort of thing to say:

Would to God I had never thought of that unhappy title for my essay. What I meant by the title was the state of mind of the man who finds an impulse in him toward a believing attitude, and who resolves not to quench it simply because doubts of its truth are possible. Its opposite would be the maxim: Believe in nothing which you can possibly doubt.

My essay hedged the license to indulge in private overbeliefs with so many restrictions and sign boards of danger that the outlet was narrow enough. It made of tolerance the essence of the situation. It defined the permissible cases. It treated the faith attitude as a necessity for individuals, because the total "evidence" which only the race can draw include their experiments among its data. It tended to show only that faith cannot be absolutely *vetoed*, as certain champions of "science" had claimed it ought to be.

I cry to heaven to tell me of what insane root my "leading contemporaries" have eaten, that they are so smitten with blindness as to the meaning of printed texts.

In my essay the evil shape was a vision of "Science" in the form of abstraction, priggishness and sawdust, lording it over all. Take the sterilest scientific prig and cad you know, compare him with the richest religious intellect you know, and you would not, any more than I would, give the former the exclusive right of way.

In these matters it is necessary to maintain a certain degree of detachment. One feels, readily enough, that James's "nature" would have led *him* to choose the "right hypothesis" for belief. But the world is full of persons who lack his powers of understanding. What about them? The root of this confusing problem lies, really, in James's initial skepticism. Following such traditions as Hume and Mill bespoke, James begins by admitting that reason is powerless to settle this question in natural theology; that there is no such thing as "rational" theology. From reason he turned to emotion. In this he resembled Pascal. And now he is attempting the somewhat difficult task of formulating a "reasonable" defense of his position. Once having thrown reason overboard, he might better have remained impervious to criticisms proceeding from persons who had, in fact, *not* made that initial concession.

There are two parts to any man's exposition of his ideas concerning God. In the first place, he should make clear why he believes that God exists. In the second, he should make clear what he conceives God's nature to be. In a phrase, the existence and nature of God. So far as God's existence goes, we know where James stands in this essay. "Why do I believe in God? Is it because I have experienced his presence? No; rather because I need it so that it must be true." Before quitting James and the whole question of natural theology, it is worth noting that he used his pragmatic principle to justify his belief in God's finiteness. Like Mill, and many other recent and contemporary theologians, James repudiated the celebrated "omni's" of traditional theology. His reasoning is much the same as Mill's.

I simply refuse to accept the idea of there being no purpose in the objective world. On the other hand, I cannot represent the existence of purpose except as based in a mind. The "not-me," therefore, so far as it contains purpose, must spring from a mind; but not necessarily a *One and Only* mind.

In saying God exists, all I imply is that my purposes are cared for by a mind so powerful as on the whole to control the drift of the universe. That is . . . merely a practical emotional faith.

The only difficulties of theism are the moral difficulties and meanness; and they have always seemed to me to flow from the gratuitous dogma of God being the all-inclusive reality. Once think possible a pluralism of which He may be one member, and piety forthwith ceases to be incompatible with manliness, and religious faith with intellectual rectitude.

In short, the only theism I defend is that of simple unphilosophic mankind. God, in the religious life of ordinary men is the name, not of the whole of things, heaven forbid, but only of the ideal tendency in things. . . . He works in an external environment, has limits, and has enemies. . . . If there be a God, how the devil can we know what difficulties he may have had to contend with? Possible difficulties! They save everything. But what are they if not limitations to the all-inclusiveness of any single being!

Having an environment, being in time, and working out a history just like ourselves, He escapes from the foreignness from all that is human, of the static, timeless, perfect absolute.

My God, being part of a pluralistic system, is responsible only for such things as He knows enough and has enough power to have accomplished. The "omniscient" and "omnipotent" God of theology I regard as a disease of the philosophy shop.

The line of least resistance, as it seems to me, both in theology and in philosophy, is to accept, along with the Superhuman Consciousness, the notion that It is not all embracing; the notion, in other words, that there is a God, but that He is finite, either in power or in knowledge, or in both at once.

Reading References. The best, the easiest, and the most continuously pleasing thing to do about William James is to read him. In so many respects, he is his own best commentary. The volume, *The Will to Believe and Other Essays*, from which this chapter has been largely drawn, is a delightful collection. But the time comes when one desires to know what other people think about an author whom one has read. The book here is Julius Bixler's *Religion in the Philosophy of William James*. The only complete account of James's life and times is to be found in R. B. Perry's two monumental volumes, *The Life and Thought of William James*. No one who once dips into this work will feel satisfied short of browsing through the whole of it. The chapter in which Perry gives an account of "The Will to Believe" will repay immediate perusal.

READING QUESTIONS

1. Can you trace the argument of natural theology from Aquinas through Pascal and Hume and Mill, to James?
2. What does James mean by an *hypothesis?*
3. How does he distinguish between a live and a dead hypothesis?
4. What does he mean by an *option?*
5. What by a living option? A forced option? A momentous option?
6. What by a genuine option?
7. Upon what principle does he propose to decide a genuine option which cannot be decided on intellectual (i.e., rational) grounds?

8. In what sense do moral questions present themselves for decision on this principle?
9. How does James state the religious hypothesis?
10. How does his statement make skepticism equivalent to denial?
11. Why does he proceed to develop the ethical case for skepticism?
12. What is the ethical case for skepticism?
13. Upon what grounds does he dismiss the skeptic finally?
14. Having disposed of the skeptic, what criticism does James turn to?
15. How does he deal with it?
16. Satisfactorily, do you think?
17. Having worked out the case for theism, on pragmatic grounds, why does James hold out for the conception of a limited deity?
18. Show how elements from Pascal and Mill are present in James.
19. Formulate one or more questions you would put to James.

TOPIC TWO. A METAPHYSICAL PROBLEM

THE PROBLEM STATED

One of the best-known remarks in the history of philosophy is ascribed to the Greek thinker, Thales. He is said to have held that "all things are made of water." On the face of it, this seems both unimportant and false. Whence its historical importance? Why has Thales been bracketed, along with Copernicus and Darwin, as having initiated a line of thought which marked an epoch in human speculation?

The reason is this. It required, in the first instance, a bold mind to conceive any proposition having the general form "All things are made of . . ."; because if there is one proposition which would appear to be justified by the facts of our everyday experience, it is that all things are not made of any one thing. Multiplicity and variety are the obvious facts about the everyday world. The effort of thought required to break down the testimony of the everyday world must have been considerable, as it certainly was subsequently fruitful.

pluralism

Thales probably had his reasons. Such apparently diverse things as ice, snow, mist, vapor, steam are all "made of" water, if we use the term loosely. Why not other things too? Whatever his reasons may have been, his remark, once made, continued to re-echo in the minds of generations which came after him. "All things are made of . . ."

In fact, the problem is with us to this day. What are all things made of? What do we intend by the phrase *made of?* If we brush aside Thales' answer, what do we propose in place of it? Speculations on this question constitute part of the general topic of metaphysics. That is, metaphysics is, in part, an inquiry into the question what all things are "made of."

Suppose we consider a miscellaneous collection of things, a clay pipe, a bird's egg, a rainbow, a copy of *Hamlet*, an uprising in Central China, an act of mercy, a cry in the night, a new planet. What are all these things made of? Varying the words, to what common substance are these all reducible? Of what "underlying reality" are they all manifestations? Is this underlying reality itself further reducible?

The notion that the observed multiplicity and variety of the everyday world are reducible to something common and uniform and *not* given as part of the everyday world is not an unreasonable notion. Few persons would care to deny it in principle, much as they might argue over what that something is to which all things are reducible. Granted the propriety of the notion of an ultimate reality, it is necessary to go one step further. In some sense or other, the everyday world is an appearance or a manifestation of it. They are the appearances; it is the real.

It is then possible to restate our central problem: What is the nature of that ultimate reality of which the everyday world is but the appearance?

Answers to this question vary. If it is held that there is *an* ultimate reality, we have what is called *monism* in metaphysics, the belief that ultimate reality is one in kind. If it is held that there are at least two ultimate realities, we have what is called *dualism* in metaphysics, the belief that ultimate reality is two in kind. If it is held that there are three or more ultimate realities, we have what is called *pluralism* in metaphysics, the belief that ultimate reality is three or more in kind.

Within these classifications others will occur. You and I

might agree that monism is a true belief. Our agreement might extend no further. When we came to the question of the nature of this ultimate reality, we might differ. I might claim that it was matter; you might claim that it was mind; a third person might claim that it was neither, but something more ultimate of which both matter and mind are manifestations.

In this topic we are to be concerned with such inquiries. A metaphysical hypothesis is any belief about the nature of ultimate reality. In considering any such hypothesis, it will be helpful to ask: What is the belief? Is it a form of monism, or dualism, or pluralism? What reasons are given, or may be given, in support of it? What reasons against it? What consequences follow from it? Do these agree with common sense? Or do they make nonsense of it? Reflection upon the nature of ultimate reality is not the whole of metaphysics, but it is a large part of it. For a beginner in metaphysics, two things are of primary importance: to demand reasons for accepting any hypothesis, and to note consequences which follow from accepting the hypothesis.

The readings and comments which follow are grouped, in an historical way, around the problem stated above. They provide material for thinking about this problem, comparable to the readings and comments grouped around the theological problem in the sections which preceded. There are five sets of them: two from the seventeenth century (Descartes and Hobbes), one from the eighteenth century (Berkeley), one from the nineteenth century (Schopenhauer), and one from the twentieth century (James). These men have been chosen because, among them, they provide a varied gallery in which to roam. No two are alike. Each is convinced of his views and eager to spread them among "all rational minds." Each is a competent metaphysician in the sense that he realizes he must be prepared to argue his case. There is, among them, no appeal to emotions; at least, not intentionally. They are all, in this respect, "hardheaded rationalists." Here, for the eye which can detect it, is man's supreme intellectual sport insofar as he is a "rational" animal. Here are corrosive skepticism, caustic (if obscure) wit, resounding thwacks, closely built arguments, relentless determination to "begin at the beginning" and "think it through," and proud gestures directing attention to "positions established" and "positions overthrown." A taste for metaphysics and a flare for the practice of metaphysics are not widely diffused, but the genuine article, like a love for poetry or painting, is irrepressible once it has had a chance to take root.

The readings which follow are in chronological order, but the chronological order itself exhibits an interesting development. Conceive each of these five authors confronted with the inquiry: What is the nature of ultimate reality? The answer of Descartes is the most conventional. Reality consists of three substances, namely, God, human souls, and matter. The position taken up by Hobbes represents a selection of one of the elements argued for by Descartes. All things, runs the argument, are matter: materialism, as full blown as one could wish it. The position taken up by Berkeley represents a deliberate reaction from Hobbes's materialism. All things, runs the argument here, are mind or spirit. Hobbes's materialism and Berkeley's idealism, between them, account for an enormous amount of modern metaphysics. The term *voluntarism*, associated with Schopenhauer in metaphysics, covers the conviction that neither matter nor spirit but "will" is the ultimate substance, the ultimately real stuff, of which all things are merely manifestations. James's "pragmatic" approach to metaphysics with which this series concludes, represents an attempt to do two things: to formulate a radically new type of argument for metaphysical beliefs, and to place this type of argument at the disposal of James's own beliefs.

1. DUALISM AND ITS IMPLICATIONS — FROM RENÉ DESCARTES

In point of time, and with respect to content, one's acquaintance with modern metaphysics cannot begin more profitably than with the speculations of René Descartes. This, for two reasons: He lived in a "climate of opinion" which is still widely prevalent, despite the lapse of three centuries, and hence brings to his task the presuppositions which most persons still possess; and he has served as the point of departure for almost all metaphysicians since his day.

Biographical Note. Descartes was born in France in 1596 and died in Sweden in 1650 at the age of fifty-four. His biography reveals three periods: years of education, years of wandering and learning, and years of maturity and production.

1. Descartes' formal education, from eight to sixteen, was received at the Jesuit college of La Flêche. Here he acquired the essentials of a "gentleman's education," a deposit which he subsequently devoted much time to erasing. Before he had turned seventeen he put aside his books and after a few lessons in fencing and horsemanship went to "the great world of Paris" Here he remained for about five years, living at first the usual life of gaiety and gambling, but retiring after a while to the quiet and seclusion of an obscure lodging house. His thoughtful temper reasserted itself. Habits of reflection acquired at La Flêche, and roused once more by a Catholic friend, one Father Mersenne, took possession of him again.

(2) In 1618 Descartes left Paris, determined to see the world. These were his true *wanderjahren*. He became a soldier, serving in three different European armies, in the Netherlands, in Bavaria, and in Hungary. It was a life which gave him much time for thought during the long months of idleness in winter quarters. He stuck to soldiering for three or four years, then resolved "no longer to carry a musket." Army days over, he continued his travels for five or six years more,

visiting Switzerland and Italy, until, in 1628, he decided that he had read enough in the "great book of the world."

(3) In 1629, his mind crowded with ideas demanding to be written down in books and essays and correspondence, he settled in Holland. He was seeking quiet and seclusion once more, but this time in earnest. His European retirement, as he called it, lasted twenty years. These were the years of fruitful production. Book followed book. His reputation spread. He had the intellectuals of his generation for his readers, and its rulers for his patrons and friends. In rapid succession he wrote his *Quest for Truth*, his *Rules for the Direction of the Mind*, his *Discourse on Method*, his *Meditations on First Philosophy*, his *Principles of Philosophy*, his *Treatise on the Passions*, and many other volumes which soon became stock in trade for the philosophically minded of his day. In 1649 he was invited by Queen Christina of Sweden to visit her at Stockholm and expound the principles of the "new philosophy." After much hesitation, and against the advice of his friends, he agreed to go. It cost him his life, for he caught a cold in his lungs which brought about his death within the following year.

THE ARGUMENT OF THE CITATIONS. The following citations are taken for the most part from Descartes' little book *Meditations on First Philosophy*. The thought of these six short soliloquies might be paraphrased as follows: I was given the usual gentlemen's education in my youth. Presently I became skeptical of most of what had been taught me. Accordingly, I determined to abandon all my learning and begin again with a clean slate upon which no one but myself should write, and upon which nothing should be written that was not luminously clear and distinct to my mind. I needed, as a starting point, something which could stand against all possible skepticism. To that end I set about the cultivation of systematic doubt. My doubts were brought to an abrupt cessation at the fact of my own existence. The fact that I was doubting entailed necessarily my own existence as a doubter. From this indubitandum my reconstruction must proceed. Could I use the fact of my own existence to prove the existence of anything else? Two great steps were in order: to demonstrate the existence of God and the existence of the material world. The steps by which I moved from doubts about things taught me at school, through an elaborate process of systematic doubt to the demonstrated existence of myself, God, and the external world, constitute the theme of these *Meditations*.

The first group of citations puts one in possession of the autobiographical facts with which Descartes wishes to begin.

I had been nourished on letters since my childhood, and since I was given to believe that by their means a clear and certain knowledge could be obtained of all that is useful in life, I had an extreme desire to acquire instruction.

But as soon as I had achieved the entire course of study at the close of which one is usually received into the ranks of the learned, I entirely changed my opinion. I found myself embarrassed with so many doubts and errors that it seemed to me that the effort to instruct myself had no effect other than the increasing discovery of my own ignorance. And yet I was studying at one of the most celebrated schools in Europe, where I thought there must be men of learning if such were to be found anywhere in the world.

I learned there all that others had learned. Moreover, not being satisfied with the sciences that we were taught, I even read through all books which fell into my hands, treating of what is considered most curious and rare. Along with this, I knew the judgments which others had formed of me, and I did not feel that I was esteemed inferior to my fellow students. And finally, our century seemed to me as flourishing, and as fertile in great minds, as any which had preceded it.

These reflections combined to make me take the liberty of judging all others by myself, and of coming to the conclusion that there was no learning in the world such as I had formerly believed it to be.

That is why, as soon as age permitted me to emerge from the control of my tutors, I entirely quitted the study of letters. I resolved to seek no other knowledge than that which could be found in myself, or at least in the great book of the world. I employed the rest of my youth in travel, in seeing courts and armies, in intercourse with men of diverse temperaments and conditions, in collecting varied experiences, in testing myself in the various predicaments in which I was placed by fortune. In all circumstances I sought to bring my mind to bear on the things that came before it so that I might derive some profit from my experience.

For nine years I did nothing but roam hither and thither, trying to be a spectator rather than an actor in all the comedies which the world displays. Especially did I ask myself, in each matter that came before me, whether anything could make it subject to suspicion or doubt.

I considered the manners and customs of other men, and found nothing to give me settled convictions. I remarked in them almost as much diversity as I had formerly seen in the opinions of philosophies. So much was this so, that I learned to believe nothing too certainly of which I had been convinced only by example and custom.

I thus concluded that it is much more custom and example that persuade us than any certain knowledge. And this despite the fact that the voice of the majority affords no proof of any value in matters a little difficult to discover. Such truths are like to have been discovered by one man, more than by a nation. But I could not, however, put my finger on a single person whose opinions seemed preferable to those of others.

I found I was constrained, so to speak, to undertake the direction of my own inquiries.

As regards all the opinions which, up to that time, I had embraced, I thought I could not do better than try once for all to sweep them completely away. Later on they might be replaced, either by others which were better, or by the same when I had made them conform to the uniformity of a rational scheme. I firmly believed that by this means I should succeed much better than if I had built on foundations and principles of which I had allowed myself to be persuaded in youth without having inquired into their truth. My design has never extended beyond trying to reform my own opinions and to build on a foundation which is entirely my own.

I was not seeking to imitate the skeptics, who only doubt for the sake of doubting and pretend always to be uncertain. On the contrary, my design was only to provide myself with good ground for assurance, to reject the quicksand and the mud in order to find the rock or clay.

These remarks give us the terms of his self-imposed task. It was twofold. On the one hand, to work himself free from the tangled mass of belief and opinion which he had accepted as part of a normal education; on the other, to avoid the flippant shallowness of the merely disillusioned skeptic. The execution of this design called for a deliberately formulated procedure. This Descartes outlines:

Like one who walks alone and in the twilight, I resolved to go slowly, to use so much circumspection that even if my advance was very small at least I guarded myself from falling. I did not wish to reject any opinion finally until I had planned out the task I had undertaken, and until I had sought out the true method of arriving at a knowledge of the things of which my mind was capable.

In my younger days I had studied logic and geometry and algebra — three sciences which, it seemed, ought to contribute something to the design I had in view.

But, in examining them, I observed in respect to logic, that syllogisms and the rest served better to explain those things which one already knows than to learn something new. As to geometry and algebra, they embrace only the most abstract matters, such as appear to have no actual use. This made me feel that some other method must be found exempt from their fault. So, in place of the many precepts of which logic is composed, and the many rules and formulae of which mathematics is composed, I settled on four rules for the direction of the understanding.

My first rule was to accept nothing as true which I did not clearly recognize to be so; to accept nothing more than what was presented to my mind so clearly and distinctly that I could have no occasion to doubt it. The second rule was to divide each problem or difficulty into as many parts as possible. The third rule was to commence my reflections with objects which were the simplest and easiest to understand, and rise thence, little by little, to knowledge of the most complex. The fourth rule was to make enumerations so complete, and reviews so general, that I should be certain to have omitted nothing.

Those long chains of reasoning which geometricians make had caused me to imagine that all parts of human knowledge might be mutually related in the same fashion; and that, provided we abstain from receiving anything as true which is not so, and always deduce one conclusion from some other, there can be nothing so remote that we cannot reach it, nor so recondite that we cannot discover it.

But what pleased me most, in this method which I was determined to follow, was that I was certain by its means to exercise my reason in all things; if not perfectly, at least as well as was in my power. I felt that, in making use of it, my mind would gradually accustom itself to think about its objects more accurately and distinctly.

The first of the above rules is perhaps the important one: to accept nothing as true which he did not clearly recognize to be so. It is one thing to lay this rule down. It is another to abide by it. The difficulty is in knowing where to start searching for one indubitable fact. But, the search is under way.

. . . it is necessary for me to reject as false everything as to which I can imagine the least ground of doubt, in order to see if anything remains that is entirely certain. So I set myself seriously and freely to the general upheaval of all my former opinions.

To that end it is not requisite that I examine each opinion in particular. That would be an endless undertaking. Owing, however, to the fact that the destruction of the foundations brings with it the downfall of the rest of the edifice, I shall only attack those principles upon which all my former opinions rested.

All that up to the present time I have accepted as most true and certain I have learned either from the senses or through the senses. But it is sometimes proved to me that these senses are deceptive. And it is wiser not to trust entirely to anything by which we have once been deceived.

But it may be objected that, although the senses sometimes deceive us concerning things which are hardly perceptible or are very far away, there are yet many things as to which we cannot reasonably have any doubt although we recognize them by their means. For example, there is the fact that I am here, seated by the fire, attired in a dressing gown, having this paper in my hand. And how could I deny that these hands and this body are mine?

At the same time I must remember that I am in the habit of sleeping, and in my dreams representing to myself the same things. How often has it happened that I dreamt I was in this particular place, dressed and seated near the fire, while in reality I was lying undressed in bed. On many occasions I have in sleep been deceived by similar illusions. In thinking carefully about this fact, I see that there are manifestly no certain indications by which we may clearly distinguish wakefulness from sleep.

Suppose we assume, then, that we are asleep; that all these particulars, e.g., opening our eyes, shaking our head, extending our hand, are but false delusions; that possibly neither our hands nor our body are such as they appear to us to be.

There is a point, however, which we must not overlook. We must admit that the things which are represented to us in sleep are like painted representations which can only have been formed as the counterparts of something real and true, i.e., not illusory. It would follow from this admission that those general things at least, i.e., eyes, head, hands, body, are not imaginary things but things really existent.

We are bound, at the same time, to confess that there are some objects yet more simple and universal than eyes, a head, a body, etc., namely, colors, shapes, size, number, etc., which are real and true. For, whether I am awake or asleep, red is not blue, two and three make five, squares have only four sides, and so on. It does not seem possible that truths so clear can be suspected of any falsity.

Nevertheless, I have long had fixed in my mind the belief that an all-powerful God existed by whom I have been created such as I am. But how do I know that He has not brought it to pass that there is no earth, no heaven, no extended body, no magnitude, no place; and that, nonetheless, I possess perceptions of all these things which seem to me to exist just exactly as I now see them?

It might be urged against this suggestion that God has not desired that I should be thus deceived. For is He not said to be supremely good? However, if it is contrary to His goodness to have made me such that I am constantly deceived, it would also seem to be contrary to His goodness to permit me to be sometimes deceived; and yet it cannot be denied that He does permit this.

Against the suggestion that I may be constantly deceived by God in the matter of what my senses tell me, I see no conclusive objection. In the end I feel constrained to admit that there is nothing, in all that I formerly believed to be true, of which I cannot in some measure doubt, not merely through want of thought or through facetiousness, but for reasons which are very powerful and maturely considered.

I shall suppose, then, that God, who is supremely good and the fountain of truth, is in reality some evil genius not less powerful than deceitful, employing His whole energies to deceive me. I shall consider that the heavens, the earth, colors, shapes, sounds, and all other external things, are nothing but illusions and dreams by which this evil genius has laid traps for my credulity. I shall consider myself as having no hands, no eyes, no flesh, no blood, nor any senses; yet falsely believing myself to possess all these things. I shall remain obstinately attached to this idea. If, by this means, it is not in my power to arrive at the knowledge of any truth, I may at least do what is in my power, namely, suspend judgment, and thus avoid belief in anything false and avoid being imposed upon by this arch deceiver, however powerful and deceptive He may be.

Determined to "doubt everything," until doubt becomes impossible of being pushed further, Descartes has had recourse to heroic measures. The senses have been discredited, and with them the credibility of the external world revealed by the senses. This, one might have thought, would have sufficed. But assurance must be made doubly sure. Hence the ingenious hypothesis of an omnipotent and malignant Deity. At this point the eagerly sought *indubitandum* begins to appear over the horizon.

I suppose, then, that all the things that I see are false. I persuade myself that nothing has ever existed of all that my fallacious memory represents to me. I consider that I possess no senses. I imagine that body, figure, extension, motion, and place are but the fictions of my mind. What, then, can be esteemed as true? Perhaps nothing at all, unless that there is nothing in the world that is certain.

But immediately I notice that while I wish to think all things false, it is nonetheless absolutely essential that I, who wish to think this, should truly exist. There is a powerful and cunning deceiver who employs his ingenuity in misleading me? Let it be granted. It follows the more that I exist, if he deceives me. If I did not exist, he could not deceive me. This truth, "I think, therefore I am; *cogito, ergo sum*," is so certain, so assured, that all the most extravagant scepticism is incapable of shaking it. This truth, "I am, I exist," I can receive without scruple as the first principle of the philosophy for which I am seeking.

I think, therefore I am. But what am I? I do not yet know; and hence I must be careful lest I imprudently take some other object in place of myself and thus go astray in respect of this knowledge which I hold to be the most certain of all that I formerly believed.

What then did I formerly believe myself to be? I considered myself as having a face, hands, arms, and all that system of members which I designate by the name of body. In addition to this, I considered that I was nourished, that I walked, that I felt, and that I thought.

But what am I, now that I assume that there is an evil and malicious genius who exploys all his powers to deceive me? Can I affirm, with as much certainty as I can affirm my existence, that I possess any of the least of all those things which I have just now ascribed to myself? I pause to consider. I resolve all these things in my mind. I find none of the bodily attributes which I can ascribe to myself.

What of thinking? I find that thought alone is an attribute which cannot be separated from me. I am, I exist; that is certain. But this certainty reposes on the "I think" which preceded. I am trying here not to admit anything which is not necessarily true. To speak thus strictly, I am nothing more than a thing which thinks, that is, to say, a mind, an understanding. I am a real thing. I really exist. But what am I? I have answered: a thing which thinks.

I am a thing which thinks. And what more? What is a thing which thinks? It is a thing which doubts, understands, conceives, affirms, denies, wills, refuses, imagines, feels. Certainly it is no small matter if all these things pertain to my nature.

But why should they not so pertain? Am I not that being who now doubts nearly everything, who nevertheless understands certain things, who affirms that only one thing is true, who denies all other things, who desires to know more, who is averse from being deceived, who imagines many things, who perceives many things? Is there, in all this, anything which is less than that I exist? Indeed, it is so evident that it is I who doubts, who understands, who desires, and so on, that there is no reason here to add anything to explain it. From this time I begin to know what I am with a little more clearness and distinctness than before.

The argument begins to move rapidly now. Doubt has been explored and exploited. Self has been isolated as the single indubitable fact. The nature of self, a thinking thing, has been noted. Can this be used as a steppingstone? Does the fact of himself and his thoughts imply any other fact?

I shall now close my eyes; I shall stop my ears. I shall call away all my senses. I shall efface from my thoughts all images of material things — or, since that is hardly possible — I shall esteem them as vain and false. Thus holding converse only with my self, and considering my own nature, I shall try to reach a better knowledge of what I am.

I am a thing which thinks; that is to say, that doubts, affirms, denies, knows, is ignorant, wills, desires, imagines, perceives. For, as I remarked before, although the things which I perceive and imagine are perhaps nothing apart from me, yet the perceptions and imaginings certainly reside in me. And in the little that I have just said, I think I have summed up all that I really know, or was hitherto aware that I knew. To extend my knowledge further, I shall look around more carefully and see whether I cannot still discover in myself some other things which I have not hitherto perceived.

I am certain that I am a thing which thinks. But if I am indeed certain of this I must know what is requisite to render me certain of anything. I must possess a standard of certainty. In this first knowledge which I have gained, what is there that assures me of its truth? Nothing except the clear and distinct perception of what I state. This, indeed, would not suffice to assure me that what I state is true if it could ever happen that I should clearly and distinctly perceive to be true something which was in fact false. Accordingly, I can establish as a general rule that all things which I perceive very clearly and very distinctly are true.

All things which I perceive very clearly and very distinctly, are true. If I have heretofore judged that such matters could be doubted, it was because it came into my mind that perhaps a God might have endowed me with such a nature that I might have been deceived even concerning things which seemed to me most manifest. I see no reason to believe that there is a God who is a deceiver; however, as yet I have not satisfied myself that there is a God at all.

I must inquire whether there is a God. And, if I find that there is a God, I must also inquire whether He may be a deceiver. For, without a knowledge of these two truths, I do not see that I can ever be certain of anything.

Now, it is obvious that there must be at least as much reality in any cause as in its effect. For whence could the effect derive its reality, if not from its cause? From this it follows that something cannot proceed from nothing; and that the more or the greater cannot proceed from the less.

The longer and more carefully I investigate these matters, the more clearly and distinctly do I perceive their truth. But what may I conclude from it all, finally? It is this: If I have any ideas which I myself cannot be the cause of, it follows of necessity that I am not alone in the world, that there is some other being which exists as the cause of this idea. Have I any such idea?

There is the idea of God. Is this idea something that could have originated in, been caused by, me? By the name *God* I understand a being that is infinite, eternal, immutable, independent, all-knowing, all-powerful, by which I myself and everything else (if anything else does exist) have been created.

Now, all these qualities are such that the more diligently I attend to them, the less do they appear capable of originating in me alone. Hence, from what was premised above, we must conclude that God necessarily exists as the origin of this idea I have of Him. For, to consider but one point, the idea of a being or a substance is within me owing to the fact that I am myself a being or substance; nevertheless, I would not have the idea of an infinite being, since I am myself finite, unless it had proceeded from some being who was infinite.

I see nothing in all that I have just said which, by the light of nature, is not manifest to anyone who desires to think attentively on the subject. It only remains to examine into the manner in which I have acquired this idea from God.

I have not received it through the senses; nor is it a fiction of my mind, for it is not in my power to take from or add to it. The only alternative is that it is innate in me, just as the idea of myself is innate in me.

It is not strange that God, in creating me, placed this idea within me to be like the mark of the workman imprinted on his work. For, from the fact that God created me it is most probable that He has placed His image and similitude upon me. The whole strength of the argument which I have here used to prove the existence of God consists in this: It is not possible that my nature should be what it is, and that I should have in myself the idea of a God, if God did not exist. God, whose idea is in me, possesses all those supreme perfections of which our mind may have some idea but without understanding them all; is liable to no errors or defects, and has none of those marks which denote imperfection. From this it is manifest that He cannot be a deceiver, since fraud and deception proceed from some defect.

Before I pass on to the consideration of other truths which may be derived from this one, it seems to me right to pause for a while to contemplate God Himself, to ponder at leisure His marvelous attributes, to consider and to admire and to adore the beauty of His light. Faith teaches us that supreme felicity of the life to come consists in this contemplation of the Divine Majesty. Even so we continue to learn by experience that a similar meditation, though less perfect, causes us to enjoy the greatest satisfaction of which we are capable in this life.

Disillusionment. Systematic doubt. Existence of self as a thinking thing. Existence of God, no longer the deceiving genius of the early part of the argument. There remains only the external world, revealed by the senses. Can this be reinstated? Can its existence be shown to be part of the network, inextricably bound up with his own and Deity's nature and existence?

And so I see that the certainty and truth of all knowledge depends alone upon the knowledge of the true God. Before I knew Him, I could not have a perfect knowledge of any other thing. Now that I know Him I have the means of acquiring a perfect knowledge of an infinitude of things.

Nothing further now remains but to inquire whether material things exist. And first of all I shall recall those matters which I hitherto held to be true, as having perceived them through the senses; in the next place I shall examine the reasons which have since obliged me to place them in doubt; and in the last place I shall consider which of them I must now believe.

First of all, I perceived that I had a head, hands, feet, and all other members of which this body is composed. Further, I was sensible that this body was placed amid many others. In them, in addition to extension, figure, and motion, I remarked hardness, heat, light, color, scents, sounds, and so forth.

Considering the ideas of all these qualities which presented themselves to my mind, it was not without reason that I believed myself to perceive objects quite different from my thought, to wit, bodies from which those ideas proceeded. For I found by experience that these ideas of all these qualities presented themselves to me without my consent being needed. Thus, I could not perceive any object unless it were present to the organs of sense; nor could I help but perceive it, when it was present.

Furthermore, because these ideas which I received through my senses were clearer, more lively, more distinct, than any ideas I could myself frame in meditation or find in memory, it appeared as though they could not have proceeded from my mind. So, therefore, I concluded that they must have been produced in me by some other things. And, since I had no knowledge of these objects except the knowledge which the ideas themselves gave me, nothing was more likely to occur to my mind than that the objects themselves were similar to the ideas which were caused.

But afterwards many experiences destroyed, little by little, all the faith which I had rested in my senses. For example, I observed that towers, which from afar appeared to me to be round, seemed square when more closely observed; that colossal statues seemed quite tiny when viewed from a distance; that persons whose legs or arms had been cut off seemed to feel pain in the part which had been amputated; that my dreams, which could not be caused by outside objects, closely resembled my waking moments; and so on.

Now, however, that I begin to know myself better ("I am a thing which thinks") and to discover more clearly the author of my being, I do not think I should rashly admit all the things which the senses seem to teach me, nor do I think that I should doubt them all universally.

This much is certain, i.e., clear and distinct: There is in me the capacity to receive and recognize the ideas of sensible things. The active cause of these ideas which I passively receive cannot be in me, since those ideas are often produced in me without my contributing in any way to the same, often even against my will. It follows that the power which produces these ideas resides in some substance different from me. This substance is either a material object or God or some other creature.

But, I have argued already, God is no deceiver. He has given me a very great inclination to believe that my ideas of sensible objects are sent or conveyed to me by external material objects. I do not see how He could be defended from the accusation of deceit if these ideas were produced in me by any cause other than material objects. Hence we must allow that material objects exist.

Descartes' meditations have brought him the full circle. It is well to remember that he wrote in the seventeenth century. The significance attaching to Descartes' thinking lies in the gesture of impatience and sincerity with which he seeks to abandon old traditions and to start over again. The full weight of the Middle Ages was pressing upon him from the past. The rising sun of the new sciences and new world was beckoning him toward the future. A clean break with the past seemed required. The *Meditations* were an attempt to see what ideas of the past must be allowed for by the future.

Reading References. There is little point in trying to read an entire book on Descartes at this stage. Much of what he himself wrote is dated; however, there are some valuable secondary items. Short of attempting a thorough study of Descartes and his influence on later speculation, one does best to concentrate on the few ideas presented in the little books from which the citations in this chapter were taken, his *Meditations* and his *Discourse on Method*. These are still readable in their entirety. An old volume by a German historian of philosophy, Kuno Fischer, translated into English under the title *Descartes and His School*, is lively and interesting. In T. H. Huxley's volume of essays, *Method and Results*, there is a good study of Descartes as a thinker.

READING QUESTIONS

It cannot be repeated too often: Descartes repays study. Master him, and you are in a fair way to proceed to other thinkers. Study his way of thinking. It is typical of most others. Be sure that no turn in his total argument goes unnoticed.

1. Why did he quit the study of letters?
2. What did he thereupon resolve to do?
3. How did this lead him to the necessity of cultivating skepticism?
4. What four rules did he formulate for the direction of the understanding?
5. How does doubting his senses fail to carry him far enough?
6. What hypothesis concerning God does he introduce at this point?
7. What indubitandum does this lead him to? How?
8. "*Cogito, ergo sum.*" Explain.
9. How does he proceed from "self" to God?
10. Why could he not have recourse, at this point, to the design argument in natural theology?
11. How does he proceed from God to the external world?
12. Descartes is sometimes described as a "rationalist." What propositions express his unbounded faith in reasoning?
13. Formulate two or more problems you would put to Descartes.

2. MATERIALISM AND ITS IMPLICATIONS — FROM THOMAS HOBBES

From Descartes to Hobbes. The problem we have been considering is stated in the question: What is the nature of ultimate reality? We have seen Descartes' answer. This, one suspects, is the metaphysics which is most congenial to the unsophisticated person. But not all men are unsophisticated in these things. There have therefore been several alternative metaphysical positions. One of the most familiar of these is a straight materialism: the belief, namely, that reality consists of particles of matter moving in space and time according to necessary laws. This metaphysical hypothesis came early to the fore, in the seventeenth century, and allowing for a certain quaintness of language, it has never received a more wholehearted exposition than is to be found in the pages of Thomas Hobbes, contemporary and friend and critic of Descartes.

Biographical Note. Thomas Hobbes was born in England in 1588 and died in 1679 at the age of ninety-one. During a long and busy life he was a close student of revolutionary politics and the new physical sciences. His life's work was a sustained attempt to formulate a philosophy which, he felt, would be more adequate to the new times than either the medieval traditions persisting from St. Thomas and others or the somewhat compromising position adopted by Descartes and his followers. The story of his own life is crowded with interest, but it is a reflected interest arising largely out of the stirring times through which he lived. He was educated at Oxford. Thereafter he became tutor and secretary to the Earl of Devonshire. In this capacity he made the acquaintance of Francis Bacon, Ben Jonson, and other literary figures. He published a translation of Thucydides. When his patron died, Hobbes took over the education of his son with whom he took the Grand Tour, making the acquaintance of Galileo, Gassendi, and other scientific luminaries on the Continent. He returned to England to study politics. It was the time of England's civil war against Charles I. Hobbes was Royalist, siding against Cromwell. Circulation of his book, *The Body Politic*, obliged him to leave England and reside in Paris. This time he met Descartes and engaged him in metaphysical controversy. The exiled Prince of Wales, afterwards Charles II, was also in Paris. Hobbes became his tutor. He published again on the subject of politics, this time rousing the wrath of some of the Royalists. He returned to England and enjoyed such peace as obtained under Cromwell's regime, making friends with William Harvey, who discovered the circulation of the blood, with the poet Cowley, and others. Upon the restoration of Charles II to the English throne, Hobbes moved once more to a place in the sun and on the pension list. He was one of the most influential men of his day among persons who were open to ideas. There is not space to outline his position in seventeenth-century thought, but this much may be summarized: He believed that matter is the ultimate reality; that our sense organs are transformers, not revealers; that man does not have a free will; that all human action is motivated by complete selfishness; that an absolute sovereign is needed, whether in the form of a monarch or a parliament, to insure peace under law; and that religion is a "pill which it is better to swallow without chewing."

THE ARGUMENT OF THE CITATIONS. The following citations give a simple formulation of metaphysical materialism. From a statement of the essential point, that all is matter moving according to laws, the quotations follow Hobbes through the principal turns of his belief. They present a development and, in some cases, a defense of the implications of the fundamental belief. It should be remembered that Hobbes is writing here as a philosopher, not as a scientist. In the strict sense of the word, he was not a scientist, either by temperament or training. He is, where it is relevant, restating or referring to the labors of Copernicus, Kepler, Galileo, Harvey, and the rest. But the point of his writings, in effect, is this: If what such men are finding out, is once accepted without reservation, then over all we are committed to these more comprehensive beliefs.

Think not, courteous reader, that the philosophy which I am going to set in order is that which makes philosophers' stones. It is the natural reason of man, busily flying up and down among the creatures, and bringing back a true report of their order, causes, and effects. Philosophy is therefore the child of the world and your own mind. Like the world, its father, as it was in the beginning, it is a thing confused. If you will be a philosopher in good earnest, let your reason move upon the deep of your own cogitations and experience; those things that lie in confusion must be set in order, distinguished, and stamped everyone with its own name.

Philosophy excludes theology, I mean the doctrine of God. It excludes the doctrine of angels and also such things as are neither bodies nor properties of bodies. It excludes history, natural as well as political, because such knowledge is but experience or authority and not reason. It excludes astrology and all such divinations. It excludes all such knowledge as is acquired by divine inspiration, or revelation, as not derived to us by reason but by some supernatural sense. Lastly it excludes the doctrine of God's worship as being not to be known by the light of natural reason but by the authority of the church.

I am not ignorant how hard a thing it is to weed out of men's minds inveterate opinions that have taken root there, and been confirmed by the authority of eloquent writers; especially since true philosophy rejects the paint and false colors, the ornaments and graces, of language. The first grounds of knowledge are not only not beautiful; they are poor and arid, and, in appearance, deformed. Nevertheless, there being some men who are delighted with truth and strength of reason, I thought I might do well to take these pains for the sake of even those few. I proceed therefore and take my beginning from the definition of philosophy.

With these preliminary observations, Hobbes closes in on his theme:

The subject of philosophy is every body [i.e., piece of matter] of which we can conceive any beginning, which we can compare with other bodies, or which is capable of composition and resolution; that is to say, every body of whose beginning or properties we can have any knowledge.

The definition of body may be this: a body is that which, having no dependence upon our thought, is coincident or coextended with some part of space.

The world — I mean the whole mass of things that are — is corporeal, that is to say, body; and that which is not body is no part of the universe. . . . The universe being the aggregate of all bodies, there is no real part thereof that is not also body.

The basic thesis once stated, Hobbes moves on to a series of implications, that is, propositions which follow from the fundamental position. The first of these is that motion is the one thing that "really" takes place; all else is mere appearance, thrown off, so to speak, by matter in motion.

There can be no cause of motion except in a body contiguous and moved.

Mutation, that is, change, can be nothing but motion of the parts of that body which is changed. We say that that which appears to our senses is otherwise than it appeared formerly. Both appearances are effects produced in the sentient creature; and, if they be different, it is necessary that some part of the agent which was formerly at rest is now moved, and so the mutation consists in the motion; or some part which was formerly moved, is now otherwise moved, and so the mutation consists in this new motion; or which, being formerly moved, is now at rest, and so again mutation is motion.

A second corollary is rigid determinism, that is, the belief that everything happens of necessity, or inevitably.

Whatever effect is produced at any time, the same is produced by a necessary cause. For whatsoever is produced had an entire cause, had all those things which, being supposed, it cannot be understood but that the effect follows; that is, it had a necessary cause. In the same manner, whatsoever effects are hereafter to be produced, shall have a necessary cause, so that all the effects that have been or shall be produced have their necessity in things antecedent.

From this determinism it would follow that, given enough knowledge of the past and present one could predict all future events in the greatest detail. Hobbes is aware of this claim. It has been made, off and on, ever since his time. Better than a century later the French astronomer, LaPlace, wrote:

We ought to regard the present state of the universe as the effect of its antecedent state and as the cause of the state that is to follow. An intelligence, who for a given instant should be acquainted with all the forces by which nature is animated, and with the several positions of the beings composing it, if his intellect were vast enough to submit these data to analysis, would include in one and the same formula the movement of the largest bodies in the universe and those of the lightest atom. Nothing would be uncertain for him, the future as well as the past would be present to his eyes.

Before resuming the elaboration of his views, Hobbes pays his lip service to natural theology:

He that from any effect he seeth come to pass, should reason to the next and immediate cause thereof, and from thence to the cause of that cause, and plunge himself profoundly into the pursuit of causes, shall come at last to this, that there must be, as even the heathen philosophers confessed, one first mover, one first cause of things which is that which men mean by the name of God.

Having disposed of that, Hobbes turns back to the more congenial task of noting further implications of his materialism. All living organisms, it would follow, are just so many complicated machines:

Seeing that life is but a motion of limbs and organs, why may we not say that all automata (engines that move themselves by springs and wheels as doth a watch) have an artificial life? For what is the heart but a spring, and the nerves but so many strings, and the joints but so many wheels, giving motion to the whole body?

Hobbes continues. Materialism in metaphysics, he urges, implies sensationism in epistemology; implies, that is, that all knowledge originates in sensations.

The original of men's thoughts is sense, for there is no conception in a man's mind which hath not, totally or by parts, been begotten upon the organs of sense. The rest are derived from that original.

As I said before, whatsoever we conceive, hath been perceived first by sense, either all at once or by parts. A man can have no thought representing anything, not subject to sense.

Imagination is nothing but decaying sense. From whence it

followeth that the longer the time is after the sense, the weaker is the imagination.

Imagination being only of those things which have been formerly perceived by sense, it followeth that imagination and memory are but one thing which for divers considerations hath diverse names.

Materialism. Determinism. Mechanism. Sensationism. And now the doctrine of representative perception, that is, the belief that sensations represent but do not reveal the real nature of the external world. Hobbes labors this point at great length.

The cause of sense is the external object which presseth the organ proper to each sense either immediately or mediately. This pressure, by the mediation of the nerves and other strings and membranes, continues inward and causeth there a reaction or counter-pressure; which endeavor because outward, seemeth to be some matter without. This seeming is that which men call sense; and consisteth, as to the eye, in a light or colored figure; to the ear, in a sound; and so on. All which qualities, called sensible qualities, are, in the object that causeth them only so many several motions of the matter by which it presseth our organs diversely. Neither in us that are pressed, are they anything else but divers motions; for motion produceth nothing but motion. For if these sensible qualities (colors, sounds) were in the object which causeth them, they could not be severed from them as by mirrors and echoes they are.

The cause of perception consisteth in this: When the uttermost part of the organ is pressed, it no sooner yields but the next part within it is pressed also. In this manner the pressure or motion is propagated through all the parts of the organ to the innermost. Also, the pressure of the uttermost part proceeds from the pressure of some more remote body, and so continually till we come to the object. Sense therefore is some internal motion in the sentient organism, generated by some internal motion of the parts of the object, and propagated through all the media to the innermost part of the organ.

I shall endeavor to make plain these points: that the object wherein color is inherent is not the object seen; that there is nothing without us, really, which we call image or color; that color is but the apparition unto us of the motion, agitation, or change which the object worketh in the brain or some internal substance of the head; that as in vision, so also in the other senses, the subject of their inherence is not the object but the sentient creature.

As a color is not inherent in the object, but an effect thereof upon us, caused by motion in the object, so neither is sound in the thing we hear, but in ourselves. The clapper hath no sound in it, but action, and maketh motion in the internal parts of the bell; so the bell hath motion, and not sound, that imparteth motion to the air; and the air hath motion, but no sound, which it imparteth by the ear and nerve unto the brain; and the brain hath motion, but not sound.

From hence it followeth that whatsoever qualities our senses make us think there be in the world, they be not there, but are seeming and apparitions only; the things that really are in the world without us are those motions by which these seemings are caused. And this is the great deception of sense.

Hobbes is stopped by a rather ingenious problem. If the sensation, say the red color of a cherry, is really so much motion of particles in the observer's head, how can we explain the fact that it appears out there in space, located where the cherry is? As Hobbes asks, "Why doth the sensation appear as something situated without the organ?" His answer is as ingenious as his question:

Why doth the sensation appear as something situated without the organ? It is thus: There is in the whole organ, by reason of its own internal natural action some reaction against the motion which is propagated from the object to the innermost part of the organ. In the organ there is an endeavor opposite to the endeavor which proceeds from the object. That endeavor inwards is the last action in the act of sense. Then from the reaction, an idea hath its being, which by reason that the endeavor is now outward, doth always appear as something situated without the organ.

But though all sense be made by reaction, as I have said, it is not necessary that everything that reacteth should have sense. I know there have been philosophers, and those learned men, who have maintained that all bodies are endued with sense. Nor do I see how they can be refuted if the nature of sense be placed in reaction only.

The argument turns from the subjectivity of sensations to the question of desires. These too must be admitted to be merely so much matter in motion.

As that which is really within us, in sensation, is only motion caused by the action of external objects, so that which is really within us in appetite or desire is nothing but motion. But the appearance of that motion we call either pleasure or pain.

When appetites and aversions arise alternately concerning the same thing, so that sometimes we have an appetite to it and sometimes an aversion from it, then the whole sum of desires and aversions is what we call *deliberation.*

In deliberation, the last appetite or aversion, immediately adhering to the act or the omission thereof, is what we call *will.*

If this be the whole story of man's preferences and desires, Hobbes is in a position to make short shrift of any lofty moral idealism. This he proceeds to do:

Moral philosophy is nothing else but the science of what is good and evil in the conversation and society of mankind. Good and evil are names that signify our appetites and aversions; which in different tempers, customs, and doctrines of men, are different, and divers men differ not only in their judgment, on the sense of what is pleasant and unpleasant to the taste, smell, hearing, touch, and sight, but also what is conformable or disagreeable to reason in the actions of common life. Nay the same man, in divers times differs from himself and at one time praiseth, that is, calleth good what at another time he dispraiseth, that is, calleth evil.

Every man calleth that which pleaseth him, *good;* and that which displeaseth him, *evil.* Since every man differeth from another in constitution, they differ also from one another concerning the common distinction of good and evil. Nor is there any such thing as absolute goodness considered without relation.

Whatsoever is the object of any man's appetite or desire, that it is which he for his part calleth good; and the object of his hate and aversion, evil. For these words *good* and *evil* are ever used with relation to the person that useth them, there being nothing simply and absolutely so, nor any rule of good and evil to be taken from the nature of objects themselves; but from the man, where there is no commonwealth.

To the commitments adduced thus far, Hobbes adds one more: a categorical denial of man's free will:

I conceive that nothing taketh beginning from itself, but from the action of some other immediate agent without itself. Therefore, when a man hath an appetite or will to something, to which before he had no appetite or will, the cause of his will is not the will itself but something else not in his own disposing.

Neither is the freedom of willing or not willing greater in man than in other living creatures. For where there is appetite, the entire cause thereof hath preceded, and, consequently, the appetite could not choose but follow; that is, hath of necessity followed. Therefore such a liberty as is free from necessity is not to be found in the will.

If by *freedom* we understand the power, not of willing but of doing what we will, then certainly that freedom is to be allowed to both men and animals.

The ordinary definition of a *free agent* is that he is one that when all things are present which are needful to produce an effect, can nevertheless not produce it. This implies a contradiction that is nonsense, being as much as to say the cause of anything may be sufficient and yet the effect shall not follow. There is no such thing as an "agent," which when all things requisite to action are present, can nevertheless forbear to produce it. Or, which is all one, there is no such thing as freedom from necessity.

The essentials of Hobbes's materialism are now before us. The position bristles with difficulties. With unerring instinct Hobbes places his finger upon the one point which, more than any other perhaps, will be disputed. I mean the denial of man's free will. The following citations show Hobbes attempting to defend his determinism against anticipated objections:

To deny necessity is to destroy the power and foreknowledge of God Almighty. For whatsoever God hath purposed to bring to pass by man, or foreseeth shall come to pass, a man might frustrate and make not come to pass if he have freedom from necessity. Then would God foreknow such things as never shall be, and decree such things as shall never come to pass.

Liberty and necessity are consistent: as in the water, that hath not only liberty but a necessity to descend by the channel. So likewise in the actions men voluntarily do; which because they proceed from their will are termed *voluntary*. And yet, because every act of man's will and every desire and inclination proceedeth from some cause, and that from some other cause, in a continual chain, it proceeds from necessity. To him that could see the connection of those causes, the necessity of all men's voluntary actions would appear manifest.

The necessity of an action doth not make the laws that prohibit it unjust. Whatsoever necessary cause precede an action, yet if the action be forbidden, he that doth it willingly may justly be punished. For instance, suppose the law on pain of death prohibit stealing. Suppose there be a man who by the strength of temptation is necessitated to steal, and is thereupon put to death. Does not this punishment deter others from theft? Is it not a cause that others steal not? Doth it not frame and make their wills to justice? To make the law is therefore to make a cause of justice, and so to necessitate justice. The intention of the law is not to grieve the delinquent for that which is past and not to be undone; but to make him and others just who might otherwise not be so. It respecteth not the evil act past, but the good to come. But you will say, how is it just to kill one man to amend another, if what were done were necessary? To this I answer: men are justly killed, not because their actions are not necessitated, but because their actions are noxious. We destroy, without being unjust, all that is noxious, both beasts and men.

Repentance is nothing but a glad returning into the right way, after the grief of being out of the way. Even though the cause that made a man go astray were necessary, there is no reason why he should not grieve. So likewise, even though the cause that made a man return into the right way were necessary, there remaineth still the cause of joy. So that I say the necessity of actions taketh away neither of those parts of repentance, neither grief for the error nor joy for the returning.

As for praise and dispraise, they depend not at all on the necessity of the action praised or dispraised. For what is it to praise, but to say a thing is good? Good for me, good for someone else, or good for the commonwealth. What is it to say an act is good, but to say it is as I wish it, or as another wish it, or according to the law of the commonwealth? Can no action please me, or another, or the commonwealth, that should happen of necessity? Doth not praise and dispraise, reward and punishment, make and conform the will to good and evil by example?

Materialism is always with us. It is as old as the records of Western philosophy, having received an elaborate presentation in the fifth century B.C. among the Greeks. Our task is to grasp the meaning of materialism and its implications. To recapitulate: It is the belief that reality is moving particles of matter. Its adherents have usually felt committed to certain further claims, as, for example, all events are rigidly predictable; all organisms are only mechanisms; all knowledge, originating in sensations, is knowledge of appearances only, since sensations are entirely subjective; human conduct is strictly determined by antecedent and concomitant events; human motives are essentially egocentric; and the achievement of happiness, in the sense of the satisfaction of desire, is the only finally good thing. These assorted doctrines are not, of course, as logically interdependent as the materialist would have us believe. But they are temperamentally interdependent. They give expression to a mood or a temperament or a frame of mind which is sufficiently widespread to demand a courteous hearing.

READING REFERENCES. The best small book on Hobbes is by Sir Leslie Stephen. It is in the series, *English Men of Letters*. The literature on materialism itself is very large. One can only suggest a few things. A good beginning may be made in T. H. Huxley's volume mentioned already under Descartes, *Method and Results*. The third and fifth essays deal with phases of materialism. Hugh Elliot's *Modern Science and Materialism* is a competent and aggressive presentation of the case. Elliot has the virtue of *caring* whether his reader believes in materialism or does not. Santayana has remarked of himself that he is today perhaps the sole surviving materialist. The volume, *Reason in Science*, in his five-volume treatise, *The Life of Reason*, provides a statement of his materialism. It is also to be found in his later book, *The Realm of Matter*.

READING QUESTIONS

1. What does Hobbes begin by excluding from philosophy?
2. What does he propose to include?
3. How does he define his ultimate reality?
4. What account of change does he give?
5. How does this entail determinism?
6. What is his view regarding the nature of animal organisms?
7. What account of thought does he give? Of imagination?
8. What do you understand by representative perception?
9. How does Hobbes find himself committed thereto?
10. On what grounds does he defend the subjectivity of sensations?
11. "And this is the great deception of sense." What is?
12. How does he seek to account for the fact that we locate our sensations "out there"?
13. What account does he give of will? Its nature? Its freedom?
14. What account does he give of good and evil?

15. What objections to determinism does he formulate?
16. How does he seek to deal with these objections?
17. Formulate two or more questions you would put to Hobbes.

3. *IDEALISM AND ITS IMPLICATIONS—FROM GEORGE BERKELEY*

From Hobbes to Berkeley. It was inevitable that Hobbes's tough-minded materialism should provoke protest and criticism. Throughout the seventeenth and eighteenth centuries, it is not too much to say, materialism was the "specter" which haunted Western metaphysics. Some resorted to the simple expedient of ignoring such views. Some reviled the personal characters of those who held them. Some, less serene or less muddleheaded, attacked the premises and disputed the validity of the conclusions which comprised the materialist's position. Among these, in the eighteenth century, was George Berkeley, the founder of modern idealism, and one of the shrewdest metaphysicians of modern times.

Biographical Note. George Berkeley was born in Ireland in 1685, and died in 1753 at the age of sixty-eight. He was educated at the Trinity College, Dublin, where while yet an undergraduate, he conceived the necessity of "refuting atheists and materialists." At the age of twenty-five he published *A Treatise Concerning the Principles of Human Knowledge*, and three years later his *Three Dialogues Between Hylas and Philonous*. These two small volumes, by the youngest and brightest philosophical mind of his generation, contain the statement and defense of his case against materialism and his case for idealism. For a while he was laughed at, as readers of Boswell's *Johnson* will remember. But the scattered ranks of those who had been troubled by the fashionable materialism launched by Hobbes and others in the preceding century soon closed to his support. Shortly after publication, Berkeley visited England and was received into the circle of Addison, Pope, and Steele. He traveled on the continent in various capacities, and on his return was appointed lecturer in divinity and Greek in Trinity College, Dublin. He received a D.D. He was made an ecclesiastical dean. He was promised aid to found a college in Bermuda for training clergymen for the colonies and missionaries for the Indians. He was made, finally, Bishop of Cloyne. He died at Oxford, beloved and respected, if not clearly understood, by all who knew him.

THE ARGUMENT OF THE CITATIONS. However much we may be left wondering about the metaphysical hypothesis which is advanced in the following citations, one thing cannot be ignored or denied. It is reached by an almost perfect embodiment of sound philosophical method. What I mean is this: Berkeley desires to establish the proposition that reality is ultimately spiritual in nature, that a man's mind provides him with a better example of the ultimately constituent "stuff" of things than is provided by a lump of matter. Now, this is strange doctrine at first notice, but the method by which Berkeley elaborates and defends his claim will repay the closest scrutiny. Once grasped, it will be seen to apply, *mutatis mutandis*, to many topics. The position to be established is idealism. The first step, therefore, must be a critique of materialism. This Berkeley proceeds to construct. Here, too, his method is sound. He starts from premises which the materialists themselves admit (any others would be irrelevant) and seeks to show that their conclusions (1) are either incompatible with these premises, or (2) do not follow from these premises. He then approaches materialism from another angle, seeking, this time, not to show its logical incoherence but to explain how, as a mere question of history, materialists have come to hold their "misguided" conclusions. Methodologically this procedure is above criticism. A communist might apply it to capitalism as the first step in a general statement of the case for communism. A free trader might apply it to protectionism as the first step in a general statement of the case for free trade. A liberal might apply it to conservatism as the first step in a general statement of the case for liberalism. To emphasize the fact that it is method and not doctrine to which attention is here directed, it should be noted that the same remarks are applicable to capitalists, protectionists, and conservatives.

The case against materialism stated, Berkeley's argument moves on to the case for idealism. The procedure is here equally sound. He formulates a few premises which anyone, he thinks, will admit. From these he seeks to deduce his idealism. He turns then to consider possible objections which might be urged against it before they are made.

The case against materialism stated, the case for idealism stated, the possible objections anticipated, he closes in on what, after all, he considers to be the most important part of the whole business, namely, an elucidation of the implications or commitments of his metaphysical idealism. By this I mean an enumeration of the propositions which, he thinks, are also true if his idealism is true.

The total argument begins as follows:

> It is plain that the notion of what is called *matter* or *corporeal substance* involves a contradiction; so much so that I should not think it necessary to spend time exposing its absurdity. But belief in the existence of matter seems to have taken so deep a root in the minds of philosophers, and draws after it so many ill consequences, that I choose rather to be thought prolix and tedious than to omit anything that might conduce to the discovery and extirpation of that prejudice.

The following distinction between primary and secondary qualities and the claim that primary qualities are alone real, whereas secondary qualities are merely subjective, were familiar notions in Berkeley's day.

> Some there are who make a distinction between primary and secondary qualities. By *primary qualities* they mean extension,

figure, motion, rest, solidity, and number. By *secondary qualities* they mean sensible qualities, as colors, sounds, tastes, and so forth.

Our ideas of secondary qualities they acknowledge not to be the resemblances of anything existing without the mind or unperceived. But they will have our ideas of the primary qualities to be patterns or images of things which exist without the mind in an unthinking substance which they call *matter*. By *matter*, therefore, we are to understand an inert, senseless substance in which extension, figure, and motion do actually exist.

Colors, sounds, heat, cold, and such like secondary qualities, they tell us, are sensations existing in the mind alone, depending on and occasioned by the different size, texture and motion of the minute particles of matter. This they take for an undoubted truth, which they can demonstrate beyond all exception.

By *materialism*, then, Berkeley proposes to mean the belief in an inert, senseless substance possessing primary qualities in its own right but not possessing secondary qualities in the same intimate fashion. His first criticism of this belief is as follows:

But can anyone conceive the extension and motion of a body without any of its secondary qualities? It is not in my power to frame an idea of a body extended and moving but I must withal give it some color or other secondary quality which is acknowledged to exist only in the mind. In short, primary qualities abstracted from secondary qualities are inconceivable. Where therefore the secondary qualities are, to wit, in the mind and nowhere else, there must the primary qualities be also.

His second criticism is this:

Great and small, swift and slow, degrees of extension and motion, are allowed to exist only in the mind, being entirely relative, and changing as the frame or position of the sense organs varies. The extension therefore which exists independently of the mind is neither great nor small; the action, neither swift nor slow. That is, they are nothing at all.

His third criticism is this:

Number is entirely a creature of the mind. Even though the other primary qualities be allowed to exist without, it will be evident that the same thing bears a different denomination of number as the mind views it with different respects. Thus the same extension is one, or three, or thirty-six, according as the mind considers it with reference to a yard, a foot, or an inch. Number is so visibly relative and dependent on men's understanding that it is strange anyone should give it an absolute existence without the mind.

His fourth criticism is this:

One argument whereby modern philosophers would prove that secondary qualities do not exist in matter but in our minds may be turned likewise against primary qualities. Thus, it is said that heat and cold are affections only of the mind and not at all qualities of real things; for the same body which appears cold to one hand seems warm to another. Thus, too, it is proved that sweetness is not really in the sapid thing; because, the thing remaining unaltered, the sweetness is changed to bitterness, as in the case of a fever or otherwise vitiated palate.

Now, why may we not as well argue that figure and extension are not real qualities existing in matter? To the same eye at different stations, or to eyes of a different texture at the same station, they appear various. By parity of reasoning, therefore, they cannot be ideas of anything settled and determinate without the mind.

In short, those arguments which are thought to prove that secondary qualities (colors, tastes, etc.) exist only in the mind, may with equal force be brought to prove the same thing of primary qualities (extension, figure, motion, etc.).

His fifth criticism is this:

Suppose it were possible that material substances possessing only primary qualities do exist independent of the mind. Yet how is it possible for us to know this? Either we know it by our senses or by our reason. As for our senses, by them we have knowledge only of our sensations: but they do not inform us that things exist independent of the mind, or unperceived by the mind, like to those which are perceived. This the materialists themselves acknowledge; nay, insist.

It remains, therefore, that, if we have any knowledge at all of material substances, it must be by our reason inferring their existence from what is immediately perceived by sense. But I do not see what reason can induce us to believe in the existence of bodies independent of the mind, from what we perceive, since the very patrons of matter themselves do not pretend there is any necessary connection betwixt them and our ideas.

His sixth criticism is this:

It may be thought easier to explain the production of our sensations by supposing external bodies, rather than otherwise; and so it might be at least probable that there are such things as bodies that excite ideas in our minds. But neither can this be said. For, though we give the materialists their "external bodies," they by their own confession are no nearer knowing how our ideas are produced, since they own themselves unable to comprehend in what manner body can act upon spirit (or mind) or how it could imprint any idea in the mind.

Hence it is evident that the production of ideas or sensations in our minds can be no reason why we should suppose matter or corporeal substances; since their production is acknowledged to remain equally inexplicable with or without this particular supposition. If therefore it were possible for bodies to exist without the mind, yet to hold that they do so must needs be a very precarious opinion. In short, if there were external bodies, it is impossible we should come to know it; and if there were not, we might have the very same reasons to think there were that we have now. Which consideration were enough to make any reasonable person suspect the strength of whatever arguments he may think himself to have, for the existence of external bodies independent of the mind.

His conclusion is this:

It is on this, therefore, that I insist, to wit, that the absolute existence of unthinking things are words without a meaning, or which include a contradiction. This is what I repeat and inculcate, and earnestly recommend to the attentive thoughts of the reader.

He turns now to an exploration of the probable reasons which led men "to suppose the existence of material substance":

It is worth while to reflect on the motives which induced men to suppose the existence of material substance; so that having observed the gradual ceasing and expiration of those motives, we may withdraw the assent that was grounded on them.

First, it was thought that the sensible qualities did really exist without the mind. And for this reason it seemed needful to suppose that some unthinking substratum or substance wherein they did exist, since they could not be conceived to exist by themselves.

Then, in process of time, men being convinced that secondary qualities had no existence without the mind, they stripped this substratum or material substance of those qualities, leaving only the primary ones, which they still conceive to exist without the mind and consequently to stand in need of a material support.

But now, it having been shown that none even of these can possibly exist otherwise than in a spirit or mind which perceives them, it follows that we have no longer any reason to suppose the being of "matter," nay, that it is utterly impossible that there should be any such thing so long as that word is taken to mean an unthinking substratum or substance for qualities wherein they exist without mind. It is an extraordinary instance of the force of prejudice that the mind of man retains so great a fondness, against all the evidence of reason, for a stupid, thoughtless Somewhat as a support of the qualities we perceive.

Thus Berkeley on materialism. One is moved to ponder its probable effect upon Thomas Hobbes, could that doughty old metaphysician have revisited the scene of his former labors. A grim smile perhaps, or an even grimmer sharpening of his tireless controversial quill as he prepared to do battle with this newcomer. His comment upon what remains would be even more interesting. For Berkeley, having "dethroned" matter, sets about to "enthrone" spirit. His first step is to secure one or two propositions which "any rational man" would admit.

It is evident to anyone who takes a survey of the objects of human knowledge, that they are either ideas imprinted on the senses; or such as are perceived by attending to the passions and operations of the mind; or lastly, ideas formed by help of memory and imagination — compounding, dividing, or merely representing those originally perceived in the aforesaid ways.

As several such ideas are observed to accompany each other, they come to be marked by one name, and so reputed as one thing. Thus a certain color, taste, smell, figure, and consistence having been observed to go together, are accounted one distinct thing, signified by the name *apple*. Other collections of ideas constitute a stone, a tree, a book, and the like.

Besides the ideas or objects of knowledge, there is something which knows or perceives them, and exercises divers operations as willing, imagining, remembering, about them. This perceiving active being I call *mind*, *spirit*, *soul*, or *myself*.

The existence of an idea consists in its being perceived. Its *esse* is *percipi*. The table I write on I say "exists"; that is, I see and feel it; and if I were out of my study, I should say it "existed"; meaning that if I was in my study, I might perceive it, or that some other spirit actually does perceive it. There was an odor, that is, it was smelt; there was a sound, that is, it was heard; there was a color or figure, that is, it was perceived by sight or touch. That is all I can understand by these and like expressions. Their *esse* is *percipi*. Nor is it possible they should have any existence out of the minds which perceive them.

All our ideas and sensations are visibly inactive. There is nothing of power or agency included in them. One idea or sensation cannot produce or alter another. The very being of an idea implies passiveness and inertness in it; insomuch that it is impossible for an idea to do anything, or be the cause of anything.

We perceive a continual succession of ideas. Some are excited anew, others are changed or totally disappear. There is therefore some cause of these ideas, whereon they depend, and which produces and changes them.

Having premised the above facts, Berkeley proceeds to argue from them:

It is clear, from what hath been said, that this cause cannot itself be any idea or sensation since all such are passive and inert. It must therefore be a substance. But it has been shown that there is no corporeal or material substance. It remains therefore that the cause of our ideas and sensations is an incorporeal active substance, or spirit.

I find I can excite some of my ideas in my mind at pleasure, and vary and shift the scene as oft as I think fit. This making and unmaking of ideas doth very properly denominate the mind active. Thus much is certain and grounded on experience. But when we talk, as do materialists, of unthinking substances producing ideas, we only amuse ourselves with words.

But whatever power I have over some of my ideas, I find that others have not a like dependence on my will. When, for example, I open my eyes in broad daylight, it is not in my power to choose whether I shall see or no, nor to determine what I shall see. It is likewise as to hearing and the other senses. The ideas imprinted on them are not creatures of my will. There is, therefore, some other will or mind or spirit that produces them.

These ideas which I cannot control, these ideas of sense are more strong, more lively, more distinct than those which I can control. They have, likewise, a steadiness, order, and coherence which belong not to those that are the effects of my will. They speak themselves the products of a Mind more powerful and wise than human minds.

Some truths there are so near and obvious to the human mind that a man need only open his eyes to see them. Such I take this important one to be, namely, that all the choir of heaven and furniture of the earth, in a word, all those bodies which compose the mighty frame of the world, have not any subsistence without a mind; that their being is to be perceived or known; that, consequently, so long as they are not actually perceived by me, or do not exist in my mind or the mind of any other created spirit, they must either have no existence at all or else subsist in the mind of some Eternal Spirit. For it is unintelligible to attribute to any single part of them an existence independent of (perception by a) Spirit.

Until his premises are effectively questioned, or his reasoning from these premises shown to be fallacious, Berkeley may now survey his work with satisfaction; however, he prefers first to look about him. Are there any loopholes? The citations which follow show Berkeley at work on this question. They should be studied carefully. They reveal a mind of penetration and persistence, seeking honestly to detect any flaws in its work.

Before we proceed any farther, it is necessary that we spend some time in answering objections which may probably be made against the principles we have hitherto laid down. In this, if I seem too prolix, I desire I may be excused, since all men do not equally apprehend things of this nature; and I am willing to be understood by every man.

It might be objected, Berkeley thinks, that:

By the foregoing principles all that is real and substantial in nature is banished out of the world. All things that exist, it will be said, exist only in the mind, that is, are purely notional. What therefore becomes of the sun, moon, and stars? What must we think of houses, rivers, mountains, trees, stones, nay even of our own bodies? Are all these but so many chimeras and illusions?

To this objection he has a ready answer:

We are not deprived of any one thing in nature. Whatever we see, hear, feel, or any wise conceive or understand remains as secure as ever, and is as real as ever. I do not argue against the existence of any one thing that we can apprehend either by sense or reflection. That the things I see with my eyes and touch with my hands do really exist, I make not the least question. The only thing whose existence I deny is that which philosophers call *matter*. There are minds which will or excite ideas in themselves at pleasure. Other ideas, which they do not so excite, speak themselves the effects of a mind more powerful and wise than human spirits. These latter are said to be more real than the former. In this sense the sun I see is the real sun. In this sense, everything in the world is as much a real being by our principles as by any other. If the word *substance* be taken for a combination of sensible qualities, we cannot be accused of denying its existence.

It sounds harsh to say we eat and drink ideas, and are clothed with ideas. But, in common discourse, the word *idea* is not used to signify the several combinations of sensible qualities which are called *things*. But this concerns not the truth of the proposition, which says no more than that we are fed and clothed with those things which we perceive immediately by our senses. The sensory qualities which, combined, constitute the several sorts of victuals and apparel, have been shown to exist only in the mind that perceives them. This is all that is meant by calling them *ideas*. If you agree that we eat and drink and are clad with the immediate object of sense, which cannot exist unperceived, I shall readily grant that it is more conformable to custom that they should be called *things* rather than *ideas*.

"I will still believe my senses and will never suffer any argument, how plausible soever, to prevail over the certainty of them." Be it so. Assert the evidence of your senses. We are willing to do the same. That what I see, hear, feel, etc. doth exist, I no more doubt of than I do of my own being. But, I do not see how the testimony of sense can be alleged as a proof for the existence of anything which is not perceived by the senses. We are not for having any man turn skeptic and doubt his senses.

Again, it might be objected that:

From these principles it follows that things are every moment annihilated and created anew. The objects of sense exist only when they are perceived. The trees are in the garden, the chairs in the parlor, only while there is someone there to perceive them. Upon shutting my eyes it is all reduced to nothing, and upon opening them it is again created.

His answer to this:

It is thought absurd that, upon closing my eyelids, all the visible objects around me should be reduced to nothing. Yet, is not this what my very critics and opponents commonly acknowledge when they agree on all hands that light and color, which are the immediate objects of sight, are mere sensations, mere "subjective states" which exist no longer than they are perceived?

Indeed we hold the objects of sense to be nothing else but ideas which cannot exist unperceived. Yet we may not hence conclude that they have no existence except only when they are perceived by us; there may be some other spirit that perceives them though we do not. It would not follow, hence, that bodies are annihilated and created every moment, or exist not at all during the intervals between our perception of them.

It might be objected that:

If primary qualities exist only in the mind, it follows that mind is extended, since extension is a primary quality of things.

The answer is clever, even if it does seem to beg the question rather subtly:

It no more follows that the mind is extended because extension is in it alone, than that it is red or blue because those qualities exist in it alone and nowhere else. Yet my opponents admit that secondary qualities exist in the mind alone; i.e., are "subjective."

It might be objected, once more that:

There have been a great many things explained by matter and motion. Take these away and you destroy the whole atomic theory, and undermine those principles of mechanics which have been applied with so much success to account for things. In short, whatever advances have been made in the study of nature, do all proceed on the supposition that "matter" doth exist.

To which Berkeley replies:

To "explain" things is all one as to show why, upon such and such occasions, we are affected with such and such ideas. But, how "matter" operates on mind, or produces any idea in it, is what no philosopher will pretend to explain. Of what use is it, therefore? Besides, things are accounted for by figure, motion and other qualities; not by "matter." Such qualities are no more than ideas, and therefore cannot be the cause of anything, since ideas cannot be the cause of anything.

It might be objected:

Does it not seem absurd to take away "natural causes" and ascribe everything to the operation of spirit? To say, not that fire heats or water cools, but that a spirit heats or a spirit cools, etc. Would not a man be deservedly laughed at who should talk after this manner?

To which Berkeley rejoins:

In such things we ought to think with the learned and speak with the vulgar. Those who are convinced of the truth of Copernican astronomy do nevertheless say "the sun rises," and "the sun sets." Yet it doth not. But if such persons affected a contrary style in common talk, it would appear ridiculous. It is the same with our tenets.

It might be objected:

Is not the universal assent of mankind an invincible argument on behalf of matter? Must we suppose the whole world to be mistaken? If so, what cause can be assigned of so widespread and predominant an error?

To which Berkeley responds:

It will perhaps not be found that so many do really believe in the existence of "matter." Strictly, to believe that which involves a contradiction, or has no meaning, is impossible. I admit men act as if the cause of their sensations were some senseless, unthinking being. But, that they clearly apprehend any meaning thereby, that they have formed a settled speculative opinion, is what I am not able to conceive.

Adding, too:

Even though we should grant a notion to be universally and steadfastly held to, yet that is but a weak argument for its truth. A vast number of prejudices and false opinions are everywhere embraced by the unreflecting part of mankind. There was a time when the antipodes and the motion of the earth were looked upon as monstrous absurdities even by men of learning.

It is demanded that we assign a cause of this prejudice that matter exists and is the cause of our sensations. I answer: Men, knowing they perceived several ideas whereof they themselves were not the author, nor depending on their wills, first maintained that those ideas had an existence independent of and external to the mind. But, seeing that the immediate objects of perception do not exist except they are being perceived, they then argued that there are objects, distinct from the colors, etc. immediately perceived by the mind, of which those latter are images or resemblances or effects imprinted on us by those objects. So the notion of an imperceived and unthinking "matter" owes its origin to the consciousness that we are not the authors of our sensations, which must therefore have some cause distinct from our minds upon which they are imprinted.

It might be objected:

You say: Though the ideas themselves do not exist without the mind, yet there may be things like them whereof they are copies or resemblances, which exist without the mind in an unthinking substance.

To which Berkeley counters:

It is indeed an opinion strangely prevailing among men that houses, mountains, rivers, in a word, all sensible objects, have an existence distinct from their being perceived by the understanding. But this principle involves a manifest contradiction. For what are the aforementioned objects but the things we perceive by sense? And what do we perceive besides our own ideas or sensations? Could any of these exist unperceived? There was an odor, that is, it was smelt; there was a sound, that is, it was heard; there was a color or figure, that is, it was perceived by sight or touch. That is all I can understand by these and like expressions. Their *esse* is *percipi*. Nor is it possible they should have any existence out of the minds which perceive them.

An idea can be like nothing but an idea; a color can be like nothing but a color. It is impossible for us to conceive a likeness except only between our ideas.

I ask whether the supposed originals or external things, of which our ideas are pictures or representations, be themselves perceivable or no? If they are, then they are ideas, and we have gained our point. If they are not, I appeal to anyone whether it be sense to say a color is like something which is invisible; to say hard or soft is like something intangible; and so of the rest.

It might be objected:

Let us admit that the notion of "matter" as the cause or support of the perceived qualities of things, is not needed. Yet there may perhaps be some inert, unperceiving substance, as incomprehensible to us as colors to a man born blind; supporting, it may be, qualities of which we know nothing because we have no senses adapted to them, but which, if we had other senses we should know of.

To which Berkeley replies:

If by *matter* you mean the unknown (and unknowable) cause or support of unknown (and unknowable) qualities, I see no point in affirming or denying its existence. I see no advantage in disputing about something we know not what and we know not why.

And adds:

If we had those other senses, they could only furnish us with new ideas or sensations. In which case we should have the same reason against their existing in an unperceiving substance that has been already offered with relation to such qualities as we do perceive: They would exist only in a mind perceiving them. This is true not only of ideas we are acquainted with at present but likewise of all possible ideas whatsoever.

The case is by now almost completed. He has stated and refuted materialism. He has stated and established idealism. He has anticipated and parried every objection which he can imagine. He proceeds to draw the conclusions which, in all justice, he feels are his due.

Having posed and met possible objections, we proceed to take a view of our principles with regard to their consequences. After what hath been premised, I think we may lay down the following conclusions.

First: It is plain that men amuse themselves in vain when they inquire for any natural cause distinct from a mind or spirit.

Second: Since the whole creation is the workmanship of a wise and good Agent, it should seem to be in order to employ our thoughts about the final causes, or purposes of things. This not only discovers to us the attributes of the Creator and Sustainer, but may also direct us to the proper uses and applications of things.

Third: The natural immortality of the soul is a necessary consequence of these principles. To assert natural immortality is not to assert that it is incapable of annihilation by the Creator who first gave it being but only that it is not liable to be broken or dissolved by the laws of nature or motion. Bodies are ideas in the mind or soul. The latter is indivisible, incorporeal, unextended, and consequently indissoluble. Changes, decays, dissolutions, which we see in bodies cannot affect a spirit which hath none of their properties. Such a being, a mind or soul or active spirit, is therefore indissoluble by the forces of nature.

Fourth: From what hath been said, it is plain that we cannot know the existence of other minds or spirits otherwise than by their operations or the ideas excited by them in us. I perceive combinations of ideas, and changes thereof, that inform me that there are agents like myself which accompany them and concur in their production. But the knowledge I have of these other spirits or minds is hence indirect; not as is the knowledge of my ideas, but depending on the intervention of ideas by me referred to minds as spirits distinct from myself.

Fifth: Though there be some things (i.e., combinations of sensations) which convince us that human agents are concerned in producing them, yet it is evident that nature, that is, the far greater part of the ideas or sensations perceived by us, is not produced by or dependent on the wills of men. There is therefore some other Spirit that causeth them. But if we consider the regularity, order, and concatenation of natural things, the surprising magnificence, beauty, and perfection of the larger, and the exquisite contrivance of the smaller parts of creation, we shall clearly perceive that the attributes One, Eternal, Infinitely Wise, Good, and Perfect, belong all of them to the aforesaid Spirit, who "works in all" and "by whom all things consist."

Hence it is evident that God is known as certainly and immediately as any other mind or spirit, distinct from ourselves. We may even assert that the existence of God is more evident than the existence of men; because the effects of nature are more numerous and considerable than those ascribed to men. There is not any one mark which denotes a man, or effect produced by him, that does not more strongly evince the being of that Spirit which is the author of nature. A human spirit is not perceived by sense: when we perceive the color, size, etc. of a man, we perceive only sensations or ideas excited in our own minds. These being exhibited to our view in sundry distinct collections, serve to mark out unto us the existence of finite spirits like ourselves. And after the same manner we see God. All the difference is that whereas some one finite and narrow assemblage of ideas denotes a particular human mind, on the other hand wherever we direct our view we perceive manifest tokens of the Divinity, "in whom we live and move and have our being."

It will be objected here that monsters, untimely births, fruits blasted in the blossom, rains falling in desert places, waste, miseries incident to human life, and so on, are evidence that the whole frame of nature is not actuated and superintended by a Spirit of infinite wisdom and goodness. If, that is to say, God is the author of all things, is He not the author of evil and undesirable things? Is this coherent with His infinite wisdom and goodness?

I answer: The very blemishes and defects of nature are not without their use. They make an agreeable variety and augment the beauty of the rest of creation, as shadows in a picture serve to set off the brighter parts.

I add: We do well, before we tax the author of nature with wastefulness, to examine whether such accusation be not the effect of prejudice contracted by our familiarity with impotent and saving mortals. In man, thriftiness with what he cannot easily secure may be wisdom. But, an Omnipotent Spirit can produce everything by a mere fiat. Hence nature's splendid profusion should not be interpreted as wastefulness in the author of nature. Rather is it an evidence of the riches of His power.

I add: As for the pain which is in the world, pursuant to the general laws of nature and the actions of finite imperfect Spirits, this is indispensably necessary to our well-being. We consider some one particular pain and account it an evil. But our view is too narrow. If we enlarge our view, so as to comprehend the various ends, connections, and dependencies of things, we shall be forced to acknowledge that those particular things which, considered in themselves, appear to be evil, have the nature of good when considered in connection with the whole system of beings.

From what hath been said, it will be manifest that it is merely for want of attention and comprehensiveness of mind that there are any atheists or Manichaeans. Little and unreflecting souls may indeed burlesque the works of Providence, the beauty and order whereof they have not the capacity or will not be at the pains to comprehend. But those who are masters of any justness and extent of thought can never sufficiently admire the traces of wisdom and goodness that shine through the economy of nature.

Since it is downright impossible that a soul pierced and illumined with a thorough sense of the omnipresence, holiness, and justice of that Spirit, should persist in a remorseless violation of His laws, we ought therefore earnestly to meditate on those important matters, that so we may attain conviction without scruple.

For, after all, what deserves the first place in our studies, is the consideration of God and duty; which to promote, was the main drift and design of my labors.

What is to be said of this flight of the metaphysical imagination? A generation later it caught the roving eye of the skeptically minded David Hume. He observed, somewhat tartly, "The speculations of the ingenious Dr. Berkeley — they admit of no refutation, but they produce no conviction," and proceeded to deal with idealism as Berkeley had dealt with materialism. But of that, more later. Meanwhile, one does well to study the argument. It has served, to this day, as a kind of rallying point for the like-minded in each generation. By this I would not be understood as saying that Berkeley produced no criticism, even among his followers. But he performed a greatly needed service. He provided an apparently coherent case against the "specter" of materialism. He gave articulation to that perennial temperament which dreads and despises and mistrusts the "appeal to matter." For his premises, others have been substituted. To his conclusions, especially his repudiation of materialism, little of importance or variety has been added.

READING REFERENCES. The citations in this chapter have been taken from Berkeley's *Principles of Human Knowledge* and his *Dialogues*. The latter are enjoyable reading. There the case for idealism is worked out in much more elaborate detail. Berkeley was an able and plausible writer. His dialogues are almost as lifelike as Plato's. A great number of books and chapters have been written about and against the philosophical position taken up by Berkeley. Any one of these will satisfy curiosity stirred up by this chapter. Perhaps mention might be made of four items. The first is a book by T. H. Huxley, *Hume, with Helps to the Study of Berkeley*. The "helps" part of this book is interesting and illuminating, inasmuch as Huxley is ordinarily credited with views which fall short of Berkeley's religiously motivated idealism. The second is a book by John Wild, *George Berkeley, a Study of His Life and Philosophy*. This is, by all odds, the most careful and elaborate exposition of Berkeley available anywhere in English. The third is the chapter on Berkeley in Mary Whiton Calkins' book, *The Persistent Problems of Philosophy*. The fourth is G. E. Moore's well-known essay, "The Refutation of Idealism," contained in his book, *Philosophical Studies*.

READING QUESTIONS

1. Enumerate the four large steps in Berkeley's argument.
2. Why does he concern himself with the case against materialism?
3. Why does he base his criticism of materialism on facts admitted or claimed by materialists?
4. From whom did he get the distinction between primary and secondary qualities?
5. And the claim that the latter are subjective?
6. What use does he make of this distinction and claim?
7. Condense into six propositions his criticism of materialism.
8. Why does he turn from refuting materialism to accounting for it?
9. On what hypothesis does he account for it?
10. Enumerate the premises upon which his idealism rests.
11. What does he mean by "*esse* is *percipi*"? To what does it apply?
12. What part does this idea play in his argument for idealism?
13. Enumerate the steps by which he proceeds from his premises to his conclusion.
14. The objections should be studied carefully. Be prepared to state each one in a single proposition. Be prepared to state his answer to each one, in a single proposition.
15. Do any of the objections seem more serious than others?
16. Are any of his answers less convincing than others? For example, his answer to the objection if primary qualities exist only in the mind, then the mind is extended?
17. What consequences, according to Berkeley, follow from his position?
18. How is he led to deal with the theological problem of evil?
19. How does he deal with it?
20. Formulate two or more questions you would put to Berkeley.

4. *VOLUNTARISM AND ITS IMPLICATIONS — FROM ARTHUR SCHOPENHAUER*

From Berkeley to Schopenhauer. It is sometimes argued that metaphysics is a question of temperament. There is a half truth in the claim. What it comes to is something like this: Descartes was an eminently commonplace individual, inclined both by nature and training to safe, middle-of-the-road opinions. This is abundantly reflected in his quite orthodox metaphysics of God, human souls, and matter. Hobbes was a rather hardheaded, realistically minded individual, inclined both by nature and training to discount flights of imagination and to stick to the "facts." What more natural, then, than his unvarnished materialism? Berkeley was a devout and genial Anglican cleric, inclined both by nature and training to share the pious aspirations enshrined in the institution for which he was a spokesman. Why not an idealism, under these circumstances? Why not the firm conviction that this world is, in the last analysis, but the manifestation of a Supreme Mind? Hume was a canny, skeptically minded Scot, impressed, above everything else, with man's seemingly boundless credulity. What more natural than his carefully reasoned refutation of Descartes, Hobbes, and Berkeley? And so one might continue, seeking to "psychologize" away any claim of metaphysics to rational consideration. There is just one fatal flaw in this notion. It is this: No explanation in terms of nature and training, of why any man believes anything, has any relevance to the question of whether the beliefs are true or false. It is well to raise this point here for two reasons: (1) One's first introduction to a variety of alternative metaphysical hypotheses is usually marked by a sense of confusion and a ready ear to the dissolving suggestion that, "After all, it's only a question of temperament." The best reply is that the truth of an opinion has nothing to do with the temperament of the man who holds the opinion. (2) In the case of Arthur Schopenhauer, there is a great tendency to "explain away" his doctrine by reference to his biography. It is well known that in life he was bitter, disillusioned, cynical, pessimistic. It is also well known that his metaphysical views amount to the claim that the nature of ultimate reality is such as to justify his cynicism and pessimism. The result has too often been that persons who reject his metaphysics, with something approaching abhorrence, do so on the ground that "his temperament explains his views." Perhaps it does, but that is not the important point. What one should ask is, "Does the nature of things justify his views?"

Biographical Note. Arthur Schopenhauer was born in Germany in 1788 and died in 1860 at the age of seventy-two. His life was filled with selfishness, suspiciousness, and bitterness. He spent some time in a commercial house before going to the universities at Göttingen, Jena, and Berlin. He left his business career in disgust. He berated most of his fellows and teachers at the universities. Upon the death of his father, his mother had moved to Weimar. Schopenhauer followed her, quarreled with her, and took separate lodgings; met Goethe, quarreled with him, and left town to settle a while in Dresden. Here he wrote his great work, *The World as Will and Idea*. As soon as it was published, he left for Italy. There he fumed jealously over the reputation and the gallantries of Lord Byron. He returned to Germany to find his book almost unnoticed. He stamped and raged at the obtuseness of his contemporaries and set himself up as a Privatdocent at the university in Berlin. Here he was outclassed by the famous Hegel, whom he denounced as a "windbag," and left Berlin for Frankfort. In Frankfort, despite squabbles with persons who shared his rooming house, he spent the remaining years of his life writing brilliant essays on various themes in his own philosophy, compiling a scrapbook of all articles and notices dealing with his work, preparing for a second and third edition of his treatise, and watching his doctrines and fame spread slowly over the whole of the Western world.

The Argument of the Citations. Schopenhauer's metaphysics is called *voluntarism*. It may be contrasted with materialism and idealism. It is the belief that will, not matter and not spirit, is the ultimate reality of which all things are manifestations. The following citations, in which this metaphysical hypothesis is set forth, fall into two groups. The first, given immediately below, without any comment, comprises what might be called the *data*. The second sets forth what might be called the *theory*. The first group requires no elucidation. Collectively, they might be inscribed "cynicism and pessimism." They are random reflections on the rottenness of things. As I read him, Schopenhauer would have these disconnected observations on nature and life fall, like so many drops of acid, into the reader's mind, preparing him to understand and appreciate the metaphysical theory which is to follow. "See," he seems to say, "see — these are the facts. Think them over. Then, but not until then, I'll give you a theory that will fit them."

Unless suffering is the direct and immediate object of life, our existence must entirely fail of its aim. It is absurd to look upon the enormous amount of pain that abounds everywhere in the world, originating in needs and necessities inseparable from life itself, as serving no purpose, as being the result of mere chance.

Let us consider the human race. Here life presents itself as a task to be performed. Here we see, in great and in small, universal need, ceaseless wars, compulsory activity, extreme exertion of mind and body. Millions united into nations, striving for a common good, each individual on account of his own. But thousands are sacrificed. Now silly delusions, now intriguing politics, excite them to wars. Then sweat and blood must flow to carry out someone's ideas or expiate someone's folly. In peace time it is industry and trade. Inventions work miracles, seas are navigated, delicacies are brought from the ends of the earth, waves engulf thousands. The tumult passes description. And all to what end? To sustain life through a brief span, and then to reproduce and begin again.

From whence did Dante take the materials for his hell but from our actual world? And a very proper hell he was able to make of it.

When, on the other hand, he came to describe heaven and its delights, he was confronted with a difficulty, for our world affords no materials for this.

In early youth we are like children in a theater before the curtain is raised, sitting in high spirits and eagerly waiting for the play to begin. It is a blessing we do not know what is actually going to happen . . . the longer you live, the more clearly you feel that life is a disappointment, nay, a cheat.

We are like lambs in a field, disporting under the eye of the butcher who chooses first one and then another. In our good days we are unconscious of the evil which fate may have in store for us — sickness, poverty, mutilation, blindness, insanity, and so on.

It is folly to try to turn this scene of misery into a garden of pleasure. It is folly to aim at joy and pleasure instead of the greatest possible freedom from pain. There is some wisdom in taking a gloomy view of things, in looking upon the world as a kind of hell and in confining one's efforts to securing a little room not too exposed to the fire.

Human life? It is like a drop of water seen through a microscope, teeming with infusoria; or a speck of cheese full of mites invisible to the naked eye. We laugh as they bustle about, and struggle. It is only in the microscope that our life looks so big. It is an almost invisible point, drawn out and magnified by the powerful lenses of time and space.

Unrest is the mark of human existence. We are like a man running down hill who cannot keep on his legs unless he runs on. We are like a pole balanced on the tip of one's finger, or like a planet which would crash into its sun the moment it should cease to hurry on its way.

As far as real physical pleasure is concerned, man is no better off than the brute. The higher possibilities of his brain and nervous system make him sensitive to more and intenser kinds of pleasure, but also to more and intenser kinds of pain. Boredom is a form of suffering unknown to brutes, except perhaps when they are domesticated. Whereas, in man it has become a scourge. Of a truth, need and boredom are the two poles of human life.

In every man there dwells, first and foremost, a colossal egotist who snaps the bands of right and justice with consummate ease. Newspapers show it every day. History shows it on every page. Does not the need of a balance of power in Europe demonstrate it? If it were egotism only, it would be bad enough. But to the egotist in man is joined, in every other human breast, a fund of hatred, anger, envy, rancor, malice, accumulated like the venom in a serpent's tooth.

I have been reading a book on the condition of the slaves in the southern states. This book constitutes one of the heaviest indictments against the so-called human race. No one can put it down without a feeling of horror. Whatever you may have heard will seem small when you read of how those human devils, those bigoted, church-going, Sabbatarian rascals treated their black brothers whom they had gotten into their clutches.

What is our civilized world but a big masquerade, where you meet knights, priests, soldiers, scholars, lawyers, clergymen, philosophers and so on? But they are not what they pretend to be. They are only masks, and behind the masks, as a rule, you will find moneymakers. It is merchants and moneylenders alone who, in this respect, constitute an honest class.

Formerly faith was the chief support of a throne. Now it is credit. The pope himself is scarcely more concerned over the faithful than over his creditors. In times past it was the guilty debt of the world which was lamented. Now it is the financial debt which arouses dismay. Formerly it was the Last Day which was prophesied. Now it is the great repudiation, the bankruptcy of nations.

Leibnitz, you know, argued that this is the best of all possible worlds. Those who agree with him are optimists. If I could conduct a confirmed optimist through hospitals, infirmaries, operating rooms, asylums; through prisons, torture chambers, and slave kennels; over battlefields, places of execution and sudden death; if I were to open to him all the dark abodes where misery hides from cold curiosity — he might come finally to understand the nature of this "best of all possible worlds."

Nature has appointed that the propagation of the species shall be the business of men who are young, strong, and handsome; so that the species may not degenerate. There is no law older or more powerful than this. Woe to the man who sets up claims and interests that conflict with it; they will be unmercifully crushed at the first serious encounter.

If we contemplate life, we behold a turmoil where most are occupied with want and misery, straining to dodge or ward off its multifarious sorrows. In the midst of this tumult, we see the stealthy glance of two lovers. Why so fearful, so secret? Because — unrealized by them, perhaps — these lovers are traitors who seek to perpetuate whole sordid rounds of want and drudgery which would otherwise come to an end.

If children were brought into the world by an act of pure reason, would human life continue to exist? Are not most of us trapped into life? Would not a man rather have so much sympathy with the coming generation that he would spare it the burden of existence?

Kant speaks much of the dignity of man. I have never seen it. It seems to me that the notion of dignity can be applied to man only in an ironical sense. His will is sinful. His intellect is limited. His body is weak and perishable. How shall a man have dignity whose conception is a crime, whose birth is a penalty, whose life is toil, whose death is a necessity?

Human life must be some kind of mistake. Else why is man a compound of needs and necessities so hard so satisfy? And why, if perchance they should be satisfied, is he thereby abandoned to boredom? This is direct proof that existence has no real value. For what is boredom but the feeling of the emptiness of life? The fact that this most perfect manifestation of life, the human organism, with the infinite cunning and complex working of its machinery, must oscillate between need and boredom and finally fall to dust and extinction, this fact, I say, is eloquent to him who has the mind to understand it.

Disillusion is the mark of old age. By that time the fictions are gone which gave life its charm and spurred on the mind to activity. By that time the splendors of the world have proved themselves null and vain. Its pomp, grandeur, ideals, and enthusiasms are faded. Not till a man has attained his three score years and ten does he quite understand the first verse of Ecclesiastes.

The world and man is something that had better not have been. This may sound strange. But it is in keeping with the facts. And it reminds us of that which is, after all, the most necessary thing in life — the tolerance, patience, regard, love of neighbor, which everyone needs and which everyone owes to his fellow.

You need only look at the way woman is formed to see that she is not meant to undergo great labor either of mind or body. She pays the debt of life not by what she does but by what she suffers: by the pains of childbearing, by caring for the child, by submission to her husband to whom she should be a patient and cheering companion.

That woman is meant by nature to obey may be seen by the fact that every woman who is placed in the unnatural position of complete independence immediately attaches herself to some man by whom she allows herself to be guided and ruled. If she is young, it will be a lover; if she is old, it will be a priest or a lawyer.

The institution of monogamy, and the marriage laws which it entails, bestow upon women an unnatural position of privilege by considering her as the full equivalent of a man, which is by no means the case. Seeing this, men who are shrewd and prudent often scruple to make so great a sacrifice and to acquiesce in so one-sided an arrangement.

The nobler and more perfect a thing is, the later and slower it is to mature. A man reaches the maturity of his reasoning powers hardly before the age of twenty-eight; a woman at eighteen — and then it is only reason of a sort, very niggard in its dimensions.

This weakness of woman's reasoning power explains why she shows more sympathy for the unfortunate than men do; present circumstances have a stronger hold over her, and those concrete things, that lie directly before her eyes, exercise a power which is seldom counteracted to any extent by abstract principles of thought, by fixed rules of conduct, or in general by consideration for the past and the future.

Women are dependent, not upon strength but upon craft. Hence their instinctive capacity for cunning and their inveterate tendency to say what is not true. For as lions are provided with claws and teeth, elephants with boars and tusks, cuttlefish with clouds of inky fluid, so nature has equipped woman with the arts of dissimulation. Therefore a perfectly truthful and straightforward woman is perhaps an impossibility. It may indeed be questioned whether women should be allowed to take an oath in court.

It is only the man whose intellect is clouded by his sexual impulses that could give the name of "fair sex" to that undersized, narrow-shouldered, broad-hipped, short-legged race. For the whole beauty of women is bound up with that impulse.

Nature proceeds with her usual economy. Just as the female ant, after fecundation, loses her wings which are then superfluous, nay, a danger to the business of breeding; so, after giving birth to one or two children, a woman generally loses her beauty; probably for similar reasons.

What can you expect of women, when you consider that the most distinguished intellects among them have never produced a single achievement in the fine arts that is really great, genuine, and original. Not even in painting, where mastery of technique is as much within their power as within man's, and where they have diligently cultivated it. The case is not altered by a few partial exceptions. Taken together, women are and remain thorough Philistines and incurable.

There is no proportion between the troubles of life and the gains of life. In the lives of the brute creation, the vanity of life's struggle is easily grasped. The variety and ingenuity of adaptation contrasts sharply with any lasting aim. Only momentary comfort, only fleeting pleasures conditioned and succeeded by want, much suffering, long strife, war of all against all as Hobbes has it, each one a hunter and a hunted, everywhere pressure, need, anxiety, shrieking, howling, and sudden death. And this, *in secula seculorum* or till once again the crust of the planet breaks.

The bulldog ant of Australia affords us a most instructive example. If it is cut in two, a battle begins between the head and the tail. The head seizes the tail with its teeth; the tail defends itself by stinging the head. The battle may last for half an hour, until they die or are dragged off by other ants.

Yunghahn relates that he saw in Java a plain, as far as the eye could reach, entirely covered with skeletons. He took it for a battlefield. They were, however, merely the skeletons of large turtles which come out of the sea to lay their eggs and are then attacked by wild dogs who drag them over onto their backs, strip off the small shell from the stomach, and devour them alive. For this, these turtles are born. Thus life preys upon itself, and in different forms is its own nourishment.

Under the firm crust of the planet dwell powerful forces of nature. Some accident affords them free play. The crust is destroyed, with every living thing on it. The earthquake of Lisbon, the destruction of Pompeii, are only playful hints of what is possible.

The only thing that reconciles me to the Old Testament is the story of the Fall. In my eyes, that is the only metaphysical truth in the book, even though it appears as an allegory. There seems to me no better explanation of our existence than that it is the result of some false step, some sin for which we are paying the penalty.

Vanini, whom his contemporaries burned, finding that easier than refuting him, put the same matter in a very forcible way: "Man is so full of misery that, if it were not contrary to the Christian religion, I should say that evil spirits, if there are any, have passed into human form and are now atoning for their crimes."

Tragedy is the summit of poetical art. The pain and wail of humanity, the triumph of evil, the mastery of chance, the fall of just and innocent, are here presented for us. And in it lies a significant hint of the nature of the world and man: the strife of the will against itself comes here into prominence. It is shown in the sufferings of men due to chance and error, reaching sometimes even the appearance of design. This we are led to see in the noblest works of the tragic muse.

Religious teachers tell us that suicide is cowardice, that only a madman could be guilty of it, and other insipidities of the same kind. Or else they make the nonsensical remark that suicide is wrong, when obviously there is nothing to which every man has a more unassailable title than to his own life and person.

The ancients did not regard the matter in that light. Pliny says "Life is not so desirable as to be protracted at any cost. Whoever you are you are sure to die, even though your life has been full of abomination and crime. The chief remedy for a troubled mind is the feeling that there is no greater blessing than an opportune death; and that every one can avail himself of."

Two Chinamen traveling in Europe paid their first visit to the theater. One of them spent all his time studying the machinery. He succeeded in finding out how it was worked. The other tried to get at the meaning of the piece being presented, in spite of his ignorance of the language. There you have the scientist and the philosopher.

The citations thus far have been expressions of Schopenhauer's pessimism and cynicism. They form a necessary prolegomenon to his metaphysical voluntarism. His general argument is to this effect: Metaphysical voluntarism is the only hypothesis which will account for the many facts upon which I base my cynicism and pessimism. The next four citations set forth his fundamental thesis.

I teach that the inner nature of everything is will.

That which makes itself known to us in the most immediate knowledge as our will is also that which objectifies or manifests itself at different grades in all the phenomena of the world.

If we observe the unceasing impulse with which the waters hurry to the ocean, the persistence with which the magnet turns to the pole, the readiness with which iron flies to the magnet; if we see the crystal take form, the attraction and repulsion of bodies; if we feel how a burden which hampers us by its gravitation toward the earth presses and strains in pursuit of its one tendency — if we note all these things, it requires no great effort of the imagination to recognize in nature what is will in us.

As the magic lantern shows many different pictures made visible by one and the same light, so in all the multifarious phenomena which fill the world, or throng after each other as events, only one will manifests itself, of which everything is the visibility, the objectivity, the manifestation. It is that which is identical in all this variety and change.

To throw his position into bolder relief, Schopenhauer contrasts it with pantheism, the belief that reality is God Himself manifested in everything.

Pantheism is the belief that God is the world — a belief which has always puzzled me. Taking an unprejudiced view of the world as it is, who would regard it as a god? A very ill-advised god, surely, who knows no better than to turn himself into such a world as ours, such a mean, shabby world; there to take the form of countless millions who are fretted and tormented, who live only by preying upon one another. What a pastime for a god!

With the pantheist, I have that One-in-All in common; but my One is not God. I do not go beyond experience, taken in its widest sense; and still less do I fly in the face of the facts which lie before me. The "God" of pantheism is, and must ever remain, an unknown "X." The will, on the other hand, is the one thing known most immediately in experience and therefore exclusively fitted for the explanation of the rest. What is unknown should always be explained by what is better known, not conversely.

The "God" of pantheism manifests himself to unfold his glory. What glory! Apart from the vanity here attributed to him by pantheism, there is immediately created the obligation to sophisticate away the colossal evil of the world. With me, there is none of this. With me alone, the evil of the world is honestly confessed in its whole magnitude. I alone have no need to have recourse to palliatives and sophistries.

From pantheism, he turns to the more orthodox alternative of theism, the belief, namely, that nature is God's handiwork:

There are two things which make it impossible to believe that this world is the successful work of a wise, good and all-powerful Being. The first is the misery which abounds everywhere. The second is the obvious imperfection of its highest product, man, who is a burlesque of what he should be.

In its explanation of the origin of the world — creation by God — Judaism is inferior to any other form of religious doctrine professed by a civilized people. That Jehovah should have created this world of misery and woe, because he enjoyed doing it, and should then have clapped his hands in praise of his own work, declaring everything to be good — that will not do at all!

I shall be told that my philosophy is comfortless — because I speak the truth. People prefer to be assured that everything the Lord has made is good. Go to the priests, then. Or go to your university professors; they are bound to preach optimism; and it is an easy task to upset their theories.

These matters of contrast noted, he resumes the exposition of his own metaphysical thesis:

That which, in us, pursues its ends by the light of knowledge, strives in nature blindly and dumbly in a one-sided and unchangeable manner. Yet in both cases it may be brought under the conception of will; just as the first dim light of dawn must share the name of sunlight with the rays of full midday.

The lowest grades of the objectification of the will are to be found in those most universal forces of nature which partly appear in all matter, as gravity, impenetrability, and so on, which it is the work of physics and chemistry to discover. They are the simplest modes of its objectification.

The conception of "will" has hitherto been subordinated to the conception of "force." I reverse the matter. I desire that every force in nature be understood in terms of will. This is not mere quibbling. For at the basis of the conception of force, as of all conceptions except will, there lies the sense-perceptual knowledge of the objective world, and the conception is constructed out of this. It is hence an abstraction from what is given in sense-perception. We have no direct experience of "forces" in nature, only of connections and sequences. The conception of will, however, is of all conceptions the one which does not have its origin in sense perception, in ideas of things. It comes from within, and proceeds from our immediate consciousness. If therefore, we refer the conception of will to the conception of force we have referred the better known to the less known.

From inanimate nature, Schopenhauer passes to the world of living things. It, too, is only a higher manifestation of the same underlying will:

Every species of animal is a longing of the will-to-live. For instance, the will is seized with a longing to live on trees, to hang from their branches, to devour their leaves. This longing becomes objectified in the sloth. It can hardly walk, being only adapted for climbing. It is helpless on the ground, agile on trees, looks like moss so as to escape its pursuers.

The will is active in nature where no knowledge guides it. This we see in the instincts and mechanical skills of animals. The ends toward which they strive are to them unknown. The bird of a year old has no idea of eggs for which it builds a nest. The young spider has no idea of the prey for which it spins its first web. Ants, marmots, bees, lay in provision for the winter they have never experienced. Insects deposit their eggs where the coming brood finds future nourishment. The larva of the stag beetle makes the hole in the wood, in which it is to await its metamorphosis, twice as big if it is going to be a male beetle as it would if it were going to be a female beetle — so that there will be room for the horns which no female beetle possesses. Has it knowledge thus in advance? The point is merely this: Knowledge is not necessary to guide will. It acts instinctively at some levels.

The instincts of plants and animals give us the best illustration of what is meant by teleology in nature. An instinct, is an action like that which is guided by a purpose, and is yet entirely without this purpose. So all constructions of nature resemble that which is guided by an aim, and yet is entirely without it. What we think to be means and end is, in every case, the manifestation of the unity of the one will.

Everywhere in nature pervading this adaptation we see strife. In this we can recognize that variance with itself which is essential to the will. Every grade of objectification fights for the matter of the others. The permanent matter must continually change its form. This strife may be followed through the whole of nature. It is most visible in the animal kingdom. For animals have the whole of the vegetable kingdom for their food, and within the animal kingdom one order is the prey and food of another. Thus the will everywhere preys upon itself and in different forms is its own nourishment.

From the lower forms of animal life, Schopenhauer turns to consider the higher levels at which instinct and impulse are somewhat modified by the emergence of intellect and knowledge.

From grade to grade, yet still without consciousness, as an obscure striving force, the will rises through matter and the vegetable kingdoms to the point at which the individuals in whom it is manifested can no longer receive food through mere movement following upon stimuli. The chances of the individual that is moved merely by stimuli would be too unfavorable. Its food must be sought out and selected. For this purpose movement following upon motive, and therefore consciousness, becomes necessary.

Consciousness, called in at this stage for the conservation of the individual, appears. It is represented by the brain, just as every other effort of the will is represented by an organ. With this new addition, the "world as idea" comes into existence at a stroke, with all its forms and categories, its subject and object, its time and space and causality and multiplicity. The world now shows its second side.

Till now mere will, it becomes now also idea, object to a knowing conscious subject. Up to this point the will followed its tendency in the dark with unerring certainty. But at this grade it kindles for itself a light as a means to an end, as an instrument needed to deal with the throng and complication of its prior manifestations; a need which would have accrued precisely to its highest manifestation.

The hitherto infallible certainty and regularity with which will worked in unorganized and vegetable matter, rested upon the fact that it alone was active in its original nature as blind impulse, as unconscious will, without interruption from a second and entirely different world, the world of perception. But with consciousness, its infallible certainty comes to an end. Animals are thereby exposed to deception and error. They have, however, only ideas arising out of perception. They have no conceptual powers, no reflective powers, and are therefore bound to the present.

This "knowledge without reason" becomes insufficient. When

the will has attained to the highest grade of its objectification, the kind of knowledge which arises out of mere perception confined to what is immediately present to the senses, does not suffice. That complicated and many-sided imaginative being, man, with his many needs, exposed to innumerable dangers, must, if he is to exist, be lighted by a double knowledge. A higher power than mere perception must be given him.

With this new power of reasoning, of framing and using abstract conceptions, there has appeared reflection, surveying the past, anticipating the future, deliberation, care, premeditated action, and finally the full and distinct awareness of one's own deliberate volition as such.

With mere knowledge of perception there arose the possibility of illusion and error, by which the previous infallibility of the blind striving of the will was done away with. With the entrance of reasoning powers that certainty and infallibility are almost entirely lost. Instinct diminishes. Deliberation, supposed to supplant everything from physical causation to instinctive reaction, begets irresolution and uncertainty. Errors become widely possible, and in many cases obstruct the will in action.

Thus knowledge, rational as well as sensuous, proceeds originally from the will itself, belongs to the inner being of the higher grades of its objectification as an instrument of selection and adaptation, a means of supporting the individual and the species like any other organ. Destined to forward the aims of the will, it remains almost entirely subject to its service. It is so in all brutes and in almost all men.

In all grades of its manifestations, from the lowest inorganic forms to the highest organic forms, the will is controlled by no final goal or aim. It always strives, for striving is its sole nature which no attaining can put to an end. Therefore it is not capable of any final satisfaction, but only of obstruction. This endless striving, of the will-to-be, the will-to-live, the will-to-conquer, the will-to-reproduce, we see everywhere, and see hindered in many ways. Wherever blocked, we see suffering. So if there be no final aim and no final satisfaction, there are no measure and end of suffering.

We ask: For what purpose does all this torment and agony exist? There is only one consideration that may serve to explain. It is this: The will-to-live, which underlies the whole world of phenomena, must satisfy its cravings by feeding on itself. This it does by forming a graduated scale of phenomena in which one level exists at the expense of another. Note two animals, one of which is engaged in eating the other.

By now man's place in nature has been indicated. Two citations conclude this somewhat evolutionary account.

In the life of man all this appears with greatest distinctness, illumined by the clearest knowledge. As the manifestation of the will rises higher, the suffering becomes more apparent. In the plant there is no sensibility and therefore no pain. In the lowest forms of animal life, a small degree of suffering may be experienced. As the level rises, sensitivity becomes wider and deeper. It appears in a high degree with the complete nervous system of backboned animals, and increases as intelligence develops. Thus, as knowledge increases, as consciousness attains to greater distinctness, pain also increases, and reaches its highest degree in man. And the more intelligent and finely formed a man is, the more pain he is open to.

Every human being is only another short dream of that endless spirit of nature, the persistent will-to-live; only another fleeting form carelessly sketched on an infinite page, and obliterated to make room for new. And every one of these fleeting forms must be paid for with many deep and long-drawn sufferings, and finally with a relentless death. Do you wonder why the sight of a corpse is never funny?

From the vantage point of his metaphysical hypothesis Schopenhauer feels himself in a position to account, in a general way, for the futility, the restlessness, the unhappiness and boredom which mark human life. If mankind is nothing but an objectification of a blindly striving universal will, what else could be expected?

Man's appetites are insatiable. Every satisfaction he gets lays the seeds of some new desire. There is hence no end to the wishes of any individual will. Why is this? The reason is simple. Will is the lord of all worlds. Everything is but a manifestation of will. Therefore no one single thing can ever give it satisfaction. Only the totality of things — which is endless.

The basis of all willing and striving is need, deficiency, pain. Thus the nature of man is subject to pain originally and in its essence. If, on the other hand, it lacks objects of desire, a terrible void and boredom comes over it. Thus man's life swings like a pendulum, backwards and forwards, between uneasiness and boredom. (Hence, in his speculations, after man had transferred all pains to hell, there remained nothing over for heaven but boredom.)

Real boredom is by no means an evil to be lightly esteemed. In the end it depicts on the countenance a real despair. It makes beings who love each other so little as men do, seek each other eagerly. Like its opposite evil, famine in every form, it provokes us to elaborate precautions. People require *panem et circenses* — bread and circuses. As want is the constant scourge of the lower classes, boredom is the lash laid across the back of the fashionable world. In the great middle classes, boredom is represented by Sunday and want by the six weekdays.

Thus, between desiring and attaining, all human life flows on. The wish is, in its nature, uneasiness. The attainment soon begets satiety. The end was only apparent, and possession drives away the charm.

It should be added to this that satisfaction, or what is commonly called *happiness*, is never positive. It is not something original, growing out of itself, so to speak; but must always be the satisfaction of some wish or longing. The wish, the want, the need, the desire, these are the positive things; and these precede, condition, and follow every satisfaction.

The life of every individual, surveyed as a whole, is a tragedy. Here and there in detail, it may have the character of a comedy. The restless irritations of a moment, the needs and vexations of a day, the mishaps and fears of a week, are scenes in a comedy. But the overarching, never-satisfied wishes, the frustrated efforts, the crushed and abandoned hopes, the deep errors of a whole life, with increasing pain or boredom, and death at the close, are always a tragedy. As if the fates would add derision to the miseries of our existence, our life must contain all the ingredients of a tragedy while in detail it will have the foolish look of a comedy.

That happiness is not something positive, that it is merely the satisfaction of some want, to be followed by another or by ennui, finds support in art, that true mirror of the world and life. Every epic and dramatic poem can only represent struggle, effort, fight for happiness; never-enduring and complete happiness. It conducts its heroes through a thousand difficulties and dangers to the goal. But, as soon as this is reached, the curtain falls, for now there remains nothing for it to do but show that what lured the hero on as happiness, materialized as disappointment.

Everyone who has awakened from the first dream of youth will realize, if his judgment is not paralyzed, that this world is the kingdom of chance and error, of folly and wickedness. Hence, everything better only struggles through with difficulty. What is noble and wise seldom attains to expression. The absurd and perverse in thought, the dull and tasteless in art, the wicked and deceitful in action, assert a real supremacy broken only by brief interruptions. In vain the sufferer calls on his gods for help. This irremediable evil is only the mirror of the will, of which himself is the objectification.

To me, optimism, when it is not merely the thoughtless verbalizing of those who have nothing but words under their low foreheads, is not merely absurd; it is wicked. It is a bitter mockery of the unspeakable misery of mankind. To me, as to the writers of the Gospels, the *world* and *evil* are almost synonymous terms.

Thus far Schopenhauer the metaphysician. Now Schopenhauer the moralist. The latter directs the argument from this point to its despairing conclusion. In our own day Thomas Hardy has expressed in poetry what Schopenhauer, up to this point, has been arguing in prose.

Given this view of things, what message does Schopenhauer deliver to mankind? It is one of pity and self-mortification. His argument turns to these matters, beginning with an explanation of the origin of humanity's pervasive egoism and selfishness, working around gradually to counsels of despair.

What I have been saying comes to this: In the whole of nature, at all the grades of the objectification of the will, there is a necessary and constant conflict, expressing the inner contradiction of the will with itself. This phenomenon exhibits itself with greater distinctness at the highest level of the will's objectification, namely in man. What I propose now is to trace to its source that egoism which is the starting point of all conflict.

The will everywhere manifests itself in separate individuals. But this separateness does not concern the will as it is in itself. The will itself is present, whole and undivided, in every one of these — as the color red is present, whole and undivided, in any red object — and beholds around it the innumerably repeated images of its own nature. Therefore everyone desires everything for himself, and would destroy whatever would oppose it. Every individual feels himself the center of the world, has a primary and inextinguishable regard for his own existence and well-being.

This disposition, which I call *egoism*, is essential to everything in nature. It is by reason of this primary fact that the inner conflict of the will with itself attains such terrible proportions. Yet this egoism has its being and continuance in that opposition of the microcosm and the macrocosm, in the fact that the objectification of the will has individualization as its form, in the fact that it manifests itself in the same way in innumerable individuals. In the highest grade of consciousness all this appears in its sharpest form.

We see the consequences of this basic fact everywhere in human life, in small things and great. We see its terrible side in the lives of great tyrants and miscreants, and in world-desolating wars. We see its absurd side in conceit, vanity, and minor selfishness. We see it writ large in history, which is the record of struggles ranging from vast armies to pairs of human alley cats. We see it when any mob of men is set free from law and order and restraint. Then that "war of all against all" which Hobbes has described so admirably, shows itself. This is the highest expression of egoism.

This "primary and ineradicable egoism" is the fact upon which Schopenhauer proceeds to build a moral philosophy, an ethics of pity and despair.

Out of this primary and ineradicable egoism arise both misery and wickedness. Do we desire to know what men so constituted, are worth in moral terms? We have only to consider their fate as a race. This is want, wretchedness, affliction, misery, and death. There is a species of eternal justice in it all. In this sense the world is the judgment of the world. Could we lay the misery of the world in one scale of the balance, and the guilt of the world in the other, the needle would point to the center.

I referred to an eternal justice in the scheme of things. To him who has grasped in all of its ramifications the thought which I have been developing, this will be evident. The world, in all its parts is the manifestation of one will. The will is free. The will is almighty. The world is its mirror. As the will is, so is the world. It alone bears the responsibility for what comes into being.

However, the world does not stand thus revealed to the knowledge of him whose mind is still bound to the service of his will, as it does to him who has risen to an entirely objective contemplation. The vision of the uncultured individual is clouded. He does not see the reality behind the phenomenon in time and space. He sees not the inner unity and identity of things, but only its separated, individualized, disunited, opposed, manifestations. For him pleasure is one thing and pain another. He sees one manifestation of the will live in abundance and ease, while at his door another dies of want and cold. He asks, "Where is Justice?"

But the vision of eternal justice is beyond him. He sees no inner connection. He sees the wicked flourish and the oppressed suffer. He cannot rise above these individual differences. Hence he does not understand the nature of this world's justice. That man only will grasp and comprehend eternal justice who raises himself above particular things, who sees through the individualizations of the real. He alone sees that the difference between him who inflicts suffering and him who bears it, is phenomenal only and concerns not the will as thing-in-itself. The inflicter of suffering and the sufferer are one. If the eyes of both were opened, the inflicter of suffering would see that he lives in all that suffers pain. The sufferer would see that all the wickedness in the world proceeds from that will which constitutes his own nature.

The comprehension of this eternal justice, of the tie that unites the evil of my crime with the evil of your misery, demands the power to rise above the limits of individuality. Therefore it will always remain unattainable by most men.

What I have been arguing is this: Hatred and wickedness are conditioned by egoism, and egoism rests on the entanglement of knowledge in the principle of individuation, in the fact that the will realizes itself in separate individuals.

If this penetration of the principle of individuation, this direct knowledge of the identity of the will in its diverse manifestations, is present in a high degree of distinctness, it will show an influence upon the will of the individual who has achieved this insight. If the veil is lifted from his eyes so that he no longer makes the egotistical distinction between his self and other selves, then he will regard the infinite suffering of all sufferers as his own.

To such a man no suffering is any longer strange to him. All the miseries of others work upon his mind like his own. It is no longer the changing joy and sorrow of his own person that he has in view. All lies equally near him. He knows the ultimately real, and finds that it consists in a constant passing away, a vain striving, an inward conflict, a continual suffering. Wherever he looks he sees suffering humanity and a world in passage. But all this now lies as near him as his own person lies to the man who is still in bondage to egoism.

The moralist, backed by the metaphysician, is now in a position to ask pointedly: Why should man, with this knowledge of ultimate reality, accept life on such terms? Why should man be a yea-sayer? Why not a nay-sayer?

Why should he, now, with this knowledge of ultimate reality, assert this very life through constant acts of will? Knowledge of the nature of the thing-in-itself becomes a quieter of the individual will. The individual will now turns away from life, now shudders at the pleasures in which it once recognized the assertion of life, now attains to voluntary renunciation, resignation, indifference, will-less-ness.

If we compare life to a course which we must run, a path of red-hot coals with here and there a cool spot, then he who is still entangled in the egoistic delusion is consoled by the cool places and sets out to run the course. But he who sees through individualization to the one will which is identical in all, is no longer susceptible to such consolation. He sees himself in all places at once, and withdraws. His will turns round, no longer asserts itself, but denies.

This denial of the will by an individual manifestation of it follows the recognition of the real nature of the thing-in-itself. It is the transition from virtue to asceticism. This is to say, when a man has once seen, it no longer suffices for him to love others as himself. There arises within him a horror of that will of which he is himself a manifestation.

Nothing but a manifestation of the will, the individual ceases now to will anything. His body he denies. His health he is indifferent to. His desires he ignores. He desires no gratification of any appetite in any form.

More concretely, what is meant by this exhortation to suppress and deny the will-to-live? Schopenhauer is clear enough about it all. Upon unhappy man he urges a program of chastity, asceticism, self-chastisement, and ultimate starvation:

Voluntary and complete chastity is the first step in asceticism, the first move in the denial of the will-to-live. It denies the assertion of the will which extends beyond the individual's own life. It gives assurance that the life of this body, the will whose manifestation it is, ceases.

Asceticism shows itself further in voluntary and intentional poverty; not only *per accidens* as when possessions are given away to mitigate the sufferings of others, but directly to serve as a constant mortification of the will, so that the satisfaction of desires, the sweet things of life, shall not rouse the will of which a penetrating self-knowledge has conceived a horror.

Asceticism extends further as humility and patience. He who denies the will as it appears in his own person will not resist if another does wrong to him. Suffering, insult, ignominy, he will receive gladly, as the opportunity of learning that he no longer stands behind his will. Patience and meekness will replace impatience and pride and anger.

Asceticism culminates in self-chastisement, fasting, and starvation. By constant privation and suffering he who has seen the nature and source of the evil of life in the will-to-live, is able more and more to break down and destroy that manifestation in himself; to crush in himself that which he recognizes and abhors as the source of his own and humanity's misery and wickedness.

When death comes to such a one, it is most welcome. Here it is not, as in the case of others, merely the manifestation of the will that ends in death. The inner nature of the will has long been restrained, denied, crushed. The last slight bond is now broken. For him who ends thus, the world also ends.

With a backward glance over the whole argument of his metaphysics and moral philosophy, Schopenhauer concludes:

What I have described here with feeble tongue and only in general terms, is no philosophical fable. It is the moral of the life of saints and ascetics in all ages and all religions. The inner nature of holiness, self-renunciation, mortification, is here expressed, abstractly and free from mythology, as the denial of the will-to-live, appearing after the complete knowledge of its own nature has become a quieter of all volition.

Before us there is certainly only nothingness. We look with deep and painful longing upon the perfect calm of the spirit which has strangled and subdued the will-to-live. Beside it, the misery and evil of life is thrown into clear contrast. Yet, only when we have recognized the incurable suffering and endless wickedness which follows upon the assertion of the will, and have ordered our days to its denial, do we attain any lasting consolation. To those in whom the will has turned against itself, this world of planets, suns, and milky ways is nothing.

READING REFERENCES. In a book by R. A. Tsanoff, *The Nature of Evil*, will be found a good, brief account of Schopenhauer's life and thought. Tsanoff writes on a gallery of pessimists, but his tenth and eleventh chapters are on Schopenhauer alone. A book by V. J. McGill, *Schopenhauer: Pessimist and Pagan*, is a popular biographical study. There is an edition of Schopenhauer, by Will Durant, which contains the best selections. There is a single-volume collection of essays, *Essays of Schopenhauer*, in which seven small volumes are bound in one. These are more easily read than the selections from *The World as Will and Idea*. Much criticism of Schopenhauer is either narrowly technical, in which case the whole point of the man is somehow overlooked, or is so pious and horror-stricken that one feels that after all there must be something to what Schopenhauer says. An exception to this might be found in the "Pessimism" chapter of Paulen's *System of Ethics*. A valuable little book, *Thomas Hardy's Universe*, by Ernest Brennecke, will show the way in which Schopenhauer's metaphysics forms a basis upon which Hardy's poems, tales, and novels can be understood.

READING QUESTIONS

1. Explain the point involved in Schopenhauer's references to the following: (*a*) Dante, (*b*) slavery, (*c*) Leibnitz, (*d*) Kant, (*e*) woman, (*f*) monogamy, (*g*) the bulldog ant, (*h*) wild dogs in Java, (*i*) the Fall, (*j*) tragedy, (*k*) suicide, (*l*) the two Chinamen.
2. What metaphysical hypothesis does he propose?
3. Wherein does he contrast his position with pantheism?
4. Wherein with theism?
5. Wherein does he consider his hypothesis as being superior to the hypothesis of force?
6. What account does he give of intelligence?
7. Between what alternatives does human life swing?
8. What has he to say of optimism?

9. What does he mean by *egoism?*
10. How does he pass from it to his conception of eternal justice?
11. What conclusions does he draw, with respect to the conduct of life?
12. Formulate two or more questions you would put to Schopenhauer.

5. *THE PRAGMATIC APPROACH TO METAPHYSICS — FROM WILLIAM JAMES*

FROM SCHOPENHAUER TO JAMES. Our problem remains: Granted a distinction between appearance and reality, what is the nature of reality? We have seen dualism in Descartes, materialism in Hobbes, idealism in Berkeley, and voluntarism in Schopenhauer. The case for any metaphysical hypothesis is, in the end, its power to account for the everyday world. Any hypothesis in metaphysics which makes the everyday world an unaccountable puzzle; any hypothesis which, if followed out, would require some other sort of everyday world than the one we have — any such hypothesis is unsatisfactory. In metaphysics, as elsewhere, the function of an hypothesis is to account for the facts, and the everyday world is, here, the "facts." Which hypothesis being true, would go furthest to account for our everyday world? Descartes'? Hobbes'? Berkeley's? Schopenhauer's? There is, no doubt, something to be said for each. It would be odd, indeed, if one of these historic hypotheses should turn out to have *no* power to account for the everyday world.

This notion, that an hypothesis in metaphysics stands or falls by its power to account for the everyday world, is the central claim made by William James. We must conceive James as thinking over the possible alternatives in metaphysics and asking himself the perennial question, "How estimate the value of each one? How justify the acceptance or rejection of any one of these?" We may proceed at once to examine his argument.

BIOGRAPHICAL NOTE. See under "A Theological Problem," page 73.

THE ARGUMENT OF THE CITATIONS. (James first explains what he means by *pragmatism*, or the *pragmatic approach*, in metaphysics. It is a way of dealing with metaphysical hypotheses. He applies it, then, to several hypotheses, to show what he means.) He begins as follows:

The pragmatic method is primarily a matter of settling metaphysical disputes that otherwise might be interminable. Is the world one or many? Fated or free? Material or spiritual? Here are notions either of which may or may not hold good of the world, and disputes over such notions are unending.

A glance at the history of the idea will show you what *pragmatism* means. The term is derived from the same Greek word *pragma* meaning "action," from which our words *practice* and *practical* come. It was first introduced into philosophy by Charles Peirce in 1878, in an article entitled "How to Make Our Ideas Clear." After pointing out that beliefs are really rules for action, Mr. Peirce said that to develop a thought's meaning we need only determine what conduct it is fitted to produce; that conduct is its sole significance.

A few years ago the German chemist, Ostwald, wrote to me: "All realities influence our practice, and that influence is their meaning for us. I am accustomed to put questions to my classes in this way: In what respects would the world be different if this alternative or that were true? If I can find nothing that would become different, then the alternative had no sense." This is genuine pragmatism.

Metaphysics has usually followed a very primitive kind of quest. The universe has always appeared to the natural mind as a kind of enigma, of which the key must be sought in the shape of some illuminating word or name, like *God*, *Matter*, *Reason*, *the Absolute*, or *Energy*.

The pragmatic method in such cases is to try to interpret each notion by tracing its respective practical consequences. What difference would it practically make to any one if this notion, rather than that notion were true?

If no practical difference whatever can be traced, then the alternatives mean practically the same thing, and all dispute is idle. Whenever a dispute is serious, we ought to be able to show some practical difference that must follow from one side or the other's being right.

But if you follow the pragmatic method, you must bring out of each word its practical cash value, set it at work within the stream of your experience. It appears more as a program for further work than as a solution. Theories thus become instruments, not answers to enigmas, in which wc can rest.

To attain perfect clearness in our thoughts of an object, then, we need only consider what conceivable effects of a practical kind the object may involve — what sensations we are to expect from it and what reactions we must prepare. Our conception of these effects is for us the whole of our conception of the object, so far as that conception has positive significance at all.

Pragmatism does not stand for any special results. It is a method only. It is an attitude of orientation. The attitude of looking away from first things, principles, "categories," supposed necessities; and of looking toward last things, fruits, consequences, facts. It has no dogmas and no doctrines save its method.

It lies in the midst of our theories like a corridor in a hotel. Innumerable chambers open out of it. In one, you may find a man writing an atheistic volume; in the next, someone on his knees praying for faith and strength; in a third, a chemist investigating a body's properties; in a fourth, a system of idealistic metaphysics being excogitated; in a fifth, the impossibility of metaphysics is being shown. But they all own the corridor, and all must pass through it if they want a practicable way of getting into or out of their respective rooms.

It is astonishing to see how many philosophical disputes collapse into insignificance the moment you subject them to this simple test of tracing their concrete consequences.

So much, then, for the meaning of pragmatism in metaphysics. There are two questions, it seems, which one should ask of any metaphysical hypothesis: (1) What sort of everyday world would there be, if it were true?" (2) "What sort of conduct would be required of me, as an intelligent being, in the everyday world, if it were true?" James was not the first person to take metaphysics thus seriously. Berkeley, it will be remembered, was not oblivious to the demands on conduct made by his hypothesis. Schopenhauer was even more explicit. William James proposes to begin by applying his pragmatic test to the question of substance and quality:

I will begin with what is driest. The first thing I shall take will be the problem of substance. Every man uses the old distinction between substance and attribute. Here is a bit of blackboard crayon. Its attributes or properties are whiteness, friability, cylindrical shape, insolubility in water, etc. But the bearer of these attributes is so much chalk, which thereupon is called the "substance" in which they inhere. So the attributes of this desk inhere in the substance "wood," those of my coat in the "wool," and so forth. Chalk, wood, and wool show again, in spite of their differences, common properties, and insofar forth they are themselves counted as modes of a still more primal substance, matter, the attributes of which are space-occupancy and impenetrability.

Now it was very early seen that all we know of the chalk is the whiteness, friability, etc., all we know of the wood is the combustibility and fibrous structure. A group of attributes is what each substance is known as. They form its sole cash value for our actual experience. The substance is in every case revealed through them; if we were cut off from them, we should never suspect its existence; and if God should keep sending them to us in an unchanged order, miraculously annihilating at a certain moment the substance that supported them, our experiences themselves would be unaltered.

Nominalism is the opinion that substance is a spurious idea due to our inveterate human trick of turning names into things. Phenomena come in groups — the chalk group, the wood group, etc. — and each group gets its name. The name we then treat as in a way supporting the group of phenomena. The low thermometer today, for instance, is supposed to come from something called *climate*. Climate is really only the name for a certain group of days, but it is treated as if it lay behind the day, and in general we place the name, as if it were a being, behind the facts it is the name of.

But the phenomenal properties of things, nominalists say, surely do not really inhere in names, and if not in names then they do not inhere in anything. They adhere, or cohere, rather, with each other, and the notion of a substance inaccessible to us, which we think accounts for such cohesion by supporting it, as cement might support pieces of mosaic, must be abandoned. The fact of the bare cohesion itself is all that the notion of the substance signifies. Behind that fact there is nothing.

The notion of a substance which underlies certain observed qualities is, by now, a familiar one. We have met it in previous chapters. What difference, we might have asked, does it make whether there *is* such a thing as substance so conceived? What difference, furthermore, does it make *how* we conceive this thing? James draws attention to a point in Catholic theology which makes the notion of substance, under some circumstances, very important indeed:

Scholasticism, that is, philosophy in Christian Europe in the Middle Ages, has taken the notion of substance from common sense and made it very technical and articulate. Few things would seem to have fewer pragmatic consequences for us than substances, cut off as we are from every contact with them. Yet in one case scholasticism has proved the importance of the substance-idea by treating it pragmatically.

I refer to certain disputes about the mystery of the Eucharist. Substance here would appear to have momentous pragmatic value. Since the accidents of the wafer don't change in the Lord's supper, and yet it has become the very body of Christ, it must be that the change is in the substance solely. The bread substance must have been withdrawn, and the divine substance substituted miraculously without altering the immediate sensible properties. But though those don't alter, a tremendous difference has been made, no less a one than this, that we who take the sacrament, now feed upon the very substance of divinity. The substance notion breaks into life, then, with tremendous effect.

From medieval, James turns to modern theology:

Material substance was criticized by Berkeley with such telling effect that his name has reverberated through all subsequent philosophy. Berkeley's treatment of the notion of matter is so well known as to need hardly more than a mention. So far from denying the external world which we know, Berkeley corroborated it. It was the notion of a material substance unapproachable by us, behind the external world, deeper, and more real than it, and needed to support it, which Berkeley maintained to be the most effective of all reducers of the external world to unreality. Abolish that substance, he said, believe that God, whom you can understand and approach, sends you the sensible world directly, and you confirm the latter and back it up by his divine authority.

Berkeley's criticism of "matter" was consequently absolutely pragmatistic. Matter is known as our sensations of color, figure, hardness, and the like. They are the cash value of the term. The difference matter makes to us by truly being is that we then get such sensations; by not being, is that we lack them. These sensations then are its sole meaning. Berkeley doesn't deny matter, then; he simply tells us what it consists of. It is a true name for just so much in the way of sensations.

These by way of historical illustrations. James is not interested, primarily, in the history of metaphysics. He has other business to attend to. Says he:

The mention of "material substance" naturally suggests the doctrine of materialism, in the wider sense of explaining higher phenomena by lower ones, and leaving the destinies of the world at the mercy of its blinder parts and forces.

In this wider sense of the word, materialism is opposed to theism. The laws of physical nature are what run things, materialism says. The highest productions of human genius might be ciphered by one who had complete acquaintance with the facts, out of their physiological conditions. This is the completion of present-day materialism, which may better be called *naturalism*. Over against it stands theism, which says that mind not only witnesses and records things, but also runs and operates them: the world being thus guided, not by its lower, but by its higher element.

Let us apply the pragmatic method to the question. What do we mean by *matter*? What practical difference can it make now that the world should be run by matter or by spirit? I think we find that the problem takes with this a rather different character.

In every genuine metaphysical debate some practical issue, however conjectural and remote, is involved. To realize this, revert with me to our question, and place yourselves this time in the world we live in, in the world that has a future, that is yet uncompleted whilst we speak. In this unfinished world the alternative of "materialism or theism" is intensely practical; and it is worth while for us to spend some time in seeing that is so.

This, then, is the meaning of *materialism*, abstractly stated. What of this, pragmatically considered?

You all know the picture of the last state of the universe which science foresees. I cannot state it better than in Mr. Balfour's words: "The energies of our system will decay, the glory of the sun will be dimmed, and the earth, tideless and inert, will no longer tolerate the race which has for a moment disturbed its solitude. Man will go down into the pit, and all his thoughts will perish. The uneasy consciousness which in this obscure corner has for a brief space broken the contented silence of the universe, will be at rest. Matter will know itself no longer. 'Imperishable monuments' and 'immortal deeds,' death itself, and love stronger than death, will be as if they had not been. Nor will anything that is, be better or worse for all that the labor, genius, devotion, and suffering of man have striven through countless ages to effect."

That is the sting of it. In the vast driftings of the cosmic weather, though many a jeweled shore appears, and many an enchanted cloud bank floats away, long lingering ere it be dissolved — even as our world now lingers, for our joy — yet when these transient products are gone, nothing, absolutely nothing remains to represent those particular qualities, those elements of preciousness which they may have enshrined. Dead and gone are they, gone utterly from the very sphere and room of being. Without an echo; without a memory; without an influence on aught that may come after, to make it care for similar ideals. This utter final wreck and tragedy are of the essence of materialism as at present understood. The lower and not the higher forces are the eternal forces, or the last surviving forces within the only cycle of evolution which we can definitely see.

The true objection to materialism is not positive but negative. It would be farcical at this day to make complaint of it for what it is, for "grossness." Grossness is what grossness does — we now know that. We make complaint of it, on the contrary, for what it is not — not a permanent warrant for our more ideal interests, not a fulfiller of our remotest hopes.

The purpose is to contrast materialism with theism. We have seen what the former amounts to, pragmatically considered. What of theism?

The notion of God, on the other hand, however inferior it may be in clearness to these notions so current in philosophy, has at least this practical superiority over them, that it guarantees an ideal order that shall be permanently preserved. A world with a God in it to say the last word, may indeed burn up or freeze, but we then think of Him as still mindful of the old ideals and sure to bring them elsewhere to fruition; so that, where He is, tragedy is only provisional and partial, and shipwreck and dissolution not the absolutely final things. This need of an eternal moral order is one of the deepest needs of our breast. And those poets, like Dante and Wordsworth, who live on the conviction of such an order, owe to that fact the extraordinary tonic and consoling power of their verse.

Here then, in these different emotional and practical appeals, in these adjustments of our concrete attitudes of hope and expectation, and all the delicate consequences which their indifferences entail, lie the real meanings of materialism and theism — not in hair-splitting abstractions about matter's inner essence, or about the metaphysical attributes of God. *Materialism* means simply the denial that the moral order is eternal, and the cutting off of ultimate hopes. *Theism* means the affirmation of an eternal moral order and the letting loose of hope. Surely here is an issue genuine enough for anyone who feels it; and, as long as men are men, it will yield matter for a serious philosophic debate.

Possibly some of you may still rally to the defense of those who belittle such disputes. Even whilst admitting that theism and materialism make different prophecies of the world's future, you may pooh-pooh the difference as something so infinitely remote as to mean nothing for a sane mind. The essence of a sane mind, you may say, is to take shorter views, and to feel no concern about such chimaeras as the latter end of the world.

Well, I can only say that if you say this, you do injustice to human nature. Religious melancholy is not disposed of by a simple flourish of the word *insanity*. The absolute things, the last things, the overlapping things, are the truly philosophic concerns; all superior minds feel seriously about them, and the mind with the shortest views is simply the mind of the more shallow man.

The central metaphysical problem is this: What is the nature of ultimate reality? We have seen how an answer to this question may carry certain corollaries along with it. Thus Hobbes, a materialist in metaphysics, is also a determinist in psychology, denying that man has any free will. James, for pragmatic reasons, rejects materialism. Where does he stand on the question of determinism? From a consideration of materialism, he turns his attention to free will. Says he: "Let me take up another well-worn controversy, the free-will problem." Why, he asks, why have men been concerned to affirm or deny free will? Because, largely, they feel that questions of moral accountability and responsibility, moral praise and blame, depend upon it. Thus:

You know how large a part questions of accountability have played in ethical controversy. To hear some persons, one would suppose that all that ethics aims at is a code of merits and demerits.

Thus does the old legal and theological leaven, the interest in crime and sin and punishment abide with us. Who's to blame? Whom can we punish?

So both free will and determinism have been inveighed against and called absurd, because each, in the eyes of its enemies, has seemed to prevent the "imputability" of good or bad deeds to their authors. Queer antinomy this! Free will means novelty, the grafting onto the past of something not involved therein. If our acts were predetermined, if we merely transmitted the push of the whole past, the free-willists say, how could we be praised or blamed for anything? We should be "agents" only, not "principals," and where then would be our precious imputability and responsibility?

But where would it be if we had free will? Rejoin the determinists. If a "free" act be a sheer novelty, that comes not from me, the previous me, but *ex nihilo*, and simply tacks itself on to me, how can I, the previous I, be responsible? How can I have any permanent character that will stand still long enough for praise or blame to be awarded? The chaplet of my days tumbles into a cast of disconnected beads as soon as the thread of inner necessity is drawn out by the preposterous indeterminist doctrine.

So it goes, or has gone, James finds. With this way of stating the case for free will, he will have nothing to do. If the sole, or main reason for believing that man has a free will lies in the fact that we cannot otherwise censure him for his misdemeanors, then James has no interest in the question. Such reasoning, from either party, he says, "is pitiful." Thus:

I ask you, quite apart from other reasons, whether any man, woman, or child, with a sense for realities, ought not to be ashamed to plead such principles. Instinct and utility between them can safely be trusted to carry on the social business of punishment and praise. If a man does good acts, we shall praise him, if he does bad acts we shall punish him — anyhow, and quite apart from theories as to whether the acts result from what was previous in him or are novelties in a strict sense.

To make our human ethics revolve about the question of "merit" is a piteous unreality — God alone can know our merits, if we have any. The real ground for supposing free will is indeed pragmatic, but it has nothing to do with this contemptible right to punish which has made such a noise in past discussions of the subject.

What, then, *is* the case for free will? It is this: Granted that men have free will, i.e., *can* mold their own destinies in part, there is some ground for the hope that they will, since they *can*, improve the general conditions of life.

Free will pragmatically means novelties in the world, the right to expect that in its deepest elements as well as in its surface phenomena, the future may not identically repeat and imitate the past. That imitation *en masse* is there, who can deny? The general "uniformity of nature" is presupposed by every lesser law. But nature may be only approximately uniform; and persons in whom knowledge of the world's past has bred pessimism (or doubts as to the world's good character, which become certainties if that character be supposed eternally fixed) may naturally welcome free will as a melioristic doctrine. It holds up improvement as at least possible, whereas determinism assures us that our whole notion of possibility is born of human ignorance, and that necessity and impossibility between them rule the destinies of the world.

Free will is thus a general cosmological theory of promise, just like the Absolute, God, Spirit, or Design. Taken abstractly, no one of these terms has any inner content; none of them gives us any picture; and no one of them would retain the least pragmatic value in a world whose character was obviously perfect from the start. Elation at mere existence, pure cosmic emotion and delight, would, it seems to me, quench all interest in these speculations, if the world were nothing but a Lubberland of happiness already.

Our interest in free will arises from the fact that our empirical future feels to us unsafe, and needs some higher guarantee. If the past and present were purely good, who could wish that the future might possibly not resemble them? Who could desire free will? Who would not say, with Huxley, "Let me be wound up every day like a watch, to go right fatally, and I ask no better freedom."

"Freedom" in a world already perfect could only mean freedom to be worse, and who could be so insane as to wish that? The only possibility that one can rationally claim is the possibility that things may be better. That possibility, I need hardly say, is one that, as the actual world goes, we have ample grounds for desiderating.

Free will thus has no meaning unless it be a doctrine of relief. As such, it takes its place with other religious doctrines Between them, they build up the old wastes and repair the former desolations. Our spirit, shut within this courtyard of sense experience, is always saying to the intellect upon the tower: "Watchman, tell us of the night, if it aught of promise bear," and the intellect gives it then these terms of promise.

Other than this practical significance, the word *free will* has none. Yet dark though it be in itself, or intellectualistically taken, when we bear it into life's thicket with us the darkness there grows light about us. If you stop, in dealing with such words, with their definition, thinking that to be an intellectual finality, where are you? Stupidly staring at a pretentious sham! Pragmatism alone can read a positive meaning into it, and for that she turns her back upon the intellectualist point of view altogether.

James has, by now, done these things: He has explained what is meant by the *pragmatic* approach to questions in metaphysics. He has illustrated his point by reference to two historical digressions. He has used the method to justify his own stand on the questions of materialism and determinism. It remains for him to commend his doctrine to his readers:

See then how all these ultimate questions turn, as it were, upon their hinges; and, from looking backwards, see, I say, how pragmatism shifts the emphasis and looks forward into facts themselves.

The really vital question for us all is, What is this world going to be? What is life eventually to make of itself? The center of gravity of philosophy must therefore alter its place. The earth of things, long thrown into shadow by the glories of the upper ether, must resume its rights.

It will be an alteration in "the seat of authority" that reminds one almost of the Protestant Reformation. And as, to papal minds, Protestantism has often seemed a mere mess of anarchy and confusion, such, no doubt, will pragmatism often seem to ulta rationalist minds in philosophy. It will seem so much sheer trash, philosophically. But life wags on, all the same, and compasses its ends, in Protestant countries. I venture to think that philosophic Protestantism will compass a note of dissimilar prosperity.

I fully expect to see the pragmatist view of truth run through the classic stages of a theory's career. First a theory is attacked as absurd; then it is admitted to be true but obvious and insignificant; finally it is seen to be so important that its adversaries claim that they themselves discovered it.

Reading References. The best thing to read on William James is more by William James. He is a delightful and inspiring author. If his breeziness and buoyancy should pall, turn to an essay by G. E. Moore in his *Philosophical Studies*. The essay is simply named "William James's Pragmatism." Or read the essay, "William James," in Santayana's *Character and Opinion in the United States*. In an earlier chapter I mentioned R. B. Perry's *The Life and Thought of William James*. In *Studies in the History of Ideas*, Volume Two, there is a good article by John Dewey on the history of pragmatism. It should be read by anyone proposing to see James in an historical perspective.

READING QUESTIONS

1. What does he say pragmatism is?
2. By whom was it first introduced into philosophy?
3. How does he define *pragmatism* more closely?
4. What has this in common with his test proposed in "The Will to Believe"?
5. "Pragmatism does not stand for any special results." Meaning?
6. Develop his corridor analogy.
7. Explain what you understand by nominalism.

8. What use does James make of the doctrine of the Real Presence to illustrate his point?
9. What does he say of Berkeley's idealism?
10. What is the meaning of materialism as James conceives it?
11. Does this differ substantially from Hobbes?
12. To what end does he quote A. J. Balfour?
13. What is James's pragmatic criticism of materialism?
14. What is his pragmatic justification of theism?
15. "Pragmatism does not stand for any special results." Explain. Illustrate. State whether you agree or disagree.
16. On what grounds, according to James, have men accepted the free-will doctrine?
17. Why does he reject these grounds?
18. What is the pragmatic case for free will?
19. In what respect does James compare pragmatism to Protestantism?
20. Through what stages does he expect pragmatism to pass?

TOPIC THREE. AN EPISTEMOLOGICAL PROBLEM

THE PROBLEM STATED

The word *epistemology* is derived from two Greek words meaning "knowledge" and "the rationale of." It means an inquiry into the nature of knowledge. If the derivation were carried out, it would provide us with a somewhat complicated conception, namely, knowledge of the nature of knowledge. How, it may well be asked, did philosophers ever find themselves launched upon so subtle an inquiry? Its full subtlety might escape notice, unless one paused to realize precisely what is intended. Suppose we refer to the sciences as theories about the nature of things. Thus we have, in astronomy, a theory of the universe at large; in economics, a theory of the production and distribution of wealth; in psychology, a theory of the mind and its relation to the body; and so forth. These are all theories of things. But in the conception of epistemology, knowledge turns in upon itself and seeks to formulate a "theory" of itself. Here knowledge is itself made the object of investigation.

From an acquaintance with the theological and metaphysical speculations which comprise the first two divisions of this book, one can see in a general way how epistemology came about. There is a cautious turn of mind to which all such speculations seem to be of doubtful value. Such a mind is impressed finally with the futility of such matters, and with the confusion which emerges when men seek to clarify their beliefs about such things. Out of this attitude toward speculation, two widely different things have resulted. There have come, in the first place, the genial and undisciplined doubts of such persons as Montaigne and Anatole France. Here the procedure is largely one of banter and ridicule. But that has not been the doubter's only defense against the speculator. For, in the second place, there has come the demand that flights of speculation be put aside until a preliminary inquiry is made into the nature of knowledge itself, and the question faced: Can it be shown, from an analysis of the nature of knowledge itself, whether such speculations are legitimate, whether they lie within the actual or possible grasp of the mind?

The chapters that follow may, therefore, be considered as five approaches to a single problem: Can we make an inquiry into the nature of knowledge? From the findings of such an inquiry can we say anything about the scope or reach of human knowledge? Can we show that some speculations carry the quest for knowledge beyond a legitimate possibility?

The authors chosen for consideration are John Locke, from the seventeenth century; David Hume and Immanuel Kant, from the eighteenth century; Auguste Comte, from the nineteenth century; and Hans Vaihinger, from the twentieth century.

1. THE APPEAL TO EXPERIENCE—FROM JOHN LOCKE

Epistemology is by no means a modern inquiry. Indeed, one of the finest pieces of epistemological analysis ever written may be found in Plato's dialogue "The Theaetetus"; but not all of Plato was continuously read by the generations which came after him, with the result that much that appeared in the early modern centuries was taken to be new. It is in this sense that John Locke is described as the founder of modern epistemology. Questions of priority aside, however, there is no reasonable doubt that the enormous literature which has grown up around this problem owes its inspiration, directly or indirectly, to Locke's epoch-making *Essay Concern-*

ing Human Understanding. This famous old book is very long, very wordy, and very repetitious, but its historical importance is exceedingly great, for it drew attention, from the year it was published, to the central place in all philosophy of the problem of knowledge. What it said, in so many words, was this: Before any man launches into speculation, he should pause to inquire concerning the human understanding itself. What things is it capable of knowing? How does knowledge arise? Are there not some questions to which the answers lie beyond the reach of human understanding? Would not a cool hour spent in a reflective consideration of the nature of knowledge reveal precisely this sort of fact?

Biographical Note. John Locke was born in England in 1632 and died in 1704 at the age of seventy-two. His life may be divided into three periods: years of education and educating, years of politics and governmental affairs, years of authorship. (1) He was educated at Westminster School and at Oxford University. After graduation he was made lecturer on Greek, and two years later, lecturer on rhetoric. While still a student, he had turned from the ancient and medieval authors and doctrines which then formed the basis of a university education. From Aristotle and the medieval schoolmen, for example, he felt drawn to Hobbes, Descartes, Bacon, and the new experimental sciences. These were the great molders of progressive opinion in his day. (2) In 1664 he left his work at the university and accepted the post of secretary to an Embassy to Brandenburg. This was the beginning of a long political and governmental career. The great political event of the times was the "bloodless" revolution of 1688. Locke allied himself, through the house of Shaftesbury, with the party which was to engineer the deposition of King James and the invitation to King William of Holland. (3) The revolution took place in 1688. Thereafter John Locke shared the prestige which attached to those who were instrumental in bringing it about. He was now a man of fifty-six, widely read, widely traveled, widely respected. He turned to publishing a series of treatises which gave expression to the ideas and aspirations of British liberalism in education, in politics, in religion, in philosophy. He had been writing these books for many years, but had not thus far ventured to publish. Now in rapid succession he issued *Letters Concerning Toleration*, *Essay Concerning Human Understanding*, *Two Treatises of Government*, *Some Thoughts Concerning Education*, *The Reasonableness of Christianity*. These volumes were published between 1689 and 1695. In six years, near the close of his life, Locke produced books which were destined to influence liberal thought for the next century.

THE ARGUMENT OF THE CITATIONS. The citations which follow pose the modern problem of knowledge. They do not solve it, but they point to the need for a solution, and they express the spirit in which this inquiry has been carried on. Locke begins by explaining why an inquiry concerning human understanding is important. He then asks the primary question: How does the human mind come by its knowledge? He pauses to state and refute one answer to this question current in his century, the hypothesis of innate ideas. He returns then to propound his own thesis: All knowledge comes from experience. This is known in philosophy as *empiricism*. He elaborates this claim in some detail. From the question of the origin of knowledge, he turns to the question of its limits. If knowledge arises in experience, how far can it reach? He distinguishes, to begin with, between intuitive and demonstrative knowledge. This suggests a further distinction between demonstrative and probable knowledge. With these distinctions made, Locke's theory of knowledge is complete; however, there were some who talked of a kind of knowledge, namely, *revelation*, which appeared not to fall anywhere within his scheme. His argument closes with some reflections on revelation and its relation to knowledge obtained through experience.)

The argument begins with a series of reflections on the value of an inquiry into the nature of mind and knowledge:

Since it is the understanding that sets man above the rest of sensible beings, and gives him all the advantage and dominion which he has over them, it is certainly a subject, even for its nobleness, worth our labor to inquire into.

This therefore is my purpose: to inquire into the original, certainty, and extent of human knowledge, together with the degrees of belief, opinion, and assent. It is worth while to search out the bounds between opinion and knowledge, and examine by what measures in things, whereof we have no certain knowledge, we ought to regulate our assent and moderate our persuasions.

If I can discover the powers of the understanding, how far they reach, to what things they are in any degree proportionate, and where they fail us, I suppose it may prevail with the busy mind of man to be more cautious in meddling with things exceeding its comprehension; to stop when it is at the utmost extent of its tether; and to sit down in a quiet ignorance of those things which, upon examination, are found to be beyond the reach of our capacities.

I shall imagine I have not wholly misemployed myself, if, in this historical, plain method, I can give any account of the ways whereby our understandings come to attain those notions of things we have, and can set down any measures of the certainty of our knowledge, or the grounds of those persuasions which are to be found among men, so various, different, and wholly contradictory.

We should not then perhaps be so forward, out of an affectation of an universal knowledge, to raise questions and perplex ourselves and others with disputes about things to which our understandings are not suited, and of which we cannot frame in our minds any clear or distinct perceptions, or whereof we have not any notion at all.

If we can find out how far the understanding can extend its view, how far it has faculties to attain certainty, and in what cases it can only judge and guess, we may learn to content ourselves with what is attainable by us in this state.

When we know our own strength, we shall the better know what to undertake with hopes of success. When we have well surveyed the powers of our own mind, and made some estimate of what we may expect from them, we shall not be inclined either to sit still and not set our thoughts on work at all, in despair of knowing anything; or, on the other side, question everything and disclaim all knowledge because some things are not to be understood.

It is of great use to the sailor to know the length of his line, though he cannot fathom all the depths of the ocean with it. It is well he knows that it is long enough to reach the bottom at such places as are necessary to direct his voyage and caution him against running upon shoals that may ruin him.

So much for purpose and plan. Before proceeding, Locke pauses to narrow and sharpen the inquiry:

Thus much I thought necessary to say concerning the occasion of this inquiry into human understanding. But, before I proceed to what I have thought on this subject, I must here in the entrance beg pardon of my reader for the frequent use of the word *idea*. It being that term which, I think, serves best to stand for whatsoever is the object of the understanding when a man thinks, I have used it to express whatever it is which the mind can be employed about in thinking; and I could not avoid frequently using it.

I presume it will be easily granted me that there are ideas in men's minds. Everyone is conscious of them in himself, and men's words and actions will satisfy him that they are in others.

Our first inquiry shall be how ideas come into the mind.

The problem has been brought to a focus: How does the mind come by its ideas? Before advancing his own hypothesis, Locke glances at an alternative explanation:

It is an established opinion amongst some men that there are in the understanding certain innate principles, primary notions, characters as it were stamped upon the mind of man, received in its very first being, brought with it into the world.

This "established opinion" to which Locke refers will be found in the writings of several of his predecessors. The most typical example is perhaps Lord Herbert of Cherbury, the author of a book, *On Truth.* In this book Lord Herbert lays it down that there are certain "common notions." Some of these common notions are formed without any assistance from experience or reason; others are developed by experience and reason, but do not originate therein. The former group is distinguished by certain marks or tests. Of these tests some are logical (such as independence, necessity, etc.); others are psychological (such as priority in time and universality). These common notions were supposed to yield the first principles of morality and religion. His book emphasizes in particular five common notions which Locke has in mind at this point. They were the notions (1) that there is a supreme Deity; (2) that He ought to be worshiped; (3) that the chief part of divine worship is virtue combined with piety; (4) that men should repent of their sins and turn from them; (5) that reward and punishment follow from the goodness and justice of God, both in this life and hereafter. With these historical references in mind, we may return to Locke's paragraphs:

> It would be sufficient to convince unprejudiced readers of the falseness of this supposition if I should only show how, barely by the use of their natural faculties, men may attain to all the knowledge they have without the help of any innate impressions, and may arrive at certainty without any such original notions or principles.
>
> But, because a man is not permitted without censure to follow his own thoughts in the search for truth when they lead him ever so little out of the common road, I shall set down the reasons that made me doubt the truth of the supposition of innate ideas.

Locke's refutation of the hypothesis of innate ideas is too long to be reproduced here. It comes to this: (1) It is a useless hypothesis, since the steps to knowledge are all discoverable. If this be the case, why assume innateness for some ideas? (2) Many ideas for which innateness is claimed are not perceived by infants. How account for this? If any ideas are genuinely innate, one would expect very young children to be in conscious possession of them. (3) Many ideas for which innateness is claimed are not known till the person "comes to the use of reason." How account for this? Why do some ideas, said to be innate, require for their discovery or recognition the use of powers which develop comparatively late in the organism's life? (4) Many ideas for which innateness is claimed are said to be "self-evident"; and their self-evidence is advanced as proof of their innateness. Locke objects. It is risky to claim self-evidence for any ideas. Self-evident to whom? Moreover, granting self-evidence, what of it? "Self-evident" is not the same as "innate"; and who shall say, without assuming the point at issue, that it is evidence of innateness? Further, are all self-evident ideas (for example, $2 + 2 = 4$) to be taken as innate? If not, by what do we distinguish, among self-evident ideas, which are innate? (5) The "universal assent of mankind" to some ideas is advanced as evidence of their innateness. Locke objects again. To what ideas do all men give assent? One genuine dissenter would be enough to spoil the argument from consensus. Moreover, that all men assent to an idea is one thing; that the idea is therefore innate is another thing. Upon what grounds are we justified in arguing from the one to the other? (6) Finally, Locke suspects that this whole notion of innate ideas has arisen from men's anxiety to place some ideas, particularly moral and religious ideas, beyond the scope of reasonable inquiry and doubt. Having disposed thus of the arguments in support of the hypothesis of innate ideas, he resumes his original inquiry:

Let us then suppose the mind to be, as we say, white paper, void of all characters, without any ideas. How comes it to be furnished? Whence comes it by that vast store which the busy and boundless fancy of man has painted on it with an almost endless variety? Whence has it all the materials of reason and knowledge?

To this I answer in one word: experience. All our knowledge is founded in experience, and from experience it ultimately derives itself.

This experience is of two sorts. Our observation is employed either about external sensible objects or about the internal operations of our mind, perceived and reflected on by ourselves. This observation supplies our understandings with all the materials of thinking. These two are the fountains of knowledge from whence all the ideas we have, or can naturally have, do spring.

First, our senses, conversant about particular sensible objects, do convey into the mind several distinct perceptions of things, according to those various ways wherein those objects do affect them: and thus we come by those ideas we have of yellow, white, heat, cold, soft, hard, bitter, sweet, and all those which we call sensible qualities. This great source of most of our ideas I call *sensation*.

Secondly, the other fountain from which experience furnisheth the understanding with ideas, is the perception of the operations of our own mind within us. Such operations are perceiving, thinking, doubting, believing, knowing, willing, and all the different actings of our own minds. We, being conscious of these operations, do from them receive into our understandings ideas as distinct as we do from bodies affecting our senses. As I call the other source *sensation*, so I call this *reflection*, the ideas it affords being such only as the mind gets by reflecting on its own operations within itself.

These two, I say, namely, external material things as the objects of sensation, and the operations of our own minds within as the objects of reflection, are to me the only originals from whence all our ideas take their beginnings. The understanding seems to me not to have the least glimmering of any ideas which it doth not receive from one of these two.

Having satisfied himself that all knowledge consists of ideas, that all ideas are derived from experience, that all experience is either sensation or reflection, Locke settles down to map out the entire field. His argument, at this point, becomes too detailed to permit of adequate reproduction by citation. Highly condensed, it comes to the following:

Considered with reference to their origin, ideas come to the mind either by way of sensation or reflection, or a combination of the two. From sensation, the mind gets ideas of the primary qualities of objects, e.g., solidity, extension, figure. These are qualities of the objects perceived. From sensation the mind gets also ideas of the secondary qualities of objects, e.g., sounds, tastes, colors, smells. These are not qualities of the objects perceived in the same sense that primary qualities are: they are effects, arising out of the operation of the object on the senses. From reflection the mind gets ideas of its operations. These operations include perceiving, retaining, discerning or discriminating, comparing, compounding or enlarging, abstracting, willing.

Considered with reference to their objects, ideas are either simple or complex. By *simple ideas* Locke means such qualities as coldness, hardness, sweetness, redness, as perceived in some particular object on some particular occasion. These simple ideas, either of sensation or reflection, are "the materials of all our knowledge." These simple ideas are sheer data, given to the mind in experience: "The mind can neither make nor destroy them." In the reception of simple ideas, the mind is passive.

By *complex ideas*, Locke means combinations of simple ideas; made by the mind out of its simple ideas, by repeating, combining, abstracting, etc. Complex ideas "may all be reduced under three heads: modes, substances, relations."

Modes are complex ideas which "do not contain in them the supposition of subsisting by themselves, but are considered as depending on or affections of things." Such are "ideas of triangle, gratitude, murder, etc." The point is, modes exist as properties or accidents or qualities of things, not in their own right. There are triangular things, grateful persons, murderers, etc., but none of these qualities exists independently.

Substances are "collections of qualities existing together" considered as "inhering" in some one thing. Thus, the color, shape, taste, weight, and other qualities of an apple exist together and "inhere" in the apple as a substance. The notion of substance causes Locke great perplexity and distress. It corresponds to no simple idea. It is nowhere given in experience. He refers to it as "something we know not what." "The idea to which we give the name *substance* is nothing but the supposed unknown support of those qualities we find existing, which, we imagine, cannot subsist without something to support them. We call that support *substance*." The need for the category is obvious. Its justification is obscure. He adds: "Whether anyone has any other clear idea of substance, beyond certain simple ideas coexisting together, I appeal to everyone's own experience." To repeat: "Because we cannot conceive how various sensible qualities, of which we have ideas, could exist alone, or in one another, we suppose them existing in and supported by some common subject which we denote by the name *substance*, though it is certain we have no clear or distinct idea of that thing we suppose a support."

Relations, the third kind of complex ideas, are many and various. Examples are identity and diversity, cause and effect, time and place, owner and owned, father and son, larger and smaller, and so on. Relations are described as "the work of the mind." Locke examines them at great length, classifies them, arranges them, defines them. They occur between two things at least. All things are capable of some kind of relation. Relations are often clearer than the things related. Relations terminate in simple ideas. Relations may change when the relata remain unchanged, and so on.

Having surveyed ideas with reference to their origin, i.e., sensation and reflection, their objects, i.e., modes, substances, relations, Locke turns to a consideration of the nature and degrees of human knowledge. Here we may resume our citations:

Since the mind, in all its thoughts and reasonings, hath no other immediate object but its own ideas, which it alone does or can contemplate, it is evident that our knowledge is only conversant about them.

Knowledge, then, seems to me to be nothing but the perception of the agreement or disagreement, connection or repugnance, of any of our ideas. In this alone it consists. Where this perception (of agreement or disagreement of our ideas) is, there is knowledge; where it is not, we come short of knowledge.

Locke's argument may be recapitulated. All knowledge may be analyzed into ideas. All ideas arise in experience. None are innate. Ideas are either simple or complex, the latter being combinations of the former. In knowing, the mind notes only ways in which its ideas agree or disagree. Upon the basis of this general analysis, Locke proceeds to discriminate between intuitive and demonstrative knowledge:

I have said that all knowledge consists in the view the mind has of its own ideas. It may not be amiss to consider a little the degrees of its evidence. The different clearness of our knowledge seems to me to lie in the different ways of perception the mind has of the agreement or disagreement of any of its ideas. There are three different ways.

1. Sometimes the mind perceives the agreement or disagreement of two ideas immediately, without the intervention of any other. Thus the mind perceives that white is not black, that a circle is not a triangle, that three are more than two, and so on. This we may call *intuitive* knowledge, for in this the mind is at no pains of proving or examining, but perceives the truth, as the eye doth light, merely by being directed toward it.

This intuitive kind of knowledge is the clearest and most certain that human frailty is capable of. On this kind of knowledge depends all the certainty and evidence of all our knowledge. He that demands a greater certainty than this, demands he knows not what, and shows only that he has a mind to be a skeptic, without being able to be so. In the next degree of knowledge, which I call *demonstrative*, this intuitive knowledge is necessary in all the intermediate ideas.

2. The next degree of knowledge is where the mind perceives the agreement or disagreement of any ideas, but not immediately. Thus, the mind being willing to know the agreement or disagreement in bigness between the three angles of a triangle and two right angles, cannot by an immediate view and comparing them do it. The three angles of a triangle cannot be brought at once and be compared with two right angles. In this case the mind is fain to find out some other angles, to which the three angles of a triangle have an equality, and, finding those equal also to two right angles, comes to know their equality to two right angles. And so, of the equality of the three angles of a triangle, to two right angles, the mind does not have immediate, intuitive knowledge. This mediated kind of knowledge we may call *demonstrative* knowledge.

When the mind cannot bring two ideas together in immediate comparison, to perceive their agreement or disagreement, it is fain, by the intervention of other ideas, to discover the agreement or disagreement which it searches. This is what we call *reasoning*. Those intervening ideas which serve to show the agreement or disagreement of any two others, are called *proofs*. Where the agreement or disagreement is by this means clearly perceived, it is called *demonstration*. A quickness in the mind to find out these intermediate ideas (that shall discover to it the agreement or disagreement which it searches) is called *sagacity*.

In every step which reason makes in demonstrative knowledge, there is an intuitive knowledge of that agreement or disagreement it seeks with the next intermediate idea which it uses as a proof. Without this intuitive knowledge of each step in reasoning, there would be no knowledge produced. If the connection between each step be perceived immediately, it is intuitive knowledge; if not, there is need of some intervening idea. This knowledge by intervening proofs, though it be certain, is thus not so clear and bright, nor assent so ready, as in intuitive knowledge.

These two, intuition and demonstration, are the degrees of our knowledge. Whatever comes short of these, with what assurance so ever embraced, is but faith or opinion.

Had Locke stopped at this point, or been satisfied merely to develop it in more detail, all might have been well. But he stumbled upon a further distinction which led him deeper and deeper into difficulties which he was never able finally to clear up. The next five citations are included merely to suggest something of what is meant.

3. There is, indeed, another perception of the mind, which I shall call *sensitive* knowledge. It is the perception of the existence of particular things about us, e.g., the sun, a rose, a fire, a table. I think we may add this knowledge of particular external objects, that by perception and consciousness we have of the actual entrance of ideas from them, to the two former sorts of knowledge, and allow these three, namely, intuitive, demonstrative, sensitive.

There is a difficulty connected with sensitive knowledge of the existence of external objects. It is this. There can be nothing more certain than that the idea we receive from an external object is in our minds. Of this fact we have intuitive knowledge. But whether there be anything more than barely the idea in our minds; whether we can thence certainly infer the existence of anything without us, which corresponds to that idea; of this some men think there may be a question made. They think so because men may have such ideas in their minds when no external thing exists, when no object affects their senses.

I think we are provided with an evidence that puts us past doubting. For I ask anyone, whether he be not invincibly conscious to himself of a different perception when he looks on the sun by day and thinks on it by night; when he actually tastes wormwood or smells a rose and thinks on that savor or odor? We find the difference between an idea revived in our mind by our memory and one actually coming into our minds by our senses, as plainly as we do between any two distinct ideas.

If any one say, a dream may do the same thing, and all these ideas may be produced in us without any external object; he may please to dream that I make him this answer: (1) Where all is dream, reason and argument are of no use, truth and knowledge nothing; so it is no great matter whether I remove this scruple or no. (2) He will allow a very manifest difference between dreaming of being in the fire, and actually being in it.

If he be resolved to appear so skeptical as to maintain that what I call "being actually in the fire" is nothing but a dream, and that we cannot certainly know that any such thing as fire actually exists without us, I answer: We certainly find that pleasure or pain follows upon the application of certain objects to us, whose existence we perceive or dream we perceive. The certainty with which we know this is as great as the pleasure or the pain. Beyond this we have no concernment to know or to be. So, I think, we may add sensitive knowledge of external objects to the two former kinds of knowledge.

Locke returns to the main argument of his inquiry. He has traced knowledge to experience. He has distinguished between intuitive and demonstrative knowledge: The former is the basis of the latter. There is, however, another possibility. Knowledge may fall short of demonstrative rigor, in which case it is "probable knowledge." Thus:

The understanding being given to man, not barely for speculation but also for the conduct of life, man would be at a great loss if he had nothing to direct him but what has the certainty of true knowledge. For that being very short and scanty, as we have seen, he would be often utterly in the dark had he nothing to guide him in the absence of clear and certain knowledge.

The faculty which supplies the want of clear and certain knowledge, in cases where it cannot be had, is judgment. In judgment the mind takes its ideas to agree or disagree (or, which is the same, any proposition to be true or false) without perceiving a demonstrative evidence in the proofs. The mind sometimes exercises this judgment out of necessity, where demonstrative proofs are not to be had; and sometimes out of laziness, unskillfulness, or haste even where demonstrative proofs are to be had.

As demonstration is showing the agreement or disagreement of two ideas by the intervention of one or more proofs, so probability is nothing but the appearance of such an agreement or disagreement by the intervention of proofs. For example, we may have a demonstration of the equality of the angles of a triangle to two right angles, or we may take the word of some mathematician that it is so, in which case the foundation of our judgment or assent is the probability of the thing.

Probability is likeness to be true. The entertainment the mind gives this sort of proposition is called *belief*, *assent*, *opinion*. Herein lies the difference between proability and certainty: In all the parts of certainty there is intuition, each step has its visible connection; in belief, not so. That which makes me believe is something extraneous to the thing I believe, something not evidently joined on both sides to those ideas that are under consideration.

Probability, being to supply the defect of our knowledge and to guide us where that fails, is conversant about propositions whereof we have no certainty but only some inducements to receive them for true. The grounds of probability are two: conformity with our own experience, or the testimony of the experience of others.

The propositions which we receive upon inducements of probability are of two sorts: concerning some particular existence falling under observation and hence capable of human testimony; concerning things which, being beyond our senses, are not capable of any such testimony.

Concerning the first of these, the concurrent experience of all other men with ours produces assurance approaching to knowledge; failing this, the concurrence of unquestionable testimony with our experience produces confidence; failing for the most part this, fair testimony in support of a proposition having no great initial improbability. When, however, experience and testimonies clash, the degrees of probability vary indefinitely.

The above probabilities are only such as concern things capable of observation and testimony. There remains that other sort, where the things are not capable of such testimony. In these matters, analogy is the only help we have, and it is from this alone that we draw all our grounds of probability.

One large question remains. Locke lived in an age when men traced some of their most valued knowledge, not to experience, but to revelation. This is not to be confused with the doctrine of "innate ideas." Many who held to revelation as a source of knowledge would take no stock in innate ideas. Locke was himself a devout person. He realized the important role which revealed knowledge played in the religious life of his friends and contemporaries. It was, however, not compatible with a thoroughgoing empiricism. Hence his rather grudging remarks:

Besides those we have hitherto mentioned, there is one sort of proposition that challenges the highest degree of our assent upon bare testimony. I mean where the testimony is of God Himself. This is called by a peculiar name, *revelation;* and our assent to it, *faith.*

Properly understood, faith is a settled and sure principle of assent and leaves no manner of room for doubt. Only, we must be sure (1) that it is a revelation from God, and (2) that we understand it aright. Otherwise we shall expose ourselves to all the error of wrong principles and all the extravagance of enthusiasm if we have faith in what is not divine revelation. Our assent, therefore, can be rationally no higher than the evidence of its being a revelation, and that we do understand the meaning of the expression by which it is delivered. If the evidence of its being a revelation, or that we do understand its true meaning, be only on probable proofs, our assent can rise no higher than that probability.

From these things thus premised I think we may come to lay down the measures and boundaries between faith and reason; the want whereof may possibly have been the cause of great disputes and perhaps mistakes in the world. For, till it be resolved how far we are to be guided by reason and how far by faith, we shall in vain dispute and endeavor to convince one another.

I find that every sect, as far as reason will help them, make use of it gladly; and where it fails them, they cry out, "It is a matter of faith and above reason." And I do not see how they can argue with anyone, or ever convince a gainsayer who makes use of the same plea, without setting down strict boundaries between faith and reason.

Reason I take to be the discovery of the certainty or probability of such truths as the mind has got by sensation or reflection, or has arrived at by deduction from such ideas. Faith is the assent to any proposition not thus arrived at but accepted upon the credit of the proposer as coming from God in some extraordinary way of communication. This way of discovering truths to men we call *revelation*.

First, I say that no man inspired by God can by any revelation communicate to others any new simple ideas which they had not before from sensation and reflection. For whatsoever impressions he himself may have received from the immediate hand of God, if it be of new simple ideas, cannot be conveyed to another either by words or any other signs; because words and other signs recall to our minds those ideas only which to us they have been wont to be signs of. They cannot introduce any new and formerly unknown simple ideas.

For our simple ideas, then, which are the foundation and sole matter of all our notions and knowledge we must depend wholly upon our natural faculties; and can by no means receive them from traditional revelation. I say traditional revelation, in distinction to original revelation. By the former I mean those impressions delivered over to others in words; by the latter I mean that first impression which is made immediately by God on the mind of any man, to which we cannot set any bounds.

Second, I say that the same truths may be discovered and handed down by revelation which are discoverable to us by reason. So God might by revelation discover the truth of any proposition in geometry, as well as men might make the discovery themselves.

Third, I say nothing can, under title of revelation, shake or overrule plain knowledge, or rationally prevail with any man to admit for true anything directly contradictory to the clear evidence of his own understanding. A proposition supposed revealed which contradicts our knowledge or reason will always have this objection hanging to it, namely, that we cannot conceive that to come from God, the bountiful author of our being, which, if received for true, must overturn all the principles and foundations of knowledge He has given us, render our faculties useless, wholly destroy the most excellent part of His workmanship (our understandings), and put a man in a condition wherein he will have less light than the beast which perisheth.

If anything shall he thought revelation which is contrary to the plain principles of reason and the evident knowledge the mind has of its own ideas, there reason must be hearkened to. And this because a man can never have so certain a knowledge that a proposition contradictory to reason was divinely revealed, or that he understands rightly the words wherein it is delivered, as he has that the contrary is true. So he is bound to consider it, and judge of it, as a matter of reason, and not swallow it, without examination, as a matter of faith.

In all things, therefore, where we have clear evidence from our ideas and principles of knowledge, reason is the proper judge. Revelation may, in consenting with it, confirm it; yet it cannot in such cases invalidate it. Nor can we be obliged, where we have the clear and evident sentence of reason, to quit it for the contrary opinion under the pretense that it is a matter of faith.

Fourth, I say that things werein we have imperfect notions or none at all, being beyond the discovery of our natural powers and above reason, are, when revealed, the proper matter of faith. Thus, that some of the angels rebelled against God, and thereby lost their first happy state; that the dead shall rise and live again — these and the like, being beyond the discovery of reason, are purely matters of faith. With them reason has nothing to do.

Thus John Locke on the problem of knowledge. A few paragraphs gather up the threads of his argument:

If, then, knowledge lies in the perception of the agreement or disagreement of any of our ideas, it follows that we can have knowledge no farther than we have ideas; and no farther than we can have perception of their agreement or disagreement.

It follows from this that we cannot have an intuitive knowledge that shall extend itself to all our ideas because we cannot examine and perceive all the relations they have one to another by an immediate comparison. Some knowledge, at least, must always remain mediated.

It follows also that our demonstrative knowledge cannot reach to the whole extent of our ideas because between two different ideas we cannot always find such intervening ideas as we can connect one to another with an intuitive knowledge. Wherever that fails, we come short of demonstrative knowledge.

From all which it is evident that the extent of our knowledge comes not only short of the reality of things, but even of the extent of our own ideas.

Nevertheless, I do not question but that human knowledge, under the present circumstances of our beings and constitutions, may be carried much farther than it has hitherto been, if men would sincerely, and with freedom of mind, employ all that industry and labor in improving the means of discovering truth which they employ to support a falsehood, to maintain a system, interest, or party they are once engaged in.

These ideas should be studied and thought about carefully. Their very simplicity tends to lull one's critical faculties. All seems too straightforward and inevitable. Only here and there does the argument show signs of getting out of hand. But, as subsequent chapters in the history of the problem were to show, these difficulties pointed to problems from which epistemology is still seeking to extricate itself.

Reading References. John Locke's *Essay Concerning Human Understanding* had both a popular and a technical influence. In this respect it was comparable in philosophy to Adam Smith's *Wealth of Nations* in the field of economic theory. It was widely read by the educated laity, not only in Great Britain, but also on the continent and in the American colonies. Its influence, for example on Voltaire in France and on Jonathan Edwards in the colonies, is a matter of common knowledge. It was made the subject of an extended chapter-by-chapter commentary by Locke's contemporary, the German philosopher Leibniz. It exercised the minds of Berkeley, Hume and Kant, to mention only a few outstanding names in the history of eighteenth-century philosophy. To the general reader it brought clarification and emancipation. For the philosopher, as will be seen, it raised difficult problems. The history of this two-fold influence has not yet been adequately studied. Suggestions of its manifold variety may be gained by reading, e.g., Gibson's *Locke's Theory of Knowledge*, or Hefelbower's *Locke and English Deism*, or Leibniz's *New Essays*. An interesting and valuable article by F. J. E. Woodbridge, "Locke's Essay," is to be found in the third volume of the Columbia University *Studies in the History of Ideas*. The standard two-volume life is by Fox Bourne. Good general accounts of Locke's life and writings are to be found in Aaron's *John Locke*, in Fraser's *Locke*, and in Fowler's *Locke*.

READING QUESTIONS

1. What value does Locke see in an inquiry into human knowledge?
2. What was the hypothesis of innate ideas?
3. By whom was it held?
4. What items were so described?
5. What motive would Locke have in criticizing such a doctrine?
6. What criticisms does he offer?
7. What alternative hypothesis does he advance?
8. What does he mean by *simple* in contrast to *complex* ideas?
9. What by *modes*, *substances*, and *relations*?
10. What problem does he note in connection with substances?
11. What is his distinction between intuitive and demonstrative knowledge?
12. What is the relation between them?
13. What does he have in mind by sensitive knowledge?

14. What problem does he note in this connection?
15. Is his reasoning here open to any criticism?
16. How does he distinguish between demonstrative and probable knowledge?
17. What does he say about probable knowledge?
18. Why is he called upon to deal with the doctrine of revelation?
19. How would you distinguish it from the doctrine of innate ideas?
20. What four points does he make with respect to revelation?
21. Why would you expect Locke's empiricism in epistemology to ramify into a general liberalism in other fields, e.g., politics, religion, education?
22. Formulate two or more questions you would put to Locke.

2. *EMPIRICISM INTO SKEPTICISM — FROM DAVID HUME*

From Locke to Hume. Epistemology is an inquiry into the nature of knowledge. It is an inquiry which is motivated by the desire to discover, from an analysis of knowledge, what range and scope we may ascribe to knowledge. All this was set forth in the previous section. For most readers, during the closing years of the seventeenth and most of the eighteenth century, the problem of knowledge meant John Locke's *Essay Concerning Human Understanding*. His general common-sense tone, his homely appeal to experience, his determination not to be led into unverifiable speculations, all combined to secure for him a wide circle of readers and followers. It was only natural, therefore, that the next stage in the development of epistemological theory should take the form of an attempt to "begin where Locke left off." His position briefly was this: All knowledge may be analyzed into ideas. All ideas come to us from experience. All experience is by way of the senses. This *empiricism*, as it is called, was Locke's contribution to epistemological theory. His successor in these matters, David Hume, wrote for a generation which was familiar with the problem as Locke had stated it, and the appeal to experience as Locke had formulated it. Hume set himself a simple task: to deduce more rigorously the implications of Locke's widely accepted position.

Biographical Note. See under "A Theological Problem," page 40.

The Argument of the Citations. Hume will be remembered, from an earlier chapter in these readings, as the critic of natural theology. His method there was to show what happens in natural theology if one sticks closely to the terms laid down by traditional speculation in these matters. He applies the same method in expistemology. It is proposed to make an appeal to experience, he writes; let the appeal be made, then, and not abandoned because it is found to lead to inconvenient consequences. The argument of his position is simple and direct. All knowledge may be analyzed into impressions and ideas. All ideas are derived from earlier impressions. We have certain metaphysical ideas, such as "matter," "mind," "causal connection," "free will," "the uniformity of nature." These ideas play a large part in human thinking and speculating. In fact, they are the fundamental terms in the modern man's general reflections upon the world about him. What are they worth? From what "impressions" are they derived? What corresponds to them in that actual experience to which Locke proposed to appeal? In each case Hume's answer is "they have no basis in experience." They are unjustifiable knowledge claims, and any speculation which incorporates them is mere waste of ink and paper. He begins, in the manner of Locke, by explaining that an inquiry into the nature of knowledge is directed toward eliminating as mere speculation all abstruse ideas which clutter up human thinking:

The only method of freeing learning from abstruse questions is to inquire seriously into the nature of human understanding and show, from an exact analysis of its powers and capacity, that it is by no means fitted for such subjects.

The premises of his theory of knowledge are to be the following:

We may divide all perceptions into two classes: impressions and ideas. By impressions I mean all our perceptions when we hear, see, feel, love, hate, desire, etc. Ideas are those less lively perceptions of which we are conscious when we reflect on any of those sensations mentioned above.

All ideas are copies of impressions. . . . Even those ideas which seem most wide of this origin are found, upon a nearer scrutiny to be derived from it. . . . We shall always find that every idea is copied from a similar impression . . . it is impossible for us to think of anything which we have not antecedently felt by our senses.

The test of all ideas is to be "show me the impression":

When we entertain any suspicion in a philosophical term, we need but inquire from what impression is that supposed idea derived. If it be not possible to assign any, this will serve to confirm our suspicion that it is employed without meaning. . . . By this means we can throw light upon ideas and render them precise. Produce the impressions or originals from which the ideas are copied.

The first idea to be tested by the appeal to impressions is the now familiar idea of substance or matter:

Some philosophers found much of their reasonings on the distinction of *substance* and *quality*. I would fain ask them whether the idea of substance be derived from impressions of sensations or impressions of reflection? Does it arise from an impression? Point it out to us, that we may know its nature and qualities. But if you cannot point out any such impression, you may be certain you are mistaken when you imagine you have any such idea.

If the impression from which we derive our idea of substance be conveyed to us by our senses, I ask, by which of them? If by the eyes, it must be a color. If by the ears, it must be a sound. If by the palate, it must be a taste. And so of the other senses.. But I believe none will assert that substance is either a color, a sound, or a taste.

Is the idea of substance, then, derived from an impression of reflection [i.e., introspection]? But impressions of reflection resolve themselves into our feelings, passions, and emotions, none of which can possibly resemble a substance. We have, therefore, no idea of substance, apart from that of a collection of qualities.

The idea of substance is nothing but a collection of ideas of qualities, united by the imagination and given a particular name by which we are able to recall that collection. The particular qualities which form a substance are commonly referred to an unknown something in which they are supposed to "inhere." This is a fiction.

We may well ask what causes us to believe in the existence of body [i.e., matter]. 'Tis certain there is no question in philosophy more abstruse. By what argument can it be proved that perceptions must be caused by external objects entirely different from them? By an appeal to experience? But here experience is and must be entirely silent. The mind has never anything present to it but its perceptions and cannot possibly have any experience of their connection with objects. The supposition of such a connection is, therefore, without any foundation in reasoning.

Philosophers distinguish betwixt *perceptions* and *objects*. The perceptions are supposed to be caused by the object, and to be interrupted, perishing and different at different times and for different people. The objects are supposed to cause the perceptions, and to be uninterrupted, continuous, and identical. But, however this new view may be esteemed, I assert that there are no principles, either of the understanding or the fancy which lead us to embrace this opinion of the double existence of perceptions and objects.

This hypothesis of the double existence of perceptions and objects has no primary recommendation to reason. The only existences of which we are certain are perceptions. Being immediately present to us by consciousness, they command our strongest assent, and must be the foundation of all our reasonings. But, as nothing is ever present to the mind but perceptions, it follows that we can never observe any "object," or any connection, causal or otherwise, between perceptions and objects.

The idea of substance as something underlying a set of qualities is unable to produce its credentials. Away with it, then. As Hume rather picturesquely remarks of all such ideas, "Commit it to the flames." From material substance he turns to the idea of mind or spiritual substance:

There are some philosophers (e.g., Berkeley) who imagine we are every moment intimately conscious of what we call our *self;* that we feel its existence and its continuance in existence, and are certain of its identity and simplicity.

Unluckily all these positive assertions are contrary to that very experience which is pleaded for them. Have we any idea of a self? From what impression could it be derived? It must be some impression that gives rise to every idea. But self or person is not any one impression. If any impression gives rise to the idea of one's self, that impression must continue to be the same, since one's self is supposed to continue to be the same. But there is no such continuing, constant impression.

For my part, when I enter most intimately into what I call my *self*, I always stumble on some particular perception or other, of heat or cold, light or shade, love or hatred, pain or pleasure, color or sound, etc. I never catch my self, distinct from some such perception.

If anyone thinks he has a different notion of his self, I must confess I can no longer reason with him. He may perceive something simple and continued which he calls his *self;* though I am certain there is no such principle in me.

Setting aside metaphysicians of this kind, I may venture to affirm of the rest of mankind that they are nothing but a bundle or collection of different perceptions which succeed each other with an inconceivable rapidity and are in a perpetual flux and movement. Our eyes cannot turn in their sockets without varying their perceptions. Our thoughts are still more variable. And all our other senses and powers contribute to this change.

The mind (or self) is a kind of theater where perceptions make their appearance, pass, repass, glide away, and mingle in an infinite variety. But there is no simplicity, no one simple thing present or pervading this multiplicity; no identity pervading this process of change; whatever natural inclination we may have to imagine that there is. The comparison of the theater must not mislead us: it persists, while the actors come and go. Whereas, only the successive perceptions constitute the mind.

The idea of mind or self or Spirit fails to reveal any basis in immediate impressions. That seals its fate. But the question persists: Why do we entertain such a notion? It is one thing to show that an idea is a mere fiction. It is another thing to account for its widespread presence in human thinking.

Why do we ascribe an identity amid these successive perceptions, and suppose our selves possessed of an invariable and uninterrupted existence through the whole course of our life? The identity which we ascribe to minds and selves is only a fictitious one, but why do we ascribe it?

Suppose we could see clearly into the mind of another, and observe that succession of perceptions which constitutes his mind. Suppose, too, that he always preserves the memory of a considerable part of past perceptions. It is evident that nothing could more readily contribute to bestowing a relation between these successive perceptions. Would not the frequent placing of these remembered perceptions in the chain of thought convey our imagination more easily from one to another? And so make the whole seem like the continuance of one object?

As memory alone acquaints us with the continuance and extent of a succession of perceptions, it is to be considered, on that account chiefly, as the source of personal identity. Had we no memory, we should never have any notion of that succession of perceptions which constitutes our self or person. But having once acquired this notion from the operation of memory, we can extend the same beyond our memory and come to include times which we have entirely forgot. And so arises the fiction of person and personal identity.

Matter, in the usual sense of the term, is gone. Mind ditto is gone. Hume turns to more serious business, namely, the notion of causal connection between events. I say "more serious business" because he is here proposing to invade the very citadel of eighteenth-century science, a structure which was believed to rest squarely on the notion of causal connection. Hume's handling of this idea should be observed closely. His first question is: What do people mean by the idea of causal connection? His answer is, By causal connection they mean necessary connection; they believe that there is a necessary connection between a cause and its effect. His next question is the inevitable one: What evidence, open to our senses, have we for believing that there is any necessity in causal connection? His answer is: None whatever.

There is no idea in metaphysics more obscure or uncertain than *necessary connection* between cause and effect. We shall try to fix the precise meaning of this term by producing the impression from which it is copied.

When we look at external objects, and consider the operation of causes, we are never able, in a single instance, to discover a necessary connection; any quality which binds the effect to the cause, and renders the one a necessary consequence of the other. We find only that the effect does, in fact, follow the cause. The impact of one billiard ball upon another is followed by the motion of the second. There is here contiguity in space and time, but nothing to suggest necessary connection.

The scenes of the universe are continually shifting, and one object follows another in an uninterrupted succession. But any "force" or necessary connection pervading the whole machine never discovers itself in any of the sensible qualities of body. We know that heat is a constant attendant of flame. But as to any necessary connection between them, we have no room so much as to conjecture or imagine.

In single instances of causal connection we never, by our utmost scrutiny, discover anything but one event following another. We detect no necessary connection between the cause and its effect. All events seem loose and separate. One event follows another. But we observe no tie between them, beyond contiguity in space and time. They are contiguous, thus; but never connected. As we can have no idea of anything of which we have had no correspondent impression, the conclusion seems to be that we have no idea of necessary connection, and that these words are absolutely without meaning.

We are apt to imagine that we could discover effects from their causes by the mere operation of our reason, without experience. We fancy that, were we brought on a sudden into this world, we could have inferred that one billiard ball would communicate motion to another upon impact; and that we need not have waited for the event, in order to pronounce with certainty concerning it.

Knowledge of this relation arises entirely from experience. We find that particular objects are constantly conjoined with each other. Knowledge of this relation is not, in any instance, attained by reasonings a priori. Causes and efforts are discoverable by experience, not by reason. Every effect is a distinct event from its cause. It could not, therefore, be discovered in the cause (prior to experience of their conjunction). Without the assistance of observation and experience, we should in vain pretend to determine any single event or infer any cause or effect. A man must be very sagacious who could discover by reasoning that ice is the effect of cold, without being previously acquainted with the operation of these qualities.

Hence no philosopher who is rational and modest has ever pretended to assign the ultimate cause of any natural operation. Ultimate springs and principles (causes) are totally shut off from human curiosity and enquiry.

As in the case of our idea of mind or self, Hume pauses to inquire why we ascribe to the connection between cause and effect something which is not revealed in experience.

Why do we imagine a necessary connection? From observing many constant conjunctions? But what is there in a number of instances which is absent from a single instance? Only this: After a repetition of similar instances the mind is carried by habit, upon the appearance of the cause, to expect the effect. This connection, which we feel in the mind, this customary and habitual transition of the imagination from a cause to its effect, is the impression from which we form the idea of necessary connection. There is nothing further in the case.

When we say a cause is necessarily connected with its effect, we mean, therefore, that they have acquired a connection in our thought: a conclusion which is somewhat extraordinary, but seems founded on sufficient evidence.

Every idea is copied from some impression. In all single instances of causal connection there is nothing that can suggest any idea of necessity. But when many instances have been experienced, we begin to entertain the idea. We then feel a new impression, to wit, a customary transition in our thoughts or imagination between the cause and its effect. This impression is the original of that idea which we seek for. For, as this idea arises from a number of similar instances, it must arise from that circumstance in which the number of instances differ from each single instance. This customary transition is the only circumstance in which they differ.

His rejection of the idea of cause as necessary connection suggests at once that he may be in a position to say something about the long-standing controversy over free will and determinism. That dispute arises because men hold (*a*) that human acts are caused, and (*b*) that causes are necessary connections. Hume's claim, here is not that he can solve the problem but that he can dissolve it.

The question of man's free will has been long disputed among philosophers. Does man have freedom of will? Or are his acts determined? If motives determine acts, are motives themselves determined? This dispute has been much canvassed on all hands, and has led into such labyrinths of obscure sophistry that a sensible reader inclines to turn a deaf ear to the question, expecting neither instruction nor entertainment. I hope to make it appear that the whole controversy has hitherto turned merely upon words.

We ascribe necessity to matter. The degree and direction of every motion are prescribed with exactness. Do we similarly ascribe necessity to persons? Are the degree and direction of every action prescribed with exactness?

Two circumstances form the whole of the necessity we ascribe to matter: a constant conjunction between cause-events and effect-events, and a consequent inference in our minds from the one to the other. Beyond these two circumstances we have no notion of any necessity in the motion of matter.

Do not these two circumstances take place in the voluntary actions of men? Are not similar motives followed by similar actions? Are there not detectable uniformities in human action? Is it impossible to collect any general observations concerning mankind? Has experience of human affairs, however accurately digested by reflection, no purpose?

The most irregular and unexpected resolutions of men may be accounted for by those who know every particular circumstance of their character and situation. A genial person, contrary to expectation, may give a peevish answer, but he has a toothache or has not dined. Even when, as sometimes happens, an action cannot be accounted for, do we not put it down to our ignorance of relevant details?

Thus it appears that the conjunction between motive and action is as regular and uniform as between cause and effect in any part of nature. In both cases, constant conjunction and inference from one to the other.

Though constant conjunction and customary transition be all that is discoverable between a cause and an effect in nature, men believe they perceive something like a necessary connection. Then, when they consider the operations of their own wills and feel no such necessary connection between motive and action, they suppose there is a difference between the cause-effect relation and the motive-action relation. And are hence led to say that man's will, unlike matter, is free.

But our knowledge of causation, like our knowledge of motivation, is merely of a constant conjunction and a consequent inference in our minds from one to the other. It is the same in both cases. It is different only if it be pretended that the mind can perceive, in the operation of matter, some other connection between cause and effect than has place in the voluntary actions of intelligent beings. It is incumbent on those who pretend thus to make good their assertion. So long as we rashly suppose that we have an idea of some necessity in the operations of external nature, beyond constant conjunction and an habitual inference in our minds; and, at the same time, admit we can find nothing such in the voluntary actions of the mind, we shall continue in confusion.

Thus far Hume has examined the ideas of substance, of mind, of causal connection, of free will. Of each in turn he has asked one question: Upon what impression, received by the senses, does it rest? From each in turn he has received only silence for an answer. One more idea remains, namely, the idea of a uniformity of nature, the unquestioned premise of all our inductions and generalizations from nature. Why do we believe, so unquestioningly, that the "future will resemble the past"? Why do we argue, for instance, that fire will always melt ice, when our only grounds for this belief is the fact that it has done so in the past?

All our conclusions from experience proceed on the supposition that the future will resemble the past. To prove that the future will resemble the past, by arguing from experience, is evidently going in a circle, and taking that for granted which is the very point in question.

As to past experience, it can be allowed to give direct and certain information of those precise objects only, and that precise period of time only, which fell under its cognizance. But why this experience should be extended to future times and other objects, is the question on which I would insist. So to extend it is a process of mind or thought of which I would willingly know the foundation.

Not by an argument from experience can we prove this resemblance of the past to the future, for all such arguments are founded on the supposition of that resemblance. Let the course of things be allowed hitherto ever so regular. That alone, without some new inference, does not prove that for the future it will continue so.

My practice, you say, refutes my doubts. But you mistake the purport of my question. In practice I am satisfied. As a philosopher, who has some share of curiosity, I will not say skepticism, I want to learn the foundation of this inference. No reading, no inquiry, has yet been able to remove my difficulty. Upon what grounds can we argue that the future will resemble the past? Upon what grounds expect similar effects from causes which are similar?

Geometry (or any mathematics) when taken into the assistance of science, is unable to remedy this defect. Every part of applied mathematics proceeds on the supposition that certain laws are established by nature in her operations. Mathematical reasonings are employed to assist experience in the discovery of these laws, or to determine their influence in particular instances. But the discovery of the law itself is owing merely to experience, and all the mathematical reasoning in the world could never lead one step toward the knowledge of it.

In all reasonings from experience, then, there is a step taken by the mind (that the future resembles the past) which is not supported by any argument. Nevertheless, we take this step. There must therefore be some other principle (than rational or demonstrative argument).

Though none but a fool or madman will ever pretend to dispute the authority of experience, it may surely be allowed a philosopher to have so much curiosity as to examine the principle of human nature which gives authority to experience.

This principle is custom, or habit. Wherever repetition produces a propensity to renew the same act, without being impelled by any reasoning, we say this propensity is the effect of custom or habit. That habit or custom is the ultimate principle of all our conclusions from experiences, seems to be the only hypothesis which explains why we draw from many instances an inference which we are not able to draw from one instance that is in no respect different from them.

All inferences from experience are, therefore, effects of habit or custom, not of reasoning. The conclusions which we draw, based on reasoning, from considering one circle, are the same which we would draw from surveying all circles. But no man, having seen only one body impelled by another, could infer that every other similar body would move after a like impulse.

Custom, then, not reason, is the great guide of human life. It is that principle alone which renders our experience useful to us, and makes us expect, for the future, a similar train of events with those which have appeared in the past. Without the influence of custom, we should be entirely ignorant of every matter of fact beyond what is immediately present to the memory or the senses.

What, then, is the conclusion of the whole matter? A simple one, though, it must be confessed, pretty remote from the common theories of philosophy. All belief concerning matters of fact or real existence, is derived merely from some object present to the memory or the senses, and a customary conjunction between that and some other object. Having found, in many instances, that two kinds of objects have been conjoined (say, flame and heat), the mind is carried by custom to expect the same in the future. This is the whole operation of the mind in all our conclusions concerning matters of fact and existence.

Here, then, is a kind of pre-established harmony between the course of nature and formation of our beliefs. Custom or habit is the principle of human nature by which this correspondence, so necessary to the subsistence of our species and the regulation of our conduct, has been effected. Did not the presence of an object excite in us the ideas of other objects commonly conjoined with it, all human knowledge would be limited to the narrow sphere of our memory and senses. Those who delight in the discovery of purposes in nature have here ample subject to employ their wonder and admiration.

As this operation of the mind, whereby we infer like effects from like causes, is so essential to human life, it is not probable that it could be trusted to the fallacious deductions of our reason, which is slow in its operation and extremely liable to error and mistake. It is more conformable to the ordinary wisdom of nature to secure so necessary an act of the mind by some instinct or mechanical tendency which may be infallible in its operations and independent of all the labored deductions of understanding.

Hume is now at the end of his review:

By way of conclusion to these reflections on diverse questions: When we run over libraries, persuaded of the principles here expounded, what havoc must we make? If we take in hand any volume, of divinity or metaphysics, for instance, let us ask: Does it contain any reasoning concerning quantity or number? No. Does it contain any experimental (probable) reasoning concerning matter of fact? No. Commit it then to the flames: for it can contain nothing but sophistry and illusion.

I am at first affrighted and confounded with that forlorn solitude in which I am placed by my philosophy, and fancy myself some strange uncouth monster, utterly abandoned and disconsolate. Fain would I run into the crowd for shelter and warmth. I call upon others to join me. But no one will hearken to me. Everyone keeps at a distance, and dreads that storm which beats upon me from every side. I have exposed myself to the enmity of all metaphysicians, logicians, mathematicians, and theologians. Can I wonder at the insults I must suffer? I have declared my disapprobation of their systems. Can I be surprised if they should express a hatred of my ideas and my person? When I look about me, I foresee on every hand, dispute, contradiction, anger, calumny, detraction. When I turn my eye inward, I find only doubt and ignorance. Every step I take is with hesitation; every new reflection makes me dread an error and absurdity in my reasoning.

READING REFERENCES. It would be advantageous to consult the pages on Hume in B. A. G. Fuller's *History of Philosophy*. They form a section in a chapter on Locke, Berkeley, Hume. The Hume portion should be read straight through. It brings together his critique of natural theology and his theory of knowledge. T. H. Huxley's little book on Hume, recommended elsewhere, is noted again here. Time given to C. W. Hendel's *Studies in the Philosophy of David Hume* will be well spent.

READING QUESTIONS

1. What is the historical relation between Locke and Hume?
2. What does Hume propose to free learning from? How does he propose to do it?
3. Into what two elements does he analyze knowledge? How does he relate the two?
4. What test does he propose for all ideas?
5. Enumerate the ideas to which he applies this test.
6. Summarize the steps by which he criticizes the idea of material substance.
7. Summarize the steps by which he criticizes the idea of spiritual substance.
8. By what hypothesis does he seek to account for the idea of spiritual substance?
9. What alternative terms can you give for *spiritual substance?*
10. Summarize the steps by which he criticizes the idea of necessary connection.
11. By what hypothesis does he seek to account for this idea?
12. Can you suggest any reason why Hume's critique of the idea of necessary connection should have caused such consternation at that time and since?
13. "Hume does not solve the problem of free will; he merely dissolves it." Explain.
14. Upon what "supposition" do "all our conclusions from experience proceed"?
15. Summarize Hume's criticism of this supposition.
16. "My practice, you say, refutes my doubts." Elucidate.
17. What is his answer to this objection?
18. "Those who delight in the discovery of purposes in nature have here ample subject to employ their wonder and admiration." Where?

3. *MIND AND THE WORLD ORDER—FROM IMMANUEL KANT*

From Hume to Kant. The problem of knowledge was, to all intents and purposes, posed for modern times by John Locke in his *Essay Concerning Human Understanding.* That problem, stated simply, was this: To suggest a theory of the nature and origin of knowledge, and from that theory to indicate the limits of human understanding. The problem persisted. It is with us yet. It has come, indeed, to occupy the center of philosophy. Hume and Kant, between them, have been, in large measure, responsible for this fact. For that reason it is important to grasp clearly what these two thinkers sought to accomplish.

Locke, it will be remembered, was led to pose the problem of knowledge as a measure of caution. His words reveal this motive:

> If by this inquiry into the nature of the understanding I can discover the powers thereof, how far they reach, to what things they are in any degree proportionate and where they fail us, I suppose it may be of use to prevail with the busy mind of man to be more cautious in meddling with things exceeding its comprehension, to stop when it is at the utmost extent of its tether, and to sit down in a quiet ignorance of those things which, upon examination are found to be beyond the reach of our capacities.

Nothing could be more straightforward than that. From an insight into the nature of knowledge, to recognize that some things lie beyond its reach. The hypothesis which Locke advanced was this: All knowledge comes from experience and all experience is by way of the senses. This was in the seventeenth century.

By the middle of the eighteenth century, in Hume's writings, things had undergone a subtle change. Indeed, it would perhaps be more accurate to say that they had come to something of an impasse. What Hume did, in effect, was to take Locke's appeal to experience and push it to its "logical conclusion." This conclusion was that much of the familiar furniture of man's world was dissolved into a series of question marks. The metaphysical notions of matter and spirit were declared to be so much verbiage. No appeal to experience showed any grounds for believing in their existence. The psychological notions of mind and will went the same way. Only the come-and-go of impressions and ideas remained. The generally accepted notions of cause and uniformity of nature met a like fate; they were mere habits, mere effect of custom. The theological notions of God as first cause and designer were weighed and found wanting. Hume tried, indeed, to undermine the credibility even of mathematics, by arguing, for example, that such geometrical notions as straight line, circle, equal angles, etc., were "mere notions" to which nothing discoverable in experience could be said to correspond. Hume's own consternation at this reduction of Locke's empiricism was genuine. His words will be recalled:

> I am at first affrighted and confounded with that forlorn solitude in which I am placed by my philosophy, and fancy myself some strange uncouth monster, utterly abandoned and disconsolate. Fain would I run into the crowd for shelter and warmth. I call upon others to join me. But no one will hearken to me. Everyone keeps at a distance, and dreads that storm which beats upon me from every side. I have exposed myself to the enmity of all metaphysicians, logicians, mathematicians, and theologians. Can I wonder at the insults I must suffer? I have declared my disapprobation of their systems. Can I be surprised if they should express a hatred of my ideas and my person? When I look about me, I foresee on every hand, dispute, contradiction, anger, calumny, detraction. When I turn my eye inward, I find only doubt and ignorance. Every step I take is with hesitation; every new reflection makes me dread an error and absurdity in my reasoning.

These conclusions, which filled Hume with grave doubts about the whole epistemological enterprise, were meanwhile being read and digested by the German philosopher, Immanuel Kant. They did not fill his mind with any fright and confusion. Their effect was, to quote his well-known words, "to rouse me from my dogmatic slumbers." Where Hume was "affrighted and confounded," Kant was stimulated and enlightened. For he detected an element of irony in the whole affair. Here was Hume, in the name of a theory of knowledge denying that there is any knowledge. Knowing that it is the function of a theory to account for that of which it is a theory, not to deny it, Kant was moved to say, in effect, "So much the worse for Hume's theory." If the appeal to experience will not serve as a satisfactory hypothesis, by means of which to account for the fact of knowledge, then so much the worse for the appeal to experience; surely, not so much the worse for knowledge. This was the point of his remark about being "roused from his dogmatic slumbers." He had been satisfied to assume dogmatically that empiricism would account for knowledge. Hume's conclusions served only to convince Kant that unrelieved empiricism must somehow be a mistaken hypothesis.

That is the first fact to be kept in mind with respect to Kant. There is another fact, equally important. It was this: Kant believed firmly in the existence of God, in the freedom of the will, and in the immortality of the soul. But, being also a man of wide reading in modern philosophy he knew that his age, the Age of Reason, was unsympathetic with such convictions. The age was willing, in theory, that a man should entertain these convictions as a matter of faith. But it would not in practice let it go at that. It was inclined to challenge, even to ridicule, such faith. It urged an appeal to reason, confident that in such an appeal faith would come off second best. Everything was to be tried at the "bar of reason." Kant's answer to all this was to carry the war into the enemies' country. He determined to put reason itself on trial. To this end he wrote his large and epoch-making treatise, *Critique of Pure Reason*. The thesis of this book, in one sentence, was this: An examination of reason itself will show that it is powerless to deny, to challenge, or to ridicule the beliefs which devout men hold on faith.

Kant's handling of the problem of knowledge was motivated, then, by these two considerations. First, a theory of knowledge was required to replace the empiricism of Hume. Second, a theory of knowledge was required to deflate the appeal to reason which was placing obstacles in the way of religious convictions. What Kant proposed was this: to replace the appeal to experience and the appeal to reason by a critical analysis of the function of reason in experience.

Biographical Note. Immanuel Kant was born in Germany in 1724 and died in 1804 at the age of seventy-nine. His parents were members of a German sect known as Pietists. What this meant, for Kant, was that he was given a very devout turn of mind from earliest infancy. This devotion to the "fundamentalism" of his parents did not outlast his adolescence, but it was succeeded by an equally rigorous adherence to the fundamentals of morality. His early education was intended to direct his thoughts toward the church. University years directed them along more secular lines. He graduated in classics, mathematics, science, and philosophy. At the age of thirty-one he became a privat-docent in the University at Königsberg. Here, for fifteen years, he provided coaching in mathematics, physics, physical geography, logic, and metaphysics. During these years he was gradually awakened to the dilemmas of the modern mind. These repay a moment's consideration. He took his mathematics and his natural sciences with great seriousness; he found, on the one hand, that the kind of world to which they pointed was "incompatible" with his belief in God, free will, immortality, and the supremacy of a high-minded morality; and he found, on the other, that the unquestioned appeal to experience among progressive minds cast grave doubts on the reliability of mathematics and the sciences. This was not the only respect in which the "modern mind" was at sixes and sevens with itself. In the fields of theology and metaphysics, confusion reigned supreme. In the name of reason there were claims and counterclaims; theism, atheism, skepticism with respect to Deity; dualism, materialism, idealism, skepticism, with respect to the nature of ultimate reality. All these eddies and cross-currents met in the mind of this young man whose business was to provide instruction in science and philosophy. The thought which gradually took shape in his speculations was this: The modern mind appears to be divided against itself. Used in one field, it has provided us with the beauties and achievements of mathematics and science; used in another field, it has created endless confusion in which unverifiable speculation is met with unverifiable denial. He looked into his own mind and found two unshakable convictions: on the one hand, mathematics and the sciences must be "saved" from the skeptics; on the other, the normal beliefs of a conscientious and God-fearing soul must be "saved" from both the sciences and the skeptics. As these various dilemmas clarified themselves, he saw his task: What was required, apparently, was an examination of the human mind itself. His thoughts began to shape themselves along these lines. He was, at the age of forty-six, appointed to the chair of philosophy in his university. In his inaugural address he communicated to his fellow professors his intention of devoting himself to a critical analysis of the mind's power to know. For the next eleven years he did just that, and in 1781, at the age of fifty-seven, published his long-awaited *Critique of Pure Reason*.

THE ARGUMENT OF THE CITATIONS. Kant's problem, in its general outlines, was clear enough. The only point was where to begin. He must find a sort of "Achilles' heel" at which to direct his first line of attack. This he found in the distinction between *a priori* and *a posteriori* knowledge. Both he held to be undoubted facts, but the current appeal to experience would account only for the latter; the former it either ignored or sought to deny. This little point gave Kant just the opening he required. It is time to let him speak for himself. As the citations begin, he is reflecting upon metaphysics. As his thoughts move around, he hits upon the strategic distinction between *a priori* and *a posteriori* knowledge.

My object is to persuade all those who think metaphysics worth studying, to pause, and, neglecting everything that has been done, to propose the preliminary question: Is metaphysics possible?

How does it come about that metaphysics, unlike other sciences, cannot obtain universal and permanent recognition? It seems almost ridiculous that, while every other science is continually advancing, we should, in metaphysics, move constantly around on the same spot gaining a single step. We do not find men, confident of their ability to shine in other sciences, venturing their reputation here. And so its followers have melted away.

Time was when metaphysics held a royal place among all the sciences. If the will were taken for the deed, the importance of her subject matter might well have secured her that place of honor. But at present it is the fashion to despise her; and like Hecuba, she languishes forsaken and alone. Time was when her rule was despotic. But intestinal war and anarchy broke out. The skeptics, a kind of nomad tribe, despising all settled cultivation of her lands, broke up all civil society. Fortunately their number was small; they could not prevent the old settlers from returning to till the ground afresh. But the old settlers returning had no fixed plan or agreement. At present there reign in metaphysics weariness and indifference, the mother of chaos and night. Near-reforms, ill-applied study, have rendered her counsels dark, confused, and useless.

It is vain, however, to assume a kind of artificial indifference with respect to inquiries to which human nature cannot be indifferent. Nay, even those who pretend indifference, if they think at all, fall back inevitably into those very metaphysical dogmas which they profess to despise.

Nevertheless, this widespread indifference to metaphysics is worth attention and consideration. It is, clearly, not the result of carelessness but of matured judgment. Our age will no longer rest satisfied with the mere appearance of knowledge in these matters. Its patience has run out. This fact constitutes a powerful challenge, a powerful appeal to reason to undertake anew the most difficult of her duties, to institute a court of appeal which, while it will protect her own rights, will dismiss all groundless claims. This court of appeal is no other than a critique of pure reason.

By a *critique of pure reason* I do not mean a criticism of books and systems. I mean a critical analysis of the power of reason itself, touching that whole class of knowledge which it may strive after unassisted by experience. This must decide the question: Is metaphysics possible or impossible?

Since the origin of metaphysics nothing has ever happened which was more decisive to its fate than the attack made upon it by David Hume. He started from a single, but important concept, namely causal connection. He challenged reason, which pretends to have given birth to this idea, to tell him by what right she thinks anything to be so constituted that it is necessarily connected with something else; for that is the meaning of causal connection. He demonstrated, beyond refutation, that it is impossible for us to see why, in consequence with the existence or occurrence of one thing, another thing must necessarily exist or occur also.

Hence he inferred that reason was deluded with reference to this conception of causal connection; that she erroneously considered it one of her children; that, in reality, it was nothing but a bastard child of imagination impregnated by experience; that a subjective necessity of habit was mistaken for an objective necessity arising from insight. I frankly confess, the suggestion of David Hume was the very thing which, many years ago first interrupted my dogmatic slumber, and gave my investigations in the field of speculative philosophy quite a new direction.

Hume's question was not whether the conception of causal connection was right, useful, even indispensable for our knowledge of nature. This he had never doubted. His question was whether that conception could be thought, by reason, *a priori;* whether it thus possessed an inner truth, independent of all experience. That was Hume's problem. It was, as we see, a question concerning the origin of the conception, not its indispensability.

I tried whether Hume's objection could not be put in a general form, and soon found that the conception of causal connection was by no means the only idea by which the understanding thinks the connection of things *a priori*.

It may be advisable to interrupt the movement of Kant's thought at this point. He has already used this fundamental term *a priori* twice. He is going to explain what it means, give an illustration of its use, and contrast it with its antonym, *a posteriori*. But, since the entire argument of his position revolves around this idea, it may be well to try to fix its meaning for ourselves. If we say that some fact is known, or can be known, *a priori*, we mean that it is known or can be known in advance of experience of it. Thus, we might say, "I don't know whether there are any triangles on the far side of the moon; but if there are, I can say *a priori* that the sum of their interior angles will equal two right angles." Or, we might say, "I don't know whether a slave economy was the cause of the fall of the Roman Empire, but I can say *a priori* that there was a cause." Or, we might say, "I don't know whether there are two chairs in the next room, and two in the hall; but if there are, I can say *a priori* that they will add up to four chairs." Or, we might say, "I don't know what happened either before or after I ate my dinner, but I can say *a priori* that something happened both before and after." These illustrations could be extended indefinitely. As Kant will indicate, the problem which they present is this: How does it happen that we can know certain sorts of facts *a priori?*

It is a question worth investigating, whether there exists any knowledge independent of experience and all sense impressions.

Such knowledge is called *a priori* and is distinguished from *a posteriori* knowledge which has its sources in experience. That there is genuine *a priori* knowledge, that we can advance independent of all experience, is shown by the brilliant example of mathematics.

This term *a priori* requires closer definition. People are wont to say, even with regard to knowledge derived from experience, that we have it or might have it *a priori*. They mean we might derive it from a general rule. Thus, of one who undermines the foundations of his house, they would say he might have known *a priori* that it would tumble down; know it, that is, from the general rule that unsupported bodies fall. But this general rule has itself been derived from experience. Whoever knows this general rule had first to learn it from experience. He could not have known this entirely *a priori*. (This Hume has shown.) In what follows, we shall use the term more strictly. We shall understand by *a priori* that which is absolutely independent of all experience, and not of this or that experience only. Opposed to this is *a posteriori* or empirical knowledge, such as is derived from experience.

Experience tells us what is, but not that it must necessarily be as it is. It therefore never gives us any necessary, *a priori*, knowledge. Experience never imparts to its judgments any strict universality, but only relative universality (by means of induction) so that we ought always to say, "so far as we have experienced, there is no exception to this or that rule." Necessity and universality are criteria of the *a priori*. If, therefore, a judgment is thought with strict universality and necessity so that no exception is admitted as possible, it cannot have been derived from experience.

We have here a mystery. We must discover the ground of *a priori* judgments. We must understand the conditions which render them possible. The real problem is contained in the question: How is *a priori* knowledge possible? That metaphysics has hitherto remained in so vacillating a condition of ignorance and contradiction is due entirely to the fact that this problem has been ignored.

David Hume, who among all philosophers approached nearest to this problem, arrived at the conclusion that *a priori* knowledge is impossible. According to his reasoning everything we call metaphysics would turn out to be mere delusion. But if he had grasped clearly the problem of the *a priori* he would never have thought of an assertion which destroys all metaphysics, because he would have seen that, according to such an argument, neither was mathematics possible (since it contains *a priori* judgments). And from such an assertion his good sense would probably have saved him.

It is to be noted that our problem is not: Are *a priori* judgments possible? For there are enough of them to hand, of undoubted certainty, that we need not argue for their possibility. (What is actual must be possible.) We must inquire into the grounds of the possibility of their existence. The proper problem, upon which all depends, when expressed precisely is this: How are *a priori* propositions possible?

It again seems advisable to break in upon Kant's meditations. The justification must be this: He is saying things quite calmly which cut very deep. He began by admitting a sort of bankruptcy on all hands in matters philosophical. He added, however, that no philosopher worth his salt would therefore feel justified in crying quits. He realized that Hume had been an important factor, despite his negative conclusions. He wants, above all, a toe hold, some fact upon which he can take a stand. His eye catches sight of this apparently neglected distinction between *a priori* knowledge and *a posteriori* knowledge. He fastens on this, realizing that this may have important implications. He sees, also, that the fact of the *a priori* raises a problem. The *a priori* is a fact. The problem is how to account for it.

Although all our knowledge begins with experience, it does not follow that it arises entirely from experience. For it is quite possible that our empirical knowledge is a compound of that which we receive through impressions and that which our own faculty of knowing (incited by impressions) supplies from itself — a supplement to impressions which we do not distinguish from that raw material (i.e., impressions) until long practice has roused our attention and rendered us capable of separating one from the other.

Hitherto it has been supposed that all our knowledge must conform to the objects, but, under that supposition, all attempts to establish any knowledge about them *a priori* have come to nothing.

The experiment therefore ought to be made, whether we should not succeed better by assuming that objects must conform to our forms of knowledge. For this would agree better with the required possibility of an *a priori* knowledge of objects; that is, with the possibility of settling something about those objects before they are given us in experience.

We have here the same case as with the first thought of Copernicus. Not being able to explain the movements of the heavenly body so long as he assumed that the stars moved around the spectator, he tried assuming the spectator to be turning around and the stars to be at rest. A similar experiment may be tried in metaphysics, so far as our knowledge of objects is concerned. If our knowledge has to conform to the nature of objects, I do not see how we could know anything *a priori*. But if the object of knowledge has to conform to the constitution of our power of knowing, I can very well conceive the possibilities of such *a priori* knowledge.

If Copernicus had not dared, by an hypothesis which contradicted the senses, to seek the observed movements in the spectator instead of in the heavenly bodies, the laws of planetary motion would have remained for ever undiscovered. I propose my own view, which has so many analogies with the Copernican hypothesis, as, at first, an hypothesis only.

Kant's argument at this point becomes too complicated for reproduction in quotation. For that reason, the next passages are mere descriptions of his argument, not selections or paraphrases from his *Critique*. Thus far, what he has been saying comes to this: Metaphysical speculation is in disrepute. Hume's criticism seems to have put an end to it. His conclusions followed from his dogma that all knowledge comes from experience. Since, on this premise, he could not account for *a priori* knowledge, he denied it. But a theory of knowledge which issues in a denial of knowledge is a poor theory. *A priori* knowledge is a fact to be accounted for, not an illusion to be denied. Since the appeal to experience has failed, something else must be tried. A new theory of knowledge is required to account for the fact of *a priori* knowledge. Kant's hypothesis is this: That knowledge is a joint product of mind and external world, arising in experience. This hypothesis raises the following problem: If knowledge is a joint product of mind and external world, then what part of the joint product is contributed by the mind? Kant answers by distinguishing between the form and the content of knowledge. The form of knowledge is contributed by the mind. The content is contributed by the external world. In the production of knowledge the mind acts to impose form on content supplied by the external world. This leads to a new problem: If knowledge is a joint product of mind and world, and mind's contribution is the form, can these formal elements in knowledge be isolated and analyzed? What, in other words, is the form which mind contributes?

Kant answers by distinguishing between perceptual, conceptual, and speculative knowledge. To our perceptual knowledge, mind contributes the forms of space and time. These Kant calls *forms of sensibility*. To our conceptual knowledge mind contributes the forms of quantity, quality, relation, and modality. These, when further analyzed, he calls *categories of understanding*. To our speculative knowledge, mind contributes the forms of self, universe, and God. These he calls *ideas of reason*. I shall refer to them as *forms of speculation*. Space and time are forms of perception, not things perceived. Things are always perceived spread-out-and-strung-along, are always perceived in a background-foreground and a before-and-after setting. This invariable spatial and temporal character is the form of all perceptual knowledge. On Kant's hypothesis, it is due to the "diffracting" action of mind or consciousness. Except as forms of consciousness, these words have no meaning. They are forms of awareness, not things of which we are aware. In Kant's words, space and time are "empirically real, but transcendentally ideal," that is, real in experience but otherwise only ideal. Quotations are here possible once more:

Space does not represent any property of things in themselves, nor does it represent them in their relation to one another. . . . Space is nothing but the form of all appearances of outer sense. It is the subjective condition of sensibility under which alone outer perception is possible for us.

Since the capacity to be affected by objects must precede all perceptions of these objects, it can readily be understood how the form of all appearances (i.e., space) can be given prior to all perceptions, and so exist in the mind *a priori;* and how, as a pure intuition, in which all objects must be determined, it can contain, prior to all experience, principles which determine the relations of these objects. It is, therefore, solely from the human standpoint that we can speak of space, of extended things. If we depart from the subjective, the representation of space stands for nothing whatsoever.

This predicate (i.e., space) can be ascribed to things only insofar as they appear to us, that is, to objects of sensibility. Since, however, we cannot treat the special conditions of sensibility as conditions of the possibility of things, but only of their appearances, we can indeed say that space comprehends all things that appear to us as external, but not all things in themselves. For we cannot judge in regard to the perceptions of other kinds of thinking beings, whether they are bound by the same conditions as limit us.

The proposition that all things are side by side in space is valid under the limitation that these things are viewed as objects of our perception. Our exposition claims the reality, the objective validity, of space in respect of whatever can be presented us; but also, at the same time, the ideality of space in respect of things when they are considered in themselves, that is, without regard to the constitution of our sensibility.

We assert, then, the empirical reality of space, as regards all possible outer experience, and, at the same time, its transcendental ideality, i.e., that it is nothing at all, immediately we withdraw the said condition, namely limitation to possible experience, and look upon it as something that underlies things in themselves.

The transcendental conception of appearances in space is a critical reminder that nothing perceived in space is a thing in itself; that space is not a form inhering in things in themselves as their intrinsic property; that objects in themselves are nothing but mere representations of our sensibility, the form of which is space. The true correlate of sensibility, the thing in itself, is not known, and cannot be known, through these representations; and in experience no question is ever asked in regard to it.

Kant's remarks on the status of time, which parallel, roughly, his remarks on the status of space, may be quoted in part:

Time is not an empirical conception that has been derived from any experience. For neither coexistence nor succession (the two modes of time) would ever have come within our perception, if the representation of time were not presupposed as underlying them *a priori*.

Time is not something which exists of itself or inheres in things. Were it a determination (i.e., property) of things in themselves, it could not be known *a priori*. But such *a priori* knowledge is quite possible if time is nothing but the subjective condition under which alone perception can take place in us. For, that being so, this form of intuition can be represented prior to the objects and therefore *a priori*.

Time is a purely subjective condition of our human perception, and, in itself, apart from the subject, is nothing. . . . What we are maintaining is the empirical reality of time, its objective validity of all objects which allow of ever being given to our senses. Since our perception is always sensible (i.e., by the senses), no object can ever be given to us in experience which does not conform to the condition of time. On the other hand, we deny to time any claim to absolute reality; that is to say, we deny that it belongs to things absolutely, as their condition or property independently of any reference to the form of our perception. Properties that belong to things in themselves can never be given to us through the senses. This, then, is what constitutes the ideality of time.

What we mean by the *ideality of time* is this: If we abstract from the subjective conditions of sensuous perception, time is nothing, and cannot be ascribed to the objects in themselves apart from their relation to our perception, neither in the way of subsistence nor of inherence.

By *categories* Kant means such forms of understanding things as unity and plurality, substance and quality, cause and effect, and so on. He enumerates twelve. The number is not so important as his recognition that conceptual knowledge has form as well as content, and his hypothesis that the form is mind's contribution. Thus, to consider one of these categories, causation is a form of understanding, not a reality in its own right. When a drop in temperature causes the water to freeze, there are not three things, namely, dropping temperature, freezing water, and a cause connecting the two. Rather, there are two things understood in terms of a category. Our understanding of anything involves many such categories. Kant's point is the simple, but revolutionary suggestion that categories of understanding are not objects of knowledge but forms of knowledge; not things known but ways of knowing. Our understanding of things given in experience is conditioned by the categories in terms of which our minds work. These categories are forms of understanding what is given in experience; they are, themselves, not given in experience.

Speculation is the attempt to carry understanding beyond the limits of experience. Since the categories are only forms to which experience gives content, any such attempt is deemed to fail. To use a common expression, it can never be anything more than "mere speculation." Kant notes, and condemns, three forms of speculation, three ways in which the mind perennially seeks to transcend the limits of experience.

The first of these is the attempt to speculate on the nature of the mind itself, to seek to understand the nature of that which contributes form to knowledge. Beyond detecting the forms, we cannot go. The mind itself is outside of experience. It is, itself, never given in experience. It can never be content for its own forms. The attempt to formulate a rational psychology, that is, to gain an understanding of the mind, soul, self, ego, is, on Kant's theory of knowledge, to attempt the impossible. We cannot pierce beyond the stream of consciousness, to a knowledge of the factors which make it to be the kind of thing it is. That there is a mind, beyond the stream of consciousness, Kant is prepared to argue, as against Hume. His reason for refusing to stop short with Hume is simple. The latter, it will be recalled, "reduced" mind to a succession of awarenesses. To this Kant has a rejoinder. The fact to be accounted for, he points out, is not a succession of awarenesses, but an awareness of succession. If that which is aware passed with the awareness, there could be no awareness of succession. But there is precisely this, namely, awareness of succession. Time indeed is one of the forms of knowledge.

The second attempt to extend knowledge beyond experience, is to speculate on the nature of the whole of things, beyond what is given piecemeal in experience. The attempt to formulate a rational cosmology, that is, to extend the categories beyond experience is to attempt the impossible. The mind's categories are valid only within experience. As the universe comes within the grasp of experience, it becomes understood in terms of the categories. Beyond that, as in the case of rational psychology, is "mere speculation."

The third attempt to extend knowledge beyond experience is to speculate on the nature of God. For reasons which will appear later, Kant believed in the existence of God, but he is prepared to argue that such belief is not to be confused with knowledge. To attempt to formulate a rational theology, that is, to know God as we know things which fall within our experience, is to attempt the impossible. Kant reiterates and extends Hume's destructive criticism of the grounds for theism. Like rational psychology and rational cosmology, rational theology is "mere speculation." A quotation from Kant is possible here:

> Human reason begins with principles which, in the course of experience it must follow. With these again, according to the necessities of its nature, it rises higher and higher to more remote conditions. Thus it becomes involved in darkness and contradictions. It may conclude that errors must be lurking somewhere, but it is unable to discover them because the principles which it follows go beyond all limits of experience and so beyond all experimental verification. Metaphysics is the battlefield of these endless controversies.

Kant contrasts the forms of sensibility and the categories of understanding with these three ideas of speculation. The two former are constitutive of knowledge. That is, within the limits of experience, they enter into and contribute to genuine knowledge. The latter, however, are merely regulative. This distinction between constitutive and regulative forms of knowledge is important. The ideas of self, cosmos, and God are regulative goals toward which knowledge moves but to which it never attains.

Kant's distinction between *phenomena* and *noumena*, between things as known and things-in-themselves, follows as a corollary from this general theory of knowledge. It arises thus: Knowledge is a joint product of mind and external world arising in experience. There are here two contributing factors: the mind and external world. The latter "appears" through the forms and categories of the former. The word *phenomena* is derived from a Greek word meaning "that which appears." Hence reality as known is appearance, is phenomenal, is to be contrasted with reality as it is, which is noumenal. As Kant sweepingly remarks, "We only know phenomena."

We are now in a position to return to the one basic fact which this elaborate theory was invoked to account for, namely, *a priori* knowledge. Our *a priori* knowledge is formal only, and arises out of the dual origin of knowledge. We know *a priori* that things perceived will be perceived as spread-out-and-strung-along. We know *a priori* that things will be understood as effects of causes. We know *a priori* that things will be understood as qualities inhering in substances. We know *a priori* that things will be understood in terms of part-whole relations. And so on through the categories. But this knowledge is purely formal. We do not know *a priori* what the content of future experiences will be. We know that it will exhibit the various forms referred to, because, by hypothesis, knowledge is a joint product of mind-imposed forms filled with experience-given content. Thus did Kant "answer" Hume. At this point we can resume quoting directly from his writings.

I must, therefore, even before objects are given me in experience, presuppose the "rules of the understanding," or the "principles of knowledge" as existing within me *a priori*. These rules are expressed in *a priori* concepts to which all objects of experience must necessarily conform and to which they must agree. By thus changing our point of view, the possibility of *a priori* knowledge can well be explained.

After a superficial view of this work, it may seem that its results are negative only, warning us against venturing beyond the limits of experience. Such is no doubt its primary use. But its results are seen to be positive, when we perceive that it leads inevitably to a narrowing, a limiting, of the employment of reason; to the impossibility of going by it beyond the frontier of possible experience.

But thus and thus alone can we cut away the very root of materialism, idealism, skepticism, fatalism, atheism, fanaticism, and superstition. If governments ever think proper to interfere with the affairs of the learned, it would be consistent with their wise regard for science and society, to favor the freedom of such a criticism as can establish the labors of reason on a firm footing.

To deny that this service, setting limits to the speculative use of reason, is a positive advantage, would be the same as to deny that the police confer any positive advantage on us in preventing that violence which citizens have to fear from citizens. The police protection enables each to pursue his vocation in peace and security. The critique of reason does as much for the powers of the mind.

To illustrate this, let us suppose that the necessary distinction, established in our critique, between things as phenomena and things-in-themselves, had not been made. In that case the principle of causality, and with it the mechanical interpretation of nature, would apply to all things and not to their appearances only. I should then not be able to say of one and the same thing, for instance, the human soul, that it is both free and subject to necessity, without involving myself in a contradiction.

If, however, we may legitimately take an object in two senses, namely, as phenomenon and as thing-in-itself; and if the principle of causality applies to things only as phenomena and not as noumena, then we can, without any contradiction, think one and the same thing when phenomenal as necessarily conforming to the principle of causality and so far not free, and yet, in itself not subject to that principle and therefore free.

Suppose morality necessarily presupposed freedom of the will while speculative reason had proved that such freedom cannot even be thought. In such case freedom, and with it morality, would have to make room for the mechanical interpretation of nature. But our critique has revealed our inevitable ignorance of things-in-themselves, has limited our knowledge to mere phenomena. So, as morality requires only that freedom should not entail a contradiction, there is no reason why freedom should be denied to the will, considered as thing-in-itself, merely because it must be denied to it as phenomenon. The doctrine of morality may well hold its place, and the doctrine of nature too; which would have been impossible without our theory of the nature and limitations of knowledge.

If I cannot deprive speculative reason of its pretensions to transcendent insight, I cannot even assume freedom of will, not even in the interests of morality. I had, therefore, to remove the possibility of knowledge of what lies beyond experience, in order to make room for faith. This question of free will is but one of many which derive positive advantage from the limitations imposed by my theory of knowledge, on the speculative reach of pure reason beyond experience.

Let any reader who finds these inquiries obscure consider that not every one is bound to study metaphysics; that many minds will succeed very well in the exact sciences more closely allied to practical experience while they cannot succeed in investigations dealing exclusively with abstract conceptions. In such cases men should apply their talents to other subjects.

The following citations from John Dewey's *Quest For Certainty* describe rather pointedly the motive and the main turns of Kant's theory of knowledge:

Kant's position bristles with points of internal difficulty; many of these are objects of controversy. Ignoring these, however, it can fairly be asserted that the main characteristic of his position is a division of territory between the objects of cognitive certitude and the objects of equally complete moral assurance.

He aims in the first place to make secure, on rational *a priori* grounds, the foundation of natural knowledge; in the second, to perform a like office for the foundations of moral and religious conceptions. Science is limited to phenomena in space and time in order that the world of higher and noumenal realities may be appropriated by ideals and spiritual values. Each has complete jurisdiction and undisputed sovereignty in its own realm.

His argument in justification of the certitude of the foundations of knowledge is couched at every point so as to indicate the necessity of a higher although intellectually unapproachable realm. There was nothing factitious, in Kant's own conception, in the way in which the two kingdoms excluded each other and yet made each other necessary. On the contrary, the neat way in which the elements of each dovetailed into those of the other was to him a convincing proof of the necessity of the system as a whole. If the dovetailing was the product of his own intellectual carpentry, he had no suspicion of the fact.

He thought he had disposed, once for all, of many of the most perplexing problems of earlier philosophy. Upon the scientific side he was concerned to provide a final philosophical justification, beyond the reach of skepticism, for the Newtonian science.

His conception of space and time as necessary forms of the possibility of perception was the justification of the application of mathematics to natural phenomena. Categories of thought, necessary to understand perceived objects — and understanding necessary to science — supplied the foundation of permanent substances and causal connection demanded by Newtonian science. The tendency of the mind to pass beyond the limits of experience to the thought of unconditioned and self-sufficient totalities, "Ideas" of the universe, soul and God, was explained; and while cognitive validity was denied these "Ideas," they were admitted as regulative ideals which directed inquiry and interpretation. Above all, the thought of these transempirical realities left room that the postulate of free choice could fill.

In its essential framework, the Kantian scheme thus agreed marvelously well with the needs of the historic crisis. It gave freedom to both science and morals, with a guarantee that they could never interfere with each other. The traditional belief was that security of moral authority depends upon some source in being apart from the experiences by which values are incarnated in concrete objects and institutions. Granted this traditional belief, the Kantian scheme has such merits that it is safe to predict that as long as this belief continues to have vitality, the main elements of the Kantian position will have devoted disciples.

Thus Kant on the problem of knowledge in his *Critique of Pure Reason*. His ideas here are closely connected with the ideas which he was to put into his second *Critique*. The latter was directed toward a clarification and defense of his convictions in the field of ethics. Since his philosophy comprises both of these *Critiques*, together with much more, we shall return to him later on in connection with the ethical problem.

Reading References. It has been said that more books have been written on Shakespeare, Goethe, and Kant than on any three other persons. Kant is a perennially attractive figure. Anyone who is familiar with the main turns of modern philosophy can feel the tug which the man's ideas exert even when had at second hand. The accounts of Kant to be found in Will Durant's *Story of Philosophy*, in Mary Whiton Calkins's *The Persistent Problems of Philosophy*, in Royce's *Lectures on Modern Idealism* are good introductory presentations. These are for beginners. For those who desire to go a little further, Lindsay's *Kant*, Paulsen's *Immanuel Kant*, and the extended account in Volume Two of Hoffding's *History of Modern Philosophy* are recommended. Beyond that, one arrives soon at specialized and monumental treatises.

READING QUESTIONS

1. "Kant's handling of the problem of knowledge was motivated by these two considerations." Namely?
2. "During these years he was gradually awakened to the dilemmas of the modern mind." What years? What dilemmas?
3. "He looked into his own mind and found two unshakable convictions." What convictions?
4. What preliminary question is it his object to propose?
5. What is the state of metaphysics as he sees it?
6. "It is vain to assume an artificial indifference." To what? Why?
7. How does he describe the impact of Hume's work on philosophy?
8. What does he mean by *a priori* knowledge?
9. "Experience tells us what is, but not that it must necessarily be as it is." Elucidate.
10. "We have here a mystery." Elucidate.
11. "Hitherto it has been supposed . . . have come to nothing." Restate the complete passage in your own words

12. By what hypothesis does he propose to account for the *a priori?*
13. Why does he liken it to the Copernican hypothesis?
14. What is his distinction between form and content?
15. How does he propose to connect this distinction with the distinction between *a priori* and *a posteriori?*
16. State his "Copernican" hypothesis in terms of this distinction between form and content.
17. What is his thesis regarding space and time?
18. What does he mean by the *empirical reality* and *transcendental ideality* of space and time?
19. Distinguish after Kant: perception, understanding, speculation.
20. What are the formal (*a priori*) elements in each?
21. What are the three forms of speculation which Kant notes?
22. By what line of reasoning does he eliminate all three?
23. In what sense are the forms of sensibility and the categories of the understanding "constitutive" whereas the ideas of speculation are "regulative"?
24. What is his distinction between phenomena and noumena?
25. How is it derived?
26. "We only know phenomena." Meaning?
27. "The one basic fact which this elaborate theory was invoked to account for, namely, *a priori* knowledge." Elucidate.
28. "After a superficial view of this work, it may seem that its results are negative only." Elucidate.
29. "But its results are seen to be positive." How so?
30. What is his policeman analogy?
31. What bearing does he suggest his theory might have on morality?
32. "Kant's position bristles with points of internal difficulty." Can you suggest some?
33. "In its essential framework, the Kantian scheme agreed marvelously well with the needs of the historic crisis." What crisis? What needs? What essential framework?
34. Under what conditions, according to Dewey, will the main elements of the Kantian position have devoted disciples?

4. POSITIVISM — FROM AUGUSTE COMTE

From Kant to Comte. Each century tackles the problem of knowledge in its own way. The seventeenth century, represented most completely in Locke's essay, differs in method from the eighteenth. The eighteenth, represented by the twin stars of Hume and Kant, differs again from the nineteenth represented in the writings of Auguste Comte. By the 1830's, it was rather unnecessary to reopen the hectic controversies which inspired and followed from earlier epistemologies. At least, Comte appears to have felt as much. The picture is altered. Comte approaches the question of knowledge from the point of view of a man who is interested primarily in the range and organization of the various bodies of science. He pins a controversial tag on himself, no doubt; for *positivism*, as will be seen, means "no more metaphysics." But he is inclined to sweep controversy to one side and ask several new leading questions: What common method has the growth of science revealed? What relations, if any, exist among the different sciences? What significance, for general education, may be ascribed to the sciences as a whole? In what fields, if any, may we look for the emergence of new sciences? For these reasons, among others, Comte is perhaps more convincing to one who is either innocent of Hume and Kant or who has lost those peculiar sensibilities which respond to their anxieties and convictions.

Biographical Note. Auguste Comte was born in France in 1798, and died in 1857 at the age of fifty-nine. He showed an early aptitude for mathematics, which he began to teach in Paris. When he was twenty-eight, he embarked on a series of public lectures designed to offer a synoptic account of the principal sciences. These attracted considerable attention; but after the third lecture, his brain temporarily gave way, and he tried to commit suicide. Two years later he had sufficiently recovered to resume his lectures. In 1830 he began the publication of his great survey of the sciences. It was completed in six large volumes and served through several generations as a storehouse of fact and generalization for advanced students in France and abroad. He continued to maintain himself by teaching mathematics and serving as an examiner in that subject. Unfortunately, however, he became embroiled in controversies which caused him to lose a great part of his means of living. The English philosopher, J. S. Mill, who had been impressed by the value of Comte's work, was instrumental in securing a considerable sum of money from Comte's admirers in England. This tided him over his immediate difficulties. When this was used up, Comte faced poverty; however, aid came eventually from admirers in France who banded together to provide the lonely polymath with a small income for the rest of his life.

Comte's interest in epistemology was not direct. To get this point as clearly and, at the same time, as sympathetically as possible, we need to recall a bit of French history. Comte wrote for the first generation after Napoleon. The old regime, the epoch of the grand monarchy, formed a remote background. It had been swept away by the French Revolution. Liberal hopes had run high, only to be disappointed by the autocratic domination of Napoleon, and now, following the Congress of Vienna, France had been made over once more into a monarchy under Louis XVIII and Charles X. These drastic changes appear to have inspired Comte with the dream of a new era in which they would no longer be possible. This new era was to be built upon science and the application of science to industry. But, as Comte saw it, several obstacles blocked the path of the new age. They were remnants from the past. They were, more particularly, beliefs or mental sets which still lingered from the Middle Ages, the period of the grand monarchy, the Age of Reason, the revolution, and

Napoleon. They were beliefs about such matters as God, the soul, ultimate reality, immortality, natural laws, inalienable rights, men of destiny, and so forth. These beliefs, Comte felt, were not only groundless, they were harmful. They had been responsible for continuous tyranny, revolt, suppression, war, and they always would be. What the world needed was a riddance of such disarranging beliefs, and Comte would supply it under cover of this new term *positivism*, which was to abolish the old loyalties and controversies, to set up the ideal of scientific method and its application to nature in the interests of human welfare.

THE ARGUMENT OF THE CITATIONS. Comte begins by elaborating what he calls the *law of the three stages*. This enables him to dispose of metaphysics and theology. He turns then to a statement of his theory of the sciences. The citations tell their own story from that point on:

In order to understand the true value and character of positivism, we must take a brief general view of the progress of the human mind; for no conception can be understood otherwise than through its history.

From the study of the development of human understanding, in all directions and through all times, the discovery arises of a fundamental law. The law is this: that each of our leading conceptions, each branch of our knowledge, passes through three different theoretical conditions: the theological or fictitious, the metaphysical or abstract, the scientific or positive. This fundamental law should henceforth be, in my opinion, the starting point of all philosophical researches about man and society.

The human mind employs in its progress three methods of explanations, the characteristics of which are essentially different and even radically opposed: the theological, the metaphysical, and the scientific. Hence arise three philosophies, or three general systems of thought, each of which excludes the other. The first is the mind's necessary point of departure; the second is merely a state of transition; the third is the mind's fixed and definitive state.

An instance of what Comte means might be the following: In the early stages of man's study of the heavens, he accounted for their motion in terms of various deities. Later he envisaged them as controlled by the force of gravitation. Finally he repudiates explanation in terms of gods and forces and is satisfied to describe the motion in terms of formulae which enable him to locate and predict:

Different departments of our knowledge have passed through the three stages at different rates. The rate depends on the nature of the knowledge in question. Any kind of knowledge reaches the positive stage early in proportion to its generality, simplicity, and independence of other branches of knowledge. Thus astronomy, which is above all made up of facts which are general, simple, and independent of other facts, was the first science to attain the positive stage, then physics, then chemistry, and finally physiology.

In the theological stage, the human mind, seeking the essential nature of things, their first and final causes, supposes all things to be produced by the immediate action of supernatural beings. Here imagination predominates over observation.

A natural and irresistible instinct disposes the human race to adopt theological ideas as its earliest principles of explanation. The personal action exerted by man on other things is, at first, the only kind he is able to understand. He is thus led to conceive, in an analogous way, the action of external bodies on himself and on each other. This is animism. Continued observation leads him to convert this primitive hypothesis into another, less enduring one: that of a "dead" inert nature guided by invisible superhuman agents, distinct and independent of one another. This is polytheism. Continued observation and reflection disposes him gradually to reduce the number of these supernatural agencies until he is led from polytheism to monotheism. The theological system arrived at its highest perfection when it substituted the providential action of a single supreme Being for the varied operations of numerous divinities; when, that is, it passed from polytheism to monotheism.

The entire theological system is based on the supposition that the earth is made for man, and the whole universe made for the earth.

Remove this supposition, and the system crumbles. Hence the true astronomical theory, proposed by Copernicus and proved by Kepler, Galileo, and Newton, would alone have sufficed to demolish the theological system. In the light of the fact that our planet, one of the smallest, is in no respect different from the others, revolving like them around the sun, the hypothesis that nature is made for mankind alone so shocks good sense and contradicts fact that it must appear absurd and collapse. With it falls the theological edifice.

In the metaphysical stage, which is only a modification of the first, the mind supposes abstract forces, personified abstractions, inherent in all things and capable of producing them, instead of supernatural beings. What is called the *explanation* of anything is, in this stage, a reference of it to its proper force, principle, or abstraction.

To explain sleep, for example, in terms of what used to be called the *dormitive principle* is to explain observed phenomena by reference to what Comte would call a *metaphysical abstraction*. Many such phrases are to be found strewn through the annals of science and philosophy. Thus Hegel's *reason* or *time-spirit*, Schopenhauer's *will*, Bergson's *élan vital*, Freud's *censor*, the erstwhile *vis viva*, *vis inertia*, and *entelechy* are, I suspect, all instances of what Comte would call *metaphysical abstractions*. His objection to them is that they are attempts to explain the known by the unknown, to postulate something which is not revealed in experience to account for what is revealed in experience.

Even today, after all our advance in positive knowledge, if we try to understand how the fact which we name a cause produces the fact which we name its effect, we should be compelled, as Hume points out, to resort to images similar to those which serve as the basis of primitive human theories. (Cause is a metaphysical notion; regularity of succession is the positive notion.)

The metaphysical system arrived at its last stage when men substituted the one great entity — nature — as the cause of everything.

In the scientific or positive stage the mind has given over the vain search after absolute knowledge; abandoned the quest for knowledge of the origin and destination of the universe, of causes and forces; and applies itself solely to the study of laws, to the study of relations of succession and resemblance. Reasoning and observation, duly combined, are the means of this knowledge. What is now called the *explanation* of anything is the establishment of a connection between it and some general laws, the number of which continually diminishes with the progress of science.

Observation of fact is the only solid basis for human knowledge. Taking this principle in its most rigorous sense, we may say that a proposition which does not admit of being reduced to a simple enunciation of fact, particular or general, can have no real or intelligible sense.

The first characteristic of positivism is that it regards all things as subject to invariable laws. Our business — seeing how vain is any search into what are called causes, either first or final — is to pursue an accurate discovery of those laws, with a view to reducing them to the smallest possible number. The best illustration of this is in the case of the law of gravitation. We say things are explained by it, because it connects an immense variety of facts under one head.

The positive system would attain its ultimate perfection if men could represent all particular facts as instances of one general law, e.g., the law of gravitation.

There is no science, which, having attained to the positive stage, does not bear marks of having passed through the two previous stages. At some earlier period it was composed of metaphysical abstractions; and, further back in its evolution, it took its form from theological conceptions. Our most advanced sciences still bear traces of the earlier stages through which they have passed.

In mentioning just now the four principal categories of phenomena — the astronomical, the physical, the chemical, the physiological — there was an omission. Nothing was said of social phenomena. These demand a distinct classification, by reason of their importance and difficulty. They are the most complicated and the most dependent on others. Their science, therefore, will be the latest to attain positivity.

This branch of science has not hitherto entered the domain of positive knowledge. Theological and metaphysical conceptions and methods, exploded and abandoned in other departments, are still used in the treatment of social subjects, though the best minds are weary of disputes about "divine rights," "sovereignty of the people," and so on. This is the great, the only, gap to be filled to constitute solid and entire the positive philosophy. This is what men have now most need of.

This once done, the philosophical system of the moderns will be complete. There will then be no phenomena which does not enter into one of the five great categories — astronomical, physical, chemical, physiological, and sociological.

So much then, for the law of the three stages. It has a certain plausibility. But, for Comte, its principal virtue seems to reside in the fact that it eliminates, at one fell swoop, a whole army of clamorous hypotheses and controversies which constitute a large portion of modern philosophy. Comte now turns his attention to the question of the classification of the positive sciences. (It should be noted that, as Comte uses it, the term *physiology* has the broader meaning which we extend today to the term *biology*.)

We propose to classify the fundamental sciences. They are six, as we shall see. We cannot make them less; and most scientists would make them more. To classify the sciences is not so easy as may appear. It always involves something, if not arbitrary, at least artificial; and in so far, it will always involve imperfection. It is perhaps impossible to exhibit the sciences, quite rigorously, in their natural relations and mutual dependence so as to avoid, in some degree, the danger of overlapping.

What we seek to determine is the dependence of scientific studies. Does physics depend upon physiology? Does sociology depend upon chemistry? Dependence among the sciences can result only from dependence among the corresponding phenomena. For a principle in terms of which to classify the sciences, then, we must look to the different orders of phenomena through which science discovers the laws which are her object.

All phenomena may be included within a very few natural categories, so arranged that the study of each may be grounded on the principal laws of the preceding and serve as the basis of the next ensuing. We have now obtained our rule. We proceed next to our classification.

We are first struck by the clear division of all natural phenomena into two classes: inorganic and organic. Each of these two great halves has subdivisions. Inorganic phenomena may be divided into two classes: celestial and terrestrial. Terrestrial inorganic phenomena may be divided into two classes according as we regard bodies in their mechanical or chemical character. Organic phenomena may be divided into two classes: those which relate to the individual and those which relate to groups.

Thus we have five basic sciences in successive dependence: astronomy, physics, chemistry, physiology, and sociology. The first considers the most general, simple, and remote phenomena known to us, and those which affect all others without being affected by them. The last considers the most particular, complex, and nearest phenomena. Between these two the degrees of speciality and complexity are in regular proportion to the place of the respective sciences in the scale exhibited. This we must regard as the true filiation of the sciences.

It is proposed to consolidate the entire body of positive knowledge into one body of homogeneous doctrine. But it must not be supposed that we are proposing to study this vast variety as proceeding from one single law. There is something so chimerical in attempts at explanation in terms of one single law, that it may be as well to repudiate any such notion. Our intellectual resources are too narrow, and the universe too complex, to justify any hope that it will ever be within our power to carry scientific perfection to this last degree of simplicity.

This notion of all phenomena referable to a single law is by no means necessary to the systematic formation of science. The only necessary unity is that of method. And this is already, in great part, attained: The scientific method of thought is the same for all fields of knowledge, however widely they may vary and however irreducible they may be in content.

Comte's meaning is probably this: In the scientific exploration of any field, the method is the same. Initial data are collected, usually in the light of some tentatively held hypothesis; this hypothesis is then assumed to be true, and its consequences or implications deduced; facts subsequently acquired, by observation or experiment, verify the deductions made from the hypothesis. The hypothesis may be with regard to some particular fact or some general law.

The most interesting point in our hierarchical classification is its effect on education, both general and scientific. This is its direct and unquestionable result. No science can be effectually pursued without a competent knowledge of the anterior sciences upon which it depends.

Your competent physicist must have at least a general knowledge of astronomy. Chemists cannot properly understand chemistry without physics and astronomy. Physiologists require some knowledge of chemistry, physics, and astronomy. Above all, students of social science require a general knowledge of the anterior sciences. As such conditions are rarely fulfilled, there is among us, no genuinely rational scientific education. To this may be attributed, in part, the imperfection of even the most important sciences at this day.

In our enumeration of the basic sciences there is one prodigious omission. We have said nothing of mathematics. The omission was intentional, and the reason was the vast importance and unique status of mathematics. It is, however, less a constituent part of the body of positive knowledge than a basis for the whole of that knowledge. It is the most powerful instrument that the human mind can employ in the investigation of the laws of natural phenomena. It must, therefore, hold the first place in the hierarchy of the sciences and be the point of departure for all education in any of the sciences.

From the question of the classification of the sciences, Comte addresses himself to certain advantages which, he thinks, will arise from the unified view which results. It is interesting to note that these include the elimination of logic and the reduction of psychology to behaviorism.

We have now considered philosophically the articulation of the positive sciences. The order that results is this: mathematics, astronomy, physics, chemistry, physiology, and sociology. We must glance at the principal advantages to be derived from a study of them. Of these advantages, four may be pointed out.

In the first place, the study of the positive sciences affords the only rational means of exhibiting the logical laws of the human mind. Looking at all scientific theories as so many great logical facts, it is only by the observation of these facts that we can arrive at the knowledge of logical laws.

Psychology pretends to discover the laws of the human mind by contemplating the mind itself. Such an (introspective) attempt, made in defiance of the physiological study of our intellectual organs, cannot succeed. The mind may observe all phenomena but its own. There can be nothing like scientific observation of mental phenomena except from without, and by another. The observing and observed organ are here the same. In order to observe its activity, your mind must pause from activity; yet it is this very activity that you want to observe. If you cannot pause, you cannot observe; if you do pause, there is nothing to observe. The results of such a method are in proportion to its absurdity.

After two thousand years of psychology, no one proposition is established to the satisfaction of psychologists. To this day they are divided into a multitude of schools, still disputing about the very elements of their doctrine. The psychologists have done some good in keeping up the activity of our understandings when there was no better work for our minds to do.

What we have said with regard to psychology as a positive science applies yet more strikingly to logic, that is, to the "study" of scientific method. Scientific method can be judged of only in action. It cannot be studied apart from the work on which it is employed. Such a study would be dead, could produce nothing of value in the mind which loses time on it. We may talk forever about scientific method, and state it in terms very wise and learned, without knowing half so much about it as the man who has once put it into practice upon a single piece of research. Thus have logicians, by dint of reading the aphorisms of Bacon and the discourses of Descartes mistaken their own dreams for science. We cannot explain the great logical procedures apart from their applications.

In the second place, a study of positive science as here conceived will regenerate education. The best minds are agreed that our European education, still essentially theological, metaphysical, and literary, must be superseded by a scientific education conformable to our time and needs.

Everything yet done to this end is inadequate. What is required is an organic conception of the sciences such as positivism presents. The exclusive specializing tendencies of our sciences spoil our teaching. If any student desires to form a conception of science as a whole, he is compelled to go through each department as it is now taught, as if he were to be only an astronomer or only a chemist. The result, be his intellect what it may, is unsatisfactory when what he requires is a general conception of the entire range of positive knowledge.

It is such a general conception of the entire range of the sciences which must henceforth be the permanent basis of all human combinations. It will constitute the mind of future generations. But to this end it is necessary that the sciences, considered as branches from one trunk, should yield us as a whole, their chief methods and results.

In the third place, the proposed study of the organically related generalizations of the positive sciences will aid the progress of each separate science. The divisions we establish between the sciences are, though not arbitrary, essentially superficial. The subject of our researches is one; we divide it for convenience, in order to deal more easily with separate problems. But it sometimes happens that we need what we cannot obtain under the present isolation of the sciences, namely a combination of several special points of view. For want of this, important problems wait for their solution.

To go into the past for an example: Descartes' grand conception with regard to analytical geometry, a discovery which has changed the whole face of mathematics, issued from the union of two sciences which had before been separately studied and pursued.

Again, it was undecided whether azote is a simple or a compound body. Almost all chemists held that azote is a simple body. But the illustrious Berzelius, influenced by the physiological observation that animals which receive no azote in their food have as much of it in their tissue as carnivorous animals, was able to throw new light on the question. Thus must physiology unite with chemistry to inform us whether azote is simple or compound, and to institute a new series of researches upon the relation between the composition of living bodies and their mode of alimentation.

In the fourth place, philosophy based on the positive sciences offers the only solid basis for that social reorganization which must succeed the critical condition in which even the most civilized nations are now living.

It cannot be necessary to argue that ideas govern the world or throw it into chaos, that all social mechanism rests upon opinions held by the members of society. The great political and moral crisis that societies are now undergoing proceeds from intellectual anarchy. Stability in fundamental principles is the first condition of genuine social order: We witness an utter disagreement on all such matters. Till a certain number of general ideas can be acknowledged as a rallying point for social doctrine, nations will remain in a revolutionary state whatever palliatives may be advised, and their institutions only provisional and makeshift.

But when the necessary agreement on first principles can be obtained, appropriate institutions will issue from them without shock or resistance. It is in this direction that those must look who desire a natural, regular, normal state of society.

Now, the existing disorder is abundantly accounted for by the existence, all at once, of three incompatible philosophies — the theological, the metaphysical, and the positive. Any one of these might alone secure some sort of social order. But while the three coexist, it is impossible for us to understand one another upon any essential point whatever. If this is true, we have only to ascertain which of the philosophies must, in the nature of things, eventually prevail.

Comte's point here might be illustrated by controversies centering in such questions as birth control, sterilization of the subnormal and criminal, etc. Consider the case of sterilization. A sincere Catholic might oppose the measure as contrary to the will of God; a sincere democrat might oppose it as contrary to the rights of man; a social scientist disregarding both grounds of opposition, might simply argue that offspring born to such parents are likely to prove a needless burden and menace to a society which must, in the end, either support them or imprison them.

This problem, once recognized, cannot remain long unsolved; for all considerations point to a philosophy based on the positive sciences as the one destined to prevail. It alone has been advancing during the course of centuries, while others have been declining. The fact is incontestable. Some may deplore it, but none deny it or destroy it, nor neglect it save on pain of being betrayed by illusory speculations.

This general revolution of the human mind is nearly accomplished. We have only to complete the hierarchy of the positive sciences by bringing the facts and problems of society within its comprehension. The preference which almost all minds, from the highest to the commonest. accord to positive knowledge over vague and mystical conceptions, is a pledge of what this philosophy will receive when it is once completed by the addition of a positive social science. When this has been accomplished, its supremacy will be automatic and will establish order throughout society.

Reading References. Comte's influence has been very great. Most unphilosophically minded scientists are probably Comteans, in the sense that they would endorse his positivism. Further reading in Comte should be done in those writings in which he sets forth his conception of the new social sciences, the new social order, and the new religion of humanity. John Morley's essay on Comte in one of the volumes of his *Miscellanies* is worth while. John Stuart

Mill's *Auguste Comte and Positivism*, published shortly after Comte's death, is still an illuminating account and, with respect to what Mill describes as Comte's "later aberrations," a vigorous polemic. The account of Comte in Volume Two of Hoffding's *History of Modern Philosophy* is excellent. The standard work on Comte is by Lucien Lévy-Bruhl.

READING QUESTIONS

1. What are the three stages which Comte notes?
2. What characterizes each stage?
3. On what basis does Comte classify the sciences?
4. What is the resulting hierarchy?
5. "The most interesting point in our hierarchical classification is its effect on education." Namely?
6. "In our enumeration of the basic sciences there is one prodigious omission." Namely? Why?
7. On what grounds does Comte eliminate logic?
8. On what grounds does he eliminate psychology, as a separate science?
9. "A study of positive science as here conceived will regenerate education." How so?
10. "The proposed study of the . . . positive sciences will aid the progress of each separate science." How so?
11. "Philosophy based on the positive sciences offers the only solid basis for social organization." Meaning?
12. Show how Hume, Kant, and Comte reach the same antimetaphysical conclusions from different premises.

5. *THE ROLE OF FICTIONS IN KNOWLEDGE—FROM HANS VAIHINGER*

FROM COMTE TO VAIHINGER. We began with Locke, and have thus far read our way from him through Hume and Kant and Comte. With Comte's positivism matters seemed likely to reach a dead end. What Comte did, in effect, was to settle the problem of knowledge by definition. That is, he described the method of natural science (observation, hypothesis, deduction, verification) and the method of mathematics (postulation, definition, deduction), and then said that anything not obtained by these methods is not knowledge. Comte was then able to write off all beliefs which he could not certify in terms of these methods, as vestiges of the theological or metaphysical stages through which the mind of man has passed, but from which, here and there, some traces yet remain.

One must go back to Kant in order to make a new beginning with Vaihinger. It will be recalled that Kant conceived of his *Critique of Pure Reason* as having set limits to knowledge in order to make room for faith. There were consequences. The first was that knowledge could deal only with the world of appearances. The second was that all beliefs concerning the real world were mere speculations. It will be recalled that he describes such notions as God, the soul, and the cosmos as regulative ideas. They were regulative, in contrast to constitutive. This was a way of stating that these ideas were useful fictions, or so, at least, our next author takes it. In this concept of a useful fiction, one passes directly from Immanuel Kant to Hans Vaihinger.

Vaihinger seized upon this notion of Kant's, and elaborated it into the general theory that all knowledge rests on useful fictions. This hypothesis was stated and documented in his treatise, *The Philosophy of As-If*. By an *as-if*, the author means a useful fiction.

Biographical Note. In place of the usual biographical facts, I am appending herewith an abridgment of Vaihinger's account of his own life. The reason for this is that his account of his life is also an account of his opinions. Anyone who has read through this volume of selections thus far is in possession of most of the names and ideas to which Vaihinger refers. This makes his autobiography both interesting and valuable to read.

I was born in a Swabian parsonage near Tübingen in 1852, and so I grew up in a very religious atmosphere. It was not exactly bigoted, but it had a limited horizon. My father, who was the author of a good many theological works, had written a pamphlet against Strauss. When I was twelve years old I was given into the charge of an excellent master and teacher. I was his favorite pupil. He used to tell me about his Sanskrit studies. He was especially interested in the great Mahabharata epic; and occasionally at the end of the lesson in religion he would tell us how this Indian epic contained the same sort of legends as the New Testament. The stories of the Old and New Testaments had already awakened doubts in my mind, so I was gradually led to the ethical value of the myth. Generally speaking, his attitude was one of rationalistic theism with a solid moral basis. I had already reached this way of thinking at the time of my confirmation in 1866. This ethical theism was a great help to me in those years, but from the time I entered grammar school it gradually evolved into pantheism, based on a deep love of nature. During this period of transition I came across Herder's book on the history of mankind. It appealed to me by its mixture of theism and pantheism. I owe a great deal to it. It gives a wide and lofty view of the whole history of mankind from the earliest origins through all kinds and varieties of civilization. The idea of evolution became one of the fundamental elements of my mental outlook. Herder draws special attention to the evolution of spiritual life out of its first animal origins; and he regards man always as linked up with that nature from which he has gradually evolved. Thus when I first heard Darwin's name, and when my school friends told me about the new theory of man's animal ancestry, it was no surprise to me.

From that time onward, one of the fundamentals in my philosophy has been this fact of man's animal ancestry. About this time I came under the influence of Plato, which acted as a counterbalancing factor. I read the usual dialogues and the *Apology*. Our professor was old, and, though very thorough, he was dull and kept us to the grammatical side. His routine teaching made nothing like the impression on me that was made by three lectures from a young man who came to replace him during an illness. This young man read us the myth on the nature of the soul, in the *Phaedrus*, and the description of the cave from the *Republic*. These opened a new world to me, and as he spoke of Plato's myths, the seed was sown of that conception which later I myself named the "World of as-if."

The introduction to philosophy which was customary at that time, with its bare outlines of logic, psychology, and ethics, played quite an insignificant part compared with the revolutionary ideas which I was discovering for myself. Philosophy should be the general principle of instruction in all subjects. It should practice the "opportunist method," which emphasizes points of philosophical significance, when the occasion arises, in other branches of study.

Last, but not least, I must mention Schiller's poems and treatises, for they too had an important influence on me at that time. Every earnest young student is inspired and fired by Schiller. His philosophic poems, in which he contrasts the ideal world of pure form with the empirical world, were easily linked up with the Platonic influences mentioned above. Many of his verses made an indelible impression on me; for instance, the words "in error only is there life, and knowledge must be death" have, in certain respects, become the foundation of my theory of fictions.

Thus equipped, I entered the University of Tübingen in the autumn of 1870, as a student at the resident theological college there. In my time the university was run on very liberal lines, and great freedom was and is given to the students to allow them to develop in their own way. In the first four terms they are given a very thorough grounding in philosophy. My first term was devoted to ancient philosophy; the second to later philosophy up to Kant; the third to the period from Kant to Hegel; and the fourth from Schleiermacher onwards. First-rate coaches gave us careful instruction. They also supervised the working out of philosophic treatises by the students, who were encouraged to think freely for themselves. No obstacles were placed in the path of my philosophical development. On the contrary, I was encouraged on all sides, especially when I started a prize essay for the faculty of philosophy on recent theories of consciousness. For this work, which took me a year, I received first prize in the autumn of 1873. This enabled me to travel in Switzerland and North Italy. This prize essay was also the decisive factor in making me abandon my theological studies. I had started them with much hesitation anyway. My transition to philosophy was made easier for me in every way. Thus I have good reason to remember the theological college of Tübingen with gratitude, particularly the open-minded and kind-hearted director at that time.

In my first term the teaching of the Greek nature philosophers made a great impression on me because of their close similarity with the modern theory of evolution. Anaximander appealed to me especially. I also worked at Aristotle very thoroughly. In my second term Spinoza absorbed me by his consistency and his dispassionate conception of the universe.

But the impression made upon me by Kant was very different from the rest. In every respect he freed my mind without fettering it. His bold theory of the ideality of space and time always liberates the mind from immediacy, from the pressure of the material world, even though one soon recognizes that in the long run it is not tenable in that form. But what impressed me most was Kant's discovery of the contradictions with which human thought is faced when it ventures into the realm of metaphysics. His theory of antinomies had a profound influence upon me. I derived permanent value from his theory of the limitation of knowledge to experience, and also from his doctrine that action, the practical, must take first place. This so-called supremacy of practical reason seemed to appeal to my innermost being.

The official plan of studies passed from Fichte, Schelling, and Hegel, direct to Schleiermacher. But I followed my own course and turned to Schopenhauer, who, until then, had been ignored, even despised, by the faculty. I had got hold of Von Hartmann's *Philosophy of the Unconscious*, and it led back to Schopenhauer. So I went straight to the source and studied Schopenhauer very thoroughly. He gave me much that was new and great and lasting: pessimism, irrationalism, and voluntarism.

1. Schopenhauer's pessimism became, with me, a fundamental and lasting state of mind; all the more so because of my own sad and difficult experiences. I have not found that this outlook tends to weaken biological and moral energy. On the contrary, I am

one of those whom only pessimism enables to endure life. Pessimism gives me the ethical strength to work and fight for myself, as well as to help others. Furthermore, I believe that pessimism has given me a more objective view of reality. For example: I have regarded the political situation of Germany, during the last thirty years, in a way quite different from the great majority. For many years I prophesied the World War and its consequences for us. I have also found that people of other nations, who have been accustomed to a more realistic philosophy than the usual German idealism and optimism, have had a far clearer view of reality. If Germany's leaders since 1871 had taken a lesson from Schopenhauer, Germany would not have fallen into her desperate condition. The development of the social question, too, might just as well have evolved toward the right as toward the left, if Schopenhauer had been the guiding influence, instead of Rousseau and Hegel. Even in Kant, as I noticed in those early days, there is a strong undercurrent of pessimism.

2. The impression which Schopenhauer made upon me was, intensively, greater than that made by Kant. To explain this I must go further afield. In all the systems of philosophy which I had hitherto met, the irrational aspect of the world and of life had not received adequate attention. The ideal of philosophy was to explain everything rationally, i.e., by logical conclusions to prove it rational, significant, fitting. The Hegelian philosophy came nearest to this ideal, and it was considered the supreme achievement in philosophy. This ideal, however, had failed to satisfy me. From my earliest days I had come across countless manifestations of the irrational in my immediate surroundings. I therefore considered it to be a lack of sincerity in most systems of philosophy that they tried more or less to hide the irrational side. Now, in Schopenhauer, I came across, for the first time, a man who recognized irrationality openly and honorably, and who attempted to explain it in his system of philosophy. Schopenhauer's love of truth was a revelation to me. I did not follow his metaphysical theories because, since I had studied Kant, the impossibility of all metaphysics had seemed to me to be obvious. But that part of Schopenhauer's teaching which can be established empirically

became my lasting possession and a source of fruitful inspiration, particularly as it could be linked up with the theory of evolution and the struggle for existence.

3. What appealed to me most in Kant was his emphasis on the practical. In Schopenhauer I found this same tendency, but much clearer, much stronger, much more comprehensive. With him "the will" was placed in the forefront. To me, much that had hitherto been inexplicable seemed suddenly to be explained, or at least capable of explanation. What struck me most was his proof of the fact that originally thought is only used by the will as a means to its own end, and that only in the course of evolution does thought free itself from the bonds of the will and become an end in itself. He pointed out that the brain of animals is quite small, yet is large enough to act as an organ for the execution of the will's purposes; whereas, in the higher animals, and particularly in man, it has grown out of all proportion. Darwin's theory of evolution, which was being worked out at this time, corroborated Schopenhauer's contention.

This theory of Schopenhauer's, that fundamentally thought is dependent on the purposes of the Life-Will, and has developed into an end in itself only as it were against all laws, became linked up in my mind with Kant's theory that human thought is bound by certain limits and that metaphysical knowledge is impossible. This limitation of human knowledge to experience, which Kant emphasizes over and over again, no longer struck me as a deplorable deficiency in the human mind. It seemed to me now to be a necessary and natural result of the fact that thought and knowledge are originally only a means to attain the life purpose. Indeed, the independence of thought signifies a breaking away from its original purpose; and by the fact of this breaking loose thought is confronted with impossible problems which are not merely insoluble to human thought but to all forms of thought as such. This conviction has become one of the most solid foundations of my conception of the universe. It has grown within me and has crystallized, with the passing of the years, into an ever clearer form.

Another powerful influence, along these same lines, was a book by Adolf Horwicz, *Psychological Analysis upon a Physiological Basis*.

In this work Horwicz showed that all psychology is based on the so-called scheme of reflexes: stimulation, sense impressions, ideas leading up to thought, expressive movement, and volitional action. The simplest reflexes are motor phenomena following upon stimulation. These stimuli must result in elementary feelings, which release corresponding movements, representing the most elementary beginning of volitional actions. In the interval between these impressions and the motor expression, ideas come to the surface, first in an elementary form, but growing more and more complicated so that in their highest form they may be described as thought processes. Thus the idea, and later on the thought, appear as merely a bridge, an intermediary between impression on the one hand and expression on the other. This theory, which Horwicz worked out most carefully and comprehensively, fitted in very well with the idea I had derived from Schopenhauer, namely, that thought is, originally, only a means for the purposes of the will. And both ideas coincided with the conviction I had gained from Kant as to the supremacy of the practical.

These comments bring Vaihinger to the year 1873. During the next three years he prosecuted his studies on a variety of fronts.

Toward the latter part of the year 1876 I wrote down my thoughts in a large manuscript to which I gave the title *Logical Studies. Part I: The Theory of Scientific Fictions*. This work is exactly the same as what was published in 1911 as *Part I: Basic Principles* of *The Philosophy of As-If*. In it I developed the whole system of scientific fictions and tried to give an exhaustive theory of this manifold as-if process.

I regarded this dissertation as only a rough outline, in need of much supplementing and correction. I made use of the next two years to work at it as much as my lectures would allow me to.

Other things intervened. His father's death obliged him to look for more remunerative work. He arranged with a publisher to write a commentary on Kant's *Critique of Pure*

Reason for the 1881 centenary. The first volume of this commentary did not appear until 1884, but it was recognized at once as perhaps the greatest work of its kind anywhere in the field of Kant studies. The author was appointed "special professor" at the University of Halle. Bad health delayed the publication of the second volume of the *Commentary* until 1892. In 1894 the author was made "regular professor" at Halle. In 1896 he founded a journal, *Kant Studien*, as a means of helping his work along. In 1904, the centenary of Kant's death, Vaihinger started a fund for the founding of a Kant Society. The drive proved a success. He was a long way from his previous 1876 essay on the theory of fictions. But events brought him back to it.

In 1906, in the midst of all these complications and crossings of my original intentions, a misfortune unexpectedly brought a happy solution and enabled me after twenty-seven years to return to my original plan which I had given up in 1879. The misfortune was the weakening of my eyesight so that it became impossible for me to continue my lectures. So I had to give up my official duties. The eyesight still remaining to me was just sufficient to allow me to publish my manuscript. I got my dissertation of 1876 copied and introduced a number of small editorial alterations. I also completed the revision I had made between 1877 and the beginning of 1879. This part took me two and a half years because of my bad eyesight. A third part took me another two and a half years. It was the spring of 1911 before the work appeared.

I called this work, *The Philosophy of As-If*, because that seemed to express more convincingly than any other possible title what I wanted to say. The point which I wished to convey was that the *as-if*, the consciously false, plays an enormous part in science, in philosophies, and in life. I wanted to give a complete enumeration of all the methods in which we operate intentionally with consciously false ideas. I wanted to reveal the secret life of these extraordinary methods. I wanted to give a complete theory of as-if.

I will end by summarizing all the conclusions which are expressed in *The Philosophy of As-If*, or which form its basis, or arise out of it:

1. From an epistemological standpoint, philosophical analysis leads to sensational contents. From a psychological standpoint it leads to sensations, feelings, and strivings or actions. Scientific analysis leads to matter and the smallest constituents and motions of matter. It is impossible for the mind to bring these two spheres of reality into a rational relation, although in intuition and experience they form a harmonious unity.

2. The strivings which probably exist in the most elementary physical processes develop in organic beings into impulses. In man, who has sprung from the animal, these higher impulses have evolved into will and action, which is expressed in movements and caused by stimuli or by the sensations arising from stimuli.

3. Ideas, judgments and conclusions, i.e., thought, act as a means in the service of the will to live and dominate. Thought is originally only a means in the struggle for existence and to this extent only a biological function.

4. It is a universal phenomenon of nature that means which serve a purpose often undergo a more complete development than is necessary for the attainment of their purpose. In this case the means, according to the completeness of its self-development, can emancipate itself partly or wholly and become established as an end in itself. This I call the law of the preponderance of the means over the end.

5. The preponderance of the means over the end has taken place in thought, which, in the course of time, has gradually lost sight of its original practical purpose and is finally practiced for its own sake as theoretical thought.

6. As a result, this thought, which appears to be independent and theoretical in its origins, sets itself problems which are impossible, not only to human thought, but to every form of thought. An instance of what I mean is the problem of the origin and nature of the universe. Another is the question of the relation between sensation and motion, popularly known as mind and matter.

7. These endless, and, strictly speaking, senseless questions, can-

not be answered by looking forward but only by looking backward, by showing how they arose psychologically within us.

8. If rationalism is the assumption of an original theoretical reason, as an inherent human faculty with certain problems to be determined by it, then my position must be termed *antirationalism* or even *irrationalism*.

9. From this standpoint all thought processes and thought constructs appear, *a priori*, to be not essentially rationalistic but biological phenomena.

10. In this light many thought processes and thought constructs appear to be consciously false assumptions, which either contradict reality or are even contradictory in themselves, but which are intentionally thus formed to overcome difficulties of thought by this artificial deviation and reach the goal of thought by roundabout ways and bypaths. These artificial thought constructs are called *scientific fictions* and are distinguished as conscious creations by their as-if character.

11. The as-if world, which is formed in this manner, is just as important as the so-called real or actual world (in the ordinary sense of the word). Indeed, it is far more important for ethics and aesthetics. This aesthetic and ethical world of as-if, the world of the unreal, becomes finally for us a world of values which, particularly in the form of religion, must be sharply distinguished in our mind from the world of becoming.

12. What we usually term *reality* consists of our sensational contents which press forcibly upon us with greater or less irresistibility and as "given" can generally not be avoided.

13. In these given sensational contents, which include what we call our body, there is an abundance of regularity in coexistence and succession, investigation of which forms the content of science. By means of the sensational contents which we call our body, we can exercise greater or less influence on the rich world of the other sensational contents.

14. In this world we find a great number of relations of fitness and much that is not fitting. We have to take this as we find it for there is little we can alter. It is a satisfying fiction for many to regard the world as if a more perfect Higher Spirit had created or at

least regulated it. But this implies the supplementary fiction of regarding a world of this sort as if the order created by the Higher Divine Spirit had been destroyed by some hostile force.

15. It is senseless to question the meaning of the universe. This is the idea expressed in Schiller's words "Know this, a sublime mind puts greatness into life, yet seeks it not therein." This is positive idealism.

The Argument of the Citations. There is no need to restate the argument of the passages quoted below. It has already been given above in Vaihinger's own words. I have introduced numbers, at irregular intervals, to indicate that the author is beginning a new line of thought at that point. The passages between any two numbers form together a more or less solid block.

I

Scientific thought is a function of the psyche. It is an active appropriation of the outer world, a useful organic elaboration of the material of sensation.

The psyche is not merely a receptacle into which foreign matter is poured. It may be compared to a machine with a chemical retort which uses foreign matter most fittingly for its own maintenance. Just as the physical organism breaks up the matter which it receives, mixes it with its own juices, so the psyche envelops the thing perceived with categories. As soon as an external stimulus reaches the psyche, it responds as though provided with delicate feelers, inner processes start, the outcome of which is the appropriation of the thing perceived for some purpose.

The procedures of the psyche are carried on, for the most part, unconsciously. Should the product finally enter consciousness, or should consciousness momentarily accompany the process, this light penetrates only to the shallows. The fundamental processes are carried on in the darkness of the unconscious. The specifically purposeful operations of the psyche are chiefly, in the beginning, wholly instinctive and unconscious, even if later they press forward into the luminous circle of consciousness.

It is the purpose of the eye to transform various waves into sensations, to make reduced images of the objective world through refraction and reflection of rays. It is suitably arranged to achieve this purpose and is able to carry out independent movements of accommodation and modification as circumstances require. In the same way, the logical or scientific function of the psyche is an activity which has a purpose and can adapt itself to circumstances and objects for the fulfillment of this purpose.

The function of the psyche is to change and elaborate perceptional material into ideas, associations of ideas and conceptual constructions consistent and coherent among themselves. Since, however, we do not know objective reality directly but only infer it, we are obliged to say that thought has fulfilled its purpose when it has elaborated the given sensations into valid conceptions and generalizations and has produced such a world that objective happenings can be calculated and our behavior successfully carried out.

2

Thought must be recognized as a mechanism, as a machine, as a tool, as an instrument, in the service of life. The test of the correctness of a logical construct lies in practice. The purpose of thought must be sought, not in the reflection of a so-called objective world, but in rendering possible the calculation of events and of operations upon them.

The purpose of the psyche in logical procedures is to keep us in a position to deal with things so that, given certain conditions and relations, we may receive an exactly ascertainable sense impression; so that, by a certain impulse, we may produce an exactly ascertainable effect. Sensations are the starting point of all logical activity and the terminus to which they must run.

We lay most stress on practical corroboration, on the experimental test of the utility of the logical constructions produced by the psyche. It is not the correspondence with an assumed objective reality (never directly accessible to us); it is not the theoretical representation of an outer world in the mirror of the mind, which, in our view, guarantees that thought has fulfilled its purpose. It is the practical test: Is it possible, with the help of the psyche's products, to calculate events and to realize our impulses?

3

To attain the purpose of its activity — namely, to deal with events and render them dependent on our will — the psyche employs the most diverse means. It undertakes ingenious operations, invents brilliant expedients, introduces complicated processes. The raw material — sensations — is remodeled, recoined, compressed . . . we emphasize the utility of the psyche's procedures because we shall be dealing with logical constructions in which this purposiveness is strikingly manifested.

It must be remembered that the purpose of the world of ideas is not to portray reality — an utterly impossible task — but to provide us with an instrument for finding our way about more easily in this world. Subjective processes of thought represent the highest and ultimate result of organic development, and the world of ideas is the fine flower of the whole process; but, for that very reason it is not a copy of reality in the ordinary sense. Its purpose is the preservation and enrichment of life. It serves as an intermediary between living beings. It is an edifice, well calculated to fulfill such purposes. But to regard it as a copy of reality is to indulge in a hasty and unjustifiable comparison.

It would indeed be strange if these concepts were actually pictures of objective reality. We need only make clear to ourselves what this term *picture* or *copy* is supposed to mean, and to ask how a logical construct could be a copy of an event in the real world. These concepts are not copies of events. They are themselves events. The world as we conceive it is only a secondary or tertiary construction, arising in our heads. This conceptual world is not a picture of the real world, but an instrument for grasping, dealing with, understanding, that world. It is only an auxiliary construct formed by the psyche in order to take its bearings. This construction can be substituted for the actual world, and in practice we all do that. But it is not a picture; it is only a sign used to deal with reality, a logical expedient devised by the psyche to enable us to act in the real world.

4

There are methods employed in scientific procedure which, up till now, have not been duly considered in logical theory. I refer to methods employed less in the natural sciences than in the mathematical and social sciences, i.e., in the most exact and the least exact sciences. The methods to which I refer may be described as irregular. In logic, a veil of secrecy has been woven about them.

5

We may distinguish between rules and artifices of thought. Rules of any function are those operations in virtue of which it is able to attain its objective directly. Artifices, on the other hand, are those operations of a somewhat mysterious character which run counter to ordinary procedure in more or less paradoxical ways. They give an onlooker the impression of magic if he be not himself initiated. They are able to overcome, indirectly, the difficulties which beset the ordinary activities. Thought has such artifices. They are strikingly purposive expressions of the organic function of thought.

Among these artifices is one which is our special concern, namely, the fiction. Fictions are mental constructions, woven by the psyche itself. It introduces these hybrid and ambiguous thought structures in order to attain its purpose indirectly where the material which it encounters resists a direct procedure.

We shall try to give an especially typical example of every variety of fiction, and to use it to study the scheme of the construct and the methodology employed.

6

A standard example is the well-known assumption of Adam Smith, according to which all human actions are dictated by egoistic motives. Human actions are excessively complicated. They present insuperable obstacles when we try to understand them and reduce them to laws. This was Smith's problem. He realized that the main cause lay in egoism. He therefore formulated the assumption that all human actions, and particularly those of an economic nature, could be looked upon as if egoism were their sole motive. Thus all other factors were neglected. By means of this as-if he succeeded in bringing the whole of economics into an ordered system. He assumed the egoism, and then deduced from it the relations in trade and commerce which followed of necessity from that assumption.

Another typical example may be found in Thünen's fiction of an imaginary city. He introduced it into economics, at the beginning of the nineteenth century, in order to explain the relations between agriculture, transportation, etc. It was this: Grant an imaginary city. Around it, in concentric zones, are arranged the different spheres of activity from which the requirements of the city are drawn. By means of this ingenious artifice agricultural and economic laws are then systematically deduced. The fictions of an isolated man, an isolated state, etc., belong to the same group.

Another instructive example of the fictional method is offered by Bentham's treatment of the problems of political science. Bentham based his general theory of the state on the assumption that men act always from self-interest. In order, then, to work up the case for constitutionalism and parliamentarism, as necessary forms of government, he reasoned as follows: If men's actions are determined by selfish interests, then the only rulers who govern in the interests of the governed are those whose selfish interests coincide with those of the governed. The interests of the rulers are brought into harmony with the interests of the ruled only by responsibility, i.e., through the dependence of the rulers upon the will of the ruled. The wish on the part of rulers to retain power and the fear of losing it are the only motives which can inspire a policy in agreement with the interests of the ruled. From this Bentham deduced representative government, responsibility of ministers, frequent elections, and so forth.

Another remarkable example of the fictional method is to be found in Condillac's statue. In his *Treatise on Sensations* he sought to show that all beliefs and conceptions could be reduced to an origin in experience. To this end he imagines a statue, similar to a human being whose mind is as yet devoid of ideas. To admit and exclude impressions at will, this imaginary man is enclosed in a marble case which prevents him from using his sense organs. In this way Condillac is able to isolate those ideas which would result from each of the senses. He limits his statue to the sense of smell, and then, in succession, to hearing, taste, sight, and touch. He then combines the various senses by opening or closing the means of access to the statue. By this means he can show the contribution of each particular sense, trace the development of consciousness, attention, memory, judgment, imagination, abstraction, reflection, and so forth.

The term *fiction* is nowhere better known than in jurisprudence. In principle the juristic fiction is identical with such others as we have considered. It consists in submitting a single case under a construct not intended for it. The basis for this is as follows: Since laws cannot include all cases, certain special examples are treated as if they belonged under them. For instance, in a recent German commercial code we find a provision that goods not returned to the sender within a specified time are to be regarded as if the recipient had definitely authorized and accepted them. Again, it is assumed, in England, that a husband is the father of a child if it can be proved that he was in the country at the time of the child's conception. This, however, is rather a *praesumptio juris* than a genuine *fictio juris*. In England in the eighteenth century every crime could be treated as if it were directed personally at the king and every plaintiff had the right to bring action under this fiction. The Code Napoléon contains a number of legal fictions, e.g., that a woman's household goods are *immobilia*, that an *enfant concu* can under certain circumstances be regarded as an *enfant ne*, etc. Elsewhere we encounter such legal fictions as that the defendant who does not put in an appearance is regarded as if he admitted the charge; an adopted son is regarded as if he were a real son; an heir who is deemed unfit to inherit is regarded as if he had died before the testator; and so forth.

In these juristic fictions the formal behavior of the psyche is identical with what we have seen it to be in other fields. Practically, the importance is great; theoretically, there is a deviation from reality. Without such deviations thought cannot attain its purposes. It is just the deviation that in the end appears to be the natural procedure, and hence the need for emphasizing the fact.

7

One of the most important fictions ever formed by man is the idea of free will. Human actions are regarded as "free," and therefore responsible, in contrast with the "necessary" course of natural events. In spite of all the contradictions which this concept contains, we use it constantly in ordinary life in making judgments, and it is the foundation of criminal law. Our judgment of our fellow men is so bound up with this construct that we can no longer do without it. Only on this basis is a high degree of culture and morality and law possible. But this does not prevent us from realizing that it is itself a logical monstrosity, a contradiction, a fiction. There is nothing in the real world corresponding to the idea of free will, but in practice it is an exceedingly necessary fiction.

Ideals are working fictions, in contradiction with reality. True morality rests upon fictions. We must act as if duty were imposed by God, as if we would be judged by Him for our conduct, as if we would be punished for immorality, etc. But as soon as we transform these as-ifs into so many "becauses," morality loses its purely ethical character and becomes merely a matter of calculating our interests. Thus, before our very eyes does a small artifice of the psyche develop into a mighty source of all the idealistic belief and behavior of mankind.

The importance of our theory for practical philosophy is obvious. Fictions enter profoundly into our practical life. Indeed, they are necessary. They are a consequence of human imperfection. But all the nobler aspects of our life are based upon fictions. A pure ethics can only be established by the recognition of its fictional basis. How closely truth and illusion thus approach one another is apparent. What we call *truth* is really only the most expedient form of error. It is an error to suppose that an absolute truth, an absolute criterion of knowledge and behavior, can be discovered. The higher aspects of life are based upon noble delusions.

8

The fundamental conceptions of mathematics are all fictions. Thus, e.g., empty space, empty time, points without extension, lines without breadth, surfaces without depth, spaces without content, are all imaginary and fictional conceptions. Upon these as foundations the psyche has constructed the entire edifice of this amazing science. Mathematicians have occasionally realized that they were dealing with fictions, but seldom have they made this the subject of any profound study. Recognition of the fictional nature of its basic concepts is, however, essential for mathematical progress. The efforts made to conceal this fact have worn threadbare.

Another ingenious mathematical fiction is that of considering lines and surfaces as composed of elements of infinitely small extension. This fiction enables us, e.g., to subsume a curve under a straight line, to subsume an ellipse under a circle, and so forth.

The same applies to such mathematical notions as zero, negative numbers, fractions, irrational numbers, imaginary numbers, infinite series, and so forth. Their very names indicate that they are constructs. The history of mathematics is full of examples of the superstitious awe with which these number-constructs have been regarded.

9

In mechanics we are confronted with many fictions. For example, such concepts as the rigid bar, the Alpha body (the immovable central point of absolute space), the center of gravity, absolute space and time, absolute motion, *actio in distans*, and so on, are, all of them, imaginary constructs, useful in the elaboration of theoretical mechanics, but corresponding to nothing in reality.

One of the most important fictions is that notorious product of the imagination, the concept of "force." If two events are constantly conjoined, we call that peculiarity of the first event which consists in its being followed by the other event, its *force;* and we measure this force in terms of the magnitude of its effect. In reality, of course, only the sequence exists. The forces that objects are supposed to possess are nothing but a necessary consequence of succession. They are raised to the rank of real entities, placed as a permanent background, given a separate existence, all in contrast with the transitory events. What we call *force*, so far as it is thought of as the cause of motion or change is nothing but a disguised outlet for our tendency to personify.

Force is a fiction. It is nothing but a reduplication of the facts, namely, of the causal relations of succession. We interpolate this construct, and imagine we have added something. The assumption of forces that "determine" the sequence of phenomena in no way aids us in giving a theoretical explanation. As the critical, positive attitude develops, these abortive branches on the tree of knowledge wither and fall off.

All the specific forces are included here. Gravitational force, life force, sleeping force, and so on. Newton himself looked upon gravitation as a fiction. The phenomena which it correlated are, of course, real enough, but to attribute some gravitational force to them is simply a summary expression for the regularity of the correlations.

10

Such terms as *soul*, *psychic force*, *vital force*, *vis inertia*, *vis dormitiva*, etc., are names of fictions. The concept soul, for example, is a glaring fiction. We still use it. We still speak of a soul as if there were a separate, integral, simple entity, though we know there is no such reality.

What we call a *natural law* is a fiction. It is nothing but an expression for the totality of relations existing in a group of phenomena. It is a summational fiction. If by *law* we intend anything more than the regular sequence of events of which it is a summary, if we intend any "force" or "power" which determines the sequence, we are misleading ourselves by a typical fiction, comparable to abstractions and generalizations.

11

All abstractions are fictions. By an *abstraction* is meant a quality or property which, in reality, always belongs to some particular thing but may be considered in abstraction from that thing; e.g., goodness, color, smoothness, equality, etc. Abstractions get built into the language and conceal their fictional nature. We begin to apply adjectives to them, and add verbs. We say, "War destroys men." We speak of "deeds of fame," of "qualities of virtues, wisdom, justice," etc. We come thus to impart substance to what are merely abstractions. We speak of them as if they were realities existing independently of the objects with which they are always, in fact, connected. In themselves they are no more real than the square root of minus one.

All generalizations are fictions. Generalization is another favorite device of thought, closely connected with abstraction. Such words as *stone*, *plant*, *book*, *tree*, *ship* are names of general concepts, or generalizations, formed from particular instances. But the particular instance is alone real. No perception exists covering, e.g., the notion "tree." There is this tree and that tree, but not tree in general. These general concepts are psychical constructs, extracted by thought from the particulars of experience; pure fictions, for nothing real can be proved to exist corresponding to them in the external world. It would not be neccessary to waste words on this subject, were it not for the fact that in philosophy it has been held that there is something objective corresponding to these constructs.

12

Our view gains real importance and value primarily through its application to the favorite ideas of philosophers, e.g., the ideas of God, free will, immortality, thing-in-itself, the Absolute, and so on through a long list. These gain their true significance when they are denied significance for truth, i.e., considered as fictions. The real value of our inquiry lies in the rigorous application of the notion of fictions to certain popular thoughts and famous ideas.

The German theologian, Schleiermacher, and the school which followed him made use of fictions in their interpretation of Christianity. The actual relationship, e.g., between God and the world, and between God and men, they hold to be incomprehensible. Take the relationship between God and men. For Schleiermacher, the philosopher, this is completely unknowable. But by Schleiermacher, the theologian, it is conceived of as if it were the relation of father to son. God is not the father of men, but He is to be regarded and treated as if He were. By means of this as-if Schleiermacher held thousands of people to Christianity. Such an interpretation proved to be of tremendous importance for the practice of religion and worship. Schleiermacher himself was well aware of the artificial and artistic aspect of his method, although he did not describe it quite as bluntly as we do here.

Schleiermacher further argues that prayer is a meaningful act so long as it is interpreted as if God would hearken to it. It is clear, however, that the conception of praying to an omnipotent and omniscient God contains a contradiction, i.e., is a fiction. This quite apart from the contradiction involved by the idea of prayer in relation to natural laws.

The materialistic conception of the world is a necessary and useful fiction. It proceeds as if the external world did assuredly exist outside ourselves, and as if, even without us as subjects, things would be as they appear; although, in reality, all that we experience is merely our sensations which thus have validity only in relation to us as subjects. Not only does the world of color and sound exist merely through and in our sensations, but the world of touch also. The old truth that secondary qualities are merely relative has been extended to primary qualities also.

The idea of substance or thing is a fiction. We speak of things having qualities; e.g., we speak of this tree as having the quality of hardness, smoothness, a given size, shape, etc. Now what is the *thing* which has these qualities? It is absolutely equivalent to the indefinite series of those qualities. If the qualities were all removed, there would be no thing. A thing is merely the sum of the qualities. A thing in any other sense is a mere fiction, and when we say that a thing "has" certain qualities, we are making use of a fiction if thereby we intend something outside of and beyond the qualities.

13

We must discuss one other idea, the last and greatest fiction, namely the thing-in-itself, Kant's *Ding-an-sich*. From all that has preceded, it is clear what our attitude must be: that the thing-in-itself is a fiction. In the first edition of his *Critique of Pure Reason* Kant indeed, in one place, calls it a "mere idea," i.e., a fiction. It is a device by means of which the whole world of reality can be dealt with. It is an *x* to which a *y*, our ego, corresponds. By means of these two the real world of sensations is ordered and understood. In order to explain the world of ideas Kant assumes that the real world consists of things-in-themselves, mutually interacting. On the basis of this interacting he explained the genesis of sensations. We must remember, however, that Kant had the right to say only that we must regard real existence as if things-in-themselves existed, as if they influenced us and gave rise to our idea of the world. In that case the thing-in-itself was a necessary fiction since only thus can we imagine actual reality or think and speak of it at all.

The division of the world into things-in-themselves and egos, into objects and subjects, is the primary fiction upon which all others depend. From the standpoint of a critical positivism sensations alone are real, and out of these the whole subjective world is constructed with its division into physical and psychical complexes. A critical positivism asserts that any further claim is fictional. For it, only the observed sequence and coexistence of phenomena exist, and upon these alone it takes its stand. Any explanation going beyond this can do so only by the instrumentalities of fictions. A critical positivism is the only fictionless doctrine.

14

The treatment of all ideational constructs as mere products of the psyche was originally accomplished by Hume and Kant and continued by Schopenhauer. We go further in pointing out that they are, from a logical point of view, identical with scientific fictions, i.e., with constructs that are practically useful and necessary though theoretically false, deviations from reality. This point is implicit in Hume and Kant but is not stressed by them. The view here presented we call *critical positivism.*

15

Now that we have examined various fictions it will be useful to collect the terms which have been applied, more or less appropriately, to them. They are frequently referred to by terms simply translated from the Latin: *inventions*, *conceits*, *figments of the brain.*

phantasies, *imaginary ideas*, and so on. Other terms are derived from the fact that fictions are an aid to thought: *conceptual aids*, *auxiliary words*, *makeshifts*, and so on. Others, again, arise from the ingenious character of the process: *expedients*, *devices*, *artifices*, *artificial concepts*, *stratagems*, *dodges*, *contrivances*, *short cuts*, and so on. Some terms for fictions are derived from their functional nature: *instrumental ideas*, *intermediate ideas*, *bridges*, *props*, *ladders to thought*, *crutches*, *surrogates*, *substitutes*, *suppositions*, *scaffoldings*, and so on. We also find: *chimeras*, *distorted concepts*, *auxiliary methods*, *play*, *idea*, *schema*, *deceptive idea*, *provisional concept*, *heuristic idea*, *regulative concept*, *modus dicendi*, *mere idea*, *interim idea*, *limiting concept*, *theoretical concept*, *provisional assumption*, and so on.

What is a *fiction?* What is an *as-if?* In the *if* lies the assumption of an unreal or impossible case. For example, "*If* there were infinitesimals, then the curved line could be treated as made up of them"; or, "*If* there were ultimate discrete particles, then matter could be treated as made up of them"; or, "*If* egotism were the only motive, then we ought to be able to deduce social relations from it." In the if clause something unreal or impossible is assumed. From this unreality or impossibility inferences are drawn.

16

We can now indicate the general characteristics of fictions. It is well to begin by distinguishing between semifictions and genuine fictions. The former is illustrated, e.g., in Adam Smith's assumption that all human action is selfishly motivated; the latter is illustrated, e.g., in the notion that the circumference of a circle is composed of an infinite number of infinitely short straight lines, or in Kant's notion of a thing-in-itself nowhere revealed to experience but conditioning experience. Bearing these cases in mind we can proceed to note four main characteristics of fictions.

1. The first is their deviation from reality. In the case of semifictions this deviation is partial; that is, they partially contradict reality. Thus, recurring to Adam Smith, some human action is selfishly motivated, and some is not. In the case of genuine fictions this deviation is complete; that is, they completely contradict reality. And, furthermore, they possess the added characteristic

that they contain a self-contradiction. This discloses itself, e.g., in the antinomies to which they give rise.

2. A second main characteristic is that they disappear in the course of history or through the operation of logic. The former holds for semifictions, the latter for genuine fictions. Those which partially contradict reality have value only if they are used provisionally until experience has become richer or methods of thought more refined and definitive. Those which completely contradict reality, and themselves contain a self-contradiction, are allowed for, when recognized for what they are, because our aim is to obtain noncontradictory results.

3. The third main feature of a fiction is the awareness accompanying its use that it is just a fiction. This holds only of normal fictions; or rather, of fictions normally held. In the history of the sciences this is frequently not the case. The first authors of a fiction are not themselves clear whether they have a fiction or an hypothesis on their hands. The realization of its fictional nature develops later.

4. The fourth characteristic of a fiction is that it is a means to a definite end, that it is expedient, or useful, not to say necessary. Where there is no such utility the fiction is unscientific, i.e., merely aesthetic. That fictions in scientific thought have this character of utility is the kernel of our position, and distinguishes it fundamentally from previous positions, e.g., Hume's or (to a less extent) Kant's. The essential element in a scientific fiction is not the mere fact of its being a conscious deviation from reality; it is that it is a useful or necessary deviation.

These four characteristics suffice to distinguish fictions from hypotheses. With them as "warrant," every fiction can be at once recognized and examined. If a survey of the whole field of science were made today, many fictions which we have not mentioned would certainly be discovered.

17

Fictions are very useful for scientific thought. It is quite wrong to reject these concepts as useless as soon as their objective impossibility has been recognized. This shows the very prejudice which dominates philosophy today; namely, that because a construct is logically contradictory, it is therefore of no value. Precisely the contrary is true. These contradictory concepts are the most valuable.

As we have seen, many of the fundamental ideas with which science operates are fictions. The problem is not how to do away with these contradictions — that would be futile — but to show that they are of utility and advantage to thought. It is an error to imagine that only what is logically noncontradictory is logically fruitful. Such an attitude, if consistently adhered to, would bring us to the conclusion that all science is valueless, since so many of the fundamental concepts are contradictory.

Our position must be sharply distinguished from this. It is, of course, true that many fundamental scientific concepts are fictional and contradictory and do not "reflect" the world of reality. But this in no way renders them valueless. They are psychical constructs which not only give rise to the illusion that the world is being comprehended but also enable us to orient ourselves in the realm of the actual.

18

It is because our conceptual world is itself a product of the real world that it cannot be a reflection of the real world. On the other hand, it can serve as an instrument within reality by means of which we can move about. It is a symbol by means of which we orient ourselves. It is in the interests of science to make this symbol more and more adequate and useful, but a symbol it will always remain.

There is no reply to the argument that the conceptual world cannot be identical with the real world because it is a product of the real world. There is no identity of thought and reality. The "world" which the psyche constructs is merely an instrument, and for that reason, the world of ideas is not the ultimate goal of thought. The ultimate purpose of thought is not thought itself, but behavior and ultimately ethical behavior. The real world, symbolized in the form of a world of ideas, is the means thereto. The world is the material of ethical behavior.

The true and final purpose of thought is action and the facilitation of action. Looked at from this point of view the world of ideas, taken as a whole, is simply a means, and its constituent elements are also merely a means. What we have in it is a system of expedients of thought which mutually help and support one another. It is just an extremely sensitive machine constructed by the psyche. It is related to a prescientific world of ideas as a modern hammer to a prehistoric stone hammer. Both are instruments and, though very different as regards delicacy and elegance, are yet identical in kind. They are instruments, products of the psyche, of the logical instinct.

The conceptual world, the world of ideas, lies between the two poles of sensation and motion, perception and action. The psyche continually adds new members between these two poles. The delicacy and elaboration of its interpolations develop with the growth of the nerve mass and the increasing isolation of the brain from the spine.

The conceptual world, the world of ideas, lies between the sensory and the motor nerves, an intermediate world, serving merely to make the interconnection between them richer and easier, more delicate and more serviceable. Science is concerned with the elaboration of this intermediate world, and with the adjustment of this instrument to the objective relations of sequence and coexistence which make themselves perceptible. But when science goes further, making of this instrument an end in itself, when it is no longer concerned merely with the perfecting of the instrument, it is to be regarded as a luxury and a passion.

It is a pardonable weakness in science to believe that its ideas are concerned with reality itself. It deals with reality only to the extent of detecting the inevitable sequence and coexistences. But the concepts, the ideas, which encompass and embrace reality are of a fictional nature, the additions of man, forming merely the frame in which man encloses the reality in order that he may thus manipulate it better.

It is this attitude alone which can free us from the pressure of the logical contradictions so constantly concealed in the basic principles of science. It is not these which really matter, for they are but a means. The psyche creates more and more delicate means of encompassing and dealing with reality. It is an error to confuse the means, the instrument, with what the instrument was created to deal with

19

The psyche is not merely a receptacle into which foreign matter is poured. It may be compared to a machine with a chemical retort which uses foreign matter most fittingly for its own maintenance. Just as the physical organism breaks up the matter which it receives, mixes it with its own juices, so the psyche envelops the thing perceived with categories. As soon as an external stimulus reaches the psyche, it responds as though provided with delicate feelers; inner processes start, the outcome of which is the appropriation of the things perceived for some purpose.

Vaihinger has some interesting defensive comments to make on his own position. They are cited hereunder:

1. The term *skepticism* has occasionally been applied to the philosophy of as-if and its systematic doctrines. This is not a correct description. Skepticism implies a theory which raises doubting or questioning to the dignity of a principle. The as-if philosophy has never had a trace of this attitude. It claims that consciously false conceptions and judgments are applied in all sciences, and it shows that these scientific fictions are to be distinguished from hypotheses. Hypotheses are assumptions which are probable, assumptions the truth of which can be proved by further experience. They are therefore verifiable. Fictions are never verifiable, because they are assumptions which are known to be false but which are employed because of their utility. When a series of assumptions in mathematics, mechanics, physics, chemistry, ethics, or the philosophy of religion are shown in this way to be useful fictions, and so to justify themselves, this does not imply skepticism. The application of the term *skepticism* to the as-if philosophy has been made, partly, no doubt, because of the doubt with which this philosophy treats God and immortality. But, as in the case of the sciences, the above consideration applies here also. The as-if philosophy does not deny that these conceptions are fictions of ethical value.

2. Many people think they can discover not exactly skepticism

but agnosticism in the as-if philosophy. Agnosticism is the belief that human knowledge is confined within more or less narrow limits. It speaks of the Unintelligible, the Unknowable. Now, the as-if philosophy holds that knowledge has certain limits, but not in the sense that these limits bound only human knowledge but do not bound a superhuman knowledge. My opinion is that the limitations are not implicit in the specific nature of man (as compared with possible minds of a higher order) but are part of the nature of thought itself. If there are higher forms of mind, these limitations will affect them, and even the highest mind of all. For thought originally only serves the will to life as a means to an end. But when, according to the law of the preponderance of the means over the end, thought has broken loose from its original aim and has become an end in itself it sets itself problems to which it is not equal because it has not developed for this purpose, for example, such problems as the origin of the world, the formation of matter, the beginning of motion, the meaning of the world, the purpose of life, etc. If thought is regarded as a biological function, it is obvious that these are impossible problems for thought to solve, and quite beyond the natural boundaries which limit thought as such. I have no inclination to fall back on the old grievance about the limitations of human knowledge. At most, we may complain that the law of the preponderance of the means over the end has led us to ask questions that are unanswerable.

3. In the same way we can dispose of another objection which is raised against the as-if philosophy, namely that the concept of reality implied in it is not uniform. On the one hand all reality is reduced to sensations; on the other hand, to the motion of matter and the smallest constituents of matter. The question is how to unify these two notions of reality. The criticism is that the as-if philosophy does nothing to effect this union.

I am going to ask a question in return. Has *any* philosophical system ever succeeded in bringing these two spheres into a rational relation? The answer is that they have never been brought into a logically satisfactory relation by any philosopher. They never will be brought into a definitely unified association by any rational formula. We stand here at a point where an impossible problem confronts our reason. This question is just as impossible of solution by rational methods as the question of the purpose of existence. Although we, who ask this question, unite in our nature these two halves of reality, our mind is not in a position to answer it satisfactorily. He who would criticize *any* system of philosophy for not answering this question, is in the same intellectual position as a man who would reproach a mathematician for not solving the problem of squaring the circle, or an engineer for not solving the problem of a perpetual-motion machine.

Naturally, the human mind is tormented by this insoluble contradiction between the world of motion and the world of consciousness, and this torment can eventually become very oppressive. One would be well advised to remember that Kant had already pointed out that there are problems which mock us perpetually, but which we cannot get rid of. But there is one solution of this and similar torturing questions, for in intuition and in experience all this contradiction and distress fade into nothingness. Experience and intuition are higher than human reason. When I see a deer feeding in the forest, when I see a child at play, when I see a man at work or sport, but above all when I am myself working or playing, where are the problems with which my mind has been torturing itself? We do not understand the world when we are pondering over its problems, but when we are doing the world's work.

Reading References. Books and articles expounding the ideas of Hans Vaihinger are few in number, unless one is prepared to read them in German. The translation of the treatise itself, and a chapter in a book by Havelock Ellis, are all that this author has encountered: Hans Vaihinger, *The Philosophy of As-If*. Havelock Ellis, "The Art of Thinking," in *The Dance of Life*.

READING QUESTIONS

1. What is the relation between Kant and Vaihinger?
2. What does he say in favor of Schopenhauer's pessimism?
3. What in favor of Schopenhauer's irrationalism?

4. In what way did he find that Darwin corroborated Schopenhauer?
5. What notion has "grown within me, and has crystallized into an ever-clearer form"?
6. What did he learn from Adolf Horwicz?
7. Why did he call his book *The Philosophy of As-If*?
8. "Scientific thought is a function of the psyche." In what sense?
9. "Thought must be recognized as an instrument." In what sense?
10. "The purpose of the world of ideas is not to portray reality." Why not? What then?
11. About what has "a veil of secrecy been woven"?
12. What is the distinction between a rule and an artifice of thought?
13. How would you define a *fiction*?
14. Cite an example in economic thought from Adam Smith.
15. In political science from Bentham.
16. In psychology from Condillac.
17. In juristic thought.
18. In what sense is the idea of free will a fiction?
19. Why does he describe it as "one of the most important fictions ever formed by man"?
20. "True morality rests upon fictions." Explain.
21. Cite an example of a fiction in mathematical thought.
22. In mechanics.
23. "What we call a *natural law* is a fiction." In what sense?
24. "All abstractions . . . all generalizations are fictions." Explain.
25. Cite an example of a fiction in religious thought from Schleiermacher.
26. "The materialistic conception of the world is a fiction." How so?
27. "The last and greatest fiction, Kant's thing-in-itself." Elucidate.
28. What does he mean by *critical positivism*?
29. What are some synonyms for the term *fiction*?
30. Distinguish between a semifiction and a genuine fiction.

31. What are the four main characteristics of fictions?
32. Distinguish between a fiction and an hypothesis.
33. Why does he repudiate the term *skepticism* as applied to his position?
34. Why *agnosticism*?
35. What criticism does he say is made of his conception of reality?
36. How does he parry this criticism?
37. "There is one solution of this and similar torturing questions." What is this question? Wherein is it torturing? What are similar questions? What is the solution?

TOPIC FOUR. AN ETHICAL PROBLEM

THE PROBLEM STATED

Ethics may be defined as an inquiry into the principles and problems of morality. It covers a wide field. From this total field, we shall select one problem and, as before, approach it through the writings of five modern philosophers. The problem proposed is this: Upon what principle do we discriminate between right and wrong? This principle, once formulated, we shall refer to as "the principle of morality," or as "the moral principle."

The notion of a principle of morality is one which we use every time we pass a moral judgment on conduct, on character, on institutions, on laws, on customs. We say, of a given act, that it is right or wrong; of a type of character, that it is the right type or the wrong type; of an institution, for example, private property, that it is right or wrong; of a law, say, capital punishment, that it is right or wrong; of a custom, that it is right or wrong. Our present problem is not which particular act, or character, or institution, or law, or custom is right or wrong. Our problem is the more general one: On what principle do we judge these things right or wrong?

The sets of citations which follow present five different approaches to this question. The first set, drawn from the writings of a celebrated eighteenth-century moralist, William Paley, argues that *right* means "according to the will of God." This way of grounding morality in theology is something with which we are all familiar. Paley's statement is therefore valuable as a starting point. His argment is clear and concise.

The second set of citations, drawn from the writings of Immanuel Kant, argues that *right* means "according to reason," or "what reason prescribes." Kant wrote in the Age of Reason which produced such characteristic figures as Voltaire, Rousseau, Thomas Paine, and others. His attempt to ground morality on an appeal to reason, with no reference to theological doctrine, represents one of the perennial possibilities open to the human mind. In any age which understands by *reason* what Kant intended by that term, his appeal would be instant and profound.

The third set of citations, drawn from the writings of John Stuart Mill, argues that *right* means "producing human happiness." Mill was the moralist *par excellence* of the age of the Industrial Revolution. The position in moral philosophy which he occupies was inspired by his experience of great and far-reaching changes in the social order, widespread wealth and poverty, the rise of nineteenth-century democratic governments, the emergence of new economic classes, and the rapid decay of old customs and institutions. It is in this context that we must understand his somewhat abrupt and impatient dismissal of the moral philosophies typified by Paley and Kant, and his forthright appeal to happiness as the foundation principle of human morality.

In the fourth set of citations, Friedrich Nietzsche argues that *right* means "productive of or giving expression to the superman." The notion that man has evolved from lower animals suggested at once that something higher may evolve from man. This, when it comes, will be the superman, and in this appeal to the struggle for existence, anything is right which either hastens his arrival or expresses his nature when arrived.

The fifth and last set of citations, drawn from the writings of William James, presents a curious return to the position argued for by Paley, namely, that the whole duty of man is summed up in the phrase "to know the will of God and keep it."

There are other philosophical problems in the field of ethical analysis and speculation, besides the one which is here traced from Paley's appeal to the will of God to James's appeal to the same, but this problem is central. The rest of one's moral philosophy, once this question has been settled, is largely a series of deductions from or applications of the principle adopted as fundamental.

1. MORALITY GROUNDED IN THEOLOGY — FROM WILLIAM PALEY

One of the most important questions we can direct at any human act, is this: "Was it right or wrong? Did the agent do as he ought to have done, or as he ought not to have done?" Implicit in any answer to this question is a moral principle; that is, a criterion in terms of which we distinguish between right and wrong. As long as men entertain a lively belief in the existence of God, and ascribe to Him an interest in human affairs, many are likely to base their moral judgments upon what they consider to be His will. They are going to say that *right* means "according to the will of God," and *wrong* means "contrary to the will of God." William Paley, one of the most popular and widely read moralists in the eighteenth century, was a man of precisely this turn of mind. One cannot do better than examine the essentials of the appeal to theology as these are to be found in his writings. Any virtues which reside in this view will be obvious in the simplicity and sincerity of his language. Any shortcomings can be the more readily pointed out, since his stand is clear and bold. The following passage by Sir Leslie Stephen in his *History of English Thought in the*

Eighteenth Century is worth reading before proceeding to Paley's biography and philosophy. Says Sir Leslie:

The different religions of the world tell us, each in its own fashion, what is the plan and meaning of this universe. Thence believers may infer what is the best method of employing our brief existence within it. We ought to be good, say all moralists, and the question remains: What is meant by *ought* and by *goodness?* Theology, so long as it was a vital belief in the world, afforded a complete and satisfactory answer to these questions. Morality was, of necessity, its handmaid. Believe in an active ruler of the universe, who reveals his will to men, who distributes rewards and punishments to the good and the evil, and we have a plain answer to most of the problems of morality. God's will, so far as known to us, determines what is good. We are obliged to be good, whether from love or from fear.

Biographical Note. William Paley was born in England in 1743 and died in 1805 at the age of sixty-two. His father was headmaster of the school of Giggleswick in Yorkshire. His early education was obtained under the paternal eye. At the age of fifteen, young Paley went to the University of Cambridge. That his father had great expectations may be gathered from a remark he made to a friend: "My son is now gone to college. He'll turn out a great man. Very great, indeed. I am certain of it. He has by far the clearest head I ever met in my life." Paley spent four years at Cambridge, obtaining his B.A. in 1762. The following anecdote suggests that he was a very normal young man during these years:

I spent the first two years of my undergraduate life happily, but unprofitably. I was constantly in society, where we were not immoral, but idle and rather expensive. At the commencement of my third year, however, after having left the usual party at a rather late hour in the evening, I was awakened at five in the morning by one of my companions, who stood at my bedside. He said: "Paley,

I have been thinking what a fool you are. I could achieve nothing worth while, even were I to try, and anyway I can afford the idle life I lead. You could achieve anything, if you were to try, and you cannot afford to waste your time. I have had no sleep during the whole night on account of these reflections, and am now come solemnly to inform you that if you persist in your indolence, I must renounce your society." I was so struck with the visit and the visitor that I laid in bed a great part of the day, and formed my plan. I ordered my bedmaker to prepare my fire every evening, in order that it might be lighted by myself the next morning. I rose at five o'clock, read during the whole of the day, except such hours as chapel and lectures required, allotting to each portion of time its peculiar branch of study; and, just before the closing of the gates (9:00 P.M.) I went to a neighboring coffeehouse, where I constantly regaled upon a mutton chop and a dose of milk punch.

After graduating, Paley rose slowly but steadily in the ecclesiastical world. In 1785 he published his *Principles of Moral and Political Philosophy*, from which the citations below have been drawn. It passed through fifteen editions during his own lifetime. One of his contemporaries remarked of this book: "It may be said to be the only work on moral philosophy fitted to be understood by every class of readers." With his other writings, equally popular, we are not concerned.

THE ARGUMENT OF THE CITATIONS. Paley's presentation of the fundamental principle of morality is simple and clear: Right is that which agrees with the will of God; wrong is that which does not. Having stated this controlling idea, he sets himself to elaborate it. He provides first a definition of *virtue*, consistent with his basic proposition; he moves on, then, to examine the meaning of moral obligation and the distinction between prudence and duty. These matters settled, he turns to the question: if *right* means "according to the will of God," how are we to tell what is and is not the will of God? His answer here is twofold: scriptural revelation and the "light of nature." The sense in which God's will may be gathered from Scripture is then explained. But what of the light of nature; what, that is, about the morality of acts where we do not have God's express declaration? Here Paley meets a real problem, and knowing, as he did, that many occasions arise with respect to which Scripture is silent, he could not treat this matter lightly. To solve his problem he adopts the assumption that human happiness is God's primary concern. Realizing, as he says, that "this assumption is the foundation of the whole system," he sets himself to "explain the reasons upon which it rests." The explanation in question occupies the remainder of the citations. The following quotation from a seventeenth-century moralist expresses so clearly the idea which Paley proposes to develop that I give it as a kind of foreword:

That God has given a rule whereby men should govern themselves, I think there is no one so brutish as to deny. He has a right to do it. We are His creatures. He has goodness and wisdom to direct our actions to what is best, and He has power to enforce it by rewards and punishments of infinite weight and duration in another life; for nobody can take us out of His hands. This is the only touchstone of moral rectitude, and by comparing them to this law, it is that men judge of the most considerable moral good or evil of their actions; that is, whether as duty or as sins, they are like to procure them happiness or misery from the hands of the Almighty.

Now Paley. First, as to ethics in general:

Ethics is that science which teaches men their duty and the reasons of it. The use of such a study depends upon this, that, without it, the rules of life by which men are ordinarily governed, oftentimes mislead them, through a defect in either the rule or in the application.

Then, as to the meaning of *right:*

Right signifies being consistent with the will of God.

Right is a quality of persons or of actions. Of persons, as when we say, "He has a right to his property"; of actions, as when we say, "His action was right on that occasion." Whether of persons or of actions, *right* means "consistent with, or according to, the will of God." In the one case, substituting the definition for the term, you may say, "It is consistent with or according to the will of God that he have his property"; in the other case, "His action, on that occasion, was consistent with or according to the will of God."

From this it follows that:

Virtue is doing good to mankind, in obedience to the will of God, and for the sake of everlasting happiness.

The division of virtues to which we are nowadays most accustomed is into duties: duties toward God; duties toward other men; duties toward ourselves. There are more of these distinctions, but it is not worth while to set them down.

And we are now in a position to explain what is meant by *duty* or *moral obligation*.

What are we to understand by *moral obligation?* Truthfulness, we say, is a moral obligation. What do we intend by this expression? Why am I obliged to keep my word?

When I first turned my thoughts to moral speculations, an air of mystery seemed to hang over the whole subject. This arose, I believe, from hence — that I supposed that to be obliged to do a thing was very different from being induced or urged to do it; that the obligation to practice virtue, for example, was quite another thing, and of another kind, than the obligation which a soldier is under to obey his officer, or a servant his master. Now in what does the difference consist?

I shall argue to the following effect: A man is said to be *obliged* when he is urged by a violent motive resulting from the command of another. First, the motive must be violent, strong, powerful. A person has done me some little service. Suppose, then, he asks me for my vote. From a motive of gratitude, or expectation, I may give it to him. But I should hardly say I was obliged to give it to him; because the motive, or incentive, or inducement, does not rise high enough. Second, it must result from the command of another.

Offer a man a gratuity for doing anything. He is not obliged by your offer to do it. But if a magistrate were to command it, he would then consider himself obliged to do it.

Wherever, then, the motive is violent enough and is coupled with the idea of a command, an authority, a law, a will, there, I take it, we always reckon ourselves to be obliged. Let it be remembered that to be obliged is to be urged by a violent motive resulting from the command of another.

And then let it be asked: Why am I "obliged" to keep my word? The answer will be: Because I am urged by the expectation of being rewarded after this life if I do, and punished if I do not, follow, in this respect, the command of God. This solution goes to the bottom of the subject, as no further question can reasonably be asked.

There is always understood to be a difference between an act of prudence and an act of duty. Thus, if I distrusted a man who owed me money, I should reckon it an act of prudence to get another bound with him; but I should hardly call it an act of duty. On the other hand, it would be a loose kind of language to say that, as my friend had placed a box of jewels in my hands when he went abroad, it would be prudent of me to preserve it for him until he returned.

Now, wherein does the difference consist? The difference, and the only difference, is this, that, in the one case, we consider what we shall gain or lose in the present world; in the other case, we consider also what we shall gain or lose in the world to come. Prudence has regard to the former; duty, to the latter. Those who would establish a system of morality, independent of a future state, must look out for some different idea of moral obligation.

To us, therefore, there are two great questions: Will there be, after this life, any distribution of rewards and punishments at all? If so, what actions will be rewarded and what actions will be punished? The first question comprises the credibility of the Christian religion. Proof of an affirmative answer to it, although we confess that it is the foundation upon which the whole fabric rests, must in this treatise be taken for granted. The second question comprises morality itself, and to this we shall now address ourselves.

By now the fundamental role of the will of God in Paley's moral philosophy should be clear. From it proceed all the principal terms in such a moralist's vocabulary. The question hence, begins to press: How do we determine what is and is not the will of God?

As the will of God is our rule, to inquire, in any instance, what is our duty or what we are obliged to do, is, in effect, to inquire what is the will of God in that instance. This consequently becomes the whole business of morality.

Now, there are two methods of coming at the will of God on any point: by his express declarations, when they are to be had, and which must be sought for in Scripture; by what we can discover of his designs and disposition from his works, or, as we usually call it, the light of nature. The object of both is the same — to discover the will of God; and, provided we do but discover it, it matters nothing by what means.

An ambassador may guide himself in many cases with safety by judging only from what he knows of his sovereign's disposition, by arguing from what he has observed of his conduct or what he knows of his designs. But if he have his commission and instructions in his pocket, it would be strange never to look into them. He will, naturally, conduct himself by both rules. When his instructions are clear and positive, there is an end of all further deliberation, unless, indeed, he suspect their authenticity. Where his instructions are silent or dubious, he will endeavor to supply or explain them by what he has been able to collect from other quarters of his master's general inclination or intentions.

Whoever expects to find in the Scriptures particular directions for every moral doubt that arises looks for more than he will meet with. Such a detail of particular precepts would have so enlarged the sacred volume that it would have been too bulky either to be read or circulated; or rather, as St. John says, "even the world itself could not contain the books that should be written."

Morality is taught in the Scriptures in this wise: General rules are laid down, of piety, justice, benevolence, and purity. Several of these rules are occasionally illustrated, either in fictitious examples, as in the parable of the good Samaritan; or in instances which actually presented themselves, as in Christ's reproof of his disciples or his praise of the poor widow; or, in the resolution of questions proposed to Christ, as in his answer to the young man who asked him, "What lack I yet?"

This is the way in which all practical sciences are taught, as arithmetic, grammar, navigation, and the like. Rules are laid down, and examples are subjoined, by way of explaining the principle of the rule, and as so many specimens of the method of applying it.

So far, so good. By reference to the will of God we determine what is right and wrong. By reference to Scripture we determine, in part, what is the will of God. But what of that part which is not provided for by Scripture?

The method of coming at the will of God concerning any action, where we do not have his express declaration, is to inquire into the tendency of the action to promote or diminish the general happiness. This rule proceeds on the assumption that God Almighty wills and wishes the happiness of His creatures, and, consequently, that those actions which promote that will and wish must be agreeable to Him; and the contrary.

As this assumption is the foundation of the whole system, it becomes necessary to explain the reasons upon which it rests.

When God created the human species, either He wished their happiness or He wished their misery or He was indifferent to both.

If He wished their misery, He might have made sure of His purpose, e.g., by forming our senses to be as many sores and pains to us as they are now instruments of gratification and enjoyment. He might, e.g., have made everything we tasted, bitter; everything we saw, loathsome; everything we touched, a sting; every smell, a stench; every sound, a discord.

If He had been indifferent to our happiness or misery, we must impute to our good fortune both the capacity of our senses to receive pleasure and the supply of external objects fitted to excite it. But either of these — and still more both of them — is too much to be attributed to accident, i.e., mere "good fortune." Nothing remains, therefore, than the first supposition; namely, that when God created the human species, He intended their happiness.

The same argument may be proposed in different terms, thus: The world abounds in contrivances, and all the contrivances with which we are acquainted are directed to beneficial purposes. Evil, no doubt, exists. But it is never, that we can perceive, the object of contrivance. Teeth are contrived to eat, not to ache. Their aching now and then is incidental to the contrivance, perhaps inseparable from it, perhaps even a defect in it; but it is not the object of it.

This is a distinction which well deserves to be attended to. In describing implements of husbandry, you would hardly say of a sickle that it is made to cut the reaper's fingers, though from the construction of the instrument, and the manner of using it, this mischief often happens.

On the other hand, if you had occasion to describe instruments of torture, the case would be different. This, you would say, is to stretch the sinews; this, to dislocate the joints; this, to break the bones; this, to scorch the soles of the feet; and so forth. Here pain and misery are the very objects of the contrivance.

Now, nothing of this sort is to be found in nature. We never discover a contrivance whose object is to bring about pain and misery. No anatomist ever discovered anything in the organism calculated to produce pain and disease. No anatomist, in explaining the parts of the human body, ever said, "This is to irritate, this is to inflame, this is to conduct stones to the kidneys, this is to secrete the humor which forms gout." The most he will say is that he does not understand some part or other, or that it is useless. He never suspects that it is put there to incommode, to annoy, to torment.

Since, then, God hath called forth His consummate wisdom to contrive and provide for our happiness, and the world appears to have been constituted with this design at first, then, so long as this constitution is upheld by Him, we must suppose the same design to continue.

We conclude, therefore, that God wills and wishes the happiness of His creatures. This conclusion being once established, we are at liberty to go on with the rule built upon it, namely, that the method of coming at the will of God concerning any action, where we do not have his express declaration, is to inquire into the tendency of that action to promote or diminish the general happiness.

By virtue of the two principles, that God wills the happiness of His creatures, and that God's will is the measure of right and wrong, we arrive at certain conclusions. These conclusions become rules. And soon we learn to pronounce actions right or wrong according as they agree or disagree with our rules, without looking any further.

Paley, in moral philosophy, like St. Thomas in natural theology and Descartes in metaphysics, starts from premises and arrives at conclusions that have an old and familiar ring. Like St. Thomas and Descartes, too, Paley is of interest for the difficulties which his position suggests. Stated very briefly, what he says comes to this: "*Right* means according to God's will. God's will is to be found in the Scriptures, or discovered by the light of nature. The light of nature tells us that God intends above all to produce and promote human happiness. Where, therefore, the Scriptures are silent, we determine the rightness of an act by the fact that it produces more happiness than any other act possible at the time." This is both clear and confused. It really raises more questions than it settles. For example, does Paley mean that an act is right because it agrees with God's will, or that it agrees with God's will because it is right? These two are not the same. Then, of course, there is the problem connected with detecting God's will in the Scriptures. Why the Scriptures? Why not in Plato's dialogues? Or in the Mohammedan *Koran*? In which parts of the Scriptures? In those parts which enjoin an eye for an eye? Or in those parts which enjoin the golden rule? If in both, what about clashes? If in one, how choose which? Passing to the second half of his argument, has he proved, at all conclusively, that God's will is directed to creating and promoting human happiness? This hypothesis may account for some of the facts. But it does not account for all of them. See Hume and Schopenhauer on the misery of man's estate. Going a step further, and admitting his argument, are we justified in arguing that an act is right, if and only if, it produces more happiness than any other act possible under the circumstances? Is this not to formulate a moral principle that swings clear of the first part of Paley's argument, and could stand on its own feet, without any aid from Scripture? If so, what about cases where the "appeal to Scripture" and "the appeal to happiness" appear to clash? Finally is it or is it not the case that we are more sure of what is right and wrong than we are of God's very existence? If so, would it not be wiser to begin with what we are more sure of, than to begin with what we are less sure of? These, and other problems which suggest themselves, were engaging the attention of Immanuel Kant during the years in which Paley was writing his *Principles of Moral and Political Philosophy*. Paley published in 1785. Kant had published his *Critique of Pure Reason* in 1781, and was meanwhile engaged on a second *Critique*, directed, this time, not at the problem of knowledge but at the problem of morality. From this prosperous and rather worldly Anglican divine one turns with something like eagerness to the austere and searching professorial moralist at Königsberg.

READING REFERENCES. None are suggested.

READING QUESTIONS

1. What do you understand by the principle of morality?
2. Cn what sorts of things do we pass moral judgments?
3. In one sentence devoted to each, contrast the positions of Paley, Kant, Mill.
4. In what sense, according to Stephen, is morality the handmaid of religion?
5. Upon what does the use of the study of ethics depend, according to Paley?

6. In what two senses does he use the term *right?*
7. How does he define the term?
8. What "air of mystery seemed to hang over the whole subject" of moral obligation?
9. When is a man "obliged" to do something?
10. What solution goes to the bottom of what subject?
11. Wherein lies the distinction between prudence and duty?
12. Wherefore are there two great questions? What are these questions?
13. "There are two methods for coming at the will of God on any point." Namely?
14. What is the point of the ambassador analogy?
15. In what way is morality taught in the Scriptures?
16. Suppose we do not have the express declaration of God's will in the Scriptures?
17. What "rule" proceeds on what "assumption"?
18. In what sense is "this assumption the foundation of the whole system"?
19. What criticism does he make of the hypothesis "When God created the human species, He wished their misery"?
20. Of the hypothesis that God was indifferent?
21. "The same argument may be proposed in different terms." Namely?
22. Formulate one or more criticisms of Paley's position.

2. *MORALITY GROUNDED IN DUTY — FROM IMMANUEL KANT*

From Paley to Kant. While Paley was engaged in arguing that morality has its roots in theology, Immanuel Kant was engaged in showing that such is not the case. Paley, it will be remembered, published in 1785. Kant, who had been developing his views in lecture form since 1775, published in 1785 and again, at greater length, in 1788. The efforts made by these two moralists to formulate the principle of morality provide an excellent starting point for the study of modern analysis and speculation in these matters.

Kant lived in the Age of Reason, the age of Hume and

Rousseau and Voltaire and the revolutions in America and France. He is a firm believer in the rationality of man. He seeks to develop the notion of a rational morality, as opposed to a theological morality. He works with the conception of man as essentially a rational animal. By *rational* as applied to man I understand him to mean two things: having (1) the power to discover what is the case, and to guide conduct by such knowledge, i.e., to develop pure and applied sciences; (2) the power to discover what ought to be the case, and to guide conduct by such knowledge, i.e., to develop a moral philosophy and a morality. Just as he could speak of rational science, so he would speak of rational conduct or rational morality. Just as, by *rational science* he would mean knowledge valid and binding for all rational minds, so by *rational morality* he would mean morality valid and binding for all rational minds. To the first kind of rationality he devoted his *Critique of Pure Reason;* to the second, his *Critique of Practical Reason.*

Biographical Note. At the end of the biographical note on Kant in the previous topic, page 220, we left him finishing his *Critique of Pure Reason* and publishing it in 1781. This treatise was the first of three, all directed to the analysis and exploration of a single theme, namely, mind and its place in nature. The first critique dealt with mind and the world order; the second is to deal with mind and the moral order; the third with mind and the aesthetic order. In other words, the relation of mind to the true, the good, and the beautiful; or to science, morality, and art. The elaboration of the ideas contained in these three studies brought Kant to a ripe old age, crowned with honors and influence. He became, and remains, one of the great formative thinkers in the history of the modern mind.

The Argument of the Citations. Kant's handling of the problem of morality follows from his conception of what morality is. Without a firm grip of this, one is likely to miss the point of his analysis. For that reason, it is necessary to emphasize his starting point. He begins by assuming that morality, whatever it may be in detail, is something which is universally binding on all rational minds, comparable, in this respect, to science. Thus, if it is true that two and two make four, then it is binding on all rational creatures to accept this proposition. If this is a truth, it is true for everyone, not merely true for those who care to believe it. If it is true, it is true necessarily and always. It is true, in and of itself, without any reference to why it is true, without any reference to who does or does not believe it, without any reference to consequences that follow from its being true or from its being believed. It is, to use a favorite phrase of Kant's, true categorically, without any strings or qualifications. To repeat, it is not true because God commands it, nor because it is according to nature, nor because it pays in the long run to believe it, nor because all or most people agree to it, nor for any other reason. It is simply true because it is true. Moreover, it is true of all cases of two's and two's. There are no possible exceptions. It is not something which holds for one period of time and not for another, for one pair of two's and not for another, for one stage of civilization and not for another. In this universality, necessity, objectivity, which we detect readily enough in the proposition that two and two make four, Kant finds the differential mark of rational knowledge. He has his own word for it. It is, he says, true *a priori*. It will be recalled that he began his *Critique of Pure Reason* by accepting and exploring the implications of *a priori* knowledge.

This notion of *a priori* he carries over into the field of morality. If there is such a thing as rational science, it is *a priori*. If there is such a thing as rational morality, it is *a priori*. Moreover, just as in the case of *a priori* knowledge he did not undertake to prove that there is such a thing, but assumed its existence as a fact, so in the case of morality he does not undertake to show that there is such a thing, but assumes its existence as a fact. His argument is after this manner: If you admit that there is any rational knowledge, then you must admit that it is *a priori* in character, and if you admit that there is any rational morality, you must admit that it is *a priori* in character. If you admit that there is any rational knowledge, you must recognize that it is binding on all rational beings; so, by analogy, if you admit that there is any rational morality, you must recognize that it is binding on all rational beings. He is content to accept both rational knowledge and rational morality as facts to be recognized, not as hypotheses to be proved.

Once the notion of a rational morality is admitted, Kant is in a position to formulate his problem. It is this: What must be its principle? It will be noticed that he is not seeking to justify morality, any more than one would seek to justify arithmetic; not seeking to explain why right is right and wrong is wrong, any more than one would seek to explain why true is true, or false is false. He is merely saying: The facts of morality are categorical facts, not dependent for their moral quality upon anything beyond themselves. Such being the case, we ask again, what principle must run through all the cases of morality, and be absent from all the cases of immorality?

His answer is simple: An act is moral if and only if the principle which it embodies is capable of universalization without self-contradiction. This notion once stated, Kant proceeds to illustrate his meaning by some examples. His next step is to approach this same notion of categorical rightness from two other angles, namely, duty and good will. When these matters have been settled, he turns to consider a question that had been hanging fire since his studies in the problem of knowledge. I mean the problem of man's free will. Here the findings of the first *Critique* are called in to help solve the difficulty. As a moralist, his fundamental problem is, "What ought I to do?" But if, as would appear from the "scientific" view of the world, everything happens "of necessity," what sense is there to claiming that some things "ought" or "ought not" to be done? Here Kant is at once clarifying and baffling. Clarifying because he has the insight and tenacity to hold on to the "ought" as being every bit as much a reality as the "is," baffling because he concludes by admitting his inability to solve the paradox involved in their joint acceptance. His treatment of this question would require too much space to be summarized here. From freedom he passes on to God and immortality. As in the case of Kant's handling of the problem of knowledge, it will be necessary to state a few of his claims in the form of a condensed summary. His own language is too involved to permit direct citation. Wherever possible, however, his own words will be introduced.

Morality, the rightness and wrongness of actions, is categorical (not dependent upon anything) and *a priori* (valid for all persons and all times and all cases). In this it resembles rational knowledge. To quote: "The morality of an action is quite a peculiar thing. When we are considering the goodness of an action, we are concerned with what constitutes the goodness in and of itself."

If morality is of this categorical and *a priori* nature, then we can rule out several misleading attempts to formulate its principle. For example, the morality of an act is said, by some, to reside in the "feeling" which one has about the act. But this could not be for two reasons: (1) If morality is a matter of someone's feelings, then it is not categorical; that is, an act would depend, for its morality, upon the fact (external to the act itself) that it was or was not felt about in some way or other by some person or other. (2) If morality is a matter of feeling, then it is not anything universally binding and valid for all men, because feelings vary notoriously from time to time and from person to person; that is, one and the same act could be both right and wrong provided merely that two persons had opposite feelings about it. But this is to rob morality of its categorical nature, to give as the defining characteristic of morality a quality in virtue of which it would fail to be categorical and *a priori*.

Much the same line of reasoning is adduced by Kant against those who seek to locate the rightness of an act in its agreement with God's will. He says:

There are those who argue that we must first have God and then morality — a very convenient principle. But ethics and theology are neither of them a principle of the other. We are not discussing, here, the fact that theology is a motive for ethics — which it is — but we are asking whether the principle of ethical discrimination is theological — and it cannot be that.

Were it so, then before a nation could have any conception of duties it would first have to know God. Nations which had no right conception of God would have no duties, and this is not the case. Nations had a right idea of their duties, e.g., were aware that lies were detestable, without having the proper notion of God. Duties must therefore be derived from some other source.

If we do as God commanded, because He has commanded, and because He is so mighty that He can force us to, or punish us if we do not, we act under orders from fear and fright, not appreciating the propriety of our actions and knowing why we should do as God has commanded. Might cannot constitute a *vis obligandi*. Threats do not impose a (moral) obligation; they extort. Such conduct does not make the heart better.

Moral laws can be right without any commander, promulgator, obligator. How do we know the divine will? None of us feels it in his heart. We cannot know the moral law from any revelation, for if we did so, then those who had no revelation would be wholly ignorant of it.

We imagine God as possessing the most holy and most perfect will. But what then is the most perfect will? The moral law shows us what it is. We say the divine will accords with the moral law and is, therefore, holiest and most perfect. Thus we recognize the perfection of the divine will from the moral law. God wills all that is morally good and proper, and His will is, therefore, holy and perfect. But what is it that is morally good? Ethics supplies the answer to this question.

These strictures may be summarized. To locate the rightness of an act in its agreement with God's will is to deny its categorical nature, i.e., to make it depend, for its rightness, upon something other than or outside of itself. It is, too, to render morality an impossibility for all who do not know what God's will is, or who have a wrong notion of that will, or (it may be) deny His existence. There is, Kant would say, such a thing as morality apart from God's existence or our knowledge of the same. Finally, the view fails to take into account that when we say, "God is good," we are making goodness prior to and independent of God. He is good because His will or His action corresponds to the good; not vice versa.

There remains for consideration what Kant calls the *pragmatic* view of morality. The pragmatic view of morality is that an act is right because of the nature of its consequences; not right in itself, but because of the results that do or do not follow from it. Kant does not need to concern himself with the question of the nature of the results. He has two objections to doing so: (1) To locate the rightness of an act in the nature of its consequences is to deny the categorical nature of morality. It is to make its morality depend upon something other than the act. (2) To find the morality of an act in its consequences is to deprive morality of its *a priori* nature, because we can never know the consequences of an act until after the act is done, and even then never know them completely. This would reduce morality to a matter of probability; make it, as Kant says, *a posteriori*, instead of *a priori*. At this point, direct citations from Kant may be resumed.

Having examined what the principle of morality is not, we must now examine what it is.

What is the one principle of morality, the criterion by which to judge everything and in which lies the distinction between moral goodness and all other goodness? What is the principle upon which we establish morality, and through which we are able to discriminate between what is moral and what immoral?

In this connection we must first notice that there are two points to be considered: the principle upon which we discriminate, and the mainspring or motive of performance. We must distinguish between the measuring rod and the mainspring. The measuring rod is the principle of discriminating; the mainspring is the motive of the performance of our obligation. If we ask, "What is morally good and what is not?" it is the principle of discrimination that is in question; but if we ask, "What is it that leads me to be moral?" it is the motive that is in question. We must guard against confusing the principle of morality with the motive to morality. The first is the norm. The second is the incentive.

The essence of morality is that our actions are motivated by a general rule. If we make it the foundation of our conduct that our actions shall be consistent with a universal rule, valid at all times and for everyone, then our actions exemplify the principle of morality.

In all moral judgments the idea which we frame is this: What is the character of the action taken by itself? If the principle of the action can, without self-contradiction, be universalized, it is moral; if it cannot be so universalized without contradicting itself, it is immoral. That action is immoral whose principle cancels and destroys itself when it is made a universal rule.

From this wholly general statement of the nature of rightness Kant turns to some concrete illustrations. He considers the case of lying and suicide. These, being instances of wrongness, illustrate his notion of rightness only indirectly.

May I, when in distress, make a promise with the intention not to keep it? Considerations of prudence aside, would such an act be moral? The shortest way to answer this question is to ask, "Would I be content that the principle (getting out of difficulties by making false promises) should hold good as a universal law, for myself and all others?"

If I ask, "Can the principle of making deceitful promises to get out of difficulties be universalized?" I realize that it cannot. For with such a law there would be no promises at all. With such a principle made universal, it would be in vain to allege my intentions in regard to future actions. As soon as it were made a universal law, the principle would necessarily destroy itself, necessarily defeat its own end.

A man finds himself forced to borrow money. He knows that he will not be able to repay it, but he sees also that nothing will be lent to him unless he promises to repay it. Would it be right to promise? The principle of his action would be: When in need, to borrow and promise to repay, knowing that I cannot do so. Could this principle become a universal law? I see at once that it could not. As a universal law, it would contradict itself. For if this principle were a universal law, such promises would become impossible. For no one would consider such promises as binding, and all would ridicule them as vain pretenses.

A man reduced to despair by a series of misfortunes feels wearied of life. Would it be right to take his own life? Could the principle of his action become a universal law of nature? The principle would be: To shorten life when its longer duration is likely to bring more evil than satisfaction. Could this principle become a universal law of nature? Clearly not. A system of nature in which it was a law to destroy life by means of the very feeling whose special office it is to impel to the improvement of life, would contradict itself, and therefore could not exist as a system of nature. Hence that principle could not possibly exist as a universal law of nature. Hence it would be wholly inconsistent with the supreme principle of all duty.

If we attend to ourselves, on occasion of any transgression of duty, we shall find that we do not will that the principle of our action should become a universal law. On the contrary, we will that the opposite should remain a universal law, only we assume the liberty of making an exception in our own favor — just for this time only, it may be. This cannot be justified to our own impartial judgment, and it proves that we do recognize the validity of the moral principle I have formulated, even while we allow ourselves a few exceptions which we think important and forced upon us.

Thus far Kant has been developing the notion of a rational morality as something categorical and *a priori*. He has used this conception of morality to eliminate certain other theories which are incompatible with it, e.g., the theory that morality is a matter of feeling or emotion. He has disentangled what he takes to be the underlying principle of morality so conceived and advanced a few illustrations of his thesis. He returns again and again throughout his ethical writings to these basic claims. One example of such a reworking is contained in his distinction between hypothetical and categorical imperatives. The statement of this is given below. But a word first on Kant's use of these terms. The term *imperative*, used as a noun, means "a command." Kant inclines to use it in this sense. We shall, I think, come closer to his real meaning if we construe it by our word *ought*. We do, as a matter of everyday usage, employ the term *ought* in precisely the sense Kant would appear to have in mind. We say, for example, "If you wish to be there on time, you *ought* to leave early." Here the force of the *ought* is hypothetical; that is, it depends on whether you do or do not wish to get there on time. But there are times, Kant would claim, when we do not so use the term; when, for instance, we are pointing out what we take to be a duty. Thus, "you *ought* to be honest," "you *ought* to respect the rights of others." Here, we might feel, the *ought* is not dependent upon any *if*. It is not an hypothetical *ought*. It is, Kant would say, a categorical *ought*. The same idea could also be expressed in the distinction between an hypothetical obligation and a categorical obligation. Kant says:

All imperatives command either hypothetically or categorically. The former represent the practical necessity of a possible action as means to something else that is willed or might be willed. The latter would be that which represented an action as obligatory of itself without reference to some other end.

If an action is good only as a means to something else, then the imperative which commands it is hypothetical only; but if it is conceived to be good in itself, that is, without reference to any further end, the imperative which commands it is categorical.

The hypothetical imperative only says that the action is good for some purpose, actual or possible. The categorical imperative declares an action to be binding in itself, without reference to any purpose or end beyond itself.

All sciences have a practical part, consisting of problems connected with ends or purposes possible for us, and of imperatives directing how these may be attained. Here there is no question whether the end is good or rational, but only what one must do in order to attain it. The precepts for the physician to make his patient healthy and for a poisoner to insure his victim's death, are of equal value in this respect, namely that each serves to effect its purpose.

There is one imperative which commands certain conduct immediately, without having as its condition any other purpose to be attained by it. This imperative is categorical. It concerns not the matter of the action, nor its intended result, but its form and principle. This imperative may be called the imperative of morality.

There is but one categorical imperative, namely, "Act only on that principle which thou canst will should become a universal law."

This imperative of duty may be expressed, by analogy with natural laws, as follows: "Act as if the principle of thy action were to become by thy will a universal law of nature."

If there is a supreme practical principle or categorical imperative.

it must be one which constitutes an objective principle, and can therefore serve as a universal practical law. From this, as a supreme practical law, all laws of the will must be capable of being deduced. Accordingly the categorical imperative may be stated in a third way: "So act as to treat humanity, whether in thine own person or in the person of another, as an end withal, never as a means only."

If all the imperatives of duty can be deduced from this one imperative, as from it as their principle, then, although it should remain undecided whether what is called *duty* is not merely a vain notion, yet at least we shall be able to show what we understand by it; be able, that is, to show what the notion means.

To act out of respect for this principle constitutes duty. To this every other motive must give place, because it is the condition of a will being good in itself, good absolutely, good without qualification; and the worth of such a will is above everything.

The direct opposite of acting on the principle of morality is acting on the principle of private happiness. This would ruin morality altogether, were not the voice of reason so clear, so irrepressible, so distinctly audible even to the commonest men. That action should be based on the principle of private happiness can only be maintained by such as are bold enough to shut their ears against that heavenly voice in order to support a theory that costs no trouble.

Two things fill the mind with ever new and increasing admiration and awe, the oftener and more steadily we reflect on them: the starry heavens above and the moral law within. I have not to search for them and conjecture them as though they were veiled in darkness or in a region transcending my horizon. I see them before me and connect them directly with the consciousness of my existence.

Duty! Thou sublime and mighty name! Thou seekest not to move the will by threatening nor by charming. Thou merely holdest forth a law which finds entrance into the mind, a law before which all inclinations and desires are dumb. What origin is worthy of thee? Where is to be found the root of thy noble descent?

I do not, therefore, need any far-reaching penetration to discern what I have to do in order that my will may be morally good. Inexperienced in the course of the world, incapable of being prepared for all its contingencies, I need only ask, "Can I will that the principle of my action should become a universal law?" If not, then it must be rejected.

A second reworking of his fundamental insight is contained in his remarks on the intrinsic goodness of a good will. This thought requires a few words of explanation. Kant has spoken thus far of the morality of acts and wherein it resides. He has, also, restated the same notion in terms of *ought* and *ought not*. But, he is quite aware, there is no such thing as an act apart from someone who does the act. We may analyze and define the morality of an act, but we must end by addressing our remarks, not to acts, but to persons who act. There can be right acts only insofar as persons act rightly; hence the need to restate the matter in terms of will or intention. Every moralist, no matter what his principle of morality, is brought around at last to this point; hence Kant's genuine concern over a good will, i.e., a will inspired and controlled by the principle he has defined.

Nothing can be called *good*, without qualifications, except a good will. We now proceed to examine what exactly constitutes that will, simply good in itself, on which moral goodness depends.

Intelligence, wit, judgment, courage, resolution, perseverance, and so on, are no doubt good and desirable in many respects. But these gifts of nature may also be bad and mischievous if the will which is to make use of them is not good.

It is the same with gifts of fortune. Power, riches, honor, even health and happiness, inspire pride and often presumption if there is not a good will to check their influence.

A good will is good, not because of what it performs or accomplishes, not because of its usefulness or fruitfulness, but is simply good in itself. Even if it should happen that, owing to a special disfavor of fortune or the niggardly provision of a stepmotherly nature, a good will should wholly lack power to achieve its purpose, should by its greatest efforts achieve nothing, yet, like a jewel it would shine by its own light as a thing which has its whole value in itself.

We have, then, to develop the notion of a will good in itself and without reference to anything further. This notion already exists in the sound natural understanding, and requires rather to be clarified than taught or proved. In order to define more closely the notion of a good will, we will consider the wider notion of duty which includes the notion of a good will.

To have moral worth an act must be done from a sense of duty alone. We must distinguish between acts which accord with what duty requires, and acts done because duty requires. The latter alone have moral worth. We must distinguish between doing what duty requires, and doing because duty requires. Only the latter possesses moral worth.

If I do a thing because it is commanded, or because it brings advantage, my action is not moral. But if I do a thing because it is absolutely right in itself, my disposition is a moral one. We ought to do a thing, not because God wills it, but because it is righteous and good in itself.

Thus, it is a matter of duty that a dealer should not overcharge an inexperienced customer. Refraining from so doing for any other motive than that duty requires it, has no moral worth. It is one's duty to maintain life and happiness. Doing so for any other reason than that duty requires it, has no moral worth. It is one's duty to be generous, kind, honest, and so on. Being so for any reason except that duty requires it, has no moral worth. An action done from a sense of duty must wholly exclude the influence of inclination. An action, to be wholly moral, must exclude wholly the influence of inclination.

Take for instance a man who pays his debts. He may be swayed by the fear of being punished if he defaults, or he may pay because it is right that he should. In the first case his conduct is legally right, but it is only in the latter case that it is morally right.

It is a very beautiful thing to do good to men out of love for them or to be just from love of order. But this is not the true moral principle, suitable to our position among rational beings as men. To pretend it were, would be to set ourselves, with fanciful pride, above the thought of duty, like volunteers independent of command;

to want to do, of our own pleasure, what we think we need no command to do.

An action done from a sense of duty derives its moral worth, not from the purpose which is to be attained by it, but from the principle upon which it is done. . . . The moral worth of an action does not lie in the results expected from it, but from the principle which it embodies.

What sort of principle, or moral law, can that be, the conception of which must determine the will, without regard to expected consequences, in order that the will may be called *good* absolutely and without qualifications?

It is this: "So act that the principle of your action might become a universal law." Canst thou will that the principle of thy action should become a universal law? If not, then it must be rejected.

Kant has now declared himself on the fundamental problem of moral philosophy. One other large problem remains. It grows out of his remarks on the nature and importance of a good will. A *good* will may be defined, after Kant, as a will to do what ought to be done. Here the crucial term is *ought*. And it is crucial because it implies that the will in question is a free will. There would be no point to the remark that a man ought to do so-and-so if, as a matter of fact, he has no free will. Furthermore, we hold a man responsible for his action, but only on the hypothesis that his action expresses his free will in the matter. The moralist in all of us is brought up short by any denial of man's free will. Such a denial would deprive our everyday ethical language of all meaning. If you doubt this, try some time to be a moralist about your own or other people's conduct, and resolutely refrain from using such words as *ought*, *ought not*, *obligation*, *responsible*, *accountable*, *answerable*, *deserved*, *undeserved*, etc. I know of no experiment better calculated to give point to Kant's far-reaching concern over the question of man's free will.

Without freedom of the will, no moral law and no moral responsibility are possible.

A man commits a theft. By the physical law of causality this deed is a necessary result of the causes preceding it in time; it was impossible that it could not have happened. How then can the moral judgment make any difference, and suppose it could have been omitted? The moral judgment says it ought to have been omitted. How can this be? How can a man be called free, at the same moment and with respect to the same act in which he is subject to an inevitable physical necessity?

Actions which are not free, and do not involve one's personality, do not give rise to obligations. Thus no man can be placed under an obligation to give up swallowing for the very reason that it would not be within his powers. Obligation, therefore, presupposes the use of freedom.

That is the difficulty. No free will, no morality. This dilemma cannot be stated too starkly. It is as unblinkable as "no eyes, no vision," or "no light, no vision." Deny freedom of will, and at one stroke you annihilate morality, and I do not mean that by denying freedom of will you "discourage" people, so that they will "give up trying to do what is right." I mean that you make the term *morality* a meaningless term. So concerned was Kant over this matter that he spent some eleven years thinking out a theory of knowledge which would legitimate the notion of free will. In this sense his *Critique of Pure Reason* was thought out with an eye to the *Critique of Practical Reason* which followed it. In the very next sentence, we are back once more in the ideas of the first *Critique:*

If we take things in time as things-in-themselves, as is commonly done, then it is impossible to reconcile the necessity of the causal relation with freedom. They are contradictory. From the former, it follows that every event, every action, is a necessary result of what existed in time preceding. So, since time past is no longer in my power, it would follow that every action I perform is the necessary result of causes which are not in my power. That is, it would follow that at the moment in which I act, I am never free.

Obligation expresses a sort of necessity which occurs nowhere else in nature except in man. It is impossible that anything in nature *ought to be* other than in fact it is. In truth, obligation, if one has before one's eyes only the succession in nature, has simply and solely no meaning. We can as little ask what ought to happen in nature as what attributes a circle ought to have.

If existence in time, that is, existence as phenomena, were the only kind we could ascribe to things-in-themselves, freedom would have to be rejected as a vain and impossible suggestion.

Consequently, if we would save freedom, no other way remains but to consider that the existence of a thing in time and therefore according to the law of physical necessity, is appearance only. Freedom we must attribute to the thing as a reality, as a thing-in-itself. This is inevitable, if we would retain both these contradictory conceptions of necessity and freedom. However, when we try to explain their combination in one and the same action, great difficulties present themselves.

Now, in order to remove the apparent contradition between freedom and mechanism in one and the same action, we must recall what was said in the *Critique of Pure Reason*, or what follows from what was said there. It was said there that the necessity of nature — which cannot coexist with the freedom of the will — pertains only to things as phenomena. The category of causation, it was argued, extends to phenomena or appearances only. The possibility of freedom was thus left open, although its reality was not thereby proved.

Kant's words are important. He says, "The possibility of freedom was thus left open." That is all the help he claims from his theory of knowledge. It is sufficient, however. As his discourse shows, he proposes to use the undeniable *ought*. That we ought to do some things and ought not to do others is a point upon which all moralists would agree. They might differ as to what we ought or ought not to do That is a mere detail. The essential point is that they would all use the notions of "oughtness" and "ought-notness." It is necessary to give Kant credit here for proposing to cut a Gordian knot which no person dare leave tied. Picking up the argument where we broke in, the only point is to change this "may be free," which Kant's theory of knowledge permits, into an "is free" which his moral insight demands.

The only point is to change this "may be free" into "is free." That is, to show, in an actual case, that certain actions do imply freedom. Now, it is a duty to realize the moral law in our acts. Therefore it must be possible. ("I ought" implies "I can.") Therefore every rational being must assume whatever is implied by this possibility. Freedom of the will, independence of causal necessity, is implied by this possibility. The assumption is as necessary as the moral law, in connection with which alone it is valid.

Freedom and duty reciprocally imply each other. It is the moral law, of which we become directly conscious, that leads directly to the conception of freedom. It is morality that first discovers to us the notion of freedom. The moral law — "I ought" — which itself does not require any proof, proves the actuality of freedom in those who recognize it as binding on themselves. A man judges he can do, or refrain from doing, a certain act because he is conscious that he ought to. No one would ever have been so rash as to introduce freedom into science had not the moral law forced it upon us.

Morality requires us only to be able to think freedom without self-contradiction, not to understand it. It is enough that our notion of the act as free puts no obstacle in the way of the notion of it as mechanically necessary. Our notion is that the act stands in quite a different relation to freedom from that in which it stands to the mechanism of nature. From the point of view of my *Critique of Pure Reason* this is possible; the doctrine of nature and necessity and the doctrine of morality and freedom may each be true in its own sphere.

How freedom of the will is possible, how we are to conceive it theoretically and positively, how man is a member of two worlds, how man's moral actions must always appear necessitated while they are nonetheless free — all this is not discoverable. Only that there is such a freedom, is postulated by the moral law. How freedom is possible no human intelligence will ever fully fathom. That freedom is possible, on the other hand, no sophistry will ever wrest from the conviction of even the commonest man.

It will be said that the solution here proposed to the problem of freedom involves great difficulty. But is any other solution easier and more intelligible?

Thus far one is inclined to let Kant have things pretty much his own way. Grant him his initial hypothesis of a rational morality, and it is difficult to challenge his argument. He gives a clarifying and convincing presentation of what is implied in this conception, but he was not satisfied to be simply a moralist; he must also say his word as a theologian. In this sense he might have anticipated the cry of Goethe's *Faust*, "*Zwei Seelen wohnen ach in meiner Brüst*." His transition from moral philosophy to theology comes about in connection with his doctrine of the postulates of morality. One of these postulates we have already seen, namely, free will. But there are two more to come, namely, immortality and God. It is perhaps as well to let Kant tell his own story. First, immortality:

The immortality of the soul is also a postulate of the moral law. By a *postulate* I mean a theoretical proposition, not demonstrable as such, but which is an inseparable result of an unconditional, *a priori*, practical (i.e., moral) law.

The connection is this. The moral law commands the perfect accordance of the will with it. This must be possible, since it is commanded. But perfect accordance of the will with the moral law is a perfection of which no rational being of the sensible world is capable at any moment of his existence. Since, nevertheless, it is commanded, it can only be realized in an infinite progression toward that perfect accordance. Now, this endless progress is only possible on the supposition of an endless duration of the existence and personality of the same rational being. This is called the *immortality of the soul*. The highest good for man, the perfect accord of his will with the moral law, is only possible on the supposition of the immortality of the soul. Consequently, this immortality, being inseparably connected with the moral law, is a postulate of pure practical reason.

For a rational but finite being, the only thing possible is an endless progress from the lower to higher degrees of perfection. . . . And thus he may hope, not indeed here nor at any imaginable point of his future existence, but only in the endlessness of his duration, to be perfectly adequate in his will.

This principle of the moral destination of our nature, namely, that it is only in an endless progress that we can attain perfect accordance with the moral law, is of the greatest use, not merely for supplementing the impotence of speculative reason, but also with respect to religion.

It is interesting to note that Kant has here reversed the usual order of things. Paley, it will be recalled, deduced morality from theology. Kant is deducing theology from morality. Some amends, one must suppose, were required in order to square accounts: From his theory of knowledge he had deduced an agnosticism with respect to speculative theology; in his analysis of the conception of a rational morality he had demonstrated its independence of theology. The argument continues:

The existence of God is also a postulate of the moral law. We proceed to exhibit this connection in a convincing manner.

Happiness is the condition of a rational being in the world with whom everything goes according to his wish and will. It rests, thus, on the harmony of physical nature with his ends and purposes. But the rational being in the world is not the cause of the world and of physical nature. There is, therefore, not the least ground in the moral law for any necessary connection between morality (i.e., virtue) and proportionate happiness.

To repeat: In a being that belongs to the world as part of it, is therefore dependent on it, and for that reason cannot by his will be a cause of nature nor by his own power make it completely harmonize, as far as his happiness is concerned, with his practical (i.e., moral) principles, in such a being there is not the least ground for any connection between morality and proportionate happiness.

Therefore, the *summum bonum*, the union of virtue and happiness, is possible in the world only on the supposition of a Supreme Being having a causality corresponding to moral character.

Accordingly, the existence of a cause of nature, distinct from nature itself, and containing the principle of this connection, this exact harmony of happiness with morality, is postulated.

Now, a being that is capable of acting on the conception of laws is an intelligence, and the causality of such a being according to this conception of laws, is his will. Therefore, the supreme cause of nature, which must be presupposed as a condition of the *summum bonum* (the union of virtue and happiness) is a being who is the cause of nature by intelligence and will, that is, its author; that is, God.

Now, in as much as it is a duty for us to promote the *summum bonum*, it is not merely allowable but a duty to presuppose the possibility of this *summum bonum*. And so, as this is possible only on condition of the existence of God, it is morally necessary, it is a matter of duty, to assume the existence of God.

These postulates of immortality, freedom, and the existence of God, all proceed from the principle of morality which is itself not a postulate but a law, an imperative. . . . These postulates are not theoretical dogmas, but suppositions practically necessary, i.e., required in the interests of practice. While they do not extend our speculative knowledge, they do give objective reality to the ideas of speculative reason in general, do give it a right to conceptions the possibility of which it could not otherwise venture to affirm. . . . Thus respect for the moral law leads, through these postulates, to conceptions which speculation might indeed present as problems but could never solve.

By way of conclusion it might be well to repeat the main turns of Kant's argument. He begins by assuming that a rational morality is the only morality. He shows that this means categorical and *a priori*. This enables him to eliminate three misleading conceptions — that it is a matter of feelings, that it is a matter of consequences, that it is a matter of agreeing with God's will, since on these counts it would be neither categorical nor *a priori*. He returns again to the conception of rational morality as categorical and *a priori*, and formulates its principle. This central thesis he then works over in terms of the notion of *ought* or *duty*, and in terms of the *good will*. These considerations raise the problem of free will. He sharpens the point of this problem. He then reaches back into his theory of knowledge for justification of the claim that free will "may be so." He returns, finally, to the conception of morality as necessitating free will as a postulate. There his moral philosophy proper stops, and his theology begins. Kant's moral philosophy, I think, contains some of the soundest and most clarifying analyses to be found anywhere in the history of human thought.

It is customary, among historians of these matters, to distinguish between the morality of principles and the morality of consequences. This distinction cannot be pressed very far, but it serves to set Kant off from those who attempt to determine the morality of actions in terms of the consequences which follow from those actions. Of moralists who have developed the latter approach, one stands out pre-eminent among the rest, and forms an instructive contrast to Immanuel Kant. I mean John Stuart Mill, who is the subject of the next chapter.

Reading References. The references given under the Kant section, in the third topic, are valuable here also. A few titles are here added which have special reference to Kant as a moralist, e.g., J. W. Scott's *Kant on the Moral Life;* A. K. Rogers' *Morals in Review*, chapter on Kant; discussion of Kant in Paulsen's *System of Ethics;* discussion of Kant in Rashdall's *Theory of Good and Evil*.

READING QUESTIONS

1. Distinguish Kant's use of *a priori* in epistemology and in ethics.
2. To what did he ascribe the *a priori* element in knowledge?
3. To what, by parity of reasoning, might he ascribe the *a priori* element in morality?
4. What is his criticism of the claim that the morality of an act resides in one's feelings about the act?
5. Show how his claim regarding the *a priori* nature of morality is the basis of this criticism; and of the next two, as you come to them.
6. What criticisms would Kant have directed at Paley?
7. Wherein does Kant find "the essence of morality"?
8. What illustrations does he offer of his general idea?
9. What is his distinction between hypothetical and categorical imperatives?
10. "There is but one categorical imperative." Namely?
11. "Two things fill the mind with ever new and increasing admiration and awe." Namely?
12. Distinguish "what duty requires" and "because duty requires."
13. "We have to develop the notion of a will good in itself." Develop it.
14. How does Kant define a *moral* act?
15. A will is good if it is motivated by what principle?
16. "Without freedom of will no moral law and no moral responsibility are possible." Elucidate.
17. How does Kant use his theory of knowledge in this connection?
18. "To change this 'may be free' into 'is free.' " Explain.
19. What does he mean when he describes freedom as a postulate of morality?
20. What is Kant's argument for immortality?
21. For the existence of God?
22. "Kant reversed the usual relation between morality and religion." Elucidate.
23. Indicate the relation between the *Critique of Pure Reason* and the *Critique of Practical Reason*.

3. MORALITY GROUNDED IN HAPPINESS—FROM JOHN STUART MILL

From Kant to Mill. Our subject is still the principle of morality. Our quest began with Paley's attempt to ground morality in theology. Paley, we found, distinguished between right and wrong by reference to God's will; that is right which agrees, and wrong which disagrees with God's will. He supplemented this principle by another, designed to help out when God's will was not known. This principle was that *right* means "producing human happiness," and *wrong* means "producing human unhappiness." Difficulties latent in Paley's position were noted and need not be repeated here. In Kant's attempt to argue that morality is categorical, that it is not grounded in anything, but "stands on its own feet," we met a complete antithesis to the position represented by Paley. Kant's effort to disengage morality from theology, as well as from happiness, repudiating both terms of Paley's argument, stands alone. The trend of moral philosophizing has been for the most part away from Kant. In J. S. Mill one meets a moralist who is prepared to argue in support of the latter half of Paley's position: that an act is right if, and only if, it produces more happiness than any other act possible under the circumstances.

Biographical Note. John Stuart Mill was born in England in 1806 and died in 1873 at the age of sixty-seven. He was educated privately by his father. He grew up in the group which included Jeremy Bentham, James Mill (father of J. S.), T. R. Malthus, David Ricardo, George Grote, and others. These men were interested primarily in political, economic, and social reform. They were the driving force behind the first Reform Bill, the early Factory Acts, and so on. They were known, in their own day, as the Utilitarians and as the Philosophical Radicals. Each term tells their story. They were utilitarians because they enquired of any law, custom, or institution, "What is its utility? Of what use is it?"

If no answer were forthcoming, beyond some vague statement about its prestige or its long standing, they proposed to scrap it. They were philosophical radicals because they aimed to go to the roots of things, the word *root* being English for the Latin word *radix*. The root to which these men proposed to go was human happiness. That, for them, was the "root question" to be addressed to any law, custom, or institution. For the most part they did not spend time seeking to justify this principle. This task J. S. Mill undertook to do. They applied the principle that *right* means "producing human happiness." He undertook to clarify and defend the principle, undertook, that is, a philosophical exposition of the principle. Most of his other writings stem from the celebrated little book in which this defense is set forth. Thus, in his *Essay on Liberty*, written a few years before his *Utilitarianism*, but based on the principles subsequently given in the later book, he argued that the greatest happiness of the greatest number is more likely to be achieved by allowing as much freedom of thought and action as possible. In his treatise, *Considerations on Representative Government*, he argued that government by elected representatives would offer a better guarantee of human happiness than government by monarchs or aristocrats. In his monograph *On the Subjection of Women* he argued that the purpose of representative government was, in part, frustrated by refusing votes to women. The range and sincerity of his writings have combined to make him one of the greatest single influences throughout the past hundred years. The heart of his work is contained in his statement of the case for human happiness as the ultimate test of right and wrong. For other biographical notes, see page 58.

The Argument of the Citations. Mill's exposition and defense of the appeal to happiness as the basis of morality moves through five turns. He first states the problem:

What is the basis or principle of morality? He then explores two "false leads," and shows grounds for rejecting them. He then states his own position at some length. He then asks the question: Is this belief open to any kind of proof or disproof? and answers as best he can. He turns then to review a long series of objections and misunderstandings which, he knows, will be brought against his claim. These he seeks to answer, one by one. With this accomplished, he is in a position to say, "I have posed an age-long problem. I have criticized two widely held theories. I have advanced my own answer. I have shown what sort of proof it is amenable to. I have stated and removed as many objections as I can think of. The defense rests."

The *Utilitarianism* begins as follows:

> There are few circumstances more significant of the backward state of speculation than the little progress which has been made in the controversy respecting the criterion of right and wrong.
>
> From the dawn of philosophy the question concerning the foundation of morality has been accounted the main problem in speculative thought, has occupied the most gifted intellects, and divided them into sects and schools carrying on a vigorous warfare against one another.
>
> After more than two thousand years the same discussions continue. Philosophers are still ranged under the same contending banners. Neither thinkers nor mankind at large seem nearer to agreement than when the youthful Socrates listened to the old Protagoras.

The problem is now before us: What is the foundation of morality? He proposes to examine two familiar answers. The first of these is the observation that this is a matter of personal opinion. Thus one reads the remarks, "There's nothing right or wrong, but thinking makes it so." "Right you are, if you think you are." That is, an act is right if you, or the community, or all mankind, think it is; right and wrong are mere matters of opinion, are merely subjective.

There are many different ways of stating this notion. Of all moralists, who hold this view Mill says:

> They all, in one phrase or another, place the test of right and wrong in a feeling of approval or disapproval . . . they find certain feelings of approval and disapproval in themselves . . . a great part of all the ethical reasoning in books and in the world is of this sort.

His criticism of this appeal to moral feeling to settle the matter is short and pointed:

> All experience shows that "moral feelings" are eminently artificial, and the product of culture; that the most senseless and pernicious "feelings" can be raised to the utmost intensity by inculcation, as hemlock and thistles could be reared to luxuriant growth by sowing them instead of wheat.
>
> Things which have been really believed by all mankind have been proved to be false, as that the sun rises and sets. Can immunity for similar error be claimed for the "moral feelings"?
>
> I do not found the morality of actions upon anybody's opinion or feeling of them. I found it upon facts.

What facts, we ask. Wait a moment, is the answer, till I glance at another doctrine. This time it is the appeal to nature. A thing is right, it will be said, if it is according to nature, if it is natural; wrong, if it is contrary to nature, if it is unnatural.

> We will inquire into the truth of the doctrines which make nature a test of right and wrong, good and evil, or which in any mode or degree attach merit or approval to following, imitating, or obeying nature. A reference to that supposed standard is the predominant ingredient in the vein of thought and feeling which was opened by Rousseau, and which has infiltrated itself most widely into the modern mind.
>
> That any mode of thinking, feeling, or acting is "according to nature" is usually accepted as a strong argument for its goodness. If it can be said, with any plausibility, that "nature enjoins" any-

thing, the propriety of obeying the injunction is considered to be made out. And, conversely, the imputation of being "contrary to nature" is thought to bar the thing so designated from being tolerated or excused. It is thought that nature affords some criterion of what we ought to do.

Mill's handling of the appeal to nature is a masterpiece of condensed refutation. He first points out that the term *nature*, or *according to nature*, is ambiguous. He states the two senses in which it might be used. He then shows that, given the first sense, the appeal to nature is meaningless; and, given the second sense, it is irrational and immoral.

The word *nature* has two principal meanings: it either denotes the entire system of things, with the aggregate of all their properties, or it denotes things as they would be, apart from human intervention.

Such being the two principal senses of the word *nature*, in which of these is it taken when the word and its derivatives are used to convey ideas of commendation, approval, and even moral obligation?

In the first of these senses, the doctrine that man ought to follow nature is unmeaning, since man has no power to do anything else than follow nature; all his actions are done through, and in obedience to, some one or many of nature's physical or mental laws.

In the other sense of the term, the doctrine that man ought to follow nature, or in other words, ought to make the spontaneous course of things the model of his voluntary actions, is equally irrational and immoral.

Irrational, because all human action whatever, consists in altering, and all useful action in improving the spontaneous course of nature. Immoral, because the course of natural phenomena being replete with everything which when committed by human beings is most worthy of abhorrence, any one who endeavored in his actions to imitate the natural course of things would be universally seen and acknowledged to be the wickedest of men.

The doctrine that the existing order of things is the natural order, and that, being natural, all innovation upon it is criminal, is vicious.

Conformity to nature has no connection whatever with right and wrong. The idea can never be fitly introduced into ethical discussions at all. That a thing is unnatural is no argument for it being blamable.

At this point we may cite Mill's own position. We have now two alternatives with which to compare it. He says:

All action is for the sake of some end, and rules of action must take their whole character and color from the end to which they are subservient.

The creed which accepts the greatest happiness principle as the foundation of morals holds that actions are right in proportion as they tend to promote happiness, wrong as they tend to produce the reverse of happiness. By happiness is intended pleasure, and the absence of pain; by unhappiness, pain, and the privation of pleasure. This theory I propose to expound and defend.

The standard is not the agent's own greatest happiness, but the greatest amount of happiness altogether. As between his own happiness and that of others, utilitarianism requires him to be as strictly impartial as a disinterested and benevolent spectator.

The test of morality is not the greatest happiness of the agent himself. Utilitarianism does not dream of defining morality to be the self-interest of the agent. The greatest happiness principle is the greatest happiness of mankind and of all sentient creatures.

He who does anything for any other purpose than to increase the amount of happiness in the world is no more deserving of admiration than the ascetic mounted on his pillar. He may be an inspiring proof of what men can do, but assuredly not an example of what they should do.

Pleasure and freedom from pain are the only things desirable as ends, and all desirable things are desirable either for the pleasure inherent in them or as means to the promotion of pleasure and the prevention of pain.

Mill has stated that morality is a matter of consequences. An act is right or wrong, according to its consequences, not because it agrees with someone's opinion, or with universal opinion, or with nature, or (by implication) with God's will. He pauses a moment to elaborate this point:

By "calculating the consequences" is meant, generally, calculating the consequences of classes of actions. There are, as we shall note, exceptions to this, but over all we must look at actions as though multiplied, and in large masses. Take murder for example. There are many persons, to kill whom would be to remove men who are a cause of no good to any human being, who are a cause of cruel physical and moral suffering to several, and whose whole influence tends to increase the mass of unhappiness and vice. Were such a man to be murdered, the balance of traceable consequences would be greatly in favor of the act. But, the counter consideration, still on the principle of utility, is that unless persons were punished for killing, and taught not to kill, nobody's life would be safe.

We say, "generally," not "universally." For the admission of exceptions to rules is a necessity equally felt in all systems of morality. To take an obvious instance: The rule against homicide, the rule against deceiving, the rule against taking advantage of superior strength, are suspended against enemies in the field and partially against malefactors in private life. In each case, the rule is suspended as far as is required by the peculiar nature of the case. That the moralities arising from special circumstances of the action may be so important as to over-rule those arising from the class of acts to which it belongs, is a liability common to all ethical systems.

The existence of exceptions to moral rules is no stumbling block peculiar to the principle of utility. The essential is that the exception should itself be a general rule; so that, being definite, and not left to the partial judgment of the individual, it might not shake the stability of the wider rule in the cases to which the reason of the exception does not extend. This is an ample foundation for "the construction of a scheme of morality."

With respect to the means of inducing people to conform in their actions to the scheme so formed, the utilitarian system depends, like all other schemes of morality, on the external motives supplied by law and opinion and the internal motives produced by education or reason.

The greatest happiness principle is now before us. Two things remain. The first is the question of whether the principle is open to any kind of proof. Mill's answer to this question should be carefully considered. It amounts to a denial that any such principle can be proved. The rationale of this denial is as follows:

Of what sort of proof is this principle of the greatest happiness susceptible?

It is evident that it cannot be proof in the ordinary and popular meaning of the term. Questions of ultimate ends are not amenable to direct proof. Whatever can be proved to be good must be shown to be a means to something admitted to be good without proof.

The medical art is proved to be good by its conducing to health. But how is it possible to prove that health is good? The art of music is good, for the reason among others, that it produces pleasure. But what proof is it possible to give that pleasure is good?

No comprehensive formula, including all things good in themselves and not as means to things good in themselves, is a subject of what is commonly meant by *proof*. It may be accepted or rejected, but not proved in the usual sense of that term.

There is a larger meaning of the word *proof* in which this question of ultimate principles is as amenable to proof as any other of the disputed questions of philosophy. The subject is within the cognizance of the rational faculty. Its acceptance or rejection does not depend on blind impulse or arbitrary choice.

The problem has been stated. False solutions have been exposed. His own solution has been given. The meaning of *proof* in these matters has been made clear. He turns to that inevitable job — seeking to formulate objections that may be raised. A careful study of these objections and replies will do a great deal to clarify and fix the doctrine in one's mind.

It may not be superfluous to notice a few of the common misapprehensions of utilitarian ethics, even those which are so obvious and gross that it might appear impossible for any person of candor and intelligence to fall into them.

The first objection is that such a moral philosophy is a godless doctrine:

> Utilitarianism is a godless doctrine: The appeal to happiness, instead of the appeal to the will of God, is a godless, i.e., irreligious, principle of morality.

Mill's answer is to carry the war into the enemy's camp:

> The question [whether the appeal to happiness is a godless ethic] depends upon what idea we have formed of the moral character of the Deity. If it be a true belief that God desires above all things the happiness of His creatures, and that this was His purpose in their creation, then utilitarianism is not only not a godless doctrine, but more profoundly religious than any other.
>
> Although the existence of God as a wise and just lawgiver is not a necessary part of the feelings of morality, it may still be maintained that those feelings make His existence eminently desirable. No doubt they do, and that is the great reason why we find that good men and women cling to the belief and are pained by its being questioned.
>
> If the objection [that utilitarianism is a godless doctrine] means that utilitarianism does not recognize the revealed will of God as the supreme law of morals, I answer: An utilitarian who believes in the perfect goodness and wisdom of God, necessarily believes that whatever God has thought fit to reveal on the subject of morals must fulfill the requirements of utilitarianism in a supreme degree.

A second objection:

> To suppose that life has no higher end than pleasure, no better and nobler object of desire and pursuit, is utterly mean and groveling; a doctrine worthy only of swine.

Mill's answer:

> This supposes that human beings are capable of no pleasures except those of which swine are capable. If this supposition were

true, the charge could not be denied; but it would then be no charge, for if the sources of pleasure were precisely the same for human beings and for swine, then the rule of life which is good enough for the one would be good enough for the other.

The comparison is felt to be degrading precisely because a beast's pleasures do not satisfy a human being's conception of happiness. Human beings have faculties more elevated than the animal appetites, and do not regard anything as happiness which does not include their gratification.

A third objection:

Utilitarianism [the appeal to the pleasure-pain consequences of action] renders men cold and unsympathizing; that it chills their moral feelings toward individuals; that it makes them regard only the consequences of actions, not taking into account the personal qualities from which those actions emanate.

Mill's answer:

If this means that utilitarians do not allow their judgment concerning the rightness or wrongness of an act to be influenced by their opinion of the quality of the person who does it, then it is a complaint not against utilitarianism but against having any standard of morality at all. For certainly no known ethical standard decides an action to be good or bad because it is done by a good or bad man; still less because it is done by an amiable, brave, or benevolent man, or the contrary. These considerations are relevant, not to the estimation of actions, but of persons; and there is nothing in utilitarianism inconsistent with the fact that there are other things which interest us in persons besides the rightness or wrongness of their actions.

The stoic moralists, indeed, were fond of saying that he who has virtue has everything. But no claim of this description is made for the virtuous man by the utilitarian moralist. There are other desirable possessions and qualities besides virtue. A right action does not necessarily indicate a virtuous character. Actions that are blamable often proceed from qualities entitled to praise. When this is so in any particular case, it modifies one's moral estimation of the agent, but not of the act.

A fourth objection is that the morality of an action, depends upon the motive, not upon the consequences. Mill answers:

As to motive, the utilitarian position is this: Motive has nothing to do with the morality of the action, though much with the worth of the agent. He who saves a fellow creature from drowning does what is morally right, whether his motive be duty or the hope of being paid for his trouble.

A fifth objection:

A stock argument against utilitarianism consists in saying that an utilitarian will be apt to make his own particular case an exception to moral rules, and when under temptation, will see an utility in the breach of a rule, greater than he will see in its observance.

Mill's answer:

But is utilitarianism the only creed which is able to furnish us with excuses for evil doing and means of cheating our own conscience? They are afforded in abundance by all doctrines which recognize as a fact in morals the existence of conflicting considerations; which all doctrines do that have been believed by sane persons.

It is not the fault of any creed, but of the complicated nature of human affairs, that rules of conduct cannot be so framed as to require no exceptions, and that hardly any kind of action can safely be laid down as either always obligatory or always condemnable.

There is no ethical creed which does not temper its laws by giving a certain latitude, under the moral responsibility of the agent, for accommodation to peculiarities of circumstances. At the opening thus made, self-deception and dishonest casuistry get in.

There exists no moral system under which cases of conflicting obligation do not arise. These are the real difficulties, the knotty points, both in a theory of ethics and in the conscientious guidance of personal conduct. But is any one less qualified to deal with cases of conflicting obligations by reason of the fact that he possesses an ultimate standard to which such cases can be referred?

A sixth objection:

Utilitarianism is only an appeal to expedience, and an appeal to expedience is not as high morally as an appeal to principle.

Mill's answer:

This objection rests on a loose use of the term *expedience*. Generally, the *expedient* means that which is expedient for the particular interests of the agent himself; as when a minister of state sacrifices the interests of his country to keep himself in place. The expedient in this sense is a branch of the hurtful; and to claim that utilitarianism is an appeal to the expedient, in this sense, is simply to misunderstand or misrepresent its meaning.

Utilitarianism does recognize in human beings the power of sacrificing their own greatest good for the good of others. I must repeat again, what critics seldom have the justice to acknowledge, that the happiness which forms the standard of what is right in conduct, is not the agent's own happiness but the happiness of all concerned.

Utilitarianism does, however, refuse to admit that sacrifice of one's own good is itself a good. A sacrifice which does not increase the sum of happiness is wasted. The only sacrifice which utilitarianism applauds is that which is made in the interests of the happiness either of mankind or of individuals within the limits imposed by the interests of mankind.

A seventh objection:

Happiness cannot be the rational purpose of life, because it is unattainable.

Mill's answer:

This objection, were it well founded, would go to the root of the matter; for if no happiness is to be had at all by human beings, the attainment of it cannot be the end of morality. However, the assertion that it is impossible that human life be happy is an exaggeration.

If by *happiness* be meant a continuity of highly pleasurable excitement, it is evident that this is impossible. A state of exalted pleasure lasts only for a few moments, or in some cases for somewhat longer periods. If this kind of intense rapture be meant by *happiness*, then happiness is unattainable.

But this is not what philosophers have meant by *happiness* when they taught that happiness was the end of life. The happiness which they meant was not a life of rapture, but moments of such in an existence made up of few and transitory pains, many and various pleasures, with a decided predominance of the active over the passive, and having as the foundation not to expect more from life than it is capable of bestowing. A life thus composed, to those who have been fortunate enough to obtain it, has always appeared worthy of the name of happiness. And such an existence is even now the lot of many.

An eighth objection:

We cannot calculate all the consequences of any action and thus cannot estimate the degree in which it promotes human happiness.

Mill's answer:

Is there any department of human affairs in which we can do all that is desirable? Because we cannot foresee everything, is there no such thing as foresight? Can no estimate be formed of consequences, which would be any guide for our conduct, unless we can calculate all consequences? Because we cannot predict every effect which may follow from a person's death, are we to say that we cannot know that murder would be destructive to human happiness? Whether morality is or is not a question of consequences, it cannot be denied that prudence is a question of consequences, and if there is such a thing as prudence, it is because the consequences of actions can be calculated.

A ninth objection:

There is not time, previous to action, for calculating and weighing the effects of any line of conduct on the general happiness.

Mill's answer:

This is exactly as if any one were to say that it is impossible to guide our conduct by Christianity, because there is not time, on every occasion on which everything has to be done, to read through the Old and New Testaments.

The answer to the objection is that there has been ample time, namely, the whole past duration of the human species. During all that time mankind have been learning by experience the tendencies of actions; on which experience all the prudence, as well as all the morality, of life is dependent.

Nobody argues that the art of navigation is not founded on astronomy, because sailors cannot wait to calculate the nautical almanac. Being rational creatures, they go to sea with it ready calculated, and all rational creatures go out upon the sea of life with their minds made up on the common questions of right and wrong.

There is no difficulty in proving any ethical standard whatever to work ill, if we suppose universal idiocy to be conjoined with it, but on any hypothesis short of that, mankind must by this time have acquired positive beliefs as to the effects of some actions on their happiness. To inform a traveler respecting the place of his ultimate destination is not to forbid the use of landmarks and direction posts on the way.

A tenth objection:

If happiness is made the ultimate standard by which other things are judged to be good or bad, then we are not in a position to distinguish among kinds of happiness with respect to their goodness or badness.

Mill's answer:

It is quite compatible with the principle of utility to recognize the fact that some kinds of pleasure are more desirable and more valuable than others. It would be absurd that while, in estimating all other things, quality is considered as well as quantity, the estimation of pleasures should be supposed to depend on quantity alone.

Of two pleasures, if there be one to which all or almost all who have experience of both give a decided preference, irrespective of any feeling of moral obligation to prefer it, that is the more desirable pleasure.

Now it is an unquestionable fact that those who are equally acquainted with, and equally capable of appreciating and enjoying, both, do give a most marked preference to the manner of existence which employs their higher faculties. It is better to be a human being dissatisfied than a pig satisfied; better to be Socrates dissatisfied than a fool satisfied. And if the fool, or the pig, is of a different opinion, it is because they only know their side of the question. The other party to the comparison knows both sides.

Few human creatures would consent to be changed into any of the lower animals for a promise of the fullest allowance of an animal's pleasures. No intelligent human being would consent to be a fool, no instructed person would consent to be an ignoramus, no person of feeling and conscience would consent to be selfish and base, even though they should be persuaded that the fool, the dunce or the rascal is better satisfied with his lot than they are with theirs.

From this verdict of the only competent judges, I apprehend there can be no appeal. On the question of which of two pleasures is the best worth having, which of two modes of existence is the most grateful to the feelings, the judgment of those who are qualified by knowledge of both must be admitted as final. . . . There is no other tribunal to be referred to.

READING REFERENCES. It is not easy to find a sympathetic account of Mill as a moralist. In a little book by George Santayana, *Some Turns of Thought in Modern Philosophy*, there is a passage, beginning on page 55, "With this dissolution always in prospect . . .," which is an exception to this rule. The trouble arose, even in Mill's own day, over his somewhat unsatisfactory handling of the tenth objection: The appeal *to* happiness does not permit criticism *of* happiness. Nor does it. In F. H. Bradley's *Ethical Studies*, chapter 3, "Pleasure for Pleasure's Sake" will be found a severely critical examination of Mill's argument. Mill's *Autobiography* is splendid reading. It gives one a picture of the man who made a bold stand for happiness in moral philosophy. There is no really first-class book on Mill. The nearest approaches are Courtney's *Life of Mill* and the third volume of Stephen's *English Utilitarians*. The subsequent elaboration and defense and modification of Mill's position is to be traced in Henry Sidgwick's *Method of Ethics* and G. E. Moore's *Principia Ethica*.

READING QUESTIONS

1. What connection exists between Paley and Mill?
2. Who were the Utilitarians? By what other name were they known? What do these names signify?
3. What is Mill's criticism of the appeal to "feeling"?
4. "The appeal to nature is unmeaning in one sense of the term *nature*." What sense? Wherein unmeaning?
5. " . . . or irrational and immoral, in the other sense." Explain.
6. What principle does Mill formulate?
7. Whose happiness is not referred to in the principle?
8. What about "exceptions"? Exceptions to what?
9. "Of what sort of proof is this principle susceptible?"
10. "Such a philosophy is a godless doctrine." Wherein? Mill's answer?
11. "It is a doctrine worthy of swine." How so? Mill's answer?
12. "Such a doctrine renders men cold and unsympathizing." Mill's answer?
13. How does Mill deal with the question of motive?
14. "The principle of utility may serve as a cloak for selfishness." Mill's answer?
15. "An appeal to expedience is not as high morally as an appeal to principle." What does that statement mean? How does Mill deal with it?
16. "Happiness cannot be the rational purpose of life." Why not? Mill's answer?
17. "We cannot calculate all the consequences." Mill's answer?

18. "There is not time, previous to action, for calculating the effects." Mill's answer?
19. Formulate the tenth objection carefully, in your own words.
20. What is Mill's answer?
21. Is it an answer?

4. *MORALITY GROUNDED IN POWER—FROM FRIEDRICH NIETZSCHE*

From Mill to Nietzsche. We have examined three attempts to formulate the principle of morality. Paley found the rightness of an act to depend upon its agreement with the will of God. Kant denied that the rightness of an act depended upon anything, asserting that an act, if right, is so categorically, without reference to anything outside of itself. Mill found the rightness of an act to depend upon its consequences, these consequences being the amount of happiness which it brought about. We have now to examine the claim of a fourth moralist whose findings differ radically from any of the other three. The difference is so great that it is rather difficult to institute a comparison. The point may be approached in terms of an example. Consider honesty, the habit of telling the truth and being "square" in one's dealings. Let us suppose each of our moralists to be asked, "Why is it right to be honest and wrong to be dishonest?" "Because it agrees with God's will," Paley would say. "There is no reason why honesty is right," Kant would say, "It is right simply because it is right." "Because it makes for the greatest amount of happiness in the long run and for the most people," Mill would say. Now our fourth moralist would be inclined to answer the question by asking another: "Who said that honesty is right, and dishonesty wrong?" That is, he would ask whether the very wording of the question doesn't beg the question. You first accept certain things as right and wrong, he would argue, then you ask what principle is involved in thus distinguishing them. That is to beg the question. In other words, you can only ask this question by first assuming, without inquiry, that some things are right and others wrong, but if you query *that* fact, then where are you?

BIOGRAPHICAL NOTE. Friedrich Nietzsche was born in Germany in 1844 and died in 1900 at the age of fifty-six. His biography may be epitomized in terms of three periods: years of preparation, years of production, and years of insanity. (1) He was born into a puritanical, religious family and was intended by his parents to enter the church. To this end he was educated privately and at a denominational school. In the University at Bonn he broke completely with his family in matters doctrinal. He moved on to the University at Leipzig. There he met Wagner, the German composer, and became a fervent Wagnerite. He discovered Schopenhauer's writings in a second-hand bookshop and became a convinced Schopenhaurian. He met Erwin Rhode, the historian of Greek culture, and became engrossed in the problems and perspectives of the cultural history of mankind. He did military service for a year in a war with Austria, returning to the University at Leipzig to complete his studies. The following year he was appointed to the chair of classical philology in the university at Bâle, received his Ph.D., and began work on his important book, *The Birth of Tragedy*. The next year he was called once more into military service in the Franco-Prussian War which had just begun, 1870. He was head of an ambulance corps, but did only three weeks' service. Diphtheria ended his military career. He returned to the university at Bâle and resumed lectures. For eight years he remained at this work. During this period he was arriving at conclusions which formed the basis of his future writings. He published *The Birth of Tragedy*. It met with a chilly reception. His prestige began to decline. His next book, *Thoughts Out of Season*, contained four essays in which he criticized Strauss, Schopenhauer, German historians, and others. Two years later for reasons of poor health he retired on a small pension from the university.

(2) It should never be forgotten that Nietzsche was, first and last, a cultural historian; that is, he was interested in, and drew his inspiration from, the study of the cultures achieved by various peoples, ancient and modern. He wrote a series of books which develop really one theme. His investigations into mankind's cultural history, understanding by the term *culture* such things as art, religion, science, morality, government, etc., left him profoundly impressed, in the first place, by the enormous diversity which has obtained in these things at different times and places. But that was not all. He was equally impressed with the fact that cultural values are local and transitory affairs. He expressed this in the notion of the relativity of cultural values. By this he meant that cultural values are relative to time and place and relative to the needs peculiar to the peoples among whom they flourish. In other words, there is nothing eternal or absolute or immutable about them, and this, he felt, holds for values of all descriptions: religious, artistic, social, moral, scientific, and so on. On the rebound from his earlier orthodox training, he dismissed them with a flourish of his pen in his book, *Human, All Too Human*. That was his "great discovery." Values, one and all, are "human-all-too-human." The rest of his work may be described as a series of studies in the natural history of human values. *Human, All Too Human*, was followed by *Dawn of Day*, and it, in turn, by *Joyful Wisdom* Clearly, a new note was being struck. What idea was Nietzsche working out in these books?

It was something like this: The cultural history of mankind shows that those aristocratic qualities flourish in the early stages of a culture and disappear gradually as that culture becomes old. In Homer's time, the Greeks were "heroes"; by the time of Pericles and the Spartan war, they had become mere "sophists" and "philosophers" and "scientists." In early Roman history there were great kings who founded a race which conquered the ancient world, but centuries later, in the days of imperial decline, this nation of "strong, silent men" had become helpless victims of their own weakening civilization and the new races of barbarians as yet "untouched" by such things. These newcomers swept over Europe, and another page in cultural history was begun, but with the same result. By the nineteenth century these "Germanic" peoples who had made over the civilization of ancient Rome had become democratic, even socialistic; they cultivated "science," "art," "morality" or (in some instances) decadent forms of "immorality," wealth, ease, the "emancipation of women," optimism, pessimism, philosophy, and so on.

There is no quarreling with Nietzsche's likes and dislikes in these matters. The sight of Achilles sulking in his tent was simply something he admired more than the sight of Karl Marx sulking in the library of the British Museum. A Greek athlete or a Roman warrior was simply not in the same degenerate class with J. S. Mill pleading for representative government and the political enfranchisement of women, or Schopenhauer brooding over the misery and folly of human affairs. Hence, the titles of his books. To "see through" modern degeneration was "the dawn of day"; to realize that "real virtues" belong in the context of fresh and vigorous young cultures was the first step in "joyful wisdom." Nietzsche was carried away on the wings of this sort of thing. Lonely, poor, sickly, unpopular, a bachelor *malgré lui*, he nevertheless lived on in the private world of "transvalued values," heaping scorn on "art" and "science" and "morality" and "religion" and "emancipation" and "democracy" and "socialism" and "humanitarianism." He poured his soul into the mold of one beautiful book, *Thus Spake Zara-*

thustra. This was the fine flower of his genius. Through the mouth of Zarathustra, the prophet of his doctrine, he preached and exhorted and satirized in pages of marvelous beauty and suggestiveness. But the nineteenth century passed Zarathustra by on the other side. Only a handful took the trouble to read him, and even these few were puzzled and disturbed. For their enlightenment, Nietzsche wrote two more books, *Beyond Good and Evil* and *The Genealogy of Morals.* They were intended as commentaries on the *Zarathustra.* The substance of their argument is given in the citations which follow. The balance of Nietzsche's writings carry further the ideas presented already. The Zarathustra group was followed by *The Twilight of the Idols*, *Antichrist*, *The Will to Power* (unfinished), and his own autobiography bearing the significant title *Ecce Homo.*

(3) In 1889, now forty-five, Nietzsche began to lose the use of his mind. For the next eleven years he was caught in the toils of a steadily increasing insanity. The picture brings to mind Schopenhauer's gloomy hypothesis and leaves one impatient with the century which had allowed the man's genius to flicker out alone and unheeded.

THE ARGUMENT OF THE CITATIONS. The following passages, chosen principally from Nietzsche's *Beyond Good and Evil* and *The Genealogy of Morals*, exhibit six turns of thought. He begins by repudiating the whole notion of trying to formulate any principle of morality, in the sense that moralists have traditionally sought to do this. He insists that there is no such thing as morality having one fundamental principle running through it; that, on the contrary, there have been and are many moralities; and that any attempt to think philosophically about morality must begin by recognizing its diversity and the fact of its having had a history like any other phase of human culture. He propounds then a tentative natural history or genealogy of morals. From this he undertakes to draw some far-reaching conclusions. These he calls collectively his *immoralism*, or *transvaluation of values*. One fundamental distinction, arising out of his account of the natural history of morals and forming the foundation of his immoralism, is that between master morality and slave morality. The characteristics of each he then describes at some length. The doctrine is now substantially complete. However, to illustrate it more concretely, he applies it in a critical way to two phenomena of modern morality, namely, the emancipation of woman, and the close connection between modern morality and Christianity. He closes with a few reflections on his own significance.

The opening citations are fundamental. In these Nietzsche draws the searching distinction between accepting morality and trying to formulate its principle, and making moralities the subject of impartial investigation. It is the historian of humanity's manifold cultures and cultural values who speaks:

Hitherto all moralists, with a pedantic and ridiculous seriousness, have wanted to give a "basis" to morality, and each has believed that he has given this "basis" to morality. Morality itself, however, has been regarded as something "given."

That which moralists have called "giving a basis to morality," has proved merely a learned form of good faith in prevailing morality, a new means of expressing prevailing morality, consequently just a phenomenon within one definite morality, a sort of denial that it is lawful for this particular morality to be called in question. In no case has the attempt to "provide a basis for morality" ever involved a testing, analyzing, doubting, and vivisecting of the prevailing moral faith.

The philosophical workers, after the pattern of Kant and Hegel, have to fix and systematize some existing body of valuations, that is to say, creations of value which have become prevalent and are for a time called "the truth." It is for these thinkers to make conspicuous, conceivable, intelligible, manageable what has happened and been esteemed hitherto.

Apart from the value of such assertions as "there is a categorical imperative in us," we can always ask: "What does such an assertion indicate about him who makes it?"

Because moralists have known the moral facts imperfectly, in an arbitrary epitome, perhaps the morality of their environment, their position, their church, their *Zeitgeist*, their climate; because they have been badly instructed with regard to nations, eras, and past ages, and were by no means eager to know about these matters; precisely because of this fact, they did not even come in sight of the real problems of morality, problems which disclose themselves only to a comparison of many kinds of morality.

There are systems of morals which are meant to justify their author in the eyes of other people; systems which are meant to tranquilize him and make him self-satisfied; systems which are meant to enable him to crucify and humble himself. By means of one system of morals, he wishes to take revenge; by means of another, to conceal himself; by means of another, to glorify himself and gain superiority and distinction. In short, systems of morals are only sign languages of the emotions.

What is still necessary is the collection of material, the comprehensive survey and classification of sentiments of worth, distinctions of worth, which live, grow, propagate, and perish; and the attempt, perhaps, to give a clear idea of the recurring and more common forms of these living crystallizations. This is necessary as preparation for a theory of types of morality.

So much as a start. The primary problem is not to formulate the principle of morality, but to recognize the existence and study the natural history of many moralities. An acquaintance with these matters, Nietzsche feels, will reveal the fact that genuine moralities arise from the presence in any group of an aristocratic or ruling-class element. He offers an hypothetical reconstruction of the natural history or genealogy of morals.

Every elevation of the type "man" has hitherto been the work of an aristocratic society, and so it will always be: a society believing in a long gradation of rank and differences of worth among human beings, and requiring slavery in some form or other.

Without the pathos of distance, such as grows out of the difference of classes, out of the constant outlooking and downlooking of the ruling class on subordinates and instruments, out of the constant practice of obeying and commanding, out of the keeping down and keeping at a distance, without these, that other more mysterious pathos could never have arisen: the longing for the continued self-surmounting of man.

To be sure, one must cherish no humanitarian illusions about the origin of aristocratic societies. The truth is hard. Every higher civilization has originated in barbarism. Men, barbarians in every respect, men of prey, still in possession of unbroken strength of will and desire for power, threw themselves upon weaker, more moral, more peaceful races, upon old mellow civilizations in which the final vital force was flickering out in brilliant fireworks of wit and depravity. In the beginnings, the noble caste was always the barbarian caste.

The essential thing in a good and healthy aristocracy is that it should regard itself not as a function of the king or the people but as the significance and highest justification thereof; that it should accept with a clear conscience the sacrifice of a legion of individuals, who, for its sake, must be suppressed and reduced to imperfect men, to slaves and instruments. Its fundamental belief must be that society is not allowed to exist for its own sake, but only as a foundation and scaffolding by which a select class may be able to elevate themselves to their higher duties: like those climbing, sun-seeking plants in Java which encircle a tree till, high above it but supported by it, they can unfold their tops in the open light and exhibit their happiness.

Consider an aristocratic commonwealth, e.g., an ancient Greek city state, as a voluntary or involuntary contrivance for rearing human beings. There men are beside one another, thrown on their own resources, who want to make their species prevail, chiefly because they must prevail or be in danger of extermination. The favor, the abundance, the protection, are lacking under which variations are fostered. The species needs itself as species; as something which by its hardness, its uniformity, its simplicity of structure, can prevail in the struggle against neighbors or rebellious vassals. Experience teaches it what are the qualities to which it owes its continued existence in spite of gods and men. These qualities it calls *virtues*, and these virtues alone it develops to maturity.

These virtues it develops with severity. Every aristocratic morality is intolerant in the education of its youth, in the control of its women, in the customs which control marriage, in the relations between old and young, in the penal laws (which have an eye only for the degenerating). It counts intolerance itself among the virtues.

Thus is established a type, with few but very marked features. The constant struggle with unfavorable conditions is the cause of the type becoming stable and hard.

Finally, however, a happy state of security results, and the enormous tension is relaxed. Perhaps there are no more enemies among neighboring peoples; perhaps the means of life and enjoyment are present in abundance. With one stroke the bond and constraint of the old discipline snaps. It is no longer regarded as a necessary condition of existence and survival. If it would continue, it can do so only as an archaizing "taste." Variations appear suddenly in the greatest exuberance and splendor. The individual dares to be individual and detach himself.

At this turning point of history there manifest themselves a magnificent manifold growth and an extraordinary decay, owing to the savagely opposed and seemingly exploding egoisms which strive for "light and sun" and can no longer assign any limit or restraint to themselves by the hitherto existing morality. It was this morality itself which piled up the enormous strength, which bent the bow in so threatening a manner, but it is now out of date, or getting out of date.

The dangerous and disquieting point has now been reached. The greater, more manifold, more comprehensive life now coming into existence is lived beyond the old morality. The "individual" stands out and is obliged to have recourse to his own law giving, his own arts and artifices for self-preservation, self-elevation, self-deliverance. Nothing but new "whys"; nothing but new "hows." No longer any common formulae; misunderstanding and disregard in league together; decay, deterioration, lofty desire, frightfully entangled; the genius of the race overflowing from all the cornucopias of good and bad; new charms and mysteries peculiar to the still inexhausted, still unwearied, corruption.

Danger, the mother of morality, is present once more. This time the danger point has shifted, into the individual, the neighbor, the friend; into the street, into their own child, into all the most personal and secret recesses of their desires and volitions.

After the fabric of a society seems established and secure against external dangers, it is the fear of our neighbor which creates new perspectives of moral evaluation.

It is by the loftiest and strongest instincts, when they break out and carry the individual above and beyond the average, above and beyond the low level of the herd conscience, that the self-reliance of the community is destroyed. Its belief in itself breaks. Consequently these instincts will be most branded and most defamed.

Strong and dangerous instincts, e.g., the love of enterprise, foolhardiness, revengefulness, astuteness, rapacity, love of power, which, up till then had to be honored and fostered and cultivated because required in the common dangers against common enemies, are now felt to be themselves dangerous, are gradually branded as immoral and given over to calumny. The opposite instincts and inclinations now attain to moral honor. The herd instinct gradually draws its conclusions.

How much danger to the community or its equality is contained in an opinion, a condition, an emotion, a character, a disposition? That is now the moral perspective. Here again fear is the mother of morals.

The lofty, independent spirit, the will to stand alone, are felt to be dangers. Everything that elevates the individual above the herd, and is a source of fear to the neighbor, is henceforth called evil. The tolerant, unassuming, self-adapting, self-equalizing disposition, the middle-of-the road desires, attain to moral distinction and honor.

Under peaceful circumstances there is always less opportunity and less need for training the feelings to severity and rigor. Now every form of severity, even severity in justice, begins to disturb the conscience. A lofty and rigorous nobleness and self-responsibility becomes now almost an offense.

The man of an age of dissolution, of an age which mixes the races with one another; who has the inheritance of a diversified descent in his body, contrary instincts and standards of value which struggle among themselves and are seldom at peace; such a man, of late culture and broken lights, will, as a rule, be a weak man.

His fundamental desire is that the war which is in him should come to an end. Happiness appears to him in the character of a soothing medicine and mode of thought; it is above all things the happiness of repose, of undisturbedness, of repletion, of final unity.

All systems of morals which address themselves to "happiness" are only suggestions for behavior adapted to the degree of danger from themselves in which the individuals live. They are thus recipes for their passions, their good and bad propensities, insofar as the individuals would like to play the master. They are all so many small and great expediences, permeated with the musty odor of old family medicines and old wives' wisdom; all grotesque and absurd because they are generalizations where generalization is not justified.

The rank-and-file man assumes an air of being the only kind of man that is allowable. He glorifies, as the peculiarly human virtues, his qualities, such as public spirit, kindness, deference, industry, temperance, modesty, indulgence, sympathy (by virtue of which he is gentle, endurable, and useful to the herd).

In cases where it is believed that a leader cannot be dispensed with, attempt after attempt is made to replace rulers by summing together clever herd-minded men. All representative constitutions, for example, are of this origin.

There arises what I call the moral hypocrisy of the ruling class. They know no other way to protect themselves from bad conscience than to play the role of executors of older and higher orders. (These "older and higher orders" may be predecessors, the constitution, justice, the law, or God himself.) Or they even justify themselves by maxims drawn from the current opinions of the herd, as, for example, "the first servants of their people," or "instruments of public weal."

The end is quickly approaching; everything decays and produces decay; nothing will endure until the day after tomorrow; nothing, that is, except one species of man, the incurably mediocre. The mediocre alone have a prospect of continuing, of propagating themselves. They will be the men of the future, the sole survivors. "Be like them! Be mediocre!" is now the only morality which has still a significance or obtains a hearing. But it is difficult to preach this morality of mediocrity. It can never avow what it is and what it desires. It has to talk of "moderation," and "dignity," and "duty," and "brotherly love." It will have difficulty in concealing its irony!

But this herding-animal morality is only one kind of morality, beside which, before which, and after which, many other moralities, above all, higher moralities, are or should be possible. Against such a possibility, this herd morality defends itself with all its strength. It says obstinately and inexorably: "I am morality and nothing else is morality."

The first corollary which follows from Nietzsche's conception of the genealogy of morals is what he calls his *immoralism*, or his proposed *transvaluation of values*. Thus:

What will the moralists who appear at this time have to preach? What shall be the message of these sharp on-lookers, these unhurried ones?

What is essential and invaluable in every system of morals, is that it is a long constraint.

A species originates, a type becomes established and strong in the long struggle with essentially unfavorable conditions. On the other hand, species which receive abundant nourishment, a surplus of protection and care, tend to develop variations, become fertile in prodigies and monstrosities.

The essential thing, to repeat, is that there should be a long obedience in the same direction. Thereby results something which makes life worth living; for instance, virtue, art, music, dancing, reason, spirituality; whatever, in short, is transfiguring, refined, or divine.

One may look at every system of morals in this light. It teaches us to hate the lax, the too great freedom. It implants the need for limited horizons, for immediate duties, for narrow perspectives. "Thou must obey some one, and for a long time; otherwise thou wilt come to grief, and lose all respect for thyself."

The tension of soul in misfortune, its shuddering in view of rack and ruin, its inventiveness and heroism in enduring and exploiting misfortune, its depth, mystery, greatness; have these not been bestowed through the discipline of great suffering?

Up to now man has been in the worst hands, has been ruled by the misfits, the physiologically botched, the cunning and revengeful, the so-called *saints* — slanderers of the world, traducers of humanity. The morality of decadence, the will to nothingness, passes as morality *par excellence*. Proof of this: Altruism is considered an absolute value, while egoism meets with hostility everywhere. He who disagrees with me on this point I regard as infected.

For a physiologist, such an opposition of altruism and egoism would leave no room for doubt. If the smallest organ in the body neglects its self-preservation, its recuperative powers, its "egoism," the whole organism will degenerate. The physiologist insists that such decayed parts be cut out. He pities them not at all. But the priest wants precisely the degeneration of mankind; hence he strives to preserve the decayed elements in humanity. This is the price of his rule. This is the "harm that good men do."

When one is no longer serious about self-preservation and the increase of bodily energy, when anemia is made an ideal and contempt of the body is construed as "salvation of the soul," what can all this be, if not a recipe for decadence? Loss of ballast, resistance to natural instincts, "selflessness," these have hitherto been called *morality*.

You want, if possible, to do away with suffering. There is not a more foolish "if possible." We would rather have it increased and made worse. Well-being, as you understand it, is certainly not a goal. The discipline of great suffering is the only discipline that has produced all the elevations of humanity hitherto.

To consider distress as something to be destroyed is sheer idiocy. Generally, it is actually harmful in its consequences, a fatal stupidity, almost as mad as the desire to abolish bad weather out of pity for the poor. In the great economy of the universe the terrors of reality, e.g., the passions, the desires, the will to power, are incalculably more essential than that petty happiness, so-called *goodness*.

It is only among decadents that pity is called a virtue. They are too ready to forget modesty, reverence, and that delicacy of feeling which knows how to keep at a distance. They forget that this sentimental emotion stinks of the mob; that pity is only one step removed from bad manners; that pitying hands may be thrust with destructive results into a great destiny, into a wounded isolation. . . . The overcoming of pity I reckon among the noble virtues.

There is nowadays a sickly irritability and sensitiveness to pain, a repulsive complaining, an effeminizing, which, with the aid of religious and philosophical nonsense, seeks to deck itself out as something superior. There is a regular cult of suffering. The unmanliness of what such groups of visionaries call *sympathy* is, I believe, the first thing that strikes the eye. One must resolutely taboo this latest form of bad taste.

There is a point of diseased mellowness and effeminacy in the history of society, at which society itself takes the part of him who injures it, the part of the criminal. To punish now appears to be somehow "unfair." Is it not sufficient, it is asked, if the criminal be rendered harmless? Why should we still punish? Punishment is barbarous! And so on. With these questions, the herd morality, the morality of fear, draws its ultimate conclusion.

On no point is the ordinary mind of Europe more unwilling to be corrected, than on this matter. People rave nowadays, even under the guise of "science," about coming social conditions in which the "exploiting character" of human relations is to be absent. Particularly is this true of socialistic shallowpates and howling anarchistic dogs. Their words sound to me as if they were promising a mode of life which should refrain from all organic functions. "Exploitation" is not the mark of a depraved or primitive society; it belongs to the nature of the living, as a primary organic function; it is a consequence of the will to power which is precisely the will to life.

You may note that I do not care to see rudeness undervalued. It is by far the most humane form of contradiction, and amid modern effeminacy, it is one of our first virtues.

To be able to be an enemy, to be an enemy, presupposes a strong nature. Strong natures need resistance, accordingly they seek it. The pathos of aggression belongs to strength as much as feelings of revenge and rancor belong to weakness. The strength of the aggressor is determined by the opposition he needs; every increase of strength betrays itself by a search for a more formidable opponent.

To refrain from mutual injury, from violence, from exploitation, to put one's will on a par with others' may result in a kind of good conduct among individuals; but only when the necessary conditions are given, namely, an equality of the individuals in force and worth, and their correlation within one organization.

To take this principle more generally, however, to use it as the fundamental principle of society, would immediately reveal what it actually amounts to, namely, a principle of dissolution and decay. Here one must think profoundly and resist all sentimentality; life itself is essentially appropriation, injury, exploitation, conquest, suppression, severity, obtrusion, incorporation.

Even the organization within which the members treat each other as equal, must, itself, do that toward other organizations which its members refrain from doing to each other; if, that is, it be a living, growing, and not a dying organization. It will endeavor to grow, to gain ground, to attract to itself, to acquire ascendency; not owing to any morality or immorality, but simply because it lives, and because life is precisely will to power.

Fortunately, the world is not built merely on those instincts in which the good-natured herd animal would find his paltry happiness. To demand that everyone become a "good man," a gregarious animal, a blue-eyed benevolent "beautiful soul," or (as Herbert Spencer wished) an altruist, would mean robbing existence of its greatest character, emasculating mankind. And this has been attempted. It is just this that men call *morality*.

The "good" man is the most harmful kind of man. He secures his existence at the cost of truth. He cannot create. He crucifies the man who writeth new values on new tables. He crucifies the whole future of humanity. Whatever harm the slanderers of the world may do, the harm which good men do is the most calamitous of all harm.

Let me say again what I have already said a hundred times. In all our principal moral judgments, that which is sure of itself, that which glorifies itself with praise and blame, that which calls itself good, is the instinct of the herding human animal: the instinct which is coming more and more to the front, coming more and more to dominate other instincts. Morality at present is herding-animal morality.

All questions of politics, of the social order, of education, have been falsified from top to bottom, because the most harmful men have been taken for great men, and because people were taught to despise the fundamentals of life.

Nietzsche's characteristic doctrines have their basis in these conceptions of the genealogy of morals and the transvaluation of values. His distinction between man and superman, between master morality and slave morality, his reiterated criticisms of the softer, more humanitarian virtues and customs, follow reasonably enough. Perhaps the most famous of all Nietzsche's teachings is in his distinction between master morality and slave morality. Its point is this:

Moral systems must be compelled to bow before the gradations of rank. Their presumption must be driven home, until they thoroughly understand that it is immoral to say that "what is right and proper for one is right and proper for another."

In a tour through the many finer and coarser moralities which have hitherto prevailed, or still prevail, on the earth, I have found certain traits recurring regularly together, until finally two primary types revealed themselves to me: There are master morality and slave morality.

Moral valuations have originated, either in a ruling class pleasantly conscious of being different from the ruled, or in a ruled class, among slaves and dependents of all sorts.

In the master morality, when it is the rulers who determine the notion of "goodness," it is the exalted, proud type of character which is regarded as the distinguishing feature, as that which determines the order of rank. The noble man separates from himself the persons in whom these characteristics are absent; them he despises.

They say: "Thus shall it be." They determine the whither and the why of mankind. They grasp at the future with a creative hand. Whatever is and was becomes for them a means, an instrument, a hammer. Their knowing is creating. Their creating is law-giving. Their will to truth is will to power.

In master morality the antithesis is between "noble" and "despicable." The cowardly, the timid, the no-accounts, the narrowly utilitarian, the distrustful, the self-abasing, the doglike who submit to abuse, the mendicant flatterers, and above all the liars, are despised.

A man who says, "I like that, I take it for my own, I mean to guard it and protect it"; a man who can carry out a resolution, keep hold of a woman, punish and overthrow insolence; a man who has his indignation and his sword; a man whom the weak, the suffering, even the animals, willingly submit to and naturally belong to; such a man is a master by nature.

The noble type of man regards himself as the determiner of values; he does not require to be approved of; he passes the judgment: "What is injurious to me is injurious in itself"; he knows that it is he himself only who confers honor on things; he is a creator of values. He honors whatever he recognizes in himself: such morality is self-glorification. In the foreground there is the feeling of plenitude, of power which seeks to overflow, the consciousness of a wealth which would fain give and bestow.

The noble man honors in himself the powerful one, him who has power over himself, who knows how to speak and how to keep silent, who takes pleasure in subjecting himself to severity and hardness and has reverence for all that is severe and hard. "Wotan placed a hard heart in my breast," says an old Scandinavian saga: it is thus rightly expressed from the soul of a proud Viking.

The noble man is furthest removed from the morality which sees the essence of the moral in sympathy, or in "acting for the good of others." Faith in oneself, pride in oneself, a radical irony and enmity toward "selflessness," belong as definitely to master morality as do scorn and precaution in the presence of sympathy and the "warm heart."

A man of this sort is carved from a single block, which is hard, sweet, fragrant. He enjoys only what is good for him. His desire ceases when the limits of what is good for him are overstepped. . . . Whatever does not kill him makes him stronger. He gathers his material from all he sees, hears, and experiences. He is a selective principle: he rejects much. . . . He reacts slowly to all kinds of stimuli, with that slowness which long caution and pride have bred in him. . . . He is always in his own company, whether mingling with men or books or nature. . . . He honors the thing he chooses.

There is an instinct for rank, which, more than anything else, is the sign of a high rank. The refinement, the goodness, the loftiness of a soul are put to a real test when something of the highest rank passes by but is not yet protected with the awe of authority; something that goes its way like a living touchstone, undistinguished, undiscovered, tentative, perhaps veiled and disguised.

The noble and powerful know how to honor; it is their art, their domain for invention. The profound reverence for age and tradition, the belief and prejudice in favor of ancestors and against newcomers, is typical of master morality. If, contrariwise, men of "modern ideas" believe in "progress" and the "future," and are increasingly lacking in respect for the past, the ignoble origin of these "ideas" is thereby betrayed.

He whose task is to investigate souls will avail himself of many varieties of this very art to determine the ultimate value of a soul, the innate order of rank to which it belongs. He will test it by its instinct for reverence. The vulgarity of many a soul spurts up like dirty water when any holy vessel, any jewel from closed shrines, any book bearing the marks of great destiny, is brought before it. Contrariwise, there is an involuntary silence, a hesitation, a cessation, by which is indicated that a soul feels the nearness of what is worthy of respect.

In the so-called *cultured* classes today, the dealers in "modern ideas," nothing is perhaps so repulsive as their lack of shame, their lack of reverence, the easy insolence of hand and eye with which they touch, finger, and examine everything. It is possible that more tact for reverence exists among the lower classes and peasants than among the newspaper-reading demimonde of "intellect" and "culture."

Much has been achieved when the sentiment of reverence has been finally instilled into the masses, i.e., the shallowpates and nitwits of every kind; when they realize that they are not allowed to touch everything, that there are some experiences before which they must take off their shoes and restrain their hand.

The master morality is especially foreign and irritating to present-day taste. It is disliked and distrusted for the sternness of its principle that one has duties only to one's equals; that one may act toward persons of a lower rank, toward all that is foreign, just as one pleases; that its values are "beyond good and evil."

It is typical of the master morality to be able and obliged to exercise prolonged gratitude and prolonged revenge, but both only within the circle of one's equals; artfulness in retaliation; a need for enemies as outlets for emotions of envy, quarrelsomeness, arrogance. This, of course, is not "modern morality," and is therefore difficult to realize, to discover.

In contrast to the master morality stands the slave morality:

It is otherwise with the second type of morality; what I have named slave morality. If the abused, the oppressed, the suffering, the unemancipated, the weary, the uncertain-of-themselves, should moralize, what will be the common element in their moral evaluations?

The slave has an unfavorable eye for the virtues of the powerful. He has a skepticism and distrust of everything which they honor. He would fain persuade himself that their happiness is not genuine.

On the other hand, those qualities which serve to alleviate the existence of sufferers are brought into prominence and flooded with light. It is here that sympathy, the kind helping hand, the warm heart, patience, diligence, humility, friendliness, attain to honor. For here these are the most useful equalities, almost the only means of supporting the burden of existence.

Slave morality is essentially the morality of utility. It is oriented around the idea of the "useful." Here is the seat of the origin of the famous antithesis of "good" and "evil," which I have distinguished from the antithesis of "good" and "bad." According to slave morality, the "evil" man rouses fear. According to master morality, the "good" man rouses fear, and seeks to rouse it, while the "bad" man is regarded as the despicable being.

According to slave morality, the good man must be the "safe" man: he must be good-natured, easily hoodwinked, perhaps a little stupid. Wherever slave morality gains the ascendency, language shows a tendency to approximate the significations of the words *good* and *stupid*.

A last fundamental difference: the desire for freedom, the enthusiasm for "liberty" the instinct of being "happy" belong as inherently to slave morality as artifice in reverence and enthusiasm in devotion belong to master morality. Hence, we can understand, love as a passion, romantic love, with its ardors and endurances and binding ties, is a phenomenon of master morality.

Nietzsche never wearied of criticizing those phases of modern morality which smacked of "degeneration" and "slaves." Among the topics singled out for castigation was the nineteenth-century enthusiasm for the emancipation of women. Says Nietzsche:

To be mistaken in the fundamental problem of "man and woman" is the typical sign of a shallow mind. To deny here the profoundest antagonism, the need for hostile tension; to dream here of "equal rights," equal training, equal claims and obligations; to prove oneself shallow at this dangerous spot, may be regarded as suspicious, nay more, as betrayed. Such an one may probably prove "too short" for all the fundamental issues of life, unable to descend into any of the depths.

In no previous age have women been treated with so much respect by men as at present. This belongs to the tendency and fundamental taste of democracy. Is it any wonder that abuse should be made of this respect? Women want more; they learn to make claims; they become rivals for rights. In a word, they lose their modesty. And, let me add, they also lose their taste.

They unlearn their fear of men. But the woman who "unlearns" her fear of men, sacrifices her most womanly instincts. That woman should venture forward when man has ceased to inspire fear, is reasonable enough, and intelligible enough. But what is more difficult to grasp is that precisely thereby woman deteriorates. That is happening these days: let us not deceive ourselves about it.

Wherever the industrial spirit has triumphed over the military and aristocratic spirit, woman strives for the economic and legal independence of a clerk. "Woman as clerk" is inscribed on the portal of that modern society which is in course of formation.

While she thus appropriates new rights, aspires to be master, and inscribes the "progress" of woman on her flags and banners, the very opposite realizes itself with terrible obviousness — woman retrogrades.

There is stupidity in this movement, an almost masculine stupidity, of which a well-bred sensible woman might be heartily ashamed. To lose the ground on which she can most surely achieve victory; to neglect her proper weapons; to let herself go before man where formerly she kept herself in control in artful humility; to neutralize man's faith in a fundamentally different ideal in woman, something eternally feminine; to emphatically and loquaciously dissuade man from the idea that woman must be preserved, protected, and indulged like some delicate, strangely wild, and often pleasant domestic animal; what does all this betoken, if not a disintegration of womanly instincts?

There are, to be sure, enough of idiotic friends and corrupters of woman amongst the learned asses of the male sex, who advise woman to defeminize herself in this manner, and to imitate all the stupidities from which man suffers, who would like to lower woman to "general culture," indeed, even to newspaper reading and meddling with politics.

In their efforts to rise to the ideal woman, to the higher woman, they have really wished to lower the general level of women, and there are no more certain means to this end than university education, trousers, and the rights of voting like cattle. Fundamentally, the "emancipated" and the "emancipators" (for example, that typical old maid, Henrik Ibsen) are anarchists, misbegotten souls whose most deep-rooted instinct is revenge.

Almost everywhere her nerves are being ruined, and she is daily being made more hysterical and more incapable of fulfilling her first and last function, namely, the rearing of robust children. These "friends of woman" wish to "cultivate" her, to make the weaker sex strong by "culture," as if history did not teach that the "cultivating" of mankind and the weakening of mankind have always kept pace with one another.

That which inspires respect in woman, and often also fear, is her real nature, her genuine, carnivora-like cunning and flexibility, her tiger claws beneath the glove, her naïveté in egoism, her untrainableness, her innate wildness, her incomprehensibleness, the extent and deviation of her virtues.

That which, in spite of fear, excites one's sympathy for the dangerous and beautiful in woman, is that she seems more afflicted, more vulnerable, more needful of love and more condemned to disillusion, than any other creature. Fear and sympathy — it is with these feelings that man has hitherto stood in the presence of woman, always with one foot in tragedy which rends while it delights. And all that is now to be at an end? The disenchantment of women is in progress? The tediousness of woman is slowly evolving?

Another object of Nietzsche's criticism was what he describes as "Christian morality." He never tires of railing at it. From among pages and pages, the following citations may be taken as representative:

All the things men have valued heretofore are not even realities. They are mere fantasies; more strictly speaking, they are lies. All the concepts, "God," "soul," "virtue," "sin," "Beyond," "truth," "eternal life," are lies arising from the evil instincts of diseased and harmful natures.

I am the first immoralist. Basically, there are two denials included in this term. First, I deny the type of man who formerly passed as the highest, the "good" man, the "benevolent" man, the "charitable" man. Second, I deny that kind of morality which has become recognized and dominant, namely Christian morality. . . . The second of these denials is the more decisive.

No one before me has felt Christian morality beneath him. To do that one must have height, far vision, depth. Up to now, Christian morality has been the Circe of all thinkers; they stood at her service. What man before me has descended into the caves from which the poisonous fumes of this ideal burst forth? Who before me ever dared to suspect they were caves? What philosopher before me was a real moralist and not a superior swindler, an idealist?

Have you understood me? What defines me is the fact that I unmasked Christian morality. For this reason I needed a word which would contain the idea of a universal challenge: immoralist. Blindness in the face of Christian morality is the essential crime. It is the great uncleanliness.

Christian morality is the most pernicious form of the will to falsehood, the denial of life. It is not error as error which infuriates me here. It is not the age-long lack of "good will," of discipline, of decency, of spiritual courage, which betrays itself in the triumph of Christian morality. It is the ghastly fact that what was unnatural received the highest honors as morality, and remained suspended over man as the law of the categorical imperative. This is the great blundering. To teach contempt of the primal life instincts; to set up a "soul," a spirit, in order to overthrow the body; to teach man to find impurity in sex; to look for the principle of evil in the need for expansion; to see a "higher moral value" in "selflessness," in "objectivity," in "neighbor love"; these things are the will to nothingness, the denial of life, the great nay-saying.

The Jews performed the miracle of the inversion of valuations, by means of which life on earth obtained a new and dangerous charm for a couple of thousand years. Their prophets fused the expressions *rich*, *godless*, *wicked*, *violent*, *sensual*, into one expression, and for the first time coined the word *world* as a term of reproach. In this inversion of values (which included the use of *poor* as synonymous with *saint* and *friend*) the significance of the Jewish people is to be found. It is with them that slave morality begins.

From the beginning, Christian morality was essentially the surfeit of life which disguised itself under the belief in "another" and "better" life. The hatred of the world, the condemnation of emotion, the fear of beauty, the distrust of sensuality, all these have always appeared to me as the most dangerous forms of the "will to perish," symptoms of the deepest weariness, exhaustion, anemia.

The teachers and preachers and leaders of mankind, including the theologians, have been decadents. Hence their inversion of values into a hostility to life; hence "morality." Here is a definition of *morality:* the idiosyncrasy of decadents actuated by a desire to avenge themselves successfully upon life. I attach great value to this definition.

Have you understood me? The unmasking of Christian morality is a unique event. It breaks the history of mankind in two. Man lives either before or after that. Everything which was until then called the *truth*, is now recognized as the most harmful, spiteful, and concealed falsehood. The sacred pretext, the "improvement of man," is recognized as a ruse to drain life of its blood. This morality is vampirism.

He who unmasks Christian morality unmasks the worthlessness of the values in which men believe. He sees in them only the most fatal kind of abortions; fatal, because they fascinate. The notion of "God" was invented as the counternotion to life. The notion of a "Beyond" was invented to depreciate the only world that exists. The notion of an "immortal soul" was invented to despise the body. The notion of "sin" was invented to mislead our instincts. Finally, the notion of a "good man" has come to mean everything that is weak, ill, misshapen, everything which should be obliterated. The law of selection is thwarted. And all this was believed in as morality! *Ecrasez l'infâme!*

We who hold a different view, we who regard Christian morality and democratic politics to be a degenerating form of organization, where have we to fix our hopes?

In new moralists and a new morality. There is no other alternative. In minds strong enough and original enough to initiate a transvaluation of values, to invert "eternal valuations," lies our only hope. In forerunners, in men of the future, who shall fix the constraints and fasten the knots which will compel millenniums to take new paths; make preparations for vast hazardous enterprises and collective attempts in rearing and educating; put an end to the frightful rule of folly and chance which has hitherto gone by the name of *history;* in such do we fix our hopes.

For these purposes a new type of moralist and ruler will some time be needed, at the very idea of which everything that has existed might look pale and dwarfed. The image of such leaders hovers before our eyes.

But their image fills our hearts with anxiety and gloom. How are they to be born? How are they to be bred? How nurtured to that elevation and power which will feel the present needs as their tasks? Of them is demanded a transvaluation of values. In them is needed a new conscience of steel, a new heart of brass, to bear the weight of such responsibility. There is always the danger that they may be lacking, or miscarry and degenerate. These are our real anxieties and glooms. These are the heavy thoughts and storms which sweep across our skies.

There are few pains so grievous as to have seen an exceptional man miss his way and deteriorate. But he who has the rare eye to see the danger of mankind itself missing its way and deteriorating; he who has recognized the element of wild chance in human affairs; he who has detected the fate that is hidden under the idiotic unwariness and blind confidence of "modern ideas," and still more of Christian morality and democratic politics; suffers from an anguish beyond comparison.

The universal degeneracy of mankind to the level of the ideals of socialistic fools and humanitarian shallowpates, the dwarfing of man to an absolutely gregarious animal, the brutalizing of man into pigmy with equal "rights" and "claims" — this is undoubtedly possible. He who has foreseen this possibility knows another loathing unknown to the rest of mankind.

From these themes, Nietzsche turns to the question of his own significance for the modern mind. Nietzsche on the genealogy of morals is interesting. Nietzsche on the distinction between master morality and slave morality is suggestive. Nietzsche on woman and Christianity is challenging. But Nietzsche on himself is unique:

Idealism is alien to me. Where you see ideal things I see human things, alas all-too-human.

He who would be a creator in good and evil must first be a destroyer, and break values into pieces. I am the most terrible man that has ever existed. But I shall be the most beneficent. I know the joy of annihilation. I am the first immoralist. I am thus the essential destroyer.

I know my destiny. I am not a man. I am a fatality. I am dynamite. Some day my name will be bound up with the recollection of something terrific, a crisis, a profound clash of consciences, a decisive condemnation of all that before me had been believed, required, hallowed.

I am the voice of truth. But my truth is terrible, for hitherto lies have been called truth. "The transvaluation of all values" is my formula for mankind's act of highest self-recognition. I contradict as no one has contradicted before. For when truth engages in a struggle with the falsehoods of ages, we must expect shocks, earthquakes, rearrangements of hills and valleys, such as never yet have been dreamt of. All the mighty forms of the old social structure I blow into space, for they rest on falsehoods. Politics on a grand scale will date from me.

My life task is to prepare humanity for a moment of supreme self-consciousness, a great noontide, a transvaluation of all values, an emancipation from all moral values, a yea-saying, a confidence in all that has formerly been forbidden, despised, and damned; when it will gaze both backwards and forwards, emerge from the tyranny of accident and priesthood, and, for the first time, pose the question of the why and wherefore of humanity as a whole.

But with all this there is nothing in me to suggest the founder of a "religion." Religions are the business of the mob. After coming in contact with a religious man, I have always to wash my hands. I want no "believers." I never address myself to the masses. I do not wish to be a saint: I would rather be a clown. Perhaps I am a clown.

READING REFERENCES. The best thing to do with Nietzsche, having read carefully the selections given here, is to try his

Thus Spake Zarathustra. This is at first a somewhat difficult book, but it has a strange, exotic charm.

It may be supplemented by chapters from *Beyond Good and Evil* and *The Genealogy of Morals.* Among items that may be consulted with profit, for a beginning, is Will Durant's chapter in his *Story of Philosophy.* The best single book on Nietzsche is George A Morgan's *What Nietzsche Means.* The author of the Philo Vance detective novels was a student of Nietzsche's works. His real name was W. H. Wright, and his book *What Nietzsche Taught* is a good introduction. The same goes for H. L. Mencken's *The Philosophy of Friedrich Nietzsche.* Among books of a more academic character may be mentioned W. K. Salter's *Nietzsche the Thinker.*

READING QUESTIONS

1. What quarrel does Nietzsche have with all previous moral philosophies?
2. What is necessary as a preparation for what?
3. Through what stages does he trace the genealogy of morality?
4. What do you understand by these phrases: "the pathos of distance," "sun-seeking plants in Java," "Danger, the mother of morality," "herd-minded," "the moral hypocrisy of the ruling class," "morality of mediocrity," "herding-animal morality," "a long constraint"?
5. What do you understand by "immoralism"? What by "the transvaluation of values"?
6. Elucidate these phrases: "the discipline of great suffering," "pity as a vice," "socialistic shallowpates," "the pathos of aggression," "the harm that good men do"?
7. How does he characterize master morality?
8. How slave morality?
9. "Slave morality is essentially the morality of utility." Meaning?
10. What are his views on the emancipation of women?
11. What are his views on what he conceives as Christian morality?
12. Formulate two or more criticisms you would make of his position.

5. *MORALITY GROUNDED IN DEMANDS — FROM WILLIAM JAMES*

From Nietzsche to James. The moral philosophy of Nietzsche assumed, on its negative side, the form of a critique of traditional morality, especially of such portions as derived from historical Christianity. Naturally, matters were not left at that. Among the many who rallied to the cause of religion, against its critics, none was more colorful and engaging than William James. We have seen him at work already, in two earlier chapters. In the present chapter we meet him once more, this time in the role of moralist. I think it would be instructive, having read this chapter carefully, to recall what the author had to say on the questions of natural theology and metaphysics. There is a general consistency among the different parts of his philosophy which endeared him to those who shared that philosophy.

Biographical Note. See under "A Theological Problem," page 73.

The Argument of the Citations. James begins by calling attention to the fact that ethical skepticism is not one among other possible moral philosophies. It is the denial or the bankruptcy of moral philosophy. If it is, in essential part at least, the aim of a moral philosophy to explain what is meant by *right*, *good*, *obligation*, and other such ethical terms, and to indicate what things or classes of things are right, good, obligatory, etc. then ethical skepticism would be the admission that we do not or cannot know the answers to questions formulated in these terms. For example: "What does it mean to say of an act that it is right?" Answer: "I don't know." "What acts are right?" Answer: "I don't know." "Is this particular act right?" "I don't know." "Is any act whatever right?" Answer: "I don't know." Ethical skepticism is the belief that the answer to all ethical questions is "I don't know." Thus James:

What is the position of him who seeks an ethical philosophy? To begin with he must be distinguished from all those who are satisfied to be ethical skeptics. He *will* not be skeptic. Therefore, so far from ethical skepticism being one possible fruit of ethical philosophizing it can only be regarded as that residual alternative to all philosophy which from the outset menaces every would-be philosopher who may give up the quest discouraged and renounce his original aim.

From this provisional warning that he will pay any price within limits to avoid ethical skepticism, James settles down to formulate his questions. What do we mean by such words as *good* and *ill*? He begins by noting that there are some things, or classes of things, to which these words are inapplicable.

First of all, such words as *good* and *ill* can have no application or relevancy in a world in which no sentient life exists. Imagine a world containing only physical and chemical facts, without a God, without even an interested spectator. Would there be any sense in saying of that world that one of its states is better than another? If there were two such worlds, would there be any rhyme or reason in calling one good and the other bad?

I am asking whether goods and evils exist in physical facts, *per se*. There is, it seems to me, no status for goods and evils to exist in, in a purely insentient world. How can one physical fact, considered simply as a physical fact, be "better" than another? A physical fact, in its mere material capacity, can no more be good or bad than it can be pleasant or painful. Physical facts simply are, or are not. No world composed of merely physical facts can possibly be a world to which ethical propositions apply.

To sharpen his initial claim that ethical terms can have no application in a world where no sentient life exists, James suggests, by way of minimum contrast, a world in which only one person exists.

Let us suppose a universe containing one person. Let us call the supposed universe which he inhabits a *moral solitude*. There is a chance now for goods and evils to exist. They have their status in that being's consciousness. So far as he feels anything to be good, he makes it good. It is good, for him, and being good for him, is absolutely good, for he is the sole creator of values in that universe, and outside of his opinion things have no moral character at all.

In such a universe as we have supposed, it would be absurd to ask whether the solitary thinker's judgments of good and evil are true or false. Truth supposes a standard outside of the thinker to which he must conform. But here the thinker is subject to no higher judge.

What happens to the argument if we add one more person to our universe?

If now we introduce a second thinker, with his likes and dislikes, into the universe, the ethical situation becomes more complex, and several possibilities are seen to obtain.

The two thinkers may ignore each other's attitude about good and evil altogether, and indulge each his own preferences, indifferent to what the other may feel or do. In such a case we have twice as much of the ethical quality in our world as we had in our moral solitude, only it is without ethical unity. The same object is good or bad, in such a universe, according as you measure it by the view which this one or the other one of the thinkers takes.

In such a universe as we are now supposing, if the two persons ignore each other, you cannot find any possible ground for saying that the opinion of one is more correct than the opinion of the other, or that one of the two has a truer moral sense than the other. There is no single point of view within it from which the values of things can be judged, since the two thinkers are supposed to be indifferent to each other.

Multiply the thinkers into a pluralism, and the result remains the same. Individual minds are the measures. No one "objective" truth can be found for moral judgments; only a multitude of "subjective" opinions.

The argument has reached an impasse. In a world of many persons, each recognizing only his private ideals, we could not give any general answer to the question, what does *good* mean? Or what things are good? There would be no single answer to such questions. This is veering around to skepticism, and as we know, James wishes to avoid that possibility.

But this is the kind of a world with which the philosopher will not put up. Among the various ideals represented, there must be, he thinks, some which have more truth or authority, and to these the others *ought* to yield.

The outcome of the discussion so far has been to show that nothing can be good or right except so far as some consciousness feels it to be good or right. Of these qualities we may say that their *esse* is *percipi*. Therefore, the moralist who seeks to know which ideal ought to have supreme weight must trace the *ought* itself to some existing consciousness. This consciousness must make the one ideal right by feeling it to be right, the other wrong by feeling it to be wrong. Now, what particular consciousness in the universe *can* enjoy this prerogative of obliging others to conform to a rule which it lays down? All one's slumbering revolutionary instincts waken at the thought of any single moralist wielding such power. Better chaos forever than an order based on any philosopher's rule, even though he were the most enlightened member of his tribe.

We can't allow skepticism. We can't allow subjectivism. We can't admit the arbitrary. How then can we say, or get into a position to say, of any particular account of the nature of the good, that all persons ought to accept it? How can any ideal impose any moral obligation upon any one to accept it?

Before we can address ourselves to this question we must deal first with the question, what is the *ground* of an ought, an obligation?

When we first try to answer this question, what is the *ground* of an obligation?, there is a tendency to imagine an abstract moral order in which the objective truth resides, and to try to prove that this pre-existing moral order is more accurately reflected in our own ideas than in the ideas held by some one else. Backed by this overarching abstract order, we think that others should submit. This attitude of regarding ourselves as subject to an overarching system of moral relations true in themselves is, taken as it stands, an out-and-out superstition.

We want an account of good and ill which will be binding upon all persons, which will be obligatory upon all persons to accept. To this end we enquire concerning the grounds upon which anything can be obligatory upon anyone. We note that such grounds are not to be discovered "in any abstract moral order which antedates and overarches the mere facts." Where then? What does set up obligations?

We cannot find the *ground* of an obligation in any such abstract moral order which antedates and overarches the mere facts, and makes it right that we should conform to it. Where then? The moment we take a steady look at the question, what is the *ground* of an obligation?, we see that it is *always* a claim actually made by some concrete person.

Claim and *obligation* are, in fact, coextensive terms. They cover each other exactly. Without a claim, actually made by some concrete person, there can be no obligation. Wherever there is a claim, there is some obligation. It is hard for those who are accustomed to what I have called the *superstitious* view, to realize that *every* claim creates, in so far forth, an obligation. We inveterately think that something which we call the *validity* of the claim gives to it its obligatory character; and that this validity is something outside of the claim's mere existence as a claim. Its validity, we think, rains down upon the claim, much as the influence of the pole rains down upon the steel of the compass needle.

Take any claim, however slight, which any creature, however weak, may make. Ought it not to be satisfied? If not, prove why not. The only possible kind of proof you could adduce would be a claim, made by some other creature, that ran the other way. The only reason why any claim ought to be satisfied is that it is made. It makes itself valid by the fact that it exists at all.

Any claim is imperative to the extent of its amount. Some claims are small claims. They are put forward by insignificant persons. We customarily make light of the obligations which they bring. But the fact that small claims impose small obligations does not keep the largest obligations from having their ground in personal claims.

Wherever persons exist and value things, wherever they make claims upon one another, there good, evil, and obligation exist, and there is an ethical world in its essential features. Were there but one rock, with two loving souls upon it, that rock would have as thoroughly moral a constitution as any possible world which the eternities and immensities could harbor. There would be real goods and real evils. There would be claims and obligations. In short, there would be a moral life whose active energy would have no limit but the intensity of interest in each other with which the two souls were endowed.

If we, on this earth of ours, are like the inhabitants of such a rock, we constitute an ethical republic. Ethics would have as genuine and real a foothold as in any possible universe. Whether this conception of an ethical republic, in which the valuers and claimants are only human beings, in which no higher consciousness exists, can gratify the moral philosopher's demands of a unified moral world, is a different question.

James is meeting his old difficulty in a new form. He didn't wish to accept skepticism or relativism or subjectivism. To avoid them, he turned from "good" to "obligation," and finds now that the ground of any obligation is the fact of a claim issued by some person or persons. But we can all make claims and have, therefore, the power to set up obligations. Whose claims shall take precedence? Whose claims are to be the grounds for the obligation that is to be binding on all persons? Hence James's puzzlement: "What can the philosopher do, then, except fall back on skepticism and thus give up the notion of being a philosopher at all?"

The controls of James's argument have been these: We cannot admit ethical skepticism, relativism, subjectivism, but if the good is only some person's good, we cannot avoid these.

Nor can we avoid them by means of the notion of obligation, if we admit that the ground of an obligation is a claim made by some one. What then?

It would seem that the stable and systematic moral universe for which the moral philosopher asks is fully possible only in a world where there is a divine thinker with all-enveloping demands. If such a thinker existed, his way of subordinating the demands to one another would be the finally valid one. His claim would be the most appealing. His ideal would be the most inclusive. In his thought would be that ethical philosophy which we ask as the pattern.

In the interests of our own ideal of systematically unified moral truth, therefore, we, as would-be philosophers must postulate a divine thinker. Exactly what the thought of the infinite thinker may be, is hidden from us, even were we sure of his existence.

God, then, is the necessary answer to the problem of avoiding the confusions of ethical skepticism and relativism. If God's conception of the good is admitted, we have something objective and independent of any individual. If God's claim is made the ground of obligation, we have an obligation that is objective, independent of any individual, and binding upon all individuals. What is God's conception of the good? Either James doesn't know, or he feels that that is another question to be dealt with elsewhere. The same holds for the claims made by God and the obligations which they set up for men. Those two questions would seem to be paramount. Otherwise, of course, we are brought around again to ethical skepticism. I presume that James knew this. The fact remains that he does nothing about it. His line of defense, at this point, is a curious one. It begins by drawing attention to a psychological distinction, that, namely, between the easygoing and the strenuous mood.

The deepest difference, in the moral life of man, is the difference between the easygoing and the strenuous mood. The easygoing mood makes us shrink from present ill. The strenuous, on the contrary, makes us indifferent to present ill, if only the greater ideal be attained.

The capacity for the strenuous mood probably lies slumbering in every man. But it has more difficulty in some than in others in waking up. It needs the wilder passions to arouse it, the big fears, loves and indignations; or else the deeply penetrating appeal of some one of the higher fidelities, like justice, truth, or freedom. Strong relief is a necessity of its vision. A world where all the mountains are brought down and all the valleys are exalted is no congenial place for its habitation.

In a solitary thinker the strenuous mood might slumber on forever without waking. In a merely human world, composed of many finite thinkers, the appeal to our moral energy would be greater, but it would still fall short of its maximal stimulating power. To be sure, in such a world, life would be a genuine ethical symphony played in a couple of poor octaves. The infinite scale of values would fail to open up. It would lack the note of infinitude and mystery. There would be no need of agonizing ourselves or making others agonize. It could all be dealt with in the easygoing mood.

The case for the strenuous mood is that when it is on, things get done. But the relativities of goods private to individuals, and obligations private to individuals, cannot set up the strenuous mood. If the good is God's good, and obligation is grounded in God's claims, then the strenuous mood will descend upon us.

When, however, we believe that a God is there, and that he is one of the claimants, the infinite perspective opens out. The scale of the symphony is incalculably prolonged. The more imperative ideals now begin to speak with an altogether new objectivity and significance, and to utter the penetrating, shattering, tragically challenging note of appeal.

The strenuous mood awakens at the sound. It saith among the trumpets, "Ha, ha!" It smelleth the battle afar off, the thunder of the captains and the shouting. Its blood is up. Cruelty to the lesser claims, so far from being a deterrent, does but add to the stern joy with which it leaps to answer the greater.

James appeals to history to document his claim that a moral philosophy which does generate the strenuous mood will always triumph over a moral philosophy which does not.

All through history, in the periodical conflicts of puritanism with the don't-care temper, we see the antagonism of the strenuous and the genial mood, and the contrast between the ethics of infinite and mysterious obligation from on high, and those of prudence and the satisfaction of merely finite need.

The capacity for the strenuous mood lies so deep down among our natural possibilities that even if there were no metaphysical or traditional grounds for believing in a God, men would postulate one simply as a pretext for living hard, and getting out of the game of existence its keenest possibilities of zest.

Our attitude toward concrete evils is entirely different in a world where we believe there are none but finite demanders, from what it is in one where we joyously face tragedy for an infinite demander's sake. Every sort of energy and endurance, of courage and capacity for handling life's evils, is set free in those who have religious faith. For this reason the strenuous type of character will always outwear the easygoing type, on the battlefield of human history, and religion will drive irreligion to the wall.

That is the defense James offers for his main argument. Morality grounded in the will of God will generate the strenuous mood, whereas others will not. He now turns, by way of conclusion, to a defense of this defense.

To some readers, such advocacy will seem a sad misuse of one's professional position. Mankind, they will say, is only too prone to follow faith unreasoningly, and needs no preaching or encouragement in that direction.

I quite agree. What mankind at large most lacks is criticism and caution, not faith. Its cardinal weakness is to let belief follow recklessly upon lively conception. Were I addressing the Salvation

Army, or a miscellaneous popular crowd, it would be a misuse of opportunity to preach as I have preached. What such audiences most need is that their faiths should be broken up and ventilated, that the northwest wind of science should get into them and blow their sickliness and barbarism away.

But I am speaking to an academic audience, and academic audiences, fed already on science, have a very different need. Paralysis of their native capacity for faith is *their* special form of mental weakness, brought about by the notion, carefully instilled, that there is something called "scientific evidence," by waiting upon which they shall escape all danger of shipwreck in regard to truth. But there is no method, scientific or other, by which men can steer safely between believing too little and believing too much. To face such dangers is apparently our duty, and to hit the right channel between them is the measure of our wisdom as men. It does not follow that, because recklessness may be a vice in soldiers, courage ought never to be preached to them.

Reading References. James wrote several topical essays which can be read to supplement the material in this chapter: "Is Life Worth Living?" "The Moral Equivalent of War," "The Dilemma of Determinism," "The Energies of Men," are a few. Perry's *The Life and Thought of William James*, already mentioned in an earlier chapter, is valuable here, too. Consult the table of contents of Perry's book.

READING QUESTIONS

1. What do you understand by *ethical skepticism*?
2. What is James's objection to it?
3. To what have ethical terms no application?
4. What is the point of his parable of a universe containing only one person?
5. What happens to the argument if we add another person?
6. How is he brought near to skepticism and relativism again?
7. What raises the question of the nature of an *ought*?
8. What does he mean by the *ground* of an obligation?
9. Wherein can it not be found? Why?

10. Wherein can it be found?
11. How is he brought near to skepticism and relativism again?
12. How does he use God to enable him to deal with the problem?
13. What new problem does this create?
14. How does he defend his appeal to God in moral philosophy?
15. What does he appeal to history to substantiate?
16. How does he defend his defense?
17. Formulate two or more criticisms of James's position.

TOPIC FIVE. A POLITICAL PROBLEM

THE PROBLEM STATED

The fact that men have religions, and that most religions include beliefs about God, provided us with the subject matter of our first topic. The fact that men distinguish between appearance and reality, and entertain beliefs about the nature of reality, provided us with the subject matter of our second topic. The fact that men distinguish between knowledge and speculation, and formulate theories to clarify and sharpen this distinction, provided us with the subject matter of our third topic. The fact that men distinguish between right and wrong, and formulate theories to clarify and sharpen this distinction, provided us with the subject matter of our fourth topic. The fact that men live in political organizations, and that political organization involves rights and duties of an imperative nature, provides us with the subject matter of our present topic.

Our subject is the state. Our problem is the justification of its claim to possess sovereign power over the wills of its subjects. Before elaborating upon this problem, we must note three terms, namely, *society*, *state*, *government*. The term *society* is not easily defined with any precision. We could perhaps say "Any group of people held together by actual or potential common interests." There seems to be intended some such meaning when we say, "Society insists that criminals be punished," or "The interests of society require a certain amount of fair dealing in business." The term *society* should not be confused with the term *state*. By the term *state* is meant a "society organized to make law possible."

The state, again, is not the government. Statehood is a kind of organization which a society can exhibit. Government is an organization, within society, whose function is to make and administer the laws. A government may be elective or hereditary; again, it may be by one man or many men. These distinctions do not apply to the state.

The government of a state differs from the government of a church or university or industrial corporation in the amount of power which it sometimes possesses and always claims over the wills of individuals who compose the society of which it is the government. Thus, the government of a church may claim and sometimes possess the power to stipulate the conditions under which an individual may belong to the church. But it does not usually claim the power to prevent an individual from leaving the church, if he chooses to do so, nor the power to inflict physical punishment upon its members, to dispossess them of their property, to imprison them, to conscript them, or to execute them.

The unique characteristic of the government of a state is that under some circumstances it does claim power to deal in these and other ways with individuals without their consent, even against their wills. This is the claim to possess and exercise sovereignty. There are several interesting things about such a claim. It may be made, but it may be disputed. It may be challenged from within, in which case there is revolt. It may be challenged from without, in which case there is conquest. Or it may be merely evaded, in which case there is crime. The criminal, the invader, the rebel are differently related to the central claim which defines the government of a state.

We have distinguished between making and making good the claim to possess sovereign power. We need, also, to distinguish between both of these and justifying the claim. It is one thing to make a claim. It is another to enforce it. It is still another to justify it. The problem of the present topic arises out of this distinction between *de facto* and *de jure* claim to possess absolute sovereignty. Upon what is this claim based? If the question of justification be raised, to what shall appeal be made? The authors included in this topic have written with this or a closely related problem in mind. The issue is clearer in some than it is in others, but if, at any time, you have a sense of having lost this point of connection, you can always restate the matter in very simple terms, thus: The government of a state claims absolute sovereignty over its subjects. Upon what grounds can this claim be justified? Then ask yourself what light the author in point is shedding or attempting to shed on this problem.

The first author, James I of Great Britain, sets himself to answer the question of what are "the true grounds of the mutual duty and allegiance betwixt an absolute monarch and his people." This is our question, somewhat differently worded. The second author, Thomas Hobbes, says that he "will consider what are the rights and just power of a sovereign, and what it is that preserveth and dissolveth it." This, too, is our question, somewhat differently worded. The third author, Jean Jacques Rousseau, begins, "Man is born free, and is everywhere in chains. . . . How does this change come about? I do not know. What can make it legitimate? That question I think I can answer." This is again our problem, somewhat differently worded. The fourth author, Edmund Burke, after denying the notion of popular sovereignty, advances the claim that the foundation of the state, meaning its principle of justification, is to be sought among the needs of human nature, and specifically in the need to be coerced and restrained in things that are our duties when we might choose to violate these in the name of supposed rights. This again is our problem. The fifth author, John Stuart Mill, argues the case for vesting the absolute power claimed by the state in a government of representatives chosen by the people.

1. THE DIVINE RIGHT OF KINGS—FROM JAMES I

There is little to say by way of introduction to the argument which follows. Many persons have doubtless heard of the doctrine of the divine right of kings; few have had an opportunity to examine a somewhat detailed statement of it. For that reason, it is included here. The author, as will be seen from the biographical note which follows, was king of Scotland at the time this argument was written. Five years later, he became king of Scotland and England, that is, Great Britain. He is aware of the threefold distinction between claiming sovereignty, making good the claim to sovereignty, and justifying the claim to sovereignty. He would justify the claim to sovereignty by an appeal to the will of God, as revealed in the Scriptures and manifested in the order of nature.

Biographical Note. James Stuart, subsequently James VI of Scotland and James I of Britain, was born in Edinburgh in 1566 and died in England in 1625 at the age of fifty-nine. He was the son of Mary, Queen of Scots. His life may be divided into three periods. (1) Until 1583 he was growing up, getting an education in the classics, the Bible, and Protestant theology, and discovering the vast difference between claiming and exercising supreme power. The question of justifying did not come until later. His mother was forced to abdicate in 1567. Scotland carried on under a regency until 1583, at which time James took matters into his own hands. (2) From 1583 to 1603 his energies were absorbed by a prolonged struggle with the still feudal nobility of Scotland. By the end of twenty years, he had reduced the anarchical baronage of sixteenth-century Scotland to obedience, and had replaced the divided sovereignty which was the essence of feudalism by a strong centralized authority. In fact, he did for Scotland what the Tudors had done for England, what

Louis XI had done for France, what Ferdinand and Isabella had done for Spain. During this period, in 1598, he wrote *The True Law of Free Monarchies*, which contains his argument for the divine right of kings. A year later, 1599, he published a treatise, *Demonologie*, denouncing witchcraft and exhorting the civil power to the strongest measures of suppression. (3) In 1603, Queen Elizabeth died closing the Tudor line in England. James VI of Scotland was invited to become James I of Britain, uniting Scotland and England under one throne. His career in England was less successful than it had been in Scotland. By disposition and conviction he was unfitted to succeed to the throne of the Henrys and Elizabeth. The Tudors had been strong monarchs, but they had not written books or made speeches in which they drew on the Bible to justify their absoluteness. They had claimed supremacy and, for the most part, made good their claim; they had not cast about for any subtle or elaborate justification.

The Argument of the Citations. James's argument may be divided into four parts. There is, first, a preamble in which he explains why and how he proposes to expound the doctrine of the divine right of kings. There is, second, a consideration of the duties of a king to his subject. These are explained, and the explanations documented by arguments drawn from the Scriptures and from the order of nature. There is, third, a consideration of the duties of a subject to his king. These are explained, and the explanations documented by arguments drawn from the Scriptures and the order of nature. This third portion of the total argument, "the duty that the lieges owe to their king, and the ground thereof" is the main thing. James's efforts to prove his case reach here a maximum. The whole doctrine of the divine right of kings is at stake. There is, finally, a consideration of objections to the doctrine. These objections are stated and refuted by arguments drawn from the Scriptures or the order of nature. They will bear careful watching, because, in disclosing what James considers a relevant objection and a relevant reply, these passages reveal quite clearly the level at which the entire argument moves. He begins:

My dear countrymen: Accept, I pray you, as thankfully this pamphlet that I offer unto you, as lovingly it is written for your weal. It may be ye miss many things that ye look for in it. But, for excuse thereof, consider rightly that I only lay down herein the true grounds, to teach you the right way, without wasting time upon refuting the adversaries.

My intention is to instruct, not to irritate. The profit I would wish you to make of it, is, to frame all your actions according to these grounds, as may confirm you in the course of honest and obedient subjects to your king in all times coming, as also, when ye shall fall in with any that shall praise or excuse the by-past rebellions that brake forth either in this country, or in any other, ye shall herewith be armed against their siren songs. Whereby ye shall soundly keep the course of righteous judgment, discerning wisely of every action only according to the quality thereof, and not according to your prejudged conceits of the committers. So shall ye, by reaping profit to yourselves, turn my pain into pleasure.

As there is nothing so necessary to be known by the people of any land, next to their knowledge of God, as the right knowledge of their allegiance, according to the form of government established among them, especially in a monarchy, so hath the ignorance and seduced opinion of the multitude (blinded by them who think themselves able to teach and instruct) procured the wreck and overthrow of sundry flourishing commonwealths, and heaped heavy calamities, threatening utter destruction, upon others.

And among others, no commonwealth that ever hath been since the beginning hath had greater need of the true knowledge of this ground, than this our so long disordered and distracted commonwealth. The misknowledge hereof is the only spring from whence hath flowed so many endless calamities, miseries, and confusions; as is better felt by many than the cause thereof well known and deeply considered.

The natural zeal, therefore, that I bear to this my native country, with the great pity I have to see the so-long disturbance thereof, hath compelled me to break silence, to discharge my conscience to you, my dear countrymen, so that, knowing the ground from whence these your many endless troubles have proceeded, ye may, by knowledge and eschewing of the cause, escape and divert the lamentable effects that ever necessarily follow thereupon.

I have chosen, then, only to set down in this short treatise, the true grounds of the mutual duty and allegiance betwixt a free and absolute monarch and his people.

First, I will set down the true grounds, whereupon I am to build, out of the Scriptures, since monarchy is the true pattern of divinity; next, from the law of nature, by divers similitudes drawn out of the same; and will end by answering the most weighty and apparent incommodities that can be objected.

From a statement of his aims and method, he turns to the first part of the argument. What have the Scriptures to say concerning the king's duties to his subjects? He begins:

The king's duty to his subjects is so clearly set down in many places of the Scriptures, and so openly confessed by all good princes, that it needeth not that I be long therein.

Kings are called Gods by the prophetical King David, in the sixth verse of the eighty-second Psalm, because they sit upon God His throne in the earth, and have the count of their administration to give unto Him. Their office is "to minister justice and judgment to the people," as the same David saith; "to advance the good and punish the evil," as he likewise saith; "to establish good laws to his people, and procure obedience to the same," as divers good kings of Judah did; "to procure the peace of the people," as the same David saith; "to decide all controversies that arise among them," as Solomon did; "to be the minister of God for the weal of them that do well, and to take vengeance upon them that do evil," as Saint Paul saith; "to go out and in before his people, as a good pastor," as is said in first Samuel; "that through the prince's prosperity, the people's peace may be procured," as Jeremiah saith.

And therefore, in the coronation of every Christian monarch, they give their oath: first, to maintain the religion presently professed within their country, according to their laws whereby it is established, and to punish all those who should seek to alter or disturb the profession thereof; next, to maintain all the lowable and good laws made by their predecessors, to see them put into execution and the breakers and violators thereof punished according to the tenor of the same; and lastly, to maintain the whole country, and every state therein, in all their ancient privileges and liberties, as well against all foreign enemies as among themselves.

In short, they take each his oath to procure the weal and flourishing of the people, not only by maintaining and executing the old lowable laws of the country, by establishing new laws (as necessity and evil manners will require), but by all other means possible to foresee and prevent all dangers that are likely to fall upon them; and to maintain concord, wealth, and civility among them as a loving father and careful watchman, caring for them more than for himself, knowing himself to be ordained for them, and not they for him, accountable therefore to that great God who placed him as His lieutenant over them, upon the peril of his soul to procure the weal of both souls and bodies as far as in him lieth.

From the Scriptures he turns to the order of nature. What does the order of nature show regarding a king's duties to his subjects? He continues:

By the law of nature the king becomes a natural father to all his lieges. As the father is bound to care for the nourishing, education, and virtuous government of his children, even so is the king bound to care for all his subjects. As all the toil and pain that the father can take for his children will be thought light and well bestowed by him, so the effect thereof redounds to their profit and weal; so ought the king to do toward his people. As the kindly father ought to foresee all the inconveniences and dangers that may arise toward his children, and with the hazard of his own person to press to prevent the same; so ought the king toward his people. As the father's wrath and correction upon any of his children that offendeth ought, by a fatherly chastisement to be seasoned with pity, as long as there is any hope of amendment in them; so ought the king towards any of his lieges that offend in that measure.

In short, as a father's chief joy ought to be in procuring his children's welfare, rejoicing at their weal, sorrowing and pitying at their woe, hazarding for their safety, traveling for their rest, waking for their sleep, thinking (in a word) that his earthly felicity and life standeth and lieth more in them than in himself; so ought a good prince to think of his people.

Having dealt with the question of the king's duties to his subject, he turns to the much more controversial question of the subject's duties to the king. What do the Scriptures say regarding "the other branch of this tie"? He begins:

The other branch of this mutual and reciprocal tie is the duty and allegiance that the lieges owe to their king. The ground hereof I take out of the words of Samuel, dited by God's spirit, when God had commanded him to hear the people's voice in choosing and anointing them a king. Because that place of Scripture is so pertinent for our purpose, I insert herein the very words of the text.

That these words and discourses of Samuel were dited by God's spirit, it needs no further probation than that it is in the Scripture; since the whole Scripture is dited by that inspiration, as Paul saith; which ground no good Christian will or dare deny.

And it came to pass, when Samuel was old, that he made his sons judges over Israel. And his sons walked not in his ways, but turned aside after lucre, and took bribes, and perverted judgment. Then all the elders of Israel gathered themselves together, and came to Samuel unto Ramah, and said unto him: "Behold, thou art old, and thy sons walk not in thy ways: now make us a king to judge us like all the nations." But the thing displeased Samuel, when they said: "Give us a king to judge us." And Samuel prayed unto the Lord. And the Lord said unto Samuel: "Hearken unto the voice of the people in all that they say unto thee: for they have not rejected thee, but they have rejected Me, that I should not reign over them. According to all the works which they have done since the day that I brought them up out of Egypt even unto this day, wherewith they have forsaken Me, and served other gods, so do they also unto thee. Now therefore hearken unto their voice: howbeit yet protest solemnly unto them, and shew them the manner of the king that shall reign over them."

And Samuel told all the words of the Lord unto the people that asked of him a king. And he said: "This will be the manner of the king that shall reign over you: he will take your sons, and appoint them for himself, for his chariots, and to be his horsemen; and some shall run before his chariots. And he will appoint him captains over thousands, and captains over fifties; and will set them to ear his ground, and to reap his harvest, and to make his instruments of war, and instruments of his chariots. And he will take your daughters to be confectionaries, and to be cooks, and to be bakers. And he will take your fields, and your vineyards, and your oliveyards, even the best of them, and give them to his servants. And he will take the tenth of your seed, and of your vineyards, and give to his officers, to his servants. And he will take your menservants, and your maidservants, and your goodliest young men, and your asses, and put them to his work. He will take the tenth of your sheep: and ye shall be his servants. And ye shall cry out in that day because of your king which ye shall have chosen you; and the Lord will not hear you in that day." Nevertheless the people refused to obey the voice of Samuel; and they said: "Nay; but we will have a king over us; that we also may be like all the nations; and that our king may judge us, and go out before us, and fight our battles." And Samuel heard all the words of the people, and he rehearsed them in the ears of the Lord. And the Lord said to Samuel: "Hearken unto their voice, and make them a king."

If ye will consider the very words of the text, as they are set down, it shall plainly declare the obedience that the people owe to their king in all respects.

First, God commanded Samuel to grant the people a king. Then, He commanded Samuel to forewarn them of what some kings will do unto them, that they may not thereafter say, "We would never have had a king of God, had He let us know how we would have been used by him."

Next, Samuel declares unto them what points of justice and equity their king will break in his behavior unto them; and putteth them out of hope that they shall have leave to shake off that yoke which God, through their importunity, hath laid upon them.

Now, the erection of this kingdom and monarchy among the Jews, and the law thereof, may and ought to be a pattern to all Christian and well-founded monarchies, as being founded by God Himself. What liberty, then, can broiling spirits and rebellious minds justly claim against any Christian monarchy? They can claim no greater liberty, on their part, than the people of God might have done. They can point to no greater tyranny than was here forwarned to the people of God; and yet all rebellion was countermanded unto them.

That this proposition, grounded upon the Scripture, may the more clearly appear to be true, we never read that ever the prophets persuaded the people to rebel against the king, howsoever wicked he was.

There never was a more monstrous persecutor and tyrant nor Ahab was. Yet all the rebellion that Elias ever raised against him was to flee to the wilderness, where, for fault of sustentation, he was fed with the corbies.

I think no man will doubt but Samuel, David, Elias, had as great power to persuade the people, had they liked to employ their credit to uproars and rebellions against wicked kings, as had any of our seditious preachers in these days of whatsoever religion, either in this country or in France. (Only love of verity, I protest, has moved me this far to be somewhat satiric.)

I could cite further. Jeremiah threatened the people of God with utter destruction for rebellion against Nebuchadnezzar, the king of Babel, although he was an idolatrous persecutor, a foreign king, a tyrant and usurper of their liberties. Yet, in respect they had once received and acknowledged him for their king, Jeremiah not only commanded them to obey him but even to pray for his prosperity, adjoining the reason to it: because in his prosperity stood their peace.

To end the grounds of my proposition as taken out of the Scripture, let a notable example from the New Testament be considered. That king, whom Paul bids the Romans obey and serve for conscience' sake, was Nero — that bloody tyrant, that infamy to his age, that monster to the world, being also an idolatrous persecutor. If then, idolatry and defection from God, tyranny and the persecution of the Saints, hindered not the spirit of God to command his people under highest pain to give all due and hearty obedience for conscience, sake, giving to Caesar what was Caesar's and to God what was God's, what shameless presumption, I say, is it in any Christian people nowadays to claim that unlawful liberty which God refused to his own peculiar and chosen people?

In short, to take up in two or three sentences, grounded upon all these arguments out of the law of God, the duty and allegiance of the people to their lawful king, I say: Their obedience ought to be to him, as to God's lieutenant on earth answerable to God alone, obeying his commands in all things as the commands of God's minister; acknowledging him as a judge set by God over them and having power to judge them; fearing him and loving him; praying for him as their protector, for his continuance if he be good, for his amendment if he be wicked; following his lawful commands and fleeing his fury in his unlawful commands; offering no resistance, but by sobs and tears to God.

Thus the Scriptures. They are clearly on the king's side. What about the order of nature? Does it, too, support the king's claim to possess absolute sovereignty? He continues:

The agreement of the law of nature with the laws and constitutions of God will by two similitudes easily appear.

The king toward his people is rightly compared (1) to a father of children, and (2) to a head of a body composed of divers members.

As fathers, the good princes and magistrates of the people of God acknowledged themselves to their subjects. And for all other well-ruled commonwealths the style of *pater patriae* was ever used of kings.

Now, for the father's part, consider, I pray you, what duty his children owe to him, and whether, upon any pretext whatsoever, it will not be thought monstrous and unnatural in his sons to rise up against him, to control him, to slay him when they think good, or to cut him off and adopt to themselves any other they please in his room.

Can any pretense of wickedness or rigor on his part be a just excuse for his children to put a hand to him? Even suppose the father hated and wronged the children never so much, will any man, endowed with the least spark of reason, think it lawful for them to meet him with the line? Yea, suppose the father were furiously following his sons with a drawn sword, is it lawful for them to turn and strike back, or to make any resistance but by flight?

I think surely, if there were no more but the example of brute beasts, it may serve well enough to qualify and prove this my argument. For instance, we read often of the pity that storks have to their old and decayed parents. And generally, we know, there are many sorts of beasts and fowls that with violence and many bloody strokes will beat and banish their young ones from them as soon as they perceive them able to fend for themselves; but we never read or hear of any resistance on the part of the young, except among the vipers. This proves such persons as unnaturally follow this example to be endowed with a viperous nature.

As for the similitude of the head and the body, the proper office of a king toward his subjects agrees very well with the office of the head toward the body. For, from the head, being the seat of judgment, proceedeth the care and foresight of guiding, and preventing all evil that may come to the body or any part thereof. The head careth for the body; so doeth the king for his people. Discourse and directions flow from the head, execution according thereunto belongs to the rest of the members every one according to his office; so it is betwixt a wise prince and his people. Judgment, coming from the head, may employ the members every one in their own office as long as they are able for it; in case any one of them be affected with any infirmity, it must care and provide for their remedy, so it be curable, and if otherwise, cut them off for fear of infecting the rest. Even so it is betwixt the prince and his people. There is always hope of curing any diseased member by the direction of the head, as long as it is whole; but, by the contrary, if the head be troubled, all the members are partakers of that pain. So it is betwixt the prince and his people.

Now, it may very well fall out that the head will be forced to cut off some rotten members to keep the rest of the body in its integrity:

but what state the body can be in, if the head, for any infirmity that can befall it, be cut off, I leave to the reader's judgment.

To conclude these similitudes: If the children may upon any pretext lawfully rise up against their father, cut him off and choose any other they please in his room; if the body may for any infirmity that can be in the head, strike it off — then I cannot deny that the people may rebel, control, displace, or cut off their king.

The case is complete. Both God and nature are on the side of the king who claims absolute sovereignty. "In case any doubts might arise," however, he proposes four possible objections to his argument:

In case any doubts might arise in any part of this treatise, I will conclude with the solution of the principal and most weighty objections.

First, it is cast up by divers who employ their pens upon apologies for rebellions and treasons: every man is born to carry such a natural zeal and duty to his commonwealth that, seeing it so rent and deadly wounded, as whiles it will be by wicked kings, good citizens will be forced, out of said zeal and duty, to put their hand to work for freeing their commonwealth from such a pest.

Whereunto I give two answers: (1) It is a sure axiom in theology that evil should not be done in order that good may come of it. The wickedness, therefore, of the king can never make them that are ordained to be judged by him, to become his judges. If it be not lawful to a private man to revenge his private injury upon a private adversary, how much less is it lawful to the people, or any part of them, to take upon them the use of the sword against the public magistrate?

(2) In place of relieving the commonwealth out of distress, they shall keep double distress and trouble upon it; and so their rebellion shall procure the contrary effects that they pretend for it. For a king cannot be imagined to be so unruly and tyrannous but the commonwealth will be kept in better order by him than it can by his way-taking. For all sudden mutations are perilous in commonwealths, hope being thereby given to all bare men to set themselves up and fly with other men's feathers, the reins being loosed to all the

insolencies that disordered people can commit by hope of impunity because of the looseness of all things.

Second, it is objected: A curse hangeth over the commonwealth where a wicked king reigneth, and, say they, there cannot be a more acceptable deed in the sight of God than to free the country of such a curse.

Whereunto for answer: I grant indeed that a wicked king is sent by God for a curse to his people, and a plague for their sins. But, that it is lawful to them to shake off that curse by their own hand, which God hath laid upon them, that I deny, and may so do justly. Will any deny that the king of Babylon was a curse to the people of God, as was plainly forespoken and threatened unto them in the prophecy of their captivity? What else was Nero to the Christian church in his time? And yet, Jeremiah and Paul commanded the people not only to obey them, but heartily to pray for their welfare. It is certain then, that patience, earnest prayers to God, and amendment of their lives, are the only lawful means to move God to relieve them of that heavy curse.

The third objection: They say that the fortunate success which God hath so often given to enterprises of rebellion proveth plainly that God favored the justness of these quarrels.

To which I answer: It is true indeed that all the success of battles lieth only in God's hands. But, to conclude on that principle that He always gives victory to the just quarrel would prove that the Philistines, and divers other enemies of the people of God, had, in respect to the many victories they obtained over the people of God, justice on their side. It hath been so in many other instances. Therefore, I say, it is oft times a very deceivable argument to judge of the cause by the event.

The last objection is grounded upon the mutual pact and adstipulation betwixt the king and his people at the time of his coronation. For there, they say, was a mutual pact whereupon it followeth that if the contract be broken upon the king's side, the people are no longer bound to keep their part of it, but are thereby freed of their oath.

My answer: I confess that a king at his coronation oath promiseth to discharge honorably and truly the office given him by God over his people. But, presuming that thereafter he breaks his promise unto them never so inexcusably, the question is: Who should be judge? A contract cannot be broken by one party and so free the other party except first a lawful trial and cognition be had by the ordinary judge of the breakers thereof. Otherwise every man may be both party and judge in his own cause: which is absurd once to be thought.

Now (I say) in this contract betwixt the king and his people, God is the only judge, because to Him only the king must make count of his administration. For in His presence, as only judge of oaths, and therefore of coronation oaths, all oaths ought to be made. Since, then, God is the only judge betwixt the two contracting parties, the trial and revenge must only appertain to Him. It follows therefore that God must first give sentence upon the king before the people can think themselves freed of their oath.

The argument stated, the objections met, he concludes:

And as ye see it manifest: the king is overlord of the whole land. . . . In the parliament (which is nothing else but the head court of the king and his vassals) the laws are but craved by his subjects. For, although the king make daily statutes and ordinances, enjoining such pains thereto as he thinks fit, yet it lies in the power of no parliament to make any kind of law or statute without his scepter be to it giving it the force of law. He is master over every person that inhabiteth the land, having power over the life and death of every one of them. For, although a just king will not take the life of any of his subjects without a clear law, yet the laws whereby he taketh them are made by him; so the power flows always from him. . . . Likewise, although a good king will frame his actions to be according to the law, yet he is not bound thereto but of his good will and for good example-giving to his subjects.

Reading References. Other items by James I will be found in *The Political Works of James I* edited by C. H. McIlwain. To this volume Professor McIlwain has contributed a long and enlightening introduction. A history of Great Britain, especially if it included a chapter on the history of

Scotland during the period of James VI, would provide good background reading.

READING QUESTIONS

1. From whence have so many calamities flowed?
2. What has he chosen "to set down in this short treatise"?
3. Specify two or three duties enjoined upon kings by the Scriptures.
4. What analogy from the order of nature does he use to indicate the duties of kings to their subjects?
5. Give the story which he reads from the book of Samuel?
6. What was his point in referring to it?
7. What is the point of his reference to Ahab? To Nebuchadnezzar? To Nero?
8. Do you detect a cumulative effect in these three references?
9. What follows from his "king as father" argument?
10. What from his "king as head" argument?
11. What moral does he draw from what brute beasts?
12. How does he meet the objection: "It is the duty of a good citizen to free the commonwealth from a wicked king"?
13. What is the second objection which he considers?
14. How does he meet the objection: "The success which God hath given to rebellion proveth the justness of these quarrels"?
15. How does he deal with the objection: "If the contract be broken upon the king's side, the people are no longer bound to keep their part of it"?
16. Quote two or three sentences which indicate that James was seeking to justify absolute sovereignty in the monarch.

2. *THE GREAT LEVIATHAN — FROM THOMAS HOBBES*

From James I to Hobbes. King James had published *The True Law of Free Monarchy*, stating the case for the divine right of kings, in 1598. In 1603 he had become king of Great Britain. Throughout his reign, he sought to act upon the assumption that he possessed an absolute sovereignty delegated to him by God. His parliaments resented this notion, but bided their time. In 1625 James I was succeeded by Charles I, who also believed strongly in the doctrine of divine rights and tried to live up to it. Indeed, for eleven years, he ruled without parliament. But in 1640, needing extra money to finance some military operations, he convoked his parliament. This parliament continued in session for twenty years. It began by passing the Triennial Act, which required its convocation every three years, and presented, in the Grand Remonstrance, a summary of its objections to Stuart absolutism. In 1642, it conducted a civil war under the leadership of Cromwell. In 1649 it executed Charles I and set up a Commonwealth which lasted eleven years. During the early years of this Commonwealth period, in 1651, Thomas Hobbes published his book, *The Leviathan*.

The Leviathan contains a restatement of the case for absolute sovereignty. But this time the argument is not carried out in theological terms. It is not made to rest upon the claim that absolute sovereignty is something delegated to governments by God. It is a statement in naturalistic instead of supernaturalistic terms. It represents, therefore, a step toward the wholly secular statement of the ciaim that sovereignty is delegated to the government by a people organized as a state.

Biographical Note. In Topic Two, "A Metaphysical Problem," we encountered Hobbes in the role of a propounder of materialism. In the present topic we are to meet him in the role of propounder of what he conceived to be the implications in political theory of his position in metaphysical theory. It will be remembered, from the previous biographical note, that Hobbes was born in 1588 and died in 1679. His political theory acquires considerable persuasiveness when one recalls the tumultuous period which it reflects. Hobbes was born ten years before James published the defense of the divine right of kings. He lived to see James I antagonize parliament by those claims, to see Charles I executed by his parliament, to see Cromwell become an absolute dictator under the Commonwealth, to see Charles II (restored to the throne in 1660) gradually alienate his parliament by absolutist claims. When Hobbes died, the reign of Charles II was six years from its close, and the reign of the House of Stuarts was but nine years from its close, for in 1688 the parliament deposed James II, thus putting an end to the Stuart dynasty and the political theory which it had exemplified. All this being so, it would seem that the argument of Hobbes's *Leviathan* reflected two elements in his own experience. He saw clearly that the divine-rights doctrine was a bankrupt trouble-maker, but he saw, equally clearly, that some person or persons not only do claim sovereignty, but must needs do so if society is not to disintegrate amid stresses and strains such as had been set up by James I, Charles I, the Civil War, and the Commonwealth, to mention only matters within the society in question.

The Argument of the Citations. There are two thoughts running through Hobbes's argument. Both refer to absolute sovereignty considered as a fact. The first thought is: On what hypothesis can the occurrence of this fact be accounted for? The second thought is: On what principle can this fact be morally justified? Hobbes does not always keep these matters distinct. We must do so. He begins with a pretty conceit, in which the body politic is likened to the body physical. From this he passes to an explanation of the formation of states. Out of this he derives a justification of the same. From this he passes to a description of the institution of sovereignty within any state; from this to an inventory of the rights and powers possessed by the person or persons in whom sovereignty is vested; from this to an inventory of the rights and powers reserved by individuals despite the absolute sovereignty supposed to exist in the government. And he ends with the thought that the universities of England would do well to propagate his views. He begins:

Two chief kinds of bodies offer themselves to such as search after their generation and properties: One is called a *natural body;* the other is called a *commonwealth* and is made by the wills and agreement of men.

Nature is imitated by the art of man in many ways; but especially in this, that it can make an artificial animal. For by art is created that great Leviathan called a *commonwealth* or *state*, which is but an artificial man, though of greater stature and strength than the natural man. The sovereignty is an artificial soul, as giving life and motion to the whole body; the magistrates and other officers of judicative and executive are artificial joints; rewards and punishments, by which every joint and member is moved to perform his duty, are the nerves; the wealth and riches of all the particular members are the strength; the people's safety is its business; councilors, by whom all things needful for it to know are suggested unto it, are the memory; equity and laws are its reason and will; concord is its health; sedition is its sickness; and civil war its death.

How and why does it come to pass that men make this "artificial animal" of which Hobbes here speaks? Why do men set up the state, limiting thereby their own liberties by the will of the person or persons in whom an absolute sovereignty is vested? Because of such facts as the following:

Nature hath made men so equal, in the faculties of the body and mind, as that though there be found one man sometimes manifestly stronger in body or of quicker mind than another, yet when all is reckoned together, the difference between man and man is not so considerable as that one man can thereupon claim to himself any benefit, to which another may not pretend as well as he. For as to strength of body, the weakest hath strength enough to kill the strongest, either by secret machinations or by confederacy with others that are in the same danger with himself.

From this equality of ability ariseth equality of hope in the attaining of our ends. And therefore, if any two men desire the same thing, which nevertheless they cannot both enjoy, they become enemies; and in the way to their end, which is principally their own conservation and sometimes their own pleasure only, endeavor to destroy or subdue one another.

So that in the first place, I put for a general inclination of all mankind a perpetual and restless desire of power after power that ceaseth only in death. And the cause of this that no man can assure the power and means to live well, which he hath at present, without the acquisition of more.

It may seem strange to some, who have not well weighed these things, that nature should thus dissociate and render men apt to invade and destroy one another. Such persons, not trusting to this inference made from the passions, may therefore desire to have the same confirmed by experience.

Let him therefore consider within himself. When taking a journey, he arms himself. When going to sleep, he locks his doors. Even in his own home, he locks his chests. What opinion has he of his fellow subjects, when he rides armed? Of his fellow citizens, when he locks his doors? Of his children and servants, when he locks his chest? Does he not there as much accuse mankind by his actions, as I do by my words?

Hereby it is manifest, that during the time men live without a common power to keep them all in awe, they are in that condition which is called war; and such a war as is of every man against every man. For war consisteth not in battle only, but in a tract of time wherein the will to contend by battle is sufficiently known.

Whatsoever therefore is consequent to a time of war, where every man is enemy to every man; the same is consequent to the time wherein men live without other security than what their own strength and their own invention shall furnish them withal.

In such condition, there is no place for industry because the fruit thereof is uncertain, and consequently no culture of the earth, no navigation, no use of commodities that may be imported by sea, no commodious buildings, no instruments of moving and removing, no knowledge of the face of the earth, no account of time, no arts, no letters, no society; and, which is worst of all, continual fear of violent death; and the life of man, solitary, poor, nasty, brutish, and short.

To this war of every man against every man this also is consequent, that nothing can be unjust. The notions of right and wrong, justice and injustice have there no place. Where there is no common power, there is no law; where there is no law, there is no injustice. Justice and injustice are faculties of neither the body nor the mind, differing herein from both the senses and the passions. They are qualities that relate to men in society, not in solitude. It is consequent also to the same condition that there be no propriety, no dominion, no mine and thine distinct, but only that to be every man's that he can get, and for so long as he can keep. Thus much for the ill condition which man by mere nature is actually placed in.

It may peradventure be thought that there never was such a time, nor condition of war such as this. And I believe it was never generally so, over all the world. But there are many places where they live so now. However, it may be perceived what manner of life there would be, where there were no common power to fear, by the manner of life that men degenerate into in a civil war.

The state, when it comes, is to be a union of wills to the end that law and order may be possible. The intolerable nature of the alternative — "the life of man, solitary, poor, nasty, brutish, and short" — is the justification. The state, man's answer to the threat of chaos, is founded upon a contract. What are the terms of this contract? Who are the parties to this contract? Hobbes continues:

Without the terror of some common power to cause them to be observed, justice, equity, modesty, mercy, doing to others as we would be done to, are contrary to our natural passions that carry us to partiality, pride, revenge, and the like. Covenants without the sword are but words, and of no strength to secure a man at all.

The only way to erect such a common power is for men to confer all their power and strength upon one man or one assembly of men that may reduce their wills unto one will: which is as much as to say, for all to appoint one man or one assembly of men to bear their person, for all to acknowledge themselves to be the authors of whatsoever he shall do or cause to be done, in those things which concern the common peace and safety, for all to submit their wills to his will, and their judgments to his judgment.

This is more than consent or concord. It is a real unity of all in one person or one assembly of persons, made by covenant of every man with every man, as if every man should say to every man, "I give up my right of governing myself to this man or assembly of men on condition that thou give up thy right in like manner." This done, the multitude so united in one person or one assembly of persons is called a *commonwealth*. This is the generation of that great Leviathan, of that mortal god to which we owe (under the immortal God) our peace and defense.

He that carrieth this power is called *sovereign*, and is said to have sovereign power. Everyone besides is said to be his *subject*. In him consisteth the essence of the commonwealth; which, to define it, is "one person of whose acts a great multitude, by mutual covenants one with another, have made themselves everyone the author to the end that he may use the strength and means of all for their peace and defense."

The difference of commonwealth consisteth in the difference of the sovereign. When the representative is one man, then is the commonwealth a monarchy; when an assembly of all, then is the commonwealth a democracy; when an assembly of part only, then is the commonwealth an aristocracy. Other kind of commonwealth there can be none, for either one, or some, or all must have the sovereign power. The difference between these three kinds of commonwealth consisteth not in the difference of power, but in the difference of convenience or aptitude to produce the peace and security of the people; which end they were instituted to. [Hobbes then argues that on six counts of efficiency an absolute monarchy is to be preferred to any other form of sovereignty.]

We have, by now, seen why men set up a state. We have seen the nature of that contract upon which it rests. We have seen the peculiar relation of the sovereignty to this contract. He is a beneficiary of it but not a party to it. What follows, if this be so? Hobbes proceeds:

From this institution of a commonwealth are derived all the rights and powers of him or them on whom sovereign power is conferred by the consent of the people.

First, because they covenant, they cannot lawfully make a new covenant among themselves to be obedient to any other, in anything whatsoever, without his permission. They that are subject to a sovereign cannot, without his leave, cast him off and return to the confusion of a disunited multitude, nor transfer to another man or assembly of men; for they are bound every man to every man.

Second, because sovereignty is given by covenant only of one to another and not him to any of them, there can be no breach of covenant on the part of the sovereign. He that is made sovereign maketh no covenant with his subject beforehand. The opinion that any sovereign receiveth his power by covenant, that is on condition, proceedeth from want of understanding this easy truth that covenants, being but words and breath, have no force to oblige any man but what it has from the public sword, that is from the untied hands of that man or assembly of men that hath the sovereignty.

Third, because every subject is by this institution the author of all the actions of the sovereign, it follows that whatsoever the sovereign doth can be no injury to any of his subjects; nor ought he to be accused of injustice by any of them. For he that doth anything by authority of another, doth no injury to him by whose authority he acteth. He that complaineth of injury from his sovereign, complaineth of that whereof he himself is the author, and therefore ought not to accuse any man but himself; nor even himself, since to do injury to oneself is impossible.

Fourth, it follows from what was said last that no sovereign can justly be put to death or otherwise punished in any manner by his subjects. For seeing every subject is the author of the actions of his sovereign, he but punisheth another for the actions committed by himself.

Fifth, it is annexed to sovereignty to be judge of what opinions and doctrines are averse and what are conducive to peace; and, consequently, on what occasions, how far, and what men are to be trusted in speaking to multitudes, and who shall examine the doctrines of all books before they be published. For the actions of men proceed from their opinions; and in all the well-governing of opinions consisteth the well-governing of men's actions in order to their peace and concord. And, though in matter of doctrine, nothing ought to be regarded but the truth, yet this is not repugnant to regulating the same by reference to peace. For doctrine repugnant to peace cannot be true. For those men that are so remissly governed that they dare take up arms to defend or introduce an opinion, are still in a state of war. Their condition is not peace, but only a cessation of arms for fear of one another, and they live as it were in the precincts of battle continually. It belongeth therefore to sovereignty to be judge, or to appoint all judges, of opinions and doctrines, as a thing necessary to peace, and to prevent discord and civil war.

Sixth, the whole power of prescribing rules whereby every man may know what goods he may enjoy and what actions he may do without being molested by any of his fellow men, is annexed to sovereignty. For before the constitution of sovereignty, as hath been shown, all men had right to all things, which necessarily causeth war. And therefore, these rules of property and conduct, being necessary to peace and depending on sovereignty, are the act of that power in order to preserve the public peace.

Seventh, the right of hearing and deciding all controversies which may arise concerning law or concerning fact, is annexed to sovereignty. For without such decision of controversies there is no protection of one subject against another, the laws concerning mine and thine are in vain, and to every man remaineth the right to protect himself by his private strength, which is the condition of war and contrary to the end for which commonwealth is instituted.

Eighth, the right of making war and peace, of judging when it is for the public good, of levying money upon the subjects to defray expenses thereof, is annexed to the sovereignty.

Lastly, to sovereignty is committed the power of rewarding every subject with riches or honor or dignity or titles; of punishing every subject by fine, by imprisonment, by corporal punishment, by ignominy, according to the law that sovereignty hath formerly made.

These are the rights which make the essence of sovereignty, and which are the marks whereby one may discern in what man or assembly of men the sovereign power is placed. For these are incommunicable and inseparable. And as the power, so also the honor of the sovereign ought to be greater than that of any or all of the subjects. Though his subjects shine, some more and some less when they are out of his sight, yet in his presence they shine no more than the stars in the presence of the sun.

Such are the rights and powers invested in government by men who form a state. Is this sovereignty absolute? Hobbes is evasive here. He seems to say, "In a sense, yes"; but, equally clearly, he means also, "In a sense, no." It appears that there are limits which define sovereignty. These take the form of rights reserved by men in case the sovereign should overreach itself. Thus:

As men, for the attaining of peace and conservation of themselves thereby, have made an artificial man which we have called a *commonwealth*, so also have they made artificial chains called *civil laws*, which they themselves by mutual covenants, have fastened at one end to the lips of that man or assembly of men to whom they have given sovereign power, and at the other end to their own ears. These bonds, in their own nature but weak, may nevertheless be made to hold, by the danger though not by the difficulty of breaking them. In relation to these bonds only it is that I am to speak now, of the liberty of subjects. What are the things which, though commanded by the sovereign, the subject may nevertheless justly refuse to do?

If the sovereign (i.e., the government) command a man, though justly condemned, to kill, to wound, or to maim himself; not to resist those that assault him; to refrain from anything without which he cannot live; that man hath the liberty to disobey.

If the sovereign interrogate a man concerning a crime done by himself, he is not bounden, without assurance of pardon, to confess it.

If a man be held in prison, he is not bounden by covenant to subjection. If he can, he may make his escape by any means whatsoever.

If the sovereign command a man to execute any dangerous or dishonorable office, and refusal to obey frustrates the end for which the sovereignty was ordained, there is no liberty to refuse; otherwise there is.

To resist the sword of the commonwealth, in defense of another man, guilty or innocent, no man hath liberty; because such liberty takes away from the sovereign the means of protecting us, and is therefore destructive of the very essence of government. But in case a great many men together have already resisted the sovereign power unjustly, or committed some capital crime, for which every one of them expecteth death, have they not the liberty to join together, and assist and defend one another?

They have, for they but defend their lives, which the guilty as well as the innocent may do. But the offer of pardon taketh from them the plea of self-defense and maketh their perseverance unlawful.

If a subject have a controversy with his sovereign, he hath the same liberty to sue for his rights as if it were against a subject.

If the sovereign, either monarch or assembly, grant any liberty to all or any subject, by virtue whereof he is disabled to provide for their safety, the grant is void.

The obligation of subject to sovereign lasts no longer than the power by which he is able to protect them. For the right men have by nature to protect themselves when none else can protect them, can by no covenant be relinquished.

If a subject be taken prisoner in war, and hath his life and liberty given him on condition he be subject to the victor, he hath liberty to accept the conditions.

If the sovereign shall relinquish the sovereignty without appointing successor, his subjects thereby return to the absolute state of nature.

If the sovereign banish the subject, during banishment he is not subject.

If the sovereign be subdued by war, subjects are delivered from their obligation and become obligated to the victor.

As for other liberties, they depend on the silence of the law. In cases where the sovereign has prescribed no rule, the subject hath the liberty to do or foredo according to his own discretion. And therefore, such liberty is in some places more and in some less, in some times more and in some times less, according as they that have the sovereignty shall think most convenient.

The argument closes with a few observations upon the wisdom of spreading these ideas among the students at the universities, and with the hope that the author may hereafter be left in that peace of mind required for the prosecution of his other studies.

I think what I have writ may be profitably printed, and more profitably taught at the universities, in case they also think so. For, seeing the universities are the fountains of civil and moral doctrine from whence the preachers and gentry, drawing such water as they find, sprinkle the same (both from the pulpit and in their conversation) upon the people, there ought to be great care taken to have it pure, both from the venom of heathen politicians and from the incantations of heathen spirits.

And thus I have brought to an end my discourse on government, occasioned by the disorders of the present time, without partiality, without application, without other design than to set before men's eyes the mutual relation between protection and obedience of which the condition of human nature and the laws both natural and positive, require an inviolable observation.

In the revolution of states there can be no very good constellation for truth of this nature to be born under. Yet I cannot think it will be condemned at this time, either by the public judge of doctrine, or by any that desire the continuance of public peace. And in this hope I return to my uninterrupted speculation of bodies natural, wherein I hope the novelty will as much please as, in the doctrine of this artificial body, it useth to offend.

Reading References. More by Hobbes is the best commentary on anything by Hobbes. Despite his somewhat archaic English, he is thoroughly readable and exceedingly suggestive. There is a refreshing cynicism about the man.

Further reading in *The Leviathan*, particularly that portion in which Hobbes describes the "kingdom of Darkness" is in order. Sir Leslie Stephen's book, *Hobbes*, in the *English Men of Letters* series, is good. So is Sir G. P. Gooch's book, *Political Thought in England: Bacon to Halifax*, in the *Home University Library* series. An older commentary will be found in the first two chapters of William Graham's *English Political Philosophy: Hobbes to Maine*.

READING QUESTIONS

1. Through what important events in English history did Hobbes live?
2. What light do these cast upon the argument of his *Leviathan*?
3. Wherein does he differ from James I?
4. To what sort of facts does he direct attention to explain the formation of states?
5. Pick out three or four apt or vivid phrases from his paragraph.
6. Who are parties to the contract upon which the state is founded?
7. What is the relation of the sovereign to this contract? Is he a contracting party? If not, why not?
8. "The difference of commonwealth consisteth in the difference of the sovereign." Explain.
9. What rights and powers comprise sovereignty?
10. What rights and powers are reserved?
11. Why does he recommend the teaching of his doctrines at the universities?
12. "Artificial chains, fastened at one end to the lips of the sovereign and at the other to their own ears." Elucidate this image.
13. Are there any inconsistencies between the rights and powers of the sovereign and those reserved by the citizens?
14. How far would a believer in democracy go along with Hobbes? A believer in fascism?

3. *THE SOCIAL CONTRACT AND THE GENERAL WILL—FROM JEAN JACQUES ROUSSEAU*

FROM HOBBES TO ROUSSEAU. Hobbes published his account of the state, in his *Leviathan*, in 1651. It had been written with reference to the Puritan revolution in England in 1649. The intention of the author had been to explain to all parties what issues had been at stake in that upheaval. Between the *Leviathan* in 1651 and Rousseau's *Social Contract* in 1762, there came a second English revolution in 1688. This is referred to, sometimes, as the "bloodless" revolution, because of the fact that James II was deposed, the Stuart line closed, a new monarch invited to come to England from Holland, with little or no actual fighting. This revolution of 1688 was celebrated in the annals of political theory by John Locke in his *Two Treatises of Government*. This book defended the revolution on the ground that government rests upon the consent of the governed, and that what the governed consent to is a satisfactory definition and protection of their natural rights. There is, between sovereign and subject, a contractual relation. If the sovereign violates this contract, revolution is justified. This doctrinal claim that government *is* founded — in contrast to the historical claim that it *was* founded — on a contract was made the central theme of Jean Jacques Rousseau's important and influential little book, *The Social Contract*. Locke and Rousseau together provided the theory upon which the revolutionary movements at the end of the eighteenth century professed to rest. Americans in 1776 and French in 1789 were convinced that their actions were susceptible of justification in terms of the *Two Treatises of Government* and the *Social Contract*. The essence of these books is perhaps expressed in the claims that an ideal government is one which permits self-government by the people; and that true self-government is the imposition by each man on himself of rules and limitations demanded by him of all others.

Biographical Note. Jean Jacques Rousseau was born in Switzerland in 1712, and died in 1778 at the age of sixty-six. His life falls into three periods. (1) During the period from

1712 to 1748 he was acquiring the elements of a formal education and a great deal more than the elements of a worldly education. These matters are set down in his *Confessions*. As might be expected from the haphazard and undisciplined way in which he conducted himself during these years, Rousseau arrived at a state of thorough maladjustment. The times looked out of joint. The mores looked cramped and artificial. Civilization looked decadent.

(2) During the period from 1749 to 1762 he formulated his criticisms of the then modern world in a series of tracts which have given him his place in the scheme of things. The first of these (1749) was addressed to the question: Have the sciences and arts contributed to purify morals? Rousseau's answer was No. The second (1755) *On the Origin of Inequality Among Men*, argued that the root of inequality is the division of labor within society which permits the strong and wealthy to subject the mass of mankind to toil and poverty. The third (1760), *The New Heloise*, was a protest against the artificialities of marriage and the family. The fourth (1762), *Émile*, was an elaborate indictment of education conceived as discipline and restraint. It stated the case for education, conceived as expression and development. The fifth (1762), *The Social Contract*, was addressed to the problem: Man is born free, and is everywhere in chains. How can this be justified? In these writings, Rousseau managed to touch on practically every phase of eighteenth-century civilization. His pronouncements were usually in terms of such words as *artificial*, *unnatural*, *narrow*, *selfish*, *ignoble*, *crass*. Art, science, society, education, religion, the family, the state — all gave evidence that mankind was paying too great a price for the fruits of "civilized" living.

(3) During the period from 1763 to 1778 he was again a wanderer. He had said "Wasteland" to his generation. The authorities ordered him out of France. He moved to

Switzerland. The authorities ordered him out of Switzerland. He moved, at the invitation of David Hume, to England. This proved no better. He returned to France. During the last years of his life his mind became unbalanced. He died suddenly in 1778, two years after the American Revolution and eleven years before the French Revolution, for both of which in *The Social Contract* he had formulated the principles of justification.

The Argument of the Citations. The problem which Rousseau set himself to explore has been stated several times already. It was this: "Man is born free, and is everywhere in chains. How did this come about? I do not know. What can make it legitimate? That question I think I can answer." It is clear, from his manner of stating it, that Rousseau does not propose to account for the fact that man is everywhere in chains. That is, he is not proposing a piece of historical research into origins. Nor is he proposing to remove the chains in question. That is, he is not proposing an argument for anarchism. His question is the more searching one: Granted that men must live in chains (i.e., under laws) what considerations will justify the fact? He begins by rejecting the notion that the right of this condition is to be found in the might that enforces it. Might does not make right. What does, then? His answer is common need, common confrontation with conditions which no individual could handle if left to himself. This idea is contained in the notion of the social contract. The terms of the contract are noted. The attributes of the sovereignty created and sustained by the contract are noted. The role of lawmaker is noted. The nature of law is noted. The separation of powers within government is argued for. The alternative forms of government (monarchy, aristocracy, democracy) are noted, together with their defining virtues and vices. He notes, finally, "the unavoidable and inherent defect which tends ceaselessly to destroy" any form of political organization in any society. The argument begins as follows:

Man is born free, and is everywhere in chains. One thinks himself the master of others, and still remains a greater slave than they. How did this come about? I do not know. What can make it legitimate? That question I think I can answer.

The first thing to be clear about is that the restrictions which law imposes cannot be justified by any appeal to the fact of force which lies back of them. Might does not make right. Thus:

Suppose that "force" creates "right." The result is a mass of nonsense. For, if force creates right, then every force that is greater than the first succeeds to its right. As soon as it were possible to disobey with impunity, disobedience would become legitimate; and, the strongest being always in the right, the only thing that would matter (so far as concerns "justification") would be to act so as to become the strongest.

But what kind of "right" is it that perishes when force fails? If we "must" obey, there is no question that we "ought" to obey. And, on the principle that force makes right, if we are not forced to obey, we are under no obligation to do so. A brigand surprises me at the edge of a wood. The pistol he holds gives him power. Does it also give him right? Even if I could withhold my purse, am I in conscience bound to give it up? Does his "might" create a "right"?

Force is a physical power, and I fail to see what moral effect it can have. To yield to force is an act of necessity, not of will; at most, an act of prudence. In what sense can it be a duty?

"Obey the powers that be." If this means "yield to force," it is a good precept; but superfluous: I can answer for its never being violated. If it means "yield, because all power comes from God," the case is no better. All power comes from God, I admit; but so does sickness. Does that mean that we are forbidden to call in a doctor?

Let us admit then that force does not create right, and that we are obligated to obey only legitimate powers. In that case my original question recurs: What is the basis of political obligation?

If might does not make right, if the "chains" cannot be justified by noting the fact that we are forced to wear them, what can we say? Rousseau shifts from the force which is admittedly necessary to the existence of law, to the conditions which justify law backed by force. Thus:

Suppose men to have reached the point at which the obstacles in the way of their preservation in the state of nature are greater than the resources at the disposal of each individual. That primitive condition can then subsist no longer, and the human race would perish unless it changed its manner of existence.

The problem is to find a form of association which will protect the person and goods of each individual with the whole common force of all; and in which each, uniting himself with all, may still obey himself alone and remain as free as before. This is the fundamental problem of which the "social compact" provides the solution.

If we disregard what is not of the essence of the social compact we shall find that it reduces itself to the following terms: "Each of us puts his person and his power in common under the supreme direction of the general will; and, in our corporate capacity, we receive each member as a part of the whole."

At one stroke, in place of the individual personality of each contracting party, this act of association creates a collective body, receiving from this act its unity, its common identity, its life, and its will. This public person, so formed by the union of all other persons, takes the name of *body politic*. It is called *state* when passive, *sovereign* when active, and *power* when compared with others like itself. Those who are associated in it take collectively the name of *people*, are severally called *citizens* as sharing in the sovereign power, and *subjects* as being under the laws of the state.

As soon as this multitude is united in one body politic, it becomes impossible to offend against one of the members without attacking the body politic, and still more to offend against the body politic. Duty and interest, therefore, equally obligate the two contracting parties to give each other help.

The social contract creates the state. It thereby creates the "chains" he had referred to. But it does more than that. The chains are seen to be, in principle, self-imposed restrictions; and they bring with them compensating advantages. Thus:

> In the social compact there is no real "renunciation" on the part of the individuals. The position in which they find themselves, as a result of the compact, is really preferable to that in which they were before. Instead of a "renunciation," they have made an advantageous exchange; instead of an uncertain and precarious way of living, they have got one that is better and more secure; instead of natural independence, they have got liberty; instead of the power to harm others, they have got security for themselves; instead of their strength, which others might overcome, they have got a right which social union makes invincible.
>
> What a man loses by the social compact is his natural liberty, and an unlimited right to everything he tries to get and succeeds in getting. What he gains is civil liberty and the proprietorship of all he possesses. If we are to avoid mistake in weighing one against the other, we must distinguish natural liberty, bounded only by the strength of the individual, from civil liberty, limited by the general will; and we must distinguish possession, the effect of force, from property, founded only on a positive title.
>
> For such physical inequalities as nature may have set up between men, the social compact substitutes an equality that is moral and legitimate: by it, men who may be unequal in strength or intelligence, become every one equal by convention and legal right.
>
> Under bad governments, this equality is only apparent and illusory: it serves only to keep the pauper in his poverty and the rich man in the position he has usurped. In fact, laws are always of use to those who possess, and harmful to those who have nothing: from which it follows that the social state is advantageous to men only when all have something and none have too much.
>
> The general will alone can direct the state according to the object for which it was instituted, i.e., the common good: for, if the clashing of particular interests made the establishing of societies necessary, the agreement of these interests made it possible. The

common element in these different interests is what forms the social tie; and, were there no point of agreement between them all, no society could exist. It is solely on the basis of this common interest that every society should be governed.

There is often a great difference between the "will of all" and the "general will." The latter considers only the common interest; the former takes private interest into account, and is no more than a sum of particular wills. But deduct from the sum of particular wills the plusses and minuses that cancel one another, and the general will remains.

Each individual may have a particular will contrary or dissimilar to the general will which he has as a citizen. His particular interest may speak to him quite different from the common interest; may make him look upon what he owes to the common cause as a gratuitous contribution, the loss of which will do less harm to others than the payment of it is burdensome to himself. He may come to regard the moral person which constitutes the state as a *persona ficta*, because not a man; and, as a result, may wish to enjoy the rights of citizenship without being ready to fulfill the duties of a subject. This, continued, would prove the undoing of the body politic.

The social contract creates sovereignty, i.e., a society organized to define and enforce its laws. This sovereignty inheres in the people. Rousseau proceeds to note several of its defining properties:

In order that the social compact may not be an empty formula, it includes the undertaking, that whoever refuses to obey the general will shall be compelled to do so. In this lies the key to the working of the body politic. This alone legitimizes civil undertakings which, without it, would be absurd, tyrannical and liable to the most frightful abuses. The social compact gives the body politic absolute power over all its members. It is this power, under the direction of the general will, which bears the name of *sovereignty*.

The sovereign, being formed wholly of the individuals who compose it, neither has nor can have any interest contrary to theirs. The sovereign, therefore, need give no guarantee to its subjects.

Merely by virtue of what it is, the sovereign is always what it should be.

Sovereignty, being nothing less than the exercise of the general will, is inalienable, and the sovereign, who is no less than a collective being, cannot be represented except by himself. The power may be delegated, but not the general will from which it derives. To be "general," the will need not be unanimous, but every vote must count; any exclusion is a breach of generality. For the same reason that it is inalienable, sovereignty is indivisible.

The social compact sets up among the citizens an equality of such a kind that they all bind themselves to observe the same conditions and should therefore all enjoy the same rights. Thus, from the very nature of the compact, every act of sovereignty binds or favors all the citizens equally; so that the sovereign recognizes only the body of the nation and draws no distinctions between those of whom it is made up.

What, then, is an act of sovereignty? It is not a convention between a superior and an inferior, but a convention between the body politic and each of its members. It is legitimate, because based on the social contract; equitable, because common to all; useful, because it can have no other object than the general good; and stable, because guaranteed by the public force and the supreme power.

The people are sovereign. Granted. But what can they do about it? They can delegate their sovereignty to a legislature and an administration. Of themselves the sovereign people cannot draw up good law nor can they administer it.

But how are the people to "regulate the conditions of society"? By a common agreement? By a sudden inspiration? Has the body politic an organ to declare its will? Who can give it the foresight to formulate and announce its acts in advance? How is it to announce them in the hour of need? How can a blind multitude, who often does not know what is good for it and hence what it wills, carry out for itself so great and difficult an enterprise as a system of legislation?

Of itself, the people always wills the good, but of itself it by no means always sees it. The general will is always in the right, but the judgment which guides it is not always enlightened. It must be got to see things as they are, and, sometimes, as they ought to appear to it. It must be shown the good road it is in search of, secured against the seductive influences of individual wills. It must be taught to see times and places, made to weigh the attractions of present and sensible advantages against the dangers of distant and hidden evils.

All stand equally in need of guidance. Individuals must be compelled to bring their wills into conformity with their reason. The public must be taught to know what is the good which it wills. If that is done, there is a union of understanding and will in the social body. The parts work together, and the whole is raised to its highest power. This makes a legislator necessary.

The function of lawmaker needs to be considered. The unique qualifications are noted. The "legislator" is a paradoxical ideal.

To discover the rules of society best suited to nations, a superior intelligence beholding all the passions of men without experiencing any of them, would be needed. This intelligence would have to be wholly unrelated to our nature, while knowing it through and through. Its happiness would have to be independent of our happiness and yet ready to occupy itself with it. It would have to look forward and, working in one century, to be able to enjoy the next. It would take gods to give men laws.

He who dares undertake the making of a people's institutions ought to feel himself capable of changing human nature, of transforming each individual into part of a greater whole, of altering men's constitution for the purpose of strengthening it, of substituting a shared and moral existence for the independent and natural existence which nature has conferred on us all. In a word, he must take away from man his own resources and give him in their stead new ones incapable of being used without the help of other men. The more completely these "natural" resources are annihilated, the greater and more lasting are those which supplant them, and the more stable and perfect are the new institutions.

The office of legislator, which gives form to the state, nowhere enters into its constitution. He who holds command over men (the government), ought not to hold command over the laws. He who holds command over the laws (the legislator) ought not to hold command over men. Else would his laws be the ministers of his passions serving to perpetuate his injustices, and his private aims mar the sanctity of his work.

When Lycurgus gave laws to Sparta, he began by resigning his throne. Most Greek towns entrusted the establishment of their laws to foreigners.

The republics of modern Italy in many cases followed this example. Geneva did the same and profited by it. Rome suffered a revival of tyranny and was brought to the verge of destruction, because it put legislative authority and sovereign power into the same hands.

Thus in the task of legislation we find two things which appear to be incompatible: an enterprise too difficult for human powers, and, for its execution, an authority that is no authority.

The great soul of the legislator is the only miracle that can prove his mission. Any man may engrave on tables, buy an oracle, feign secret intercourse with the gods, train a bird to whisper into his ear, or find some other trumpery way to impose on the people. He whose knowledge goes no further may perhaps gather round him a band of fools, but he will never found an empire, and his extravagances will perish with him. Idle tricks form a passing tie; only wisdom can make it lasting.

Provided the miracle of a good law can be performed, what does society have at its disposal? An instrument, essentially, for dealing with general conditions. The particulars must be seen to fall under the law by the wisdom of the executive.

What is a law? When the whole people declares for the whole people, this is what I call a *law*.

The matter about which such decree is made is, like the decreeing will, general. When I say that the matter is "general," I mean that law considers subjects *en masse* and actions in the abstract, never a particular person or action. Thus law may declare that there shall be privileges; but it cannot confer them on any one by name. It may set up classes of citizens. It may specify qualifications for membership of these classes. But, as law, it cannot nominate such and such persons as belonging to these classes. Law may, e.g., establish a monarchical form of government and an hereditary succession. It cannot choose a king or nominate a royal family. In a word, no function which has a particular object in view can be a matter of law.

On this view, we see at once that it can no longer be asked whose business it is to make laws, since they are acts of the general will; nor whether "government is above the law," since governors are part of the state; nor whether laws can be unjust, since no one is unjust to himself; nor how we can be both "free" and at the same time subject to laws, since they are but registers of our wills.

The law unites universality of will with universality of object. What any man commands of his own motion cannot be law. Even what sovereignty commands with regard to some particular matter cannot be law; it is then merely a decree of the government.

Laws are, strictly speaking, the conditions of civil association. The people, being subject to the laws, ought to be their author: the conditions of the society ought to be regulated by those who unite to give it form.

Thus far we have had society, the contract, the sovereign people, the legislator, and laws. We come now to government, what we would call the executive arm of government. It is not to be confused with any of the other terms:

I have argued that the power to make laws belongs to the sovereign people, and can belong to it alone. On the other hand, the power to execute these laws cannot belong to the generality, because such power consists wholly of particular acts which fall outside the competency of lawmaking as such.

The body politic, therefore, needs an agent of its own to bind it together, to set it to work under the direction of the general will, to serve as a means of communication between the (people as) state and the (people as) sovereign. Here we have the basis of government, something which is often confused with the sovereign whose minister it is.

What then is government? It is an intermediate body, set up

between the (people as) subjects and the (people as) sovereign, to secure their mutual correspondence, to execute the laws and to maintain liberty. The members of this body are called governors.

Government is hence simply and solely a commission, in which the governors, mere officials of the sovereign people, exercise in their own name the power which is invested in them by the people. This delegated power the sovereign people can limit, modify, or recover at pleasure.

The government gets from the (people as) sovereign the orders which it gives to the (people as) subjects. For the state to be properly balanced there must be an equality between the power of the government and the power of the citizens, for the latter are, on the one hand, sovereign, and, on the other hand, subject.

None of these three terms — *sovereign*, *subjects*, *government* — can be altered without the equality being instantly destroyed. If the sovereign tries to govern, if the government tries to give laws, or if the subjects refuse to obey, disorder replaces order, force and will no longer act together, and the state is dissolved into despotism or anarchy.

Government, then, is distinct from such matters as society, sovereignty, legislator, etc. Its function is to administer the laws. What form should it have?

There has been at all times much dispute concerning the best form of government. Is it democratic? Aristocratic? Or monarchical? This question, "What, absolutely, is the best form of government?" is unanswerable and indeterminate. The fact is that each is in some cases the best, and in others the worst.

Let us see. Consider first the notion of democracy:

The sovereign people may commit the charge of the government to the whole people or to a majority of the people. The result would be that more citizens would be actual governors than mere private subjects. This form of government is called *democracy*.

If we take the term in the strict sense, there never has been a real democracy, and there never will be. It is unimaginable that the people should remain continually assembled to devote their time to public affairs.

Besides, how many conditions, difficult to unite, would such a form of government presuppose! First, a very small state, where the people can readily be got together and where each citizen can with ease know all the rest. Second, great simplicity of manners, to prevent business from multiplying and raising thorny problems. Third, a large measure of equality in rank and fortune, without which equality of rights and authority cannot long subsist. Fourth, little or no luxury, for luxury either comes of riches or makes them necessary.

Moreover, it is a certainty that promptitude in execution diminishes as more people are put in charge of it. Where prudence is made too much of, not enough is made of fortune; opportunity is let slip, and deliberation results in the loss of its object.

It may be added that no form of government is so subject to civil wars and intestinal agitations as democracy, because there is none which has so strong and persistent a tendency to change to another form, or which demands more vigilance and courage for its maintenance. Were there a people of gods, their government would be democratic. So perfect a government is not for men.

Obviously, pure democracy is unsuited to the needs of the modern state. Another possibility is an elected aristocracy. It holds more promise:

The sovereign people may restrict the government to a small number, so that there are more private citizens than magistrates. This is named *aristocracy*.

There are three sorts of aristocracy: natural, elective, and hereditary. The first is only for simple peoples; the second is the best, and is aristocracy properly so-called; the third is the worst of all governments.

There is much to be said for an elective aristocracy. It has the advantage of keeping clear the distinction between the two powers, sovereignty and government. Besides this, its members are chosen to be governors, not born to this office, as in the case of a pure democracy or an hereditary aristocracy. By this means uprightness, understanding, experience, and all other claims to pre-eminence become so many guarantees of wise government.

It is more efficient. Assemblies are more easily held; affairs are better discussed and carried out with more order and diligence; the credit of the state is better sustained abroad.

It is more economical. There is no need to multiply instruments, or get twenty thousand men to do what a hundred picked men can do better.

However, if an elective aristocracy does not demand all the virtues needed by popular government, it demands others which are peculiar to itself; for instance, moderation on the side of the rich, and contentment on the side of the poor. If this form of government carries with it a certain inequality of fortune, this is justifiable on the grounds that the administration of public affairs may be entrusted to those who are most able to give them their whole time.

In Rousseau's day the commonest form of government was hereditary monarchy. It has its good points and its bad points. Thus:

The sovereign people may concentrate the whole government in the hands of a single person from whom all others hold their power. This form of government is the most usual, and is called *monarchy*.

No form of government is more vigorous than this. All answer to a single motive power. All the springs of the machine are in the same hands. The whole moves toward the same end. There are no conflicting movements to cancel one another. In no constitution does a smaller amount of effort produce a greater amount of action. Archimedes seated quietly on the bank of a river, easily drawing a great floating vessel, stands in my mind for a skillful monarch governing vast estates from his study, moving everything while he seems himself unmoved.

For a monarchical state to have a chance of being well governed, its population and extent must be proportionate to the abilities of its governor. It is easier to conquer than to rule. With a lever long enough, the world could be moved with a single finger; to sustain it requires the shoulders of Hercules.

Everything conspires to take away from a man who is set in authority the sense of justice and reason.

Kings desire to be absolute, and men are always crying out to them from afar that the best means is to get themselves loved by their people. This is all very well, and true enough in some respects. Unfortunately, it will always be derided at court. The power that comes of a people's love is no doubt the greatest; but it is precarious and conditional, and princes will never rest content with it. The best of kings desire to be in a position to be wicked, if they so please, without forfeiting thereby their mastery. Political sermonizers may tell them, to their hearts' content, that the people should be prosperous, numerous, and formidable. Kings know this to be untrue. Their personal interest is that the people should be weak, wretched, and unable to resist them.

There is an essential and inevitable defect which will always rank a monarchy below a republic. It is this. In a republic the people hardly ever raises men who are unenlightened and incapable to the highest positions; whereas, under a monarch, those who rise to power are most often petty blunderers, petty swindlers, petty intriguers, men whose petty talents cause them to get into stations of the greatest eminence at court. The people is far less often mistaken in its choice than the monarch. A man of real worth among the king's ministers is almost as rare as a fool at the head of a republic.

Another disadvantage in monarchical government is the lack of any continuous succession. When one king dies, another is needed. In the case of an elective monarchy, dangerous interregnums occur, and are full of storms; unless, that is, the citizens are upright and disinterested to a degree which seldom goes with this kind of government.

What has been done to prevent these evils? Succession has been made hereditary in certain families. That is to say, men have chosen rather to be ruled by children, monstrosities, or imbeciles than to endure disputes over the choice of good kings. Apparent tranquillity has been preferred to wise administration.

These difficulties have not escaped our political writers. But they are not troubled by them. The remedy, they say, is to obey without a murmur: God sends bad kings in His wrath, and they are to be borne as the scourges of heaven. Such talk is doubtless edifying, but it would be more in place in a pulpit than in a political book. What are we to say of a doctor whose whole art is to exhort the sufferer to patience?

By way of conclusion we may note the fundamental fact from which political instability continually proceeds:

All forms of government contain within them the seeds of destruction and dissolution. As the particular will acts constantly in opposition to the general will, the government continually exerts itself against the sovereign. The greater this exertion becomes, the more the constitution changes. This is the unavoidable and inherent defect which, from the very birth of the body politic, tends ceaselessly to destroy it, as age and death end by destroying the human body.

Such is the natural and inevitable tendency of the best constituted governments. If Sparta and Rome perished, what state can hope to endure for ever? We desire a long-lived form of government? Let us not dream of making it eternal. If we are to succeed, we must not attempt the impossible; nor must we flatter ourselves that we are endowing the work of man with a stability which human conditions do not permit.

The body politic begins to die as soon as it is born, and carries in itself the causes of its own destruction. The state is a work of art, not of nature. It is for men to prolong its life as much as possible, by giving it the best possible constitution. But even the best will have an end.

The life principle of the body politic lies in the sovereign authority. The legislative power is the heart of the state; the executive power is its brain. The brain may become paralyzed, and the body still live. But as soon as the heart ceases to perform its function, the organism is dead. Wherever the laws grow weak as they become old, there is no longer a legislative power, and the state is dead.

Reading References. The number of books written on Rousseau is exceedingly large. Each generation has found it necessary to take stock of his ideas. Lord Morley's *Rousseau* is good reading for those who continue to share Lord Morley's typically nineteenth-century rationalism and liberalism. A most provocative chapter on *The Social Contract* is to be found in Bernard Bosanquet's *Philosophical Theory of the State*. The author stresses the fact that Rousseau's self-imposed problem was *not* how to justify revolution, but how to justify restraint of the individual by the state. A good biography is to be found in Matthew Josephson's *Jean Jacques Rousseau*. The best comprehensive accounts of Rousseau's ideas are to be found, so far as books written in English are concerned, in C. W. Hendel's two volumes, *Rousseau as Moralist*, and in Matthew Josephson's *Jean-Jacques Rousseau*.

READING QUESTIONS

1. What is Rousseau's problem?
2. What does he say is *not* his problem?
3. On what grounds does he deny that force or might makes right?
4. What is the fundamental problem of which the social compact provides the solution?
5. What compensations attend the adoption of the social compact?
6. What "continued, would prove the undoing of the body politic"?
7. "Sovereignty is inalienable." Explain.
8. "And indivisible." Explain.
9. "It would take gods to give men laws." Why?
10. "The office of legislator nowhere enters into the constitution." Meaning? Why not?
11. "Law must deal with general considerations." Meaning? Reason?
12. Explain the status of government in Rousseau's argument?
13. What is his case against a democratic government?
14. What are the virtues and requirements of an elective aristocratic government?

15. "There is an essential and inevitable defect which will always rank a monarchy below a republic." Namely?
16. "The unavoidable and inherent defect which tends ceaselessly to destroy the body politic." Namely?

4. PRINCIPLES OF CONSERVATISM — FROM EDMUND BURKE

From Rousseau to Burke. Rousseau published *The Social Contract* in 1762. The American Revolution began in 1775. It was scarcely over when the French Revolution began, in 1789. This political restlessness in the colonies and in Europe was accompanied by a sharp demand for parliamentary reform in England. The revolutionary Society for Constitutional Information was organized in 1780. Prime Minister Pitt tried three times, and each time in vain, to persuade a reluctant House of Commons to consider the case for parliamentary reform. During these years, Tom Paine was gaining his reputation as spokesman for liberal and revolutionary movements in America and Europe. Jeremy Bentham published in 1789 his epoch-making treatise on liberal social reform, *Principles of Morals and Legislation*, in which he argued that customs, laws, institutions, and constitutions should be evaluated in terms of one standard, namely, the greatest happiness of the greatest number.

Such was the climate of opinion in which Edmund Burke wrote his exposition and defense of political conservatism. On all hands he saw, or thought he saw, signs that the old regimes of monarchies and aristocracies were weakening before popular demand for democratic politics. Wherever he looked, he detected "factions now busy amongst us who endeavor to propagate an opinion that the people, in forming their commonwealth, have by no means parted with their power over it." He set himself to stem this tide. He might as well have bade the sun stand still. These democratizing tendencies swept on and left the memory of his plea stranded amid the welter of wars, revolutions, reforms, and changes. If this were all, there would be little need to include Burke among spokesmen of political philosophy. But there is more to Burke than a neglected warning against democratic politics. In his words may be found a careful account of the principles of political conservatism. It is an expression of one of man's perennial needs.

Biographical Note. Edmund Burke was born in Ireland in 1729 and died in England in 1797 at the age of sixty-eight. He received his academic education at Trinity College, Dublin. He spent some time acquiring the rudiments of a legal training in London in the Middle Temple. He entered Parliament in the 1760's and rose there to a position of great prestige. In 1775 he delivered his famous speech, "Conciliation with America." In 1785 he opened his attack on Warren Hastings' India administration with his equally famous speech "The Nabob of Arcot's Debts." In 1790 he published his *Reflections on the French Revolution*. The ideas advanced in this tract were subsequently elaborated in his *Appeal from the New to the Old Whigs*, his *Letter to a Noble Lord* and his *Letter on a Regicide Peace*. The citations in this chapter are, for the most part, from the *Reflections* and the *Appeal* and the *Letters*.

The Argument of the Citations. Burke begins by noting that there are certain "factions now busy amongst us who endeavor to propagate an opinion that 'the people' in forming their commonwealth have by no means parted with their power over it." In other words, the notion of popular sovereignty is being argued for. The substance of such claims is noted. A general criticism is passed upon them. The concept of "the people," upon which the whole argument turns, is then proposed for analysis. What does one mean by *the people?* If by *the people* one means a numerical majority, then certain criticisms may be advanced. At this point the argument is suspended while Burke makes two long excursions into recent French history with a view to documenting his critique of the concept of the people as sovereign. The first aside is addressed to a Frenchman, pointing out the extent to which, in Burke's mind, alternative steps had been possible in France at the time the revolution was launched. Various excesses are noted. "Were all these dreadful things necessary?" he demands. The second aside recounts the fate of the French king and queen and laments the absence of wisdom and decency exhibited by those who put them to death. "Alas, the age of chivalry is gone." From these historical asides, he returns to his criticism of the "barbarous philosophy" which has led to this havoc.

At this point Burke's arguments become positive. He sketches the foundation in which government is laid. From this, there results a more austere conception of the state than is held by those who launch and defend revolution in the name of the "rights of man." Does this commit Burke to a repudiation of the notion of the rights of man? "I am far from denying the real rights of man," he protests. The notion of "real" rights, in contrast to spurious rights, is outlined. This involves a clarification of "real" liberties in contrast to spurious liberties. The "real" rights and liberties, which Burke is prepared to ascribe to "the people" presuppose government by a natural aristocracy. This notion is outlined. It is then contrasted with a sham aristocracy of mere lords and dukes.

The fundamental claim is disclosed at this point: Burke will entertain the notion of rights only in terms of the notion of duties. We have rights because we have duties, and, within limits, we do not choose our duties. They await us in the society into which we are born and in which we grow up. This idea may involve difficult problems and nice distinctions. In all such cases, it is wiser to keep an eye on duties than on rights. The burden of proof rests with those who violate obligations in the name of their rights. This, however, is not to be taken as a categorical denial of all change and reform, merely an insistence that wisdom ordinarily lies with custom and tradition, and that an individual should address himself to the problem of extracting the wisdom which these contain. It is folly to "trade each on his own private stock of reason." This conservative political philosophy rests upon a recognition of the fact that wise politics has, in the last analysis, a religious basis. "On religion all our laws and institutions stand." "The awful author of our being has disposed and marshaled us by a divine tactic." The argument concludes with several eloquent paragraphs setting forth the great wisdom which attends the policy, arising out of these views, of regarding "liberties as an entailed inheritance" to be held as a sacred trust and passed on intact to one's posterity.

Factions now busy amongst us, in order to divest men of all love for their country, and remove from their minds all duty with regard to the state, endeavor to propagate an opinion that the "people," in forming their commonwealth, have by no means parted with their power over it. Discuss any of their schemes, and their answer is, It is the act of the people and that is sufficient.

These theorists hold, that sovereignty, whether exercised by one or many, did not only originate from the people, but that in the people the same sovereignty constantly and unalienably resides; that the people may lawfully depose kings; not only for misconduct, but without any misconduct at all; that they may set up any new fashion of government for themselves, or continue without any government at their pleasure; that the people are essentially their own rule, and their will the measure of their conduct; that the tenure of rulers is not a proper subject of contracts, because rulers have duties, but no rights; and that if a contract *de facto* is made with them in one age, allowing that it binds at all, it binds only those who are immediately concerned in it, but does not pass to posterity.

They hold that to a majority of the people belongs the right of altering the whole frame of their society, if such should be their pleasure. They may change it, say they, from a monarchy to a republic today and tomorrow back again from a republic to a monarchy, and so backward and forward as often as they like. They are masters of the commonwealth, because in substance they are themselves the commonwealth.

The ceremony of cashiering kings, of which these gentlemen talk so much, can rarely, if ever, be performed without force. It then becomes a case of war, and not of constitution. Laws are commanded to hold their tongues amongst arms, and tribunals fall to the ground with the peace they are no longer able to uphold.

Whilst they are possessed by these notions, it is vain to talk to them of the practice of their ancestors, the fundamental laws of their country, the fixed form of a constitution, whose merits are confirmed by the solid test of long experience, and an increasing public strength and national prosperity. They despise experience as the wisdom of unlettered men, and as for the rest, they have wrought underground a mine that will blow up, at one grand explosion, all examples of antiquity, precedents, charters, and acts of parliament.

Burke now has the political heresy stated. It is the claim that the people are sovereign and need acknowledge no masters save of their own choosing. Those who hold this view are, Burke feels, beyond the reach of argument. Nevertheless, over against the time when experience shall have disclosed to them the folly of their ways, he proposes to analyze and evaluate their claim:

These doctrines concerning "the people" tend, in my opinion, to the utter subversion, not only of all government, in all modes, but all stable securities to rational freedom, and all the rules and principles of morality itself.

On such principles every individual would have a right to originate what afterwards is to become the act of the majority. Whatever he may lawfully originate, he may lawfully endeavor to accomplish. He has a right therefore to break the ties and engagements which bind him to the country in which he lives, and he has a right to make as many converts to his opinions, and to obtain as many associates in his designs, as he can procure: for how can you know the dispositions of the majority to destroy their government, but by tampering with some part of the body? You must begin by a secret conspiracy, that you may end with a national confederation.

The mere pleasure of the beginning must be the sole guide, since the mere pleasure of others must be the sole ultimate sanction, as well as the sole actuating principle in every part of the progress. Thus, arbitrary will (the last corruption of ruling power) step by step poisons the heart of every citizen.

No sense of duty can prevent any man from being a leader or a follower in such enterprises. Nothing restrains the tempter; nothing guards the tempted. Nor is the new state, fabricated by such arts, safer than the old. What can prevent the mere will of any person, who hopes to unite the wills of others to his own, from an attempt wholly to overturn it? It wants nothing but a disposition to trouble the established order, to give a title to the enterprise.

By such doctrines, all love to our country, all pious veneration and attachment to its laws and customs, are obliterated from our minds; and nothing can result from this opinion, when grown into a principle, and animated by discontent, ambition, or enthusiasm, but a series of conspiracies and seditions, sometimes ruinous to their authors, always noxious to the state.

There is, it appears, much to be said against this popular doctrine. A few obvious things have already been noted. But nothing fundamental has been offered as yet. Burke moves, accordingly, to the essential point. Everything turns upon the meaning of this phrase, *the people*. So he proceeds:

Believing it a question at least arduous in theory, and in practice very critical, it would become us to ascertain what our incantations are about to call up from darkness and the sleep of ages when the supreme authority of "the people" is in question. Before we attempt to extend or to confine, we ought to fix in our minds, with some degree of distinctness, an idea of what it is we mean, when we say *the people*.

We are so little affected by things which are habitual, that we consider this idea of the decision of a majority as if it were a law of our original nature, but such constructive whole, residing in a part only, is one of the most violent fictions that ever has been or can be made on the principles of artificial incorporation. Out of civil society nature knows nothing of it; nor are men, even when arranged according to civil order, otherwise than by very long training, brought at all to submit to it.

In a state of rude nature there is no such thing as "a people." A number of men in themselves have no collective capacity. The idea of a people is the idea of a corporation. It is wholly artificial, and made like all other legal fictions, by common agreement. What the particular nature of that agreement was, is collected from the form into which the particular society has been cast. Any other is not their covenant.

When men, therefore, break up the agreement which gives its corporate form and capacity to a state, they are no longer a people; they have no longer a corporate existence; they have no longer a legal, coactive force to bind within, nor a claim to be recognized abroad. They are a number of vague, loose individuals and nothing more. With them all is to begin again. Alas! They little know how many a weary step is to be taken before they can form themselves into a mass, which has a true, political personality.

The phrase *the people* cannot be identified with a mere voting majority. Such an idea, namely that a voting majority shall be "the people" is a product of late political experience. Men must have learned much from long trial and error before they can act on that notion. It expresses an agreement or consensus that political experience alone makes possible. If this meaning of the phrase is a product of group experience of state organization, then it cannot be argued to be prior to and more fundamental than state organization. To overlook or to deny this fact is to court much trouble. Thus:

I see as little of policy or utility, as there is of right, in laying down a principle that a majority of men, told by the head are to be considered as "the people," and that as such their will is to be law. What policy can there be in arrangements made in defiance of every political principle? To enable men to act with the weight and character of a people, and to answer the ends for which they are incorporated into that capacity, we must suppose them to be in that state of habitual social discipline, in which the wiser, the more expert, and the more opulent conduct, and by conducting enlighten and protect the weaker, the less knowing, and the less provided with the goods of fortune. When the multitude are not under this discipline, they can scarcely be said to be in civil society.

It is not necessary to teach men to thirst after power. But it is very expedient that by moral instruction, they should be taught, and by their civil constitutions they should be compelled, to put many restrictions upon the immoderate exercise of it, and the inordinate desire for it. The best method of obtaining these great points forms the important, but at the same time the difficult problem to the true statesman. No legislator, at any period of the world, has willingly placed the seat of active power in the hands of the multitude: because there it admits of no control, no regulation, no steady direction whatsoever.

The people are not to be taught to think lightly of their engagements to their governors; else they teach their governors to think lightly of their engagements toward them. In that kind of game in the end the people are sure to be the losers. To flatter them into a contempt of faith, truth, and justice, is to ruin them; for in those virtues consists their whole safety. To flatter any man, or any part of mankind, in any description, by asserting that in engagements he or they are free whilst any other human creature is bound, is ultimately to vest the rule of morality in the pleasure of those who ought to be rigidly submitted to it, to subject the sovereign reason of the world to the caprices of weak and giddy men.

The democratic commonwealth is the foodful nurse of ambition.

Under other forms of government it meets with many restraints. Whenever, in states which have a democratic basis, the legislators have endeavored to put restraints upon ambition, their methods were as violent, as in the end they were ineffectual: as violent indeed as any the most jealous despotism could invent. The caution could not very long save the state which it was meant to guard, from the attempts of ambition, one of the natural, inbred, incurable distempers of a powerful democracy.

I am well aware that men love to hear of their power, but have an extreme disrelish to be told of their duty. This is a matter of course; because every duty is a limitation of some power. Indeed arbitrary power is so much to the depraved taste of the vulgar of every description, that almost all dissensions, which lacerate the commonwealth, are not concerning the manner in which it is to be exercised, but concerning the hands in which it is to be placed.

The people are, to a far less extent than are princes and other persons of exalted station, under responsibility to one of the greatest controlling powers on earth, the sense of fame and estimation. The share of infamy that is likely to fall to the lot of each individual in public acts is small indeed; the operation of opinion being in the inverse ratio to the number of those who abuse power. Their own approbation of their own facts has to them the appearance of a public judgment in their favor. A perfect democracy is therefore the most shameless thing in the world. As it is the most shameless, it is also the most fearless.

At this point Burke turns from his criticism of the notion of "the people" to some of the facts in recent French history. These facts, he feels, will amply bear out what he claims.

We hear much from men, who have not acquired their hardiness of assertion from the profundity of their thinking, about the omnipotence of a majority, in such a dissolution of an ancient society as hath taken place in France.

It appears to me as if I were in a great crisis, not of the affairs of France alone, but, of all Europe, perhaps of more than Europe. All circumstances taken together, the French Revolution is the most astonishing that has hitherto happened in the world. The most wonderful things are brought about in many instances by means the most absurd and ridiculous; in the most ridiculous modes; and apparently, by the most contemptible instruments. Everything seems out of nature in this strange chaos of levity and ferocity, and of all sorts of crimes jumbled together with all sorts of follies. In viewing this monstrous tragicomic scene, the most opposite passions necessarily succeed, and sometimes mix with each other in the mind; alternate contempt and indignation; alternate laughter and tears; alternate scorn and horror.

His estimate at this point is addressed to a citizen of France under the new regime. Hence his use of the second person:

Your constitution was suspended before it was perfected, but you had the elements of a constitution very nearly as good as could be wished. In your old estates you possessed that variety of parts corresponding with the various descriptions of which your community was happily composed; you had all that combination, and all that opposition of interests; you had that action and counteraction which, in the natural and in the political world, from the reciprocal struggle of discordant powers, draws out the harmony of the universe.

You had all these advantages in your ancient states, but you choose to act as if you had never been molded into civil society, and had everything to begin anew. You began ill, because you began by despising everything that belonged to you. You set up your trade without a capital. If the last generations of your country appeared without much luster in your eyes, you might have passed them by, and derived your claims from a more early race of ancestors. Under a pious predilection for those ancestors, your imaginations would have realized in them a standard of virtue and wisdom, beyond the vulgar practice of the hour, and you would have risen with the example whose imitation you aspired. Respecting your forefathers, you would have been taught to respect yourselves. You would not have chosen to reconsider the French people as a people of yesterday, as a nation of low-born servile wretches until the emancipating year of 1789.

You might, if you pleased, have given to your recovered freedom a dignity. Your privileges, though discontinued, were not lost to memory. Your constitution, it is true, whilst you were out of possession, suffered waste and dilapidation, but you possessed in some parts the walls, and, in all, the foundations of a noble and venerable castle. You might have repaired those walls; you might have built on those old foundations.

You would have rendered the cause of liberty venerable in the eyes of every worthy mind in the nation. You would have shamed despotism from the earth, by showing that freedom was not only reconcilable, but, as when well disciplined, it is auxiliary to law. You would have had an unoppressive but a productive revenue. You would have had a flourishing commerce to feed it. You would have had a free constitution; a potent monarchy; a disciplined army; a reformed and venerated clergy; a mitigated but spirited nobility, to lead your virtue, not to overlay it; you would have had a liberal order of commons, to emulate and to recruit that nobility; you would have had a protected, satisfied, laborious, and obedient people, taught to seek and to recognize the happiness that is to be found by virtue in all conditions; in which consists the true moral equality of mankind, and not in that monstrous fiction, which, by inspiring false ideas and vain expectations into men destined to travel in the obscure walk of laborious life, serves only to aggravate and embitter that real inequality, which it never can remove; and which the order of civil life establishes as much for the benefit of those whom it is able to exalt to a condition more splendid, but not more happy.

From a consideration of what the citizens might have done, Burke turns to note some of the things they have done. Thus:

Who that had not lost every trace of humanity could think of casting down men of exalted rank and sacred function, some of them of an age to call at once for reverence and compassion; casting them down from the highest situation in the commonwealth, wherein they were maintained by their own landed property; casting them down to a state of indigence, depression, and contempt.

Who but a tyrant could think of seizing on the property of men, unaccused, unheard, untried, by wholesale descriptions, by hundreds and thousands together? I hope we shall never be so totally lost to all sense of the duties imposed upon us by the law of social union, as, upon any pretext of "public service," to confiscate the goods of a single unoffending citizen.

That a man should rejoice and triumph in the destruction of an absolute monarchy; that in such an event he should overlook the captivity, disgrace, and degradation of an unfortunate prince, and the continual danger to a life which exists only to be endangered; that he should overlook the utter ruin of whole orders and classes of men, extending itself directly, or in its nearest consequences, to at least a million of our kind, and to at least the temporary wretchedness of a whole community, I do not deny to be in some sort natural: when people see a political object, which they ardently desire, they are apt extremely to underrate the evils which may arise in obtaining it. This is no reflection upon the humanity of those persons. Their good nature I am the last man in the world to dispute. It only shows that they are not sufficiently informed or sufficiently considerate. When they come to reflect seriously on the transaction, they will think themselves bound to examine what the object is that has been acquired by all this havoc.

This was unnatural. The rest is in order. They have found their punishment in their success. Laws overturned; tribunals subverted; industry without vigor; commerce expiring; the revenue unpaid, yet the people impoverished; a church pillaged, and a state not relieved; civil and military anarchy made the constitution of the kingdom; everything human and divine sacrificed to the idol of public credit, and national bankruptcy the consequence; and, to crown all, the paper securities of new, precarious, tottering power, the discredited paper securities of impoverished fraud, and beggared rapine, held out as a currency for the support of the empire, in lieu of the two great recognized species that represent the lasting, conventional credit of mankind, which disappeared and hid themselves in the earth from whence they came, when the principle of property, whose creatures and representatives they are, was systematically subverted.

Compute your gains; see what is got by those extravagant and presumptuous speculations which have taught your leaders to despise all their predecessors, and all their contemporaries, and even to despise themselves, until the moment in which they became truly despicable. By following those false lights, France has bought undisguised calamities at a higher price than any nation has purchased the most unequivocal blessings! France has bought poverty by crime! France has abandoned her interest, that she might prostitute her virtue. All other nations have begun the fabric of a new government, or the reformation of an old, by establishing originally, or by enforcing with greater exactness, some rights or other of religion. All other people have laid the foundations of civil freedom in severer manners and a system of more austere and masculine morality. France, when she let loose the reins of regal authority, doubled the license of a ferocious dissoluteness in manners, and of an insolent irreligion in opinions and practices; and has extended through all ranks of life, as if she were communicating some privilege, or laying open some secluded benefit, all the unhappy corruptions that usually were the disease of wealth and power. This is one of the new principles of equality in France.

Were all these dreadful things necessary? Were they the inevitable results of the desperate struggle of determined patriots, compelled to wade through blood and tumult, to the quiet shore of a tranquil and prosperous liberty? No! nothing like it. The fresh ruins of France, which shock our feelings wherever we can turn our eyes, are not the devastation of civil war; they are the sad but instructive monuments of rash and ignorant counsel in time of profound peace. They are the display of inconsiderate and presumptuous, because unresisted and irresistible authority. The persons who have thus squandered away the precious treasure of their crimes, the persons who have made this prodigal and wild waste of public evils, have met in their progress with little, or rather with no opposition at all. Their whole march was more like a triumphal procession, than the progress of a war. Their pioneers have gone before them, and demolished and laid everything level at their feet. Not one drop of their blood have they shed in the cause of the country they have ruined. They have made no sacrifices to their projects of greater consequence than their shoe buckles, whilst they were imprisoning their king, murdering their fellow citizens, and bathing in tears, and plunging in poverty and distress, thousands of worthy men and worthy families. Their cruelty has not even been the base result of fear. It has been the effect of their sense of perfect safety, in authorizing treasons, robberies, rapes, assassinations, slaughters, and burnings, throughout their harassed land.

So far his indictment has been in terms of rather large general issues. He moves to consider more specific outrages, particularly the case of the king and queen. Burke's prose here should be read aloud.

Let those who have the trust of political or of natural authority ever keep watch against the desperate enterprises of innovation; let even their benevolence be fortified and armed. They have before their eyes the example of a monarch, insulted, degraded, confined, deposed; his family dispersed, scattered, imprisoned; his wife insulted to his face like the vilest of the sex, by the vilest of all populace; himself three times dragged by these wretches in an infamous triumph; his children torn from him, in violation of the first right of nature, and given into the tuition of the most desperate and impious of the leaders of desperate and impious clubs; his revenues dilapidated and plundered; his magistrates murdered; his clergy proscribed, persecuted, famished; his nobility degraded in their rank, undone in their fortunes, fugitives in their persons; his armies corrupted and ruined; his whole people impoverished, disunited, dissolved; whilst through the bars of his prison, and amidst the bayonets of his keepers, he hears the tumult of two conflicting factions.

All this accumulation of calamity, the greatest that ever fell upon one man, has fallen upon his head, because he had left his virtues unguarded by caution; because he was not taught that, where power is concerned, he who will confer benefits must take security against ingratitude.

It is now sixteen or seventeen years since I saw the queen of France, then the dauphiness, at Versailles; and surely never lighted on this orb a more delightful vision. I saw her just above the horizon, glittering like the morning star, full of life and splendor and joy.

Oh! what a revolution, and what a heart must I have, to contemplate without emotion that elevation and that fall. Little did I dream, when she added titles of veneration to those of enthusiastic, distant, respectful love, that she should ever be obliged to carry the sharp antidote against disgrace concealed in that bosom. Little did I dream that I should have lived to see such disasters fallen upon her in a nation of gallant gentlemen, a nation of men of honor and of cavaliers. I thought ten thousand swords must have leaped from their scabbards to avenge even a look that threatened her with insult!

But alas, the age of chivalry is gone. The age of sophisters, economists, and calculators has succeeded, and the glory of Europe is extinguished for ever. Never, never more shall we behold that generous loyalty to rank and sex, that proud submission, that dignified obedience, that subordination of the heart, which kept alive, even in servitude itself, the spirit of an exalted freedom. The unbought grace of life, the cheap defense of nations, the nurse of manly sentiment and heroic enterprise, is gone. That sensibility of principle, that chastity of honor, which felt a stain like a wound, which inspired courage while it mitigated ferocity, which ennobled whatever it touched, under which vice lost half its evil by losing all its grossness, is gone.

Now all is changed. All the pleasing illusions, which made power gentle and obedience liberal, which harmonized the different shades of life, which by a bland assimilation incorporated into politics the sentiments which beautify and soften private society, are to be dissolved by this new conquering empire of "light and reason." All the decent drapery of life is to be torn off. All the superadded ideas, furnished from the wardrobe of a moral imagination, which the heart owns and the understanding ratifies as necessary to cover the defects of our naked shivering nature and raise it to dignity in our own estimation, are to be exploded as ridiculous, absurd, and antiquated fashion.

Back of all this chaos and cruelty and injustice and folly lies the doctrine of popular sovereignty. That was what

Burke set out to criticize. His asides have been intended merely to document his claims:

The pretended "rights of man," which have made this havoc, cannot be the rights of the people. For to be a people, and to have these rights, are things incompatible. The one supposes the presence, the other the absence of a state of civil society. The very foundation of the French commonwealth is false and self-destructive; nor can its principles be adopted in any country, without the certainty of bringing it to the very same condition in which France is found.

On the scheme of this barbarous philosophy, which is the offspring of cold hearts and muddy understandings, which is void of solid wisdom, which is destitute of all taste and elegance, laws are to be supported only by their own tenors and by the concern which each individual may find in them from his own private speculations or can spare to them from his own private interests. In the groves of their academy, at the end of every vista, you see nothing but the gallows.

On the principles of this philosophy institutions can never be embodied in persons. That sort of "reason" which banishes the affections is incapable of filling their place. These public affections, combined with manners, are required, sometimes as supplements, sometimes as correctives, always as aids, to law.

At this point he returns to his original argument. "The people" cannot be the foundation of government, it seems, or he has misread French history of late. What then? If the foundation of coercive government is not to be found in the doctrine of the "rights of man," where then? He settles down to this more positive question:

The dislike I feel to revolutions, the signals for which have so often been given from pulpits; the spirit of change that is gone abroad; the total contempt which prevails of all ancient institutions, when set in opposition to a present sense of convenience, or to the bent of a present inclination — all these considerations make it not unadvisable, in my opinion, to call back our attention to the true principle of laws.

The foundation of government is laid, not in imaginary rights of men, but in political convenience, and in human nature; either as that nature is universal, or as it is modified by local habits and social aptitudes. The foundation of government is laid in a provision for our wants, and in a conformity to our duties; it is to purvey for the one; it is to enforce the other.

Among men's wants is to be reckoned the want of a sufficient restraint upon their passions. Society requires not only that the passions of individuals should be subjected, but that even in the mass and body, as well as in the individuals, the inclinations of men should frequently be thwarted, their will controlled, and their passions brought into subjection. This can only be done by a power out of themselves; not subject to that will and those passions which it is its office to bridle and subdue.

In this sense the restraints on men, as well as their liberties, are to be reckoned among their rights. But as the liberties and the restrictions vary with times and circumstances, and admit of infinite modifications, they cannot be settled upon any abstract rule; and nothing is so foolish as to discuss them upon that principle.

The state ought to be considered as something better than a partnership agreement in a trade of pepper and coffee, calico or tobacco, to be taken up for a little temporary interest, and to be dissolved by the fancy of the parties. It is to be looked on with reverence, because it is not a partnership in things subservient only to the gross animal existence of a temporary and perishable nature.

The state is a partnership in all science, a partnership in all art, a partnership in every virtue and in all perfection. As the ends of such a partnership cannot be attained in many generations, it becomes a partnership not only between those who are living, but between those who are living, those who are dead, and those who are to be born. People will not look forward to posterity who never look backward to their ancestors.

Each contract of each particular state is but a clause in the great primeval contract of eternal society, linking the lower with the higher natures, connecting the visible and the invisible world, according to a fixed compact sanctioned by the inviolable oath which holds all physical and all moral natures each to their appointed places.

The "rights of man" are not the foundation of the state. They are not "prior" to the state. Indeed, they are made possible by the state; and the foundation of anything is not to be sought in that which the things in question makes possible. What then does he think about the "real" rights of men which *proceed* from political organization?

I am far from denying the real rights of men. In denying their false claims of right, I do not mean to injure those which are real, and are such as their pretended rights would totally destroy. If civil society be made for the advantage of man, all the advantages for which it is made become his right.

Men have right to the fruits of their industry, and to the means of making their industry fruitful. They have a right to the acquisitions of their parents; to the nourishment and improvement of their offspring; to instruction in life, and to consolation in death. Whatever each man can separately do, without trespassing upon others, he has a right to do for himself, and he has a right to a fair portion of all which society, with all its combination of skill and force, can do in his favor.

In this partnership all men have equal rights, but not to equal things. He that has but five shilling in the partnership, has as good a right to it as he that has five hundred pounds has to his larger proportion. But he has not a right to an equal dividend in the product in the joint stock, and as to the share of power, authority, and direction which each individual ought to have in the management of the state, that I must deny to be amongst the direct original rights of man in civil society; for I have in my contemplation the civil social man, and no other. It is a thing to be settled by convention.

Circumstances (which with some gentlemen pass for nothing) give in reality to every political principle its distinguishing color and discriminating effect. The circumstances are what render every civil and political scheme beneficial or noxious to mankind.

I must be tolerably sure, before I venture publicly to congratulate men upon a blessing, that they have really received one. Flattery corrupts both the receiver and the giver, and adulation is not of more service to people than to kings. I should therefore suspend my congratulations on the acquisition of liberties, until I was informed how it had been combined with government; with public force; with the discipline and obedience of armies; with the collection of an effective and well-distributed revenue; with morality and religion; with solidity and property; with peace and order; with civil and social manners.

All these (in their way) are good things too, and, without them, liberty is not a benefit whilst it lasts, and it is not likely to continue long. The effect of liberty to individuals is that they may do what they please; we ought to see what it will please them to do, before we risk congratulations, which may be soon turned into complaints. Prudence would dictate this in the case of separate, insulated, private men; but liberty, when men act in bodies, is power. Considerate people, before they declare themselves, will observe the use which is made of power, and particularly of so trying a thing as new power in new persons, of whose principles, tempers, and dispositions, they have little or no experience, and in situations where those who appear the most stirring in the scene may possibly not be the real movers.

I flatter myself that I love a manly, moral, regulated liberty as well as any gentleman, be he who he will; and perhaps I have given as good proofs of my attachments to that cause, in the whole course of my public conduct. I think I envy liberty as little as they do, to any other nation. But I cannot stand forward, and give praise or blame to anything which relates to human actions, and human concerns, on a simple view of the object, as it stands stripped of every relation, in all the nakedness and solitude of abstraction.

Is it because liberty in the abstract may be classed amongst the blessings of mankind, that I am seriously to felicitate a madman, who has escaped from the protecting restraint and wholesome darkness of his cell, on his restoration to the enjoyment of life and liberty? Am I to congratulate a highwayman and murderer, who has broke prison, upon the recovery of his natural rights?

If true rights and liberties presuppose government, and therefore, coercion, the question, as in Rousseau, presents itself: What is the best form of government? Again as in Rousseau, the answer is an aristocracy. But where Rousseau had suggested an elective, Burke suggests a natural aristocracy. Thus:

Believe me, those who attempt to level never equalize. In all societies, consisting of various descriptions of citizens, some description must be uppermost. The levelers therefore only change and pervert the natural order of things; they load the edifice of society, by setting up in the air what the solidity of the structure requires to be on the ground. Tailors and carpenters cannot be equal to the situation, into which, by the worst of usurpations, an usurpation on the prerogatives of nature, you attempt to force them.

You will hear it said that all occupations are honorable. If this means only that no honest employment was disgraceful, it does not go beyond the truth. But in asserting that anything is honorable, we imply some distinction in its favor. The occupation of a hairdresser, or of a working tallow chandler, cannot be a matter of honor to any person — to say nothing of a number of other more servile employments. Such men ought not to suffer oppression from the state, but the state suffers oppression, if such as they, either individually or collectively, are permitted to rule. In this you think you are combatting prejudice, but you are at war with nature.

A true natural aristocracy is not a separate interest in the state, or separable from it. It is an essential integrant part of any large body rightly constituted. It is formed out of a class of legitimate presumptions, which, taken as generalities, must be admitted for actual truths. To be bred in a place of estimation; to see nothing low and sordid from one's infancy; to be taught to respect oneself; to be habituated to the censorial inspection of the public eye; to look early to public opinion; to stand upon such elevated ground as to be enabled to take a large view of the widespread and infinitely diversified combinations of men and affairs in a large society; to have leisure to read, to reflect, to converse; to be enabled to draw the court and attention of the wise and learned wherever they are to be found; to be habituated to command and to obey; to be taught to despise danger in the pursuit of honor and duty; to be formed to the greatest degree of vigilance, foresight, and circumspection, in a state of things in which no fault is committed with impunity, and the slightest mistakes draw on the most ruinous consequences; to be led to a guarded and regulated conduct, from a sense that you are considered as an instructor of your fellow citizens in their highest concerns, and that you act as a reconciler between God and man; to be employed as an administrator of law and justice, and to be thereby amongst the first benefactors to mankind; to be a professor of high science, or of liberal and ingenuous art; to be amongst rich traders, who from their success are presumed to have sharp and vigorous understandings, and to possess the virtues of diligence, order, constancy, and regularity, and to have cultivated an habitual regard to commutative justice — these are the circumstances of men that form what I should call a *natural* aristocracy, without which there is no nation.

Men, qualified in the manner I have just described, form in nature, as she operates in the common modification of society, the leading, guiding, and governing part. It is the soul to the body, without which the man does not exist. To give therefore no more importance, in the social order, to such men, than that of so many units, is a horrible usurpation.

When great multitudes act together, under that discipline of nature, I recognize the people. I acknowledge something that perhaps equals, and ought always to guide the sovereignty of convention. In all things the voice of this grand chorus of national harmony ought to have a mighty and decisive influence.

But when you disturb this harmony; when you break up this beautiful order, this array of truth and nature, as well as of habit and prejudice; when you separate the common sort of men from their proper chieftains so as to form them into an adverse army, I no longer know that venerable object called *the people* in such a disbanded race of deserters and vagabonds. For a while they may be terrible indeed, but in such a manner as wild beasts are terrible. The mind owes to them no sort of submission. They are, as they have been reputed, rebels.

Woe to the country which would madly and impiously reject the service of the talents and virtues, civil, military, or religious, that are given to grace and serve it, and would condemn to obscurity everything formed to diffuse luster and glory around a state. Woe to that country too that, passing into the opposite extreme, considers a low education, a mean contracted view of things, a sordid, mercenary occupation, as a preferable title to command.

He wishes to be clear about one point. His doctrine of a natural aristocracy does not commit him to a theory of government by lords and dukes. Thus:

I am accused of being a man of aristocratic principles. If by *aristocracy* they mean the peers, I have no vulgar admiration, nor any vulgar antipathy, toward them; I hold their order in cold and decent respect. I hold them to be of absolute necessity in the constitution, but I think they are only good when kept within their proper bounds.

I am no friend to aristocracy, in the sense at least in which that word is usually understood. If it were not a bad habit to moot cases on the supposed ruin of the constitution, I should be free to declare that, if it must perish, I would rather by far see it resolved in any other form than lost in that austere and insolent domination.

Do not imagine that I wish to confine power, authority, and distinction to blood and names and titles. There is no qualification for government but virtue and wisdom, actual or presumptive. Wherever they are actually found, they have, in whatever state, condition, profession or trade, the passport of Heaven to human place and honor.

From the notion of a natural aristocracy, Burke returns to his earlier theme that government is justified by reason of the fact that men have duties which they need to have enforced. He desires to point out that "duties" is a basic notion, and that duties are seldom a matter of choice:

Look through the whole of life, and the whole system of duties. Much the strongest moral obligations are such as were never the result of our option.

I cannot too often recommend it to the serious consideration of all men, who think civil society to be within the province of moral jurisdiction, that if we owe to it any duty, it is not subject to our will. Duties are not voluntary. *Duty* and *will* are even contradictory terms.

Men without their choice derive benefits from association; without their choice they are subjected to duties in consequence of these benefits; and without their choice they enter into a virtual obligation as binding as any that is actual. Look through the whole of life and the whole system of duties. Much the strongest moral obligations are such as were never the result of our option.

When we marry, the choice is voluntary, but the duties are not matter of choice. They are dictated by the nature of the situation. Dark and inscrutable are the ways by which we come into the world. The instincts which give rise to this mysterious process of nature are not of our making. But out of physical causes, unknown to us, perhaps unknowable, arise moral duties, which as we are able perfectly to comprehend, we are bound indispensably to perform.

Parents may not be consenting to their moral relation; but consenting or not, they are bound to a long train of burdensome duties toward those with whom they have never made a convention of any sort. Children are not consenting to their relation, but their relation, without their actual consent, binds them to its duties, or rather it implies their consent, because the presumed consent of every rational creature is in unison with the predisposed order of things.

Nor are we left without powerful instincts to make this duty as grateful to us, as it is awful and coercive. Our country is not a thing of mere physical locality. It consists, in a great measure, in the ancient order into which we are born. We may have the same geographical situation, but another country; as we may have the same country, in another soil. The place that determines our duty to our country is a social civil relation.

Obviously, the notion of duties contains problems. There is always the problem of a clash between duties and rights. There is, too, the more difficult problem of a clash between one duty and another, and of deciding when, precisely, one is confronted with a duty. Burke acknowledges all this, but would not emphasize it:

I admit, indeed, that in morals, as in all things else, difficulties will sometimes occur. Duties will sometimes cross one another. Then questions will arise: Which of them is to be placed in subordination? Which of them may be entirely superseded? These doubts give rise to that part of moral science called *casuistry*. It requires a very solid and discriminating judgment, great modesty and caution, and much sobriety of mind in the handling; else there is a danger that it may totally subvert those offices which is its object only to methodize and reconcile.

Duties, at their extreme bounds, are drawn very fine, so as to become almost evanescent. In that state some shade of doubt will always rest upon these questions, when they are pursued with subtlety. But the very habit of stating these extreme cases is not very laudable or safe, because, in general, it is not right to turn our duties into doubts. They are imposed to govern our conduct, not to exercise our ingenuity; and therefore, our opinions about them ought not to be in a state of fluctuation, but steady, sure, and resolved.

Amongst these nice, and therefore, dangerous points of casuistry, may be reckoned the question so much agitated at the present hour — whether, after the people have discharged themselves of their original power by an habitual delegation, no occasion can possibly occur which may justify the resumption of it. This question, in this latitude, is very hard to affirm or deny, but I am satisfied that no occasion can justify such a resumption, which would not equally authorize a dispensation with any other moral duty, perhaps with all of them together.

However, if, in general, it be not easy to determine concerning the lawfulness of such devious proceedings, which must be ever on the edge of crimes, it is far from difficult to see the perilous consequences of the resuscitation of such a power in the people. The practical consequences of any political tenet go a great way in deciding upon its value. Political problems do not primarily concern truth or falsehood. They relate to good or evil. What in the result is likely to produce evil, is politically false; that which is productive of good politically true.

The natural conservative in him has the floor by now. He cannot abide the thought of all the nice problems in casuistry which he sees rising before him:

I confess, I never liked this continual talk of resistance and revolution, or the practice of making the extreme medicine of the constitution its daily bread. It renders the habit of society dangerously valetudinarian; it is taking periodical doses of mercury sublimate, and swallowing down repeated provocatives of cantharides to our love of liberty.

As it was not made for common abuses, so it is not to be agitated by common minds. The speculative line of demarcation, where obedience ought to end, and resistance must begin, is faint, obscure, and not easily definable. It is not a single act, or a single event, which determines it. Governments must be abused and deranged indeed, before it can be thought of, and the prospect of the future must be as bad as the experience of the past.

The subversion of a government, to deserve any praise, must be considered but as a step preparatory to the formation of something better, either in the scheme of the government itself, or in the persons who administer it, or in both. These events cannot in reason be separated.

This, I think, may be safely affirmed: that a sore and pressing evil is to be removed, and a good, great in its amount and unequivocal in its nature, must be probable almost to certainty, before the inestimable price of our own morals, and the well-being of a number of our fellow citizens, is paid for a revolution. If ever we ought to be economists even to parsimony, it is in the voluntary production of evil. Every revolution contains in it something of evil.

The burden of proof lies heavily on those who tear to pieces the whole frame and contexture of their country, that they could find no other way of settling a government fit to obtain its rational ends, except that which they have pursued by means unfavorable to all the present happiness of millions of people, and to the utter ruin of several hundreds of thousands.

It is not worth our while to discuss, like sophisters, whether, in no case, some evil, for the sake of some benefit, is to be tolerated. Nothing universal can be rationally affirmed on any moral, or any political subject. Pure abstraction does not belong to these matters. The lines of morality are not like ideal lines of mathematics. They are broad and deep as well as long. They admit of exceptions; they demand modifications. These exceptions and modifications are not made by the process of logic, but by the rules of prudence.

This line of argument against emancipation by citing hard cases reaches its high point in the paragraphs which follow:

I would not exclude alteration, but even when I changed, it should be to preserve, not to destroy. I should be led to my remedy by a great grievance. In what I did, I should follow the example of our ancestors. I would make the reparation as nearly as possible in the style of the building.

We know that we have made no discoveries, and we think that no discoveries are to be made, in morality; nor many in the great principles of government; nor in the ideas of liberty, which were understood long before we were born, altogether as well as they will be after the grave has heaped its mold upon our presumption, and the silent tomb shall have imposed its law on our pert loquacity.

Prejudice is of ready application in the emergency; it previously engages the mind in a steady course of wisdom and virtue, and does not leave the man hesitating in the moment of decision, sceptical, puzzled, and unresolved. Prejudice renders a man's virtue his habit, and not a series of unconnected acts. Through just prejudice, his duty becomes a part of his nature.

Prescription [i.e., tradition] is the most solid of all titles, not only to property, but, which is to secure that property, to government. All titles terminate in prescription. Nor is prescription of government formed upon blind unmeaning prejudices for man is a most unwise and most wise being. The individual is foolish . . . but the species is wise, and when time is given to it, as a species it almost always acts right.

If you apprehend that on a concession you shall be pushed by metaphysical process to the extreme lines, and argued out of your whole authority, my advice is this: When you have recovered your old, your strong, your tenable position, then face about — stop short — do nothing more — reason not at all — oppose the ancient policy and practice of the empire as a rampart against the speculations of innovators on both sides of the question, and you will stand on great, manly, and sure ground.

We are afraid to put men to live and trade each on his own private stock of reason . . . individuals would do better to avail themselves of the general bank and capital of nations and of ages. Thanks to our sullen resistance to innovation, thanks to the cold sluggishness of our national character, we still bear the stamp of our forefathers.

Burke has one last point to make. It is that politics, like morals, is based ultimately on religion. This is for him the taproot of his conservatism. It brings him rather close to James I whom we have already read. He begins:

Nothing is more certain than that manners, civilization, and all good things connected with manners and civilization, have, in this European world of ours, depended for ages upon two principles, and were indeed the result of both combined: I mean, the spirit of a gentleman and the spirit of religion.

We know, and what is better, we feel inwardly that religion is the basis of civil society, and the source of all good and all comfort; that on religion, according to our mode, all our laws and institutions stand as upon their base.

The religious sense of mankind, like a wise architect, hath built up the august fabric of states; like a provident proprietor, to preserve the structure from profanation and ruin, as a sacred temple purged from all the impurities of fraud and violence and injustice and tyranny, it hath solemnly and forever consecrated the commonwealth and all that officiate therein.

This consecration is made that all who administer in the government of men should have high and worthy notions of their function and destination; that their hope should be full of immortality; that they should not look to the paltry pelf of the moment, nor to the temporary and transient praise of the vulgar, but to a solid, permanent existence, in the permanent part of their nature, and to a permanent fame and glory, in the example they leave as a rich inheritance to the world.

This principle ought to be impressed, even more strongly, upon the minds of those who compose the collective sovereignty. For the people at large can never become the subject of punishment by any human hand. They ought therefore to be persuaded that they are fully as little entitled and far less qualified, with safety to themselves, to use any arbitrary power whatsoever; that they are not, under a false show of "liberty," tyranically to exact, from those who officiate in the state, an abject submission to their occasional will.

When the people have emptied themselves of all the lust of selfish will, which without religion it is utterly impossible they ever should; when they are conscious that they exercise a power, which to be legitimate must be according to that eternal and immutable law in which will and reason are the same, they will be more capable how they place power in base and incapable hands.

In their nomination to office they will not appoint to the exercise of authority as to a pitiful job, but as to a holy function; not according to their sordid selfish interest, nor to their wanton caprice, nor to their arbitrary will. They will confer that power, which any man may well tremble to give or to receive, on those only in whom they discern a predominant portion of active virtue and wisdom.

Those who believe that God willed the state think some part of the wealth of the country is as usefully employed in maintaining a church and a clergy as in fomenting the luxury of individuals. It is the public ornament. It is the public consolation. It nourishes the public hope. The poorest man finds his own importance and dignity in it. It is for the man in humble life — to raise his nature, to put him in mind of a state in which the privileges of opulence will cease, when he will be equal by nature, and may be more than equal by virtue — that his portion of the general wealth of the country is thus employed and sanctified.

The awful author of our being is the author of our place in the order of existence. Having disposed and marshalled us by a divine tactic, not according to our will, but according to His, He has, in and by that disposition, virtually subjected us to act the part which belongs to the place assigned us. We have obligations to mankind at large, which are not in consequence of any special voluntary pact. They arise from the relation of man to man, and the relation of man to God, which relations are not matters of choice.

An "alliance" between church and state in a Christian commonwealth is, in my opinion an idle and a fanciful speculation. An alliance is between two things that are in their nature distinct and independent, such as between two sovereign states. But in a Christian commonwealth, the church and state are one and the same thing, being different integral parts of the same whole.

Religion is so far, in my opinion, from being out of the province or duty of a Christian magistrate that it is, and ought to be, not only his care, but the principal thing in his care; because it is one of the great bonds of human society.

Against infidels [i.e., unbelievers] I would have the laws rise in all their terrors. . . . I would cut up the very root of atheism. The infidels are outlaws of the constitution; not of this country, but of the human race. They are never to be supported, never to be tolerated.

The concluding paragraphs sum up the argument. Rights and liberties are products of the political organization of society. In the political organization of society one is confronted, largely, with matters of tradition — *prescription* is his word — matters of slow growth and gradual change:

From Magna Charta to the Declaration of Right, it has been the uniform policy of our constitution to claim and assert our liberties as an entailed inheritance from our forefathers and to be transmitted to our posterity; as an estate, specially belonging to the people of this realm without any reference whatever to any other more general or prior right.

By thus regarding our liberties as an entailed inheritance, our constitution preserves a unity in the great multiplicity of its parts. We have an inheritable crown; an inheritable peerage; and a house of commons and a people inheriting privileges, franchises, and liberties, from a long line of ancestors.

This policy appears to me to be the result of profound reflection; or rather, the happy effect of following nature, which is wisdom without reflection, and above it. The idea of inherited liberties, rights, and privileges furnishes a sure principle of conservation and transmission, without at all excluding a principle of improvement. It leaves acquisition free, but it secures what it acquires. Whatever advantages are obtained, are locked fast as in a sort of family settlement, grasped as in a kind of mortmain forever.

We receive, we hold, we transmit our government and our privileges, in the same manner in which we enjoy and transmit our property and our lives. The institutions of policy, the goods of fortune, the gifts of Providence, are handed down to us and from us in the same course and order. Our political system is placed in a just correspondence and symmetry with that mode of existence decreed to a permanent body composed of transitory parts, by the disposition of a stupendous wisdom, molding together the great mysterious incorporation of the human race, the whole at one time, is never old or middle-aged or young, but in a condition of unchangeable constancy moves on through the varied tenor of perpetual decay, fall, renovation, and progression.

By preserving thus the method of nature in the conduct of the state, in what we improve we are never wholly new; in what we retain, we are never wholly obsolete. By adhering in this manner and on those principles to our forefathers, we are guided, not by the superstition of antiquarians but by the spirit of philosophic analogy. In this choice of entailment, inheritance, we have given to our frame of polity the image of a relation in blood; binding up the constitution of our country with our dearest domestic ties; adopting our fundamental laws into the bosom of our family affections; keeping inseparable, and cherishing with the warmth of all their combined and mutually reflected charities, our state, our hearths, our sepulchers, and our altars.

We procure reverence to our civil institutions on the principle upon which nature teaches us to revere individual men, on account of their age, and on account of those from whom they are descended. All your sophisters cannot produce anything better adapted to preserve a rational and manly liberty than the course we have pursued, who have chosen our nature rather than our speculations, our breasts rather than our inventions, for the great conservatories and magazines of our rights and privileges.

A politic caution, a guarded circumspection, a moral timidity, were among the ruling principles of our forefathers in their most decided conduct. They were not illuminated with that "light of reason," of which the gentlemen of France tell us they have got so abundant a share. They acted under a strong sense of the ignorance and fallibility of mankind. He that made them thus fallible, rewarded them for having in their conduct attended to their nature. Let us imitate their caution, if we wish to deserve their fortune or retain their bequests. Let us add, if we please; but let us preserve what they have left; let us be satisfied to admire, rather than attempt to follow in their desperate flights the aeronauts of France.

Reading References. John Maccun has a good book, *The Political Philosophy of Burke.* It is not easy reading. Lord Morley has done the Burke volume in the *English Men of Letters* series. It is easier reading. Chapter six in Volume One and Chapter one in Volume Two of C. E. Vaughan's *Studies in the History of Political Philosophy* are good. Chapters eight, ten, and eleven in Sir Leslie Stephen's *English Thought in the Eighteenth Century* are also good. An interesting contrast between author and subject will be found in Harold Laski's pages on Burke in *Political Thought in England from Locke to Bentham.* A good recent biography will be found in R. H. Murray's *Edmund Burke.* But better than any of these would be a careful reading of Burke's *Letter to a Noble Lord, Appeal from the New to the Old Whigs,* or any hundred pages from his *Reflections.*

READING QUESTIONS

1. What doctrine does Burke propose to criticize?
2. Cite one of Burke's criticisms.
3. What does he make of the notion of "the people"?

4. Cite one warning from Burke of what may well befall a country which entertains the false idea of "the people."
5. Why does he turn to French history?
6. Cite any two things the French might have done.
7. What did they do?
8. "Compute your gains." Elucidate.
9. "Were all these dreadful things necessary?" What things?
10. "To be a people and to have these rights are things incompatible." What rights? Wherein incompatible?
11. "The foundation of government is laid. . . ." Where?
12. "Among these wants is to be reckoned. . . ." What?
13. "In this sense restraints are to be reckoned among rights." Meaning?
14. In what sort of thing is the state to be considered a partnership?
15. What "real" rights will he recognize?
16. What must he know about a liberty before he will congratulate its possessor?
17. "When great multitudes act together under that discipline of nature I recognize the people." What discipline of nature?
18. "I am accused of being a man of aristocratic principles." Why? What does he say?
19. "*Duty* and *will* are ever contradictory terms." How so?
20. "Difficulties will sometimes occur . . . some shade of doubt will always rest upon these questions. . . . Among these nice points of casuistry may be reckoned. . . ."
21. What is his advice, in view of the things noted in question 20?
22. What does he mean by *prescription*?
23. Why does he urge it on men?
24. In what sense is religion the base of "all our laws and institutions"?
25. "This principle ought to be impressed even more strongly upon. . . ." Whom? Why? What principle?
26. What about state appropriation of funds to pay for the church?
27. What is the "divine tactic" of which he speaks?
28. What about infidels?
29. "Liberties as an entailed inheritance." Elucidate.

5. *THE CASE FOR REPRESENTATIVE GOVERNMENT—FROM JOHN STUART MILL*

From Burke to Mill. Burke, it will be remembered, published his *Reflections on the French Revolution* in 1790, one year after the outbreak of the revolution in France. His book attained to an immediate and widespread prestige. It was read with approval in the chancelleries of Europe. Here, it was felt, was the answer to radical political philosophy. A year later, in 1791, Thomas Paine, newly returned from the revolutionary war in America, and now settled in revolutionary Paris, published his celebrated reply to Burke's *Reflections*. He called his book *The Rights of Man*, thus drawing attention to the root of the matter which, he felt, Burke had misunderstood. With the argument of this eighteenth-century defense of the democratic idea, we are not concerned. Its importance lay in its readability and vigor and consequent great popularity. It contributed vastly to clarifying and fixing in the public mind the case for the democratic idea. This was timely, since agitation for parliamentary reform in England was brought to a standstill two years later, in 1793, when the British Government declared war on France with a view to checking the spread of revolutionary politics in Europe. By that time, Napoleon Bonaparte was beginning to emerge in French politics. His power continued to grow, in France and then over Europe. The war dragged on for twenty-two years, until 1815, at which time Napoleon was exiled and the monarchy restored in France. It was then feasible to reopen the question of a democratic reform of British politics. The idea met with considerable opposition from entrenched interests. The task of breaking down this inertia was undertaken by the Philosophical Radicals. Among these was James Mill, who was invited to contribute articles on government and related topics to the supplement to the fifth edition of the *Encyclopedia Britannica*. These articles were subsequently published in volume form in 1825. They contained the clearest and most persuasive statement of the aims of the reform party. They circulated widely. They performed, during the years 1825 to 1832, somewhat the same function which Tom Paine's *Common Sense* had performed in the American colonies in 1776. The movement to which they gave written articulation culminated in 1832 with the passage of the first Reform Act.

By this time, James Mill's son, John Stuart Mill, a young man of twenty-six, was engrossed in the questions which were involved in the democratizing of British politics. He watched the reform experiment with close interest. In 1859 he published *Thoughts on Parliamentary Reform* and *On Liberty*. Both were seasoned comments upon the experiment of 1832. Two years later, in 1861, he published *Considerations on Representative Government*. This became at once the best single statement and defense of the claim that representative government is the method of democracy in politics. In 1865 Mill himself was elected to Parliament. In 1867, during Mill's term of office, the House of Commons passed the second Reform Act which carried further the democratizing process begun in 1832. Mill's book *Considerations on Representative Government* (1861) stood to the second Reform Act (1867) much as his father's *Essay on Government* (1825) stood to the first Reform Act (1832).

Biographical Note. The main facts of Mill's life have been stated already in connection with the reading from Mill under Topics One and Four (see pages 58 and 321).

Argument of the Citations. The form of government is open, in some degree, to choice. By what test should society's choice be directed? The test is twofold: To what extent does a proposed form of government make for the moral and intellectual development of the people? To what extent does it make use of the present moral and intellectual resources at its command? On these grounds the ideal form of government would be a complete democracy. Reasons for this. But a complete democracy is not practicable. Reasons for this. The device of governing by elected representatives is as close as a modern state can come to straight democracy. Three fundamental conditions which representative government must fulfill. The proper functions of representative government.

The argument of the following citations is so simple and direct that it seems superfluous to add any comment. I have, accordingly, left the Mill citations to speak for themselves, grouping paragraphs by a number when they state or develop some single thought. He begins:

I

The form of government for any given country being within limits amenable to choice, it is pertinent to ask by what test the choice should be directed. What are the distinctive characteristics of the form of government best fitted to promote the interests of any given society?

If we ask ourselves on what conditions good government depends, we find that the principal of them is the qualities of the human beings composing the society over which the government is exercised.

The first question in respect to any political institution is, how far it tends to foster in the members of the community various desirable qualities, moral and intellectual. The government which does this the best has every likelihood of being the best in all other respects, since it is on these qualities, so far as they exist in the people, that all possibility of goodness in the practical operations of the government depends.

The other constituent element of the merit of a government is the degree in which it is adapted to take advantage of the amount of good qualities which may at any time exist, and make them instrumental to the right purposes.

2

There is no difficulty in showing, if the above considerations be granted, that the ideally best form of government is that in which the sovereignty, or supreme controlling power is vested, in the last resort, in the entire aggregate of the community; every citizen not only having a voice in the exercise of that ultimate sovereignty, but being, at least occasionally, called on to take an actual part in the government, by the personal discharge of public function, local or general.

To test this proposition, it has to be examined in reference to the two branches into which, as pointed out, the inquiry into the goodness of a government conveniently divides itself; namely, how far it promotes the good management of the affairs of society by means of the existing faculties, moral, intellectual, and active, of its various members; and what is its effect in improving or deteriorating those faculties.

3

The superiority of popular government in reference to present well-being rests upon two principles. The first is that the rights and interests of every or any person are only secure from being disregarded when the person interested is himself able, and habitually disposed to stand up for them. The second is, that the general prosperity attains a greater height, and is more widely diffused, in proportion to the amount and varieties of the personal energies enlisted in promoting it.

Human beings are only secure from evil at the hands of others in proportion as they have the power of being, and are self-protecting; and they only achieve a high degree of success in their struggle with nature in proportion as they are self-dependent, relying on what they themselves can do, either separately or in concert, rather than on what others do for them.

Thus stands the case as regards present well-being, the good management of the affairs of the existing generation. If we now pass to the influence of the form of government upon character, we shall find the superiority of popular government over every other to be, if possible, still more decided and indisputable.

4

This question really depends upon a still more fundamental one, viz., which of two common types of character, for the general good of humanity, it is most desirable should predominate — the active, or the passive type; that which struggles against evils, or that which endures them; that which bends to circumstances, or that which endeavors to make circumstances bend to itself.

The commonplaces of moralists, and the general sympathies of mankind, are in favor of the passive type. Energetic characters may be admired, but the acquiescent and submissive are those which most men personally prefer. The passiveness of our neighbors increases our sense of security, and plays into the hands of our willfulness. Passive characters, if we do not happen to need their activity, seem an obstruction the less in our own path. A contented character is not a dangerous rival.

Yet nothing is more certain than that improvement in human affairs is wholly the work of the uncontented characters; and, moreover, that it is much easier for an active mind to acquire the virtues of patience than for a passive one to assume those of energy.

The striving, go-ahead character is only a fit subject of disapproving criticism on account of the very secondary objects on which it commonly expends its strength. In itself it is the foundation of the best hopes for the general improvement of mankind.

Inactivity, unaspiringness, absence of desire, are a more fatal hindrance to improvement than any misdirection of energy, and are that through which alone, when existing in the mass, any very formidable misdirection by an energetic few becomes possible.

5

Now there can be no kind of doubt that the passive type of character is favored by the government of one or a few, and the active, self-helping type by that of the many. Irresponsible rulers need the quiescence of the ruled more than they need any activity but that which they can compel. Submissiveness to the prescriptions of men as necessities of nature is the lesson inculcated by all governments upon those who are wholly without participation in them.

The will of superiors, and the law as the will of superiors, must be passively yielded to.

Very different is the state of the human faculties where a human being feels himself under no other external restraint than the necessities of nature, or mandates of society which he has his share in imposing, and which it is open to him, if he thinks them wrong, publicly to dissent from, and exert himself actively to get altered. What is still more important than even this matter of feeling is the practical discipline which the character obtains from the occasional demand made upon the citizens to exercise, for a time and in their turn, some social function.

It is not sufficiently considered how little there is in most men's ordinary life to give any largeness either to their conceptions or to their sentiments. Their work is a routine; not a labor of love, but of self-interest in the most elementary form, the satisfaction of daily wants; neither the thing done, nor the process of doing it, introduces the mind to thoughts or feelings extending beyond individuals; if instructive books are within their reach, there is no stimulus to read them; and in most cases the individual has no access to any person of cultivation much superior to his own. Giving him something to do for the public, supplies, in a measure, all these deficiencies. If circumstances allow the amount of public duties assigned him to be considerable, it makes him an educated man.

Still more salutary is the moral part of the instruction afforded by the participation of the private citizen, if even rarely, in public functions. He is called upon, while so engaged, to weigh interests not his own; to be guided, in case of conflicting claims, by another rule than his private partialities; to apply, at every turn, principles and maxims which have for their reason of existence the common good: and he usually finds associated with him in the same work minds more familiarized than his own with these ideas and operations, whose study it will be to supply reasons to his understanding and stimulation to his feeling for the general interest.

Where this school of public spirit does not exist, scarcely any sense is entertained that private persons, in no eminent social situation, owe any duties to society, except to obey the laws and submit to the government. There is no unselfish sentiment of identification with the public. Every thought or feeling, either of interest or of duty, is absorbed in the individual and in the family. The man never thinks of any collective interest, of any objects to be pursued jointly with others, but only in competition with them, and in some measure, at their expense.

From these accumulated considerations it is evident that the only government that can fully satisfy all the exigencies of the social state is one in which the people participate: that any participation, even in the smallest public function, is useful; that the participation should everywhere be as great as the general degree of improvement in the community will allow; and that nothing less can be ultimately desirable than the admission of all to a share in the sovereign power of the state.

6

But, in a community exceeding a single small town, all cannot participate personally in any but some very minor portions of the public business. It follows that the ideal type of a perfect government must be representative.

The meaning of representative government is that the whole people, or some numerous portion of them, exercise through deputies periodically elected by themselves, the ultimate controlling power, which, in every constitution, must reside somewhere. This ultimate power they must possess in all completeness. They must be masters, whenever they please, of all the operations of government.

7

We have recognized in representative government the ideal type of the most perfect polity, for which, in consequence, any portion of mankind are better adapted in proportion to their degree of general improvement. As they range lower and lower in development, that form of government will be, generally speaking, less suitable to them. Let us examine at what point in the descending series representative government ceases altogether to be admissible, either through its own unfitness, or through the superior fitness of some other regimen.

Representative government must fulfill three fundamental conditions. 1. The people should be willing to receive it. 2. They should be willing and able to do what is necessary for its preservation. 3. They should be willing and able to fulfill the duties and discharge the functions which it imposes on them.

8

The willingness of the people to accept representative government only becomes a practical question when an enlightened ruler, or a foreign nation or nations who have gained power over the country, are disposed to offer it. To individual reformers the question is almost irrelevant, since, if no other objection can be made to their enterprise than that the opinion of the nation is not yet on their side, they have the ready and proper answer, that to bring it over to their side is the very end they aim at. When opinion is really adverse, its hostility is usually to the fact of change, rather than to representative government in itself.

When a people have no sufficient value for, and attachment to, a representative constitution, they have next to no chance of retaining it. Representative institutions necessarily depend for permanence upon the readiness of the people to fight for them in case of their being endangered. If too little valued for this, they are almost sure to be overthrown, as soon as the head of the government, or any party leader who can muster a force for a *coup de main*, is willing to run some small risk for absolute power.

These considerations relate to the first two causes of failure in a representative government. The third is, when the people lack either the will or the capacity to fulfill the part which belongs to them in a representative constitution.

When nobody, or only some small fraction, feels the degree of interest in the general affairs of the state necessary to the formation of a public opinion, the electors will seldom make any use of the right of suffrage but to serve their private interest, or the interest of their locality, or of some one with whom they are connected as adherents or dependents. The small class who, in this state of public feeling, gain the command of the representative body, for the most part use it solely as a means of seeking their fortune.

9

The preceding are the cases in which representative government cannot permanently exist. There are others in which it possibly might exist, but in which some other form of government would be preferable. These are principally when the people, in order to advance in civilization, have some lesson to learn, some habit not yet acquired, to the acquisition of which representative government is likely to be an impediment.

The most obvious of these cases is the one in which the people have still to learn the first lesson of civilization, that of obedience. A race who have been trained in energy and courage by struggles with nature and their neighbors, but who have not yet settled down into permanent obedience to any common superior, would be little likely to acquire this habit under the collective government of their own body. A representative assembly drawn from among themselves would simply reflect their own turbulent insubordination. It would refuse its authority to all proceedings, which would impose, on their savage independence, any improving restraint.

Another of the strongest hindrances to improvement, up to a rather advanced stage, is an inveterate spirit of locality. Portions of mankind, in many other respects capable of, and prepared for, freedom, may be unqualified for amalgamating into even the smallest nation. They may not yet have acquired any of the feelings or habits which would make the union real, supposing it to be nominally accomplished. They may have had considerable practice in exercising their faculties on village or town interests, and have even realized a tolerably effective popular government on that restricted scale, and may yet have but slender sympathies with anything beyond, and no habit or capacity of dealing with interests common to many such communities.

A people are no less unfitted for representative government by the contrary fault to that last specified; by extreme passiveness, and ready submission to tyranny. If a people thus prostrated by character and circumstances could obtain representative institutions, they would inevitably choose their tyrants as their representatives, and the yoke would be made heavier on them by the contrivance which *prima facie* might be expected to lighten it.

Among these tendencies which, without rendering a people absolutely unfit for representative government, seriously incapacitate them from reaping the full benefit of it, another deserves particular notice.

There are nations in whom the passion for governing others is so much stronger than the desire for personal independence, that for the mere shadow of the one they are found ready to sacrifice the whole of the other. An average individual among them prefers the chance, however distant or improbable, of wielding some share of power over his fellow citizens, above the certainty, to himself and others, of having no unnecessary power exercised over them.

These are the elements of a people of place hunters; in whom the course of politics is mainly determined by place hunting; where equality alone is cared for, but not liberty; where the contests of political parties are but struggles to decide whether the power of meddling in everything shall belong to one class or another; where the idea entertained of democracy is merely that of opening offices to the competition of all instead of a few; where the more popular the institutions, the more innumerable are the places created, and the more monstrous the overgovernment exercised by all over each, and by the executive over all.

10

We have examined, thus far, several questions fundamental to the philosophy of government. We began by a consideration of the general question: What is the criterion of a good form of government? We argued that the ideally best form of government is representative government. We turned aside, at that point, to consider what conditions render such government inapplicable. It remains to consider what are the proper functions of representative bodies.

While it is essential to representative government that the practical supremacy in the state should reside in the representatives of the people, it is an open question what actual functions shall be directly and personally discharged by the representative body. Great varieties in this respect are compatible with the essence of representative government, provided the functions are such as secure to the representative body the control of everything in the last resort.

There is a radical distinction between controlling the business of government and actually doing it. The same person or body may be able to control everything, but cannot possibly do everything; and in many cases its control over everything will be more perfect the less it personally attempts to do.

Some things cannot be done except by bodies; other things cannot be well done by them. It is one question, therefore, what a popular assembly should control, another what it should itself do.

It should, as we have already seen, control all the operations of government. But in order to determine what portion of the business of government the representative assembly should hold in its own hands, it is necessary to consider what kinds of business a numerous body is competent to perform properly. That alone which it can do well it ought to take personally upon itself. With regard to the rest, its proper province is not to do it, but to take means for having it well done by others.

The principles which are involved and recognized in this constitutional doctrine, if followed as far as they will go, are a guide to the limitation and definition of the general functions of representative assemblies.

II

In the first place, bodies ought not to administer. The maxim is grounded not only on the most essential principles of good government, but on those of the successful conduct of business of any description. No body of men, unless organized and under command, is fit for action in the proper sense.

What can be done better by a body than by an individual is deliberation. When it is necessary or important to secure hearing and consideration to many conflicting opinions, a deliberative body is indispensable. Those bodies, therefore, are useful in general only as advisers.

A popular assembly is still less fitted to dictate in detail to those who have charge of administration. Even when honestly meant, the interference is almost always injurious. Every branch of public administration is a skilled business, which has its own peculiar principles and traditional rules, many of them not even known, in any effectual way, except to those who have at some time had a hand in carrying on the business, and none of them likely to be duly appreciated by persons not practically acquainted with the department. I do not mean that the transaction of public business has esoteric mysteries, only to be understood by the initiated. Its principles are all intelligible to any person of good sense, who has in his mind a true picture of the circumstances and conditions to be dealt with: but to have this he must know those circumstances and conditions; and the knowledge does not come by intuition.

Difficulties are sure to be ignored by a representative assembly which attempts to decide on special acts of administration. At its best it is inexperience sitting in judgment on experience: ignorance on knowledge; ignorance which never suspecting the existence of what it does not know, is equally careless and supercilious, making light of, if not resenting, all pretensions to have a judgment better worth attending to than its own. . . . Thus it is when no interested motives intervene; but when they do, the result is jobbery more unblushing and audacious than the worst corruption which takes place in a public office under a government of publicity.

It is not necessary that the interested bias should extend to the majority of the assembly. In any particular case it is often enough that it affects two or three of their number. Those two or three will have a greater interest in misleading the body, than any other of its members will have in putting it right. The bulk of the assembly may keep their hands clean, but they cannot keep their minds vigilant or their judgment discerning in matters they know nothing about; and an indolent majority, like an indolent individual, belongs to the person who takes most pains with it.

To a minister, or the head of an office, it is of more importance what will be thought of his proceedings some time hence than what is thought of them at the instant; but an assembly, if the cry of the moment goes with it, however hastily raised or artificially stirred up, thinks itself and is thought by everybody to be completely exculpated however disastrous may be the consequences. Besides, an assembly never personally experiences the inconveniences of its bad measures until they have reached the dimensions of national evils.

The proper duty of a representative assembly in regard to matters of administration is not to decide them by its own vote, but to take care that the persons who have to decide them shall be the proper persons. Even this they cannot advantageously do by nominating the individuals. There is no act which more imperatively requires to be performed under a strong sense of individual responsibility than the nomination to employments. The experience of every person conversant with public affairs bears out the assertion, that there is scarcely any act respecting which the conscience of an average man is less sensitive; scarcely any case in which less consideration is paid to qualifications, partly because men do not know, and partly because they do not care for, the difference in qualifications between one man and another.

The qualifications which fit special individuals for special duties can only be recognized by those who know the individuals, or who make it their business to examine and judge of persons from what they have done, or from the evidence of those who are in a position to judge.

Numerous bodies never regard special qualifications at all. Unless a man is fit for the gallows, he is thought to be about as fit as other people for almost anything for which he can offer himself as candidate. When appointments made by a public body are not decided, as they almost always are, by party connection or private jobbing, a man is appointed either because he has a reputation, often quite undeserved, for *general* ability, or frequently for no better reason than that he is personally popular.

12

It is equally true, though only of late and slowly beginning to be acknowledged, that a numerous assembly is as little fitted for the direct business of legislation as for that of administration.

There is hardly any kind of intellectual work which so much needs to be done, not only by experienced and exercised minds, but by minds trained to the task through long and laborious study, as the business of making laws. This is a sufficient reason, were there no other, why they can never be well made but by a committee of very few persons. A reason no less conclusive is that every provision of a law requires to be framed with the most accurate and long-sighted perception of its effect on all the other provisions, and the law when made should be capable of fitting into a consistent whole with the previous existing laws.

It is impossible that these conditions should be in any degree fulfilled when laws are voted clause by clause in a miscellaneous assembly. The incongruity of such a mode of legislating would strike all minds, were it not that our laws are already, as to form and construction, such a chaos, that the confusion and contradiction seem incapable of being made greater by any addition to the mass.

If that as yet considerable majority of the House of Commons who never desire to move an amendment or make a speech would no longer leave the whole regulation of business to those who do; if they would bethink themselves that better qualifications for legislation exist, and may be found if sought for, than a fluent tongue and the faculty of getting elected by a constituency; it would soon be recognized that, in legislation as well as administration, the only task to which a representative assembly can possibly be competent is not that of doing the work, but of causing it to be done; of determining to whom or to what sort of people it shall be confided, and giving or withholding the national sanction to it when performed.

Any government fit for a high state of civilization would have as one of its fundamental elements a small body, not exceeding in number the members of a cabinet, who should act as a commission of legislation, having for its appointed office to make the laws, to watch over the work, protect it from deterioration, and make further improvements as often as required.

No one would wish that this body should of itself have any power of enacting laws: The commission would only embody the element of intelligence in their construction; Parliament would represent that of will. No measure would become a law until expressly sanctioned by Parliament: and Parliament would have the power not only of rejecting but of sending back a bill to the commission for reconsideration or improvement.

By such arrangements as these, legislation would assume its

proper place as a work of skilled labor and special study and experience; while the most important liberty of the nation, that of being governed only by laws assented to by its elected representatives, would be fully preserved, and made more valuable by being detached from the serious, but by no means unavoidable, drawbacks which now accompany it in the form of ignorant and ill-considered legislation.

13

Instead of the function of governing, for which it is radically unfit, the proper office of a representative assembly is to watch and control the government; to throw the light of publicity on its acts; to compel a full exposition and justification of all of them which any one considers questionable; to censure them if found condemnable; and, if the men who compose the government abuse their trust, or fulfill it in a manner which conflicts with the deliberate sense of the nation, to expel them from office, and either expressly or virtually appoint their successor. This is surely ample power, and security enough for the liberty of the nation.

14

Representative assemblies are often taunted by their enemies with being places of mere talk. There has seldom been more misplaced derision. I know not how a representative assembly can more usefully employ itself than in talk, when the subject of talk is the great public interest of the country, and every sentence of it represents the opinion either of some important body of persons in the nation, or of an individual in whom some such body have reposed their confidence. A place where every interest and shade of opinion in the country can have its cause even passionately pleaded, in the face of the government and of all other interests and opinions, can compel them to listen, and either comply, or state clearly why they do not, is in itself, if it answered no other purpose, one of the most important political institutions that can exist anywhere, and one of the foremost benefits of free government.

Such "talking" would never be looked upon with disparagement if it were not allowed to stop "doing"; which it never would, if assemblies knew and acknowledged that talking and discussion are their proper business, while doing, as the result of discussion, is the task not of a miscellaneous body, but of individuals specially trained to it; that the fit office of an assembly is to see that those individuals are honestly and intelligently chosen, and to interfere no further with them, except by unlimited latitude of suggestion and criticism, and by applying or withholding the final seal of national assent.

Their part is to indicate wants, to be an organ for popular demands, and a place of adverse discussion for all opinions relating to public matters, both great and small; and, along with this, to check by criticism, and eventually by withdrawing their support, those high public officers who really conduct the public business, or who appoint those by whom it is conducted. Nothing but the restriction of the function of the representative bodies within these rational limits will enable the benefits of popular control to be enjoyed in conjunction with the not less important requisites (growing ever more important as human affairs increase in scale and in complexity) of skilled legislation and administration. There are no means of combining these benefits except by separating the functions which guarantee the one from those which essentially require the other; by disjoining the office of control and criticism from the actual conduct of affairs, and devolving the former on the representatives of the many, while securing for the latter, under strict responsibility to the nation, the acquired knowledge and practiced intelligence of a specially trained and experienced few.

Parliament is at once the nation's committee of grievances, and its congress of opinions; an arena in which not only the general opinion of the nation, but that of every section of it, and as far as possible of every eminent individual whom it contains, can produce itself in full light and challenge discussion; where every person in the country may count upon finding somebody who speaks his mind as well or better than he could speak it himself — not to friends and partisans exclusively, but in the face of opponents, to be tested by adverse controversy; where those whose opinion is overruled, feel satisfied that it is heard, and set aside not by a mere act of will, but for what are thought superior reasons, and commend themselves as such to the representatives of the majority of the nation; where every party or opinion in the country can muster its strength, and be cured of any illusion concerning the number or power of its adherents; where the opinion which prevails in the nation makes itself manifest as prevailing, and marshals its hosts in the presence of the government, which is thus enabled and compelled to give way to it on the mere manifestation, without the actual employment, of its strength; where statesmen can assure themselves, far more certainly than by any other signs, what elements of opinion and power are growing, and what declining, and are enabled to shape their measures with some regard not solely to present exigencies, but to tendencies in progress.

READING REFERENCES. The above citations are taken from J. S. Mill's *Considerations on Representative Government*. The entire book, which is not long, should be read. It is an excellent example of the author's ability to deal with the whole question of democratic politics. It can, with profit, be read along with his *On Liberty*. The third volume of Sir Leslie Stephen's *English Utilitarians* gives an account of Mill's views. Emery Neff's *Carlyle and Mill: An Introduction to Victorian Thought* is also well worth consulting, although it is more favorable to Carlyle than to Mill. Perhaps the best short account is to be found in W. L. Davidson's *Political Thought in England: The Utilitarians*. There does not, however, exist in English any good single book devoted to the life and philosophy of J. S. Mill. In the second volume of Hoffding's *History of Modern Philosophy* will be found sixty or seventy pages which, if expanded to two or three hundred, would fill the bill. The Danish historian, apparently alone among historians of modern philosophy, had a sense for the many-sidedness and vitality of Mill's ideas.

READING QUESTIONS

1. What twofold test does Mill propose by which a form of government would be chosen?
2. On this test, which form of government would be ideally best?

3. Show this for each of the two elements in his proposed test.
4. Why does he shift from this form of government to representative government?
5. "Representative government must fulfill three fundamental conditions." What conditions?
6. What are the proper functions of representative governments?
7. What are not the proper functions? Why?
8. The nature and function of the commission of legislation?
9. "Representative governments . . . are mere places of talk." Elucidate.
10. Be prepared to trace the main turns of the argument from James I to John Stuart Mill.

TOPIC SIX. AN HISTORICAL PROBLEM

THE PROBLEM STATED

Our first problem arose out of the distinction between nature and God; our second, out of the distinction between appearance and reality; our third, out of the distinction between speculation and knowledge; our fourth, out of the distinction between moral and immoral; our fifth, out of the distinction between society and state. In each case, we have been concerned with the justification for these distinctions, and with the justification for beliefs about the second member of each set. Thus, for example, we distinguish between appearance and reality. With what justification? We proceed to assert beliefs about reality. Upon what grounds can such beliefs be justified?

Our sixth, and final, problem arises out of the distinction between event and history. We make this distinction readily enough. We distinguish between the death of Caesar and the history of Rome, between the taking of the Bastille and the history of the French Revolution, between the production of *Hamlet* and the history of Elizabethan drama, between the invention of the steam engine and the history of the Industrial Revolution. We "stumble upon" events in the context of a history. We "understand" events in terms of a history. We "isolate" events within a history. We "abstract" events from a history. We "locate" events by referring them to a history.

What is a *history?* It is not easy to say. We cannot say that a history is "nothing but" the events which "make it up," because an event, in turn, is soon seen to be "nothing but'' a moment in its history. These terms are correlative. Each is useless without the other.

If we cannot define *history* in terms of events, except on pain of involving ourselves in a circular definition, can we describe *history* by means of a metaphor? Can we say, that a history is a pattern, a plot, a theme, a motif, a frame, a structure, a plan, a *schema*, an outline? The term *pattern* is perhaps the most neutral of these metaphors. The idea which it is intended to convey is illustrated in the familiar newspaper drawing containing scattered numbers which the reader is invited to connect up by means of lines. The result is a "picture," perhaps of a horse or a man's head. The scattered numbers occur in a pattern. When we first look at them, we do not detect the pattern. Gradually, as we fill in the lines from number to number, we begin to "see" the pattern. It was "there" all the time.

Now, suppose we liken a history to the pattern which is implicit or latent in the scattered numbers in the cartoon. The scattered numbers would be the events. Drawing lines between them would be tracing connections between the events. Seeing the picture which gradually emerges would be grasping the history within which the events occur.

Granted the legitimacy of this pattern metaphor, we can pose the problem of the present topic: What is the pattern which holds the events of history together, which gradually emerges as we fill in the events, which is merely latent in the events considered in their bare particularity. Is there one such pattern which takes in all events? Or many limited patterns? If there are many limited patterns, do they themselves form parts of a more inclusive pattern? If there are many limited patterns, do single events occur in more than one of these? Do they belong equally fundamentally to each of the patterns in which they occur?

We could use this pattern metaphor to avail ourselves of

some terminology. The claim that there is "patternedness" we could call historical *rationalism*. The claim that there is one overarching and all-inclusive pattern we could call historical *monism*. The claim that there is more than one pattern, each equally fundamental and irreducible, we could call historical *pluralism*. The claim that there is no pattern, we could call historical *nihilism* or historical *irrationalism*. The claim that we do not know whether there is a pattern we could call historical *skepticism*. The claim that a pattern is something which we arbitrarily impose, one pattern being no more there than any other, we could call historical *subjectivism*.

When we think about events, we use a pattern as an hypothesis. How many facts does it enable us to account for? Does it do this better than any alternative hypothesis? Are there any facts which it ought to account for, but will not? This is not to suggest that historical patterns are merely in our heads. Unless, of course, we would be prepared to admit that the pattern marked out by the planets around the sun, is also merely in our heads; because this pattern we also use as an hypothesis to account for the facts, the observed or recorded positions and changes of the planets.

There are three fundamental types of philosophy of history. The first, historical rationalism, is the claim that there is "patternedness." The second, historical nihilism, is the claim that there is no "patternedness." The third, historical skepticism, is the claim that we do not know whether or not there is "patternedness." What was referred to above as historical subjectivism is a form of historical nihilism. It asserts that the "patternedness" is not there in history, but merely in our heads.

There are accordingly two fundamentally distinct sorts of controversy possible within the field of philosophy of history. (1) The first sort of controversy would be whether historical rationalism, historical nihilism, or historical skepticism can be justified. An extension of this controversy, which would be possible only after historical rationalism had been proved or postulated, would be whether historical monism or historical pluralism has truth on its side. (2) The second sort of controversy, possible only after historical monism or historical pluralism had been proved or postulated, would be over what the pattern is, or what the patterns are, which events hold implicit in their apparent particularity.

The first sort of controversy is not illustrated by any of the authors assembled in this topic. Each of the five is, in his own way, a rationalist. That is, he believes there is a rationale, or pattern, to history. Each differs from the other in respect to what the precise pattern is. Each offers a different interpretation of history. Each reads a different meaning out of the events. The first, St. Augustine (presented by George Santayana) sees in history the realization of God's plan for man's salvation. The second, Kant, sees in history the story of rationality in the social order. The third, Hegel, sees in history the self-realization of the world spirit in the self-realization of individual spirits and nations. The fourth, Karl Marx, sees in history the struggle between economic classes, and the eventual triumph of the proletariat class. The fifth, Oswald Spengler, sees in history the recurrence of a cyclical movement which begins in a culture and ends in a civilization.

1. *THE MEDIEVAL INTERPRETATION OF HISTORY — FROM GEORGE SANTAYANA*

Not many persons hold a philosophy of history. The reason may be that they do not know enough history to be able to catch at the notion of a vast pattern detectable amid its manifold particulars. Or it may be that they know too much history, with the result that they are skeptical about any single theme amid so great a welter of particulars. Time was when a majority of persons with any pretensions to historical knowledge would have expressed themselves in no uncertain terms. They would have begun with Creation. They would have continued with the Fall. They would have concluded with the Incarnation, the Crucifixion, the Ascension, the Redemption, the Last Judgment, and the Life to Come. This "golden thread" they would have detected amid the myriad beads. This inclusive "meaning" they would have read into or out of the story of the past.

If we should ask who proposed this interpretation of history, in the sense that we might ask who proposed the idea of evolution, the answer would perhaps be: St. Augustine, fifth-century Bishop of Hippo, in his book, *City of God*. We would not intend thereby to suggest that Augustine invented the idea, any more than we would say that Darwin invented the idea of evolution. Others had held it before him, but he gave it something like definitive expression. It is hence sometimes referred to as the Augustinian interpretation. In its essentials it has probably been held in the Western world by more people and over a longer period than any other single interpretation of history. It seems fitting, therefore, to go back to Augustine for a point of departure, despite the fact that he flourished so many centuries before the Renaissance and that we are concerned with philosophy since the Renaissance.

Biographical Note. St. Augustine was born in the middle of the fourth century A.D., and died in the year 430. He was made Bishop of Hippo, a town in North Africa, in 395. These were times that tried men's souls. The "barbarian tribes" were "invading" the Roman Empire. In 410, for example, the West Goths under Alaric captured and sacked the city of Rome. A few years later, the Vandals under Genseric moved into Roman territory in North Africa, thus bringing matters close to home for Augustine. The presence of these wandering peoples within the confines of the Roman Empire, and their destructive activities raised a large problem for the Christian world of Augustine's day. What were they doing here? Why were they allowed to come? Had not Emperor Constantine accepted the Christian religion? What more did God want? Where, in His plan of things, did all these misfortunes belong? Was Rome to be the Eternal City no longer? What had the civilized world done to deserve such calamitous treatment?

Augustine set himself to straighten out this tangle. He wrote the *City of God* to account for the decline of Rome. His argument, very briefly, was this: The eternal city is not Rome, but the congregation of all who shall be saved through the death of Christ, and shall pass their eternity in Paradise. To lament the possible destruction of Rome or the Empire is to admit only temporal and human values. Of what significance is Rome or the Empire in that great sweep of events between Creation and the Life to Come? Only from the perspective of that world is it possible to place a proper evaluation upon the affairs of this world.

The Argument of the Citations. The selection which follows is not taken from Augustine's *City of God*. It is from George Santayana's *Reason in Religion*. It is a paraphrase of Augustine's argument. The justification for having recourse to a second-hand account is twofold: The original is exceedingly difficult to quote from, by reason of its enormous length and prolixity, and the passage from Santayana is an example of such fine prose that one welcomes almost any excuse for making use of it. It requires no comment or summary.

There was in the beginning, so runs the Christian story, a great celestial King, wise and good, surrounded by a court of winged musicians and messengers. He had existed from all eternity, but had always intended, when the right moment should come, to create temporal beings, imperfect copies of himself in various degrees. These, of which man was the chief, began their career in the year 4004 B.C., and they would live on an indefinite time, possibly, that chronological symmetry might not be violated, until A.D. 4004. The opening and close of this drama were marked by two magnificent tableaux.

In the first, in obedience to the word of God, sun, moon, and stars, and earth with all her plants and animals, assumed their appropriate places, and nature sprang into being with all her laws. The first man was made out of clay, by a special act of God, and the first woman was fashioned from one of his ribs, extracted while he lay in a deep sleep. They were placed in an orchard where they often could see God, its owner, walking in the cool of the evening. He suffered them to range at will and eat of all the fruits he had planted save that of one tree only. But they, incited by a devil, transgressed this single prohibition, and were banished from that paradise with a curse upon their head, the man to live by the sweat of his brow and the woman to bear children in labor. These children possessed from the moment of conception the inordinate natures which their parents had acquired. They were born to sin and to find disorder and death everywhere within and without them.

At the same time God, lest the work of his hands should wholly perish, promised to redeem in his good season some of Adam's children and restore them to a natural life. This redemption was to come ultimately through a descendant of Eve, whose foot should bruise the head of the serpent. But it was to be prefigured by many partial and special redemptions. Thus, Noah was to be saved from the deluge, Lot from Sodom, Isaac from the sacrifice, Moses from Egypt, the captive Jews from Babylon, and all faithful souls from heathen forgetfulness and idolatry. For a certain tribe had been set apart from the beginning to keep alive the memory of God's judgments and promises, while the rest of mankind, abandoned to its natural depravity, sank deeper and deeper into crimes and vanities.

The deluge that came to punish these evils did not avail to cure them. "The world was renewed and the earth rose again above the bosom of the waters, but in this renovation there remained eternally some trace of divine vengeance. Until the deluge all nature had been exceedingly hardy and vigorous, but by that vast flood of water which God had spread out over the earth, and by its long abiding there, all saps were diluted; the air, charged with too dense and heavy a moisture, bred ranker principles of corruption. The early constitution of the universe was weakened, and human life, from stretching as it had formerly done to near a thousand years, grew gradually briefer. Herbs and roots lost their primitive potency, and stronger food had to be furnished to man by the flesh of other animals. . . . Death gained upon life, and men felt themselves overtaken by a speedier chastisement. As day by day they sank deeper in their wickedness, it was but right they should daily, as it were, stick faster in their woe. The very change in nourishment made manifest their decline and degradation, since as they became feebler they became also more voracious and bloodthirsty."

Henceforth there were two spirits, two parties, or, as St. Augustine called them, two cities in the world. The City of Satan, whatever its artifices in art, war, or philosophy, was essentially corrupt and impious. Its joy was but a comic mask and its beauty the whitening of a sepulcher. It stood condemned before God and before man's better conscience by its vanity, cruelty, and secret misery, by its ignorance of all that it truly behooved a man to know who was destined to immortality. Lost, as it seemed, within this Babylon, or visible only in its obscure and forgotten purlieus, lived on at the same time the City of God, the society of all the souls predestined to salvation; a city which, however humble and inconspicuous it might seem on earth, counted its myriad transfigured citizens in heaven, and had its destinies, like its foundations, in eternity.

To this City of God belonged, in the first place, the patriarchs and the prophets who, throughout their plaintive and ardent lives, were faithful to what echoes still remained of a primeval revelation, and waited patiently for the greater revelation to come. To the same city belonged the magi who followed a star till it halted over the stable in Bethlehem; Simeon, who divined the present salvation of Israel; John the Baptist, who bore witness to the same and made straight its path; and Peter, to whom not flesh and blood, but the spirit of the Father in Heaven, revealed the Lord's divinity. For salvation had indeed come with the fullness of time, not, as the carnal Jews had imagined it, in the form of an earthly restoration, but through the incarnation of the Son of God in the Virgin Mary, His death upon a cross, His descent into hell, and His resurrection at the third day according to the Scriptures. To the same city belonged finally all those who, believing in the reality and efficacy of Christ's mission, relied on His merits and followed His commandment of unearthly love.

All history was henceforth essentially nothing but the conflict between these two cities; two moralities, one natural, the other supernatural; two philosophies, one rational, the other revealed; two beauties, one corporeal, the other spiritual; two glories, one temporal, the other eternal; two institutions, one the world, the other the church. These, whatever their momentary alliances or compromises, were radically opposed and fundamentally alien to one another. Their conflict was to fill the ages until, when wheat and tares had long flourished together and exhausted between them the earth for whose substance they struggled, the harvest should come; the terrible day of reckoning when those who had believed the things of religion to be imaginary would behold with dismay the Lord visibly coming down through the clouds of heaven, the angels blowing their alarming trumpets, all generations of the dead rising from their graves, and judgment without appeal passed on every man, to the edification of the universal company and his own unspeakable joy or confusion. Whereupon the blessed would enter eternal bliss with God their master and the wicked everlasting torments with the devil whom they served.

The drama of history was thus to close upon a second tableau: long-robed and beatified cohorts passing above, amid various psalmodies, into an infinite luminous space, while below the damned, howling, writhing, and half transformed into loathsome beasts, should be engulfed in a fiery furnace. The two cities, always opposite in essence, should thus be finally divided in existence, each bearing its natural fruits and manifesting its true nature.

Let the reader fill out this outline for himself with its thousand details; let him remember the endless mysteries, arguments, martyrdoms, consecrations that carried out the sense and made vital the beauty of the whole. Let him pause before the phenomenon; he can ill afford, if he wishes to understand history or the human mind, to let the apparition float by unchallenged without delivering up its secret. What shall we say of this Christian dream?

Those who are still troubled by the fact that this dream is by many taken for a reality, and who are consequently obliged to defend themselves against it, as against some dangerous error in science or in philosophy, may be allowed to marshal arguments in its disproof. Such, however, is not my intention. Do we marshal arguments against the miraculous birth of Buddha, or the story of Cronos devouring his children? We seek rather to honor the piety and to understand the poetry embodied in those fables. If it be said that those fables are believed by no one, I reply that those fables are or have been believed just as unhesitatingly as the Christian theology, and by men no less reasonable or learned than the unhappy apologists of our own ancestral creeds. Matters of religion should never be matters of controversy. We neither argue with a lover about his taste, nor condemn him, if we are just, for knowing so human a passion. That he harbors it is no indication of a want of sanity on his part in other matters. But while we acquiesce in his experience, and are glad he has it, we need no arguments to dissuade us from sharing it. Each man may have his own loves, but the object in each case is different. And so it is, or should be, in religion. Before the rise of those strange and fraudulent Hebraic pretensions there was no question among men about the national, personal, and poetic character of religious allegiance. It could never have been a duty to adopt a religion not one's own any more than a language, a coinage, or a costume not current in one's own country. The idea that religion contains a literal, not a symbolic representation of truth and life is simply an impossible idea. Whoever entertains it has not come within the region of profitable philosophizing on that subject. His science is not wide enough to cover all existence. He has not discovered that there can be no moral allegiance except to the ideal. His certitude and his arguments are no more pertinent to the religious question than would be the insults, blows, and murders to which, if he could, he would appeal in the next instance. Philosophy may describe unreason, as it may describe force; it cannot hope to refute them.

The eclectic Christian philosophy thus engendered constitutes one of the most complete, elaborate, and impressive products of the human mind. The ruins of more than one civilization and of more than one philosophy were ransacked to furnish materials for this heavenly Byzantium. It was a myth circumstantial and sober enough in tone to pass for an account of facts, and yet loaded with enough miracle, poetry, and submerged wisdom to take the place of a moral philosophy and present what seemed at the time an adequate ideal to the heart. Many a mortal, in all subsequent ages, perplexed and abandoned in this ungovernable world, has set sail resolutely for that enchanted island and found there a semblance of happiness, its narrow limits give so much room for the soul and its penitential soil breeds so many consolations. True, the brief time and narrow argument into which Christian imagination squeezes the world must seem to a speculative pantheist childish and poor, involving, as it does, a fatuous perversion of nature and history and a ridiculous emphasis laid on local events and partial interests. Yet just this violent reduction of things to a human stature, this half-innocent, half-arrogant assumption that what is important for a man must control the whole universe, is what made Christian philosophy originally appealing and what still arouses, in certain quarters, enthusiastic belief in its beneficence and finality.

Nor should we wonder at this enduring illusion. Man is still in his childhood; for he cannot respect an ideal which is not imposed on him against his will, nor can he find satisfaction in a good created by his own action. He is afraid of a universe that leaves him alone. Freedom appals him; he can apprehend in it nothing but tedium and desolation, so immature is he and so barren does he think himself to be. He has to imagine what the angels would say, so that his own good impulses (which create those angels) may gain in authority, and none of the dangers that surround his poor life make the least impression upon him until he hears that there are hobgoblins hiding in the wood. His moral life, to take shape at all, must appear to him in fantastic symbols. The history of these symbols is therefore the history of his soul.

Reading References. A good essay on Augustine's *City of God* is contained in the volume of King's College lectures edited by F. J. C. Hearnshaw, *The Social and Political Ideas of Some Great Medieval Thinkers*. The lecture in question occurs in two parts. The first part is by A. J. Carlyle. The second part is by Hearnshaw; it should be read. Professor Hearnshaw's lecture may be supplemented by J. N. Figgis' *The Political Aspects of Saint Augustine's "City of God."*

READING QUESTIONS

1. When did men begin their career?
2. Why might their career close in 4004 A.D.?
3. "The opening and close of this drama were marked by two magnificent tableaux." What drama? What tableaux?
4. "They transgressed this single prohibition." Who did? What prohibition? With what result? How is this episode described in theological or biblical language?
5. "It was to be prefigured with many partial and special redemptions." What was? By whom?
6. Why was the deluge sent? What results did it produce?
7. Contrast the City of Satan and the City of God.
8. "Two moralities." Namely?
9. "Two philosophies." Namely?
10. "Two beauties." Namely?
11. "Two glories." Namely?
12. "Two institutions." Namely?
13. Who will behold what with dismay?
14. "Matters of religion should never be matters of controversy." Why?
15. What is the point of Santayana's reference to Buddha and Cronos?
16. "And so it is, or should be, in religion." What is? Agreed?
17. "The idea . . . is an impossible idea." What idea? Why impossible?
18. Who has not come within the region of profitable philosophizing on what subject?
19. What must seem childish and poor to whom?

20. What made the Christian philosophy of history originally appealing?
21. "The history of these symbols is therefore the history of his soul." What symbols? Why "therefore"?

2. *HISTORY AS THE EVOLUTION OF A RATIONAL SOCIAL ORDER—FROM IMMANUEL KANT*

From Augustine to Kant. The overview that Augustine proposed for history was the drama of salvation; man's creation, fall, redemption, and destiny in heaven. This overview died hard; indeed, it may be an exaggeration to say that it is dead yet. But from Augustine to Kant is a shift from an "age of faith" to an "age of reason." Kant wrote toward the end of the eighteenth century, in the period following the rise of modern science, and itself crowded with the American Revolution, the French Revolution, the Encyclopedists, Hume, Voltaire, Condorcet, Rousseau, Tom Paine. These men repudiated the whole Augustinian standpoint. What philosophy of history could a man propose that would command their belief and support? That is the problem which Immanuel Kant tackled in his *Idea of a Universal History*, published in 1784, just three years after his *Critique of Pure Reason*.

Biographical Note. See under "An Epistemological Problem," page 220, and under "An Ethical Problem," page 299.

The Argument of the Citations. Can we find a clue to any plan implicit in human history? Kant answers yes, and outlines his idea as follows: If creatures are predisposed by nature to develop any latent tendencies, they will do so. Men are predisposed by nature to develop tendencies which will involve the use of their reason. This development will take place in the species as a whole, not in any individual. Nature intends that man should owe to himself alone the development of his rational powers and the sort of happiness that attends their exercise and growth. To this end she has so created man that his distinctively human tendencies can develop only in the antagonism, conflict, give-and-take of life in a society. The highest problem she has set man is, therefore, the formation of a social order in which the fruitfulness of conflict will not be destroyed by conflict. This problem is not only the highest, it is also the hardest and the last. The problem requires for its final solution the formation of a world state. History is the unraveling of nature's plan for establishing this perfect political order.

Whatever difference there may be in our notions of the freedom of the will, it is evident that the manifestations of this will, viz., human actions, are as much under the control of universal laws of nature as any other physical phenomena. It is the province of history to narrate these manifestations; and let their causes be ever so secret, we know that history, simply by taking its station at a distance and contemplating the agency of the human will upon a large scale, aims at unfolding to our view a regular stream of tendency in the great succession of events; so that the very same course of incidents, which taken separately and individually would have seemed incoherent and lawless, yet viewed in their connection never fail to discover a steady and continuous though slow development of certain great predispositions in our nature. Thus for instance deaths, births, and marriages, considering how much they are separately dependent on the freedom of the human will, should seem to be subject to no law according to which any calculation could be made beforehand of their amount; and yet the yearly registers of these events in great countries prove that they go on with as much conformity to the laws of nature as the oscillations of the weather; the latter again are events which in detail are so far irregular that we cannot predict them individually, and yet taken as a whole series we find that they never fail to support the growth of plants, the currents of rivers, and other arrangements of nature in a uniform and uninterrupted course. Individual men, and even nations, are little aware that, whilst they are severally pursuing their own peculiar and often contradictory purposes, they are unconsciously following the guidance of a natural purpose which is wholly unnoticed by themselves, and are thus promoting and making efforts for a process which, even if they perceived it, they would little regard.

Considering that men, taken collectively as a body, do not proceed like animals under the law of an instinct, nor yet like wholly rational beings under the law of a preconcerted plan, one might imagine that no systematic history of their actions (such, for instance, as the history of bees or beavers) could be possible. At the sight of the actions of man displayed on the great stage of the world, it is impossible to escape a certain degree of disgust; with all the occasional indications of wisdom scattered here and there, we cannot but perceive the whole sum of these actions to be a web of folly, childish vanity, and often even of the idlest wickedness and spirit of destruction. Hence at last one is puzzled to know what judgment to form of our species so conceited of its high advantages. In this perplexity there is no resource for the philosopher but this: that, finding it impossible to presume in the human race any rational purpose of its own, he must endeavor to detect some natural purpose in such a senseless current of human actions, by means of which a history of creatures that pursue no plan of their own may yet admit a systematic form as the history of creatures that are blindly pursuing a plan of nature. Let us now see whether we can succeed in finding out a clue to such a history, leaving it to nature to produce a man capable of executing it.

Proposition the First. All tendencies of any creature, to which it is predisposed by nature, are destined in the end to develop themselves perfectly and agreeably to their final purpose.

External as well as internal (or anatomical) examination confirms this remark in all animals. An organ which is not to be used, a natural arrangement that misses its purpose, would be a contradiction in physics. Once departing from this fundamental proposition, we have a nature no longer tied to laws, but objectless and working at random; and a cheerless reign of chance steps into the place of reason.

Proposition the Second. In man, those tendencies which have the use of his reason for their object are destined to obtain their perfect development in the species only and not in the individual.

Reason in a creature is a faculty for extending the rules and purposes of the exercise of all its powers far beyond natural instinct, and it is illimitable in its plans. It works however not instinctively, but stands in need of trials, of practice, and of instruction in order to ascend gradually from one degree of illumination to another. On this account either it would be necessary for each man to live an inordinate length of time in order to learn how to make a perfect use of his natural tendencies; or else, supposing the actual case that nature has limited his term of life, she must then require an incalculable series of generations (each delivering its quota of knowledge to its immediate successor) in order to ripen the germs which she has laid in our species to that degree of development which corresponds with her final purpose. Otherwise man's own natural predispositions must of necessity be regarded as objectless; and this would at once take away all practical principles, and would expose nature — the wisdom of whose arrangements must in all other cases be assumed as a fundamental postulate — to the suspicion of capricious dealing in the case of man only.

Proposition the Third. It is the will of nature that man should owe to himself alone everything which transcends the mere mechanical constitution of his animal existence, and that he should be susceptible of no other happiness or perfection than what he has created for himself, instinct apart, through his own reason.

Nature does nothing superfluously, and in the use of means to her ends does not play the prodigal. Having given to man reason, and freedom of the will grounded upon reason, she had hereby sufficiently made known the purpose which governed her in the choice of the furniture and appointments, intellectual and physical, with which she has accoutered him. Thus provided, he had no need for the guidance of instinct, or for knowledge and forethought created to his hand; for these he was to be indebted to himself. The means of providing for his own shelter from the elements — for his own security, and the whole superstructure of delights which add comfort and embellishment to life — were to be the work of his own hands. So far indeed has she pushed this principle, that she seems to have been frugal even to niggardliness in the dispensation of her animal endowments to man, and to have calculated her allowance to the nicest rigor of the demand in the very earliest stage of existence: as if it had been her intention hereby to proclaim that the highest degree of power — of intellectual perfection — and of happiness to which he should ever toil upwards from a condition utterly savage, must all be wrung and extorted from the difficulties and thwartings of his situation — and the merit therefore be exclusively his own, thus implying that she had at heart his own rational self-estimation rather than his convenience or comfort. She has indeed beset man with difficulties; and in no way could she have so clearly made known that her purpose with man was not that he might live in pleasure; but that by a strenuous wrestling with those difficulties he might make himself worthy of living in pleasure. Undoubtedly it seems surprising on this view of the case that the earlier generations appear to exist only for the sake of the latter — viz., for the sake of forwarding that edifice of man's grandeur in which only the latest generations are to dwell, though all have undesignedly taken part in raising it. Mysterious as this appears, it is however at the same time necessary, if we once assume a race of rational animals, as destined by means of this characteristic reason to a perfect development of their tendencies, and subject to mortality in the individual but immortal in the species.

Proposition the Fourth. The means, which nature employs to bring about the development of all the tendencies she has laid in man, is the antagonism of these tendencies in the social state — no farther however than to that point at which this antagonism becomes the cause of social arrangements founded in law.

By antagonism of this kind I mean the unsocial sociality of man; that is, a tendency to enter the social state combined with a perpetual resistance to that tendency which is continually threatening to dissolve it. Man has gregarious inclinations, feeling himself, in the social state, more than man by means of the development thus given to his natural tendencies. But he has also strong antigregarious inclinations prompting him to insulate himself, which arise out of the unsocial desire (existing concurrently with his social propensities) to force all things into compliance with his own humor; a propensity to which he naturally anticipates resistance from his consciousness of a similar spirit of resistance to others existing in himself. Now this resistance it is which awakens all the powers of man. It drives him to master his propensity to indolence, and, in the shape of ambition or avarice, impels him to procure distinction for himself amongst his fellows. In this way arise the first steps from the savage state to the state of culture, which consists peculiarly in the social worth of man: Talents of every kind are now unfolded, taste formed, and by gradual increase of light a preparation is made for such a mode of thinking as is capable of converting the rude natural tendency to moral distinctions into determinate practical principles, and finally of exalting a social concert that had been extorted from the mere necessities of the situation into a moral union founded on reasonable choice. But for these antisocial propensities, so unamiable in themselves, which give birth to that resistance which every man meets with in his own self-interested pretensions, an Arcadian life would arise of perfect harmony and mutual love such as must suffocate and stifle all talents in their very germs. Men, as gentle as the sheep they fed, would communicate to their existence no higher value than belongs to mere animal life, and would leave the vacuum which exists in reference to the final purpose of man's nature, as a rational being, unfilled. Thanks be, therefore, to nature for the enmity, for the jealous spirit of envious competition, for the insatiable thirst after wealth and power! These wanting, all the admirable tendencies in man's nature would remain for ever undeveloped. Man, for his own sake as an individual, wishes for concord; but nature knows better what is good for man as a species, and she ordains discord. He would live in ease and passive content; but nature wills that he shall precipitate himself out of his luxury of indolence into labors and hardships, in order that he may devise remedies against them and thus raise himself above them by an intellectual conquest — not sink below them by an unambitious evasion. The impulses, which she has laid in his moral constitution, the sources of that antisociality and universal antagonism from which so many evils arise, but which again stimulate a fresh reaction of the faculties and by consequence more and more aid the development of the primitive tendencies — all tend to betray the adjusting hand of a wise creator, not that of an evil spirit that has bungled in the execution of his own designs, or has malevolently sought to perplex them with evil.

Proposition the Fifth. The highest problem for the human species, to the solution of which it is irresistibly urged by natural impulses, is the establishment of a universal civil society founded on political justice.

Since it is only in the social state that the development of all man's tendencies can be accomplished; since such a social state must combine with the utmost possible freedom, and consequent antagonism of its members, the most rigorous determination of the boundaries of this freedom in order that the freedom of such individual may coexist with the freedom of others; and since this as well as all other objects of man's destination should be the work of men's own efforts, on these accounts a society in which freedom under laws is united with the greatest possible degree of irresistible power is the highest problem nature sets for man; because it is only by the solution of this problem that nature can accomplish the rest of her purpose with our species. Into this state of restraint man, who is otherwise so much enamored of lawless freedom, is compelled to enter by necessity, his natural inclinations making it impossible for man to preserve a state of perfect liberty for any length of time in the neighborhood of his fellows. But, under the restraint of a civil community, these very inclinations lead to the best effects — just as trees in a forest, for the very reason that each endeavors to rob the other of air and sun, compel each other to shoot upwards in quest of both; and thus attain a fine erect growth; whereas those which stand aloof from each other under no mutual restraint, and throw out their boughs at pleasure, become crippled and distorted. All the gifts of art and cultivation which adorn the human race — in short, the most beautiful forms of social order — are the fruits of the antisocial principle — which is compelled to discipline itself, and by means won from the very resistance of man's situation in this world to give perfect development to all the germs of nature.

Proposition the Sixth. This problem is at the same time the most difficult of all, and the one which is latest solved by man.

The difficulty, which is involved in the bare idea of such a problem, is this: Man is an animal that, so long as he lives amongst others of his species, stands in need of a master. For he inevitably abuses his freedom in regard to his equals; and, although as a reasonable creature he wishes for a law that may set bounds to the liberty of all, yet do his self-interested animal propensities seduce him into making an exception in his own favor whensoever he dares. He requires a master therefore to curb his will, and to compel him into submission to a universal will which may secure the possibility of universal freedom. Now where is he to find this master? Of necessity amongst the human species. But, as a human being, this master will also be an animal that requires a master. Lodged in one or many, it is impossible that the supreme and irresponsible power can be certainly prevented from abusing its authority. Hence it is that this problem is the most difficult of any; nay, its perfect solution is impossible; out of wood so crooked and perverse as that which man is made of, nothing absolutely straight can ever be wrought. An approximation to this idea is therefore all which nature enjoins. That it is also the last of all problems, to which the human species addresses itself, is clear from this — that it presupposes just notions of the nature of a good constitution, great experience, and a will favorably disposed to the adoption of such a constitution; three elements that can hardly, and not until after many fruitless trials, be expected to concur.

Proposition the Seventh. The problem of the establishment of a perfect constitution of society depends upon the problem of a system of international relations adjusted to law; and, apart from this latter problem, cannot be solved.

To what purpose is labor bestowed upon a civil constitution adjusted to law for individual men, i.e., upon the creation of a commonwealth? The same antisocial impulses, which first drove men to such a creation, is again the cause — that every commonwealth in its external relations, i.e., as a state in reference to other states, occupies the same ground of lawless and uncontrolled liberty. Consequently each must anticipate from the other the same evils which compelled individuals to enter the social state. Nature accordingly avails herself of the spirit of enmity in man, as existing even in the great national corporations of that animal, for the purpose of attaining through the inevitable antagonism of this spirit a state of rest and security. That is, by wars, by the exhaustion of incessant preparations for war, and by pressure of evil consequences which war at last entails even through the midst of peace, she drives nations to all sorts of experiments and expedients; and finally after devastations, ruin, and exhaustion of energy, to one which reason should have suggested without the cost of so sad an experience; viz., to quit the condition of lawless power, and to enter into a federal league of nations, in which even the weakest member looks for its rights and for protection not to its own power, or its own adjudication, but to this great confederation, to the united power, and the adjudication of the collective will. Visionary as this idea may seem, it is, notwithstanding, the inevitable resource and mode of escape under that pressure of evil which nations reciprocally inflict; and, hard as it may be to realize such an idea, states must of necessity be driven at last to the very same resolution to which the savage man of nature was driven with equal reluctance — viz., to sacrifice brutal liberty, and to seek peace and security in a civil constitution founded upon law. All wars therefore are so many tentative essays (not in the intention of man, but in the intention of nature) to bring about new relations of states, and by revolutions and dismemberments to form new political bodies. These again, either from internal defects or external attacks, cannot support themselves, but must undergo similar revolutions, until at last, partly by the best possible arrangement of civil government within and partly by common concert and legal compact without, a condition is attained which, like a well-ordered commonwealth, can maintain itself.

Now, whether (in the first place) it is to be anticipated that states, like atoms, by accidental shocking together, should go through all sorts of new combinations to be again dissolved by the fortuitous impulse of fresh shocks, until at length by pure accident some combination emerges capable of supporting itself; or whether (in the second place) we should assume that nature is pursuing her course of raising our species gradually from the lower steps of animal existence to the very highest of a human existence, and that not by any direct interposition in our favor but through man's own spontaneous and artificial efforts (spontaneous, but yet extorted from him by his situation), and in this apparently wild arrangement of things is developing with perfect regularity the original tendencies she has implanted; or whether (in the third place) it is more reasonable to believe that out of all this action and reaction of the human species upon itself nothing in the shape of a wise result will ever issue, that it will continue to be as it has been, and therefore that it cannot be known beforehand but that the discord, which is so natural to our species, will finally prepare for us a hell of evils under the most moral condition of society such as may swallow up this very moral condition itself and all previous advance in culture by a reflex of the original barbaric spirit of desolation; to all this the answer turns upon the following question: Is it reasonable to assume a final purpose in all natural processes and arrangements in the parts, and yet a want of purpose in the whole?

What therefore the condition of savage life effected, viz., checked the development of the natural tendencies in the human species, but then, by the very evils thus caused, drove man into a state where those tendencies could unfold and mature themselves, that same service is performed for states by the barbaric freedom in which they are now existing — viz., by causing the dedication of all national energies and resources to war, it checks the full development of the natural tendencies in its progress; but on the other hand by these very evils and their consequences, it compels our species at last to discover some law of counterbalance to the principle of antagonism between nations, and in order to give effect to this law to introduce a federation of states and consequently an international police corresponding to national internal police.

This federation will itself not be exempt from danger, else the powers of the human race would go to sleep. It will be sufficient that it contain a principle for restoring the equilibrium between its own action and reaction, and thus checking the two functions from destroying each other. Before this last step is taken, human nature — then about half way advanced in its progress — is in the deepest abyss of evils under the deceitful semblance of external prosperity. We are at this time in a high degree of culture as to arts and sciences. We are civilized to superfluity in what regards the graces and decorums of life. But, to entitle us to consider ourselves moralized, much is still wanting. Nothing indeed of a true moral influence can be expected so long as states direct all their energies to idle plans of aggrandizement by force, and thus incessantly check the slow motions by which the intellect of the species is unfolding and forming itself, to say nothing of their shrinking from all positive aid to those motions. But all good, that is not engrafted upon moral good, is mere show and hollow speciousness — the dust and ashes of morality. And in this delusive condition will the human race linger, until it shall have toiled upwards in the way I have mentioned from its present chaotic abyss of political relations.

Proposition the Eighth. The history of the human species as a whole may be regarded as the unraveling of a hidden plan of nature for accomplishing a perfect state of civil constitution for society in its internal relations (and, as the condition of that, in its external relations also) as the sole state of society in which the tendencies of human nature can be all and fully developed.

This proposition is an inference from the preceding. The question arises: Has experience yet observed any traces of such an unraveling in history? I answer: Some little. The entire period of this unraveling is probably too vast to admit of our detecting the relation of the parts to the whole from the small fraction of it which man has yet left behind him.

Meantime our human nature obliges us to take an interest even in the remotest epoch to which our species is destined, provided we can anticipate it with certainty. So much less can we be indifferent to it, inasmuch as it appears within our power by intellectual arrangements to contribute something toward the acceleration of the species in its advance to this great epoch. On this account the faintest traces of any approximation in such a direction becomes of importance to us. At present all states are so artificially interconnected, that no one can possibly become stationary without retrograding with respect to the rest; and thus if not the progress yet the nondeclension of this purpose of nature is sufficiently secured through the ambition of nations. Moreover, civil liberty cannot at this day any longer be arrested in its progress but that all the sources of livelihood, and more immediately trade, must betray a close sympathy with it, and sicken as that sickens; and hence a decay of the state in its external relations. Gradually too this liberty extends itself. If the citizen be hindered from pursuing his interest in any way most agreeable to himself, provided only it can coexist with the liberty of others, in that case the life of general business is palsied, and in connection with that again the powers of the whole. Hence it arises that all personal restriction is more and more withdrawn; religious liberty is established; and thus, with occasional interruptions, arises illumination; a blessing which the human race must win even from the self-interested purposes of its rulers, if they comprehend what is for their own advantage. Now this illumination, and with it a certain degree of cordial interest which the enlightened man cannot forbear taking in all the good which he perfectly comprehends must by degrees mount upwards even to the throne, and exert an influence on the principles of government.

Finally, war itself becomes gradually not only so artificial a process, so uncertain in its issue, but also in the afterpains of inextinguishable national debts so anxious and burthensome; and, at the same time, the influence which any convulsions of one state exert upon every other state is so remarkable in our quarter of the globe — linked as it is in all parts by the systematic intercourse of trade — that at length, those governments, which have no immediate participation in the war, under a sense of their own danger, offer themselves as mediators — though as yet without any authentic sanction of law, and thus prepare all things from afar for the formation of a great primary state body, such as is wholly unprecedented in all preceding ages. Although this body at present exists only in rude outline, yet already a stirring is beginning to be perceptible in all its limbs — each of which is interested in the maintenance of the whole; even now there is enough to justify a hope that, after many revolutions and remodelings of states, the supreme purpose of nature will be accomplished in the establishment of an international state as the bosom in which all the original tendencies of the human species are to be developed.

Proposition the Ninth. A philosophical attempt to compose a universal history tending to unfold the purpose of nature in a perfect civil union of the human species is to be regarded as possible, and as capable even of helping forward this very purpose of nature.

At first sight it is apparently an extravagant project — to propose a history of man founded on any idea of the course which human affairs would take if adjusted to certain reasonable ends. On such a plan, it may be thought, nothing better than a romance could result. Yet, if we assume that nature proceeds not without plan even in the motions of human free will, this idea may possibly turn out very useful; and, although we are too shortsighted to look through the secret mechanism of her arrangements, this idea may yet serve as a clue for connecting into something like unity the great abstract of human actions that else seem a chaotic and incoherent aggregate. For, if we take our beginning from Greek history; if we pursue down to our own times its influence upon the formation and malformation of the Roman people as a political body that swallowed up the Greek state, and the influence of Rome upon the barbarians by whom Rome itself was destroyed; and if to all this we add the political history of every other people so far as it has come to our knowledge through the records of the two enlightened nations above mentioned; we shall then discover a regular gradation of improvement in civil polity as it has grown up in our quarter of the globe, which quarter is in all probability destined to give laws to all the rest. If further we direct an exclusive attention to the civil constitution, with its laws, and the external relations of the state, insofar as both, by means of the good which they contained, served for a period to raise and to dignify other nations and with them the arts and sciences, yet again by their defects served also to precipitate them into ruin, but always so that some germ of illumination survived which, being more and more developed by every revolution, prepared continually a still higher step of improvement; in that case, I believe that a clue will be discovered not only for the unraveling of the intricate web of human affairs and for the guidance of future statesmen, but also such a clue as will open a consolatory prospect into futurity, in which at a remote distance we shall discover the human species seated upon an eminence won by infinite toil where all the germs are unfolded which nature has implanted — and its destination upon this earth accomplished. Such a justification of nature, or rather of providence, is no mean motive for choosing this station for the survey of history. For what does it avail to praise and to draw forth to view the magnificence and wisdom of the creation in the irrational kingdom of nature, if that part in the great stage of the supreme wisdom, which contains the object of all this mighty display — viz., the history of the human species — is to remain an eternal objection to it, the bare sight of which obliges us to turn away our eyes with displeasure, and (from the despair which it raises of ever discovering in it a perfect and rational purpose) finally leads us to look for such a purpose only in another world?

My object in this essay would be wholly misinterpreted, if it were supposed that under the idea of a universal history which to a certain degree has its course determined *a priori*, I had any wish to discourage the cultivation of empirical history in the ordinary sense. On the contrary, the philosopher must be well versed in history who could execute the plan I have sketched, which is indeed a most extensive survey of history, only taken from a new station. However the extreme and, simply considered, praiseworthy circumstantiality, with which the history of every nation is written in our times, must naturally suggest a question of some embarrassment: In what way will our remote posterity be able to cope with the enormous accumulation of historical records which a few centuries will bequeath to them? There is no doubt that they will estimate the historical details of times far removed from their own, the original monuments of which will have long perished, simply by the value of that which will then concern themselves — viz., by the good or evil performed by nations and their governments in a universal view. To direct the eye upon this point as connected with the ambition of rulers and their servants, in order to guide them to the only means of bequeathing an honorable record of themselves to distant ages, may furnish some small motive (over and above the great one of justifying providence) for attempting a philosophic history on the plan I have here explained.

Reading Reference. Kant's *Idea of a Universal History* was published in 1784. It was followed, in 1795 by his essay, *Toward Everlasting Peace*. This latter can be read with profit as an extension of the claims set forth in the former. Among secondary sources, the following are useful: Edward Caird's *Critical Philosophy of Kant*, Volume II, Book II, Chapter 6; and Friedrich Paulsen's *Immanuel Kant*, Part II, Book II, Section II.

READING QUESTIONS

1. What are Kant's views on history and man's free will?
2. Why must the philosopher endeavor to detect some natural purpose in human actions?
3. Be prepared to formulate each numbered proposition, e.g., Proposition the First, as briefly as you can.
4. "This would expose nature, the wisdom of whose arrangements must in all other cases be assumed, as a fundamental postulate, to the suspicion of capricious dealing with man only."
   a. What would expose nature thus?
   b. Why must the wisdom of her arrangements be assumed, in all other cases, as a fundamental postulate?
   c. What is the wisdom of her arrangements?
   d. Do you imagine that Kant would criticize the design argument in natural theology?
5. Where, do you suppose, Kant finds out that the arrangement noted in Proposition the Third is the will of nature? What does such an expression mean, if not the will of God? Can nature be said to have a will?
6. What *appears* mysterious, but *is* necessary, if we once assume what?
7. What is the means which nature employs to bring about the development of the tendencies she has laid in man?
8. "No farther, however, than to that point." What point?
9. "Man wishes for concord; but nature knows better, and she ordains discord." Why?
10. What is the highest problem for the human species?
11. "This problem is at the same time the most difficult of all." Elucidate.
12. "This problem depends upon a system of international relations adjusted to law." Elucidate.
13. "The human race will linger in this delusive condition until

it shall have toiled upwards in the way I have mentioned." What delusive condition? What way?

14. "The history of the human species may be regarded as the unraveling of a hidden plan of nature." Namely?
15. Of what value is such a history?
16. "I have no wish to discourage, under the idea of a universal history, which is to a certain degree *a priori*, the cultivation of empirical history." Explain.

3. *IDEALISTIC INTERPRETATION OF HISTORY — FROM G. W. F. HEGEL*

FROM KANT TO HEGEL. Kant's essay was published in 1784. His views on history did not command much attention at that time. Hegel on history, however, has been much more widely read and influential. He is the real successor to Augustine. For this reason it may be well to begin with a few remarks on the period between Augustine and Hegel, before noting the period between Kant and Hegel.

Augustine died in the year 430; Hegel, in the year 1831, just one year over fourteen centuries later. Into these fourteen centuries were crowded the final break-up of the Roman Empire, the Dark Ages, the Middle Ages, the Renaissance, the Reformation, the long religious wars, the rise of modern science, the discovery and peopling of the New World, the rise of modern nationalism, the American, French, and Industrial Revolutions, the career of Napoleon and the post-Napoleonic era of conservatism symbolized by Metternich. What was the pattern now? What would be a nineteenth century equivalent of Augustine's City of God? For an answer to this question, we can most profitably turn our attention to the argument of Hegel's *Philosophy of History*, delivered as lectures in the University at Berlin for some years prior to his death, and published posthumously in 1837.

Between Kant and Hegel the two great historical events were the French Revolution and the career of Napoleon. These made a difference, for persons who lived on into the period of reaction under Metternich, in the interpretation of history. The Revolution, which began as a demand for liberty, seemed to culminate in a demand for licence; and its licence, in turn, seemed to have invoked the heavy-handed regime of Napoleon. The result, in the sphere of practical politics, was a period of illiberalism, of distrust of revolutionary politics, and of fear of the tyranny which they seem to generate. From 1815 to 1830 was the period during which this distrust was at its height. Hegel's philosophy of history is the attempt to restate the appeal to reason, such as one meets in Kant's pamphlet, by an appeal to reason somewhat disillusioned and chastened by the events which fell between him and Kant. Three things at least Hegel had to do: save the great concept of freedom, by means of the distinction between law and licence; provide recognition of the fact that the argument of history includes a place for the great man, or hero, e.g., Napoleon, whom Hegel referred to as the world-spirit on horseback; and justify the attempt of the Reaction to save Europe from licence and tyranny in the name of "rational freedom" or freedom under law.

Biographical Note. Georg Wilhelm Friedrich Hegel was born in 1770 and died in 1831 at the age of sixty-one. He wrote many volumes elucidating the general thesis that reality is spirit manifesting itself in nature, in man, and in their combination which is history. These books are difficult reading, partly because the thought they contain is unfamiliar and elusive, partly because the words they contain are obscure and technical. Early in life, Hegel arrived at the conclusion that the totality of things is an objectification or manifestation of "Geist" or spirit. With his reasons for this conclusion we are not here concerned. They were not similar to Berkeley's argument in support of a comparable conclusion. Hegel's writings are directed, for the most part, towards elaborating his central thesis, not proving it. In his *Phe-*

nomenology of Spirit he offered an account of nature, of man, of society, of morality, of art, of religion, of philosophy, as so many "fields" in which the nature of "Geist" is disclosed. His *Philosophy of Right* was a treatise on the state and law in which these are analyzed and described to show wherein they disclose the nature of "Geist," spirit. After his death, his disciples published his lectures in a series of volumes, *Philosophy of History*, *Philosophy of Art*, *Philosophy of Religion*, in which similarly motivated analyses and descriptions are carried out.

The external facts of Hegel's life are few and unimportant. He was trained for the church. He early became an academic. Outwardly at least, he never ceased to be one. He taught at several universities before he was called to occupy the chair of philosophy in the University at Berlin. He died, at the height of his fame, from an attack of cholera which had broken out in Berlin. His writings provided the great synthesis of European thought between the age of Newton and Kant before him, and Darwin and Marx after him.

The Argument of the Citations. After defending the notion of a philosophy of history against the charge of forcing facts to fit theories, Hegel proposes that history be construed as the realm of mind, in contrast to nature as the realm of matter. In history, mind, or spirit, is engaged in working out the form and substance of freedom. Freedom is the capacity to act. It presupposes rules. Rules which permit the exercise and growth of the capacity to act are rules which define freedom under law, which is true freedom, in contrast to false freedom or licence. The career of spirit has been marked with violence and conflict. This breeds pessimism and cynicism only in little men. Hegel's claim is that they are the necessary conditions under which freedom comes into being. The process is blind, in the sense that the successive steps are not marked out in advance. But it is also beneficent in the sense that each step forward, no matter what the cost in individual misery, marks an increase in the conditions which make freedom possible. The pain and sorrow which characterize the history of humanity, the conflicts within states and between states are blind stumblings toward that form of organized living in which spirit will achieve a maximum of realization in the freedom of individuals. This is a kind of long-range optimism; but in the short range it is harsh and blood-thirsty in the extreme.

The world-spirit makes use of certain individuals to initiate new and difficult turns in the history of civilization. These are the great men, or heroes, of history. They serve a power and an end which transcends them. The goal of history is the evolution of the state, that is, a union of rational wills making possible the continuous exercise and development of freedom. This is the march of God on earth. The state is the organization of the nation. Since there are many nations, war is a necessary ingredient in history. Such conflict purifies and strengthens the national state. There is no judge of the nations, beyond their survival in the strenuous march of God on earth. The world's history is the world's tribunal.

The most general definition that can be given of the philosophical treatment of history is contained in the word *rational*. The *philosophy of history* means the "rationale of history." The only thought which philosophy brings to the contemplation of history is the simple conception of reason; that reason is the sovereign of the world; that the history of the world, therefore, presents us with a "rational" process. This conviction and intuition are an hypothesis in the domain of history as such.

Before elaborating this view of history, Hegel turns to consider a possible objection. May this not lead a man to set up a plan and then force the facts to fit it?

This presupposition that history has an essential and actual goal or end is called an *a priori* view of it. Philosophy is reproached with "*a priori* history-writing." On this point we must go into further detail. This seems to be the legitimate demand that the historian should proceed with impartiality; there should be no prepossession in favor of an idea or opinion, just as a judge should have no special sympathy for one of the contending parties.

Now, in the case of the judge it is admitted that he would administer his office ill and foolishly if he had no interest in justice; indeed, if he did not have an exclusive interest in justice. That is assumed to be his one sole aim. This requirement, which we make of a judge, may be called partiality for justice.

But, in speaking of the impartiality required from an historian, this self-satisfied, insipid, chatter lets the distinction between legitimate, responsible partiality and mere subjective partiality, disappear. It demands that the historian shall bring with him no definite aim, no definite conception by which he may sort out, describe, evaluate events. It demands that he shall narrate them exactly in the casual mode he finds them, in all their incoherent and unintelligent particularity. A history must have an object, e.g., Rome and its fortunes, or the greatness and decline of Rome. This lies at the basis of the events themselves, and therefore at the basis of the critical examination into their comparative importance. A history without some such criticism would be only an imbecile mental digression — not so good as a fairy tale, for even children expect a motif in their stories, at least dimly surmisable, with which events and actions are put in relation.

To presuppose such a theme is blameworthy only when the assumed conception is arbitrarily adopted, and when a determined attempt is made to force events and actions to conform to this conception. For this kind of *a priori* handling of history, however, those are chiefly to blame who profess to be "purely historical," who raise their voice against any attempt to deal philosophically with history. Philosophy is to them a troublesome neighbor; for she is the enemy of all arbitrariness and hasty suggestion.

So much, then, for an objection to his view. He asks of history what a scientist asks of nature, namely, that it be reasonable, that the use of reason on the details of history shall not *ipso facto* mislead a man. This granted, much may be expected. However, this rationality of history is not to be confused with a pious belief in a superintending providence:

The time must come for understanding that rich product of active Reason which world history offers to us. It was for a while the fashion to profess admiration for the wisdom of God as displayed in animals, plants, and isolated occurrences. But, if it be allowed that Providence exhibits itself in such objects and forms of existence, why not also in the world history? Is this too great a matter to be thus regarded? But divine wisdom, that is, reason, is one and the same in the great as well as in the little.

In those to whom such a conception is not familiar, I may at least presume the existence of a belief in reason, a desire, a thirst, for an understanding of it. Indeed, it is the wish for rational insight, not the ambition to amass a mere heap of facts, that should be presupposed in the mind of every learner. If the clear idea of reason, of pervading rationality, is not already in our minds, in beginning the study of history, we should at least have the firm faith that it does exist there, that the scene of intelligence and conscious volition — human history — is not abandoned to chance. . . . To him who looks upon the world rationally, the world in its turn presents a rational aspect. The relation is mutual.

This conviction involves much more than the mere belief in a "superintending Providence." Pious folk are encouraged to see in particular circumstances, something more than mere chance; to acknowledge the "guiding hand" of God when help has unexpectedly come to an individual in great perplexity and need. But these instances of "providential design" are of a limited kind. They concern the accomplishment of nothing more than the desires of the individual in question. But in world history the "individuals" we have to deal with are whole peoples, e.g., the Jews, the Greeks, the Romans. We cannot, therefore, be satisfied with what we may call this "trifling" view of Providence.

But *reason*, whose presence in the world and sovereignty over the world has been maintained, is as vague and indefinite a term as

Providence. Unless we can characterize it distinctly, unless we can show wherein it consists, we cannot decide whether a thing is rational or irrational. An adequate definition of *reason* is therefore the first desideratum to an inquiry into "reason in history." Without such a definition we can get no further than mere words.

To begin with, it must be observed that world history belongs to the realm of spirit, not to the realm of matter. The term *world*, indeed, includes both physical and psychical. But our concern is not with nature at large. On the stage of world history spirit displays itself in its most concrete reality. The development of spirit is our central theme.

The nature of spirit may be understood by a glance at its direct opposite — matter. As the essence of matter is gravity, so the essence of spirit is freedom. It involves an appreciation of its own nature, a power to know itself as also an energy enabling it to realize itself, to make itself actually that which it is potentially. Accordingly it may be said of world history that it is the exhibition of spirit in the process of working out that which it is potentially.

The spirit which thinks in world history, stripping off the limitations of its several national manifestations and temporal restrictions, lays hold of its actual transcendence and universality, rises to apprehend itself for what it essentially is, while the necessity of nature and the necessity of history but minister to its revelation and are vessels of its honor.

It is the spirit which not merely broods over history as over the waters, but lives in it and is alone its principle of movement. And in the path of that spirit, liberty is the guiding principle and its development the final aim. Such a doctrine — reason in history — will be partly a plausible faith, partly a philosophical insight.

If the essence of spirit is freedom, then the history of the world, if it is the history of spirit, is none other than the progress of the consciousness of freedom.

The [ancient] Orientals had not attained the knowledge that spirit, man as such, is free. And because they did not know this, they lived in bondage. They knew only the freedom of one among the many. That one was therefore only a despot, a tyrant, not a free man. The freedom of that one was only caprice; ferocity.

brutal recklessness of passion; or, equally an accident of nature, mildness and tameness of desire.

The consciousness of freedom first arose among the Greeks. And therefore they were free. But they, and the Romans likewise, knew only that some are free, not man as such. They therefore had slaves. Their whole life, and the maintenance of their splendid liberty, was implicated with the institution of slavery. Liberty, among them, was therefore only an accidental, a transient, a limited growth; and this very fact constituted it a rigorous thraldom of our common human nature.

The Germanic peoples, under the influence of Christianity, were the first to realize that man, as man, is free; that it is freedom which constitutes the essence of spirit. To introduce this realization into the various relations of the actual world was a large problem, whose solution required a severe and lengthened process of culture. Slavery did not cease immediately upon the reception of Christianity. Liberty did not all at once predominate in states. Governments and constitutions did not all at once adopt a rational organization, or recognize freedom as their basis. The application of the principle to political relations the thorough molding and interpenetration of society by it, has been a process identical with history itself. But the history of the world has been none other than the progress of the consciousness of freedom.

In the process before us, world history, the essential nature of freedom is displayed as coming to a consciousness of itself, as realizing itself. This is the result at which the process of world history has been aiming. To this end have the sacrifices that have ever and anon been laid on the vast altar of the earth, through long lapse of ages, been offered. This is the only aim that sees itself realized and fulfilled; the only pole of repose amid the ceaseless change of events and conditions; the sole efficient principle that pervades the whole. Translating this into the language of religion, we may say that this realization by spirit of the nature and conditions of freedom is God's final aim and purpose with the world.

Freedom, the capacity to act, is the essence of spirit. Spirit is both manifested as nature and our bodies, and present in us. This "present-in-us" part is latent. We can potentially do many things that we cannot do actually; e.g., "I cannot, actually, play bridge; but, potentially, I can; that is, I can develop that freedom." Now, Hegel asks: By what means does the spirit present in humanity develop its freedoms?

If, as we have argued, the history of the world is the history of the further and further realization of freedom, we are moved to pose a question: By what means does freedom develop? By what means is it brought to further and further realization?

A first glance at history convinces us that the actions of men proceed from their needs, their passions, their characters, their abilities. A first glance impresses us, too, with the belief that these needs, passions, private interests, are the sole springs of human action. Here and there may be found, perhaps, some aims of a liberal kind; benevolence, maybe; or noble patriotism. But such aims and virtues are insignificant on the broad canvas of history. They bear only a trifling proportion to the mass of the human race, and their influence is limited accordingly.

Passions, private aims, the satisfaction of selfish desires, are the most effective springs of human action. Let no illusions be cherished on this point. Their power lies in the fact that they respect none of the limitations which justice and morality would impose on them. These natural impulses have a more direct influence over men than the artificial and tedious discipline which tends to order and self-restraint, law and morality.

If I am to exert myself for any object, principle, aim, design, it must in some way or other be mine. In its realization I must find my satisfaction; although the purpose for which I exert myself includes a complication of results, many of which have no interest for me. This is the absolute right of personal existence — to find itself satisfied in its activity and labor. If men are to interest themselves in anything, they must find their individuality gratified by its attainment. Nothing therefore happens, nothing is accomplished, unless individuals seek their own satisfaction in the issue.

We assert, then, that nothing has been accomplished without

interest on the part of those who brought it about. If *interest* be called *passion*, where the whole individuality is concentrating all its desires and powers to the neglect or exclusion of all other actual or possible interests or claims, we may affirm without qualification that nothing great has been accomplished in the world without passion.

Two elements, therefore, enter into our investigation: first, the aim, principle, destiny, namely the realization of freedom; second, the complex of human passions. The one the warp, the other the woof, of the vast arras web of world history.

The spirit which is both manifested as and present in humanity must come out, must gain freedom, must achieve the capacity to act. It must learn and master the conditions of its freedom. Now, Hegel has it, the medium in which this spirit works is the totality of blind drives that compose an unenlightened and undisciplined humanity. The spirit must achieve its freedom through and in these drives, or not at all. In themselves these drives are neither good nor bad. They are, it happens, necessary to that freedom which spirit is seen as seeking in the history of humanity.

Passion is by many regarded as a thing of sinister aspect, more or less immoral. Man is required to have no passions. We need only repeat, to silence such pallid moralizing, that nothing great has been accomplished without passion, without the concentration of energy and will upon some private interests — self-seeking, if you will — to the exclusion of all things else.

World history is controlled by a general aim — the realization of the essence of spirit, which is freedom. In the beginning this is only implicit — a profoundly hidden, unconscious instinct. The whole process of history is directed to rendering this unconscious impulse a conscious one. At the very dawn of world history, physical craving, animal instinct, private interest, selfish passion, prejudiced opinion, spontaneously present themselves. This vast congeries of wills, interests, and activities, constitute the instruments, the means, the media, of the world spirit for attaining its object.

At this point Hegel introduces a line of thought which is not easy to grasp at first. But it is central to his whole philosophy of history. We may approach it by way of what he has already said: The story of humanity is the story of the conquest by the spirit present in humanity of the conditions of its freedom, its power to act. The spirit which is present in man encounters no difficulty in acting, in exerting its will, in the realm of the natural order. And the reason is that "nature" is the realm of law and order. Nature is calculable. She "obeys" rules. When these are known they provide a basis for action. A law in nature is a possible basis for action by men. If there were no law, no order, no pattern, in nature, we could not act. We would be reduced to sheer guesswork; even lower, since if there were no law or order, we could not even guess. When we turn from nature to society, we turn from the realm of law to the realm of freedom. If man is to act in the "medium" of private wills, there must be something corresponding to laws as they are in nature. To this end man needs the state. The *state* may be defined as "society organized to make law possible." Some laws are left without the pressure of the state immediately behind them. Such laws are moral. Law and morality then, between them, are self-imposed limitations for which the justification is that they make it possible to act. They extend the realm of freedom, from the natural into the social order.

The concrete union of the two elements which we find in history — that freedom which is the essence of spirit, and those individual needs and desires which supply the driving power — is liberty under the conditions of law and morality in the state.

A state is well constituted and internally powerful when the private interests of its citizens are one with the common interest of the state, when the one finds its gratification and realization in the other.

The epoch during which a state attains this harmonious condition marks the period of its bloom, its vigor, its virtue and prosperity.

I will endeavor to make my point more vivid by means of an example. The building of a house is, on the one hand, a subjective aim and design. On the other hand we have, as means, the several substances required for the undertaking — iron, wood, stone, etc. The elements are used to work up this material — fire to melt the iron, wind to blow the fire, water to drive the wheels to cut the wood, and so on. The result is that the wind which has helped to build the house is shut out by the house. So also are the rains and floods which supplied the water to drive the wheels; and the destructive power of fire, so far as the house is fireproof. The stones and beams obey their law of gravity — press downwards — and so high walls are carried up.

Thus the elements are used according to their natures, and yet cooperate for a product by which their operation is limited. Thus, in the building of a state, where freedom is realized under conditions of law and order, the passions of men are gratified; they develop themselves and their aims in accordance with their natural tendencies, and build up the edifice of human society; thus fortifying a position for law and order against themselves.

Lest anyone should feel that Hegel is growing optimistic, viewing humanity and the state through rosy spectacles, he turns aside to note that the price of freedom is not merely eternal vigilance; it is eternal strife and violence.

When we contemplate this display of passions, and the consequences of their violence, the unreason which is associated with them; when we see the evil, the vice, the ruin that has befallen the most flourishing kingdom which the mind of man ever created, we can scarce avoid being filled with sorrow at this universal taint and corruption. Since, moreover, this perversion and decay are not the work of mere nature, but the work of human will, we are liable to a moral bitterness, a revolt of the good will, as a result of our reflections.

Without rhetorical exaggeration, a simple truthful account of the miseries that have overwhelmed the noblest of nations and the finest exemplars of private virtue, provides a picture of most fearful aspect, excites emotions of the profoundest and most hopeless sadness, counterbalanced by no consolatory results. History appears as the slaughter bench at which the happiness of peoples, the wisdom of states, and the virtue of individuals have been victimized.

In beholding it we endure a mental torture allowing no defense or escape save the consideration that what has happened could not have been otherwise; that it has been a fatality which no intervention could alter. We draw back at last in disgust. We turn from these intolerable sorrows, from these blackened pages of humanity's history, to the more agreeable environment of our own individual life.

The philosophy of history which Hegel has been marking out threatens to end in a kind of pessimism. Spirit is the capacity to act. It is therefore freedom. It is manifested as nature. It is present in humanity. It requires a social order comprising a moral and political order. These orders are the battleground of private passions and private wills controlled by private passions. The spirit must work out its destiny in terms of these factors, or not at all. They are the matter to which it will give the form, the form of freedom. This entails tension and conflict. We turn from it, as from a slaughter bench. But where to? To our own private selves. Only by withdrawing from humanity do we see any prospect of relief from the price which it continuously pays. But we withdraw from the human scene in the name of precisely those human values and ideals which the human scene alone makes possible, and toward which it is the endless struggle. Are we caught here in a vicious circle? The "great man" as hero is Hegel's partial answer. The "great man" is he who "breaks ground" for spirit's further advance.

But whither do we thus retreat? Into the present, formed by our own private aims and interests! In short, we retreat into the selfishness that stands on the quiet shore, enjoying thence in safety the distant spectacle of wreckage and confusion.

To what final aim have these enormous sacrifices been offered? To what paradox, moreover, have we come? We point to the gloomy facts presented by history — but we point to them as the very field which we regard as exhibiting the means for realizing what we have described as the essential destiny, the final aim, of world-history. In what terms can this paradox be resolved? We pick up our analysis again. The steps to which it will lead us will also evolve the conditions required for answering the question suggested by the panorama of sin and suffering that history unfolds.

Those manifestations of vitality on the part of individuals and nations, in which they seek and satisfy their own purposes, are at the same time the means and instruments of a higher and broader purpose of which they know nothing, which they realize unconsciously. This has been questioned, denied, condemned, as mere dreaming and "philosophy." So be it. On this point I announced my view at the very outset: Reason governs the world, and has consequently governed history. All else is subordinate to it, subservient to it, and the means for its development.

In the sphere of world history we see momentous collisions between established, acknowledged duties, laws, rights on the one hand and forces adverse to this fixed system on the other. These forces realize themselves in history. They involve principles different from those on which depend the permanence of a people or a state. They are an essential phase in the creative advance of the world spirit. Great historical men — world figures — are those in whose aims such principles are present.

Caesar belongs to this category. His enemies had the *status quo* and the power conferred by an appearance of justice on their side. Caesar was contending for his own position. But his victory secured for him the conquest of the empire. This realization of his own aim, however, was an independently necessary feature in the history of Rome and of the world. It was not merely his private gain. An unconscious impulse occasioned the accomplishment of that for which the time was ripe.

Such are all great historical men. Their own private aims involve those larger issues which are the will of the world spirit. They derive their purposes from a concealed fount, from that inner spirit still hidden beneath the surface which impinges on the outer world as on a shell and bursts it to pieces; not from the calm, regular course of things sanctioned by the existing order.

Such world figures have no consciousness of the general idea they are unfolding while prosecuting their own private aims. On the contrary, they are practical, political men, but possessed of an insight into the requirements of the time, an understanding of what was ripe for development. It is theirs to realize this nascent principle; the next step forward which their world is to take. It is theirs to make this their aim and spend their energies promoting it. They are the heroes of an epoch; must be recognized as its clear-sighted ones. Their deeds, their words, are the best of their time.

World historical figures form purposes to satisfy themselves, not others. Whatever they might learn from others would limit their role. It is they who best understand. From them others learn; or with them, they acquiesce. For that spirit which, in their persons, takes a fresh step in history is the inmost soul of all individuals; but in them it is in a state of unconsciousness which great men arouse. Their fellows therefore follow them, for they feel the irresistible power of their own indwelling spirit embodied in them.

If we contemplate the fate of the world historical person, whose destiny is to be the agent of the world spirit, we find it to be no happy one. He attains no calm enjoyment. His whole life is labor and trouble, driven by some master passion. And when his object is attained, he falls off like an empty shell from the kernel. He dies early, like Alexander; he is murdered, like Caesar; he is exiled, like Napoleon. This consolation those may draw from history who stand in need of it, vexed at what is great and transcendent, striving to belittle it because it is beyond them.

The special interests of private passion are thus inseparable from the development of general principles. But the principle is not implicated in the opposition and combat through which it comes into being. It remains in the hinterland, untouched. This may be called the cunning of reason; it sets the passions to work for it, while what which develops through the conflict of passions pays the penalty and suffers the loss.

A world historical figure is not so unwise as to permit many wishes to divide his energies. He is devoted to one aim. He frequently overrides great and sacred interests. Such conduct is indeed morally reprehensible, but so mighty a form must trample down many an innocent flower, and crush to pieces many an object in its path.

What pedagogue has not demonstrated of Alexander the Great, or of Julius Caesar, that they were immoral men? Whence the conclusion follows that he — the pedagogue — is a better man than they, because he is not driven by their passion. For proof of this he can point to the fact that he does not conquer Asia, does not vanquish Darius, does not subdue an empire. He enjoys life and lets others enjoy it too.

No man is a hero to his valet. Not because he is no hero, but because his valet is only a valet. World historical figures, waited upon in historical literature by psychological valets, come off poorly. They are brought down to the level — or usually a few degrees below the level — of their biographers, those exquisite discerners of true spirits!

Hegel returns, at this point, to his central thought about the state. It is society organized to make law possible. Under the shadow of state law, we can gradually get moral law. Under the discipline of "legal" law man may rise to "moral" law. Law is the possibility of action. It is therefore the basis of freedom, since freedom is the capacity to act. This Hegelian freedom, with its deification of the state, is sometimes confused with freedom in the sense of "permission" or absence of restraint. He wishes to obviate any such confusion.

In world history, only those people can come under our notice which form a state. For it must be understood that the state is the realization of freedom.

The state exists for its own sake. All the worth which any human being possesses, he possesses only through the state. Thus only is he fully conscious. Thus only is he a partaker of morality — of a just and moral social and political life. The state is the march of

God on earth. We have in it the object of history, that in which freedom obtains realization; for only that will which obeys law is free.

In our time various errors are current, respecting the state. We shall mention only one, but one which is the direct contradictory of our principle that the state is the realization of freedom. It is this misconception: that man is free by nature, but that in society, in the state, he must limit this natural freedom. In this sense a "state of nature" is assumed, in which mankind possess their "natural rights," with the unconstrained exercise and enjoyment of their freedom.

This assumption of "natural freedom" and "natural rights" is not, indeed, given the dignity of being an historical fact. It would be difficult to point to any such condition as existing or having existed. Examples of savage social organization can be pointed to; but not in support of this idea, for they are marked by brutal passion and violence, and, however primitive their conditions, they involve social organizations which actually function to restrain freedom.

Freedom does not exist as primitive and natural. On the contrary, freedom must be sought and won, and by an incalculable discipline of intellectual and moral powers. The "state of nature" is a state of injustice and violence, of untamed natural impulse, of inhuman deeds and feelings. Limits are certainly imposed by social organization; but they are limits imposed on emotions and instincts. In more advanced stages, they are limits imposed on self-will, caprice, passion. Limitation of this kind is, in part, the means whereby rational freedom, contrasted with unbridled license, can be obtained.

To the conception of freedom, law and morality are indispensably necessary. They are discovered only by the activity of thought, separating itself from the merely sensuous and developing itself in opposition thereto. They must be introduced and incorporated into the originally desire-controlled will, contrarily to its "natural" inclination. The widespread misapprehension of the true nature of freedom consists in conceiving it to be a constraint imposed upon desire, something pertaining to the individual as such.

Thus a limitation of caprice and selfwill is regarded as a limitation of freedom. Instead, we argue, such limitation is the indispensable proviso of freedom. Society and the state, with the law and morality upon which they rest, are the very conditions in which freedom is realized.

The state, its laws and morality, constitute the rights of its members. (Thus wide of the facts is the conception of "natural" rights.) Its natural features, its mountains, its rivers, its forests and fields, are their country, their homeland, their material property. Its history is their history. What their forefathers have produced, belongs to them and lives now in their memory. All is their possession, and they are possessed by it. It constitutes their being. This is the meaning of *patriotism*.

The state, then, is the hero of Hegel's philosophy of history. In it the spirit which is manifested as nature and present in man comes to self-realization. When these unions of wills clash, there is war. This conflict clarifies and strengthens the parties. War, like every other genuine expression of will, has its place in the growth of freedom.

In world history each nation is to be regarded as an individual. For world history is the story of the growth of spirit in its highest forms. The forms which this progress assumes are the characteristic "national spirits" of history; the peculiar tenor of their moral life, their government, their art, religion, science. To realize these successive forms is the boundless impulse of the world spirit, the goal of its irresistible longing. [The state is the march of God through the world . . . the world which the spirit has made for itself . . . a great architectonic edifice, a hieroglyph of reason, manifesting itself in reality.]

All the worth which any human being possesses, all his "spiritual reality," he possesses only through the state. For his "spiritual reality" consists in this, that his own essential nature — rationality — is objectively present to him. Thus only is he fully conscious. Thus only is he a partaker of morality, of a just and moral social and political life. For truth, in these matters, is the unity of the objective and subjective will; and the objective will is to be found in the state, in its laws and arrangements.

Just as the individual is not a real person unless related to other persons, so the state is not a real state unless it is related to other states.

The relation of one state to another presents, on the largest possible scale, the most shifting play of individual passions, interests, aims, talents, virtues, power, injustice, vice, and mere external chance. It is a play in which even the independence of the state is exposed to accident.

When the wills of the particular state can come to no agreement, the matter can only be settled by war. What shall be recognized as a violation of treaty, of respect, of honor, must remain indefinite since many and various injuries can accrue from the wide range of interests and complex relations among states. A state may identify its majesty and honor with any one of its aspects. And if a state, as a strong individuality, has experienced an unduly protracted internal rest, it will naturally be more inclined to irritability in order to find an occasion for intense activity.

There is an ethical element in war. It must not be regarded as an absolute ill, or as merely an external calamity accidentally based upon the passions of despotic individuals or nations, upon acts of injustice and what ought not to be.

War has the deep meaning that by it the ethical health of nations is preserved and their finite aims uprooted. And as the winds which sweep over the ocean prevent the decay that would result from its perpetual calm, so war protects a people from the corruption which an everlasting peace would bring on it.

In times of peace, civic life becomes more extended, every sphere is hedged in and grows immobile, and at last men stagnate, their particular nature becoming more and more hardened and ossified. Where the organs become still, there is death. Eternal peace is often demanded as an ideal toward which mankind should move. But nations issue forth invigorated from their wars. Nations torn by internal strife win internal peace as the result of war abroad. War indeed causes insecurity of property, but this is a necessary commotion.

From the pulpits one hears much concerning the insecurity, the vanity, the instability of temporal things. Everyone is touched by the words. Yet, let insecurity really come, in the form of Hussars with flashing sabers, and that edification which foresaw all this and acquiesced, now turns upon the enemy with curses. Wars break out whenever necessity demands them; but the seeds spring up anew, and speech is silenced before the grave repetitions of history.

The principles which control the many national spirits are limited. Each nation is guided by its particular principles. No judge exists to adjust differences, save the universal spirit of which these are but moments. Only as a particular individuality can each national spirit win objectivity and self-realization; but states, in their relation one to another, reveal the dialectic, the claims and counterclaims, which arise out of their finitude. Out of this dialectic of history rises the universal spirit, pronouncing its judgment upon the nations of the worlds. For the world's history is the world's tribunal.

Reading References. Hegel has been written about, almost as much as Kant, but the result is not encouraging. In English, there is a small volume by G. S. Morris, *Hegel's Philosophy of History*. It is more understandable, perhaps, than Hegel's own volumes, *Philosophy of History* and *Philosophy of Right*. The Hegelian conception of the state, and thus the central theme in his philosophy of history, is adopted by Bernard Bosanquet in his *Philosophical Theory of the State*. A sharply critical and not altogether satisfactory account of the Hegelian notion of the state as the significance of history may be found in L. T. Hobhouse's *The Metaphysical Theory of the State*. It should be offset by a few chapters from M. B. Foster's small volume, *The Political Philosophies of Plato and Hegel*. The fact is that Hegel is difficult to read, and that no expositor has succeeded, as yet, in translating him into the language and idiom of ordinary discourse. When that is done, it will be as though the clouds had lifted from the Matterhorn.

READING QUESTIONS

1. What is the *a priori* view of history?
2. On what grounds does Hegel defend himself against any imputation of apriorism?
3. Can you explain his use of the terms *reason*, *spirit*, *freedom?*
4. How is he led to introduce questions of private interests and passions?
5. "The one the warp, the other the woof, of the vast arras web of world history." Elucidate.
6. "The concrete union of the two elements is liberty under law and morality." Elucidate.
7. "The state is well constituted and internally powerful when. . . ."
8. "I will endeavor to make my point more vivid by means of an example." What is the example?
9. What renders us "liable to a moral bitterness, a revolt of the good will"?
10. What is the role of the great man in history?
11. "No man is a hero to his valet." Why not?
12. "In our time various errors are current respecting the state. We shall mention only one. . . ." Namely?
13. "All the worth which any human being possesses, he possesses only through the state." Elucidate.
14. "There is an ethical element in war." Namely?
15. "The world's history is the world's tribunal." Meaning?

4. THE ECONOMIC INTERPRETATION OF HISTORY — FROM KARL MARX

FROM HEGEL TO MARX. Hegel died in 1831. Seventeen years later, in 1848, Karl Marx and Friedrich Engels published *The Communist Manifesto.* This slight document, not much longer than the shorter catechism, propounded a theory of history which has since been very widely held. The theory in question is known by various names, e.g., *dialectical materialism*, *historical materialism*, *economic determinism*, *the economic interpretation of history.* It was proposed by the authors as an alternative to Hegel's idealism, and as a statement of the principles believed by them to be implicit in the many revolutionary movements which occurred around 1848. Few things in modern history have exercised such an instant and persistent influence. Tom Paine's *Common Sense*, published in this country at the time of the American Revolution, might be cited by way of a comparison.

The theory, of which this fiery pamphlet was a popular expression, is to the following effect. Suppose you distinguish within society between the polity and the economy. A polity is a society organized to make law possible. An economy is a society organized to make possible production by division of labor and distribution by exchange. Now an *economic* interpretation of political history is one which traces the events and changes in the polity to events and changes in the economy. No changes in the polity without changes in the economy. This is perhaps the most general meaning one can attach to the phrase *economic interpretation of history*.

More specifically, however, Marx's theory holds that within the economy the most fundamental thing is the way in which production takes place. If a change takes place here, it will be reflected throughout the entire economy, and hence will have important consequences in the polity. Politics mirrors economics. The defining characteristic of any one type of economy is its method of production.

More specifically still, Marx's theory holds that among the many different *kinds* of economies, one particular kind exists in the Western world today. It is the capitalist economy. Capitalism is one economy among many possible economies. He wrote his large book, *Capital*, to analyze and describe the capitalist economy. The *Manifesto* is a brief and colorful statement of what later went into the *Capital* at great length.

The central historical thesis which Marx argues, with respect to the capitalist economy, is this: It evolved out of the feudal economy, and it will evolve into the communist economy.

Biographical Note. Marx was born in 1818 and died in 1883 at the age of sixty-five. He was educated in the universities at Bonn and Berlin, beginning with law, but subsequently devoting his entire attention to philosophy. Hegelianism was the fashionable doctrine at the time. It found no favor with young Marx. So, when he graduated and looked about for a job teaching philosophy, he found no openings. For the next few years, amid a life of newspaper work and radical agitation, he devoted his spare time to writing a series of highly critical studies of those portions of the Hegelian philosophy which he understood and rejected. By 1848 he had joined the Communist League. For it he wrote the celebrated *Manifesto*. Exiled from Germany, from Belgium, from France, he settled in London. From here, in 1864, he organized the First International. In 1867 he published Volume One of *Capital*. The remainder was edited and published by Engels after Marx's death. In life, judged by ordinary standards, he was unhappy, unsuccessful, and largely unknown. In death he has become, like Darwin and Freud and Einstein, one of the makers of the modern mind.

The Argument of the Citations. The history of all hitherto existing society is the history of class struggles. In early modern times the bourgeoisie triumphed over the feudal masters. They thus became masters of the modern world. An account of their multifarious doings. They have, among other things, brought into being a new class, the proletariat. The class struggle is now between bourgeoisie and proletariat. When the latter win out, as they are destined to do, the world will see its first classless society. The bourgeoisie economy will be replaced by the communist economy. Injustices arising out of the fact that modern society has been, in respect to production and distribution, a capitalist economy, will cease to exist. To the Finland station!

Ths history of all hitherto existing society is the history of class struggles.

Freeman and slave, patrician and plebeian, lord and serf, guild master and journeyman, in a word, oppressor and oppressed, stood in constant opposition to one another, carried on uninterrupted, now hidden, now open fight, a fight that each time ended, either in a revolutionary reconstitution of society at large, or in the common ruin of the contending classes.

In the earlier epochs of history we find almost everywhere a complicated arrangement of society into various orders, a manifold gradation of social rank. In ancient Rome we have patricians, knights, plebeians, slaves; in the Middle Ages, feudal lords, vassals, guild masters, journeymen, apprentices, serfs; in almost all of these classes, again, subordinate gradations.

The modern bourgeois society that has sprouted from the ruins of feudal society, has not done away with class antagonisms. It has but established new classes, new conditions of oppression, new forms of struggle in place of the old ones.

Our epoch, the epoch of the bourgeoisie, possesses, however, this distinctive feature; it has simplified the class antagonisms. Society as a whole is more and more splitting up into two great hostile camps, into two great classes directly facing each other: bourgeoisie and proletariat.

From the serfs of the Middle Ages sprang the chartered burghers of the earliest towns. From these burgesses the first elements of the bourgeoisie were developed.

The discovery of America, the rounding of the Cape, opened up fresh ground for the rising bourgeoisie. The East Indian and Chinese markets, the colonization of America, trade with the colonies, the increase in the means of exchange and in commodities generally, gave to commerce, to navigation, to industry, an impulse never before known, and thereby, to the revolutionary element in the tottering feudal society, a rapid development.

The feudal system of industry, under which industrial production was monopolized by closed guilds, now no longer sufficed for the growing wants of the new market. The manufacturing system took its place. The guild masters were pushed on one side by the manufacturing middle class; division of labor between the different corporate guilds vanished in the face of division of labor in each single workshop.

Meantime the markets kept ever growing, the demand ever rising. Even manufacture no longer sufficed. Thereupon, steam and machinery revolutionized industrial production. The place of manufacture was taken by the giant, modern industry, the place of the industrial middle class, by industrial millionaires, the leaders of whole industrial armies, the modern bourgeois.

Modern industry has established the world market, for which the discovery of America paved the way. This market has given an immense development to commerce, to navigation, to communication by land. This development has, in its turn, reacted on the extension of industry; and in proportion as industry, commerce, navigation, railways extended, in the same proportion the bourgeoisie developed, increased its capital, and pushed into the background every class handed down from the Middle Ages.

We see, therefore, how the modern bourgeoisie is itself the product of a long course of development, of a series of revolutions in the modes of production and of exchange.

The preceding paragraphs trace the origin of the class whom Marx refers to as the *bourgeoisie*. He means the capitalists, the money masters of the modern economy. In the paragraphs which follow, he traces the influence which this class in turn has had on modern society. Before passing to the details, he pauses to note that, having become masters of the economy, they are naturally masters of the polity.

Each step in the development of the bourgeoisie was accompanied by a corresponding political advance of that class. An oppressed class under the sway of the feudal nobility, an armed and self-governing association in the medieval commune, here independent urban republic (as in Italy and Germany), there taxable "third estate" of the monarchy (as in France), afterwards, in the period of manufacture proper, serving either the semi-feudal or the absolute monarchy as a counterpoise against nobility, and, in fact, cornerstone of the great monarchies in general, the bourgeoisie has at last, since the establishment of modern industry and of the world market, conquered for itself, in the modern representative state, exclusive political sway. The executive of the modern state is but a committee for managing the common affairs of the whole bourgeoisie.

Historically the members of the bourgeoisie have played a most revolutionary part. That is the theme of the paragraphs which follow. They have "abolished the Middle Ages." They have converted the professions into trades. They have placed everything, even the family upon "a cash nexus." They found things static. They have made constant change the order of the new day. They have spread over the world in quest of materials and markets. They have given an "international" cast to modern living. And so on.

The bourgeoisie, historically, has played a most revolutionary part.

The bourgeoisie, wherever it has got the upper hand, has put an end to all feudal, patriarchal, idyllic relations. It has pitilessly torn asunder the motley feudal ties that bound man to his "natural superiors," and has left no other nexus between man and man than naked self-interest, than callous "cash payment." It has drowned the most heavenly ecstasies of religious fervor, of chivalrous enthusiasm, of Philistine sentimentalism, in the icy water of egotistical calculation. It has resolved personal worth into exchange value, and in place of the numberless indefeasible chartered freedoms, has set up that single, unconscionable freedom — free trade. In one word, for exploitation, veiled by religious and political illusions, it has substituted naked, shameless, direct, brutal exploitation.

The bourgeoisie has stripped of its halo every occupation hitherto honored and looked up to with reverent awe. It has converted the physician, the lawyer, the priest, the poet, the man of science, into its paid wage laborers.

The bourgeoisie has torn away from the family its sentimental veil, and has reduced the family relation to a mere money relation.

The bourgeoisie has disclosed how it came to pass that the brutal display of vigor in the Middle Ages, which reactionists so much admire, found its fitting complement in the most slothful indolence. It has been the first to show what man's activity can bring about. It has accomplished wonders far surpassing Egyptian pyramids, Roman aqueducts, and Gothic cathedrals; it has conducted expeditions that put in the shade all former exoduses of nations and crusades.

The bourgeoisie cannot exist without constantly revolutionizing the instruments of production, and thereby the relations of production, and with them the whole relations of society. Conservation of the old modes of production in unaltered form was, on the contrary, the first condition of existence for all earlier industrial classes. Constant revolutionizing of production, uninterrupted disturbance of all social conditions, everlasting uncertainty and agitation distinguish the bourgeois epoch from all earlier ones. All fixed, fast frozen relations, with their train of ancient and venerable prejudices and opinions, are swept away, all new formed ones become antiquated before they can ossify. All that is solid melts into the air, all that is holy is profaned, and man is at last compelled to face with sober senses, his real conditions of life, and his relations with his kind.

The need of a constantly expanding market for its products chases the bourgeoisie over the whole surface of the globe. It must nestle everywhere, settle everywhere, establish connections everywhere.

The bourgeoisie has through its exploitation of the world market given a cosmopolitan character to production and consumption in every country. To the great chagrin of reactionists, it has drawn from under the feet of industry the national ground on which it stood. All old-established national industries have been destroyed or are daily being destroyed. They are dislodged by new industries, whose introduction becomes a life and death question for all civilized nations, by industries that no longer work up indigenous raw material, but raw material drawn from the remotest zones; industries whose products are consumed, not only at home, but in every quarter of the globe. In place of the old wants, satisfied by the productions of the country, we find new wants, requiring for their satisfaction the products of distant lands and climes. In place of the old local and national seclusion and self-sufficiency, we have intercourse in every direction, universal interdependence of nations. And as in material, so also in intellectual production. The intellectual creations of individual nations become common property. National one-sidedness and narrow-mindedness become more and more impossible, and from the numerous national and local literatures there arises a world literature.

The bourgeoisie, by the rapid improvement of all instruments of production, by the immensely facilitated means of communication, draws all, even the most barbarian nations into civilization. The cheap prices of its commodities are the heavy artillery with which it batters down all Chinese walls, with which it forces the barbarians' intensely obstinate hatred of foreigners to capitulate. It compels all nations, on pain of extinction, to adopt the bourgeois mode of production; it compels them to introduce what it calls *civilization* into their midst, i.e., to become bourgeois themselves. In a word, it creates a world after its own image.

The bourgeoisie has subjected the country to the rule of the towns. It has created enormous cities, has greatly increased the urban population as compared with the rural, and has thus rescued a considerable part of the population from the idiocy of rural life. Just as it has made the country dependent on the towns, so it has made barbarian and semibarbarian countries dependent on civilized ones, nations of peasants on nations of bourgeois, the East on the West.

The bourgeoisie keeps more and more doing away with the scattered state of the population, of the means of production, and of property. It has agglomerated population, centralized means of production, and has concentrated property in a few hands. The necessary consequence of this was political centralization. Independent, or but loosely connected provinces, with separate interests, laws, governments, and systems of taxation, became lumped together in one nation, with one government, one code of laws, one national class interest, one frontier, and one customs tariff.

The bourgeoisie, during its rule of scarce one hundred years, has created more massive and more colossal productive forces than have all preceding generations together. Subjection of nature's forces to man, machinery, application of chemistry to industry and agriculture, steam navigation, railways, electric telegraphs, clearing of whole continents for cultivation, canalization of rivers, whole populations conjured out of the ground — what earlier century had even a presentiment that such productive forces slumbered in the lap of social labor?

We see then: The means of production and of exchange on whose foundation the bourgeoisie built itself up, were generated in feudal society. At a certain stage in the development of these means of production and of exchange, the conditions under which feudal society produced and exchanged, the feudal organization of agriculture and manufacturing industry, in one word, the feudal relations of property became no longer compatible with the already developed productive forces; they became so many fetters. They had to burst asunder; they were burst asunder.

Into their places stepped free competition, accompanied by social political constitution adapted to it, and by economical and political sway of the bourgeois class.

The capitalist economy makes trouble for itself. Where production is motivated by profit, overproduction is to be expected. Then the whole system buckles and staggers, only to regain its equilibrium and plunge on again. In this matter of overproduction, says Marx, the modern bourgeoisie economy is like the sorcerer. It conjures up a jinni which it is unable to control.

A similar movement is going on before our own eyes. Modern bourgeois society with its relations of production, of exchange and of property, a society that has conjured up such gigantic means of production and of exchange, is like the sorcerer, who is no longer able to control the powers of the nether world whom he has called up by his spells. For many a decade past, the history of industry and commerce is but the history of the revolt of modern productive forces against modern conditions of production, against the property relations that are the conditions for the existence of the bourgeoisie and of its rule. It is enough to mention the commercial crises that by their periodical return put on its trial, each time more threateningly, the existence of the entire bourgeois society. In these crises a great part not only of the existing products, but also of the previously created productive forces, are periodically destroyed. In these crises there breaks out an epidemic that, in all earlier epochs, would have seemed an absurdity — the epidemic of overproduction. Society suddenly finds itself put back into a state of momentary barbarism; it appears as if a famine, a universal war of devastation, had cut off the supply of every means of subsistence; industry and commerce seem to be destroyed; and why? Because there is too much civilization, too much means of subsistence, too much industry, too much commerce. The productive forces at the disposal of society no longer tend to further the development of the conditions of the bourgeois property; on the contrary, they have become too powerful for these conditions by which they are fettered, and as soon as they overcome these fetters, they bring disorder into the whole of bourgeois society, endanger the existence of bourgeois property. The conditions of bourgeois society are too narrow to comprise the wealth created by them. And how does the bourgeoisie get over these crises? On the one hand by enforced destruction of a mass of productive forces; on the other, by the conquest of new markets, and by the more thorough exploitation of the old ones. That is to say, by paving the way for more extensive and more destructive crises, and by diminishing the means whereby crises are prevented.

The bourgeoisie have not only produced an unmanageable economy, they have also produced an opposition class who will do for them what they did for the masters of the feudal order. This new class is the wage earners, the proletarians. He continues:

The weapons with which the bourgeoisie felled feudalism to the ground are now turned against the bourgeoisie itself.

But not only has the bourgeoisie forged the weapons that bring death to itself; it has also called into existence the men who are to wield those weapons — the modern working class — the proletarians.

In proportion as the bourgeoisie, i.e., capital, is developed, in the same proportion is the proletariat, the modern working class, developed, a class of laborers who live only so long as they find work, and who find work only so long as their labor increases capital. These laborers, who must sell themselves piecemeal, are a commodity, like every other article of commerce, and are consequently exposed to all the vicissitudes of competition, to all the fluctuations of the market.

Owing to the extensive use of machinery and to division of labor, the work of the proletarians has lost all individual character, and, consequently, all charm for the workman. He becomes an appendage of the machine, and it is only the most simple, most monotonous and most easily acquired knack that is required of him. Hence, the cost of production of a workman is restricted almost entirely to the means of subsistence that he requires for his maintenance, and for the propagation of his race. But the price of a commodity, and also of labor, is equal to its cost of production. In proportion, therefore, as the repulsiveness of the work increases the wage decreases. Nay more, in proportion as the use of machinery and division of labor increases, in the same proportion the burden of toil increases, whether by prolongation of the working hours, by increase of the work enacted in a given time, or by increased speed of the machinery, etc.

Modern industry has converted the little workshop of the patriarchal master into the great factory of the industrial capitalist. Masses of laborers, crowded into factories, are organized like soldiers. As privates of the industrial army they are placed under the command of a perfect hierarchy of officers and sergeants. Not only are they the slaves of the bourgeois class and of the bourgeois state, they are daily and hourly enslaved by the machine, by the overlooker, and, above all, by the individual bourgeois manufacturer himself. The more openly this despotism proclaims again to be its end and aim, the more petty, the more hateful, and the more embittering it is.

The less the skill and exertion or strength implied in manual labor, in other words, the more modern industry becomes developed, the more is the labor of men superseded by that of women. Differences of age and sex have no longer any distinctive social validity for the working class. All are instruments of labor, more or less expensive to use, according to their age and sex.

No sooner is the exploitation of the laborer by the manufacturer, so far at an end, that he receives his wages in cash, than he is set upon by the other portions of the bourgeoisie, the landlord, the shopkeeper, the pawnbroker, etc.

The lower strata of the middle class — the small tradespeople, shopkeepers and retired tradesmen generally, the handicraftsmen and peasants — all these sink gradually into the proletariat, partly because their diminutive capital does not suffice for the scale on which modern industry is carried on, and is swamped in the competition with the large capitalists, partly because their specialized skill is rendered worthless by new methods of production. Thus the proletariat is recruited from all classes of the population.

With the evolution of the capitalist economy, then, proceeds the evolution of this class which is its social antithesis. Gradually every one is drawn into one side or the other. The economy is divided into the "haves" and the "have-nots," the "masters" and the "slaves," the "bourgeoisie" and the "proletariat," the "owners" and the "workers." The new class acquires its structure gradually. He proceeds:

The proletariat goes through various stages of development. With its birth begins its struggle with the bourgeoisie. At first the contest is carried on by individual laborers, then by the work people of a factory, then by the operatives of one trade, in one locality, against the individual bourgeois who directly exploits them. They direct their attacks not against the bourgeois conditions of production, but against the instruments of production themselves; they destroy imported wares that compete with their labor, they smash to pieces machinery, they set factories ablaze, they seek to restore by force the vanished status of the workman of the Middle Ages.

At this stage the laborers still form an incoherent mass scattered over the whole country, and broken up by their mutual competition. If anywhere they unite to form more compact bodies, this is not yet the consequence of their own active union, but of the union of the bourgeoisie, which class, in order to attain its own political ends, is compelled to set the whole proletariat in motion, and is moreover yet, for a time, able to do so. At this stage, therefore, the proletarians do not fight their enemies, but the enemies of their enemies, the remnants of absolute monarchy, the landowners, the non-industrial bourgeois, the petty bourgeoisie. Thus the whole historical movement is concentrated in the hands of the bourgeoisie, every victory so obtained is a victory for the bourgeoisie.

But with the development of industry the proletariat not only increases in number; it becomes concentrated in greater masses; its strength grows; and it feels that strength more. The various interests and conditions of life within the ranks of the proletariat are more and more equalized, in proportion as machinery obliterates all distinctions of labor, and nearly everywhere reduces wages to the same low level. The growing competition among the bourgeois, and the resulting commercial crises, make the wages of the workers even more fluctuating. The unceasing improvement of machinery, ever more rapidly developing, makes their livelihood more and more precarious; the collisions between individual workmen and individual bourgeois take more and more the character of collisions between two classes. Thereupon the workers begin to form combinations (trades' unions) against the bourgeois; they club together in order to keep up the rate of wages; they found permanent associations in order to make provision beforehand for these occasional revolts. Here and there the contest breaks out into riots.

Now and then the workers are victorious, but only for a time. The real fruit of their battle lies not in the immediate result but in the ever-expanding union of workers. This union is helped on by the improved means of communication that are created by modern industry, and that places the workers of different localities in contact with one another. It was just this contact that was needed to centralize the numerous local struggles, all of the same character, into one national struggle between classes. But every class struggle is a political struggle. And that union, to attain which the burghers of the Middle Ages with their miserable highways required centuries, the modern proletarians, thanks to railways, achieve in a few years.

This organization of the proletarians into a class, and consequently into a political party, is continually being upset again by the competition between the workers themselves. But it ever rises up again, stronger, firmer, mightier. It compels legislative recognition of particular interests of the workers by taking advantage of the divisions among the bourgeoisie itself. Thus the ten hours' bill in England was carried.

Altogether collisions between the classes of the old society further, in many ways, the course of development of the proletariat. The bourgeoisie finds itself involved in a constant battle. At first with the aristocracy; later on, with those portions of the bourgeoisie itself whose interests have become antagonistic to the progress of industry; at all times, with the bourgeoisie of foreign countries. In all these battles it sees itself compelled to appeal to the proletariat, to ask for its help, and thus, to drag it into the political arena. The bourgeoisie itself, therefore, supplies the proletariat with its own elements of political and general education; in other words, it furnishes the proletariat with weapons for fighting the bourgeoisie.

Further, as we have already seen, entire sections of the ruling classes are, by the advance of industry, precipitated into the proletariat, or are at least threatened in their conditions of existence. These also supply the proletariat with fresh elements of enlightenment and progress.

Finally, in times when the class struggle nears the decisive hour, the process of dissolution going on within the ruling class — in fact, within the whole range of an old society — assumes such a violent, glaring character that a small section of the ruling class cuts itself adrift and joins the revolutionary class, the class that holds the future in its hands. Just as, therefore, at an earlier period, a section of the nobility went over to the bourgeoisie, so now a portion of the bourgeoisie goes over to the proletariat, and in particular, a portion of the bourgeois ideologists, who have raised themselves to the level of comprehending theoretically the historical movements as a whole.

The bourgeois have driven the feudal society off the field. They have created the modern world. Their creation is getting out of hand. Among other things it is generating an opposition class which is slowly organizing itself for large-scale revolt.

Of all the classes that stand face to face with the bourgeoisie today the proletariat alone is a really revolutionary class. The other classes decay and finally disappear in the face of modern industry; the proletariat is its special and essential product.

The lower middle class, the small manufacturer, the shopkeeper, the artisan, the peasant, all these fight against the bourgeoisie, to save from extinction their existence as fractions of the middle class. They are therefore not revolutionary, but conservative. Nay, more; they are reactionary for they try to roll back the wheel of history. If by chance they are revolutionary, they are so only in view of their impending transfer into the proletariat; they thus defend not their present, but their future interests; they desert their own standpoint to place themselves at that of the proletariat.

The "dangerous class," the social scum, that passively rotting mass thrown off by the lowest layers of old society, may, here, be swept into the movement by a proletarian revolution; its conditions of life, however, prepare it far more for the part of a bribed tool of reactionary intrigue.

In the conditions of the proletariat, those of the old society at large are already virtually swamped. The proletarian is without property; his relation to his wife and children has no longer anything in common with the bourgeois family relations; modern industrial labor, modern subjection to capital, the same in England as in France, in America as in Germany, has stripped him of every trace of national character. Law, morality, religion, are to him so many bourgeois prejudices, behind which lurk in ambush just as many bourgeois interests.

All the preceding classes that got the upper hand sought to fortify their already acquired status by subjecting society at large to their conditions of appropriation. The proletarians cannot become masters of the productive forces of society, except by abolishing their own previous mode of appropriation, and thereby also every other previous mode of appropriation. They have nothing of their own to secure and to fortify; their mission is to destroy all previous securities for and insurances of individual property.

All previous historical movements were movements of minorities, or in the interest of minorities. The proletarian movement is the self-conscious independent movement of the immense majority. The proletariat, the lowest stratum of our present society, cannot stir, cannot raise itself up without the whole superincumbent strata of official society being sprung into the air.

When the social revolution occurs, it will involve the whole of society. It must first gather momentum in national movements, then it will spread into an international movement.

Though not in substance, yet in form, the struggle of the proletariat with the bourgeoisie is at first a national struggle. The proletariat of each country must, of course, first of all settle matters with its own bourgeoisie.

In depicting the most general phases of the development of the proletariat, we traced the more or less veiled civil war, raging within existing society, up to the point where that war breaks out into open revolution, and where the violent overthrow of the bourgeoisie, lays the foundations for the sway of the proletariat.

Hitherto every form of society has been based, as we have already seen, on the antagonism of oppressing and oppressed classes. But in order to oppress a class, certain conditions must be assured to it under which it can, at least, continue its slavish existence. The serf, in the period of serfdom, raised himself to membership in the commune, just as the petty bourgeois, under the yoke of feudal absolutism, managed to develop into a bourgeois. The modern laborer, on the contrary, instead of rising with the progress of industry, sinks deeper and deeper below the conditions of existence of his own class. He becomes a pauper, and pauperism develops more rapidly than population and wealth. And here it becomes evident that the bourgeoisie is unfit any longer to be the ruling class in society, and to impose its conditions of existence upon society as an overriding law. It is unfit to rule, because it is incompetent to assure an existence to its slave within his slavery, because it cannot help letting him sink into such a state that it has to feed him, instead of being fed by him. Society can no longer live under this bourgeoisie; in other words, its existence is no longer compatible with society.

The essential condition for the existence, and for the sway of the bourgeois class, is the formation and augmentation of capital; the condition for capital is wage labor. Wage labor rests exclusively on competition between the laborers. The advance of industry, whose involuntary promoter is the bourgeoisie, replaces the isolation of the laborers, due to competition, by their involuntary combination, due to association. The development of modern industry, therefore, cuts from under its feet the very foundation on which the bourgeoisie produces and appropriates products. What the bourgeoisie therefore produces, above all, are its own grave-diggers. Its fall and the victory of the proletariat are equally inevitable.

When the great day arrives, the new order will embody many deep-going reforms. Marx cites ten such proposals:

1. Abolition of property in land and application of all rents of land to public purposes
2. A heavy progressive or graduated income tax
3. Abolition of all right of inheritance
4. Confiscation of the property of all emigrants and rebels
5. Centralization of credit in the hands of the state, by means of a national bank with state capital and an exclusive monopoly
6. Centralization of the means of communication and transport in the hands of the state
7. Extension of factories and instruments of production owned by the state, the bringing into cultivation of waste lands, and the improvement of the soil generally in accordance with a common plan

8. Equal liability of all to labor; establishment of industrial armies, especially for agriculture
9. Combination of agriculture with manufacturing industries; gradual abolition of the distinction between town and country by a more equable distribution of the population over the country
10. Free education for all children in public schools, abolition of children's factory labor in its present form, combination of education with industrial production, etc.

When, in the course of development, class distinctions have disappeared, and all production has been concentrated in the hands of a vast association of the whole nation, the public power will lose its political character. Political power, properly so called, is merely the organized power of one class for oppressing another. If the proletariat during its contest with the bourgeoisie is compelled, by the force of circumstances, to organize itself as a class; if, by means of a revolution, it makes itself the ruling class, and as such sweeps away by force the old conditions of production, then it will, along with these conditions, have swept away the conditions for the existence of class antagonism, and of classes generally, and will thereby have abolished its own supremacy as a class.

In place of the old bourgeois society, with its classes and class antagonisms, we shall have an association in which the free development of each is the condition for the free development of all. Let the ruling classes tremble at a Communistic revolution. The proletarians have nothing to lose but their chains. They have a world to win. Workingmen of all countries, unite!

Reading References. For Marx as philosopher, one cannot do better than consult Sidney Hook's book, *Toward an Understanding of Karl Marx*. It may be supplemented by the same author's paper on "Marxism" in his recent volume, *Reason, Social Myth, and Democracy*. Bertrand Russell's *Freedom versus Organization* is also excellent on Marx as theoretical philosopher. A. D. Lindsay's little book, *Karl Marx's Capital* is well worth the effort required to read it.

For Marx as social critic, one cannot do better than consult

Edmund Wilson's book, *To The Finland Station*. This is one of the finest pieces of historical writing so far published upon the revolutionary movement. Less deftly written, but valuable, is Max Nomad's *Apostles of Revolution*.

The standard biography of Marx is by Franz Mehring. It is long and very detailed. Another, not so exhaustive, by Otto Ruhle, is good reading. A recent short work, *Karl Marx*, by I. Berlin, in the *Home University Library* series, is perhaps the best single item for busy students.

READING QUESTIONS

1. What is "the history of all hitherto existing society"?
2. Name any two pairs of "oppressor" and "oppressed."
3. He speaks of "a series of revolutions in the modes of production and exchange." Name any two.
4. "The bourgeoisie, historically, has played a most revolutionary part." Specify any three items.
5. "They had to burst asunder." What had to? Why?
6. "Modern bourgeois society . . . is like the sorcerer." Wherein?
7. "It has also called into existence the men who are to wield those weapons." What men? What weapons?
8. Mention any three items characterizing the lot of the proletarian in the modern economy.
9. "The proletariat goes through various stages of development." Cite two or three.
10. "The proletariat alone is a really revolutionary class." How so?
11. "They have nothing of their own to secure and fortify." How not? So what?
12. "What the bourgeoisie produces are its own grave-diggers." Elucidate.
13. Be prepared to cite any four of the proposed reforms.
14. And to comment in detail on any two.
15. "The public power will lose its political character." What does Marx mean by this statement? When does he say this event will take place?

16. ". . . and will thereby have abolished its own supremacy as a class." Elucidate.
17. "The free development of each is the free development of all." Elucidate.

5. *CULTURES DECLINE INTO CIVILIZATIONS—FROM OSWALD SPENGLER*

From Marx to Spengler. *The Communist Manifesto* was published by Marx and Engels in 1848. It broached the theory that history discloses a pattern of class struggles moving toward a social revolution which will end the class struggle by ushering in a classless social order based upon a socialist economy. Exactly seventy years later, in 1918, Oswald Spengler published his massive work, *The Decline of the West*. The years between were crowded with events and ideas. These should be recalled to mind in passing from Marx to Spengler.

1. In the first place, the period from 1848 to 1918 was crowded with much lively history. If we recall merely wars and revolutions, the list is imposing. In the year 1848 itself, revolutionary uprisings occurred throughout Europe on an unprecedented scale. The Crimean War and the Indian Mutiny came in the 1850's; the American Civil War, in the 1860's; the Franco-Prussian War and the third French revolution, in the 1870's; a number of colonial and "imperialistic" wars, in the 1880's and 1890's, culminating in the Boer War at the opening of the new century; the Russian-Japanese War and the first Russian revolution, in 1904–1905; an intricate tangle of Balkan wars, in the years preceding 1914; the important Chinese revolution, in 1912; the World War, in 1914; the two Russian revolutions under Kerensky and Lenin, in 1917; and the German revolution in 1918. This list is representative. It is not exhaustive. These wars and revolutions formed an almost unbroken accompaniment to enormous population growth, tremendous economic expansion, vast

and complex political and social reform movements, the rise of organized labor, the formation of overseas empires by European great powers, and much more besides. Consult the table of contents of any good history of the world since 1848. The cultural history of the period is no less intense. The scientific theories of Darwin, Pavlov, Freud, and Einstein fall between Marx and Spengler. The challenging problem literature of modern England, Russia, France, Germany, and the Scandinavias falls between Marx and Spengler. The heated controversies associated with the names of Colenso, Bradlaugh, Huxley, Pasteur, Dreyfus, Pankhurst, Nietzsche, to name only a few, fall between Marx and Spengler. The movements in the arts associated with such persons as Wagner, William Morris, Rodin, Cézanne, Matisse, and others, fall between Marx and Spengler. The tendencies in modern philosophy covered by such terms as *neo-Hegelianism*, *neo-positivism*, *pragmatism*, *creative evolutionism*, *instrumentalism*, *realism*, *anti-intellectualism*, etc., fall between Marx and Spengler.

2. In the second place, the period from 1848 to 1918 was exceedingly rich in historical writing. More and, with a few notable exceptions, greater histories were written during these years than during any comparable period in the past. In Germany the latter half of the historical writings of Leopold von Ranke, the historical writings of Theodor Mommsen, of Heinrich von Treitschke, of Eduard Zeller, of Kuno Fischer, of Adolph Harnack, of Theodor Gomperz, to name only a few, fall between Marx and Spengler. So, also, in France, do the historical writings of Jean Victor Duruy, Ernest Renan, Hippolyte Taine, and others. In England the historical writings of Macaulay, Froude, Stubbs, Green, Maine, Gardiner, Lecky, Seeley, Creighton, Acton, Maitland, the Trevelyans, fall within the same period; as, also, in the United States, do the works of John Lothrop Motley, of Francis

Parkman, of John Fiske, of James Ford Rhodes, Alfred Mahan, Henry Adams, and others. The point of listing these names — no more than a selection — is to indicate that a philosophy of history formulated during or at the close of this period had to take account of a vastly increased amount of sheer data. The inviting simplicity presented by the picture of world history between Augustine and Hegel is gone. The man who proposes to discourse on these matters now, must be prepared to take account of a greater number and a larger range of facts than confronted his predecessors in other centuries.

3. In the third place, the period from 1848 to 1918 was prolific in theories or philosophies of history. In England, Carlyle's "great man" theory carried over from a previous generation. It was followed by the hypothesis of geographic determinism and the central role of intellectual progress, in the writings of H. T. Buckle. Buckle was followed by Walter Bagehot, whose *Physics and Politics* proposed an application to human history of the categories applied to natural history by Darwin. On the continent philosophies of history were set forth by Hippolyte Taine, by Friedrich Nietzsche, by Anatole France, by Benedetto Croce, by Vilfredo Pareto, and many others. And mention should be made, in the United States, of the interesting and suggestive theory advanced by Henry Adams in his two papers, "The Tendency of History" and "The Rule of Phase Applied to History,"s and illustrated in his two books, *Mont-Saint-Michel and Chartres* and *The Education of Henry Adams*.

No matter who is read, following Augustine, Kant, Hegel, and Marx, the facts which comprise the history of the world since 1848 would have to be brought to mind. The problem of a philosophy of history remains what it has always been: an hypothesis in the light of which to interpret the events. But, as already noted, the number and range of events known is greater, and the tempo of reflection upon them has been stepped up. In selecting Spengler with whom to close this set of five, I do not wish to suggest that valuable alternatives are lacking. Spengler, in our own day, is worth reading, in the wake of Augustine and Kant and Hegel and Marx. But so, too, are several others, particularly Benedetto Croce, Flinders Petrie, Henry Adams, Vilfredo Pareto, Pitrim Sorokin, and Arnold Toynbee. If science has been the greatest fertilizer of modern philosophy, history runs it a close second.

Biographical Note. Oswald Spengler was born in Germany in 1880 and died in 1936, at the age of fifty-six. He was educated in the universities at Halle, Munich, and Berlin. He studied mathematics and philosophy particularly, we are told, but, like Francis Bacon, seems to have taken all knowledge for his field. After teaching for seven years in the secondary schools of Germany, he retired to do private tutoring and to write his books. His one great work, *The Decline of the West*, was published, Volume One in 1918 and Volume Two in 1922. Over a hundred thousand copies were sold in Germany in a few years. The *Decline* was followed by two small volumes, *Man and Technics* and *The Hour of Decision*, in which the author formulates a philosophy of life and a call to action, based upon the premise that the argument of the large treatise is substantially correct.

The Argument of the Citations. Spengler begins with the usual questions: "Is there a logic of history? Is there, beyond all the casual and incalculable elements of the separate events, something that we may call a structure of historic humanity? Does world history present certain grand traits?" The first step toward an answer to this question is the critique of what he calls the "ancient-medieval-modern" scheme of history. Reasons for rejecting this "Ptolemaic" view of history. In place of it, the author proposes his

"Copernican" view, reminding us of an earlier "Copernican revolution" in philosophy. Granted the Copernican hypothesis in history, he pauses to emphasize the fact that analogy thereby becomes fundamental in historical thinking. The essence of Spengler's Copernican revolution in historiography is the distinction between a culture and a civilization, and the claim that history reveals many cultures maturing and declining into civilizations. The culture of the West, declining into the civilization of the West, is a case in point. The book is to tell the story of this decline, once the general theory has been established. One of the characterizing features of a culture degenerating into a civilization is the emergence of "world cities" and their contributary "provinces." Our own period is then given some attention. Finally, the futility and fate of philosophizing, in our own period, are pointed out. *Sic transit gloria mundi.*

Is there a logic of history? Is there, beyond all the casual and incalculable elements of the separate events, something that we may call a structure of historic humanity? Does world history present certain grand traits? And if so, what are the limits to which reasoning from such premises may be pushed?

The above quotation shows at once that Spengler is proposing the same question as St. Augustine, Kant, Hegel, Marx. Is there a logic of history? If so, what is it? Before presenting his own views to the reader, the author pauses to repudiate the usual textbook division of history into ancient, medieval, and modern. He calls this the *Ptolemaic* view of history, likening it to Ptolemaic astronomy according to which our earth was the center of the universe. His criticisms should be noted.

What is world history? An ordered presentation of the past, no doubt. Everyone, if asked, would say that he knew "the form" of history, quite clearly and definitely. He would be under an illusion.

The illusion is there because no one has seriously reflected upon the question of the form of world history, still less conceived any doubts as to his knowledge of it. In fact, the common notion of world history is an unproved and subjective affair handed down from generation to generation, and badly in need of a little of that skepticism which, from Galileo onward, has regulated and deepened our ideas of nature.

Thanks to the subdivision of history into "ancient," "medieval," and "modern" — an incredibly jejune and meaningless scheme, which has, however, entirely dominated our historical thinking — we have failed to perceive the true position in the general history of mankind of the little part world that has developed in Western Europe from the time of the Roman Empire, to judge of its relative importance, and to estimate its direction.

The ages that are to come will find it difficult to believe that such a scheme, with its simple rectilinear progression and its meaningless proportions, becoming more preposterous with each century, incapable of bringing into itself the new fields of history as they come into the light of our knowledge, was never wholeheartedly attacked.

The criticisms that it has long been the fashion for historical students to level at this scheme mean nothing. They have only obliterated the scheme without substituting any other for it. To toy with such phrases as "the Greek middle ages" or "Germanic antiquity" does not help us to form a clear picture in which China and Mexico, the empire of Axum and that of the Sassanids have their proper places. And the expedient of shifting the initial point of "modern history" from the Crusades to the Renaissance, or from the Renaissance to the French Revolution, only goes to show that the scheme is still regarded as unshakably sound.

It is not only that the ancient-medieval-modern scheme circumscribes the area of history. What is worse, it rigs the stage. Western Europe is treated as a steady pole, and great histories of millenial duration and mighty far-away cultures are made to revolve around this pole in all modesty. We select a single patch of ground, for no better reason, it seems, than because we live on it, and make it the center of the historical system. From it all the events of history receive their light, from it their importance is judged. But this phantom "world history," which a breath of skepticism would dissipate, is acted out only in our own West European conceit.

We have to thank this conceit of ours for the immense optical illusion whereby distant histories, such as those of China and Egypt, are made to shrink to mere episodes while in the neighborhoods of our own position the decades since Luther or Napoleon loom large as Brocken specters.

For the cultures of the West, it is evident that Athens, Florence, or Paris, is more important than Lo-Yang or Pataliputra. But is it permissible to found a scheme of world history on such estimates? The Chinese historian is equally entitled to frame a world history in which Caesar, the Crusades, the Renaissance, Frederick the Great are passed over in silence as insignificant. From the morphological point of view, why should our eighteenth century be more important than any of the sixty centuries that preceded it? Is it not ridiculous to oppose a "modern" history of a few centuries to an "ancient" history which covers as many millennia? This is no exaggeration. Do we not, for the sake of keeping the hoary scheme of ancient-medieval-modern, dispose of Egypt and Babylon as a prelude to classical history? Do we not relegate the vast cultures of India and China to footnotes? Do we not entirely ignore the great American cultures?

As mentioned above, this ancient-medieval-modern scheme is to be repudiated as Ptolemaic and replaced by a Copernican view of history.

The most appropriate designation for this ancient-medieval-modern scheme of history, in which great cultures are made to follow orbits around us, is the Ptolemaic system of history. The system that is put forward in this book, in place of it, I regard as the Copernican system in the historical sphere. It admits no privileged position to the classical culture, or the Western culture, as against the cultures of India, Babylon, China, Egypt, the Arabs, Mexico. Each of these non-Western cultures, being separate worlds, count, in point of mass for just as much in the general picture of history as the classical culture, while they frequently surpass it in point of spiritual greatness and soaring power.

I see, in place of that empty figment of ancient-medieval-modern, the drama of a number of mighty cultures, each springing from the soil of a mother region; each stamping its material in its own image; each having its own idea, its own passions, its own life, its own will and feeling, its own death. Here indeed are colors, lights, movements, that no eye has yet discovered.

Here cultures, peoples, languages, truths, gods, bloom and age as the oaks and the stone pines. Each culture has its own new possibilities of self-expression, which arise, ripen, decay, and never return. There is not just one sculpture, one painting, one mathematics, one physics, one religion, one morality, one philosophy, but many, each different from the others, each limited in duration, each having its special type of growth and decline. Each grows with the same superb aimlessness as the flowers of the field. I see world history as a picture of endless formations and transformations. The professional historian sees it as a sort of tapeworm industriously adding onto itself one epoch after another.

The substitution of the Copernican for the Ptolemaic view of history effects an unmeasurable widening of horizon. This idea once attained, the rest is easy. To this single idea one can refer all those separate problems of religion, art, philosophy, morals, politics, economics with which the modern mind has busied itself so passionately and so vainly. This idea is one of those truths that have only to be expressed with clarity to become indisputable. It is capable of transforming the world outlook of one who fully understands it. It immensely deepens the world historical picture. By its aid we are enabled to follow the broad lines into the future, a privilege till now permitted only to the physicist.

The Copernican view, then, resolves history into a number of different epochs. Each epoch, it is to be argued, begins as a "culture" and ends as a "civilization." The first step will be to clarify these terms *culture* and *civilization*. Do the epochs have any common characteristics? Does each have a "life" of its own?

Is it possible to find in life a series of stages which must be traversed? For everything organic, the notions of birth, youth, age, lifetime, death, are fundamentals. May not these notions possess, in the realm of history, a meaning which no one has yet extracted? In short, is all history founded upon general biographic archetypes?

At this point Spengler pauses to develop the thought that a history of many different epochs will inevitably develop analogies between one epoch and another. Something in one epoch will be "analogous" to something in another epoch. How reliable is the analogy?

The means whereby to identify dead forms is mathematical law. The means whereby to understand living forms is analogy.

From any technique of analogies we are far distant. It is neither a principle nor a sense of historic necessity, but simple inclination, that governs the choice of the analogies we draw. They throng up without scheme or unities. If they do hit upon something that is apt, it is thanks to luck, more rarely to instinct, never to a principle. No one has hitherto set himself to work out a technique or method for striking upon apt and revealing analogies in the region of world history. Nor has anyone had the slightest inkling that there is here a root, in fact the only root, from which can come a broad solution of the problems of history.

Insofar as they lay bare the structure of history, analogies might be a blessing to historical thought. Their technique, developing under the influence of a comprehensive idea, might eventuate in inevitable conclusions and logical mastery. But, as hitherto understood and practiced, they have been a curse, for they have enabled historians to follow their own tastes, instead of realizing that their first task was the symbolism of history and its analogies. Superficial in many cases, these analogies are worse than superficial in others, while occasionally they are bizarre to the point of perversity.

Napoleon has hardly ever been discussed without a side glance at Caesar and Alexander. Napoleon himself conceived of his situation as akin to Charlemagne's. The French Revolutionary Convention spoke of Carthage when it meant England, and the Jacobins styled themselves Romans. Cecil Rhodes, the organizer of British South Africa, felt himself akin to the Emperor Hadrian. And so on, through an indefinitely long list.

I have not hitherto found anyone who has carefully considered the morphological relationship that binds together the expression forms of all branches of a single culture; who has, e.g., gone beyond politics to grasp the ultimate and fundamental ideas in mathematics, ornamentation, architecture, philosophy, literature, craftsmanship, etc., within a single culture.

Who among historians realizes that there are deep uniformities between the differential calculus and the dynastic principle of politics in the age of Louis XIV; between the classical city state and Euclidean geometry; between the space perspective of Western oil painting and the conquest of space by railroad; between telephone and long-range weapon; between contrapuntal music and credit economics? Yet, viewed from this morphological standpoint, such things as the Egyptian administrative system, the classical coinage, analytical geometry, the cheque, the Suez Canal, the book printing of the Chinese, the Prussian army, the Roman road engineering, can be made uniformly understandable as symbols.

The historian, then, despite risks, must be prepared to make large use of analogies. He will be interested in noting what things in epoch A are "contemporary" with things in epoch B. The word *contemporary* in Spengler's use means happening in one epoch at relatively the same point as in another epoch. Two events can be contemporary, in this sense, even if the epochs in question are several centuries apart. However, the whole point of working up these analogies is to throw light on the common characteristics of an epoch. Now, an epoch, it was said, begins as a culture and ends as a civilization. Accordingly, we turn to these two key terms.

If we are to discover the form in which the destiny of Western culture will be accomplished, we must first be clear as to what a culture is. What are its relations to visible history? How far may we point to peoples, tongues and epochs, battles and ideas, states and goods, arts and crafts, sciences, laws, economic types, great men, great events, world ideas, as symbols of a culture?

Every culture has its own civilization. In this book, these two words are used in a periodic sense, to express an organic succession. The civilization is the destiny of the culture. In this principle we obtain the viewpoint from which the problems of historical morphology become capable of solution. Civilizations are the most external and artificial states of which a species of developed humanity is capable. Civilizations are a conclusion, death following upon life, rigidity following expansion. They are an end, irrevocable, yet, by an inward necessity reached again and again. They consist in a progressive taking-down of forms that have become dead.

To the culture belongs gymnastics, the joust, the tournament. To the civilization belongs sport. Art itself bcomes a sport, to be played before a highly intelligent audience of connoisseurs or buyers; and this, whether the feat consist in mastering absurd instrumental tone masses and taking harmonic fences, or in some *tour de force* of coloring. Then a new fact philosophy appears, which can spare only a smile for metaphysical speculations; and a new literature that is a necessity for the megalopolitan palate and nerves but is both unintelligible and ugly to the provincial.

What is the hallmark of a politic of civilization, in contrast to a politic of culture? It is, for the classical and the West European, money. The money spirit penetrates the historical forms of the people's existence. Though the forms persist, the great political parties cease to be more than reputed centers of decision. The decisions in fact lie elsewhere. A small number of superior heads, whose names are often little known, settle everything, while below them are the great mass of second-rate politicians selected through a franchise to keep alive the illusion of popular self-determination.

Imperialism is to be taken as the typical symbol of passing away. Imperialism is civilization unadulterated. The energy of culture-man is directed inwards; of civilization-man, outwards. In this form the destiny of the West is now set. Thus I see in Cecil Rhodes a man of the age. He stands for the political style of a far-ranging future. His phrase "expansion is everything" is the Napoleonic reassertion of the tendency of every civilization that has fully ripened. It is not a matter of choice. The expansive tendency is a doom which grips man of the world-city stage.

Rhodes is to be regarded as the precursor of a Western type of

Caesar whose day is to come, though yet distant. He stands midway between Napoleon and the force-men of the next centuries. It was only before his maps that he could fall into a sort of poetic trance, this son of a parson who, sent out to South Africa without means, made a gigantic fortune and employed it as the engine of political aims.

His idea of a trans-African railway from Cape to Cairo, his project of a South African empire, his hold on the hard metal souls of the mining magnates, his capital planned as the future residence of an all-powerful statesman who yet stood in no definite relation to the state, his wars, his diplomatic deals, his road systems, his syndicates, his armies, all this is the prelude of a future which is still in store for us and with which the history of Western man will be definitely closed.

The civilization of an epoch crystallizes always into the "world city" and "the province": megalopolis and its surrounding territory. What about these two units of social organization?

World city and province, the two basic ideas of every civilization, bring up a wholly new form-problem of history, the very problem that we are living through today with hardly any notion of its immensity. In place of a people true to a type, born of the soil and grown on the soil, there is a new sort of nomad, cohering unstably in fluid masses, the parasitical city dweller, traditionless, utterly matter-of-fact, without religion, clever, unfruitful, contemptuous of the countryman. This is a great stride toward the end. What does it signify? France and England have already taken the step. Germany is beginning to do so. After Syracuse, Athens, Alexandria, comes Rome. After Madrid, Paris, London, come Berlin and New York. It is the destiny of whole regions that lie outside the circle of one of these great cities to become "provinces."

The world city means cosmopolitanism in place of home, matter-of-fact coldness in place of reverence for tradition, scientific irreligion in place of the older religion of the heart, society in place of the state, "natural" in place of hard-earned rights. It was in the conception of money, entirely disconnected from the notion of the fruitful earth, that the Romans had the advantage over the Greeks. Thereafter any high ideal of life becomes largely a question of money. Unlike the Greek stoicism, Roman stoicism presupposes a private income. Unlike the social and moral ideals of the eighteenth century, the ideals of the twentieth century are matters for millionaires. To the world city belongs not a folk, but a mass.

The uncomprehending hostility of the mass of the world city to all the traditions of the culture — nobility, church, privilege, dynasties, conventions in art, limits of knowledge — the keen and cold intelligence that confounds the wisdom of the peasant, the new-fashioned naturalism in sex and society, the reappearance of *panem et circenses* in the form of wage disputes and large-scale organized spectator sports, all these things betoken the definite closing down of the culture and the setting in of the civilization, anti-provincial, late, futureless, but inevitable.

At this level civilizations enter upon a stage of depopulation. The whole pyramid of culture vanishes. It crumbles from the summit, first the world cities, then the provinces, and finally the land itself whose best blood has incontinently poured into the towns. At last only the primitive blood remains alive, but robbed of its strongest and most promising elements. The residue is Fellah type.

Thus far by way of preliminary: Has history a logic? Repudiation of the Ptolemaic theory of history. Proposal of the Copernican theory. History deals with great epochs. Hence analogy as the historical method. Epochs begin as cultures and end as civilizations. The world city and its province characterize the end of an epoch. With these general ideas in mind Spengler turns to the particular subject of his book: the history of our own times or, as he calls it, *The Decline of the West*. We live at the end of an epoch. We live in a civilization, not in a culture. And his massive book is an inductive survey of the evidence for this claim. He says:

Our narrow task, then, is to determine, from such a survey of world history, the state of Western Europe and America for the epoch, 1800–2000; to establish the chronological position of this period in the cultural history of the West; to indicate its significance as a chapter that is found in the story of every culture; and to make clear the meaning of its political, artistic, intellectual, and social expression forms.

Every culture is a four-act drama with an ascending movement of religion, aristocracy, and art, and a descending movement of irreligion, democracy, socialism, and the great city. The culture of the West, whose "decline" is referred to in the title of this book, originated in that feudal system of lord and serf which Roman conquest left like a network over Europe. Its basis is a stolid peasantry, bearing on its back the economic life of the world.

Considered in the spirit of analogy the period appears as chronologically parallel to the epoch we call *Hellenism;* and its present culmination, marked by the World War, corresponds to the transition from the Hellenistic to the Roman age. Rome, with its rigorous realism, uninspired, barbaric, disciplined, practical, will always give us, working as we must by analogies, the key to our own future.

Long ago we should have seen in the classical culture a development which is the counterpart of our own, differing indeed in surface detail, but similar as regards the power driving the great organism toward its end. We might have established the correspondence, item by item, from the Trojan War and the Crusades, Homer and the *Nibelungenlied*, through Doric and Gothic, Dionysian and Renaissance, Polycletus and Bach, Athens and Paris, Aristotle and Kant, Alexander and Napoleon, to the world city and imperialism.

The transition from culture to civilization was accomplished for the classical world in the fourth century A.D.; for the Western world in the nineteenth century. From these periods onwards, the great decisions take place. And they take place in three or four world cities that have absorbed into themselves the whole content of history.

Let it be realized, then, that the nineteenth and twentieth centuries, hitherto looked upon as an ascending straight line of world history, are in reality a stage of life which may be observed in every culture that has ripened to its limit. Let it be realized, then, that the future of the West is not a limitless tending upwards and onwards toward our present ideals, but a single phenomenon of history, strictly limited and defined as to form and duration, covering a few centuries and, in essentials, calculated from available precedents.

He who does not understand that this outcome is obligatory, that our choice is between willing this and willing nothing, between cleaving to this destiny or despairing of the future; he who cannot feel that there is grandeur in the achievements of powerful intelligence, in the energy and discipline of metal-hard natures, in battles fought with the coldest and abstractest means; he who is obsessed with the ideals of past ages, must forego all desire to comprehend history, to live through history, or to make history.

So much, then, for a few of the analogies by means of which Spengler locates the West and the period of its decline. He turns to some of the characteristic phenomena of the period. Here we can only quote a few scattered items from an enormous mass comprising two stout volumes. For example, the press:

A more appalling caricature of freedom cannot be imagined. There is today no need to impose military service on people. Whip their souls with articles, telegrams, pictures, till they clamor for weapons and force their leaders into a conflict. In preparation for the World War the press of whole countries was brought financially under the control of a few world cities, and the peoples belonging to them reduced to an unqualified intellectual slavery.

As for the modern press, the sentimentalist may beam with contentment when it is constitutionally "free." But the realist merely asks at whose disposal it is. For the multitude, that is true which it continually reads and hears. Its "truth" is a product of the press. What the press wills is true. Three weeks of press work, and the truth is acknowledged by everybody. The press and the news service keep whole peoples and continents under a deafening drumfire of theses, catchwords, standpoints, scenes, feelings.

Or the modern omnipresent machine:

These machines become less and less human; more ascetic, mystic, esoteric. They weave over the earth an infinite web of subtle forces, currents, tensions. Their bodies become ever more immaterial, ever less noisy. The wheels, rollers, levers, are vocal no more. All that matters draws itself into the interior. The center of this artificial and complicated realm is the engineer, the priest of the machine.

Or the modern masses:

. . . the fluid megalopolitan populace; the newspaper readers of our time; the "educated" who makes a cult of intellectual mediocrity and a church of advertisement; the man of the theaters and places of amusement, of sport and "best sellers," of expressionism, the movies, theosophy, nigger dances, poker, and racing. The Roman *panem et circenses* we have in our wage disputes and football games.

Such "men" constitute the "masses." The masses reject the matured culture of our epoch. The mass is formless. It persecutes with hatred all distinctions of rank, the orderliness of tradition, of property, of knowledge. They are the new nomads of cosmopolis. They recognize no past and possess no future. They are the end.

Or modern art:

It is all irretrievably over with the arts of the West. What is practiced as art today is impotence and falsehood: a faked music, filled with artificial noisiness of massed instruments; a faked painting, full of idiotic, exotic, and show-card effects; a lying plastic that steals from Assyria, Egypt, Mexico, indifferently. For Western people there can no longer be any question of great painting or great music. We are today playing out a tedious game with dead forms to keep up the illusion of a living art.

Coming, at last, to philosophy, the story makes very unpalatable reading. To begin with, Herr Spengler dislikes and distrusts the "thinker" type:

There are born destiny men and causality men. A whole world separates the man born to prosper, to rule, to fight, to dare, to organize, from the man who is destined by the power of his mind or the defect of his blood to be an intellectual — the saint, the priest, the scholar, the idealist. The eye for men and situations, the belief in his star, things which every born man of action possesses, are something wholly different from the belief in the "correctness of a standpoint," and are denied to the critical, meditative man. Even the footfall of the fact man sounds different from that of the thinker.

With that as a beginning, it is not hard to see what is likely to follow: Modern philosophers are nobodies and busybodies:

It still remains to consider the relation of a morphology of world history to philosophy. For me the test to be applied to a thinker is his eye for the great facts of his own time. Only this can settle whether he is merely a clever architect of systems and principles, versed in definitions and analyses, or one in whom the soul of his time speaks in his works and intuitions.

A philosopher who cannot grasp and command actuality will never be of the first rank. The early Greek philosophers were merchants and politicians *en grande*. The desire to put his political ideas into practice nearly cost Plato his life. Confucius was several times a minister of state. Pythagoras organized an important political movement. Goethe, besides being an executive minister, was interested in the Suez and Panama Canals and their effects upon the economy of the world. Hobbes was one of the originators of a plan for winning South America for England. Leibnitz, without doubt the greatest intellect in Western philosophy, founder of the differential calculus and the analysis situs, conceived or cooperated in a number of major political schemes.

Turning from men of this world to the "philosophers" of today, one is dismayed and ashamed. What they do not possess is real standing in actual life. Their personalities are poor. Their political and practical outlook are commonplace. Not one of them has intervened effectively in politics, in the development of modern techniques, in matters of communication, in economics, or in any other big actuality, with a single act or a single compelling idea. Not one of them counts in mathematics, in physics, in politics. Why is it that the mere idea of calling upon one of them to prove his intellectual eminence in government, diplomacy, large-scale organization, the direction of any big colonial or commercial or transport concern, is enough to evoke our pity? This insufficiency indicates, not that they possess profundity but that they lack weight. I look around in vain for an instance in which a modern "philosopher" has made a name by even one deep or far-seeing pronouncement on an important question of the day. I see nothing but provincial opinions of the same kind as any one else's. Whenever I take up a work by a modern philosopher I find myself asking: Has he any idea of the actualities of world politics, world-city problems, capitalism, the future of the state, the relation of techniques to the course of civilization, Russia, science? Goethe would have understood all this and reveled in it. There is not one living philosopher capable of taking it in. This sense for actualities is, of course, not the same thing as the content of a philosophy; but, I repeat, it is an infallible symptom of its necessity, fruitfulness and importance.

We must allow ourselves no illusions as to the gravity of this negative result. We have lost sight of the final significance of effective philosophizing. We have descended from the perspective of the bird to that of the frog. We confuse philosophy with preaching, with agitation, with novel-writing, with lecture-room jargon. It were better to become a colonist or an engineer, to do something that is real and true, than to chew over once more the old dried-up themes under cover of some "new wave of philosophic thought"; better to construct an aero-engine than a new theory of apperception that is not wanted. It is indeed a poor life's work to restate once more the views of a hundred predecessors on the will or on the psychophysical parallelism. This may be a profession. It is emphatically not a philosophy. A doctrine that does not attack and affect the life of one's period is no doctrine, and had better not be taught.

To me, the depths and refinement of mathematical and physical theories are a joy. By comparison, the aesthete and the physiologist are fumblers. I would sooner have the fine mind-begotten forms of a fast steamer, a steel structure, a precision lathe, the subtlety and elegance of many chemical and optical processes, than all the pickings and stealings of present-day "arts and crafts."

This is a situation that regularly repeats itself at a certain historical level. I maintain that today many an inventor, many a diplomat, many a financier, is a sounder philosopher than all those who practice the dull craft of experimental psychology. It would have been absurd in a Roman of intellectual eminence, who might, as consul or praetor, have led armies, organized provinces, built cities and roads, to want to hatch out some new variant of post-Platonic philosophy at Athens. Consequently no one did so. It was not in harmony with the tendency of the age. Therefore it attracted only third-class men of the kind that always advances as far as the Zeitgeist of the day before yesterday.

I prefer one Roman aqueduct to all the Roman temples and statues. I love the Colosseum and the giant vault of the Palatine, for they display the real Rome and the grand practical sense of her engineers. It was not for nothing, that the genuine Roman despised the "artist" and the "philosopher." The time for art and philosophy had passed; they were exhausted, used up, superfluous, and his instinct for the realities of life told him so. One Roman law weighed more than all the lyrics and school metaphysics of the time put together.

Modern philosophy, like modern art, is played out. With Kant and Schopenhauer, the curtain went down for the last time. What remains is merely the possibility of becoming competent and understanding historians of philosophy.

Systematic philosophy closed with the end of the eighteenth century. Kant put its utmost possibilities in forms that are grand and, for the Western soul, final. He is followed, as Plato and Aristotle were followed, by a specifically megalopolitan philosophy that is not speculative, but practical, irreligious, social-moral. This philosophy begins in the West with Schopenhauer. He was the first to make the will-to-live a central thought. It is the same will-to-live that was Schopenhauer-wise denied in *Tristan* and Darwin-wise asserted in *Siegfried;* that led Marx to an economic and Darwin to a biological hypothesis which have together subtly transformed the world-outlook of the Western megalopolis; and that produced a series of tragedies from Hebbel to Ibsen and Hardy.

It has embraced, therefore, all the possibilities of a philosophy, and has exhausted them.

We have not chosen our time. We cannot help it if we are born in the early winter of a civilization, instead of in the golden summer of a culture. Everything depends upon seeing our own position clearly; on realizing that we may lie to ourselves about it but cannot evade it. He who does not acknowledge this ceases to be counted among the men of his generation.

One must begin, therefore, by asking what today is possible and what is not. In the case of a genuine adept this question is answered in advance by a kind of instinct.

Systematic philosophy, then, lies far behind us, and ethical philosophy has been wound up. But a third possibility, corresponding to the classical skepticism, still remains. And it can be brought to light by the hitherto unknown methods of historical morphology. Classical skepticism was ahistoric. Our skepticism, a symbol of the autumn of spirituality, is historical. Its solutions are got by treating everything as relative, as historical. Classical skepticism is the negation of philosophy, declaring it to be useless. Our skepticism, on the contrary, regards the history of philosophy as, in the last resort, philosophy's gravest theme. This is *skepsis* in the true sense; for, where classical skepticism is led to renounce absolute standpoints by contempt for the past, we are led to do so by comprehension of the past.

It is our task to sketch out this unphilosophical philosophy — the last that the West will know. Skepticism is the expression of a pure civilization, and it dissipates the world picture of the culture that has gone before. For us, its success will lie in resolving all the older problems into one, the historical. With that, the claim of higher thought to possess general and eternal truths falls to the ground. Truths are truths only in relation to a particular mankind. Thus, my own philosophy is able to express and reflect only the Western mind, and that mind only in its present civilized phase by which its conception of the world, its practical range, and its sphere of effect, are specified.

Reading References. The best single account of Spengler and his *Decline* is to be found in Will Durant's book *Adven-*

tures in Genius. This book was reissued under the title *Great Men of Literature.* The Spengler essay, fifty pages or so, is good. A book on Spengler's interpretation of history, *Civilization or Civilizations*, has been written by E. H. Goddard and P. A. Gibbons. A volume of selections from the *Decline*, with introduction and notes by Edwin F. Dakin, has been published under the title *Today and Destiny.* The *Decline* itself is not easy reading. The author's style and his constant stream of esoteric references slow things up considerably. The two short books, *Man and Technics* and *The Hour of Decision* are much less encumbered, and in them, therefore, the author's thought moves more swiftly and vividly.

READING QUESTIONS

1. What is the Ptolemaic view of history?
2. Why is it so named?
3. Give three of Spengler's criticisms of this view.
4. What is the Copernican view of history?
5. Why is it so named?
6. Why is Spengler led to a consideration of analogy in history?
7. Name one or two he suggests.
8. In what sense does he propose to use the word *contemporary?*
9. What distinguishes a culture from its civilization?
10. What is a world city?
11. Name two or three from history.
12. How does Spengler characterize world cities?
13. What, roughly, is the period of the decline in our case?
14. What about the press in our day?
15. Or the machine?
16. Or the masses?
17. Or the fine arts?
18. What is a causality man?
19. Some items in Spengler's appraisal of modern philosophers.
20. "A third possibility . . . still remains." Namely?
21. Can you name one or more contemporary philosophers whose influence, Spengler notwithstanding, strongly affects our time?
22. Give two or more questions you would put to Spengler.

INDEX

"An ode to literature, a satiric[al] ... and, of course, a love story . . . Replete with surpluses of intellect and fancy that define Rushdie's earlier fiction."

—*Boston Sunday Globe*

"THE GROUND BENEATH HER FEET is a triumphant hymn to the transforming power of love, boldly asserting that fate is only a fiction and that you can sometimes strengthen history by speculating on its alternative outcome."

—*The Times*, London

"It's the best thing ever written about rock and roll. It IS rock and roll . . . Comparison to James Joyce's *Ulysses* is inevitable, and earned . . . It's a book of profound affirmation, of indomitable humanity. Of love. A book of greatness."

—*Baltimore Sun*

"Inspired . . . uplifting . . . This book is so rich in wit and erudition, fantasy and wordplay—in sheer playfulness—that it's never less than splendid, impressive, sublime."

—*The Dallas Morning News*

"[A] playful, highly allusive journey through the last 40 years of pop culture . . . A writer of undeniable genius."

—*Publishers Weekly*

Also by Salman Rushdie

FICTION

Grimus
Midnight's Children
Shame
The Satanic Verses
Haroun and the Sea of Stories
East, West
The Moor's Last Sigh

NON-FICTION

The Jaguar Smile
Imaginary Homelands
The Wizard of Oz

SCREENPLAY

Midnight's Children

ANTHOLOGY

Mirrorwork (co-editor)

SALMAN
RUSHDIE

The Ground Beneath Her Feet

PICADOR USA

HENRY HOLT AND COMPANY
NEW YORK

Grateful acknowledgement is made to the following for permission to reprint previously published materials:

"Jailhouse Rock" by Jerry Leiber, Mike Stoller
© 1957 (Renewed) Jerry Leiber Music, Mike Stoller Music;
All rights reserved; Used by permission.

"What a Wonderful World" by George David Weiss,
Bob Thiele © 1967 (Renewed) Quartet Music, Inc.,
Range Road Music, Abilene Music;
All rights reserved; Used by permission.

"Rubber Ball," words and music by Aaron Schroeder and Anne Orlowski;
Published by Rachel's Own Music and Dandy Dittys; Used by
permission; International Copyright Secured.

"The Great Pretender" by Buck Ram
© 1955 (Renewed) by Panther Music Corporation;
All rights reserved; Used by permission;
International Copyright Secured.

"Orpheus. Eurydice. Hermes," by Rainer Maria Rilke in *Neue Gedichte: New Poems*, trans. Stephen Cohn (Evanston, Ill.: Northwestern University Press). © 1992, 1997 Stephen Cohn;
All rights reserved.

For information on Picador USA Reading Group Guides and titles, as well as ordering, please contact the Trade Marketing department at St. Martin's Press. Phone: 1-800-221-7945 extension 488
Fax: 212-677-7456 E-mail: trademarketing@stmartins.com

ISBN: 0-312-97474-4

First published in the United States by Henry Holt.

First Picador USA Paperback Edition: January 2000

10 9 8 7 6 5 4 3 2 1

FOR MILAN

Set up no stone to his memory.
Just let the rose bloom each year for his sake.
For it is Orpheus. His metamorphosis
into this and that. We should not trouble

about other names. Once and for all
it's Orpheus when there's singing.

—R.M. Rilke, *Sonnets to Orpheus*
translated by M.D. Herter Norton

CONTENTS

CHAPTER ONE

The Keeper of Bees

On St. Valentine's Day, 1989, the last day of her life, the legendary popular singer Vina Apsara woke sobbing from a dream of human sacrifice in which she had been the intended victim. Bare-torsoed men resembling the actor Christopher Plummer had been gripping her by the wrists and ankles. Her body was splayed out, naked and writhing, over a polished stone bearing the graven image of the snake-bird Quetzalcoatl. The open mouth of the plumed serpent surrounded a dark hollow scooped out of the stone, and although her own mouth was stretched wide by her screams the only noise she could hear was the popping of flashbulbs; but before they could slit her throat, before her lifeblood could bubble into that terrible cup, she awoke at noon in the city of Guadalajara, Mexico, in an unfamiliar bed with a half-dead stranger by her side, a naked mestizo male in his early twenties, identified in the interminable press coverage that followed the catastrophe as Raúl Páramo, the playboy heir of a well-known local construction baron, one of whose corporations owned the hotel.

She had been perspiring heavily and the sodden bed-sheets stank of the meaningless misery of the nocturnal encounter. Raúl Páramo was unconscious, white-lipped, and his body was galvanized, every few moments, by spasms which Vina recognized as being identical to her own dream writhings. After a few moments he began to make frightful noises deep in his windpipe, as if someone were slitting his throat, as if his blood were flowing out through the scarlet smile of an invisible wound into a phantom goblet. Vina, panicking, leapt from the bed, snatched up her clothes, the leather pants and gold-sequinned bustier in which she had made her final exit, the night before, from the stage of the city's convention centre. Contemptuously, despairingly, she had surrendered herself to this nobody, this boy less than half her age, she had selected him more or less at random from the backstage throng, the lounge lizards, the slick, flower-bearing suitors, the industrial magnates, the aristo-trash, the drug underlords, the tequila princes, all with limousines and champagne and cocaine and maybe even diamonds to bestow upon the evening's star.

The man had begun to introduce himself, to preen and fawn, but she didn't want to know his name or the size of his bank balance. She had picked him like a flower and now she wanted him between her teeth, she had ordered him like a take-home meal and now she alarmed him by the ferocity of her appetites, because she began to feast upon him the moment the door of the limo was closed, before the chauffeur had time to raise the partition that gave the passengers their privacy. Afterwards he, the chauffeur, spoke with reverence of her naked body, while the newspapermen plied him with tequila he whispered about her swarming and predatory nudity as if it were a miracle, who'd have thought she was way the wrong side of forty, I guess somebody upstairs wanted to keep her just the way she was. I would have done anything for such a woman, the chauffeur moaned, I would have driven at two hundred kilometres per hour for her if it were speed she wanted, I would have crashed into a concrete wall for her if it had been her desire to die.

Only when she lurched into the eleventh-floor corridor of the hotel, half dressed and confused, stumbling over the unclaimed newspapers, whose headlines about French nuclear tests in the Pacific and political unrest in the southern province of Chiapas smudged the bare soles of her feet with their shrieking ink, only then did she understand that the suite of rooms she had abandoned was her own, she had slammed the door and didn't have the key, and it was lucky for her in that moment of vulnerability that the person she bumped into was me, Mr. Umeed Merchant, photographer, a.k.a. "Rai," her so to speak chum ever since the old days in Bombay and the only shutterbug within one thousand and one miles who would not dream of photographing her in such delicious and scandalous disarray, her whole self momentarily out of focus and worst of all looking her age, the only image-stealer who would never have stolen from her that frayed and hunted look, that bleary and unarguably bag-eyed helplessness, her tangled fountain of wiry dyed red hair quivering above her head in a woodpeckerish topknot, her lovely mouth trembling and uncertain, with the tiny fjords of the pitiless years deepening at the edges of her lips, the very archetype of the wild rock goddess halfway down the road to desolation and ruin. She had decided to become a redhead for this tour because at the age of forty-four she was making a new start, a solo career without Him, for the first time in years she was on the road without Ormus, so it wasn't really surprising that she was disoriented and off balance most of the time. And lonely. It has to be admitted. Public life or private life, makes no difference, that's the truth: when she wasn't with him, it didn't matter who she was with, she was always alone.

Disorientation: loss of the East. And of Ormus Cama, her sun.

And it wasn't just dumb luck, her bumping into me. I was always there for her. Always looking out for her, always waiting for her call. If she'd wanted it, there could have been dozens of us, hundreds, thousands. But I believe there was only me. And the last time she called for help, I couldn't give it, and she died. She ended in the middle of the story of her life, she was an unfinished song abandoned at the bridge, deprived of the right to follow her life's verses to their final, fulfilling rhyme.

TWO HOURS after I rescued her from the unfathomable chasm of her hotel corridor, a helicopter flew us to Tequila, where Don Ángel Cruz, the owner of one of the largest plantations of blue agave cactus and of the celebrated Ángel distillery, a gentleman fabled for the sweet amplitude of his countertenor voice, the great rotunda of his belly and the lavishness of his hospitality, was scheduled to hold a banquet in her honour. Meanwhile, Vina's playboy lover had been taken to hospital, in the grip of drug-induced seizures so extreme that they eventually proved fatal, and for days afterwards, because of what happened to Vina, the world was treated to detailed analyses of the contents of the dead man's bloodstream, his stomach, his intestines, his scrotum, his eye sockets, his appendix, his hair, in fact everything except his brain, which was not thought to contain anything of interest, and had been so thoroughly scrambled by narcotics that nobody could understand his last words, spoken during his final, comatose delirium. Some days later, however, when the information had found its way on to the Internet, a fantasy-fiction wonk hailing from the Castro district of San Francisco and nicknamed <elrond@rivendel.com> explained that Raúl Páramo had been speaking Orcish, the infernal speech devised for the servants of the Dark Lord Sauron by the writer Tolkien: *Ash nazg durbatulûk, ash nazg gimbatul, ash nazg thrakatulûk agh burzum-ishi krimpatul.* After that, rumours of Satanic, or perhaps Sauronic, practices spread unstoppably across the Web. The idea was put about that the mestizo lover had been a devil worshipper, a blood servant of the Underworld, and had given Vina Apsara a priceless but malignant ring, which had caused the subsequent catastrophe and dragged her down to Hell. But by then Vina was already passing into myth, becoming a vessel into which any moron could pour his stupidities, or let us say a mirror of the culture, and we can best understand the nature of this culture if we say that it found its truest mirror in a corpse.

One ring to rule them all, one ring to find them, one ring to bring them all and in the darkness bind them. I sat next to Vina Apsara in the helicopter to Tequila, and I saw no ring on her finger, except for the talismanic moonstone she always wore, her link to Ormus Cama, her reminder of his love.

She had sent her entourage by road, selecting me as her only aerial companion, "of all of you bastards he's the only one I can trust," she'd snarled. They had set off an hour ahead of us, the whole damn zoo, her serpentine tour manager, her hyena of a personal assistant, the security gorillas, the peacock of a hairdresser, the publicity dragon, but now, as the chopper swooped over their motorcade, the darkness that had enveloped her since our departure seemed to lift, and she ordered the pilot to make a series of low passes over the cars below, lower and lower, I saw his eyes widen with fear, the pupils were black pinpricks, but he was under her spell like all of us, and did her bidding. I was the one yelling *higher, get higher* into the microphone attached to our ear-defender headsets, while her laughter clattered in my ears like a door banging in the wind, and when I looked across at her to tell her I was scared I saw that she was weeping. The police had been surprisingly gentle with her when they arrived at the scene of Raúl Páramo's overdose, contenting themselves with cautioning her that she might become the subject of an investigation herself. Her lawyers had terminated the encounter at that point, but afterwards she looked stretched, unstable, too bright, as if she were on the point of flying apart like an exploding lightbulb, like a supernova, like the universe.

Then we were past the vehicles and flying over the hills and valleys turned smoky blue by the agave plantations, and her mood swung again, she began to giggle into her microphone and to insist that we were taking her to a place that did not exist, a fantasy location, a wonderland, because how was it possible that there could be a place called Tequila, "it's like saying that whisky comes from Whisky, or gin is made in Gin," she cried. "Is the Vodka a river in Russia? Do they make rum in Rúm?" And then a sudden darkening, her voice dropping low, becoming almost inaudible beneath the noise of the rotors, "And heroin comes from heroes, and crack from the Crack of Doom." It was possible that I was hearing the birth of a song. Afterwards, when the captain and copilot were interviewed about her helicopter ride, they loyally refused to divulge any details of that in-flight monologue in which she swung moment by moment between elation and despair. "She was in high spirits," they said, "and spoke in English, so we did not understand."

Not only in English. Because it was only me, she could prattle on in Bombay's garbage argot, *Mumbai ki kachra-pati baat-cheet,* in which a sentence could begin in one language, swoop through a second and even a third and then swing back round to the first. Our acronymic name for it was *Hug-me.* Hindi Urdu Gujarati Marathi English. Bombayites like me were people who spoke five languages badly and no language well.

Separated from Ormus Cama on this tour, Vina had discovered the limitations, musical and verbal, of her own material. She had written new songs to show off that celestial voice of hers, that multiple-octave, Yma Sumac stairway to heaven of an instrument which, she now claimed, had never been sufficiently stretched by Ormus's compositions; but in Buenos Aires, São Paulo, Mexico City and Guadalajara she heard for herself the public's tepid responses to these songs, in spite of the presence of her three demented Brazilian percussionists and her pair of duelling Argentine guitarists who threatened to end each performance with a knife fight. Even the guest appearance of the veteran Mexican superstar Chico Estefan had failed to enthuse her audiences; instead, his surgery-smoothed face with its mouthful of unreal teeth only drew attention to her own fading youth, which was mirrored in the average age of the crowds. The kids had not come, or not enough of them, not nearly enough.

But roars of acclaim followed each of the old hits from the VTO back catalogue, and the inescapable truth was that during these numbers the percussionists' madness came closest to divinity, the duelling guitars spiralled upwards towards the sublime, and even the old roué Estefan seemed to come back from his green pastures over the hill. Vina Apsara sang Ormus Cama's words and music, and at once the minority of youngsters in the audiences perked up and started going crazy, the crowd's thousand thousand hands began moving in unison, forming in sign language the name of the great band, in time to their thundering cheers:

V! T! O!

V! T! O!

Go back to him, they were saying. We need you to be together. Don't throw your love away. Instead of breaking up, we wish that you were making up again.

Vertical Take-Off. Or, Vina To Ormus. Or, "We two" translated into Hug-me as V-to. Or, a reference to the V-2 rocket. Or, V for peace, for which they longed, and T for two, the two of them, and O for love, their love. Or, a homage to one of the great buildings of Ormus's home town: Victoria Terminus Orchestra. Or, a name invented long ago when Vina saw a neon sign for the old-time soft drink Vimto, with only three letters illuminated, Vimto without the *im*.

V . . . T . . . Ohh.
V . . . T . . . Ohh.

Two shrieks and a sigh. The orgasm of the past, whose ring she wore on her finger. To which perhaps she knew she must, in spite of me, return.

THE AFTERNOON heat was dry and fierce, which she loved. Before we landed, the pilot had been informed of mild earth tremors in the region, but they had passed, he reassured us, there was no reason to abort the landing. Then he cursed the French. "After each one of those tests you can count five days, one, two, three, four, five, and the ground shakes." He set the helicopter down in a dusty football field in the centre of the little town of Tequila. What must have been the town's entire police force was keeping the local population at bay. As Vina Apsara majestically descended (always a princess, she was growing into queenliness) a cry went up, just her name, *Veeenaaa,* the vowels elongated by pure longing, and I recognized, not for the first time, that in spite of all the hyperbolic revelry and public display of her life, in spite of all her star antics, her *nakhras,* she was never resented, something in her manner disarmed people, and what bubbled out of them instead of bile was a miraculous, unconditional affection, as if she were the whole earth's very own new-born child.

Call it love.

Small boys burst through the cordon, chased by perspiring cops, and then there was Don Ángel Cruz with his two silver Bentleys that exactly matched the colour of his hair, apologizing for not greeting us with an aria, but the dust, the unfortunate dust, it is always a difficulty but now with the tremor the air is full of it, please, señora, señor, and with a small cough against the back of his wrist he shepherded us into the lead Bentley, we will go at once, please, and commence the programme. He seated himself in the second vehicle, mopping himself with giant kerchiefs, the huge smile on his face held there by a great effort of will. You could almost see the heaving distraction beneath that surface of a perfect host. "That's a worried man," I said to Vina as our car drove towards the plantation. She shrugged. She had crossed the Oakland Bay Bridge going west in

October 1984, test driving a luxury car for a promotional feature in *Vanity Fair,* and on the far side she drove into a gas station, climbed out of the car and saw it lift off the ground, all four wheels, and hang there in the air like something from the future, or *Back to the Future,* anyway. At that moment the Bay Bridge was collapsing like a children's toy. Therefore, "Don't you earthquake me," she said to me in her tough-broad, disaster-vet voice as we arrived at the plantation, where Don Ángel's employees waited with straw cowboy hats to shield us from the sun and machete maestros prepared to demonstrate how one hacked an agave plant down into a big blue "pineapple" ready for the pulping machine. "Don't try and Richter me, Rai, honey. I been scaled before."

The animals were misbehaving. Brindled mongrels ran in circles, yelping, and there was a whinnying of horses. Oracular birds wheeled noisily overhead. Subcutaneous seismic activity increased, too, beneath the increasingly distended affability of Don Ángel Cruz as he dragged us round the distillery, these are our traditional wooden vats, and here are our shining new technological marvels, our capital investment for the future, our enormous investment, our investment beyond price. Fear had begun to ooze from him in globules of rancid sweat. Absently he dabbed his sodden hankies at the odorous flow, and in the bottling plant his eyes widened further with misery as he gazed upon the fragility of his fortune, liquid cradled in glass, and the fear of an earthquake began to seep damply from the corners of his eyes.

"Sales of French wines and liquors have been down since the testing began, maybe as much as twenty percent," he muttered, shaking his head. "The wineries of Chile and our own people here in Tequila have both been beneficiaries. Export demand has shot up to such a degree you would not credit it." He wiped his eyes with the back of an unsteady hand. "Why should God give us such a gift only to take it away again? Why must He test our faith?" He peered at us, as if we might genuinely be able to offer him an answer. When he understood that no answer was available, he clutched suddenly at Vina Apsara's hands, he became a supplicant at her court, driven to this act of excessive familiarity by the force of his great need. She made no attempt to free herself from his grasp.

"I have not been a bad man," Don Ángel said to Vina, in imploring tones, as if he were praying to her. "I have been fair to my employees and amiable to my children and even faithful to my wife, excepting only, let me be honest, a couple of small incidents, and these were maybe twenty years ago, señora, you are a sophisticated lady, you can understand the weaknesses of middle age. Why then should such a day come to me?" He actually bowed his head before her, relinquishing her hands now to lock his own together and rest them fearfully against his teeth.

She was used to giving absolution. Placing her freed hands on his shoulders, she began to speak to him in That Voice, she began to murmur to him as if they were lovers, dismissing the feared earthquake like a naughty child, sending it to stand in the corner, forbidding it to create any trouble for the excellent Don Ángel, and such was the miracle of her vocal powers, of the sound of her voice more than anything it might have been saying, that the distressed fellow actually stopped sweating and, with a hesitant, tentative rebirth of good cheer, raised his cherubic head and smiled. "Good," said Vina Apsara. "Now let's have lunch."

At the family firm's old hacienda, which was nowadays used only for great feasts such as this, we found a long table set in the cloisters overlooking a fountained courtyard, and as Vina entered, a mariachi band began to play. Then the motorcade arrived, and out tumbled the whole appalling menagerie of the rock world, squealing and flurrying, knocking back their host's vintage tequila as if it were beer from a party can, or wine-in-a-box, and boasting about their ride through the earth tremors, the personal assistant hissing hatred at the unstable earth as if he were planning to sue it, the tour manager laughing with the glee he usually displayed only when he signed up a new act on disgracefully exploitative terms, the peacock flouncing and exclamatory, the gorillas grunting monosyllabically, the Argentine guitarists at each other's throats as usual, and the drummers—ach, drummers!—shutting out the memory of their panic by launching into a tequila-lubricated series of high-volume criticisms of the mariachi band, whose leader, resplendent in a black-and-silver outfit, hurled his sombrero to the floor and was on the point of reaching for the silver six-gun strapped to his thigh, when Don Ángel intervened and, to promote a convivial spirit, offered benevolently, "Please. If you permit it, I will intent, for your diversion, to sing."

A genuine countertenor voice silences all arguments, its sidereal sweetness shaming our pettiness, like the music of the spheres. Don Ángel Cruz gave us Gluck, *"Trionfi Amore,"* and the mariachi singers did a creditable job as Chorus to his Orfeo.

Trionfi Amore!
E il mondo intiero
Serva all'impero
Della beltà.

The unhappy conclusion of the Orpheus story, Eurydice lost forever because of Orpheus's backwards look, was always a problem for composers and their librettists.—Hey, Calzabigi, what's this ending you're giving me here? Such a downer, I should send folks home with their faces long like a wurst? *Hello?* Happy it up, ja!—Sure, Herr Gluck, don't get so agitato. No problem! Love, it is stronger than Hades. Love, it make the gods merciful. How's about they send her back anyway? "Get outa here, kid, the guy's crazy for you! What's one little peek?" Then the lovers throw a party, and what a party! Dancing, wine, the whole nine yards. So you got your big finish, everybody goes out humming.—Works for me. Nice going, Raniero.—Sure thing, Willibald. Forget about it.

And here it was, that showstopper finale. Love's triumph over death. *The whole world obeys the rule of beauty.* To everyone's astonishment, mine included, Vina Apsara the rock star rose to her feet and sang both soprano parts, Amor as well as Euridice, and though I'm no expert she sounded word and note perfect, her voice in an ecstasy of fulfilment, finally, it seemed to be saying, you've worked out what I'm for.

. . . E quel sospetto
Che il cor tormenta

Al fin diventa
Felicità.

The tormented heart doesn't just find happiness, okay: it *becomes happiness*. That's the story, anyway. That's the way the song goes.

THE EARTH began to shake just as she finished, applauding her performance. The great still life of the banquet, the plates of meats and bowls of fruits and bottles of the best Cruz tequila, and even the banquet table itself, now commenced to jump and dance in Disney fashion, inanimate objects animated by the little sorcerer's apprentice, that overweening mouse; or as if moved by the sheer power of her song to join in the closing *chaconne.* As I try to remember the exact sequence of events, I find that my memory has become a silent movie. There must have been noise. Pandemonium, city of devils and their torments, could scarcely have been noisier than that Mexican town, as cracks scurried like lizards along the walls of its buildings, prying apart the walls of Don Ángel's hacienda with their long creepy fingers, until it simply fell away like an illusion, a movie façade, and through the surging dust cloud of its collapse we were returned to the pitching, bucking streets, running for our lives, not knowing which way to run but running, anyway, while tiles fell from roofs and trees were flung into the air and sewage burst upwards from the streets and houses exploded and suitcases long stored in attics began to rain down from the sky.

But I remember only silence, the silence of great horror. The silence, to be more exact, of photography, because that was my profession, so naturally it was what I turned to the moment the earthquake began. All my thoughts were of the little squares of film passing through my old cameras, Voigtländer Leica Pentax, of the forms and colours being registered therein by the accidents of movement and event, and of course by the skill or lack of it with which I managed to point the lens in the right or wrong direction at the wrong or right time. Here was the eternal silence of faces and bodies and animals and even nature itself, caught—yes—by my camera, but caught also in the grip of the fear of the unforeseeable and the anguish of loss, in the clutches of this hated metamorphosis, the appalling silence of a way of life at the moment of its annihilation, its transformation into a golden past that could never wholly be rebuilt, because once you have been in an earthquake you know, even if you survive without a scratch, that like a stroke in the heart, it remains in the earth's breast, horribly potential, always promising to return, to hit you again, with an even more devastating force.

A photograph is a moral decision taken in one eighth of a second, or one sixteenth, or one one-hundred-and-twenty-eighth. Snap your fingers; a snapshot's faster. Halfway between voyeur and witness, high artist and low scum, that's where I've made my life, making my eyeblink choices. That's okay, that's cool. I'm still alive, and I've been spat at and called names only a couple of hundred times. I can live with the name-calling. It's the men with the heavy weaponry who worry me. (And they are men, almost always, all those arnolds carrying terminators, all those zealous suicidists, with their toilet-brush beards and no hair on their baby-naked upper lips; but when women do such work, they're often worse.)

I've been an event junkie, me. Action has been my stimulant of choice. I always liked to stick my face right up against the hot sweaty broken surface of what was being done, with my eyes open, drinking, and the rest of my senses switched off. I never cared if it stank, or if its slimy touch made you want to throw up, or what it might do to your taste buds if you licked it, or even how loud it screamed. Just the way it looked. That's where for a long time I went for feeling, and truth.

What Actually Happens: nothing to beat it, when you're pressed up against it, as long as you don't get your face torn off. No rush like it on earth.

Long ago I developed a knack for invisibility. It allowed me to go right up to the actors in the world's drama, the sick, the dying, the crazed, the mourning, the rich, the greedy, the ecstatic, the bereft, the angry, the murderous, the secretive, the bad, the children, the good, the newsworthy; to shimmy into their charmed space, into the midst of their rage or grief or transcendent arousal, to penetrate the defining instant of their being-in-the-world and get my fucking picture. On many occasions this gift of dematerialisation has saved my life. When people said to me, do not drive down that sniper-infested road, do not enter that warlord's stronghold, you'd do well to circumnavigate that militia's fiefdom, I was drawn towards it almost irresistibly. Nobody has ever gone in there with a camera and come out, alive, somebody would warn, and at once I'd head off past the checkpoint of no return. When I got back people looked at me oddly, as if seeing a ghost, and asked how I managed it. I shook my head. Truthfully, I often didn't know. Perhaps if I knew I wouldn't be able to do it any more and then I'd get killed in some half-baked combat zone. One day that may happen.

The closest I can get to it is that I know how to make myself small. Not physically small, for I am a tallish guy, heavy-set, but psychically. I just smile my self-deprecating smile and shrink into insignificance. By my manner I persuade the sniper I do not merit his bullet, my way of carrying myself convinces the warlord to keep his great axe clean. I make them understand that I'm not worthy of their violence. Maybe it works because I'm being sincere, because I truly mean to deprecate myself. There are experiences I carry around with me, memories I can draw on when I want to remind myself of my low value. Thus a form of acquired modesty, the product of my early life and misdeeds, has succeeded in keeping me alive.

"Bullshit," was Vina Apsara's view. "It's just another version of your technique for pulling chicks."

Modesty works with women, that's true. But with women I'm faking it. My nice, shy smile, my recessive body language. The more I back off in my suede jacket and combat boots, smiling shyly beneath my bald head (how often I've been told what a beautiful head I have!), the more insistently they advance. In love one advances by retreating. But then what I mean by love and what Ormus Cama, for example, meant by the same word were two different things. For me, it was always a skill, the *ars amatoria:* the first approach, the deflection of anxieties, the arousal of interest, the feint of departure, the slow inexorable return. The leisurely inward spiral of desire. *Kama.* The art of love.

Whereas for Ormus Cama it was just a simple matter of

life and death. Love was for life, and endured beyond death. Love was Vina, and beyond Vina there was nothing but the void.

I'VE NEVER been invisible to the earth's little creatures, however. Those six-legged dwarf terrorists have got my number, no question about it. Show me (or, preferably, don't show me) an ant, lead me (don't lead me) to a wasp, a bee, a mosquito, a flea. It'll have me for breakfast; also for other, more substantial repasts. What's small and bites, bites me. So at a certain moment in the heart of the earthquake, as I photographed a lost child crying for her parents, I was stung, once, hard, as if by conscience, on the cheek, and as I jerked my face away from my camera I was just in time (thank you, I guess, to whatever horrible *aguijón*-wielding thing it was; not conscience, probably, but a snapper's sixth sense) to see the beginning of the tequila flood. The town's many giant storage vats had burst.

The streets were like whips, snaking and cracking. The Ángel distillery was one of the first to succumb to this lashing. Old wood burst open, new metal buckled and split. The urinous river of tequila made its frothing way into the lanes of the town, the leading wave of the torrent overtook the fleeing populace and turned it head over heels, and such was the potency of the brew that those who swallowed mouthfuls of that angelic surf came up not only wet and gasping but drunk. The last time I saw Don Ángel Cruz, he was scurrying in the tequila-drowning squares with a saucepan in his hand and two kettles on strings slung around his neck, trying pathetically to save what he could.

This is how people behave when their dailiness is destroyed, when for a few moments they see, plain and unadorned, one of the great shaping forces of life. Calamity fixes them with her mesmeric eye, and they begin to scoop and paw at the rubble of their days, trying to pluck the memory of the quotidian—a toy, a book, a garment, even a photograph—from the garbage heaps of the irretrievable, of their overwhelming loss. Don Ángel Cruz turned panhandler was the childlike, fabulous image I needed, a figure eerily reminiscent of the surreal Saucepan Man from some of Vina Apsara's favourite books, the Faraway Tree series of Enid

Blyton that travelled with her wherever she went. Cloaking myself in invisibility, I began to shoot.

I don't know how long all this took. The shaking table, the collapse of the hacienda, the roller-coaster streets, the people gasping and tumbling in the tequila river, the descent of hysteria, the deathly laughter of the unhoused, the bankrupted, the unemployed, the orphaned, the dead . . . ask me to put an estimate on it and I'd come up empty. Twenty seconds? Half an hour? Search me. The invisibility cloak, and my other trick of switching off all my senses and channelling all my powers of perception through my mechanical eyes—these things have, as they say, a downside. When I'm facing the enormities of the actual, when that great monster is roaring into my lens, I lose control of other things. What time is it? Where is Vina? Who's dead? Who's alive? Is that an abyss opening beneath my combat boots? What did you say? There's a medical team trying to reach this dying woman? What are you talking about? Why are you getting in my way, who the fuck do you think you're trying to push around? *Can't you see I'm working?*

Who was alive? Who was dead? Where was Vina? Where was Vina? Where was Vina?

I snapped out of it. Insects stung my neck. The torrent of tequila ceased, the precious river poured away into the cracking earth. The town looked like a picture postcard torn up by an angry child and then painstakingly reassembled by its mother. It had acquired the quality of brokenness, had become kin to the great family of the broken: broken plates, broken dolls, broken English, broken promises, broken hearts. Vina Apsara lurched towards me through the dust. "Rai, thank God." For all her fooling with Buddhist wisemen (Rinpoche Hollywood and the Ginsberg Lama) and Krishna Consciousness cymbalists and Tantric gurus (those *kundalini* flashers) and Transcendental™ rishis and masters of this or that crazy wisdom, Zen and the Art of the Deal, the Tao of Promiscuous Sex, Self-Love and Enlightenment, for all her spiritual faddishness, I always in my own godless way found it hard to believe that she actually believed in an actually existing god. But she probably did; I was probably wrong about that too; and anyway, what other word is there? When there's that gratitude in you for life's dumb luck, when there's nobody to thank and you need to thank somebody, what do you say? God, Vina said. The word sounded to me like a way of disposing of emotion. It was a place to put something that had no place else to go.

From the sky, a larger insect bore down upon us, burdening us with the insistent downdraft of its raucous wings. The helicopter had taken off just in time to escape destruction. Now the pilot brought it down almost to ground zero, and beckoned, hovering. "Let's get out of here," Vina shouted. I shook my head. "You go," I yelled back at her. Work before play. I had to get my pictures on to the wires. "I'll see you later," I bellowed. "What?" "Later." "What?"

The plan had been for the helicopter to fly us, for a weekend's relaxation, to a remote villa on the Pacific coast, the Villa Huracán, co-owned by the president of the Colchis record company and located to the north of Puerto Vallarta, in privileged isolation, sandwiched like a magic kingdom between the jungle and the sea. Now there was no way of knowing if the villa still stood. The world had changed. Yet, like the townspeople clinging to their framed photographs, like Don Ángel with his saucepans, Vina Apsara clung to the idea of continuity, of the prearranged itinerary. She was staying with the programme. Until my kidnapped images were off to the world's news desks to be ransomed, however, there could be no tropical Shangri-la for me.

"I'm going, then," she screamed.

"I can't go."

"What?"

"Go."

"Fuck you."

"What?"

Then she was in the helicopter, and it was rising, and I had not gone with her, and I never saw her again, none of us did, and the last words she screamed down at me break my heart every time I think of them, and I think of them a few hundred times a day, every day, and then there are the endless, sleepless nights.

"Goodbye, Hope."

I BEGAN to use the workname "Rai" when I was taken on by the famous Nebuchadnezzar Agency. Pseudonyms, stage names, worknames: for writers, for actors, for spies, these are useful masks, hiding or altering one's true identity. But when I began to call myself *Rai,* prince, it felt like removing a disguise, because I was letting the world in on my most cherished secret, which was that ever since childhood this had been Vina's private pet name for me, the badge of my puppy love. "Because you carry yourself like a little rajah," she'd told me, fondly, when I was only nine and had braces on my teeth, "so it's only your friends who know you're just some no-account jerk."

That was Rai: a boy princeling. But childhood ends, and in adult life it was Ormus Cama who became Vina's Prince Charming, not I. Still, the nickname clung to me. And Ormus was good enough to use it too, or let's say he caught it off Vina like an infection, or let's say he never dreamed I could give him any competition, that I could be a threat, and that's why he could think of me as a friend. . . . But never mind that just now. *Rai.* It also meant desire: a man's personal inclination, the direction he chose to go in; and will, the force of a man's character. All that I liked. I liked that it was a name that travelled easily; everyone could say it, it sounded good on every tongue. And if on occasion I turned into "Hey, Ray" in that mighty democracy of mispronunciation, the United States, then I was not disposed to argue, I just took the plum assignments and left town. And in another part of the world, Rai was music. In the home of this music, alas, religious fanatics have lately started killing the musicians. They think the music is an insult to god, who gave us voices but does not wish us to sing, who gave us free will, *rai,* but prefers us not to be free.

Anyway, now everybody says it: Rai. Just the one name, it's easy, it's a style. Most people don't even know my real name. Umeed Merchant, did I mention that? Umeed Merchant, raised in a different universe, a different dimension of time, in a bungalow on Cuffe Parade, Bombay, which burned down long ago. The name Merchant, I should perhaps explain, means "merchant." Bombay families often bear names derived from some deceased ancestor's line of work. Engineers, Contractors, Doctors. And let's not forget the Readymoneys, the Cashondeliveris, the Fishwalas. And a Mistry is a mason and a Wadia is a shipbuilder and a lawyer is a Vakil and a banker is a Shroff. And from the thirsty city's long love affair with aerated drinks comes not only Batliwala but also Sodawaterbatliwala, and not only Sodawaterbatliwala but Sodawaterbatli*opener*wala too.

Cross my heart and hope to die.

"Goodbye, Hope," cried Vina, and the helicopter went into a steep banking climb and was gone.

Umeed, you see. Noun, feminine. Meaning hope.

WHY DO we care about singers? Wherein lies the power of songs? Maybe it derives from the sheer strangeness of there being singing in the world. The note, the scale, the chord; melodies, harmonies, arrangements; symphonies, ragas, Chinese operas, jazz, the blues: that such things should exist, that we should have discovered the magical intervals and distances that yield the poor cluster of notes, all within the span of a human hand, from which we can build our cathedrals of sound, is as alchemical a mystery as mathematics, or wine, or love. Maybe the birds taught us. Maybe not. Maybe we are just creatures in search of exaltation. We don't have much of it. Our lives are not what we deserve; they are, let us agree, in many painful ways deficient. Song turns them into something else. Song shows us a world that is worthy of our yearning, it shows us our selves as they might be, if we were worthy of the world.

Five mysteries hold the keys to the unseen: the act of love, and the birth of a baby, and the contemplation of great art, and being in the presence of death or disaster, and hearing the human voice lifted in song. These are the occasions when the bolts of the universe fly open and we are given a glimpse of what is hidden; an eff of the ineffable. Glory bursts upon us in such hours: the dark glory of earthquakes, the slippery wonder of new life, the radiance of Vina's singing.

Vina, to whom even strangers would come, following her star, hoping to receive redemption from her voice, her large, damp eyes, her touch. How was it that so explosive, even amoral, a woman came to be seen as an emblem, an ideal, by more than half the population of the world? Because she was no angel, let me tell you that, but try saying so to Don Ángel. Maybe it's just as well she was not born a Christian, or they'd have tried to make her a saint. Our Lady of the Stadiums, our arena madonna, baring her scars to the masses like Alexander the Great rousing his soldiers for war; our plastered Unvirgin, bleeding red tears from her eyes and hot music from her throat. As we retreat from religion, our ancient opiate, there are bound to be withdrawal symptoms, there will be many side effects of this Apsaran variety. The habit of worship is not easily broken. In the museums, the rooms with the icons are crowded. We always did prefer our iconic figures injured, stuck full of arrows or crucified upside down; we need them flayed and naked, we want to watch their beauty crumble slowly and to observe their narcissistic grief. Not in spite of their faults but *for* their faults we adore them, worshipping their weaknesses, their pettinesses, their bad marriages, their substance abuse, their spite. Seeing ourselves in Vina's mirror, and forgiving her, we also forgave ourselves. She redeemed us by her sins.

I was no different. I always needed her to make things all right: some botched job, some bruise on my pride, some departing woman whose last cruel words succeeded in getting under my skin. But it was only near the very end of her life that I found the courage to ask for her love, to make my bid for her, and for a heady moment I truly believed I might tear her from Ormus's clutches. Then she died, leaving me with a pain that only her magic touch could have assuaged. But she wasn't there to kiss my brow and say, It's okay, Rai, you little jerk, let it pass, let me put my witchy ointment on those bad, naughty stings, come here to mama and watch the good times roll.

This is what I feel now when I think of Don Ángel Cruz weeping before her in his fragile distillery: envy. And jealousy too. *I wish I'd done that, opened my heart and begged for her before it was too late,* and also *I wish she hadn't touched you, you snivelling squeaky-voiced bankrupt capitalist worm.*

We all looked to her for peace, yet she herself was not at peace. And so I've chosen to write here, publicly, what I can no longer whisper into her private ear: that is, everything. I have chosen to tell our story, hers and mine and Ormus Cama's, all of it, every last detail, and then maybe she can find a sort of peace here, on the page, in this underworld of ink and lies, that respite which was denied her by life. So I stand at the gate of the inferno of language, there's a barking dog and a ferryman waiting and a coin under my tongue for the fare.

"I have not been a bad man," Don Ángel Cruz whimpered. Okay, I'll do some whimpering of my own. Listen, Vina: I am not a bad man, either. Though, as I will fully confess, I have been a traitor in love, and being an only child have as yet no child, and in the name of art have stolen the images of the stricken and the dead, and philandered, and shrugged (dislodging from their perch on my shoulders the angels that watched over me), and worse things too, yet I hold myself to be a man among men, a man as men are, no better nor no worse. Though I be condemned to the stinging of insects, yet have I not led a wicked villain's life. Depend upon it: I have not.

Do you know the Fourth *Georgic* of the bard of Mantua, P. Vergilius Maro? Ormus Cama's father, the redoubtable Sir Darius Xerxes Cama, classicist and honey-lover, knew his Virgil, and through him I learned some too. Sir Darius was an Aristaeus admirer, of course; Aristaeus, the first beekeeper in world literature, whose unwelcome advances to the dryad Eurydice led her to step on a snake, whereupon the wood nymph perished and mountains wept. Virgil's treatment of the Orpheus story is extraordinary: he tells it in seventy-six blazing lines, writing with all the stops pulled out, and then, in a perfunctory thirty lines more, he allows Aristaeus to perform his expiatory ritual sacrifice, and that's that, end of poem, no more need to worry about those foolish doomed lovers. The real hero of the poem is the keeper of bees, the "Arcadian master," the maker of a miracle far greater than that wretched Thracian singer's art, which could not even raise his lover from the dead. This is what Aristaeus could do: *he could spontaneously generate new bees from the rotting carcase of a cow.* His was "the heavenly gift of honey from the air."

Well, then. And Don Ángel could produce tequila from blue agave. And I, Umeed Merchant, photographer, can spontaneously generate new meaning from the putrefying carcase of what is the case. Mine is the hellish gift of conjuring response, feeling, perhaps even comprehension, from uncaring eyes, by placing before them the silent faces of the real. I, too, am compromised, no man knows better than I how irredeemably. Nor are there any sacrifices I can perform, or gods I can propitiate. Yet my names mean "hope" and "will," and that counts for something, right? Vina, am I right?

Sure, baby. Sure, Rai, honey. It counts.

MUSIC, LOVE, death. Certainly a triangle of sorts; maybe even an eternal one. But Aristaeus, who brought death, also brought life, a little like Lord Shiva back home. Not just a dancer, but Creator and Destroyer, both. Not only stung by bees but a bringer into being of bee stings. So, music, love and life-death: these three. As once we also were three. Ormus, Vina and I. We did not spare each other. In this telling, therefore, nothing will be spared. Vina, I must betray you, so that I can let you go.

Begin.

CHAPTER TWO

Melodies and Silences

Ormus Cama was born in Bombay, India, in the early hours of May 27, 1937, and within moments of his birth began making the strange, rapid finger movements with both hands which any guitarist could have identified as chord progressions. However, no guitar players were included among those invited to coo over the new-born baby at the Sisters of Maria Gratiaplena Nursing Home on Altamount Road, or, later, at the family apartment on Apollo Bunder, and the miracle might have gone unnoticed had it not been for the single reel of 8 mm monochrome film shot on June 17 on a hand-held Paillard Bolex, the property of my own father, Mr. V. V. Merchant, a keen amateur of home movies. The "Vivvy movie," as it came to be known, luckily survived in reasonable condition until, many years later, the new computer technologies of film enhancement allowed the world to see, in digitally magnified close-ups, the pudgy hands of baby Ormus incontestably playing air guitar, moving soundlessly through a complex series of monster riffs and dizzy licks with a speed, and feeling, of which the instrument's greatest practitioners would have been proud.

Back at the beginning, though, music was the last thing on anyone's mind. Ormus's mother, Lady Spenta Cama, had been told in the thirty-fifth week of pregnancy that the child she was carrying had died in her womb. At that late date she had no choice but to go through the full agony of labour, and when she saw the stillborn corpse of Ormus's elder brother Gayo, his non-identical, dizygotic twin, her wretchedness was so great that she believed the continued movement within her was her own death trying to be born, so that she could be united with her lifeless child at once.

Until that unhappy moment she had been a placid individual, an astigmatic endomorph, heavy-spectacled and heavy-bodied, given to a certain bovine rotation of the jaw, which her voluble, irascible, erratic husband, Sir Darius Xerxes Cama, tall, ectomorphic, extravagantly moustachioed, and gimlet-eyed under his red, golden-tasselled fez, often deliberately mistook for stupidity. It was not stupidity. It was the unflappability of a soul fully occupied on the spiritual level, or, more exactly, a soul who found in her everyday routines a means of communing with the divine. Lady Spenta Cama was on speaking terms with two of the Parsi angels, the Amesha Spentas for whom she was named: the Angel Good Thoughts, silent conversations with whom occupied her for an hour each morning (she steadfastly declined to reveal the nature of these chats to her husband or anyone else); and the Angel Orderly Righteousness, under whose tutelage she became minutely attentive to household affairs, the supervision of which took up most of her afternoons. Of the various supernatural Spentas, this was the duo with whom Lady Spenta Cama felt the most affinity. The Angel Excellence and the Angel Immortality were far beyond her, she humbly allowed, and as to the Angel Perfect Sovereignty and the Angel Divine Piety, it would have been immodest to claim too close a connection with them.

The Christian and Muslim concept of angels, she liked to boast, was "derived" from these Zoroastrian originals, just as devils descended from "our own Daevas"; such was her proprietorial feeling, her pride in Parsi primacy, that she spoke of these malignant forces as if they were personal pets, or one of the many china ornaments with which she littered the Camas' thing-stuffed Apollo Bunder apartment, that much-coveted Bombay belvedere with its five high windows facing saltily out to sea. It was nevertheless startling that one so close to virtue should give way so spectacularly to the Daevas Misery, False Appearance and Evil Mind, and wretchedly cry out for woe.

"Arré, come on, then, take me, why not, O death be my dominion," Lady Spenta squalled. The two grandly Valkyrian ladies by her bedside frowned disapprovingly. Ute Schaapsteker, the chief consultant gynaecologist at the Maria Gratiaplena (known throughout the city's upper echelons as "Snooty Utie" or, alternatively, "Sister Adolf"), made a number of sharply admonitory remarks concerning the impropriety of prematurely wishing for death, which would certainly come, unwished for, at the proper time. Her aide, the midwife Sister John, was still young in those days but was well on the way to becoming that dark galleon of a bedside presence whose formidable gloom and upper-lip mole blighted many a Bombay birth over the next fifty years. "Great tidings of gladness and joy!" she boomed sourly. "For He that is Mighty hath harvested unto Himself the soul of this fortunate infant, like as though it were a grain of blessed rice." The pair of them would no doubt have continued in this vein for some considerable time, had Lady Spenta not suddenly added, in entirely altered, indeed comprehensively astonished tones, "Such pressure on my back passage, either I am in danger of passing a stool or else there is some other *chokra* trying to make an appearance."

It had not been her death wriggling inside her, of course. Nor were her bowels in danger of opening. She quickly gave birth to a small but healthy baby, a little four-and-a-half pound eel of a boy whose living form had been concealed from Dr. Schaapsteker's examinations, during both pregnancy and labour, by his dead twin's larger body. Remarkably, the Camas already had a five-year-old pair of dizygotic male twins, Khusro and Ardaviraf, known to one and all as "Cyrus and Virus." Sir Darius Xerxes Cama, who knew his Greek mythology, was familiar with the Olympian deities' practice of inserting a babe (Idas, Polydeuces) of semi-divine parentage into a womb that was also preparing to bear (Lynceus, Castor) a fully human child. In the case of the precocious, multi-talented Khusro—a child with the genuinely malign ruthlessness of a true hero—and the slow-witted, sweet-natured Ardaviraf, the ancient Greeks would have had little difficulty in identifying the child with a god for a father. On this second occasion, presumably, the dead Gayo was the earthly child and the living Ormus the one with the immortal pedigree as well as yearnings. Thus Sir Darius would be deemed the father of one duffer and one corpse, an inglorious fate. But scholarship is one thing, parenthood quite another, and Sir Darius Xerxes Cama, "the Apollonian of Apollo Bunder," was a staunch Cantabrigian rationalist and an eminent barrister-at-law who had "eaten his dinners" at Middle Temple and had subsequently dedicated his life to what he called, in an intentionally oxymoronic flash of wit, "the miracle of reason." He yielded up rights of paternity to no god, whatever his origin, took up the reins of fatherhood and, in strict fairness, oppressed all his children equally.

The living baby was taken away to the incubator by scowling Sister John, who found it harder to celebrate a birth than a "harvesting." The dead baby was removed (there are sights too powerful for mere men's eyes), and at last Sir Darius Xerxes Cama was allowed to enter the delivery room. Spenta was gripped by remorse. "In the moment of his birth I allowed the servants of the Lie to seize my tongue," she confessed. Sir Darius had long found the various manifestations of his wife's literalist religiosity difficult to handle. He did his best to conceal his unease, but could not shut out the image of Lady Spenta's tongue being worked by little bat-winged creatures despatched by Angra Mainyu, a.k.a. Ahriman himself. He closed his eyes and shuddered.

Lady Spenta rallied. "Whose idea was it to name that poor boy Gayo, anyway?" she demanded, forgetting in the heat and emotional ambiguity of the moment that it had been her own. Her husband, too gallant to remind her, bowed his head and took the blame. The First-Created Man, Gayomart, had indeed been killed by Angra Mainyu long ago. "*Bad* choice of name," Lady Spenta cried, bursting once again into tears. Sir Darius Xerxes Cama's head bowed lower; Lady Spenta found herself addressing the tasselled top of his fez. She knocked on it, firmly. It yielded a hollow sound. "The only way of compensating," she insisted, sobbing, "is at once to name the surviving boy with the name of god."

Hormuz or Ormazd, local derivatives of Ahura Mazda, were her stated options, which Sir Darius Xerxes Cama the classicist at once Latinized as Ormus. His wife was placated. She dried her eyes and together the couple visited the incubator room, where Ute Schaapsteker confirmed that the child was expected to live. "My little Ormie," Lady Spenta Cama purred at the under-sized little fellow through incubator glass. "My little shrimpy boy. Now you're safe from Hell. Now they can't open up the ground and take you down."

* * *

Sir Darius, having received Snooty Utie's reassurances about little Ormus's prospects, made his excuses, went so far as to kiss his wife and rushed off, somewhat too eagerly for Lady Spenta's taste, to play cricket. It was a big match. That year the annual Quadrangular Tournament between the city's British, Hindu, Muslim and Parsi teams had become Pentangular, and on this day Sir Darius had been put down to turn out for the Parsis against the new boys, The Rest, an XI drawn from the ranks of Bombay's Christians, Anglo-Indians and Jews. Sir Darius Xerxes Cama at forty-three still possessed the physical strength and godlike musculature of an all-round sporting hero, body-builder and ex–amateur wrestling champion. His elegant left-handed batsmanship remained much in demand; his trademark stroke was a lazily executed, and therefore alarming, but still highly effective late cut. And in short spells he could still produce bowling of discomforting speed: "the thunderbolts of Darius," as they had long been known. When he pulled on his whites, divesting himself of the long coat and high fez of a Parsi gentleman after his anxious nocturnal hours at the nursing home, he felt a sense of proud relief steal over him. No longer was he obliged to prowl peripherally at the edges of women's business! He was a tiger unchained, and his bursting pride at becoming the father of a third male child would shortly be visited upon the enemy in the form of doughty deeds with bat and ball. This transformation from citizen to sportsman in the privacy of a changing tent at the edge of the great Maidan was, of all life's rituals, the one Sir Darius most keenly enjoyed. (When, after a day's ferocious advocacy, he would strip away the gown and wig of the Law and take up his willow cudgel, he felt as if he were entering into his better nature, into a finer self of Olympian fibre and grace.) His fellow opening batsman, a dashing young blade named Homi Catrack, asked him if he felt able to play after missing a night's sleep. "Pish!" cried Sir Darius, and strode forth to do battle for his race.

On the Maidan, a large, noisy crowd awaited his coming. Sir Darius had always disapproved of the behaviour of Bombay's spectators. It was the one small blemish on these otherwise delightful days. The hooting, the shrieking, the blaring of tin horns, the banging of *dhols*, the rising chant as a pace merchant ran in to bowl, the barracking, the cries of snack vendors, the howling laughter, in short the incessant clamour, created, in Sir Darius's opinion, an unsuitable environment for the practice of the game's noble arts. The country's imperial overlords, observing the bawdiness of the populace, could only feel disappointed at the continuing backwardness of those over whom they had ruled so wisely for so long. Sir Darius Xerxes Cama, walking out to bat, wanted to cry aloud, "Brace up! Do yourselves justice! The British are watching."

It was a "fine day," the day of Ormus Cama's birth. This old Bombay term, long fallen into disuse, used to mean a day on which unexpected cloud cover brought cool relief from the heat. Schoolchildren had been given a "fine day holiday," as was the occasional practice in those far-off times. This particular fine day, however, was ill-starred. True, a child had been born alive, but another had been born dead. Demons, Daevas, had been conjured, and there were disapprovals hanging in the air. At the Sisters of Maria Gratiaplena Nursing Home, Snooty Utie Schaapsteker's disapproval of Lady Spenta's self-pity had mingled with Sir Darius's disapproval of what he might on another occasion have called his wife's "superstitions," to create a less than celebratory mood. Here at the cricket ground, too, there were unexpected noises of reproof. A band of nationalist sympathizers had arrived with a variety of deafening musical instruments, and from the beginning of the game they set out to disrupt the players' concentration by what Sir Darius thought to be a particularly tasteless type of musical heckling.

"Don't be wicket," the hecklers chanted, to the beat of drums and the tooting of trumpets, "Ban communal cricket." Sir Darius Xerxes Cama was aware that Mahatma Gandhi and his followers had denounced the Pentangular Tournament as a communally divisive, anti-national throwback, in which men of colonialized mentality performed like monkeys for the amusement of the British and gave unhelpful assistance to the policy of divide-and-rule. Sir Darius was no Independence merchant. Nationalists! He entertained the gravest doubts about the wisdom of surrendering the governance of India to men of such limited musical sense. For Mr. Gandhi personally he conceded a grudging respect but felt that if he could only persuade the great man to don flannels and learn the basics of the game, the Mahatma was bound to be persuaded of the tournament's value in honing that spirit of competition without which no people can take its place at the forefront of the world community.

As he arrived at the crease, one of the hecklers sang out, "Lady Daria's come to play!" At once a distressingly large section of the crowd—must be Christians, Anglos or Jews, huffed Sir Darius in displeasure—took up the insulting chant. "Lady Cama, give us drama! Give a catch and be a charmer!" Toot, rattle, clank. "Give us drama, Lady Cama."

Now Sir Darius noticed that his own boys, the five-year-old twins Cyrus and Virus, were sitting with their ayah on the grass close by the nationalist hecklers, grinning happily, giving every appearance of enjoying the spoilsports' antics. He moved a few paces towards them, waving his bat. "Khusro! Ardaviraf! Move on!" he called. The boys and the ayah were unable to hear him in the din and assumed he was waving. They all waved back. The hecklers, thinking he was shaking his bat at them, and happy to have so provoked him, redoubled their efforts. The music of their merry hostility clamoured in his ears. Sir Darius Xerxes Cama faced the bowling in an imperfect frame of mind.

Mr. Aaron Abraham, opening the bowling for The Rest, was able to make the new ball swing discomfortingly in those overcast conditions. Sir Darius was lucky to survive his first three deliveries. Seeing him struggle, the nationalist claque grew even noisier. Clank, rattle, toot. The drummers and trumpeters improvised a tune, and over and over his tormentors sang, "Lady Daria, don't be slack. Make a duck and off you quack." And then came a variant, and evidently popular, version: "Lady Donald, make a duck."

Sir Darius strode down the pitch to confer with his partner.

"Quack, is it?" he fumed, swishing his bat. "I'll soon give them quack, but what is this Donald?" As he asked the question, however, he remembered a recent visit to the cinema with the twins to see Chaplin's *Modern Times,* a film Sir Darius admired for, among other things, staying "silent." In the supporting programme they had seen a cartoon short, "Orphans' Benefit," featuring a new, anarchically violent, web-footed and horribly noisy anti-hero. Sir Darius brightened. "Donald, is it?" he roared. "Ha! Ha! Ha! I'll quickly make those bounders Duck."

Homi Catrack tried in vain to calm him. "Never mind the crowd. Play yourself in; then we'll show them what-for." But Sir Darius had lost his head. The fourth ball of Aaron Abraham's over was a loose delivery, eminently hittable, and Sir Darius seized his chance. He swung with all his might, and there can be no question that he was trying to hit the ball right at the group of heckling nationalist musicians. Afterwards, in the grip of an unassuageable remorse, he conceded that his injured vanity had overcome the fatherly prudence that should have been his uppermost concern, but by then it was too late; the cricket ball had travelled towards the boundary at high velocity and could not be re-called.

It was not going to hit the hecklers and there was no way of correcting its course, but many spectators were diving out of its way, for it was travelling at genuinely frightening speed, and there, smack in its path, moving neither to left nor to right, were Sir Darius Xerxes Cama's non-identical twin sons, standing up to applaud their father's great stroke, fearless, because how could their beloved father possibly cause either of them the slightest harm?

No doubt the ayah's slow reactions were partly responsible for the accident, but from the moment that he saw what was about to happen, Sir Darius never blamed anyone except himself. He bellowed out a warning at the top of his voice, but the drums and horns were louder than his screams, music prevented him from sounding the alarm, and an instant later, sweet, slow Ardaviraf Cama was struck by the rocketing cricket ball, right between the eyes, and fell down flat, as if he were made of wood, like a stump.

PERHAPS AT the very moment when the story of the Cama family was being re-written forever by the addition of that cruel line, the trajectory of a red cricket ball from a father's bat to a son's forehead, my mother and father were meeting for the first time at the Sisters of Maria Gratiaplena Nursing Home.

When it comes to love there's no telling what people will convince themselves of. In spite of all the evidence that life is discontinuous, a valley of rifts, and that random chance plays a great part in our fates, we go on believing in the continuity of things, in causation and meaning. But we live on a broken mirror, and fresh cracks appear in its surface every day. People (like Virus Cama) may slip through those cracks and be lost. Or, like my parents, they may be thrown by chance into each other's arms, and fall in love. In direct contradiction of their predominantly rational philosophies of life, however, my father and mother always believed that they were drawn together by Destiny, which was so determined to unite them that it manifested itself in no less than four different forms: that is to say, social, genealogical, gastronomical and Sister John.

They had both come to visit Lady Spenta Cama and were both inappropriately dressed in mournful attire, because they had not heard of the birth of little Ormus and were simply and kindly intending to console Lady Spenta for having had to endure the experience of a still-birth. My parents were younger than Sir Darius and Lady Spenta by a generation, and both were relatively recent friends of the family. An unlikely friendship had developed between the two men, who had found common ground in the subject of Bombay itself; Bombay, that great metropolitan creation of the British, whose foremost chronicler my father—the England-returned architect and devoted local historian V. V. Merchant (soon to be the diffident *auteur* of a subsequently celebrated home movie)—would in time become. Sir Darius Xerxes Cama, honoured with a baronetcy for services to the Indian Bar, liked to say with a great laugh that he, too, was a great metropolitan creation of the British, and proud of it. "When you write this city's history, Merchant," he roared one night over a clubhouse dinner of mulligatawny and pomfret, "you might just find it's my biography you've penned." As for my mother, she had come to know Lady Spenta Cama at meetings of the Bombay Literary Society. Lady Spenta was the least well read of women, but her serene insouciance in the face of her almost Himalayan ignorance inspired in the younger (and immensely more brilliant) Ameer a kind of amused awe that, had events taken a different course, might have deepened towards friendship.

In the nursing home's waiting room, surrounded by the beaming relatives of new-born male children and the determinedly cheerful relatives of new-born girls, my future parents made an odd pair, he wearing a dark suit and a lugubrious expression, she in a plain white sari, without jewellery, and wearing minimal make-up. (Many years later, she confided to me that "I was always certain of your father's love, because when he fell for me I was looking less attractive than a water buffalo.") As the only mourners in a place of rejoicing, it was natural that they should move towards each other and introduce themselves.

Both of them would have been feeling awkward at the prospect of facing Lady Spenta and Sir Darius in what they believed to be a moment of deep grief. My mild, tender-hearted father would have been shifting his weight and smiling his embarrassed, buck-toothed smile on account of a strangling emotional inarticulacy that made it hard for him to reveal to the outside world the great depths of feeling within his breast, and an unworldly temperament that led him to prefer the mustinesses of records offices to the unfathomable messiness of Bombay life. Ameer, my mother—"rich by name, and the real money in the family," in her own subsequent, sardonic self-description—would also have been ill at ease, because neither condolences nor congratulations came easily to her lips. I do not mean to suggest that she was unfeeling or cold; quite the contrary. My mother was a disappointed altruist, an angry woman who had come down to earth expecting a better place, who had landed in the lap of luxury and never recovered from the disillusioning discovery that dismal suffering, not easeful joy, was the human norm. Neither her philanthropy nor her temper tantrums—though both were impressive—sufficed to assuage her disappointment in the planet and her own species. Her reactions to birth and death, shaped and coloured as they were by her sense of having been let down by the cosmos, could therefore seem, to the untutored ear, just a trifle, well, cynical. Or, to be frank, heartless, brutal and mortally offensive too. *Dead baby? What else to expect? He's well out of it, anyway. Living baby?*

Poor kid. Think what he's got in store. That was her natural style.

However, before she could launch on some such speech and alienate my future father forever, she was forestalled by a startling discovery, and history moved, like a railway train diverted by a sudden switching of points, down an entirely different path.

"I am Merchant," my father introduced himself. "Like Vijay, but no relation, though I am also V. In fact, V. V." Ameer frowned, not because she was unaware that Vijay Merchant was a rising star of Indian cricket, but . . .

"How can you be 'Merchant'?" she objected. "You can not be 'Merchant.' I," she pointed at her chest for emphasis, "*I* am Merchant. Ameer."

"You?" (Bewildered.)

"I." (Emphatic.)

"Are Merchant?" (A shake of the head.)

"*A.* Merchant. Miss." (A shrug.)

"Then we are both Merchants," confirmed V. V., wonderingly.

"Don't be silly," Ameer rejoined.

Now V. V. Merchant emitted a long blurt. "Until my grandfather's time we were Shettys or Shetias or Sheths. He Englished it up, standardized it. Also, he converted. Became a sort of bad Muslim. Strictly non-practising, as we have all remained. You may ask, Then why bother? To which I answer only, Why not?"

"Sheths, you say," Ameer mused, sticking to the point.

"And now Merchant."

"So you *are* Merchant," she conceded.

"At your service."

"But not related."

"Misfortunately not."

My mother had come to an important, if still provisional, decision during the above conversation. Beneath V. V. Merchant's shyness and behind his buck teeth she had divined the existence of a great soul, a soul of profound constancy, a rock upon which, as she afterwards liked blasphemously to boast, she could build her church. Therefore, and with great daring, she declared in a voice that permitted no arguments, "Between one merchant and another there is no middle way.

Either we must be sworn rivals or we must merge, as partners."

My father blushed, so deeply that his unkempt and already thinning hair began to quiver with delight.

What social circumstances initiated and nomenclatural coincidence encouraged was further confirmed by the small consoling gifts they had brought for Lady Spenta. With surprise, Mr. V. V. Merchant saw the small bag in Miss Ameer Merchant's hand; with equal surprise, Miss Ameer Merchant noted that Mr. V. V. Merchant was carrying an identical bag. Prominently displayed on both bags was the name of a certain highly respected food store near Kemp's Corner; and within the bags, identical glass jars lay concealed.

"Honey," explained V. V. Merchant. "Honey from the Kashmir Valley. To remind her of the sweetness of life."

"How can it be Kashmiri honey?" cried Ameer. "*This* is Kashmiri honey."

She showed him her jar; he showed her his. She began to be angry, and then, instead, started laughing. My father also laughed.

The handiwork of distant bees had eased the path of love.

Finally, and conclusively, their destiny was incarnated as an angry nun, for at this moment they found themselves faced with the stern, voluminous presence of a woman with a penumbra like a partial eclipse of the sun. "Yes?" barked Sister John, so savagely that, alas, it plunged the already tickled Merchants into a fit of the giggles. "We are here," explained V. V. Merchant, splitting his sides, "to comfort Lady Spenta Cama in her tragic hour."

"Such a terrible thing," my mother lamented, wiping away tears of mirth. "The birth of a dead child."

"Beware," said Sister John, in a voice like Judgement Day. "Or you may burn in hell-fire for your sins."

The waiting room fell silent. The two Merchants, stung by the midwife's admonition, instinctively moved closer together: closing ranks. A hand (his, hers) brushed against another hand (hers, his). In the years that followed, they would always enjoyably disagree about who had made the first move, whose fingers had reached for whose, which of them had been the clasper and which the claspee. What cannot be denied—"forward" and "loose" as the behaviour must undoubtedly be termed—is that Sister John united their hands, which were not often thereafter untwined. Until, many years later, they were driven apart by a third party. Yes, a lover of sorts, or, at any rate, a Beloved. An old lady who was not even a human being. I mean the city itself.

"Anyway," added Sister John, shrugging, "there is a birth as well."

FROM SISTER John the two Merchants now received news of the unlooked-for live arrival whom nobody knew quite how to celebrate, because his birth was so mixed up with the tragedy of Gayomart Cama, who was finished before he began. In Sir Darius's absence, the surly nun was in charge and stood barring my parents' way. "Lady Spenta rests now. Come later." After much persuasion, this embattled quinquereme of a midwife agreed to take Vivvy and Ameer to see the under-sized but undoubtedly finger-wiggling Baby Ormus asleep in his light-filled incubator of glass, lying on his back with one knee raised, not at all unlike a god, with, on his left eyelid, a small purplish bruise, like the shadow of an eyeball. When my mother saw him glowing in that case she could not forbear to say, "Little tom thumb looks more like a snow white in this glass coffin," whereupon two sharp intakes of breath informed her that this ill-advised simile had shocked not only Sister John but Lady Spenta Cama herself, Lady Spenta who had risen to greet her visitors and tottered up behind them to be hit with this ice-cold verbal douche right between the eyes. "Oh," Lady Spenta said, blinking with shock, rooted to the spot, rotating her slack jaw. "A coffin, you say. Oh, my, my. A witch has come to put a curse upon my child."

My father tried stumblingly to pacify her, but it was too late. Too late to salvage things on that not-so-fine day.

I repeat: until the day of Ormus's birth Lady Spenta Cama had been, by nature, almost preternaturally calm. The new wildness of her formulations was thus an indication of the moment's star-crossed, transformational nature. From that time onwards her personality changed, becoming nervy, unsettled, easily flustered. Also, after hearing my mother's so-called curse, Spenta became incapable of loving the accursed child as he deserved. Instead, she shied away from him, as if he bore a disease.

It was thanks to the Ratty-and-Mole affection between Sir Darius Cama and V.V. Merchant—the older man a flamboyant, blazered sportsman and bon vivant, the younger one of life's subfusc burrowers—that an opportunity for making amends was given, and speedily accepted, three weeks later. By then Ameer and Vivvy had become inseparable. They went to Apollo Bunder arm in arm. V. V. Merchant took his Paillard Bolex along, filmed the infant Ormus in his crib and presented the film to Lady Spenta as a peace offering, which she, outwardly restored to her habitual evenness of nature, was prepared to accept. My mother and Ormus's mother, however, never became really close.

But I mustn't get too far ahead of my tale.

AFTER MISS Ameer Merchant's unintentional faux pas, my father quickly escorted my grumpily unembarrassed mother away from the scene. Lady Spenta Cama took to her bed in a frenzy of superstition. Her son Ormus's birthday, already an ambiguous event, had been further stained by Ameer's image of glass-coffined death. And when, soon afterwards, Sister John dolorously brought her the news that Sir Darius Xerxes Cama had run all the way from the cricket match on the Oval Maidan to the emergency room of the Parsi Lying-In Hospital with the limp body of his son Virus in his arms, Lady Spenta's hold on her sanity was, for a time, released.

Ardaviraf Cama regained consciousness in the intensive care unit a few hours later, apparently suffering from nothing worse than concussion and double vision. His reluctance to speak was ascribed by doctors to shock. Soon, however, it became plain that his mind had been impaired. He stopped speaking entirely, and responded to questions with slow, sad nods or melancholic shakes of the head. However, gradually even these gestures ceased, and Virus retreated into an impassive silence from which he would never emerge. As if he had become a photograph of himself. As if he were a motion picture, a "talkie" unaccountably denuded of its sound track, restored to the era before sound, without so much as the addition of title cards or piano accompaniment. As if his father's misdirected drive had so damaged his faith in all fathers, his trust in trust itself, as to necessitate this permanent retreat.

Though he would not speak, he did react to simple requests and commands. If told there was food on the table, he would quietly sit down to eat. When instructed that it was time for bed, he went to his room without a word and lay with his face to the wall. It was not long before the best medical opinion in town declared itself incapable of helping him any further. He went back to his studies at the Cathedral School, where, during lessons, he sat at his desk much as before, but never raised his hand to speak or deigned to answer any teacher's questions. After an initial period of adjustment the school accepted the new state of affairs. Virus had always been a slow child, and was slower now, but the teachers were willing to let him stay on and listen in the hope that he might improve over time.

It also became obvious that Virus no longer wished to participate in games of any sort. At school, in break periods, he sat cross-legged in a corner of the quad with, on his face, a yogi's look of perfect meditative calm, apparently oblivious to the rackety mayhem around him. Wordlessly, as he grew, he absented himself from all sporting activities, field hockey as well as cricket, and athletics too. That was the year the Maharaja of Patiala found time to open the great Brabourne Stadium in between his various extramarital liaisons, and the School Sports Day was held in that august location thereafter. On Sports Day, however, Virus would simply stay in bed, wearing his customary look of serene absence, and nobody had the heart to force him out of doors. After school hours, his twin brother Cyrus and his friends often tried, without luck, to entice him into their street games of seven-tiles or gilli-danda. Even board and card games were banished from Virus's life: Carrom and rummy, Totopoly and Happy Families, Chinese chequers and Snap. He had moved into the mystery of inner space and had no time for play.

Faced with a child who, at the age of five, had decided to put away childish things, Sir Darius Xerxes Cama punished himself by giving up his beloved game of cricket forever; also his lesser loves, wrestling, fencing, swimming and squash. And because as well as himself he blamed music for having caused the accident, music of all types was banned from the Cama apartment, without hope of return. Sir Darius sold the radiogram and broke every record in his collection, and when, during the wedding season, rowdy processions would pass along Apollo Bunder en route to receptions at the Taj Hotel, he would rush about in a frenzy, slamming windows so as to shut out the wedding guests' songs. Cyrus and Virus had begun to receive lessons on the piano and the Indian flute. These were halted. The teacher was dismissed and the baby grand in the drawing room was locked. At her husband's request, Lady Spenta Cama placed the key in a silver locket, which for many years she wore around her neck.

Virus's silence became familiar, even pleasant. Sir Darius realized he was actually relieved that his afflicted son never disturbed the peace of the breakfast table by chirping up with goodness knows what meaningless childish remarks. His silence had gravitas. It was, Sir Darius decided, eloquent. History was going the wrong way. Virus's silence began to look like a grand refusal. The Independence bandwagon was rolling now—Independence, whose mob of hooligan supporters had provoked Sir Darius into injuring his own child!—and the *Pax Britannica* would shortly be at an end. "Bad times ahead," Sir Darius took to saying. "Too many people spouting too many words, and in the end those words will turn to bullets and stones. Ardaviraf's silence speaks for all of us who fear the power of these metamorphic words."

So it was that Sir Darius Xerxes Cama half persuaded himself that his son Virus's muteness was in fact a kind of sophisticated speech. This made him feel a little better, but curiously, as he exonerated himself from at least some portion of blame, his anti-musical rhetoric grew more extreme. He began to hold music responsible for the world's ills and would even argue, in his cups, that its practitioners should be wiped out, eradicated, like a disease. Music was a virus, an infection, and music-lovers were comparable to those globe-trotting sexual immoralists whose nameless activities had resulted in the global spread of syphilis. They were sick, and it was Virus Cama, with his dignified silence, who was well.

* * *

After Virus's retreat into silence, Lady Spenta beat a retreat of her own, into that spiritual world which now, more than ever, seemed like a better habitation than our own. "I know where my son has gone," she announced to her husband in a tone that brooked no argument. "He has crossed the Chinvat Bridge on his soul's journey. It is for us to keep his body safe until his soul's return." With the aid of her ally the Angel Orderly Righteousness, she dedicated herself to this task, washing Virus's body in the bath as if he were a baby, spoon-feeding him at mealtimes as if he did not know how to use his own hands. "All his efforts are engaged in his mighty journey through the otherworld," she explained. "So we must spare him worldly exertion of all types." To all these ministrations Virus Cama passively submitted, showing neither pleasure nor dislike. Nor could Sir Darius, with his heavy burden of guilt, find it in his heart to object.

The washing and feeding of Baby Ormus, however, was left in the hands of the household's employees.

Virus Cama had been named after a Zoroastrian mystic who lived at some point between the third and seventh centuries of the Christian Era and left behind him a detailed account of the journey on which Lady Spenta was convinced that her son had also embarked. If she was right, then on the Chinvat Bridge to the world of the spirit Virus Cama first witnessed a dead soul's encounter with the incarnation of his own good deeds, a beautiful girl whose enormous breasts "swelled downwards, which is charming to heart and soul," and was then guided by the Angel Divine Obedience and the Angel Flaming Fire of Thought on a tour of the limbo of the Permanently Still, where those who were equally good and sinful were transformed into statues; the place of the stars and the moon, where those who were irreligious but good in other ways had ended up; and past higher levels of virtue and radiance to the pure light of Ahura Mazda himself; and then—for this was a journey in the opposite direction to Dante's—he had a good long look at Hell, where snakes crawled into men's arseholes and emerged from their mouths, etc. He would have noted the extraordinary concentration upon the female breast and also on excreta, and the ferocious glee with which the legions of the sinful were gnawed by Noxious Beasts. Adulteresses were hung by their breasts, or forced to gash their breasts with iron combs; women who had not breast-fed their children were obliged to use their breasts to dig into rocky hills. Urinating while standing up was punished especially harshly, and women who approached water or fire during menstruation were forced to eat cup after cup of male piss and shit. It is scarcely to be wondered at that Lady Spenta, imagining her Ardaviraf following her namesake on this jaunt, should become obsessed with keeping him clean and feeding him from less vilely replenished cups.

The longer Virus Cama's silence lasted, the more desperate Lady Spenta grew. She had come to rely so much upon the fantasy of her son's journey, from which he must surely return, that it began to engulf her, as if she were the soul crossing the Chinvat Bridge to see great and terrible sights, to be faced with the droopy-bosomed evidence of her good deeds and the suppurating manifestations of her sins. When she was not busy with Virus and his needs, she wore an absent yet uncalm look, and behaved in a manner at once agitated and remote. (To Ormus she continued to be distant, never fond. Events had neutered her maternal feelings towards him. Raised by servants, he was left to find love where he could.)

What a cricket ball started could not be stopped. One by one, the members of the Cama family were seceding from reality into private worlds of their own.

Sir Darius Xerxes Cama himself became the next member of his family to withdraw from everyday life. The Law, which had given him such moral sustenance all his adult life, had become, as many of his colleagues had begun openly to proclaim, "an ass." In this period the imperial administration had begun to use the full force of the legal system against the nationalists, and even though Sir Darius was a leading advocate of British civilisation and opponent of the Congress, he began to experience a profound sense of unease at what was going on. Many of his respected colleagues had joined the Independence johnnies, whose leader, Mr. Gandhi, was after all a pretty crafty legal eagle himself. Taken by surprise by the storm within himself, Sir Darius Xerxes Cama gave up his practice and retreated into the sumptuous library of classical texts which was the glory of the Apollo Bunder apartment, and he sought in the groves of scholarship that peace of mind which had been so comprehensively destroyed by the private and public history of his time.

Along with his fellow Freemason William Methwold, Sir Darius began an investigation of Indo-European myths. Methwold was a wealthy Englishman from a family of landowners and diplomats, and as a property developer had had a hand in many of the new villas and apartment blocks springing up on Malabar Hill and along Warden Road. Rendered egg-bald by alopecia, a condition which he concealed beneath a wig, he was a brilliant Greek scholar, and plunged into Sir Darius's library with the thirst of a parched wanderer who stumbles upon the purest mountain stream. Sir Darius Xerxes Cama had in his younger days fallen under the influence of the German-born scholar Max Müller, whose work in comparative mythology had led him to the conclusion that all the ancient myths of the Proto-Indo-European or Aryan cultures—Zoroastrians, Indians, Greeks—were in essence stories about the sun. This theory pleased a secularized Parsi like Sir Darius, who saw in it the rational source of the spiritual flummery that had gained almost complete mastery over his beloved wife. (Ahura Mazda, Ormazd, Hormuz was after all nothing else but Light; and Apollo was the sun.) However, after Müller's disciples attempted to prove that Jesus Christ and his disciples were nothing more than fairy-tale versions of the sun and the twelve signs of the zodiac, William Methwold had turned against "solar mythology," and at meetings of the Malabar Hill Lodge, to which they both belonged, he outraged Sir Darius by a brilliant series of spoof monologues in which he proved, first, that the Emperor Napoleon and his dozen generals were, like Christ and his followers, no more than zodiacal fictions; and, second, that Oxford University and Professor Müller himself could not possibly exist, either. Methwold hurled at Müller's philosophy the attacks formulated by the Scots journalist Andrew Lang, who held that there was no need for these unprovable Aryan theories; the gods of the Greeks had simply emerged from the large number of savage beliefs the world over. "Savage beliefs?" Sir Darius had roared, coming to his feet, brandy in hand, and silencing the lodge. "Including ours, I suppose?" William Methwold held his ground. "There are barbarians the world over, my dear fellow," he equably rejoined. "Present company excepted, of course."

For a time, the two friends saw little of each other. They patched things up when William Methwold came over a few months before the day of Ormus's birth and Virus's accident to applaud Sir Darius's victory in a local badminton tourney. Over tumblers of Scotch, Methwold admitted that he had been lured back into the Aryan fold by the work of the Frenchman Georges Dumézil, who had "shown" that the Greek god Ouranos was none other than India's own Varuna, thus proving the common heritage of all Aryan culture. "Good show," cried Sir Darius, happily. "We both turned out to be barbarians, after all."

During the next few years, Sir Darius and Methwold met from time to time to explore the relationships between the Homeric and Indian mythological traditions. The abduction of Helen of Troy by Paris and that of Sita of Ayodhya by the demon king Ravana; the relationship between Hanuman, the wily monkey god, and the devious Odysseus; the parallels between the tragedy of the House of Atreus and that of Rama's clan: these and many other matters, like the gentlemen scholars they were, they expatiated upon and enjoyed. Sir Darius was particularly drawn to the so-called tripartite theory of Dumézil. Could it be true that all Aryan cultures rested on the triple concept of religious sovereignty, physical force and fertility—that this was the real Trinity that defined both Eastern and Western civilisation, their common bond? In the time after he gave up the Bar, this became the great question of Sir Darius Xerxes Cama's life. With William Methwold by his side, he plunged deeper and deeper into the technical aspects of the problem, and the further from the surface of life they journeyed, the happier they became. Outside the library, the last phases of the colonial history of England and India took their well-known course, and a great war, greater than the wars over Helen and Sita, was brewing. But Sir Darius and William Methwold had sealed themselves away from the contemporary and sought refuge in the eternal. Inside the Cama library, Odysseus became a monkey god and Paris a demon king, and the Parsi knight and the English property-wallah grew so close that it became hard to tell them apart. Sir Darius lost much of his hair; William Methwold divested himself of his black wig and hung it on the back of his chair. And in the privacy of the universe of books, at an oak table groaning with ancient learning, they worked in joyful solitude, eternally alone except, on occasion, for the silent phantom-like figure of Virus Cama, sitting solemnly on a step stool in a corner.

One day, however, Sir Darius took off his half-rimmed spectacles, banged his fist on the table and shouted: "It isn't enough."

William Methwold looked up from his books, startled. What wasn't enough? Could Sir Darius conceivably be tiring of this idyllic existence, which had given them both such pleasure? "P-perhaps you could reconsider your self-denying ordinance," he stammered, "and we could have a game of squash. *Mens sana,* you know, *in* bally *corpore sano.*" Sir Darius made a dismissive noise. He was trembling on the edge of new knowledge, and this was no time for squash.

"Three functions aren't enough," he said feverishly. "There must be a fourth."

"Can't be," said Methwold. "Those three concepts of old Georges's fill out the insides of the whole social picture."

"Yes," said Sir Darius. "But what about *outsideness*? What about all that which is beyond the pale, above the fray, beneath notice? What about outcastes, lepers, pariahs, exiles, enemies, spooks, paradoxes? What about those who are remote? Damn it," and here he turned to face his silent child, sitting in the shadows of the room, *"what about Virus?"*

"I'm not sure I understand." William Methwold was out of his depth.

"What about people who just don't belong?"

"Where? Belong where?"

"Anywhere. To anything, to anyone. The psychically unattached. Comets travelling through space, staying free of all gravitational fields."

"If there are people like that," Methwold offered, "aren't they, well, *rarae aves*? Few and far between? Does one really need a fourth concept to explain them? Aren't they, well, like waste paper, and all the stuff one puts in the bin?

Aren't they simply surplus to requirements? Not wanted on the voyage? Don't we just cross them off the list? Cut them? Blackball them out of the club?"

But Sir Darius Xerxes Cama wasn't listening. He was standing at the great window of the library, staring out at the Arabian Sea. "The only people who see the whole picture," he murmured, "are the ones who step out of the frame."

TRY TO imagine the scene: the Parsi grandee in the sanctum of his library, with his English friend and the living ghost of his child, a man driven by life into books, standing by an open window. So he's not completely sealed off, the library isn't a closed tomb, and through the window comes all the tumultuous sensation of the city: the scents of channa and bhel, of tamarind and jasmine; the shouting voices, because nobody ever says anything in these parts without first raising his voice; and the quarrel of traffic, the hooves, the sputtering exhausts, the bicycle bells; the brilliant light of the sun on the harbour, the hooting of warships and the electricity of a society at a point of transformation.

Now imagine a gust of wind, sweeping a crumpled page of newsprint off the filthy street, tossing it upwards in slow spirals like a dirty butterfly; until at last it passes through the window, the outside world penetrates the world within, and lands neatly by Sir Darius's polished oxfords, pleading for attention. This is a picture I keep seeing, although it couldn't be, could it, how it really happened. Maybe someone wrote Sir Darius a letter; or he chanced upon a learned journal which contained the information that broke his heart. Prefer, if you please, some such prosaic version, but I'll stick with mine. Through the window came the newspaper, and Sir Darius, picking it up distastefully, was on the point of disposing of it when four words caught his eye. *Aryan, Nazi, Müller, Dumézil.*

Neither Sir Darius Xerxes Cama nor William Methwold ever believed for a moment that either of the great maligned scholars, dead Max or living Georges, had had a single racial-supremacist cell in his body. But when language is stolen and poisoned, the poison works its way backwards through time and sideways into the reputations of innocent men. The word "Aryan," which, for Max Müller and his generation, had a purely linguistic meaning, was now in the hands of less academic persons, poisoners, who were speaking of races of men, races of masters and races of servants and other races too, races whose fundamental impurity necessitated drastic measures, races who were not wanted on the voyage, who were surplus to requirements, races to be cut, blackballed and deposited in the bin of history. By one of the wild improbabilities that, taken collectively, represent the history of the human race, the arcane field of research in which Sir Darius and William Methwold had chosen to sequester themselves had been twisted and pressed into the service of the great evil of the age. History had captured their field, and their love of it had placed them on the wrong side—the side of the poisoners, of the unutterable, of those whose crime was beyond words.

At the moment when things changed for them, Sir Darius and Methwold had been full of the delight of examining the parallels between the Viewing from the Walls in the *Iliad* (when the Trojans survey the besieging army while, for their benefit, Helen identifies Agamemnon, Odysseus, Idomeneus and the greater Ajax) and the similar scene in the *Ramayana* (in which a pair of spies, standing with the abductor Ravana on the ramparts of his fortress, identify the heroes Rama, Lakshmana, Vibhishana and Hanuman). Sir Darius read the scrap of newspaper that had blown in through the window and passed it to Methwold without saying a word. When the Englishman had finished reading, he shook himself, as if emerging from a long sleep, and said, "Let's call it quits." Sir Darius inclined his head and began to close the beloved books. It was September 1939. Rip van Cama and William Winkle stumbled blinking into the light, the roar, the stink of the real world.

"One of these days," Sir Darius mumbled as Methwold replaced his wig on his head and took his leave, "let's have that game of squash."

AFTER HE gave up the study of comparative mythology, Sir Darius Xerxes Cama began to change. He saw little of William Methwold, who, it was rumoured, had developed a predilection for Indian women from the bottom of the social scale. Breaking the vow he had made after injuring his son

Ardaviraf, Sir Darius also returned to the pursuit of sporting excellence: not cricket, admittedly, but wrestling, badminton, squash. His regular opponent was the much younger Homi Catrack, and even though Sir Darius was the more gifted athlete of the two, and a tormented soul who needed the release of physical effort, the years had taken their toll, and he lost more contests than he won. The two individuals who suffered most as a result of Sir Darius's decline were his sons Cyrus and Ormus, both of whom he took to berating regularly on the subject of the decay of Parsi youth, whose alleged feebleness Sir Darius had begun to hold in contempt. The worse he played, the more vociferously he accused the next generation of decadence, of defeatism, of weakness, of homosexuality. He made the boys arm-wrestle him and laughed in their faces when he won. In that apartment which had grown accustomed to many different kinds of tragic silence, to those collected silences which had driven away friends, colleagues, even my own parents, this new, bullying sound of bombast was doubly shocking.

Three years went by. Sir Darius Xerxes Cama took to drink. (It was a time of total prohibition, but for men of Sir Darius's breeding and connections, there was always a bottle to be found.) He took to hemp and opium. Homi Catrack led him into the dark side of the city and showed him a world whose existence he had never suspected. The lower he sank, the louder grew his remonstrations. Returning from the cages of Kamathipura, from the rooms of the dancing whores, he would often shake his sons awake to accuse them of moral turpitude, of going to hell, to the dogs, to pot. Ten-year-old Cyrus and five-year-old Ormus heard him out and never said a word. Being Camas, they knew how to armour themselves in dumbness. Whatever they said would have fanned his hypocritical fire; elder and younger child knew enough to remain mute.

The early years of Ormus Cama imprisoned him within an emotional isolation so oppressive that he temporarily lost the ability to sing. From the moment of his birth, he had given many extraordinary indications of the depth of his precocious musical talent—not only the chord progressions of his finger movements but also the syncopated drumming of his tiny feet against his crib and the perfect-pitch gurgles that went up and down the musical scale, *saregama padhanisa, sanidhapa magaresa*. But his mother was lost in mysticism, his brother Virus was cocooned in silence, and his father wasn't listening. Only Cyrus Cama, his older brother, was paying attention, and Cyrus's heart was full of hatred.

Unnerved by his twin brother Ardaviraf's transformation into a zip-lipped zombie, and unwilling to blame either his father or poor Virus himself for the calamity, Cyrus had decided to blame his baby brother. "If Daddy hadn't been up all night waiting for Ormus to get himself born," he wrote in the diary he kept hidden under his mattress, "then it is certain-sure that his hit would have gone straight down one of those stupid hecklers' throats." In those days Cyrus worshipped his father and spared no effort to please him. But when he topped the class he returned home, report card in hand, to hear a tirade on the decline of the intellect of Parsi children; when he starred in junior races at the Brabourne Stadium Sports Day, his father declined to come and watch. Afterwards, when Cyrus came home loaded with little silver trophies, Sir Darius would pour scorn on his competitors. "Such namby-pamby weaklings you must've run and jumped against, no wonder you beat the lot." Cyrus, unable to blame his father for these cruelties, directed all his anger towards his brother Ormus instead.

One night in 1942, Cyrus Cama was woken in the middle of the night by the sound of little Ormus, with whom he still shared a room, singing in his sleep, so sweetly that birds had woken, thinking the dawn had come, and gathered on his windowsill to listen. This sleeper's melody contained such joy in life, such optimism and hope, that it drove Cyrus Cama insane, and clutching his pillow in his hand he went to Ormus's bed, intent on murder. The family ayah, Roxana, was asleep on a mat on the bedroom floor. This was the same slow-reacting ayah who had been standing beside Virus Cama when the cricket ball struck him, but on this occasion she more than redeemed herself, because she too had been woken by Ormus's singing, she had been lying peacefully on her mat in the moonlit bedroom, enjoying the sleeping child's song, so she saw Cyrus place his pillow over his brother's face and hold it there. The song stopped, the birds screamed, little Ormus's arms and legs began to kick, and Roxana threw herself at Cyrus Cama and dragged him weeping away.

"I couldn't stand it," was Cyrus's only explanation to his parents, Lady Spenta loose of hair and wild of eye, Sir Darius in his dressing gown, rubbing his head. "I couldn't stand the noise."

Sound and silence, silence and sound. This is a story of lives pulled together and pushed apart by what happens in (and between) our ears. Cyrus Cama was sent away to boarding school, still with murder in his eyes, banished to an implacable hill-station establishment which based its methods upon the tried and true British principles of cold baths, bad food, regular beatings and high-quality academic instruction, and which helped him to develop into the full-blooded psychopath he afterwards became.

And Ormus? Ormus Cama did not sing again for fourteen years. Not a ditty, not a warble, not a note. Not until Vina Apsara set his music free.

Sir Darius Xerxes Cama's gradual decline slowly stripped away the stiff veneer of decorum beneath which his true nature had lain concealed most of his life, revealing the prodigious vanity under that formal exterior, taking the brakes off the love of showing off which was his Achilles' heel. At the wealthy Malabar Hill Masonic Lodge, where he spent much of his leisure time among the leading officials of the fraying Raj and their local cronies, there was ample opportunity for self-display. In 1942, at one of the grand, men-only, bimonthly dinners held by the lodge, Sir Darius Xerxes Cama in his cups gave a performance that nobody who witnessed it ever forgot. After eating heartily, in a manner resolutely unaffected by the food shortages and rationing laws, the membership retired to a noble smoking room complete with humidor and string quartet, where the blackout drapes over the windows were the only concessions to the realities of the age; however, by way of compensation, an excellent supply of imported brandies and whiskies was available to members, in spite of the prohibition laws. In this congenial setting, the great men relaxed, telling ribald jokes, demonstrating bits of card magic, oiling the wheels of business and Empire, and doing party tricks. Sir Darius—drunk, opium-addled, filled with self-hatred—ordered the tail-coated musicians to "have a bash" at the movie tune "We're Off to See the Wizard (The Wonderful Wizard of Oz)." Sir Darius, the music hater! Sir Darius, the declaimer of interminable jeremiads against anything with a tune, making a musical request! Well, *that* got everyone's attention.

As the band struck up, Sir Darius Xerxes Cama stripped off his dress shirt and treated the cream of British-Indian Bombay—wartime Bombay, in which the nationalist movement was gathering momentum and every one of these high colonial nights felt a little more like a last waltz than the one before—to the idiosyncratic art of Musical Muscle Control. His pectoral and abdominal muscles jerking along to the music like tango dancers with roses between their teeth, or skirt-swirling, sliding and twirling queens of the jitterbug or lindy hop, he cried out, "This is what we could do in our heyday! Behold mind and body working as one! Behold the perfect union of the intellectual and physical spheres!" At the end of the performance, buttoning up his shirt, he bowed and declared, like a fabulist delivering the moral of his tale: *"Mens sana in corpore sano."* His fellow Masons responded with a weary politeness that concealed their mild, end-of-Empire ennui.

I can only imagine that Sir Darius was introduced to this garish skill by some louche crony of his fellow Mason Homi Catrack's, in a den on Falkland Road. That he had not walked away from the demonstration with a haughty laugh, that he had, in fact, returned week after week and actually learned the trick of it, is a sign of how far he had fallen, of the vulgarity that had entered that once noble soul. Or to put it another way: it showed that for all his bluster, he was indeed his son's father. His son Ormus, I mean, the future star of stars.

In more robust imperial times such outré exhibitionism—too extreme even by Masonic standards—would undoubtedly have tarnished Sir Darius's reputation and might have damaged his legal practice, but he had retired and was therefore invulnerable; besides, these were demoralized, rudderless days for the smart set that revolved around the British Presence in India. Suicides and crack-ups were not infrequent events. A cigar-smoking Parsi grandee removing his shirt and twitching his muscles to music seemed relatively mild by comparison. All present understood his pain and could foretell the future: his future, their own. Anglophilia, for so long the basis of these people's ascendancy, would henceforth be like the mark of Cain. It would be the dark star hanging over their interminable but also irreversible decline.

One day in 1942, soon after the Quit India Resolution was launched from the maidan at Gowalia Tank, leading to the eruption across the city of violent demonstrations, lootings and acts of arson in the wake of Mr. Gandhi's immediate arrest, Sir Darius Xerxes Cama spoke heated words on the subject of the "country's surrender to mob rule and firestarters" and added, for the first time, a thought that was to become an obsession. "Anyway, Bombay isn't India. The British built her and the Parsis gave her her character. Let them have their independence elsewhere if they must, but leave us our Bombay under beneficent Parsi-British rule."

Sir Darius was persuaded by Homi Catrack, to whom he had addressed this *cri de coeur*, to venture out of his shrinking Anglocentric milieu and "meet the future." Homi was a cards-and-horses gambler and a movie producer with—in spite of his rolled trouser leg and his activities "on the square"—a surprising commitment to the nationalist movement concealed behind his Brylcreem-and-cravat, playboy-or-gigolo smoothery. Sir Darius had started regarding him as something of a race traitor (for were not the Parsis' interests inseparable from those of the British, whose presence they had so vigorously supported, whose culture they had so successfully integrated with their own?). But the fellow's charm was irresistible, and his prowess at badminton and squash and even golf was the equal—all too often, gallingly, more than the equal!—of Sir Darius's own. "Rackets and clubs," Homi Catrack panted as they sweated happily in the nude democracy of the Wellesley Club locker room. "That's the kind of guy you're dealing with here. A clubman, *par excellence*. And, in his very water, a racketeer." He actually winked at Sir Darius to emphasize the play on words.

Wink or no wink, Homi was telling the simple truth, for in addition to being a member of every worthwhile club in the city, from the (now-defunct) Wellesley to the Governors of the Mahalaxmi Racecourse, he had also, during those days of scarcities, made a rogue's fortune by cornering the market in cement, and also from a chain of bootleg stills and illegal speakeasies. It is said that Homi Catrack was the first man to use the term "parallel economy" and that his stashes of black money would, if piled high, have formed an edifice larger than the Gateway of India. It is one of the paradoxes of human nature that this same Homi, who profited so greatly from the turmoil of the 1940s, was one of the greatest admirers of the "honest men who would clean up India," as he called the Congress leadership. His rage at Gandhi's arrest was genuine and intense.

In the locker room after a keen contest which, for once, he had narrowly won, Sir Darius Xerxes Cama was in generous mood, imagining himself in ancient Greece or Persia, sweating among philosophers, discoboli, chariot racers, sprinters, maguses and kings. In the grip of such a reverie, he was inclined to forgive a wink, and an invitation to the future seemed appropriate enough. "Very well," he glowered, tolerantly. "Let us see what type of scum is presently rising to the top."

The future turned out to be a bunch of bohemians, painters, writers and movie people, who gathered to drink whisky and discuss civil disobedience in Homi's substantial apartment (with partially obstructed sea view) in an Art Deco apartment block called Côte d' Azur on Warden Road. Within minutes Sir Darius Xerxes Cama knew it had been a mistake to come. He felt like a visitor from the moon, an alienated alien, unable to breathe this heady, illicit air. He moved uncertainly at the fringes of the night, largely ignored in spite of his striking physical presence—the fez, the moustache, the long frock coat, the natural physical grace of his movements, the fierce shine of power in his eyes: human power, that is, the force that comes from a man's nature and cannot be learned, or bought, or bestowed.

Clusters of intellectuals had formed around certain beautiful women—the starlet Pia Aziz, the artist Aurora Zogoiby—while most of the other women in the room were sitting at the feet of a boozy but celebrated Muslim writer of low-life stories who was shocking them by providing, in the most exquisite and ornate Urdu Sir Darius Xerxes Cama had ever heard, detailed and hair-raising descriptions of the worst things in the world, undisguised by circumlocution, unfettered by good taste. He spoke naturally in that famous glittering prose which was somehow both voluptuous and precise, at once dainty and appalling, telling tales of the degraded interiors of the local insane asylums, of the brutal murders and casual rapes that were the city's hidden news, of the corruption of those in authority and the violence in the hearts of the poor, of incestuous love affairs in high society and the killing of daughters in the slums, of the caged whores of Falkland Road and of the mafias who ran the city's organized crime as well as its prostitution and would order men's penises to be severed as casually as they would call for a bunch of red bananas in the bazaar. The contradiction between the high jewellery work of the writer's language and the pornographic nature of his material left Sir Darius more shocked and revolted than he felt able to show. Also, of course, he was rather more familiar with some of the storyteller's source material than he cared to reveal.

He turned away and half collided with the only Englishman at the gathering. It was William Methwold, whom he hadn't seen in years. "And how do *you* come to be here?" Sir Darius in his unnerved condition found himself speaking more bluntly than was polite, and immediately attempted to apologize. "I'm afraid I'm out of sorts," he began, but Methwold stopped him, and greeted him with evident affection.

"I'm a little disoriented myself," he said. "But then that's our destiny, as most of the assembled company would readily agree. And to answer your question, I have a house Mr. Catrack wants to buy. And there will come a time when I want to sell it."

They left it at that and began to drink seriously. Human history clanked along, and the hot, blind stars wheeled overhead. They mentioned neither Homer nor Max Müller, neither the *Ramayana* nor Dumézil. It was a night for whisky and defeat. Sir Darius Xerxes Cama forgot his wife waiting for him in the Apollo Bunder apartment, forgot his sleeping sons, forgot where he was, forgot himself, drank too heavily, and at a certain point he tore open his shirt and, bellowing out the words of "Let's Do It (Let's Fall in Love)," introduced the gathering to the gentle art of Musical Muscle Control. His fellow guests fell silent; even the obscene writer's oral narratives were stilled; and when Sir Darius Xerxes Cama finished, with a blurted *"Mens sana in corpore sàno,"* he understood in spite of his drunken stupor that what was acceptable among the bread-roll-hurling, jolly-jape-urinating, Eton-and-Oxford, men-only Freemasonry of the last years of British India had led, on this occasion, in more radical, and mixed, society, to his making a great ass of himself. Nobody spoke for a long moment, though there were several suppressed giggles and loud, irrepressible snorts of joy. Then Aurora Zogoiby, that damned painter woman with the sharp tongue, spoke up loud and clear, and stabbed him in the heart.

"Quoteofy your Latin tags by all means, Daryoosh darling," she drawled, "but the general opinion round here is that this *corpore* of yours is stark raving *insano.* As, quite possibly, Sir Circus Camasaurus, are you."

Sir Darius Xerxes Cama never met Aurora Zogoiby again. They lived in a great city, a metropolis of many narratives that converged briefly and then separated for ever, discovering their different dooms in that crowd of stories through which all of us, following our own destinies, had to push and shove to find our way through, or out. In Bombay the stories jostled you in the street, you stepped over their sleeping forms on the sidewalks or in the doorways of pharmacies, they hung off the local trains and fell to their deaths from the doors of B.E.S.T. buses or—once upon a time but no more—under an onrushing tram. Aurora the painter forgot the inebriated lawyer soon enough, never gave him another thought, but Sir Darius carried her words to the grave, like a spear.

He came to a decision. Homi Catrack and his vaunted "future" had nothing to offer him. He would dissociate himself from them both. He was, after all, a clown, a dinosaur, a species on the verge of extinction. Something immense was about to strike his world, and the cloud the impact threw up would obliterate the likes of him. Very well. Let it be so. He would make of his remaining days a lament for the mistakes of progress and the failure of the young to learn the lessons of the past. He would be a terror, as the great lizards had been, the terror of the earth, until the long night fell.

He was a natural leader of men caught in a dead end of history and deprived of followers. Where he led was backwards, in a direction nobody wanted to go. He was a father who loved his sons and came to be hated by all of them because of the harangue that never ended, the critique that reached no final summation but surged on through the days of their youth, while they, swimmers caught by the mighty wave of his disappointment, fought for breath and feared at every moment that they might drown.

And Ormus Cama, who ran furthest from his shadow, was the child most shaped by him, the only one in all the family who would always secretly acknowledge his own kinship with his father's exhibitionist streak, and of course his muscles' vulnerability to cheap music, which made them bop and twitch.

MY OWN mother, Mrs. Ameer Merchant, correctly prophesied a further problem for young Ormus. While everyone's attention was focused on the accident to Virus, on Cyrus's murderous streak, on the mystical absentness of Lady Spenta and the decay of Sir Darius, it was Ameer who kept her eye on the ball. "It is not Cyrus or Virus who is that boy's twin," she pointed out. "The disaster that sealed his fate didn't happen on any cricket pitch but inside his mother, before he was even born." For many years after Ormus and I unexpectedly became pals, in spite of the ten-year difference in our ages, my mother would return to her theme. "Born in his dead brother's shadow," she would say, tut-tutting, shaking her head. "He never could get out of it. Doesn't matter how far he ran, that dead boy's shadow was stuck hard to his heels. Doesn't matter that he ran right round the world a hundred and one times. His fate was sealed there and then, before he took one step down his badmash road."

SUCH WERE the factors that detached Ormus Cama from the ordinary ties of family life. The ties that strangle us, which we call love. Because of the loosening of these ties he became, with all the attendant pain of such becoming, free.

But love is what we want, not freedom. Who then is the unluckier man? The beloved, who is given his heart's desire and must for ever after fear its loss, or the free man, with his unlooked-for liberty, naked and alone between the captive armies of the earth?

MY MOTHER'S intuition proved to be correct. Born in his dead twin's shadow, Ormus Cama turned out to be what the ancients called a psychopomp, one concerned with the retrieval of lost souls, the souls of the beloved dead. As he grew older, he began to suffer from the family affliction of silence, of inwardness. In the beginning, until the miracle of the music, he feared, but could do nothing to resist, these spells of what he called "Cama obscura." During these "darknesses," Ormus would lie still, with his eyes shut, for hours on end, while the purple stain on his eyelid seemed to be searching the empires of the unseen, probing the depths of the worlds that lay concealed beneath the surface of the apparent, hunting (and eventually finding) Gayomart.

After the death by spearing of mortal Castor, Polydeuces the son of Zeus spent alternate days below the earth with his dead brother, at a place named Therapne; and in return the dead twin was allowed to spend alternate days with his brother on the surface, with the ground beneath his feet instead of over his head. Gayomart Cama did not return, however; unless it was in the form my mother named, as Ormus's shadow, conceived of as something like that roguish, independent silhouette which once escaped from Peter Pan until sewn back to his feet by Wendy Darling. For it was true that Ormus had shadow selves, the many Others who plagued and came to define his life. It might not be so fanciful (my own nature has a weakness for fancy) to say that his dead twin was, in the shifting shape of Ormus's monochrome, protean shade, still alive.

"MY LITTLE Ormie," Lady Spenta Cama had once greeted her unexpected son. *"My little shrimpy boy. Now you're safe from Hell. Now they can't open up the ground and take you down."* But Lady Spenta was wrong about the ground beneath his feet. I'm not saying that he was carried by demons down to some ancient supernatural inferno. No, no. But chasms did open. They can, and did. They consumed his love, stole his Vina from him and would not give her up. And they did send him, as we shall see, all the way to Hell and back.

The ground, the ground beneath our feet. My father the mole could have told Lady Spenta a thing or two about the unsolidity of solid ground. The tunnels of pipe and cable, the sunken graveyards, the layered uncertainty of the past. The gaps in the earth through which our history seeps and is at once lost, and retained in metamorphosed form. The underworlds at which we dare not guess.

We find ground on which to make our stand. In India, that place obsessed by place, belonging-to-your-place, knowing-your-place, we are mostly given that territory, and that's that, no arguments, get on with it. But Ormus and Vina and I, we couldn't accept that, we came loose. Among the great struggles of man—good/evil, reason/unreason, etc.—there is also this mighty conflict between the fantasy of Home and the fantasy of Away, the dream of roots and the mirage of the journey. And if you are Ormus Cama, if you are Vina Apsara, whose songs could cross all frontiers, even the frontiers of people's hearts, then perhaps you believed all ground could be skipped over, all frontiers would crumble before the sorcery of the tune. Off you'd go, off your turf, beyond family and clan and nation and race, flying untouchably over the minefields of taboo, until you stood at last at the last gateway, the most forbidden of all doors. Where your blood sings in your ears, *Don't even think about it.* And you think about it, you cross that final frontier, and perhaps, perhaps—we'll see how the tale works out—you have finally gone too far, and are destroyed.

"At the frontier of the skin." They made a song about it, as they did about everything. You remember it. You remember the nasal elongation of his phrasing, and above and behind him the high purity of her voice. You remember his words, her words. If you remember the music the words are impossible to forget. At the frontier of the skin no dogs patrol. That was it. At the frontier of the skin. Where I end and you begin. Where I cross from sin to sin. Abandon hope and enter in. And lose my soul. At the frontier of the skin no guards patrol.

Yeah, but there was a second verse. At the frontier of the skin mad dogs patrol. At the frontier of the skin. Where they kill to keep you in. Where you must not slip your skin. Or change your rôle. You can't pass out I can't pass in. You must end as you begin. Or lose your soul. At the frontier of the skin armed guards patrol.

Vina Apsara, the beautiful, the dead. Her very name, too good for this world. Vina, the Indian lyre. Apsara, from *apsaras,* a swanlike water nymph. (In Western terms, a naiad, not a dryad.) Look out, Vina. Nymph, watch your step. Beware the ground beneath your feet.

CHAPTER THREE

Legends of Thrace

Nobody in my family could sing a note, let alone hold a line or carry a tune. Nor could any of us produce a credible sequence of musical sounds by any other means. No string instruments were played, no flutes blown, no keyboards thumped. We couldn't even whistle. From deep within the dusty trunk of childhood I can still dig out the memory of my mother Ameer when young, Ameer on our Cuffe Parade verandah, sitting on a low stool facing the sea, with an old-fashioned churn between her knees, making mango ice cream and trying, unwisely, to whistle while she worked. The churning and the whistling made for hard, hot labour, they furrowed and moistened her high-arched brow, but when I tasted the result of her struggles I gagged and retched; her off-key *siti-bajana* had curdled my favourite dessert. I begged her to desist in future, knowing she would not. "Ma, keep mum." "Silent ice is wholly nice." "Ice cream not youce cream." And, parodying the Kwality brand's famous slogan, "A dream without scream." That was how we spoke, my mother and I: in puns and games and rhymes. In, you might say, lyrics. This was our tragedy. We were language's magpies by nature, stealing whatever sounded bright and shiny. We were tinpan alleycats, but the gift of music had been withheld. We could not sing along, though we always knew the words. Still, defiantly, we roared our tuneless roars, we fell off the high notes and were trampled by the low ones. And if bitter ices were the consequence, well, there were worse fates in the world than that.

Villa Thracia, where I was raised, was one of the series of wedding-cake fantasy bungalows that formerly lined that gracious promenade like proud courtiers standing in a row before their queen, the sea. On Cuffe Parade in the cool of

Bombay evenings, the city's strollers, complete with kids and pets, would come out to amble and flirt and "eat the air." From itinerant vendors they would buy channa for the children, Gold Flake cigarettes for the gents, and fragile garlands of chambeli flowers to wind into the ladies' hair. My memories of that childhood home seem now like dreams of Olympus, of a sojourn with the gods in the days before I was cast out into the world. Clutching at what remains of the past, I hear its spooky laughter as it eludes me. I snatch at wisps of faery dresses but yesterday's creatures no longer return. I must do the best I can with echoes.

That Cuffe Parade has gone now, and the process of its going was assisted, if one believes certain unsubstantiated suggestions regarding the laying of a fire, by the young Vina Apsara; and what Vina may or may not have facilitated was completed by my mother, who loved the city but for whom the future was a force more powerful than love. Cities are not immortal; nor are memories; nor are gods. Of the deities of childhood's Olympus, hardly any now remain.

For many Indians, our parents are as gods. Vina, who had most reason to deny her parentage, took to saying, at the height of her fame and after reading Erich von Däniken, that her true ancestors had been godlike entities who arrived in silver chariots from outer space, tall, lucent, androgynous beings one of whom had extruded her painlessly from "her" navel. "They watch over me always," she told more than one bewildered reporter. "I am in permanent contact. Permanent." In those days she was presenting herself as an androgynous alien on stage as well as off, and no doubt such guff was good for business. But I could hear the savagery beneath her airhead quotes. I could hear the goat songs of her past.

("Goat songs"? Excuse me. A literal translation, from the Greek, of a more familiar word: "tragedies." And Vina's story, with its echoes of the high old yarns of, oh, Helen, Eurydice, Sita, Rati and Persephone—tall Vina's tall tale, which in my circumambulatory way I am hastening to tell, certainly had a tragic dimension. But it also had a good deal to do with goats.)

If our parents are to be thought of as godlike, might the gods actually be our parents? Tales of divine paternity began, let us agree, at the beginning of things, and will end only at the end of time. As I learned in boyhood from my father, the gods themselves quarrelled over the "putative procreative interventions" of other deities. Shiva, suspecting that the new-born Ganesh might not be his son, struck off the baby's head; then remorse set in, and in a panic, he replaced the lost head with the first that came to hand: viz., the trunker's noddle we know and love today. And who was the father of Orpheus, by the by; Apollo the glorious Sun God, or merely Oeagrus, ruler of the outlying, the more than somewhat hickish, province of Thrace? For that matter, who was the father of Jesus Christ?

As we grow, we lose our belief in our progenitors' superhuman nature. They shrivel into more or less unimpressive men and women. Apollo turns out to be Oeagrus, god and Joseph the carpenter end up being one and the same. The gods we worship, we discover, are not different from ourselves.

I'm in this god-bothered mood because it's time to unveil the central mysteries of my own family life. Without further ado, therefore, I present you with an image from childhood of my own at-that-time divine-seeming father, Mr. V.V. Merchant. On Juhu Beach, *circa* 1956, in his middle forties, skinny as an excuse, earnest as a promise, joyful as a birth, grinning his shy, buck-toothed grin; bare-footed, hairlessly bare-chested, with his trouser legs rolled up; straw hat on head, sweat pouring down his cheeks, spade in hand; and digging.

How my father loved to dig! Other parents stood by, bored, while their eager children scrabbled in sand; or, leaving the world of silicon to urchins and ayahs, strolled off to take (and also shoot) the breeze. In my case, it was a question of having to go flat out to keep up with my feverishly burrowing sire. At the age of nine I was, I must admit, hankering for forms of beach life existing beyond the bucket and spade. Juhu Beach was an idyllic spot in those days, not the urbanized Bombay-Bondi it has become. A journey there felt like a trip beyond the frontier of the city into enchanted space. And slowly, as I grew older and raised my eyes from the sand and beyond the conventional weekend pleasures of snack vendors, and boys shinning up coco-palms, and racing camels, I heard a new voice speaking to me, not in any language I had ever learned, but in the secret language of my heart.

It was the sea. Its come-hither murmur, its seductive roar. That was the music that could wash my soul. The lure of a different element, its promises of elsewhere, gave me my first intimation of something hidden within me that would pull me across the water, leaving my parents stranded. The sea, the wine-dark, the fish-rich. The lap and suck of waves dying on sand. Rumours of mermaids. Touch the sea and at once you're joined to its farthest shore, to Araby (it was the Arabian Sea), Suez (it was the year of the Crisis), and Europa beyond. Perhaps even—I remember the thrill of the whispered word on my young lips—America. America, the open-sesame. America, which got rid of the British long before we did. Let Sir Darius Xerxes Cama dream his colonialist dreams of England. My dream-ocean led to America, my private, my unfound land.

(Allow me to add: while you're in the sea, the bugs don't bite.)

I was, I remain, a strong swimmer. Even my nine-year-old self would strike boldly out beyond my depth, heedless of danger. My mother would wade anxiously after me, her sari ballooning in the water like a jellyfish. When I swam safely back to shore, she cuffed me on the ear. "Don't you know the Old Man of the Sea is waiting to drag you down?" Mother, I know, I know.

That sandy shore, on which my barefoot father dug like an overworked undertaker, that beloved homeland, came to seem like a prison to me. The sea—over the sea, under the sea, it scarcely seemed to matter—the sea and only the sea would take me where I could be free.

V. V. Merchant, however, dreamed of the past. That was his promised land. The past was the truth, and like all truths, it lay hidden. You had to dig it out. Not just any past; just the city's. V. V. was a Bombayite through and through. And yes, many Bombayites now associate those initials with the crooked billionaire financier V. V. "Crocodile" Nandy, but my father is not under any circumstances to be confused with that mighty rogue. Of all Nandy's many embezzlements, swindles and thefts, his purloining of Vivvy Merchant's initial letters is the one that rankles most with me. But that's life, I guess. A big crook counts for more in the world than a small and honest man.

My father's given names were Vasim Vaqar, in case you were wondering, the inaccurate Ws of his names' traditional transliterations from the Urdu having been replaced by phonetically correct Vs. However, in spite of the switch, my strongly secularist father much disliked the "unacceptably religious iambs" of his names and wouldn't have been pleased to see them given an airing here; the more informal, and ideologically neutral, "Vivvy" had long been good enough for him. Still, he was the Digger of Bombay, and even if he did choose to bury his own names, he'd be on shaky ground if he complained that I'd dug them up.

(He's dead. He can't complain.)

The rest of India held no interest for Vivvy, while his home town—that single grain of sand whirling through the immensity of the cosmos—contained, for him, all the mysteries of the universe. And as his only son, I, of course, was his preferred repository of knowledge, his deposit account, his security box. Every father wishes his son to inherit the best of himself, and Bombay was what my father gave to me. Instead of children's books, I got local legends. The *Chronicles of Bimb*, or *Bimbakyan*.

In the end I ran a mile from the place. Hundreds of miles. Thousands.

Bombay? Don't ask. I could pass any exam you care to set. I can see the ghosts of old times walking down new streets. Take me to Churchgate and I'll show you where the Church Gate once stood. Show me Rampart Row and I'll show you the Ropewalk, where the British Navy's ropemakers plied their twisting, twining trade. I can tell you where the bodies are buried (F. W. Stevens, the city's architect supreme, d. 5 March 1900, lies in the Sewri cemetery), where the ashes are spilled, where the vultures fly. Graveyards, burning ghats, doongerwadis. I can even locate the bodies of islands, reclaimed long ago into the downtown peninsula. Old Woman's Island—dig into that name and you get *Al-Oman*—is now a somewhat raised lump of ground on the east side of Colaba Bazaar. My father liked digging into place names, so allow me to inform you, just off the top of my head, that Chinchpokli is "tamarind hollow" and Cumballa Hill is named after the lotus flower and Bhendi Bazaar is situated where once the ladies'-fingers grew.

From this kindergarten vegetable stuff, this urban "eaty-mology," as Vivvy Merchant called it, we proceeded on to more adult territory. Vivvy is digging on Juhu Beach, but what of Chowpatty? No problem. "Four rivulets," though nobody now knows where they might trickle . . . And Foras Road? If you know it, you'll know it's a street of whores. But V. V. dug down beneath the brothels, dug down in time as well as earth, down through one meaning to another, and showed me the building of the "foras dykes" which had reclaimed this old marshland from the sea. Where a swamp of morals now stands, was once simply a swamp. . . . And Apollo Bunder, where Ormus Cama grew up? Originally Palva Bunder, of course. "Apollo," my father pronounced, "was a nomenclatural interloper." He spoke like that. Nomenclatural interloper, putative procreative interventions, subterranean veracity. "Greek gods, like everybody else, have invaded India from time to time."

Apollo grabbed the Bunder, but it was Dionysus who really made his mark. Came this way when young, conquering and boozing, and taught us Indians how to make wine. (Alas, we forgot his lessons, and had to settle for arrack and toddy, until the British taught us, much later, about beer and rum and yo-ho-ho.) Dionysus won all his battles, did his share of slaughtering and laying waste, and departed with many elephants; the usual. That kind of show-off behaviour just doesn't impress us any more. Sounds like the old colonial boasting to me. No place for it in today's world.

Dionysiac goddesses: that's closer to my personal experience. What I know about is Vina. Vina, who came to us from abroad, who laid waste to all she saw, who conquered and then devastated every heart. Vina as female Dionysus. Vina, the first bacchante. That, I could buy.

DEEPER AND deeper my father delved beneath the ferocity of the Juhu sun, perhaps hoping to find Portuguese moidores (he dug into the name, naturally. *Moedas de ouros,* if you want to know; coins of gold) or maybe just the petrified skeletons of primeval fish. See him scoop away the present, behold the sands of time climb up around him in surprised dunes crawling with tiny see-through crabs! Listen for his scholarly cries, "Aha! Oho!" as lo! he chances upon a buried bottle, empty, broken, containing no message, he pounces on it as if it were a relic of ancient kingdoms, Rome, Mohenjo-Daro, Gondwana, perhaps even Gondwanaland, the proto-continent upon which no man ever walked, let alone blew glass into bottle shapes, or poured Dionysian liquid into the same; but Gondwanaland is still where India began, if you dig down deep enough in time. India broke off it, sailed across the ocean and smashed into what remained of the northern proto-continent, thus bringing into being the Himalayas. (My father liked to shock me by saying, "The collision is still taking place, India continues to experience impactual consequences, meaning that the mountains are getting bigger.") Now he's invisible from the waist down, glowing, happy; and now only his hat can be seen; and down and down he digs, towards Hell or the Antipodes, while I splash about in the future, further and further out to sea until my mother the jellyfish calls me in.

For twenty years, through one of the greatest upheavals in the history of nations, the end of the British Empire, my father, architect, excavator and local historian, burrowed away into the underground memory of the city the British built, becoming the undisputed master of a subject in which nobody else had the slightest interest; for Bombay forgets its history with each sunset and rewrites itself anew with the coming of the dawn. Can it be that his preoccupations blinded him to the momentous nature of those years, to the Navy Strike and Partition and all that followed? In those days of upheaval the ground itself seemed uncertain, the land, the physical land, seemed to cry out for reconstruction, and before you took a step you had to test the earth to see if it would bear your weight. A great transformation was afoot; and if my father found the uncertainty too much to bear, if he dug himself into the past, seeking fixity in knowledge, seeking solid ground beneath the shifting sands of the age, well, there's no shame in that.

We all have to deal with the uncertainty of the modern. The ground shivers, and we shake. To this day, when I'm strolling down a sidewalk, I always avoid the joins. Step on one of those cracks and they could widen, all of a sudden they could swallow you with a lazy yawn. And of course I know that superstition is a retreat, a way of not facing the real. But the real was Vina, and it's still hard to look her ending in the face.

I will. When I come to it, I will.

FINALLY, MY father gave up his digging. We had ignored him for an eternity, the indolent beach-world had turned its gaze away from his absurd hyperactivity. Exhausted, he needed help to climb out of the hole he'd dug. Grinning coconut salesmen lent him their hands, keeping their baskets balanced on their heads. Even though I had not yet learned the word, I recognized, with some embarrassment, the kitschiness of the image. My father was wearily unconcerned. Happily smacking the sand off his body with his hat, he bought us coconuts from his helpers, waited while they hacked the tops off with their great knives, and then gulped down the coco-milk making loud gluggy noises, like a bath. A moment later, he was asleep in the shade of a coco-palm; whereupon, placing a finger against her lips for silence, smiling secretly, my mother embarked upon some sand madness of her own.

LIKE MICHELANGELO, who believed that the figures of his Titans lay imprisoned within lumps of Carrara marble from which it was his duty as an artist to release them, who sculpted the *David* by simply removing everything in the stone that was not David, Ameer Merchant detected a form concealed within the great mound of sand flung up by V. V.'s beach archaeology. But my mother was no artist. She was an entrepreneur, a "developer," to use the new word of those days. She saw no godly figures in the hill of moisture-darkened sand. "I will build," she declared, "my mansions fit for gods, but men will live in them." While V. V. snored, Ameer shaped the maquette of such a mansion out of sand. While he dreamed of unknown depths, she brought into being a dream of heights. Painstakingly, she worked from the top down, in the manner of the master builders of the great Kailash temple at Ellora, that overwhelming monolith hewn by successive generations out of the living rock. And yes, it was a building that appeared, but one entirely free of devotional content. It is true that a tall spire was seen first, but this was a radio mast. And though the building seemed to soar from the sand like a steeple, yet the profusion of delicate indentations suggestive of windows showed that this was a design on an altogether grander scale than any sacred site. Small twigs, carefully inserted by Ameer into her fragile vision, served as gargoyles, and the building's surfaces were distinguished by its architect's addition of much geometric decoration along its various planes. Surplus sand fell away from her creation like a redundant garment, until at length it stood before me in magnificent nudity.

"Skyscraper," she named it. "How'd you like to own a penthouse at the top?" Skywhatter? Where was a penthouse pent? These were words I did not know. I found myself disliking them: the words, and the building to which they belonged. Besides, I was bored and wanted to swim.

"Looks like a big matchbox to me." I shrugged. "Live in it? As if."

Ameer bristled at this assault upon her handiwork. I deemed it a good time to head for the water. "You don't know anything," she cried, rounding on me like an eight-year-old. "Just wait on and see. One day they'll be all over the place." Then she heard herself sulking and began to giggle. "They'll be here," she waved an arm gaily. "All along here." That set me off too. "Beachscrapers," I said. "Sandscrapers," she agreed. "Camelscrapers, cocoscrapers, fishscrapers." We were both laughing now. "And I suppose chowscrapers at Chowpatty Beach," I wondered. "And hillscrapers on Malabar Hill. And on *Cuffe Parade*?"

"Cuffescrapers," laughed my mother. "Go and swim now and stop being so *bad-tameez*."

"Where are you going to put them, anyway?" Emboldened by her good humour, I delivered an unanswerable last word on the subject. "Here, nobody'll want them, and in town, there are houses everywhere already."

"No room, then," she mused, pensively.

"Exactly," I confirmed, turning towards the water. "No room at all."

ON THAT momentous day at the beach, I had my unforgettable first glimpse of Vina. It was the day of my instant infatuation, the commencement of a lifelong enslavement. . . . But at once I halt myself. It is possible I am pouring the wine of several beach weekends into the bottle of a single day. Damn it, there are things I can't remember. Was it on this day, or another day? In November, or the following January? While my father was snoozing, or after I went for a swim? So much is lost. Hard to believe that all this sand has accumulated, obscuring the years. Hard to believe that it's so long ago, that flesh is mortal, that everything slides towards its end. Once, I belonged to the future. The beloved future of my beloved mother, that was what counted; the present was a means, and the past no more than a dull shard of pottery, a bottle dug up by my father on the beach. Now, however, I belong to yesterday.

Is that a line from a song? I forget. Is it?

AT ANY rate: on this golden afternoon or another, bronzer p.m., at this instant or that one, the celebrated Mr. Piloo Doodhwala and his famous "magnificentourage" marched forth on to Juhu's sands. I should say that at the time, I knew nothing about him whatsoever. I was wholly ignorant of his growing citywide renown as a "character" and "coming man" and statewide purveyor of milk; I had no idea that his real name was Shetty—just as our family's had been until it got Englished years ago—but nobody called him that any more, because, as he himself liked to say, "milkman by fame, I am Milkman by name"; I had never heard of the term he had coined to describe the intimate clique of family members and servitors with which he liked to surround himself—a term gleefully taken up by the local rags and much satirised ("magnificentestine," "arrogantourage," etc.); but Piloo Shetty alias Doodhwala was impervious to satire. I simply beheld a small, plump, white-kurta-pajamaed man in his middle twenties, a young man with so great a sense of his own value that he already looked middle-aged, a fellow with a strutting walk like a peacock's and plentiful dark hair so sleekly plastered down with oil that it resembled a sleeping mongoose. He carried himself like a king, Caligula or Akbar, monarchs who entertained fantasies of being divine. Behind him strode a tall Pathan bearer in full sash-and-turban regalia, holding a large, many-coloured parasol, winking with sequins and mirrorwork, over the little emperor's head.

Piloo was preceded by musicians—a drummer, a raucous flautist, a horn player as blaringly aggressive as a motorist, and a pair of writhing, mumming singer-dancers who were probably hired *hijras,* transsexuals—whose appalling racket launched an irresistible assault upon the late-afternoon gentility of the beach. Scurrying along at his right and left elbows were male secretaries, leaning in to hear the great man's words and taking rapid shorthand notes. Following this extraordinary group was a tiny, almost spherical lady, Piloo's unusually but accurately named wife Golmatol, sheltering her mottled skin beneath a black umbrella; two little girls, aged about seven and eight, whose names, Halva and Rasgulla, bore witness to their parents' sweet teeth; and another, much taller, darker girl of around twelve or thirteen, whose face was entirely obscured beneath an enormous, low-brimmed straw hat, so that all I could see was her Stars-and-Stripes swimsuit and the white lungi she was wearing over it, tied at the hip. There was an ayah and there were two domestic servants bearing picnic hampers. A trinity of security guards sweltered in militaristic uniforms. The primary responsibility of these guards—which they discharged with enthusiasm, vigour and the liberal use of long lathi sticks—was to bat away the cluster of anxious individuals who swarmed and buzzed in the wake of the magnificentourage, for a great man will always attract supplicants and hangers-on, and must be protected from same when he is trying to have a nice day out.

Who was this pocket giant, this mighty mouse? What might be the source of such display? Whence came his power, his wealth? Ameer Merchant, her good humour befouled by the Doodhwala party's noisy advent, was in no mood for questions. "Goats," was her snappish reply. I didn't know what to make of that. He'd got *her* goat, that was plain. "Mummy? Excuse me?" She actually bleated at me in annoyance. "You don't know goats? *Mè-è-è?* Billies, nannies. Don't be stupid now. *Bakra-bakri* is all." And that was all the explanation I could get.

V. V. Merchant came awake in a confused state, jolted out of deep sleep by the noise; whereupon, to his further bewilderment, his beloved wife rounded on him. "Blasted *tamasha,*" she snorted, explosively. "Seems like one side of this family never learned how to behave."

Well, *that* was a bombshell. "We're related? How? Where?"

The Piloo gang had come to a halt no more than forty feet away, and its less exalted members were busy laying out sheets and sweets, acting on Golmatol's stentorian instructions, and raising a gay *shamiana* marquee on poles over the festive spread. A card school got going, and Piloo soon showed himself to be a fierce bidder and big winner, although perhaps his servitors, understanding where their interests lay, allowed him his successes. From a thermos flask a bearer poured Piloo a large aluminum tumblerful of thin, blue-white goat's milk. He drank open-mouthed, careless of dribbles. Halva and Rasgulla began to wail for their own drinks, but the girl in the straw hat and swimsuit had walked off and was standing at some distance with her back to the Doodhwalas, hugging herself, and slowly shaking a disenchanted (though still largely invisible) head. And what with the musicians' noise, the supplicants' pleas, the thwacking of lathi sticks, the shrieks of the wounded, the young girls' wails and the orders bellowed by Golmatol Doodhwala, it was necessary to raise one's voice; my enquiries about these high-decibel family members were made at top volume.

Ameer clutched at her brow. "Oh God, Umeed, get out of my head just now. They're nothing to do with me, I can tell you. Ask your father about his relatives."

"Distant relatives," yelled V. V. Merchant, on the defensive.

"Poor relations," rudely shouted Ameer Merchant.

"They don't look so poor to me," I objected, at the top of my voice.

"Rich in goats," Ameer bellowed into a sudden pause in the music, and her words hung irretrievably in the air, as inescapable as if they'd been lit up in neon like the Jeep sign on Marine Drive, "but poor in quality. Shoddy human goods."

An awful stillness descended. It was a hot year, 1956, one of the hottest on record; the afternoon was well advanced, but the heat had not diminished. Now the temperature actually seemed to rise, the air began to buzz, the way it's supposed to do before lightning strikes, and Shri Piloo Doodhwala began to swell in the heat, to redden, to exude liquid from every pore, as if he were filling up so fast with words that there wasn't room for anything else inside him.

His younger daughter, Halva, emitted a nervy giggle, got two tight slaps from her mother, began to cry, saw Golmatol Doodhwala's hand rising again, and shut up fast. War was very close. The sand between the Doodhwala encampment and our own had become a no-man's-land. Heavy artillery was moving into position. And at this moment the tall girl, the twelve- or thirteen-year-old in the Stars-and-Stripes swimsuit, strolled idly into that embattled zone, looked interestedly from Doodhwalas to Merchants and back again, and tilted back her big straw hat. I regret to report that I failed to control myself when I saw her face. That Egyptian profile which, many years later, I saw again in a portrait of the female pharaoh, Queen Hatshepsut, the first woman in recorded history, whom dismissive Vina, unimpressed by divine monarchs even though she became a sort of god-queen herself, referred to as Hat Cheap Suit; those sardonic eyes, that mouth so dryly twisted, caused me to let out a gasp. No, it was more than a gasp. It was a loud, strangled noise, choking, formless, and it ended in something like a sob. In short, I made, for the only time in my life, the noise of a badly smitten human male falling instantly, heavily, painfully in love. And I was only nine years old.

Let me try and remember the great moment with maximum accuracy. I had, I think, only recently emerged from the sea, my tooth braces were smarting, and I was feeling a little peckish—or else I had been planning a swim when I was distracted by the arrival of the magnificentourage. At any rate, when Ameer Merchant spoke the sentence that Piloo Doodhwala heard as a declaration of war, I had just reached down into a bag of fruit and come up with a juicy apple in my fist. Apple in hand, I gazed upon the beautiful dark girl in the Old Glory swimsuit, apple in hand I emitted my awful, naked noise of adoration; and when my feet began to move of their own accord and propelled me forward until I stood before her, gazing up into the light of her beauty, I was still holding that apple out in front of me, like an offering, like a prize.

She smiled, amused. "Is that for me?" But before I could articulate a reply, the two other girls—damn it, the two ugly sisters!—had run up with gleaming faces, ignoring their ayah's injunctions to return. "Appo," said Halva Doodhwala, making baby eyes and affecting baby talk in a doomed attempt at appearing winsome; and Rasgulla Doodhwala, older but no wiser, poutingly confirmed, "Ppl." The tall girl laughed, rather cruelly, and struck an attitude, head cocked sideways, hand on hip. "You see, you must choose, young master. To which of us will you offer your good gift?"

That's easy, I wanted to say, for it is the gift of my heart. But Piloo and (especially) Golmatol were glaring at me in savage anticipation of my decision, and when, hesitating for a moment, I cast a glance at my own parents, I saw that they were unable to help me make a choice that would affect their lives as much as mine. I did not know then (though it would have been easy to guess) that the tall girl was not the younger girls' sibling, that her place in the entourage was more Cinderella than Helen; or a curious amalgam of the two, a sort of Cinderella of Troy. But it wouldn't have made any difference if I had known; for though my tongue said nothing, my heart was speaking loud and clear. Without a word, I held out the apple to my beloved; who, with a curt nod, somewhat ungraciously received the gift and gave it a goodly bite.

So it was that my deliberate spurning of the charms of Halva and Rasgulla, those little mistresses of the insincerely batted eyelash, was added by the Doodhwalas to my mother's more accidental insult, and that was that. The Hindustani word *kutti* is inadequate for my purposes, suggesting as it does a rather petulant, almost childish level of quarrel. This was not *kutti.* This was vendetta. And in Piloo Doodhwala—who was now, to my horror, beckoning me to approach—I'd made a powerful enemy, and for life.

"Boy!"

Now that the point of no return had passed, Piloo had miraculously relaxed. He had lost the swollen look of a man over-full of furious vocabulary, and even the sweating had stopped. I, however, found myself being bitten by insects. It was that moment of the late afternoon when the mordant armies of the air manifest themselves, appearing like little clouds from some aerial dormitory. As I approached Piloo, who was reclining in splendour on *gao-takia* bolsters beneath his mirrorwork marquee, I was obliged to slap and rub at my face and neck, for all the world as if I were punishing myself for my judgement in the matter of the apple. Piloo smiled his deadly, glittering smile and continued to beckon.

"And your goodname, please?" I told him my name. "Umeed," he repeated. "Hop. That is good. All persons should be having hop, ewen when their situation is hopliss." He fell into a period of contemplation, munching on a morsel of dried bummelo; then spoke again, waving a piece of the fish in his hand. "Bombay duck," he smiled. "You know what is it? You know that this *bombil* phish declined to help Lord Rama to build the bridge to Lanka, phor purpose of rescuing Lady Sita? And therephore he squeezed it tight-tight and crushed all its bones, so now it is boneless wonder? No, how can you know, for you are conwerts." This word led to much shaking of the head, and many more mouthfuls of the fish, before he renewed his harangue. "Conwert," he said. "You know what is it? I will tell. Religious conwersion, it is like getting on a train. Afterwards, only the train itself is where you are belonging. Not departure platform, not arriwal platform. In both these places you are totally despised. Such is conwert. It is your goodfather's phorefather."

I opened my mouth; he indicated that I should close it. "Seen and not heard," he stated. "Keep your trap shut is best policy." He munched on mango. "When man conwerts," he mused, "it is like a powver cut. Load shedding. He is shedding, you see?, the Load of Human Destiny in a basically cowvardly way. Phundamentally an unserious phashion. In doing so he detaches himself from the history of his race, isn't it? Like pulling out a plug, okay? And then the toaster will not work. What is life, boy? I will tell. Life is not just a single hair plucked out phrom the head of God, okay? Life is a cycle. In this poor life of ours we must pay phor the sins of our past existence, and also if appropriate reap reward of prewious good behawiour. The conwert is like a guest in a hotel who will not pay his bill. Therephore conwersely he cannot expect benephits if there is billing error in his phavour."

Piloo's thesis wasn't easy to grasp, what with all the trains, toasters, cycles and hotels tumbling around in there, but I understood the essential point: he was insulting my father, and my father's (Muslim) branch of the family, and therefore, by extension, me. Now, however, as my adult self observes the scene through my nine-year-old eyes and ears, I see and hear other things too: the class differences, for example, the note of snobbishness in my mother's disdain for Piloo's coarser behaviour and vulgar accent; and of course communal differences. The old Hindu-Muslim rift. My parents gave me the gift of irreligion, of growing up without bothering to ask people what gods they held dear, assuming that in fact, like my parents, they weren't interested in gods, and that this uninterest was "normal." You may argue that the gift was a poisoned chalice, but even if so, that's a cup from which I'd happily drink again.

In spite of my parents' godlessness, however, the old family rift persisted. It was so deep that the family's two branches, converts and unconverted, had erased each other from their social maps. At the age of nine I had not even known of the Doodhwalas' existence, and I'm sure Halva and Rasgulla had been equally unaware of their distant cousin Umeed Merchant. As for the tall girl, the swimsuit queen with my apple in her mouth, I still had no clue as to how and where she fitted in.

"Umeed," called my mother, and her voice was angry, "come back here, now."

"Go, little Hop." Piloo dismissed me. He had begun idly to roll a set of poker dice on his carpet. "But I wonder, when you are a big Hop, what-all you will be."

I already knew the answer to that. "Ji, a photographer, ji."

"So," he said. "Then you must learn how a picture can be false. Take my photo just now, isn't it? What do you see? Only some big sahib acting big. But this is a dastardly lie. I am a man of the people, Hop. Simple phellow, humble origins, and because I am accustomed to hard work, so I also know how to enjoy. Just now I am enjoying. But you, Hop, you and your daddy-mummy, you are the guys acting big. Too big, maybe, for boots." He paused. There were milky crescents rimming the pupils of his eyes. "I think perhaps we have phought bephore, in other lives. Today we will not phight. But one day we will surely phight again."

"Umeed!"

"Say also to your goodmother," murmured Piloo Doodhwala, the smile fading from his lips, "that this sand building like a *Shiv-lingam* is a philthy blasphemy. To all decent eyes it is offensiwe and obscene."

In my mind's eye I see again my nine-year-old self, an envoy leaving the enemy camp and returning to his own. But I can also see what's really going on, the process by which power, like heat, is slowly draining from the world of my angry mother to that of Piloo the newly cool. Which is not fancy but hindsight. He hated us; and in time he would inherit, if not *the* earth, then *ours*.

"I hate India," my swimsuit queen mentioned savagely as I passed her. "And there's plenty of it to hate. I hate the heat, and it's always hot, even when it rains, and I really hate that rain. I hate the food, and you can't drink the water. I hate the poor people, and they're all over the place. I hate the rich people, they're so goddamn pleased with themselves. I hate the crowds, and you're never out of them. I hate the way people speak too loud and dress in purple and ask too many questions and order you around. I hate the dirt and I hate the smell and I specially hate squatting down to shit. I hate the money because it can't buy anything, and I hate the stores because there's nothing to buy. I hate the movies, I hate the dancing, I hate the music. I hate the languages because they're not plain English and I hate the English because it's not plain English either. I hate the cars except the American cars and I hate those too because they're all ten years out of date. I hate the schools because they're really jails and I hate the holidays because you're not free even then. I hate the old people and I hate the kids. I hate the radio and there's no tv. Most of all I hate all the goddamn gods." It was an astonishing utterance, spoken in a casual, world-weary monotone, with her eyes fixed on the horizon. I had no idea how to reply, but a reply did not appear to be required. At that time I did not understand her anger, and it shocked me deeply. Was this the girl with whom I had fallen so hopelessly in love? "I hate the apples too," she added, driving a sword into my heart. (But she'd eaten mine, I noticed.) Lovelorn, slapping at bugs, I turned to go on my difficult way. "Want to know what I like, what's the only thing I like?" she called after me. I paused and turned back to face her.

"Yes, please," I humbly said. I may even have bowed my head in misery.

"I love the sea," she said, and ran off to swim. My heart almost burst with joy.

I heard Piloo's dice begin to click and roll; and then, at Golmatol Doodhwala's command, the musicians started up again, and I heard nothing else.

For a long while I have believed—this is perhaps my version of Sir Darius Xerxes Cama's belief in a fourth function of *outsideness*—that in every generation there are a few souls, call them lucky or cursed, who are simply *born not belonging,* who come into the world semi-detached, if you like, without strong affiliation to family or location or nation or race; that there may even be millions, billions of such souls, as many non-belongers as belongers, perhaps; that, in sum, the phenomenon may be as "natural" a manifestation of human nature as its opposite, but one that has been mostly frustrated, throughout human history, by lack of opportunity. And not only by that: for those who value stability, who fear transience, uncertainty, change, have erected a powerful system of stigmas and taboos against rootlessness, that disruptive, anti-social force, so that we mostly conform, we pretend to be motivated by loyalties and solidarities we do not really feel, we hide our secret identities beneath the false skins of those identities which bear the belongers' seal of approval. But the truth leaks out in our dreams; alone in our beds (because we are all alone at night, even if we do not sleep by ourselves), we soar, we fly, we flee. And in the waking dreams our societies permit, in our myths, our arts, our songs, we celebrate the non-belongers, the different ones, the outlaws, the freaks. What we forbid ourselves we pay good money to watch, in a playhouse or movie theatre, or to read about between the secret covers of a book. Our libraries, our palaces of entertainment tell the truth. The tramp, the assassin, the rebel, the thief, the mutant, the outcast, the delinquent, the devil, the sinner, the traveller, the gangster, the runner, the mask: if we did not recognize in them our least-fulfilled needs, we would not invent them over and over again, in every place, in every language, in every time.

No sooner did we have ships than we rushed to sea, sailing across oceans in paper boats. No sooner did we have cars than we hit the road. No sooner did we have airplanes than we zoomed to the furthest corners of the globe. Now we yearn for the moon's dark side, the rocky plains of Mars, the rings of Saturn, the interstellar deeps. We send mechanical photographers into orbit, or on one-way journeys to the stars, and we weep at the wonders they transmit; we are humbled by the mighty images of far-off galaxies standing like cloud pillars in the sky, and we give names to alien rocks, as if they were our pets. We hunger for warp space, for the outlying rim of time. And this is the species that kids itself it likes to stay at home, to bind itself with—what are they called again?—*ties*.

That's my view. You don't have to buy it. Maybe there aren't so many of us, after all. Maybe we are disruptive and anti-social and we shouldn't be allowed. You're entitled to your opinion. All I will say is: sleep soundly, baby. Sleep tight and sweet dreams.

ACCORDING TO the Doodhwala version of the universe, it all started because my paternal great-grandfather "embraced Islam," as they say: Islam, that least huggable of faiths. As a result of that prickly embrace, Vivvy Merchant (and Ameer too, and indeed every Muslim in the sub-continent, for we are all the children of converts, whether we admit it or not, every single one of us) lost his connection with history. Thus we can interpret my father's desperate diggings into the city's past as a quest for his mislaid personal identity; and Ameer Merchant, dreaming of Cuffescrapers and such, was likewise seeking lost certainties in visions of high-rise apartment blocks and Art Deco cinemas, in bricks and mortar, in reinforced cement-concrete.

No shortage of explanations for life's mysteries. Explanations are two a penny these days. The truth, however, is altogether harder to find.

ALWAYS, FROM my earliest remembered days, I longed above all to be—to use once more a phrase to which I remain (perhaps excessively) attached—worthy of the world. To this end I was fully prepared to be tested, to perform labours. I began to learn about the heroes of Greece and Rome through Nathaniel Hawthorne's *Tanglewood Tales,* and of Camelot I became aware thanks to MGM's *Knights of the Round Table,* starring Robert Taylor as Lancelot and Mel Ferrer as Arthur, and as Guinevere, if memory serves, the incomparable Ava, that palindromic goddess who looked just as good when seen from the back as from the front. I devoured children's versions of the Norse Sagas (I particularly recall epic journeys made in a boat called Skidbladnir, the "ship that flew") and of the adventures of Hatim Tai and Haroun al-Rashid and Sindbad the Sailor and Marco Polo and Ibn Battuta and Rama and Lakshmana and the Kurus and Pandavas and anything else that came to hand. However, this high moral formulation, "being worthy of the world," was too abstract to be easily applicable to daily life. I told the truth and was a reasonably upstanding, if also rather solitary and inward, child; but heroism escaped me. There was even a brief interlude, at around the time I am describing, when I began to believe the world to be unworthy of me. Its false notes, its constant fallings-short. This was, perhaps, my mother's disappointed idealism, her growing cynicism, leaking into me. Now, looking back, I can say that we have been more or less on a par, the world and I. We have both risen to occasions and let the side down. To speak only for myself, however (I do not presume to speak for the world): at my worst, I have been a cacophony, a mass of human noises that did not add up to the symphony of an integrated self. At my best, however, the world sang out to me, and through me, like ringing crystal.

When I met Vina at the beach, I knew for the first time how to measure my worth. I would look for my answers in her eyes. I would ask only to wear my lady's favour on my helm.

I MUST say that I had the best possible start in life. I was the fortunate and only son of loving parents who, in order to do justice to their beloved child without giving up their own private and professional passions, chose to have no more children after me. Looking over the foregoing account of fun at the beach, I see that I have omitted to touch on the many small affectionate gestures with which V.V. and Ameer Merchant habitually demonstrated their love: her wry but adoring smiles at her digging husband, his shy, toothy grins in return, the brushings of her hand against his cheek, of his hand against the nape of her neck, the tiny solicitudes of a happy marriage—sit here, it's more shady; drink this, it's cool and sweet—that, though they be murmured ever so privately, do not escape the camera-eyed, antenna-eared, all-recording child. I, too, was well loved, and had never for a day been left in an ayah's care, a fact that aroused amazement, and attracted considerable criticism, in our social circle. Lady Spenta Cama, who never wholly forgave Ameer for her faux pas on the day of Ormus's birth, was in the habit of telling people that any woman who would not even look for a good ayah "must have a little too much of the servant in her own family background." The remark reached Ameer's ears at high speed, malice being the most eager of postmen, and relations between the two women were further strained. My parents' resolve was only strengthened by such gibes. During my babyhood and early infancy, they drew up a weekly rota of duties and pleasures on a rigorously fifty-fifty basis, arranging their work schedules and even their sleep patterns to fit the principle of parental equality. I was not breast-fed; my father would not allow it, for then he would be unable to do his share of feeding. And in his gentle way he insisted on fulfilling his appointed quota of bottom-wiping and nappy-boiling and colic-comforting and play. My mother sang her tuneless songs, and my father also sang his. So it was that I grew up thinking of this, too, as "normal." The world had many shocks in store for me.

They gave up most of their social lives without even noticing that they had done so. The arrival of a child (me) had completed them in some profound way, and they no longer appeared to need other people. Their friends remonstrated with them at first. Some were hurt. Many believed, with Lady Spenta Cama, that there was something "unhealthy" in the Merchants' "obsessive" behaviour. In the end, however, everyone simply accepted the new pattern of life as a fact, as merely one eccentricity among life's many perplexities. V. V. and Ameer were able to concentrate on their boy (me) without concerning themselves about injured feelings or wagging tongues.

Was it on account of their smothering love, or something less explicable in myself, that I began to look out to sea, and dream of America? Was it because, between them, they had possessed the city so completely—was it because I felt that the land was theirs—that I decided to award myself the sea? Did I quit Bombay, in other words, because the whole damn city felt like my mother's womb and I had to go abroad to get myself born? Such are the psychological explanations on offer, readily available from stock.

I would like to reject them all. My parents, I repeat, loved me and gave me the best they could afford. No childhood home could be more evocative, or linger more sweetly in the memory, than Villa Thracia on Cuffe Parade; and in addition to the best of homes, I had good friends, went to a good school, and had excellent prospects. How churlish, then, to blame one's parents for providing precisely what every parent hopes to offer! How disgustingly improper to hold against them just that loving attentiveness which is every father and mother's ideal! You will not hear such words from me, be sure that you won't. Detachment, a weakened sense of affiliation, was simply in my nature. Already, at the age of nine, I not only had secrets but was proud of them. My high longings, my dreams of ancient knights and heroes, I hugged to myself; to reveal them would have been to shame myself, to plunge into the humiliating gulf between the greatness of my intentions and the paltry nature of my few achievements. I cultivated silence, while dreaming that, one day, I might sing.

This overly defended self of mine had certain uses. Sometimes, of an evening, I played poker with Vivvy and Ameer. Almost always, I ended up with the largest pile of matchsticks in front of me. "Maybe you should go in for pro gambling when you grow up," my mother shockingly suggested. "Because, darling boy, that poker face of yours is already working fine." I nodded. Success loosened my tongue a little. "Nobody ever knows what I'm thinking," I told her. "That's the way I like it."

I saw the shock on both their faces, and the bewilderment too. They simply had no idea what to say to me. "It's better to speak your heart, Umeed," my father finally got out. "Better to show your hand than hide it, eh?" My father, the very model of the upstanding gent, the most honourable of men, the most honest, the least corruptible, the gentlest of manner but also the most iron-principled, the most tolerant, was in short the best of men, a godless saint (how he'd have hated the term!) who could be sold a cheap watch in the street and think it an Omega, who always lost at cards and later, tragically, lost at life. And I, his crafty, feigning son, I grinned wide-eyed at this genuinely unworldly innocent man, I made as if to echo his innocence, and then made my checkmate move. "In that case," I murmured, "why aren't all the matchsticks piled up in front of you?"

In retrospect it seems plain that the sea was just a metaphor for me. Certainly I liked to swim, but I was just as happy to do so at, for example, the Willingdon Club swimming pool, just as content with fresh water as with salty. Nor did I ever learn to sail, or regret not learning. Water was simply the magic element that would bear me away on its tides; when I grew up, and air was offered instead, I switched allegiances at once. But I remain grateful to water, because Vina loved it, and we could swim in it together.

Air and water, earth and fire: all four shaped our stories (I mean, of course, Ormus's story, Vina's tale, and mine). In the first two was our beginning. But then came middles, and ends.

When you grow up, as I did, in a great city, during what just happens to be its golden age, you think of it as eternal. Always was there, always will be. The grandeur of the metropolis creates the illusion of permanence. The peninsular Bombay into which I was born certainly seemed perennial to me. Colaba Causeway was my Via Appia, Malabar and Cumballa hills were our Capitol and Palatine, the Brabourne Stadium was our Colosseum, and as for the glittering Art Deco sweep of Marine Drive, well, that was something not even Rome could boast. I actually grew up believing Art Deco to be the "Bombay style," a local invention, its name derived, in all probability, from the imperative of the verb "to see." *Art dekho.* Lo and behold art. (When I began to be familiar with images of New York, I at first felt a sort of anger. The Americans had so much; did they have to possess our "style" as well? But in another, more secret part of my heart, the Art Deco of Manhattan, built on a scale so much grander than our own, only increased America's allure, made it both familiar and awe-inspiring, our little Bombay writ large.)

In reality that Bombay was almost brand-new when I knew it; what's more, my parents' construction firm of Merchant & Merchant had been prominent in its making. In the ten years between the birth of Ormus Cama and my own coming into the world, the city had been a gigantic building site; as if it were in a hurry to become, as if it knew it had to provide itself in finished condition by the time I was able to start paying attention to it. . . . No, no, I don't really think along such solipsistic lines. I'm not over-attached to history, or Bombay. Me, I'm the under-attached type.

I return to my muttons. It is true, though it's got nothing to do with me, that the building boom that created the Bombay of my childhood went into overdrive in the years before my birth and then slowed down for about twenty years; and that time of relative stability tricked me into believing in the city's timeless qualities. After that, of course, it turned into a monster, and I fled. Ran for my wretched life.

Me? I was a Bombay *chokra* through and through. But let me confess that, even as a child, I was insanely jealous of the city in which I was raised, because it was my parents' other love, the daughter they never had. They loved each other (good), they loved me (very good), and they loved her (not so good). Bombay was my rival. It was on account of their romance with the city that they drew up that weekly rota of shared parental responsibilities. When my mother wasn't with me—when I was riding on my father's shoulders, or staring, with him, at the fish in the Taraporewala Aquarium—she was out there with *her,* with Bombay; out there bringing her into being. (For of course construction work never stops completely, and supervising such work was Ameer's particular genius. My mother the master builder. Like her dead father before her.) And when my father handed me over to her—when we sang our hideous ditties and ate our curdled ice-cream—he went off, wearing his local-history hat and a khaki jacket full of pockets, to dig in the foundations of building sites for the secrets of the city's past, or else sat hatless and coatless at a designing board and dreamed his lo-and-behold dreams.

V. V. Merchant's first love would always be the city's prehistory; it was as if he were more interested in the infant's conception than in her actuality. Give him his head and he would prattle happily for hours of the Chalukya settlements on Elephanta and Salsette islands two and a half thousand years ago, or Raja Bhimdev's legendary capital at Mahim in the eleventh or twelfth century. He could recite the clauses of the Treaty of Bassein under which the Mughal emperor Bahadur Shah ceded the Seven Isles to the Portuguese, and was fond of pointing out that Queen Catherine of Braganza, wife of Charles II, was the secret link between the cities of Bombay and New York. Bombay came to England in her dowry; but she was also the Queen in the N.Y. borough of Queens.

Maps of the early town afforded him great joy, and his collection of old photographs of the edifices and *objets* of the vanished city was second to none. In these faded images were resurrected the demolished Fort, the slummy "breakfast bazaar" market outside the Teen Darvaza or Bazaargate, and the humble mutton shops and umbrella hospitals of the poor, as well as the fallen palaces of the great. The early city's relics filled his imagination as well as his photo albums. Hats were of particular interest. "Time was, you could tell a man's community at once by the thing he wore on his head," he lamented. Sir Darius Xerxes Cama with his chimney-pot fez was a last relic of those days when Parsis were called Topazes on account of their headgear. And banias had round hats and the chow-chow Bohras crying their unlistably various wares in the streets seemed to be carrying balls upon their heads. . . . It was from my father that I learned of Bombay's first great photographers, Raja Deen Dayal and A. R. Haseler, whose portraits of the city became my first artistic influences, if only by showing me what I did not want to do. Dayal climbed the Rajabai tower to create his sweeping panoramas of the birth of the city; Haseler went one better and took to the air. Their images were awe-inspiring, unforgettable, but they also inspired in me a desperate need to get back down to ground level. From the heights you see only pinnacles. I yearned for the city streets, the knife grinders, the water carriers, the Chowpatty pickpockets, the pavement moneylenders, the peremptory soldiers, the whoring dancers, the horse-drawn carriages with their fodder-thieving drivers, the railway hordes, the chess players in the Irani restaurants, the snake-buckled schoolchildren, the beggars, the fishermen, the servants, the wild throng of Crawford Market shoppers, the oiled wrestlers, the moviemakers, the dockers, the book sewers, the urchins, the cripples, the loom operators, the bully boys, the priests, the throat slitters, the frauds. I yearned for life.

When I said this to my father he showed me still lives of hats and storefronts and piers and told me I was too young to understand. "Comprehension of historical appurtenances," he assured me, "reveals the human factor." This required translation. "See where people lived and worked and shopped," he clarified, with a rare flash of irritation, "and it becomes plain what they were like." For all his digging, Vivvy Merchant was content with the surfaces of his world. I, his photographer son, set out to prove him wrong, to show that a camera can see beyond the surface, beyond the trappings of the actual, and penetrate to its bloody flesh and heart.

The family construction business had been developed by his late father-in-law, Ishak Merchant, a man so interminably choleric that at the age of forty-three his inner organs literally burst with anger and he died, bleeding copiously inside his skin. This was soon after his daughter's marriage. The daughter of an angry man, my mother had chosen a partner wholly lacking in anger, but couldn't handle even his gentle—and rare—reproofs; the mildest of cavils would unleash in her an astonishing storm of emotion that was more tearful than explosive, but otherwise, in respect of its extreme and damaging force, not at all unlike her dead father's rage. V. V. treated her gingerly, like the fragile thoroughbred she was. Which was necessary; but also spoke of trouble ahead, or would have, had either of the happy couple been listening. But they turned a deaf ear to all words of warning. They were deeply in love; which beats earplugs.

The happy newlyweds, Vivvy and Ameer, were plunged in at the deep end. Fortunately for them, the city needed every builder it could get. Two decades later, they could point out several of the *art dekho* mansion blocks along the west side of the Oval Maidan, and on Marine Drive too, and say with justifiable pride, "We built that" or "This one's ours." Now they were busy further afield, in Worli and Pali Hill and so on. As we drove home from Juhu, we made a number of detours to take a look at this or that site, and not only those with Merchant & Merchant boards on the wire perimeter fences. Building sites are, to a family of builders, what tourist sights are to the rest of the populace. I had grown accustomed to such behaviour and, in addition, was so excited about my encounter with my swimsuit goddess that I didn't even bother to complain. I did, however, ask questions.

"What's her name?"

"Arré, whose name? What do I know? Ask your father."

"What's her name?"

"I'm not sure. Nissa or some such."

"Nissa what? Nissa Doodhwala? Nissa Shetty? What?"

"I can't remember. She grew up far from here, in America."

"America? Where in America? New York?"

But my father had run out of information; or else there were things he did not wish to reveal. Ameer, however, knew it all.

"New York State," she said. "Some stupid *gaon* in the backyard of beyond."

"What *gaon*? Oh, Ammi, come on."

"You think I know every village in the U.S.? Some Chickaboom-type name."

"That's not a name. Is it?"

She shrugged. "Who knows what-all kind of crazy names they have there. Not just Hiawatha-Minnehaha but also Susquehanna, Shenandoah, Sheboygan, Okefenokee, Onondaga, Oshkosh, Chittenango, Chickasha, Canandaigua, Chuinouga, Tomatosauga, Chickaboom." They were her last words on the subject. Chickaboom, N.Y., it was.

"Anyway," added my mother, "you don't want anything to do with her. For one thing, that Piloo is her guardian now, and plus, she is well known to be nothing but trouble. One thousand and one percent bad egg. She has had a life of tragedy, that is so, my heart goes out to her, but just keep away from her. You heard how she talks. No discipline. She's too old, anyway; find friends your own age. And plus," as if this clinched it, "she's a vegetarian."

"I liked her," I said. My parents both ignored me.

"You know," my mother changed the subject, "those Red Indian names sound darn South Indian to me. Chattanooga, Ootacamund, Thekkady, Schenectady, Gitchee-Gummee, Ticklegummy, Chittoor, Chitaldroog, Chickaboom. Maybe some of our Dravidian co-nationals sailed off to America yonks ago in a beautiful pea-green boat. Indians get everywhere, isn't it? Like sand."

"Maybe they took some honey and plenty of money," my father joined in. I saw that we had embarked on one of our traditional family kidabouts and there was no point trying to get things back on track.

"What's the point of wrapping honey in a five-pound note, anyway," I said, giving in. "And, p.s.," I added, my thoughts turning back to my swimsuit girl, "what self-respecting pussycat would marry a stupid owl?"

"Minnehaha, Laughing Water," Ameer followed her own train of thought. "So *haha* must be laughing, which means *Minne* is water. Then what's Mickey?"

"Mickey," said my father sternly, "is a mouse."

THE PHILOSOPHER Aristotle was dismissive of mythology. Myths were just fanciful yarns, or so he opined, containing no valuable truths about our natures or our surroundings. Only by reason, he argued, will men understand themselves and master the world in which they live. For this view Aristotle had, in my childhood, some minority local support. "The true miracle of reason," Sir Darius Xerxes Cama once (or, actually, rather too often) said, "is reason's victory over the miraculous." Most other leading minds, I'm bound to report, disagreed; Lady Spenta Cama, for example, for whom the miraculous had long ago supplanted the quotidian as the norm, and who would have been utterly lost, without her angels and devils, in the tragic jungle of the everyday.

Also ranged against Aristotle and Sir Darius was Giovanni Battista Vico (1668–1744). In Vico, as for so many present-day theorists of childhood, the early years are the crucial ones. The themes and dramas of those first moments set the pattern for all that follows. For Vico, mythology is the family album or storehouse of a culture's childhood, containing that society's future, codified as tales that are both poems and oracles. The private drama of the vanished Villa Thracia colours and prophesies our subsequent way of living in the world.

"Keep away from her," said Ameer Merchant, but once the inexorable dynamic of the mythic has been set in motion, you might as well try and keep bees from honey, crooks from money, politicians from babies, philosophers from maybes. Vina had her hooks in me, and the consequence was the story of my life. "Bad egg," Ameer called her, and "rotten apple" too. And then, dripping and bruised, she arrived at our door in the middle of the night, begging to be taken in.

JUST SEVEN days after our Juhu experiences, at six o'clock in the evening, it began to rain out of a clear sky, in hot, fat drops. Heavy rain, whose warmth did nothing to cool down the maximum-humidity heat wave. And as the rain increased in force, so too, in a freak of nature, the temperature also rose, so that the water, falling, evaporated before it hit the ground and turned to mist. Wet and white, rarest of all Bombay's meteorological phenomena, the mist rolled in across the Back Bay. The citizenry, strolling on the Parade for the customary "eating of the air," fled in search of shelter. Mist obliterated the city; the world was a white sheet, waiting to be written upon. V. V., Ameer and I stayed indoors, clutching our poker hands, and in that bizarre whiteness our bidding became extreme, reckless, as if we intuited that the moment required extravagant gestures of us all. My father lost even more matchsticks than usual, and at higher speed. A white night fell.

We went to our beds, but none of us could sleep. When Ameer came to kiss me good night, I said, "I keep waiting for something to happen." Ameer nodded. "I know."

Later, after midnight, it was Ameer who first heard the noises outside, the bumping and thumping, as if an animal were loose on the front verandah, and then an exhausted, tearful panting. She sat straight up in bed and said, "Sounds like whatever Umeed was hoping for has turned up at last."

By the time we reached the verandah the girl had passed out on the boards. She had a black eye and there were cuts on her forearms, some of them deep. Glistening serpents of hair lay across the wooden verandah floor. Medusa. It crossed my mind that we should look at her face only in a burnished shield, lest we be turned to stone. Her white T-shirt and jeans were sodden. I could not help looking at the outlines of her thick nipples. Her breathing was too fast, too heavy, and she was groaning as she breathed. "It's her," I said, stupidly.

"And we have no choice," my mother said. "And what will be will be."

Dry, warm, bandaged, and eating hot porridge from a bowl, with a towel wound over her hair like a pharaoh's crown, the girl held court in my parents' bed, and we three Merchants stood before her like courtiers; like bears. "He tried to kill me," she said. "Piloo, the yellow-belly. He attacked me. So I ran away." Her voice failed. "Well, he threw me out," she said. "But I won't go back, anyway; whatever happens." And Ameer, who had warned me off her, said fiercely, "Go back? Out of the question. Nissa Doodhwala, you will kindly just stay put." Which utterance was rewarded by a tentative, though still suspicious, smile.

"Don't call me by that bastard's name, okay?" the girl said. "I left there with nothing. From now on I'll be whatever name I choose."

And a few moments later: "Vina Apsara. That's my name."

My mother soothed her, reassured her—"Yes, Vina, okay, baby, whatever you want"—and then probed: what had provoked so violent an attack? Vina's face slammed shut, like a book. But the next morning the answer arrived on our doorstep, anxiously ringing the bell: Ormus Cama, beautiful and dangerous as the revenant sun, nineteen years old, with a "reputation." And in search of forbidden fruit.

IT WAS the beginning of the end of my days of joy, spent with those Thracian deities, my parents, amidst legends of the city's past and visions of its future. After a childhood of being loved, of believing in the safety of our little world, things would begin to crumble for me, my parents would quarrel horribly and die before their time. Fleeing this frightful disintegration, I turned towards my own life, and there, too, I found love; but that existence also came to an untimely end. Then for a long time there was just me, and my painful remembering.

Now there is at last a new flowering of happiness in my life. (This, too, will be told at the proper time.) Perhaps this is why I can face the horror of the past. It's tough to speak of the beauty of the world when one has lost one's sight, an anguish to sing music's praises when your ear trumpet has failed. So also it is hard to write about love, even harder to write lovingly, when one has a broken heart. Which is no excuse; happens to everyone. One must simply overcome, always overcome. Pain and loss are "normal" too. Heartbreak is what there is.

CHAPTER FOUR

The Invention of Music

Even though Ormus Cama, our absurdly handsome and impossibly gifted hero, has just returned to the centre of my stage—a little too late to provide prompt comfort to the young lady for whose distress he is largely to blame!—I must briefly halt my runaway bus of a narrative, so that I may help the reader to a better understanding of how matters had arrived at so sorry a pass. And so I take you back to Ormus's father, Sir Darius Xerxes Cama, now in his middle sixties, stretched out on a British-style button-back leather chesterfield sofa in his Apollo Bunder library; with his eyes closed and a cut-glass tumbler and a decanter of whisky by his side; and dreaming.

Whenever he dreamed, he dreamed of England: England as a pure, white Palladian mansion set upon a hill above a silver winding river, with a spreading parterre of brilliant green lawns edged by ancient oaks and elms, and the classic geometry of flower beds orchestrated by unseen master gardeners into a four-seasons symphony of colour. White curtains were blowing at the open French windows of the great house's orangery wing. In the dream Sir Darius was once again a young boy in short trousers, and the mansion was a magnet drawing him forward across its perfect lawns, past the topiary hedges and the ornamental fountain pullulating with figures from ancient Greece and Rome, the hirsute, lecherous gods, the naked heroes with their upraised swords, the serpents, the ravished women, the severed heads, the centaurs. The curtains wound themselves around him, but he fought free, for somewhere in this house, waiting for him, combing her long hair and singing a sweet song, was his mother, whom he had lost so long ago, whom he mourned every day, and to whose bosom his dreaming self hastened to return.

He couldn't find her. He searched the house in vain, scurrying through the interconnecting grandeur of anachronistic state rooms; boudoirs of murderous Restoration miladies who had hidden their daggers and poisons in secret cavities behind fleur-de-lys panelling; Baroque offices of power where bewigged grandees with perfumed kerchiefs had once dispensed patronage and largesse to their malodorous, genuflecting protégés, and where, too, conspiracies of state had been hissed by great men into the ears of murderers and thieves; grand carpeted *Jugendstil* stairways down which betrayed princesses had hurled themselves in fits of lonely despair; and medieval star chambers where summary justice had once been handed down beneath artists' impressions of whirling galaxies and dying suns . . . until he stumbled out into an inner courtyard of the white house, where at the far end of a pool of cold black water stood the naked figure of a beautiful and blindfolded woman, her arms spread wide, as if she was preparing to dive. But she did not dive. The palms of her hands turned invitingly towards him, and he couldn't resist, he was no longer a boy in short trousers but a man full of desire; he ran towards her, even though he knew the scandal would unmake him. Dreaming, he intuited that the dream spoke of something buried in his past, buried so deep that he himself had entirely forgotten what it was.

"Yes, come to me," whispered Scandal, enfolding him in her arms, "my darling, my favourite servant of the Lie."

WHEN HE was awake, and the memory of the blindfolded nude by the swimming pool had faded into the limbo of things half remembered and uncertain, and the whisky had loosened his tongue, Sir Darius Xerxes Cama would soliloquize yearningly about the country houses of old England—Boot Magna, Castle Howard, Blandings, Chequers, Brideshead, Cliveden, Styles. As he grew older and thickened by drink, certain boundaries blurred in his memory, and nowadays he drew only the vaguest of distinctions between Toad Hall and Blenheim Palace, Longleat and Gormenghast. His nostalgia applied equally to the dream houses of fiction and the real country seats of "bluebloods" and prime ministers and rich arrivistes like the Astor clan. Real or fictional, these mighty piles represented for Sir Darius the closest approximation to earthly Paradise that human imagination and ingenuity had managed to create. He spoke more and more often of moving the family to England on a permanent basis. On Ormus Cama's nineteenth birthday his father gave him the first volume of Sir Winston Churchill's new *History of the English-Speaking Peoples.* "Not content with winning the war," Sir Darius said, shaking his head admiringly, "the old bulldog went off and won the Nobel Prize in Literature also. No wonder they call him Winnie. British youth looks up to him, seeks to follow where he trod. Great things are consequently expected of the younger generation in England. Our youth, by sad contrast," he said, looking disapprovingly at Ormus, "is in a state of advanced decay. Old virtues—service of community, discipline of personality, memorizing of poetry, mastery of firearms, pleasure in falconry, formal dancing, building of character through sport—these things have lost meaning. Only in the mother country can they be rediscovered."

"On the cover of this book the King of England has an arrow stuck in his eye," Ormus pointed out. "I guess archery must not be a specialty of the bulldog breed."

Sir Darius was predictably provoked, and would have relieved himself of a further tirade had Lady Spenta not added, immovably, "If you are dreaming again of relocating in London, be assured that I personally will never consent to upping sticks." Which turned out, like all prophecies, to be untrue.

Ormus Cama withdrew. Abandoning his parents to their ancient rituals of disagreement, he wandered through the sprawling Apollo Bunder apartment. While he remained in Sir Darius's field of vision his movements were exaggeratedly adolescent, that is, indolent and listless, the very picture of decadent Parsi youth. Once he was out of his father's sight, however, a remarkable transformation occurred. It should be remembered that Ormus, a born singer, had not opened his lips in song since the night he was almost smothered in his bed by his elder brother Cyrus; and a stranger, watching him now, might easily have concluded that all the unsung music of his silenced years had accumulated in him, causing acute discomfort, even agony; and that the pent-up melodies were actually trying to burst out of his body as he walked.

Oh, how he swayed and twitched!

If I say that Ormus Cama was the greatest popular singer of all, the one whose genius exceeded all others, who was never caught by the pursuing pack, then I am confident that even my toughest-minded reader will readily concede the point. He was a musical sorcerer whose melodies could make city streets begin to dance and high buildings sway to their rhythm, a golden troubadour the jouncy poetry of whose lyrics could unlock the very gates of Hell; he incarnated the singer and songwriter as shaman and spokesman, and became the age's unholy unfool. But by his own account he was more than that; for he claimed to be nothing less than the secret originator, the prime innovator, of the music that courses in our blood, that possesses and moves us, wherever we may be, the music that speaks the secret language of all humanity, our common heritage, whatever mother tongue we speak, whatever dances we first learned to dance.

From the beginning he claimed that he was literally years ahead of his time.

At the moment of which I now speak, the butterfly was still in its chrysalis, the oracle had not found its voice. And if I mention, as I must, the grinding rotation of his hips as he moved through the apartment on Apollo Bunder, and the increasing explicitness of his pelvic thrusts and the dervish thrashings of his arms; if I linger upon the baby-cruel curl of his upper lip, or the thick black hair hanging in sensual coils around his brow, or the sideburns that were straight out of a Victorian melodrama—if, above all, I attempt to reproduce the few strange sounds he was managing to produce, those *unnhhs, uhh-hhhs,* those *ohhs*—then you, stranger, might excusably write him off as a mere echo, just another of that legion of impersonators who first rejoiced in, and afterwards rendered grotesque, the fame of a young truck driver from Tupelo, Miss., born in a shotgun shack with a dead twin by his side.

I don't deny that, one day in early 1956, a girl named Persis Kalamanja—with whom Lady Spenta Cama was hoping to arrange Ormus's marriage; indeed, Lady Spenta was in those days actively and urgently negotiating the same with Kalamanja *père et mère*—took Ormus Cama down to the Rhythm Center store in Fort, Bombay, that rhinestone treasure chest full of the antiquated ditties of an older generation's moonsters, junesters and toupéed croonsters, which just occasionally came into possession of true jewels, perhaps from sailors on shore leave from an American naval vessel in the harbour. There, in a listening booth, hoping to impress her putative husband-to-be by her cultural savvy (for Persis was much taken with the idea of the match; Ormus, as I may have mentioned before, and will no doubt have occasion enviously to repeat, was an almost irresistibly sweet-featured fellow), eager Persis played Ormus a new, but already crackly, 78 rpm record, and to her deep, though short-lived, satisfaction, the young man's eyes widened in what might have been terror, or love, just like any other teenager hearing in the voice of Jesse Garon Parker, as he sang "Heartbreak Hotel," the sound of his own unarticulated miseries, his own hunger, isolation and dreams.

But Ormus was no ordinary teenager. What Persis had mistaken for enchanted bliss was actually surging anger, an uncontainable rage spreading in him like the plague. Halfway through the song it burst out of him. "Who is he?" shouted Ormus Cama. "What's the name of this blasted thief?"

He came out of the booth at high speed, as if he believed he might be able to grab the singer by the collar of his shirt if he moved fast enough. Facing him was a tall, amused girl, perhaps twelve or thirteen years old, but sophisticated enough for both of them, in a baggy sweatshirt that declared its allegiance to certain unnamed Giants in New York. "Thief?" she enquired. "I've heard him called lots of names, but that's a new one on me."

Many different versions of the first encounter between Vina Apsara and Ormus Cama are presently in circulation, thanks to the clouds of mythologisation, regurgitation, falsification and denigration that have surrounded their story for years: depending which journal you read, you might have heard that he transformed himself into a white bull and carried her away on his back while she, warbling gaily, clutched with erotic delight at his two long, curved and gleaming horns; or that she was indeed an alien from a galaxy far, far away who, having identified Ormus as the most perfectly desirable male specimen on the planet, beamed down smack in front of him at the Gateway of India, holding a space flower in her hand. The Rhythm Center encounter is dismissed as "apocryphal" by many commentators; too contrived, they shrug, too banal, and what *is* all that about having written the song? Plus, these cynics add, if you want yet more proof that the story is phoney baloney, try this for size. The whole thing simply makes no sense at all unless you accept that Ormus Cama, quiffed, sideburned and pelvis-swivelling Ormus, had never previously heard of the reigning king of rock 'n' roll. "This was apparently *1956,*" the critics jeer. "In 1956 even the Pope had heard of Jesse Parker. Even the Man in the Moon."

In Bombay in those days, however, communications technology was in its infancy. There was no tv, and radios were bulky items under strict parental control. Also, the state broadcasting corporation, All-India Radio, was forbidden to play Western popular music, and the only Western records pressed in India, at the Dum Dum factory in Calcutta, tended to be selections from Placido Lanza, or the sound-track music from the MGM movie *Tom Thumb.* Print media were likewise parochial. I cannot remember seeing a single photograph of American singing stars in any local showbiz magazine, let alone the daily papers. But of course there were imported American magazines, and Ormus could have seen pictures of Jesse Parker (perhaps alongside the sinister figure of "Colonel" Tom Presley, his manager) in *Photoplay* or *Movie Screen.* And that was also the year of *Treat Me Tender,* Jesse's first movie, which played at the New Empire cinema, certified for adults only. However, Ormus Cama always insisted he had neither heard of Parker nor seen his photograph until that day in the Rhythm Center store; he always claimed that his dead twin Gayomart was his only style guru—Gayomart, who apparently came to him in dreams.

So I will cling to my record shop anecdote, if only because I heard Ormus and Vina repeat it a hundred times during the years of their great love, fondly lingering here or there, in the booth or outside it, now on one part of the tale, now on another. Each loving couple cherishes the tale of its coming together, and Ormus and Vina were no exception. However, as they were—it must be said—consummate mythologisers of themselves, the tale they told was inaccurate in one important particular: Miss Persis Kalamanja was omitted completely from their reminiscing. This is an injustice which I am now able to put right. I call the heartbroken Miss K., my witness, to the stand.

Poor Persis, who had already lost her loving heart to Ormus Cama, lost a great deal more that day in the Rhythm Center store. She lost Ormus himself, and with him her whole future. Once he had come face-to-face with Vina, it was all over for Persis; she could see that at a glance. Vina and Ormus hadn't even touched, they didn't know each other's names, but already their eyes were making love. After Ormus dumped Persis she learned how a human being may believe two contradictory things at once. For a long time she believed he would surely return to her once he realized how true a love he had spurned, truer than anything that America-returned child could give him; and at the same time she also knew he would never come back. These two propositions, of equal and opposite power, paralysed her, and she never married, nor did she stop loving him until the very end, when, after the cycle of catastrophes had run its course, I received a letter from her. Poor Persis, still in Ormus's power even though he no longer lived, poured out her heart to me in an elegant, mature hand that spoke of her strong character. Yet even this impressive woman had been defenceless against the sheer force of Ormus Cama, his desirability, his voltage, his charm, his casual cruelty, his life. He broke her and forgot her. They did that to people, both of them, Vina too, as if the vastness of their own love excused them from the ordinary decencies, from responsibility, from care. Vina did it to me. Which didn't set me free, either.

"The worst thing," Persis wrote, "was that he rubbed me out of the picture, as if I hadn't been there, as if I'd never existed, as if it wasn't me who took him there that day and started everything up." I attempted, in my reply, to offer what comfort I could. She was by no means the only part of their story that Vina and Ormus tried to erase. For much of their public lives, they chose to conceal their origins, to shed the skin of the past, and Persis was shucked off along with everything else; it was, one might say, nothing personal.

That's what I told Persis, anyway, while privately believing that in her case it might indeed have been very personal indeed. Sometimes I thought of Ormus and Vina as worshippers at the altar of their own love, which they spoke of in the most elevated language. Never were there such lovers, never had feelings of such depth, such magnificence, been felt by other mortals. . . . The presence of another woman at the meeting of such godlike *amants* was a detail the deities preferred to gloss over.

But Persis existed; she still exists. Ormus and Vina have gone, and Persis, like me, is a part of what remains.

In the record store, while Ormus and Vina's eyes made love, Persis tried to defend her territory. "Listen, jailbait," she hissed, "shouldn't you be in KG?"

"Kindergarten's out, grandma," said Vina, and turned her back on the Kalamanja heiress, bathing Ormus Cama in the cascade of her liquid regard. Distantly, like a sleepwalker, he answered her question. "I called him a thief because that's what he is. That's my song. I wrote it years ago. Two years, eight months and twenty-eight days ago, if you want to know."

"Oh, come on, Ormie," Persis Kalamanja battled on. "The record only came out a month ago, and that was in America. Here, it's hot off the boat." But Vina had begun to hum another tune; and Ormus's eyes blazed once again. "How do you know that song?" he demanded. "How could anyone have sung to you what only ever existed in my own head?"

"I suppose you wrote this one too," Vina challenged him, and sang a snatch of a third melody. "And this, and this."

"Yes, all of them," he said, seriously. "The music, I mean; and the vowel sounds. Those cockeyed words may be somebody else's—a song about *blue shoes*? What *bakvaas,* I swear!—but the vowel sounds are mine."

"When you're married to me, Mr. Ormus Cama," said Persis Kalamanja in a loud voice, gripping his arm tightly, "you're going to have to start acting a lot more sensible than you are right now." At which reproof the object of her affections simply laughed: merrily, in her face. Weeping, routed,

Persis fled the scene of her humiliation. The process of removing her from the record had begun.

FROM THE beginning, Vina accepted Ormus's prophetic status without question. He claimed to be the true author of some of the most celebrated songs of the day, and did so with such uncontrolled intensity that she found she had no option but to believe him. "Either that," she told me many years later, "or else he was dangerously insane, and the way I was feeling about living in Bombay, the way things were for me in old Uncle Piloo's clutches, a madman for a boyfriend was just fine." After Persis fled, a brief awkwardness hung in the air; and then Vina, to hold the interest of the man to whose life she had already privately joined her own, asked if he knew the story of the invention of music.

Once upon a time the winged serpent Quetzalcoatl ruled the air and the waters, while the god of war ruled the land. Theirs were rich days, full of battles and the exercise of power, but there was no music, and they both longed for a decent tune. The god of war was powerless to change the situation, but the winged serpent was not. He flew away towards the house of the sun, which was the home of music. He passed a number of planets, and from each of them he heard musical sounds, but there were no musicians to be found. At last he came to the house of the sun, where the musicians lived. The anger of the sun at the serpent's invasion was a terrible thing to witness, but Quetzalcoatl was not afraid, and unleashed the mighty storms that were his personal specialty. The storms were so fearsome that even the house of the sun began to shake, and the musicians were scared and fled in all directions. And some of them fell to earth, and so, thanks to the winged serpent, we have music.

"Where is that story from?" Ormus asked. He was hooked.

"Mexico," said Vina. She came towards him and brazenly took his hand in her own. "And I am the winged serpent, and this is the house of the sun, and you, and you, are music."

Ormus Cama stared at his hand lying in hers; and felt something lift from him, the shadow, perhaps, of a pillow with which, long ago, his brother had smothered his voice.

"Would you like," he asked, amazing himself by the question, "maybe one day soon, to hear me sing?"

WHAT'S A "culture"? Look it up. "A group of micro-organisms grown in a nutrient substance under controlled conditions." A squirm of germs on a glass slide is all, a laboratory experiment calling itself a society. Most of us wrigglers make do with life on that slide; we even agree to feel proud of that "culture." Like slaves voting for slavery or brains for lobotomy, we kneel down before the god of all moronic micro-organisms and pray to be homogenized or killed or engineered; we promise to obey. But if Vina and Ormus were bacteria too, they were a pair of bugs who wouldn't take life lying down. One way of understanding their story is to think of it as an account of the creation of two bespoke identities, tailored for the wearers by themselves. The rest of us get our personae off the peg, our religion, language, prejudices, demeanour, the works; but Vina and Ormus insisted on what one might call auto-couture.

And music, popular music, was the key that unlocked the door for them, the door to magic lands.

In India it is often said that the music I'm talking about is precisely one of those viruses with which the almighty West has infected the East, one of the great weapons of cultural imperialism, against which all right-minded persons must fight and fight again. Why then offer up paeans to culture traitors like Ormus Cama, who betrayed his roots and spent his pathetic lifetime pouring the trash of America into our children's ears? Why raise low culture so high, and glorify what is base? Why defend impurity, that vice, as if it were a virtue?

Such are the noisome slithers of the enslaved micro-organisms, twisting and hissing as they protect the inviolability of their sacred homeland, the glass laboratory slide.

THIS IS what Ormus and Vina always claimed, never wavering for a moment: that the genius of Ormus Cama did not emerge in response to, or in imitation of, America; that his early music, the music he heard in his head during the unsinging childhood years, was not of the West, except in the sense that the West was in Bombay from the beginning, impure old Bombay where West, East, North and South had always been scrambled, like codes, like eggs, and so Westernness was a legitimate part of Ormus, a Bombay part, inseparable from the rest of him.

It was an amazing proposition: that the music came to Ormus before it ever visited the Sun Records studio or the Brill Building or the Cavern Club. That he was the one who heard it first. Rock music, the music of the city, of the present, which crossed all frontiers, which belonged equally to everyone—but to my generation most of all, because it was born when we were children, it spent its adolescence in our teenage years, it became adult when we did, growing paunchy and bald right along with us: this was the music that was allegedly first revealed to a Parsi Indian boy named Ormus Cama, who heard all the songs in advance, two years, eight months and twenty-eight days before anyone else. So according to Ormus and Vina's variant version of history, their alternative reality, we Bombayites can claim that it was in truth our music, born in Bombay like Ormus and me, not "goods from foreign" but made in India, and maybe it was the foreigners who stole it from us.

Two years, eight months and twenty-eight days, by the way, adds up (except in a leap year) to one thousand and one nights. Nineteen fifty-six, however, was a leap year. Go figure. This kind of spooky parallel doesn't always exactly work out.

HOW COULD such a thing happen?

We must wait a little longer for the answer, until Ormus Cama has returned home from the record store, stunned by joy (because of his meeting with that under-age nymphet, Vina Apsara) and horror (because of his discovery of the "theft" of his secret music by Jesse Parker, Jack Haley's Meteors and sundry other quiffed and finger-snapping Yanks). The answer cannot be given until Ormus has first encountered his inquisitive matchmaker of a mother, who is anxious to know how things went with "dear Persis, such an able girl, with so many good qualities, so dutiful, so well educated, such good marks in her Matric and Senior Cambridge, and quite pretty in a way, don't you think so, Ormus dear," to which somewhat perfunctory encomium he makes no other reply than a shrug. Then he must lounge lazily through the dining room, past the decrepit old domestic servant pretending to polish the silver candelabrum on the sideboard, Gieve, the kleptomaniac head bearer, whom his father took on from the departed William Methwold and who now bears the title of "butler," thanks to Sir Darius's fondness for Lord Emsworth's immortal Beach, and who has been very, very slowly stealing the family silver for years. (The disappearances have been so petty and so rare that Lady Spenta, guided by the Angel Good Thoughts, to say nothing of the Angel Blind Stupidity, has ascribed them to her own carelessness. Hardly anything except this candelabrum still remains, and even though the identity of the thief is well known to Ormus, he has never mentioned it to his parents, on account of his lofty disdain for material possessions.) And—at last!—Ormus must, he does, enter his own room, he stretches out on his bed, he looks up at the slow ceiling fan and drifts—now!—into reverie. A shadow falls. This is the fabled "Cama obscura," his stricken family's curse of inwardness, which he and he alone has learned how to harness, to transform into a gift.

There is a trick he can play on his mind. As he stares at the fan he can "make" the room turn upside down, so that he seems to be lying on the ceiling looking down at the fan which is growing like a metal flower from the floor. Then he can change the scale of things, so that the fan seems gigantic, and he can imagine himself sitting beneath it. Where is this? (His eyes close. The purple birthmark on his left eyelid seems to pulse and throb.) It's an oasis in the sands, and he's stretched out in the shade of a tall date palm, whose head tosses slowly in the warm breeze. Now, by dint of deeper dreaming, he populates that desert-ceiling; large airplanes land on the runway of the curtain rail, and all the raucous medley of a magical metropolis pours out of them, roads, tall buildings, taxicabs, policemen with guns, gangsters, saps, pianists dripping cigarettes from their lips and composing songs to other men's wives, poker games, big rooms featuring star entertainers, wheels of fortune, lumberjacks with money to burn, whores saving up for that little dress shop back home.

He is no longer in an oasis but in a city of dazzling lights, standing in front of a building that might be a theatre or a casino or some other secular temple of delights. He plunges in and at once he knows who he's looking for. He can hear his brother, whose voice is faint but not so very far away. His dead twin is singing to him, but he can't make out the song. "Gayomart, where are you going," Ormus calls. "Gayo, I'm coming, wait for me."

The place is swarming with people, all of them in too much of a hurry, spending too much money, kissing each other too lubriciously, eating too quickly so that meat juices and ketchup dribble down their chins, getting into fights over nothing, laughing too loud, crying too hard. At one end of the room is a giant silver screen, bathing the great room in glittering light. From time to time, the people in the room look up to it longingly, as if towards a god, but then shake their heads regretfully and continue with their carousing, which is oddly melancholy. All the people give off an air of incompleteness, as if they have not fully come into being. There are soldiers boasting to their fiancées about their deeds. There is a blonde with a fabulous décolletage wading through a fountain in full evening dress. In a corner, Death plays chess with a knight on his way home from the Crusades, and in another corner a Japanese samurai scratches desperately at an itch he cannot reach. Outside, in the street, a beautiful woman with cropped blond hair is hawking copies of the *Herald Tribune*.

Like a dark shade detached from its owner, Gayomart Cama slips through this gathering of brighter shadows, singing his elusive song. Ormus, pursuing him, is jostled and obstructed by a bald policeman sucking a lollipop, two absurd Indian clowns who speak in rhymes, and an underworld gang boss with cotton-wool padding in his cheeks. Their eyes fix briefly upon him, interrogating him fiercely. *Are you the one?* they seem to ask. *Is it you who will save us from this appalling place, this anteroom, this limbo, and give us the key to the silver screen?* But at once they know he is useless to them, he's not the one, and they return to their zombie dances.

Gayomart slips through a door at the far end of this first chamber, and Ormus struggles after him. The chase continues down staircases of decreasing grandeur, through rooms of growing gloom. Less glamorous than the hall of uncreated film and television characters is the room of unmade stage rôles, and tawdrier still is the parliament chamber of future betrayals, and the saloon bar of uninvented books, and the back alley of uncommitted crimes, until finally there is just a series of narrow iron steps descending into pitch blackness, and Ormus knows his twin brother is down there, waiting, but he's too afraid to descend.

Sitting on the top step of his dreamworld, staring into the dark, the purple stain on his eyelid glowing with the effort of searching out his lost sibling, his shadow self, who is down there somewhere in the blackness, Ormus Cama can hear Gayo singing his songs. Gayo has a fine, even a great, singing voice: perfect pitch, immense vocal range, effortless control, expert modulation. But he's too far away; Ormus can't make out the words. Just the vowel sounds.

The noise without the meaning. Absurdity.

Eck-eck eye ay-ee eck ee, ack-eye-ack er ay oo eck, eye oock er aw ow oh-ee ee, oo . . . ah-ay oh-eck . . .

Two years, eight months and twenty-eight days later he burst out of a listening booth in Bombay, having heard the same sounds issuing from the throat of the new American phenomenon, the first blazing star of the new music, and in the midst of his bewilderment he saw in his mind's eye the expressions on the faces of the shadows he had seen in his dream underworld, the melancholy and desperation of proto-entities longing to become and fearing their great day would never dawn; and he knew that his own face wore the selfsame expression, for the same terror was snatching at his own heart, *someone was stealing his place in history,* and it was to that look of naked fear that Vina had responded when she caught at his trembling nineteen-year-old hand and squeezed it tightly between her own, precocious palms.

I'm the least supernaturally inclined of men, but this tall story I have no option but to believe.

THREE PEOPLE, two living, one dead—I mean his ghostly brother, Gayomart, his lover, Vina, and his father, Sir Darius Xerxes Cama—were severally responsible for making sure that Ormus's day did, in the end, show up. On Gayo's lip-curled features he modelled his own sensualist's scowl; and

Gayomart's elusive songs, those devil-tunes wafting up from satanic darkness, became Ormus's own. In Gayo, Ormus found the Other into which he dreamed of metamorphosing, the dark self that first fuelled his art.

Of Vina's part in his story, much more will soon be said. As for Sir Darius, who dreamed whisky dreams of England while asleep on his leather chesterfield and yearned for fictional mansions when he was awake, his son certainly inherited his capacity for leading a vivid dream-life. And more; Sir Darius's disenchantment with his home town became Ormus's too. The son inherited his father's discontent. But the land of Ormus's dreams was never England. No white mansion for him, but that other house, the place of light and horror, of speculation and danger and power and wonder, the place where the future was waiting to be born. America! America! It pulled him; it would have him; as it pulls so many of us, and like Pinocchio on Pleasure Island, like all the little donkeys, we laugh (as it devours us) for joy.

Hee-haw!

AMERICA, THE Great Attractor, whispered in my ears too. But on the topic of Bombay, the city we would both leave behind, Ormus and I never agreed. Bombay was always something of a hick town, a hayseed provincial ville, in his eyes. The greater stage, the true Metropolis, was to be found elsewhere, in Shanghai, in Tokyo, in Buenos Aires, in Rio, and above all in the fabled cities of America, with their pinnacled architecture, the outsize moon rockets and giant hypodermic syringes towering over their cavernous streets. It is no longer permissible to speak of places like Bombay, as people spoke of them in those days, as being situated on the *periphery;* or to describe Ormus's yearnings, which were also Vina's and mine, as some sort of *centripetal force.* Yet finding the centre was what drove Ormus and Vina on.

My reasons were different. Not contempt, but surfeit and claustrophobia, made me leave. Bombay belonged too completely to my parents, V.V. and Ameer. It was an extension of their bodies, and, after their deaths, of their souls. My father, Vivvy, who adored both my mother and the city of Bombay so deeply that he sometimes referred to himself, only half jokingly, as a polygamist, had taken to referring to

Ameer as if she were a metropolis herself: her fortifications, her esplanades, her traffic flow, her new developments, her crime rate. Sir Darius Xerxes Cama had once equated himself, the arch-Anglophile product of the city the British built, with Bombay; but Vivvy's heart-city would never be Darius's. It was his own wife, Ameer.

Many youngsters leave home to find themselves; I had to cross oceans just to exit *Wombay,* the parental body. I flew away to get myself born. But like a longtime cigarette smoker who manages to quit, I have never forgotten the taste and kick of the old abandoned drug. Imagine, if you will, the elaborately ritualised (yes, and marriage-obsessed) formal society of Jane Austen, grafted on to the stenchy, pullulating London beloved of Dickens, as full of chaos and surprises as a rotting fish is full of writhing worms; swash & rollick the whole into a Shandy-and-arrack cocktail; colour it magenta, vermilion, scarlet, lime; sprinkle with crooks & bawds, and you have something like my fabulous home town. I gave it up, true enough; but don't ask me to say it wasn't one hell of a place.

(And there were other reasons too, let's be frank. For example, the threats against my person. If I'd stayed, it could have cost me my life.)

NOW MY story begins to strain in opposite directions, backwards, forwards. The forward pull, which every storyteller ignores at his peril, and to which for the moment I must yield, is nothing less than the tug of forbidden love. For even as the twenty-year-old German poet Novalis, "he who clears new territory," took a single look at twelve-year-old Sophie von Kühn and was doomed, in that instant, to an absurd love, followed by tuberculosis and Romanticism, just so the nineteen-year-old Ormus Cama, the most handsome young fellow in Bombay (though not, on account of the shadow that had lain over his family ever since the accident to Ardaviraf, the most eligible), fell for twelve-year-old Vina, fell flat, as if someone had pushed him in the back.

But their love was not absurd. Never that. We all filled it up with meanings, a surfeit of meanings; as we did their deaths.

"He was a proper gentleman," Vina as an adult would say

with genuine pride in her voice—Vina, whose taste ran to the roughest low-lifes, the most louche, least gentlemanly types on earth! "The second time we met," she would continue, "he declared his love?, and also swore a solemn oath that he would not so much as touch me until the day after my sixteenth birthday. My Ormus and his goddamn oaths." I suspected her of whitewashing the past, and said as much more than once. It never failed to rile her. "Extremes of experience is one thing," she'd snarl. "You know my views on that: I'm for 'em. Bring 'em on! I want to have them for myself?, not just read about them in the paper. But Bombay's Lolita I was not." She'd shake her head, angry at herself for being angry. "I'm telling you something beautiful, you bastard. I'm telling you it was over three years before I even got to hold his hand again! All we did was sing. And ride those goddamn trams." Then she laughed; she could never resist the memory, and gave up her wrath. "Ding-ding!" she pealed. "Ding!"

Anyone who has listened to the lyrics of Ormus Cama will certainly know of the central place reserved in his personal iconography for tramcars. They recur many times, along with street entertainers, cardplayers, pickpockets, wizards, devils, union men, evil priests, fisherwomen, wrestlers, harlequins, vagabonds, chameleons, whores, eclipses, motorbikes and cheap dark rum; and without fail, they lead to love. Your love is bearing down on me, there can be no escape, he sings. Oh cut my captured heart in two, oh crush me like a grape. No, I don't care. It's who I am. Oh you can tram me, baby, but I will derail your tram.

It was on the tramcars of Bombay, now departed, much mourned by those who remember them, that Ormus and Vina conducted their long courtship: she playing truant from school, he absenting himself from the Apollo Bunder apartment without explanation. Back then young people were kept on a tighter leash, so it was inevitable that a day of reckoning would come, but in the meanwhile they clattered round the city, hour after enchanted hour, and learned each other's stories. And so I, too, am—at last!—able to go backwards into the past; Vina's past. Satisfying my narrative's other need, I offer up for general consumption what Vina whispered into her future lover's ear.

* * *

THE MAKING of a bad girl: Born Nissa Shetty, she grew up in a shack in the middle of a cornfield outside Chester, Virginia, above Hopewell, between Screamersville and Blanco Mount, down a nothing track snaking east from 295. Corn on both sides of her and goats in the back. Her mother, Helen, Greek-American, full-figured, nervy, a reader of books, a dreamer, a woman of humble origins who carried herself well and hoped for much, fell during the World War II man shortage for a sweet-talking Indian gent, a lawyer—how'd he get all the way out there? *Indians get everywhere, isn't it? Like sand*—who married her, fathered three daughters in three years (Nissa, born during the Normandy landings, was the middle one), went to jail for malpractice, got struck off the register, came out of jail after Nagasaki, told his wife he had revised his sexual preferences, went off to Newport News to set up as a butcher with his beefy male lover, "as the female in the relationship," in Vina's words, and never wrote or called or sent money or presents for his daughters on their birthdays or Christmas. Helen Shetty in that loveless peace tumbled into a downward spiral of drink, pills and debt, couldn't hold a job, and the kids went to hell at high speed, until she was rescued by a jack-of-all-trades builder, John Poe, a widower with four kids of his own, who met her drunk and blurting in a bar, heard her out, reckoned she had good reason to despair, called her a good-looking woman who deserved a break, swore to look after her, got her off the sauce, took her and her three kids into his simple home and never differentiated between her children and his own, never commented on their dark skins, gave the girls his own name (so that at the age of three Nissa Shetty became Nissy Poe), worked hard earning money to put food in his family's mouths and clothes on their backs, asked nothing from Helen in return but conventional woman's work and an agreement that they have no more children, and though she had hoped for high things in her life, she knew how close she'd come to the gutter, so she was lucky to have found this instead, stability, a kind of gruff monosyllabic average love, a generous-hearted man, solid ground under her feet, and if he wanted things old-fashioned, that was an adjustment she was prepared uncomplainingly to make, so the shack was kept spotless, the clothes were cleaned, the children fed and bathed, John Poe's dinner was hot on the table every night when he came home, and he was right about the children thing too, so she went into the city and had the operation, and that was okay, that was really okay, she had her hands full and this made things easy, he was old-fashioned in bed as well as out of it, didn't hold with rubbers and such, and now everything was just fine, it was finer than fine, it was fine. Once a week they all went out to the drive-in in John's pickup, and Helen Poe looked at the stars above instead of those on the screen and thanked them, with certain reservations, for her luck.

If John Poe had a dream, it was of goats. In the corral behind his home there was a white Saanen doe who provided the family with milk, and a small, transient population of Spanish and myotonic goats being bred for the slaughter. Nissy Poe grew up without knowing the taste of cow milk. John Poe told her that goat milk was easier to digest, and even encouraged her to wash her face in it as a beauty treatment, as Queen Cleopatra used to do. She had learned from her mother never to contradict this big, kindly but dominating man, and she meekly drank down that thin bluish rancid-smelling liquid which she had come to hate. And after the doomed Spanish goats were taken off to the abattoir in their season, there would be nothing but chevon, goat meat, to eat for weeks at a stretch. Helen Poe was not a woman of great culinary skills, and little Nissy came to fear mealtimes above all things, because of the smile she had to paint on her face. John Poe was a man who needed regular thanking for the blessings he bestowed.

After a big goat dinner he would push back his chair and tell the future. These few creatures out back, in the paddock surrounded by a five-foot-high fence with the wire spaces just five inches or so apart, these were just the start, Nissy's stepfather declared. He wasn't going to labour for other folks all his days, you bet. A goat farm was what he had in mind. Not a meat farm, though; he held meat goats in something like contempt, especially the myotonics, whose genetic disorders caused them to fall over stiff-legged if they were startled. Some nights, John Poe looked forward to the day when he would go into the dairy-goat business, in Oregon, maybe, or Florida. He rhapsodised about the virtues of the "Swiss" Alpines and Toggenburgs and the "desert" Nubians. He spoke of the delights of goat cheese and goats' milk soap. On other nights, his vision was of angora and cashmere, and a future in fibre farming in Texas or Colorado. "You'll like that, with your Oriental blood, huh," he told Helen's daughters. "Cashmere is from Kashmir, India, originally, and angora came from Ankara, Turkey, and the name mohair, which is what we call the cloth made from the hair of the angora goat, is Arabic or such, meaning 'what we prefer.' " The Uzbek black goat, whose wool fibre was longer than the guard hairs and was of high, cashmere-type quality, often cropped up in these reveries. Nissy Poe, Eastern blood and all, came to detest the very words mohair, cashmere and Uzbek. But she smiled and said thank you as required. And John Poe, beer in hand, wafted off into his private Oriental fantasy.

Ormus Cama and I, growing up in India, felt our hearts striving towards the West; how strange it is to think of Vina's early years under the aegis of that good plain man with his lust for the East, or at least its hairy beasts.

Sometimes John Poe told goat jokes. (Two goats break into the projection room at the drive-in and start munching. "God, this film is good," sez the first, and the second goes, "Yeah, but I thought the book was better.") However, he did not tolerate such levity in others. A new neighbour dropped by once and said, "Goats, hey. Sure, we dig goats, we were thinking of getting a pet goat, but this guy said to us, 'Thing about goats is, they'll eat your car.' " After he left, John Poe placed him, his family and their land off limits. The man received a life sentence without ever knowing what he'd done, and John Poe being the man he was, it was a sentence from which there was no possibility of appeal.

It was a home without privacy, the children stacked in their bunks three and four to a room. Some of them grew up quiet, inward, defended. Nissy ran wild. In kindergarten she became notorious as a biter of other kids and teachers too, and she had to be withdrawn from class. John Poe whaled her soundly and she went back and bit harder. The war escalated and then suddenly stopped, because both combatants realized that if it went any further there might be a fatality.

John Poe told Nissy he loved her and put away his belt, and Nissy Poe told her terrorised classmates, "It's okay, I ain't gonna kill ya."

In the matter of race John Poe was close to being a liberal. He went with Helen to see the school authorities to explain that the girls' darkness was not Negro darkness, they were Indians from India and didn't need to be discriminated against, they could ride on the bus along with the regular kids. This argument the school accepted, though it brought problems of its own.

As Nissy grew older she learned that the other kids, the white kids, called her Blackfoot Indian, and also goatgirl. And then there were these three neighborhood boys, they looked Negro and spoke Spanish—boy, were *they* confused—and they used to jeer at Nissy Poe because she could ride on the bus to the white folks' school. And then one day the three boys were waiting for her bus, they kept saying there was a law now and they were going to her school too, except the driver wouldn't let them aboard, not on his bus. As she climbed on, she heard them shouting insults at her, something about her family's *cabritos* when she was the *kid* of a *cabronito*. She looked it up. *Cabrito* meant kid goat and *cabronito* meant small homosexual. The next day they were waiting for the bus again, with their daddy this time, but so what, she just took them all on. The father pulled her off his boys, she was kicking and punching air as he hauled her away, but she was satisfied, because in that short time she had inflicted a startlingly disproportionate amount of damage on the slanderers. John Poe got his belt out again, but his heart wasn't in it, because he knew that her will was greater than his. He began to ignore her, and didn't accompany Helen when she went to the school to plead with the staff to let her daughter stay on, and get an education, and escape from the trap of poverty, as she herself had once hoped to do. "It is a hard thing," Helen Poe told her daughter's class teacher, "for a child to live without hope."

Goatgirl. Not far from the shack, up towards Redwater Creek, there was a wooded hollow called Jefferson Lick. According to local legend, a kind of centaur lived there, a refugee from a Canadian travelling circus, mad and dangerous on account of all those years spent in a cage for the pleasure of the public, whipped and half starved. The Goat Monster of Jefferson Lick was the local bogeyman, used to frighten small children into obedience, and at the annual fancy-dress dance during the summer fair there would always be a Lick Man or two, the great god Pan come to Virginia, dressed in rags. When children were sure they were far enough away from Nissy Poe to be safe, they would call her the Goat Man's daughter and then run for their lives.

Helen attempted to steer her daughter on to a better road. When the girl was almost ten years old the mother stood with her (this was Memorial Day weekend, 1954) and looked up at the galaxy blazing out of the night sky. "Just follow your star, honey, don't get sidetracked by anyone or anything," Helen said, with a tremor in her voice that made Nissy glance at her sharply. The mother broke out a quick, thin, hard little smile that didn't fool Nissy for a minute. "Not like me, hey," Helen grinned, like a skull. "Just pick one of those beauties and follow where it leads." A meteor flashed. "I'll take that one," said Nissy Poe. "Looks like it's going places." Don't pick that one, her mother thought, a shooting star's bad luck. But she didn't say it, and the girl nodded firmly. "Yes, ma'am. That's the one that I want."

THAT WEEKEND, after finishing her chores, Nissy Poe went down to Jefferson Lick on her own, unafraid. She didn't expect to meet any monsters but she did want to be in there, as far in as she could go. The woods were lovely, dark and deep, and as she pushed her way through springy foliage into the depths of the hollow she felt something quite unknown fall upon her, like a blessing. It was solitude. To see the birds, you have to become part of the silence. Who said that? Some numskull. In here it was like *Snow White.* Birds everywhere, like butterfly clouds, and if you sang, they sang right along with you. Hooded warblers, yellow-breasted warblers, provided back-up vocals; woodpeckers laid down the beat. Nissy Poe let everything go, and sang. Shake, rattle and roll! This was her great secret, this voice like a rocket blast of power. Sometimes when John Poe was at work, and when John Poe's children were all out of the house, so they couldn't tell tales—John Poe might treat everyone alike, but the kids were another thing entirely—

Helen would turn on the radio and find a station that played the new stuff, the Driftwoods, Jack Haley, Ronnie "Man" Ray. Sometimes they'd even find one of the Negro rhythm and blues stations, and Helen would swing her hips and join in with that music, the segregated music, the music John Poe called the devil's boogie. "Come on, honey," Helen urged, "sing up here along with me," but Nissy Poe would always refuse and press her mouth into a white, bloodless line, and Helen would shake her head. "I don't know what it'd take to get you to have a good time," she'd say, and then the music would seize her again, she'd roll her eyes, and dance, and whoop it up, under the loyal, impassive eyes of her own daughters. (Two out of three; the youngest was usually placed on sentry duty in the front yard, in case John Poe returned unexpectedly.) Helen seemed in those moments to be a child herself, to be reaching out for a version of herself that had been crushed beneath the adult she had been forced by necessity to become.

Nissy Poe never sang for her mother but would go to Jefferson Lick to be alone, and only then, far from the world, protected by an apocryphal ogre, would she unleash the voice that revealed her heart's deepest desire. Music! It was all she wanted in life; to be a part not of silence, but of sound.

If there had been a Lick Monster present, he would have applauded. From the beginning, Vina had the voice, and the relentless attack. She sang her young heart out, then lay back on a bank of earth though she knew she would have to suffer for her dirty clothes later on, fell asleep, woke with a start, to find it was dark, scrambled out of the Lick and began to run, and when she got home she found she could have taken her time, because everybody was dead.

The children had been murdered in their beds, stabbed in their hearts with a large kitchen knife. They died without waking up. But John Poe had had his throat cut, and from the wreckage in the room it was plain he had staggered around for long moments before crashing down on top of the old tv cabinet. Blood was smeared down the tv screen, and he lay at its feet in a great sticky puddle, the swamp of his lost life. The tv was on, and somebody was saying something about a war starting up involving the Vietwhat? At

Dienbienwhere? In Indochina, right. That was between India and China? And really had a whole lot to do with a girl in a shack near Hopewell, Va., standing knee-deep in her dead family's blood.

Helen wasn't in the shack, but Nissy found her soon enough, because all the goats were dead too, and Helen was hanging by her neck from one of the cross-beams of the three-sided loafing shed John Poe had built with his own hands to give the livestock someplace to stand when the weather turned mean. In the dirt below her dangling feet was a large kitchen knife coated thickly with dark, congealing blood.

BECAUSE SHE didn't go for help until morning; because she set up a stepladder and cut her mother down with the murder weapon; because she stayed out there in the loafing shed all night, alone with the knife and her mother and the dead goats and the universe on fire in the sky, the shooting stars shooting every which way, the Milky Way pouring down (it was probably made of fucking goat milk and smelled like fucking piss); because of her bad-girl track record, the biting, the fighting, she was a suspect for about five minutes, five minutes in which she, goatgirl, the goat monster's daughter of Jefferson Lick, saw the thing in the officers' eyes that's there only when they look at big-time killers. Call it respect. But after five minutes even Sheriff Henry had worked out it would've been pretty tough for the kid to have done it, hanged her mother, for Chrissake, she was only ten. It wasn't a hard case to crack, crazy woman ran amuck, big handsome woman like her, still plenty there for a man to hold on to and be comforted by, too bad, things got to her, she snapped. Shit happens.

AFTER THAT, her father, Butcher Shetty, showed up with his lover, but she didn't like the sound of Newport News, she'd had enough of butchery for one lifetime, she'd be a vegetarian for the rest of her days. She finally agreed to go live with Helen's distant relatives the Egiptuses of Chickaboom, up near the Finger Lakes in western New York State: and all the way there, alone on the bus, she was wondering why her mother had chosen that precise moment to crack, that

Memorial Day when her middle daughter had fallen asleep in Jefferson Lick. Maybe it wasn't a spur-of-the-moment thing. Maybe Helen had waited until she, Nissa, was out of danger. She had been picked to survive, selected by her mother as the only one in the family who deserved life. Her mother had seen or heard something in her, something other than the wildness and violence, and so had spared her life. Nissa, her shooting star.

"She heard me!" The power of her sudden realization made her shout the words aloud. The passengers nearest her looked at her, shifted in their seats, but she was oblivious to their unease. *Helen heard me. She must've followed me to the Lick one day, and I never knew, and that's why she waited, she knew I'd be gone for a long while. I'm alive because she wanted me to sing.*

Welcome to Chickaboom, said a sign.

OF THE year or so she spent in that northern clime, in that Egiptian exile, Vina Apsara never told anyone very much. Ask her a question too many and she'd turn on you like a snake. She spoke to me about it only a couple of times in her life. The moment she arrived, she buried poor Nissy Poe, I know that. Mr. Egiptus offered her the use of his family name and said he had always wanted a daughter named Diana. She became Diana Egiptus without regret. The new name was not, however, lucky. "There was a woman who was not good to me," she said. "I was not treated well in that family." I could hardly get her to speak their given names. "The woman who I stayed with then," she called her chief tormentor, Mrs. Marion Egiptus; the other family members were "the people I was not happy with." These people ran, I was able to establish, the Egypt, a small cigar store, outside which stood the half-size figure of a pharaonic charioteer holding, in one hand, the reins of his single horse and, in the other, a fistful of stogies. "It was a one-horse town," Vina said, "and the one horse was made of wood." This small town was her first Troy. Bombay would be her second, and the rest of her life her third; and wherever she went, there was war. Men fought over her. In her own way, she was a Helen too.

What happened in Chickaboom? I can't tell you much;

Vina told me very little; and those who have investigated the story since have given conflicting, often purely fictitious accounts. Marion Egiptus was foulmouthed and harsh and repulsed by the future Vina's dark skin. Other members of the Egiptus household saw the same dark skin as an invitation to sexual relations. The young Nissy-Diana-Vina had to fight her cousins off.

The Egypt faltered, or was bought out. There was a fire, or there was not. It was an insurance scam, or arson, or it didn't happen. Marion Egiptus, the "woman she stayed with then," the "woman who was not good to her," refused, perhaps on account of the blow to the family's fortunes, or (if there was not, in fact, such a blow) on account of her profound aversion to the girl, to keep Diana Egiptus with her any more. There are suggestions that Vina's delinquency continued, the truancy, the violence, the excessive use of pills.

Rejected by Mrs. Egiptus, she was sent to India because no American options remained. Butcher Shetty of Newport News wrote a begging letter to his rich relations the Doodhwalas of Bandra, Bombay, failing to mention he was no longer a lawyer, no longer a fat cat getting fatter off a daily diet of high-calorie American mice, but that omission was a matter of honour, a way of preserving his self-respect. He also omitted to mention his daughter's many run-ins with authority, and somewhat overstated young Nissa Shetty's girlish charms (in this letter she reverted to her original name). At any rate, the rich Doodhwalas, seduced by the glamorous prospect of acquiring an America-returned niece, agreed to take her in. Nissa Shetty's father met her off the Greyhound at the Port Authority Terminal and spent a night with her in Manhattan. He took her to dinner at the Rainbow Room and danced with her on the revolving stage and held her close, and she understood what he was telling her; not only that business was good but also that he was saying goodbye for ever, she couldn't count on him any more. Don't call, don't write, have a good life, goodbye. The next morning she went to Idlewild by herself, took a deep breath and headed east. East to Bombay, where Ormus and I were waiting.

* * *

IF WE are to understand Vina's rage, which drove her art and damaged her life, we must try to imagine what she would not tell us, the myriad petty cruelties of the unjust relations, the absence of fairy godmothers and glass slippers, the impossibility of princes. When I met her on Juhu Beach and she delivered herself of that astonishing tirade against the whole of India, past, present and future, she was in reality only indulging in a kind of masquerade, concealing herself from me behind her bitter ironies. In cosmopolitan Bombay it was she who was provincial; if she praised American sophistication at our expense, it was because sophistication was a quality she utterly lacked. After a lifetime of poverty, it was India, in the overblown form of Piloo Doodhwala, that had offered her a first taste of affluence; therefore, by inversion, she filled her dialogue with ersatz rich-American contempt for the impoverishment of the Orient. In Chickaboom the winters had been savage (that was a detail I did manage to extract from her); loathing the cold, she complained, in warm Bombay, about the heat.

Finally, and above all else, if we are to understand Vina's rage, we must put ourselves in her shoes and try to imagine her sentiments when, after a gruelling journey across the planet to Bombay's Santa Cruz airport, she disembarked from the Pan American Douglas DC-6, to find that her father—oh, the unforgivable thoughtlessness of the man!—had delivered her once more, and with scant hope of escape, into the hated company of goats.

DING-DING! Ding!

For a big city, Bombay can operate remarkably like a small village; it isn't long before everyone knows everything, especially about a cocky twelve-year-old beauty taking tramcar rides with a grown nineteen-year-old man with movie star good looks and a whispered success rate with the girls that is fast acquiring legendary proportions. Memories being what they are, none of the three of us could agree on how long it took, days, weeks, months. What is beyond doubt is that when the news reached the ears of Pilo Doodhwala he tried to beat her up; whereupon she attacked him with an abandoned savagery that obliged Golmatol, Halva, Rasgulla and several other members of the "magnificentourage" to help subdue her, a process during which she both inflicted and received a number of wounds. The rain came; she was put out of doors; she arrived on our doorstep; and Ormus, who loved her, who swore he had not touched her, let alone defiled her honour, was not far behind.

And this in the far-off 1950s! In "underdeveloped" India, where boy-girl relations were so strictly controlled! True, true: but permit me to say, "underdeveloped nation" or not, one of our prime cultural artifacts was a highly developed apparatus of hypocritical disapproval, not only of any incipient change in social mores, but also of our own historically proven and presently hyperactive erotic natures. What's the *Kama Sutra*? A Disney comic? Who built the Khajuraho temples? The Japanese? And of course in the 1950s there were no girl tarts in Kamathipura working eighteen hours a day, and child marriages never took place, and the pursuit of the very young by lecherous old humberts—yes, we'd already heard of the new Nabokov shocker—was utterly unknown. (Not.) To hear some people talk, you'd conclude that sex hadn't been discovered in India by the mid-twentieth century, and the population explosion must have been made possible by some alternative method of fertilisation.

So: Ormus Cama, in spite of being an Indian, had a way with girls; and Vina, in spite of being just twelve, had a history of extreme violence towards males who stepped out of line. Yet their meeting transformed them both. From that moment on, Ormus lost interest in all other females of the species, and never regained it, even after Vina's death. And Vina had found, for the first and only time, a man whose approval she constantly needed, to whom she turned, after everything she said or did, for confirmation, for validation, for meaning. He became the meaning of her life, and she of his. Also, she owned a battered old acoustic guitar, and on those long afternoons riding the tramcars or sitting on the rocks at Scandal Point or walking in the Hanging Gardens or fooling around the Old Woman's Shoe in Kamala Nehru Park, she taught him how to play. What's more, when she'd listened to his incoherent, eavesdropped songs, the prophetic ditties of the late Gayomart Cama, she gave him the advice that led to his second, true birth into music and made possible the whole astonishing Cama songbook, the long stream of hits by which he will always be remembered. "It's good you love your brother, and want to follow where he's leading. But maybe it's the wrong way. Try another room in that dream-palace of yours. Or another one, or another one, or another one. Maybe you'll find your own noises someplace in there. Maybe then you'll be able to hear the words."

AT THE end of one cycle of time, they say, we experience *kenosis,* an emptying. Things lose meaning, they erode. This is what had been happening, I believe, not only to Ormus Cama and Vina Apsara, but also to all those whose lives touched theirs. The decay of time, at the end of a cycle, leads to all manner of poisonous, degrading, defiling effects. A cleansing is required. The love that was born between Ormus and Vina, the love that was prepared to wait years for fulfilment, provided that new cleanness, and a new cycle of time began. *Plerosis,* the filling of time with new beginnings, is characterised by a time of superabundant power, of wild, fruitful excess. Alas, however, such shapely theories are never quite up to the task of accounting for the messiness of real life. The cleansing and renewal of time did indeed have some beneficial results, but only on the lives of the lovers themselves. They were, it's true, greatly energized by their new love; but all around them, the catastrophes continued.

HE LOVED her like an addict: the more of her he had, the more he needed. She loved him like a student, needing his good opinion, playing up to him in the hope of drawing forth the magic of his smile. But she also, from the very beginning, needed to leave him and go elsewhere to play. He was her seriousness, he was the depths of her being, but he could not also be her frivolity. That light relief, that serpent in the garden, I must confess, was me.

CHAPTER FIVE

Goat Songs

Begin, today, with an animal sacrifice. (Or, at least, an account of same.)

O twice-born Dionysus, O madness-strengthened bull, inexhaustible fount of life energy, divine drunkard, conqueror of India, god of women, master of the snake-changing maenads, the chewers of laurels! In lieu of burnt offerings, accept from us, ere we proceed with our humble entertainments, a bloody tale of slaughtered milk-givers; and, being pleased, bestow upon our poor efforts the benison of your crazy, lethal grin!

Whereas the large-scale farming of goats had been, for Vina Apsara's late stepfather, John Poe, no more than a distant, utopian fantasy, Shri Piloo Doodhwala, her most recent "loco parentis," as my mother called him, "more loco than parentish," was the dairy-goat king of what became the state of Maharashtra, a person of immense, even feudal significance in the rural areas where the care and handling of his herds accounted for almost all local employment. From his earliest days to his present pre-eminence, Piloo the milkman thought of his "little business," his "milk round," as a mere stepping-stone to far higher things: that is to say, public office, and the immense wealth that such office can bring to a man who knows how the world works. The opening of the Exwyzee Milk Colony, and its promise to provide the Bombay citizenry with top-grade, full-cream, pasteurized cows' milk, was therefore an event which Piloo took as a personal insult.

"Cowvs?" he shrieked at his wife, Golmatol. "Let them worship cowvs, but leawe their udders alone! A person should not squveeze the titties of a goddess! Isn't it, wife? What do you say?" To which Golmatol hesitantly replied,

"But and all, the milk is OK." Piloo exploded. "OK? To my phace you are saying it? Arré, how to surwiwe when I am beset by traitors? When I must phight not only these sacred mooing gods but also my own wife as vell."

Golmatol, colouring, eyes downcast, retreated. "No, dear, I only said." But Piloo's anger had been re-targeted at the primary enemy. "Exwyzee," he snorted. "If they are so wyzee, then they will surely know that pretty soon they will be ex."

Piloo went to war. Attended by the scurrying magnificentourage, he stalked the corridors of power in the Bombay Sachivalaya, dispensing bribes and threats in equal measure, demanding the investigation, condemnation and cancellation, as a matter of priority, of the "blasphemous cow-abuse phacility just opened north of Town." He sought out zoning inspectors, tax inspectors, livestock inspectors, hygiene inspectors and of course police inspectors. He paid for giant advertising billboards on which, in a large speech-bubble issuing from his own leering face, and under the legend *Your Milkman Says,* the following argument was made: *EX—means Expensive! WY—means Why Buy It?? ZEE—means Zero Enjoyment Exists!!!* And at the bottom, next to his trademark cartoon goat, the slogan: *Vote Goat—Buy PILOO—the Dude with Doodh.*

It didn't work. In all his life he never suffered a more complete, a more humiliating rebuff. The city authorities declined even to investigate, let alone condemn or cancel the Milk Colony's licenses. Neither blasphemy nor abuse was being committed, all analysts agreed. Zoning inspectors declined to cancel permits, tax inspectors refused to harass, livestock and hygiene inspectors heaped Exwyzee with praise, police inspectors said they had nothing to inspect. Worse still, the Exwyzee grounds became a popular weekend picnic resort; and worst of all, month by month Piloo's sales figures declined, while those of the hated cows went from strength to strength. The goat villages, blaming Piloo for the crisis, simmered with the possibility of violence. Faced with the erosion of his power base, Piloo Doodhwala admitted to his lady wife that he had no idea what to do.

"And my poor Halva and Rasgulla?" demanded Golmatol Doodhwala, sheltering one weeping daughter under each arm. "What will you say to them? You think they have an idea in their dear heads? They are not lovely! Their skin is not wheatish! In education they are deficient! Sweets by name, they are sour by nature! All their hope was pinned on you! And now if you remove from them even their fortune, then what? Will husbands drop from the skies? Poor girls have no chance—no hope in hell!"

INTO THIS time of crisis came that half-breed girl, all the way from New York. She turned out to be poor, badly connected, with more scandals in her history than a Pompadour: damaged goods, in short. The Doodhwalas closed ranks against her, barely acknowledging her existence. They offered her the bare minimum: food (though their dining table groaned with dishes, she was usually served rice and lentils in the kitchen, in ungenerous quantities, and often went hungry to bed); simple clothing (the swimsuit had come with her from America, a gift from her absentee father); and an education (this was what Piloo begrudged most, because the fees cost good money, and the brat didn't seem to want to learn anything, anyway). Other than providing her with these necessities, they abandoned her to her fate. She quickly perceived that rich Bombay offered her the worst of both her previous, much poorer worlds: the detested goats of John Poe and the heartless cruelties of the Egiptus family of cigar store fame.

NOW THAT day at Juhu Beach begins to look very different. It becomes clear that, strangely enough, Piloo and Vina had both come to the same conclusion: all they had left in life was attitude, but it was a steed which would get you a long way if you knew how to stay on its back. So Piloo and his magnificentourage had come to perform, in public, a masque of power, to enact the lie of continued success in the hope that the sheer force of the performance would somehow make it true, would reverse the slow defeat that Exwyzee cows were inflicting upon the Doodh-Dude's goats. And Vina, too, was struggling to survive: in reality she wasn't Piloo's spoiled rich American bitch kid, but a poor brat brazening it out while staring the bleakest of futures in the eye.

* * *

THE FUTURE of the milk business became Piloo Doodhwala's only topic of discussion, his fixation. At home in his Bandra villa, pacing up and down in the garden, he would shriek and gibber like a caged langur. He was a man of his generation, the last for whom breast-beating and hair-tearing were still legitimate pursuits. His family and the magnificentourage, both, in different ways, fearful of the future, would hear him out in silence. His weepings, his shakings of fists, his speeches addressed to the empty, cloudless heavens. His complaints about the injustice of human life. Vina, who had seen too many things in her short life, was less tight-lipped, and the day came when she could stand it no longer.

"Oh, to hell with your stupid goats," Vina burst out. "Why don't you just cut their horrible throats and turn them into meat and coats?" Parrots flew from the trees, alarmed by the timbre of her voice; their droppings polluted Piloo's garments and, indeed, his agitated hair. She herself, tickled by the accident of the triple rhyme, began, in spite of her profound annoyance, to giggle.

The watching Doodhwala girls braced themselves delightedly for the lashing fury with which their father would now surely chastise the upstart pauper. But—in spite of her blatant insubordination, and what Ameer Merchant would have called her "fit of the gigglics"; in spite of the rain of parrot shit—no such fury manifested itself. Like unlooked-for sunshine when there has been talk of storms, Piloo Doodhwala's smile arrived, first a little hesitantly, and then breaking out in all its full-beam glory. "Thanking you, Miss America," he said. "Meat phor the interior, owercoat phor exterior. Idea is good, but"—and here he tapped a finger against his temple—"it has prompted one further idea, which is ewen betterer. It may be, madamoozel, that you hawe rescued, albeit inadwertently, our poor phamily phortunes." At which unexpected (and, in their view, entirely inappropriate) lavishing of praise upon the household's Cinderella, Halva and Rasgulla knew not whether to take umbrage or rejoice.

After this unusual exchange, Piloo Doodhwala ordered the slaughter of all his herds and the distribution of the meat, gratis, to the deserving and non-vegetarian poor. It was a royal massacre; the gutters near the abattoirs bubbled over with blood, flooding the streets, which grew sticky and stank. Flies crowded so thickly that in places it became inadvisable, for reasons of low visibility, to drive. But the meat was good, and plentiful, and Piloo's political prospects began to improve. Vote goat indeed. If Piloo had run for governor that week, no man could have stood against him.

His distressed goatherds, seeing the approach of destitution as clearly as if it were the mail train from the north, sought urgent assurances. Piloo toured the countryside, whispering conundrums in their ears. "Newer phear," he said. "The goats we will hawe in phuture could not be depheated by Exwyzee or any other alphabetists. They will be top-quality goats, and you will all grow phat and lazy, becaase you will still get all your pay, though the goats will not require any maintenance, and also, they will not cost one single rupee to pheed. Phrom now on," he concluded cryptically, "we will raise not simply goats but ghoasts."

THE RIDDLE of the "ghoasts"—or ghoats, or goasts, or what you will—must remain unsolved awhile. We have arrived once again, by recirculation, at the moment of Vina's expulsion from Piloo's portals. News of her scandalous liaison with Ormus Cama has reached her latest guardian's ears; a quarrel, which has already been alluded to, has already taken place. I offer no further details of those vituperative exchanges, or of the violent struggles that immediately preceded Vina's flight south in the pouring rain, which took her all the way from the Doodhwalas' Bandra mansion to our doorstep at Villa Thracia, Cuffe Parade. Instead, I take up the story from its last resting place: namely, the arrival of Ormus at our family home on Cuffe Parade, urgent with concern for Vina's well-being; and the further arrival, hard on Ormus's heels, of Shri Piloo Doodhwala, accompanied by wife, daughters and the full "magnificentourage."

My mother, Ameer, had telephoned him earlier to inform him that Vina was safe and well, and had gone on to speak a few home truths about his treatment of her. "She will not return to your house," Ameer finished. "Return?" barked Piloo. "Madam, I hawe put her out of doors, like a common bitch. Return is not the question." In the light of this telephonic washing of hands, the arrival of Piloo & Co. was something of a surprise. Vina sprang up and retreated at high speed to the room my mother had given her. Ormus rushed forward to stand face-to-face with his beloved's tormentor. It was left to my mild father to ask Piloo his business. The milkman shrugged. "Regarding that ungratephul girl," he said. "Monies hawe been paid. Phees, cash, spending on account. There has been major outlay of phunds, and in consequence one is considerably out of pocket. Reimbursement is not unreasonably required."

"You're asking us to purchase her?" My fine, high-minded father took a moment to grasp the horrible truth. Piloo made a face. "Not as such purchase," he insisted. "I do not insist on a profit. But you are an honourable man, isn't it? I am certain you would not ask me to swallow the loss."

"We are not speaking here of goods and chattels—" began V.V. Merchant, in outrage, but at this point Ormus Cama interrupted him. We were all standing like statues in our living room—the shock of the encounter had driven all thoughts of relaxation from our minds—and Ormus Cama's eye had fallen upon a pack of cards and a heap of matchsticks on a low table in a corner, the remnants of a light-hearted game of poker a couple of nights back, before the world began to change. He riffled the pack under Piloo's nose. "Hey, big-mouth," he said. "I'll play you for her. What do you say, hot shot? All or nothing. Do you dare to do it, or are you a gutless cutlass?"

Ameer began to protest, but my father—whose own fatal weakness would turn out to be gambling—silenced her. Piloo's eyes were gleaming, and the members of his magnificentourage, who were eavesdropping on the confrontation from the porch outside, began to hoot and cheer. Piloo nodded slowly. His voice grew very soft. "All or nothing, is it. Either I must giwe up 'all' my legitimate claim to recompense or . . . but what is 'or'? What is 'nothing'? If you lose, what do I win?"

"You win me," said Ormus. "I will work for you, any work you name, until I have worked off Vina's debt."

"Stop it, Ormus," said Ameer Merchant. "This is childish, absurd."

"I accept," sighed Piloo Doodhwala, and bowed.

Ormus bowed back. "One cut each," he said. "High card wins all. Suit immaterial. Aces high, jokers beat aces. Further cuts to decide if we draw equal cards."

"Agreed," breathed Piloo. "But we will play vith my pack." He snapped his fingers. His Pathan bearer marched into our living room carrying, on the white-gloved palm of his outstretched right hand, a silver salver upon which lay a pack of red playing cards whose seal had not been broken. "Don't," I begged Ormus. "There's some trick." But Ormus picked up the pack, broke the seal and nodded. "Let's begin."

"No shuffle," Piloo whispered. "Just cut."

"Good," said Ormus, and did so. And drew the two of hearts.

Piloo laughed. And cut. And drew the two of spades. The smile died on his lips, and the Pathan bearer recoiled from the ferocity of his master's glare.

Ormus cut again. The ten of diamonds. Piloo became very stiff. His hand jerked forward to the salver. He drew the ten of clubs. The Pathan bearer's arm began to tremble. "Hold the tray with both hands," Piloo snarled, "or else phind somebody whose shit hasn't turned to water."

On the third cut they both drew eights. On the fourth it was one-eyed jacks and on the fifth, the jacks with both eyes. By the sixth round, when they both drew fives, the silence in the room had become so noisy that even Vina emerged from her retreat to find out what all the fuss was about. Piloo Doodhwala was sweating heavily; his white kurta was sticking to the curve of his belly as well as the small of his back. Ormus Cama, however, was perfectly calm. In the seventh round both men drew kings; in the eighth, nines. In the ninth it was kings again, and in the tenth it was fours.

"That's enough," Piloo broke the silence. "From now on I'm drawing first."

On the eleventh cut, Piloo Doodhwala drew the ace of spades, and gave a great, deep sigh. Before he had finished exhaling, Ormus had cut for his card. It was the joker. Ormus remained impassive, looking down at the grinning clown on the silver dish. Piloo Doodhwala sagged visibly.

Then he rallied, clicked his fingers under Ormus's nose, snapped, "Keep the bitch," and walked out.

Ormus Cama went over to Vina, who was looking, for once, like a scared twelve-year-old. "You heard the man," he grinned. "I won you fair and square. Now you belong to me."

He was wrong. Vina belonged to no man, not even to him, though she loved him till the day she died. She reached out towards him, offering a caress of thanks. He stepped back, seriously. "No touching," he reminded her. "Not until you are sixteen years and one day old."

"And not then, not until you're decently married," said my mother, "if I have anything to do with it."

It is time to accentuate the positive. For are there no noble qualities, no high achievements, no exaltations of the spirit to praise in the life of the great sub-continent? Must it always be violence or gambling or crooks? These are touchy times. National sensitivities are on permanent alert, and it is getting harder by the moment to say boo to a goose, lest the goose in question belong to the paranoid majority (goosism under threat), the thin-skinned minority (victims of goosophobia), the militant fringe (Goose Sena), the separatists (Goosistan Liberation Front), the increasingly well organized cohorts of society's historical outcasts (the ungoosables, or Scheduled Geese), or the devout followers of that ultimate guruduck, the sainted Mother Goose. Why, after all, would any sensible person wish to say boo in the first place? By constantly throwing dirt, such booers disqualify themselves from serious consideration (they cook their own goose).

It is in the most constructive spirit imaginable, therefore, that I record the heartwarming news that Vina Apsara, who once, while standing on a beach wrapped up in Old Glory, hurled abuse at all things Indian, began at Villa Thracia to fall in love with her biological father's great country of origin. She had to wait for Ormus Cama until after her sixteenth birthday, but this other love entailed no waiting period. She consummated it right away.

To her last day, I could always see in her the skittish, disintegrated creature she'd been when she first came to us, looking as if she might run away again at any moment. What a piece of jetsam she was then, what a casualty! Literally selfless, her personality smashed, like a mirror, by the fist of her life. Her name, her mother and family, her sense of place and home and safety and belonging and being loved, her belief in the future, all these things had been pulled out from under her, like a rug. She was floating in a void, denatured, dehistoried, clawing at the shapelessness, trying to make some sort of mark. An oddity. She put me in mind of one of Columbus's sailors, close to mutiny, fearing that at any moment she might plunge off the edge of the earth, staring longingly at the lookout in the crow's-nest, whose spyglass probed the liquid emptiness, searching vainly for land. Later, when she was famous, she herself often mentioned Columbus. "He went looking for Indians and found America. I hadn't planned on going anywhere, but I found more Indians than I could handle." Vina's smart mouth, her lippiness. That, at the age of twelve, she already had.

She was a rag-bag of selves, torn fragments of people she might have become. Some days she sat crumpled in a corner like a string-cut puppet, and when she jerked into life you never knew who would be there, in her skin. Sweet or savage, serene or stormy, funny or sad: she had as many moods as the Old Man of the Sea, who would transform himself over and over again if you tried to grab him, for he knew that if you did capture him he would have to grant your deepest wish. Fortunately for her, she found Ormus, who just hung on to her, held her spirit tight in his love without laying a finger on her body, until at last she stopped changing, was no longer ocean then fire then avalanche then wind, and was just herself, one day after her sixteenth birthday, in his arms. And then she kept her side of the bargain and, for one night, gave him his heart's desire.

That she was in bad trouble, she already knew. That sassiness, delinquency, nihilism and unpredictability didn't add up to a person, she had worked out for herself. In her own way, and in spite of all her surface insouciance and defiance, she possessed a constructive spirit, and it's my belief that she was spurred on in her heroic act of self-construction by the experience of living *chez nous,* where talk of building was constant (these were the days when V. V. and Ameer started work on the great Orpheum movie theatre, the project that would eventually ruin them). What she set about constructing was put together with the materials that came immediately to hand: that is to say, Indian goods. What she built was "Vina Apsara," the goddess, the Galatea with whom the whole world would fall, as Ormus fell, as I fell, in love.

She began with music. "Vina." She'd heard a musician in Piloo's entourage playing, coarsely and without feeling, an instrument that in spite of such brutalisation "made a sound like god; and when I found out what it was called, I knew that was the name for me." The music of India, from northern sitar ragas to southern Carnatic melodies, always created in her a mood of inexpressible longing. She could listen to recordings of ghazals for hours at a stretch, and was entranced, too, by the complex devotional music of the leading *qawwals*. Longing for what? Not, surely, for an "authentic" Indianness that she could never attain? Rather, I must conclude—and this is hard for a lifelong sceptic like me to write—that what Vina wanted was a glimpse of the unknowable. The music offered the tantalising possibility of being borne on the waves of sound through the curtain of *maya* that supposedly limits our knowing, through the gates of perception to the divine melody beyond.

A religious experience, to be brief, was what she wanted. In a sense, this meant she understood the music far better than I, for its spiritual element is of central importance to so many people, not least the musicians themselves. I, however, am my parents' child, in that I have always been deaf to religious communications of all types. Unable to take them at face value—what, you *really* think there was an angel there? Reincarnation, *honestly?*—I have made the mistake (encouraged by a childhood in which I hardly ever heard the name of any deity mentioned with approval in our home) of assuming that everyone else was of the same mind, and thought of such speech as metaphorical, and nothing more. This has not always proved a happy assumption to make. It gets one into arguments. And yet—though I know that dead myths were once live religions, that Quetzalcoatl and Dionysus may be fairy tales now but people, to say nothing of goats, once died for them in large numbers—I can still give no credence whatsoever to systems of belief. They seem flimsy, unpersuasive examples of the literary genre known as "unreliable narration." I think of faith as irony, which is perhaps why the only leaps of faith I'm capable of are those required by the creative imagination, by fictions that don't pretend to be fact, and so end up telling the truth. I am fond of saying that all religions have one thing in common, namely that their answers to the great question of our origins are all quite simply wrong. So when Vina made, as she would repeatedly make, announcements of her latest conversion, I would reply, "Oh, sure," and convince myself that she was, in a profound sense, just kidding. But she wasn't. She meant it, every time. If Vina had decided to worship the Great Pumpkin, then assuredly, come Hallowe'en, hers—and not poor Linus's—would have been the sincerest pumpkin patch of all.

"Apsara" was a clue too, if I hadn't been too stupid to pick it up. It indicated a quantity of serious reading, and even though Vina liked to claim that she'd taken the name from a magazine advertisement in *Femina* or *Filmfare* for beauty soap or luxury silks or some such frippery, hindsight shows up that subterfuge for the ruse it was. She had plunged into the great matter of this strange, huge land in which she had been exiled, far from everything she'd ever thought or been or known. A refusal of the customary marginalised rôle of the exile, it was—I see it now—heroic.

"Vina Apsara" sounded to her twelve-year-old self like someone who might plausibly exist. She would bring her into being, using, as her tools, her love for Ormus Cama, her incredible will, her fabulous hunger for life, and her voice. A woman who can sing is never entirely beyond salvation. She can open her mouth and set her spirit free. And Vina's singing needs no paeans of praise from me. Put on one of her records, lie back and float downstream. She was a great river, which could bear us all away. Sometimes I try to imagine how she would have sounded singing ghazals. For even though she dedicated her life to another music entirely, the pull of India, its songs, its languages, its life, worked upon her always, like the moon.

I do not flatter myself (or not always) that she came back for me.

* * *

To MY parents, Vina was the daughter they never had, the child they had chosen to forgo so that they could concentrate on me and on their work; she was the life they thought they did not have room for in their lives. But now that she had arrived, they were filled with joy, and there turned out to be time for everything, after all. She picked up languages as easily as, throughout her life, she picked up lovers. It was in those years that she perfected her use of "Hug-me," our polyglot trash-talk. "Chinese khana ka big mood hai," she learned to say, when she wanted a plate of noodles, or—for she was a great hobbit fancier—"Apun J.R.R. Tolkien's *Angootiyan-ka-Seth* ko too-much admire karta chhé." Ameer Merchant, the family's great word-gamester, paid Vina the compliment of incorporating many of the girl's locutions into her own personal lexicon. Ameer and Vina were, linguistically at least, two of a kind. (And my mother saw, in her new ward, some deeper echoes of her own unconventional spirit.) Ameer was always convinced of the deep meanings hidden in euphony and rhyme: that is to say, she was a popster *manqué*. So, in her increasingly intimate moments of Vina-teasing and general raillery, Ameer would conflate Ormus Cama and Vasco da Gama—"Ormie da Cama, your great explorer, discovering you like a new world full of spices"—and it was a short step from Gama to *Gana,* song, and between Cama and *Kama,* the god of love, the distance was even less. Ormus Kama, Ormus Gana. The embodiment of love, and also of song itself. My mother was right. Her word games said more than she knew.

Vina was already much the same size and build as my mother, and Ameer let her dress up, not only in saris of lavish silk, but also in the slinky sequinned sheath dresses—plunging necklines and all—with which Ameer loved to display her figure to the city's sophisticated set. Vina grew her hair long, and once a week Ameer personally applied fresh coconut oil to the growing tresses and massaged the young girl's scalp. She showed Vina the traditional way of drying long hair, spreading it over a wickerwork surface, under which she set a pot of live coals sprinkled with incense. For her skin, Vina learned how to mix rose water and *multani mitti,* a clay named after Multan in Pakistan, and apply it as a face mask. Ameer rubbed ghee into Vina's feet to keep them soft and to draw out "surplus temperature" from the body during the hot season. Best of all, she taught Vina the connection between jewellery and good fortune; godless Ameer was not without her superstitious foibles. Vina took to wearing a gold chain round her waist. (However, nothing could induce her to wear toe rings, once she had been told that they heightened a woman's fertility.) And for the rest of her life, the great singer would never wear a precious stone until she had "road-tested" it by putting it under her pillow every night for a week, to see what effect it had on her dreams. This tried the tolerance of various illustrious international jewellery stores, but for a good customer, and a star, people were willing to stretch a point.

(If she had known that her last sexual companion, the playboy Raúl Páramo, had covertly slipped the gift of a ruby necklace under her pillow during their night of befuddled love—rubies had been absolutely forbidden her, years before, by Ameer's personal astrologer—she would have understood at once why she had dreamed of blood sacrifice, and been warned, perhaps, of the nearness of her doom. But she never found the necklace. It was discovered by the police during their search of her hotel room, and before she could be informed, it was all over.

And besides, all this jewel reading is pure malarkey. Nothing to it at all.)

AS WELL as Hindi-Urdu and the secrets of beauty and gems, Vina also drank down the city of Bombay in great thirsty gulps—in particular, to the delight of my father, the language of its buildings. V.V. became her eager instructor, and she his star pupil. My parents had just sunk a great deal of money in a prime property near the Bombay Central railway terminus, the site of the proposed Orpheum theatre, which, my father was determined, would be built in the Deco style that Bombay had made her own, even though the city's other Deco movie houses were already twenty years old and more "modern" theatres were presently the rage. Vina wanted to know everything. After a while, whenever we went to English-language movies, she paid more attention to the cinemas than to anything on the screen. At the great Deco masterpiece, the red-sandstone-and-cream Eros Cinema (Paramount Pictures, in VistaVision: Danny Kaye in *The Court Jester,* warning that on account of the pellet with the poison, the chalice from the palace was the one you must shun, while the vessel with the pestle had the brew that was true), Vina couldn't remember the plot but was able to mention casually that while the building had been designed by local boy Sohrabji Bhedwar, the fabulous interiors, black, white, gold and chromium, were the work of Fritz von Drieberg, who also renovated the New Empire (20th Century–Fox, Todd-AO, Rodgers, Hammerstein, a bright golden haze on the meadow, surreys with fringes, Rod Steiger singing his great self-pitying ditty, none of it enough to get her to remember a word of the fabulous score of *Ooooooo-klahoma!*). At the Metro with its MGM spectaculars—Stewart Granger in *Scaramouche,* winning the longest sword fight in movie history—her attention wandered to the chairs and carpets (American, imported) and the murals (by students at the J.J. School of Arts, where once Rudyard Kipling's dad had been in charge). And at the Regal—Maria Montez unforgettable in Universal's *Cobra Woman*—architecture-obsessed Vina failed to notice that La Montez was playing twins, but whispered credit was duly given to the Czech Karl Schara for the dazzling sun-ray design of the auditorium. At the Hindi movies, she behaved better and seemed more interested, though we did learn of the merits of Angelo Molle (interior, Broadway Cinema, Dadar). Vina professed unoriginally to be in love with Raj Kapoor, and Ormus was touchingly annoyed. I, however, was half sick of cinemas. Fortunately, the hot-season holidays came, and we went to Kashmir.

Vina blossoming towards womanhood in that once blessed valley is one of my most treasured memories. I remember her in the Shalimar Gardens beside running water, slowing suddenly from a child's gallop to a woman's walk and beginning to turn heads. I remember her on a palomino pony in the mountain meadow of Baisaran, her hair streaming behind her as she rode. I remember her on the Bund in Srinagar, falling in love with the names of the magic emporia full of papier mâché and carved walnut furniture and numdah rugs: Suffering Moses and Cheap John and

Subhana the Worst. I remember her on a pony trek through the high hamlet of Aru, being horrified that the villagers pretended they had no food to sell us, because they heard me call her "Vina" and assumed we were Hindus, and I also remember the equally intense disgust on her face when, having heard we were Muslims, these same villagers brought us a feast of shirmal and meatballs and refused to let us pay.

I remember her reading voraciously, devouring books—all in English, for she never could read Indian languages as well as she spoke them. In a field of flowers at Gulmarg, she read *On the Road* (she and Ormus could recite passages by heart, and when she did the book's elegiac conclusion, *I think of Dean . . . I think of Dean Moriarty,* there were tears in her eyes). Or, in a wood of tall trees near Pahalgam, she wondered if any of these conifers might be Enid Blyton's Faraway Tree, which—in an inspired inversion of the normal rules of travel—was regularly visited, at its cloud-concealed top, by fantastic lands. Most heart-piercingly of all, I remember her at the Kolahoi Glacier, talking excitedly about Jules Verne's *Journey to the Centre of the Earth,* and her dream of travelling to another high snowscape, that of the Snaefellsjokull in Iceland, so that on the summer solstice she could position herself in the right place at the right time and watch a rock's shadow point its swivelling finger, exactly at noon, to the entrance to the Underworld—an Arctic Taenarus Gate. In the light of what happened to her, this memory, I must confess, now gives me a bad attack of the creeps.

(All those cinemas show Hindi movies now. And Kashmir is a battle zone. But the past is not less valuable because it is no longer the present. In fact, it's more important, because forever unseen. Call it my brand of mysticism, one of the rare spiritual propositions I am prepared to make.)

Ormus Cama did not accompany us on holiday, or to the movies. On the subject of Vina's extraordinary liaison, Ameer Merchant had laid down the law. With great tolerance—and in spite of vociferous opposition from Lady Spenta Cama, whom, you will recall, she didn't much care for—she accepted the possibility that this was the beginning of a genuine love match, "but all proprieties must be observed." Ormus was allowed to call five times a week at tea-time and stay for one hour exactly. My mother agreed not to inform Lady Spenta of Ormus's visits, on the understanding that she herself would be present throughout them, or, if business appointments made it impossible for her to be there, that the entire encounter take place out of doors, on the porch. Vina agreed without argument. This was not the mutinous inwardness of Nissy Poe, or the frightened yielding of a girl with no options in life. Family life had begun to mend Vina, to make her whole, and she submitted happily to Ameer's maternal discipline because it sounded like love. Indeed, it was love; hard to say which of them needed the other more.

(Besides, as it turned out, Vina and Ormus had another, unexpected ally, who made possible a series of more private trysts.)

For me, Ormus's visits were the worst hours of the week. I tried to be absent as often as I could. When I was home, I sulked in my room. After he'd gone, however, things would look up. She'd come to see me. "Come on, Rai," she'd say. "You know how it is. I'm just killing time with Ormie, waiting for you to grow up and be my man." She'd stroke my cheek and even kiss me lightly on the mouth. And the years passed, and I turned thirteen, and her sixteenth birthday was round the corner, and still Ormus Cama refused to touch her, whether chaperones were present or not, and still I sulked in my room, and in she came, "Come on, Rai," and caressed me. In the light touch of her fingers and lips I could feel all the weight of her forbidden love for Ormus, all that inexpressible desire. I was forbidden fruit too, oppositely vetoed on account of my youth rather than hers. But although there wasn't anybody chaperoning us, because my parents were just too innocent to think of the possibility of my becoming Ormus's surrogate, his body double, I would have been prepared to settle for that lesser rôle, to be his shadow, his echo; in fact I was longing for it. But she refused to gratify me, she left me feeling worse than before, she kept me waiting.

It was a long wait. But Vina was worth waiting for.

Vina's weakness for mentors, for leaders and teachers, the addiction to mumbo jumbo which was her way of papering over the radical uncertainties of life, meant that Ormus could always, and effortlessly, claim her for his own. But I repeat: she was never wholly his possession. Card-game victories and worldwide celebrity notwithstanding, she kept coming back to me.

FROM DEATH Valley, the lowest point in the continental United States, you can see Mount Whitney, the highest. So, from the depths of my frustrated misery when Ormus Cama came to tea, I offer the following remembered glimpse of the high days when she and I were lovers:

Many years later in New York, in my third-floor walk-up on a block near St. Mark's noted for its population of gay Cuban refugees, Vina rolled off my sweating body immediately after we had finished making love, and lit a cigarette. (I have always perspired freely, a slight disadvantage in daily life but a definite plus during sex, when slipperinesses of all sorts, including moral, are efficacious.) "Did I tell you? I saw a light on him," she said. "A radiance, an aura, that first day in the record store. Not excessive?, but definitely emanating. About equivalent to a hundred-watt bulb, that is to say, enough to illuminate an average-size room. Which was plenty."

Vina was never one for the niceties of sexual betrayal. She thought nothing of discussing her *fidanzato* with her back-door man twenty seconds after reaching orgasm, which she reached easily and which, in that period of her life, was noisy and prolonged. (Later, after their marriage, she still came easily but her pleasure would last only an instant before she switched it off, zap, as if she were responding to some invisible conductor's baton. As if she were playing that beautiful instrument, her own body, and suddenly heard a shockingly false note.) I had learned to accommodate myself to her conversational indelicacies. However, then as now, I lacked the patience for such low-grade material as this "aura," this "light."

"Bushwah," I retorted. "Ormus is no god-man with portable lighting effects. Trouble with you is, you came to India and caught a dose of Wisdom-of-the-East-itis, a.k.a. gurushitia, our incurable killer brain disease. I told you not to drink the water if it wasn't boiled."

"Trouble with *you*," her smoke blew in my face, "is that

you *never* drink the water unless it's been boiled for a fucking *year.*"

She caught India, and it almost killed her. She contracted malaria, typhoid, cholera and hepatitis, and they didn't reduce her appetite for the place at all. She wolfed it down like a cheap snack from a roadside stall. Then it rejected her, as cruelly as she had been rejected in Virginia or New York State. By that time, however, she had grown strong enough to absorb the blow. She had Ormus, and the future was no longer in anyone else's gift. She could hit back and survive. But her years of good behaviour ended at that moment. After it, she embraced instability, her own and the world's, and made up her own rules as she went along. Nothing was certain in her vicinity any more, the ground was always trembling, and of course the fault lines spread through her from top to toe, and faults in human beings always open up in the end, like cracks in the groaning earth.

"THE SWIMMER," one of the last songs Ormus Cama wrote for himself and Vina, was recorded on the island of Montserrat beneath a grumbling volcano. The hard rhythm-and-blues guitar riff that drives the song had been in his head for days. He had woken with it pounding in his ears, and grabbed a guitar and a tape deck to record it before it went away. They weren't getting along in those days, and the studio sessions were scratchy, wasteful, clenched. Finally, he plugged into the poisoned atmosphere, he turned towards what was blocking things and harnessed it, made the quarrel his subject, and that bitter, prophetic song of doomed love was the result. For himself, he wrote some of his darkest lines. "I swam across the Golden Horn, until my heart just burst. The best in her nature was drowning in the worst." This in a nasal, dragging delivery that alarmed his admirers, was described by one notoriously waspish music critic (who was unconsciously echoing the singer's father, Sir Darius Xerxes Cama) as resembling the dying agonies of an aged goat, and proved that he had begun to sink even before the tragedy. But because he still loved her, even in their worst moments he couldn't deny it, he gave her high, hopeful lines to sing against his own low despair, lines as seductive as the sirens' song; as if he were both John and Paul, both sour and sweet.

There's a candle in my window, Vina sang, but I don't have to tell you, you're feeling it already, the memory of it, pulling at your emotions. *Swim to me.* I can't listen to it myself. Not any more.

THE BEST in our natures is drowning in the worst. It was Ormus's mother who used to say that. Lady Spenta Cama in the late 1950s fell into a deep sadness, under whose influence she became blasphemously convinced that the Monster of the Lie, Ahriman or Angra Mainyu, was gaining the victory over Ahura Mazda and the Light, in spite of what was prophesied in the great books, the Avesta, the Yasna and the Bundahish. Priests in their white garments were invited with increasing frequency into the apartment on Apollo Bunder, and they brought their little fires with them and chanted nobly. "Hear ye then with your ears, and see the bright flames with the eyes of the Better Mind." Ardaviraf Cama, Lady Spenta's silent son, would sit with her and haltingly participate in the fire rituals, wearing that sweet expression which was his hallmark; Ormus, however, absented himself. As for her ageing, drink-blurred husband, his impatience with her orisons only increased with the passing years. "Blasted priests make the place look like a blasted hospital," he would grumble, passing through the chamber of her devotions. "Blasted fire'll probably end up burning the blasted house down."

The house of Cama was indeed in danger, but not from holy fire. On the tenth anniversary of the independence of India, Spenta received a letter from William Methwold, who was now a peer of the realm, a Foreign Office grandee, and wrote to wish his old friends well "on so auspicious a date." However, the letter also had a less auspicious purpose. "If I address this to you, my dear Spenta, rather than to Brother D.X.C., it is because I have, I fear, difficult tidings to impart." Then followed a series of contorted, digressive animadversions on the general subject of banquets he had recently attended, in particular one "rather jolly affair" involving a re-staging of *Twelfth Night* at Middle Temple on Twelfth Night, Middle Temple being the place where *Twelfth Night* had first been staged on an earlier Twelfth Night; at any rate—and at last Lord Methwold accelerated towards his dreadful point—he had been seated by the purest chance next to the eminent judge Henry "Hang'em" Higham, who turned out to be a former classmate of "Brother D.X.C.'s" and revealed, over the brandy, that while Sir Darius Xerxes Cama had been an enthusiastic eater of dinners, in his legal studies he "hadn't come up to scratch." He had flunked his examinations, and had never been admitted to the Bar "in any shape or form."

Lord Methwold had "found the accusation well-nigh impossible to credit." In London he had required enquiries to be made, and found, to his dismay, that Henry Higham had been right. "I can only conclude," he wrote in his letter, "that your husband's papers were forgeries, forgeries of the highest quality, may I say; that he simply decided to brazen it out, on the assumption that nobody in India would bother to check; and if they did, it is not impossible, as you must know, nor indeed overly expensive, to buy a fellow's silence in that great country of yours, for which I have never ceased to feel the keenest nostalgia."

Lady Spenta Cama loved her husband in spite of everything, and he loved her. Ormus Cama always believed that the foundation of his parents' mutual affection was a sexual compatibility which old age had done nothing to erode. "The old folks went at it most nights," he'd say. "We all had to pretend we hadn't heard anything, which wasn't easy, because they made plenty of noise, particularly when my boozy father insisted upon what he called the English position, which I don't think my mother enjoyed. Those shrieks weren't really of pleasure, but she was prepared to suffer a lot for the sake of love." After she discovered that Sir Darius had built his entire professional life on a falsehood—that he was, covertly, a Servant of the Lie—Lady Spenta moved into a separate bedroom, and at night the apartment was full of the sad silence of that ending. She never gave Sir Darius a reason for her departure from the conjugal bed, and wrote to Lord Methwold imploring him, in the name of their long friendship, to keep her husband's secret. "He has not practised law for many years, and when he did, all agreed that he gave sterling service, so no harm done, eh?" Methwold wrote back to agree, "on the single condition, my very dear Spenta, that you continue to write and give me all the news, as I no longer feel comfortable about writing to D.X.C. himself, knowing what I now know."

"I fear I may be succumbing to error," Spenta confided unhappily in a later letter to Lord Methwold. "As Parsis we are proud to believe in a forward-moving view of the cosmos. Our words and deeds are part, in their small way, of the battle in which Ahura Mazda will vanquish Ahriman. But how may I believe in the perfectibility of the universe, when in my small backwater there are so many slippery slopes? Maybe our Hindu friends are right, and there is no progress but only an eternal cycle, and right now it is the long age of darkness, *kalyug*."

To combat her doubts and justify the prophet Zarathustra's innovative world picture, Lady Spenta Cama plunged into good works. Under the tutelage of the Angel Health, late-night hospital visits became her specialty. Small, heavy, bustling Spenta in her horn-rim specs, leaning forward slightly as she scuttled along, with her handbag held tightly in both hands, became a familiar figure in the neon-lit nocturnal corridors of the Lying-In Hospital and the Gratiaplena Nursing Home, particularly in those grim wards and intensive care units reserved for the gravely ill, the incurables, the horribly crippled and the dying. The nursing staff at these institutions—even the Gratiaplena's redoubtable Sister John—quickly formed a high opinion of the little lady. She seemed instinctively to know when to prattle on to the patients—gossiping about little Bombay nothings, the latest shop, the latest scandal—and when to maintain a pure silence that somehow exuded comfort. In the matter of silences she appeared to have learned something from her son Ardaviraf. Virus Cama began accompanying his mother on her rounds, and his tranquil muteness, too, brought the succour of serenity to the sick. Deeply affected by what she saw at the hospital—the many cases of malnutrition, and polio, and tuberculosis, and other poverty-related illnesses, including the self-inflicted injuries of unsuccessful suicides—Lady Spenta became, with Mrs. Dolly Kalamanja of Malabar Hill, the joint convenor and driving force of a group of Parsi ladies like herself, whose purpose was to alleviate the suffering of their community, which was widely believed to be exclusively composed of prosperous and powerful citizens, but which was, in reality, plunging into extreme hardship and even, in some cases, destitution. Sir Darius Xerxes Cama, an increasingly remote figure, disapproved of the morning teas at which the ladies would plan their fund-raising work. "Stupid beggars've only got themselves to blame," he would mutter, passing through the drawing room like a ghost. "No backbone. Weaklings. Sissies. I'm sorry, but it's the truth." The ladies ignored him and got on with their work.

There were malicious whisperers who opined that Lady Spenta Cama's sickbed visits were themselves unhealthy, that they smacked of obsession, that she had become addicted to holding the hands of the dying and playing the sainted, bountiful grande dame. I do not agree. If I am to criticise Lady Spenta's high-energy charity offensive, I would say only this: that charity begins at home.

In 1947, at the age of fifteen, Cyrus Cama had made his own declaration of independence. By then he had spent five years at the famous—and famously disciplinarian—Templars School in the southern hill station of Kodaikanal, as a punishment for his attempted smothering of his brother Ormus. During his early days at the Templars School he had given every sign of being a disturbed child, capable of violence towards his fellow students and also towards members of staff. However, at other times, he came across as a completely different child, possessed of a sweetness of nature fully as disarming and winsome as his brother Ardaviraf's. This "second self" earned him more chances than another such child would have been allowed.

Sir Darius and Lady Spenta had chosen the Templars' "year round" option, which permitted Cyrus to live at school during the holidays as well as term time, an option normally taken up only for boys whose parents were abroad or deceased. In the early days the school had twice written to the Camas asking them to reconsider this decision, because the boy appeared troubled and would no doubt benefit from a family environment; but Lady Spenta, in particular, had been adamant. "The boy needs an iron hand," she wrote back, "and you have boasted of having such a hand. Do you say that your school's reputation is undeserved?" Sir Darius, too, was of the opinion that, as the British used to say, "board is best." One may ascribe the Camas' harsh decision to the widespread Indian abhorrence of psychiatric problems and mental illness, but to explain is not to condone.

At any rate, after Lady Spenta's challenge, Cyrus was treated with maximum severity. Corporal punishment was frequent, prolonged and intense. He responded quickly. The violence ceased, his academic performance improved dramatically, Cyrus the delinquent vanished, and Cyrus the charmer took over completely. In addition, he developed a passionate interest in fitness and gymnastics, becoming the star of the school gymnasium, equally adept on horizontal and parallel bars, pommel horse and rings. His reports began to glow with his teachers' pride and satisfaction, and no doubt Lady Spenta felt herself justified by these reports.

In August 1947 the Templars School was in recess. Cyrus Cama was still in residence, along with half a dozen other boys, mostly the sons of diplomats whose fathers were newly taking up ambassadorial posts around the world. The mass murder of these children—all smothered in their beds while they slept—was an atrocity that would at any other time have captured the nation's full attention. However, the agony of the Partition massacres and the counterpointing ecstasy of the Independence festivities, coupled with the fact that these murders had taken place not in Delhi, Calcutta or Bombay but in remote Kodaikanal, meant that the deaths were ignored by the national newspapers, in spite of the eminence of the dead boys' families. The disappearance of Cyrus Cama did not initially cause him to be suspected of wrongdoing. The attempted smothering of little Ormus was a family matter, which the Camas had kept to themselves; nor, when they learned of the atrocity, did they volunteer any information to the police.

Cyrus was thought either to have escaped the assassin, in which case he was hiding out somewhere, perhaps wounded and certainly terrified, and would probably emerge after a time (he did not); or to have been taken hostage by the criminal, in which case a ransom demand might follow, or else his body would be found later, in another place (it was not). The assassin's purposes were obscure, but those were murderous days, and the Kodaikanal C.I.D., with its limited resources, did not succeed in establishing motive.

The "Pillowman," as the psychopathic serial killer Cyrus Cama later came to be known, was as intellectually brilliant and physically strong as his father longed for all young Parsi men to be, and was, in addition, responsible in the next few weeks for murders in Mysore, Bangalore and Madras. Owing to the dispersed locations of his crimes, the lack of a communal factor and the overwrought temper of the times, no connection was at first made between these separate killings—though the use of an identical method, smothering by pillows, provided an obvious link—nor was Cyrus implicated. (By now the Kodaikanal police were favouring the hostage-and-subsequent-murder theory and waiting for his dead body to turn up.) Finally, Cyrus could no longer stand the anonymity, and sent a fifteen-year-old's boastful letter to all the relevant police chiefs, incriminating himself while insisting that he would never be caught by duffers such as they.

When Lady Spenta was informed of these facts, she wept shocked tears. "Our world has lost its moorings," she told her husband. "Nothing is certain. Common humanity, what is it? How to counter so much violence, so many betrayals, such fear?" *The best in our natures is drowning in the worst.* Then for a time she retreated, as was the family practice, into a suffocated silence, emerging from it to declare in an airless voice that she no longer had a son called Khusro alias Cyrus Cama and that his name was never to be spoken in her presence again; with which Sir Darius Xerxes Cama grimly concurred. The disowning of Cyrus Cama was formalized. Sir Darius changed his will, disinheriting his murderous child. Which Virus, his twin brother, accepted without saying a word.

Cyrus Cama's technique was to charm people to their deaths. He looked and acted several years older than his age, and in respectable public places—cinemas, coffeehouses, restaurants—he befriended his victims, usually foolish young people with money to burn, to whom he came across as an unusually attractive and original young man with an exceptional force of intellect. They asked him what a young Parsi blade might be doing travelling in south India by himself (in those days few Indians travelled for pleasure in their own country, even to Kashmir); he replied in well-modulated, articulate, boarding-school accents, singing the praises of his liberal parents, C.B. and Hebe Jeebeebhoy of Cusrow Baag, Bombay, who understood that a young man must do his growing up on his own, and had acceded to his wish to see the glories of newly independent India, travelling solo on a kind of pilgrim's *yatra,* before he went up to read Law at Oxford University, England, in one year's time. He regaled his victims with traveller's tales of the great sub-continent, describing glittering cities and mountain ranges like the devil's teeth, and river deltas prowled by tigers, and lost temples in distant cornfields, in such idiosyncratic detail that it was impossible to doubt the authenticity of his entirely fictional accounts. By the end of the first evening the intrepid traveller had so completely seduced his marks that they invited him into their homes as their house guest.

Then he would transfix them by speaking passionately, night after eloquent night, of the "moral short circuit" of the age, the nationwide "loss of soul-greatness" of which he had been made so painfully aware on his journeyings, and of his dream of forming a "people's movement for the salvation by spiritual energy-force of this poor, bloodied land." Such was his charisma, and his skill at identifying his dupes, that the victims quickly began to think of him as some sort of great new leader, a guru or even a prophet, and willingly handed over substantial sums of money for the foundation of his movement and the propagation of his ideas; whereupon he visited them softly in their idiotic bedrooms and allowed the pillows, which seemed to move of their own volition into his hands, to do their work, which was necessary work, for the foolish did not deserve to live. To be killable was also to be worthy of being killed. (Adulatory descriptions of Cyrus Cama had also been found in the private diaries of the boys he killed at the Templars School, with whose freely donated pocket money he had financed his initial flight.)

Cyrus was prone to exaggerated mood swings, however, plunging at times into a lightless, cavernous underworld of self-loathing; and it was during one of these periods, early in 1948, that he returned to Kodaikanal, walked into the town police station and surrendered to the terrified duty officer, saying, "I could do with a rest, yaar." Only just sixteen, he admitted sole responsibility for a total of nineteen smotherings, was adjudged by the courts to be "profoundly disordered, utterly immoral and highly dangerous," and was transported north to be locked up for the rest of his days, "for the protection of the public," in a cell without a pillow at the maximum security facility of Tihar Jail, Delhi. Within weeks he had made a favourable impression on his jailers, who spoke effusively of his wisdom, learning, excellent manners and immense personal charm.

This was the living skeleton in Ormus's family cupboard, and another thing he had in common with Vina. There was a multiple murderer in his family too.

When I think about the three brothers Cama, I see them as men who were all incarcerated for a time, enclosed within their own bodies by the circumstances of their lives. A cricket ball jailed Virus within his silence; a pillow silenced Ormus's music for fourteen years; banishment and punishment caused Cyrus, too, to conceal himself beneath a falsehood, a self he had borrowed from his sweet-natured twin, which was not truly his. Each found something different in that internal exile. Cyrus found the wellspring of mayhem, Virus discovered the nature of peace, and Ormus, first by chasing Gayomart's shade through his dreams, and then—following Vina's advice—by learning how to listen to his own inner voices, found his art.

They were also, all three of them, men who attracted followers. Cyrus had his victims, and Ormus had his fans. Virus, however, attracted children.

Not long after Ormus Cama's epochal encounter with Vina Apsara at the Rhythm Center record store, his brother Ardaviraf was wandering, as was his habit, along the seafront to the Gateway of India in the cool hour between the heat and the darkness. He had started in those days to acquire a following of street urchins, who neither asked him for money nor offered to shine his shoes, but simply grinned at him in the hope (usually fulfilled) that he would smile back. The beautiful smile of Virus Cama had become infectious; it was spreading through the street urchin community at high speed and dramatically increasing their earning power. Few foreign visitors could resist its winsome innocence. Even seasoned Bombayites, hardened by years of refusing the children's entreaties, were melted by its warmth and gave out handfuls of silver *chavanni* bits to the incredulous brats.

It is true that there were times when Ardaviraf Cama did not smile. At these times he was assailed by feelings of claustrophobia, and of a malevolence so powerful that he had to sit down on the sea wall and gasp for breath. Terrible thoughts arrived in his head from nowhere. "Eight years. Can you imagine how much bitterness can accumulate during eight years in jail, how great a flood of vengeance must be unleashed to wash away such pain?" He couldn't answer the question. He didn't want to know the answer. But he knew that his twin brother was still alive and crazy and dreaming only of the day of his inevitable escape. Virus closed his eyes and breathed deeply, and the transmission from the Pillowboy—now a Pillowman of twenty-four—came to an end. Children clustered around him, offering up their smiles, which were also his. He smiled back. The children cheered.

"Who dat man?" Who can forget the immortal Harpo and his infant followers in *A Day at the Races*? Although Virus Cama's habitual mode of attire was nattily printed bush shirt and cream slacks, his ragamuffin-wreathed strolls always put me in mind of that beloved (and voluntarily mute) genius in his clown's battered hat and tattered coat. Virus's shock of curly hair increased his resemblance to Mr. Adolph Marx . . . and maybe one of his little ruffian pals had sneaked a look at the old movie, because one day this little fellow came up to Virus, grinning widely and bold as brass, and wordlessly held out a wooden flute; which Virus wonderingly examined; and put to his lips; and blew.

Rooty-toot-toot! Music came naturally to all the Cama boys, including the late Gayomart, and the hunger and ease with which Ardaviraf now played his flute—instinctively, with a few inevitable hesitations, but on the whole with a fluency that bordered on the magical—said much about the pain of melody's long absence from his life. The haunting, ghostly notes of the evening raga stopped the promenaders in their tracks. Children squatted down at his feet; the birds forbore to sing. The flute's sound was like the weeping of the soul, the soul at the Chinvat Bridge, perhaps, waiting for judgement. After a time, as the dusk closed in and the street lights glowed, Ardaviraf stopped, and looked gawkily, goofily pleased. "Come on, Mister Virus," pleaded the boy who had handed him the flute, "something with a smile." Virus set the flute against his lips once more; and played, with considerable gusto, "The Saints." And now he was not only Harpo but the Pied Piper too, leading his children nowhere; and after that he was Mickey Mouse as the Sorcerer's Apprentice, surrounded by Walt Disney's uncontrollable brooms, because the urchins' gleeful dancing had spiralled out of control, they were twirling in the headlights of motor cars and scooters, running wild, until the whistling of policemen scattered them, leaving Virus, flute in hand, to look dumbly shamefaced and hang his head as a white-gloved officer lectured him about the dangers of obstructing traffic.

The next morning, a Sunday, Ardaviraf Cama broke his father's nineteen-year-old embargo on music and brought melody back to the flat at Apollo Bunder. When Sir Darius was closeted in his library and Lady Spenta was taking "charitea" at Dolly Kalamanja's, Virus searched his mother's boudoir; found what he was looking for in a small chest of jewellery that sat on his mother's dressing table; knocked on Ormus's door; and held out, for his amazed brother to inspect, a silver locket containing a small key. Ormus Cama, hardly able to believe his eyes, meekly followed the newly determined Virus into the drawing room, where his silent sibling removed the dust cover from the long-forbidden baby grand, unlocked the magic keys with his own magic key, sat down, and launched into what had already become one of the most celebrated riffs in popular music. Ormus shook his head, amazed. "When did *you* learn about Bo Diddley?" he demanded; received no answer; and began to sing.

Enter Sir Darius Xerxes Cama, his hands over his ears, listing slightly to port, followed by the butler Gieve bearing a whiskey tumbler on a tray. "You sound like a goat with its throat cut," he raged at Ormus, in unconscious imitation of all the fathers raging at that very moment, all around the world, against these devil's tunes. But then Sir Darius caught Ardaviraf's eye and stopped, discomfited. Virus began to smile.

"It was because of you," Sir Darius said weakly.

"Because of the injury to you. But of course, if you want—I can't stop you—how can I deny?"

Virus's smile grew broader. In that awesome instant, which signalled the end of his patriarchal power over his own home, and in spite of the turbulence of his emotions, Sir Darius felt his own facial muscles twitch, as if a smile were trying to climb on to his face, like a spider, against his will. He turned and fled. "Tell Spenta," he called over his shoulder, "I've gone to the club."

Virus launched into a new tune, *Oh, yes, I'm the Great Pretender,* sang Ormus Cama, *pretending that I'm over you.*

HIS TONGUE untied by his tongue-tied brother, Ormus Cama at last began to utilize his prodigious gifts; for he was a prodigy from the start, he had only to touch an instrument to become a virtuoso player, only to attempt a style of singing to master it. Music flooded from him. Liberated, he sat beside smiling Ardaviraf at the piano every day and taught him a dozen new tunes. And when he visited Vina at Villa Thracia he plucked and strummed and whanged away at her battered old three-quarter-size guitar (Piloo Doodhwala had sent her few possessions round the day after Ormus's joker trumped his ace), and our house too grew full of the new music. At first Ormus played only the songs he had half learned from Gayomart in his dreams, singing those strange vowel sequences of his that made no sense to anyone, or fitting nonsensical words to them that utterly undermined the mysterious authority of the dream-music:

"The ganja, my friend, is growing in the tin; the ganja is growing in the tin."

(And then, diminuendo:)

"The dancer is glowing with her sin. The gardener is mowing with a grin. The ganja is growing in the tin."

"For Pete's sake, Ormus," Vina protested, giggling.

"But that's what it sounds like," he'd complain, sheepishly. "It's hard to hear."

After a few such failures he agreed to stick to the current hit parade. Sure enough, however, one thousand and one nights later, "Blowin' in the Wind" hit the airwaves in its authentic version and Ormus shouted at me, "Do you see now? Don't you see?"

Such things kept happening, there's no denying it; and whenever one of Gayomart Cama's melodies burst through from the world of dreams into the real world, those of us who had heard them for the first time in garbled form in a Bombay villa on the old Cuffe Parade were forced to concede the reality of Ormus's magic gift.

If he found opportunities to play Vina his other creations, the ones she had sent him in search of—I mean his own songs, the music that belonged to him alone—I never knew it. But it was during these years of waiting, when he was writing copiously, flowing like an undammed stream, that he wrote those first, naked love songs. I didn't know how to be in love, he wrote, until she came home from Rome. And I believed in god above until she came home from Rome. (Well, no, he didn't, as a matter of fact, but truth yielded to the harsh necessities of rhyme.) But now you fit me like a glove. You be my hawk, I'll be your dove. And we don't need no god above, now that you're home from Rome. And even more devotional than that was the joyful genuflection, the teenage prayer, of the anthemic "Beneath Her Feet": What she touches, I will worship it. The clothes she wears, her classroom seat. Her evening meal, her driving wheel. The ground beneath her feet.

This is the tale of Ormus Cama, who found the music first.

Lady Spenta Cama's feelings for Ormus remained, let us say, muted. Ardaviraf was her darling, however, and so, although she shared her husband's low opinion of the grunts and hiccups of Ormus's so-called singing, she was unable to ask the brothers to desist. The return of music to Apollo Bunder only increased her determination to marry off her youngest son as soon as possible. Ever since he had finished school with an academic record that brought shame and dishonour to his family, Ormus had been on the loaf: idle, without direction, except with regard to girls. Parents of students at the Cathedral Girls' School had lately started complaining to Lady Spenta that her son was in the habit of lounging against a wall across the road from the school entrance, idly picking his teeth while allowing his hips, very slowly, to gyrate, and that these gyrations were putting the girls off their homework. Ormus, when confronted by Lady Spenta, did not attempt to deny the charge. From the start the extreme sensuality of his body was an effect he produced unconsciously; he never felt responsible for it and so, naturally, accepted no responsibility for its effects. He had music on the brain, he shrugged, and it made his body move without his knowing why or how. What the girls thought about it was neither his business nor his fault. "Boy seems feckless," Lady Spenta complained to Sir Darius. "Lacking in ambition, giving backchat, nothing but music between his ears. Good for nothing, he will turn bad for everything if we do not intervene."

Persis Kalamanja was the perfect answer. The girl was beautiful, had the disposition of a saint, and unaccountably gave every sign of adoring Ormus. Also, her parents were loaded. Sir Darius's long retirement had severely eroded the Cama bank balances, and—at least in Lady Spenta's opinion—Ormus owed it to his mother and father to restore the family's financial health. Patangbaz "Pat" Kalamanja and his wife Dolly hailed from Kenya but had made their fortune in post-war London, manufacturing cheap radios and alarm clocks under the Dollytone name, and diversifying, as Kalatours, into the travel agency business, specializing in flights between the countries of the then-exploding Indian diaspora. Business was booming in fifties Britain, and Pat Kalamanja was obliged to base himself in Wembley most of the year, but Dolly had "fully relocated to the mother country," bought one of the finest old bungalows on Malabar Hill from old Mr. Evans of the Bombay Company, spent a fortune on ruining it, developed a hunger for respectability, and wanted a piece of Sir Darius's baronetcy as passionately as Lady Spenta wanted Pat Kalamanja's cash.

"Wants to sing, eh?" Lady Spenta snorted at her husband. "Dollytone radios will sing for him. Wants to dance up a storm? Travel business will lead him to calmer waters. Also, there is the British connection," she added, slyly, knowing the effect it would have on Sir Darius the arch-Anglophile.

Sir Darius's eyes glittered. He agreed at once to his wife's plan. "Older families are put off by the mistakes of you-know-who," she reasoned (it was the closest she would come to mentioning Cyrus Cama's nineteen murders), "so these Kalamanjas have fallen from the heavens, like a beautiful cut kite."

The problem was Vina. After their meeting, Ormus gravely informed his mother that as he had inadvertently fallen in love, the engagement to the beauteous Persis was unfortunately out of the question. When he identified the object of his improbable affections, his mother—who had assumed that the new light in Ormus's eye, the new lightness in his step, the new eagerness with which he greeted each new day, was because of Persis, and was therefore the result of her parental good judgement—flew into a pop-eyed rage. "You devil! That twelve-year-old penniless brat from nobody and nowhere?" she shrieked. "Get this into your head: that's a non-starter, sonny jim." Lady Spenta and Dolly Kalamanja both agreed to proceed with their plans as if nothing had happened. "It will blow over," Dolly assured her friend determinedly. "Boys will be boys, before and after marriage, but they can still be good husbands and all." This remark rather shocked Lady Spenta, but she held her tongue.

A few days later, Persis Kalamanja and Ormus Cama were taken by their respective parents on a joint family outing to the Exwyzee Milk Colony. They were encouraged to wander off by themselves among the greenery and cows, and when they were out of earshot, gorgeous Persis, whom most young men would happily have died for, asked about her under-age rival. "Look, you can tell me, it's okay, I won't be upset," she said. "Never mind what our mothers want. Love is too important to lie about." Ormus, looking awkward for once in his graceful life, confessed that he had no idea how it had happened, but that day at the record store he had met the only girl he would ever love. Persis took it on the chin, set aside all her own hopes, nodded seriously and promised to help. From that moment until Vina's sixteenth birthday, Persis joined Ormus and Vina in a conspiracy of small and large deceits. For a start, she announced to her mother that she was not at all sure about this supposed god's gift, Ormus Cama; she was one pretty high-calibre female herself and did not intend to buy the first goods her mother picked off the peg, and if it was to be Ormus then she would need a good long period in which to satisfy herself that he was an option which she was prepared, after weighing all the pros and cons, to select. "Girls today, too modern, I swear," sighed Dolly Kalamanja, and might have tried to force the marriage through, except that Persis appealed to her father Pat in England, and Patangbaz Kalamanja told Dolly that his beloved daughter wasn't going to be parcelled off to anybody if she didn't want to be posted, so that was that: Dolly sulked, but settled for a long "pre-engagement." Every month or so, Dolly would complain that her daughter was taking too long to decide, and Persis would invariably reply, "But a wife is for life, and that's too long to be wrong." Persis the Great Pretender, the beard. At night she would cry herself to sleep. And Ormus and Vina were so wrapped up in each other that they never really paid attention to the beautiful girl who gave up her own hope for their sake. Yet it is Persis who, in many ways, was the true heroine of the story of their love.

She would tell her mother she had arranged to meet Ormus for coffee, or "chips and swimming at the Willingdon"; or that he was taking her to one of the Sunday morning jazz "jam sessions" that were becoming popular, back then, in certain Colaba restaurants; or that there was a "good flick" on. "Love picture?" Dolly would greedily enquire, and Persis would nod, giving every appearance of excitement. *"Love Is a Many-Splendored Thing,"* she would reply, or, later, *"An Affair to Remember,"* and Dolly would nod, "Excellent! Get him in the mood!" And off Persis would go, driving herself down Malabar Hill in her Hindustan Ambassador to her empty assignation. For indeed she did meet Ormus at the club or restaurant or café or cinema in question, so that technically she had not lied to her mother; but a few moments later, Vina would arrive, and Persis would leave without a word. Those lonely hours, when she roamed the city alone until she could go home without blowing the lovers' alibi, were like a hole in her life, a wound through which all her hope and much of her joy seeped out. "I think of those times covering up for Ormie as the love affair we never had," she wrote to me. "He was with me, I told myself, he was right there by my side, but of course he wasn't, it was all foolishness. Not many-splendoured. Not worth remembering. But me, I couldn't forget."

BETWEEN THE self and the other, between the visionary and the psychopath, between the lover and his love, between the overworld and the underworld, falls the Shadow.

Time passes. Now, in his dreams, Ormus still chases Gayomart through that Las Vegas of the subterranean world, but as often, or perhaps more often, he stands face-to-face with himself on the streets of an unknown but familiar city, and listens to what his own dream-image has to say. He is still young.

The world is not cyclical, not eternal or immutable, but endlessly transforms itself, and never goes back, and we can assist in that transformation.

Live on, survive, for the earth gives forth wonders. It may swallow your heart, but the wonders keep on coming. You stand before them bareheaded, shriven. What is expected of you is attention.

Your songs are your planets. Live on them but make no home there. What you write about, you lose. What you sing, leaves you on the wings of song.

Sing against death. Command the wildness of the city.

Freedom to reject is the only freedom. Freedom to uphold is dangerous.

Life is elsewhere. Cross frontiers. Fly away.

VINA APSARA is looking for someone to follow, and Ormus is discovering how to lead. They read books together, looking for answers. In the beginning was water and slime, Vina reads aloud. Out of this, Time was born, three-headed, a snake. Time made the shining air and a yawning gulf, and in the air he hung a silver egg. The egg split, and so on. The part that interests Ormus is the twofold nature of man. Who is both Titanic and Dionysiac, both earthly and divine. By purification, asceticism and ritual, we may purge the Titanic element, we may cleanse ourselves of what is earthly, physical. The flesh is weak, evil, contaminated and corrupt. We must strip ourselves of it. We must prepare for becoming divine.

No, Ormus shouts. They are in the Hanging Gardens, surrounded by topiary elephants and evening hedonists, and his cry attracts attention. He moderates his voice. It is the opposite that's true. We must purge ourselves of the divine and prepare to enter fully into the flesh. We must purge ourselves of the natural and prepare to enter fully into what we ourselves have built, the man-made, the artificial, the artifice, the construct, the trick, the joke, the song.

Yes, she murmurs. The flesh, the living flesh.

What is apparent is what there is. The hidden world is a lie.

There are contradictions here. Even as she believes him, believes with the force of her needing to believe, the force of her need of him, she is half aware of another side, not only to her nature, but to his. For she is—will be—Dionysiac, divine, and so is—so will—he. They will drive people mad with desire, with music, will leave behind them long trails of destruction and delight. Is pleasure an aspect of reason or of dreams?

She asks: Why do you look for your brother in that dream-house?

My brother is dead, he shouts, turning more heads. Leave him out of this. My brother Gayomart who was never even alive.

Touch me, she pleads. Hold me, hold my hand.

He will not. He has sworn an oath.

He cannot touch her. She is not a child, not remotely a child, and yet she is a child. In his dreams, and in waking visions, he sees her body growing, sees her breasts begin to bud and flower, the coming of bodily hair and the red blood staining her thighs. He feels her move beneath his hand, feels himself tense and grow at her rough and tender touch. In the privacy of his thoughts he is a voluptuary, feral, criminal, but in the real world, which feels daily more unreal, he plays, for the first time in his life, the perfect gentleman.

She, Vina, will always boast about this on his behalf. "He waited for me." It makes her proud: of him, but also of herself. To be worth so serious a love. (I waited for her too, but she did not boast about me.)

The bruise on his eyelid is sore. His mother and father fight in him, Lady Spenta's angels and mysteries, Sir Darius's vaunted Apollonian rationalism. Though it could also be said that Lady Spenta with her good works is battling with the real world, its diseases, its cruelties, while Sir Darius, sunk in the unreality of his library, is living more than one kind of lie.

Living brothers fight in him too, violent and serene. His dead twin recedes.

Reason and the imagination, the light and the light, do not coexist peacefully.

They are both powerful lights. Separately or together, they can blind you.

Some people see well in the dark.

VINA, WATCHING him grow, hearing the struggle of his thoughts, feeling the anguish of his controlled desires, sees a light around him. It is the future, perhaps. He will be bathed in light. He will be her perfect lover. He will command multitudes.

He is fragile too. Without her love, terminally alienated, he might go horribly wrong. The idea of family, of community, is almost dead in him. There is only silent Virus and their piano sessions. Otherwise he has come loose, like an astronaut floating away from a space capsule. He is a layabout who hears only the vowel sounds of cheap music, who makes meaningless noises. He could easily amount to nothing. He might fail to add up to a person.

(IT IS said that when Kama, the love god, committed the crime of trying to shoot mighty Shiva with a dart of love, the great god burned him to ashes with a thunderbolt. Kama's wife, the goddess Rati, pleaded for his life, and softened Shiva's heart. In an inversion of the Orpheus myth, it was the woman who interceded with the deity and brought Love—Love itself!—back from the dead. . . . So also Ormus Cama, exiled from love by the parents whom he had failed to transfix with love's arrow, shrivelled by their lack of affection, is restored to the world of love by Vina.)

HE CLINGS to her, without touching her. They meet and whisper and shout and make each other up. Each is Pygmalion, both are Galatea. They are a single entity in two bodies: male and female constructed they themselves. You are my only family, he tells her. You are my only earth. These are heavy burdens, but she bears them willingly, asks for more, burdens him identically in return. They have both been damaged, are both repairers of damage. Later, entering that world of ruined selves, music's world, they will already have learned that such damage is the normal condition of life, as is the closeness of the crumbling edge, as is the fissured ground. In that inferno, they will feel at home.

CHAPTER SIX

Disorientations

In the autumn of 1960, when Vina Apsara was about to reach the magic age of sixteen, Sir Darius Xerxes Cama at last made the journey to England of which he had dreamed for so many years. In these latter days of his life Sir Darius had yielded to his wife's entreaties and resumed his studies in the field of Indo-European myth. (Lady Spenta hoped for the eradication of her husband's ruinous whisky addiction by an earlier, more valuable intoxication.) A new generation of European scholars, including many brilliant young Englishmen, was ridding the field of its unjust Nazi taint and introducing new levels of sophistication to what now looked like the first stumblings of Müller, Dumézil and the rest. Sir Darius in his library tried to excite Lady Spenta, as he himself was excited, by this new thinking, which had done so much to refine and amplify understanding of "sovereignty," "physical force" and "fertility," the three primary concepts of the Indo-European world-view. However, no sooner had he begun to explain the thrilling new proposition that each member of the conceptual triad also functioned as a subconcept within each category than Lady Spenta's heavy body appeared to deliquesce into a languid jelly. Sir Darius, pressing on, insisted that "sovereignty" was now to be subdivided into "sovereignty within sovereignty," "force within sovereignty," and "fertility within sovereignty"; while "physical force" and "fertility" were likewise, "by the same token," to be rendered tripartite. "I have a headache," said the jelly at this point, and wobbled off at high speed.

Sir Darius did indeed turn away from whisky. However, his distress at what he saw as the culture's general decline did not diminish. Left to his own devices, Sir Darius reflected on how his own family circumstances reflected this decline. As head of the household, he possessed sovereignty within sovereignty by right, both in its magical, terrifying and remote aspect and in the more legalistic and familiar meaning of the term; but while he had certainly grown remote from his children, it was a long time since anyone had thought him the smallest whit magical or terrifying. As for force within sovereignty, which he interpreted as the protection of the family's solidarity and continuity, especially by its younger members, its "warriors," well, that was just a joke. "We have slipped," he reflected aloud, "to the point at which we are mired in the lowest sub-section of the third concept, fertility within fertility, which, in our case, means no more than indolence, dreams and music."

Sir Darius's own scholarly efforts received their reward: a paper under his name—" 'Sent to Coventry': or, Is There a Fourth Function?"—was accepted for publication in the esteemed *Proceedings of the Society of Euro-Asiatic Studies,* and he was invited to deliver it, in the form of a lecture, at the Society's annual general meeting in Burlington House. His subject was the hypothetical "fourth concept" of "outsiderness," the condition of the leper, pariah, outcast or exile, whose necessity he had intuited long ago, and his evidence in support of his arguments ranged from the casteless Untouchables of India (Gandhi's Harijans, Ambedkar's Dalits) to the Judgement of Paris; for did not Paris himself embody the outsider in this vitally significant myth? Alternatively, the outsider was Strife, the goddess who produced the golden apple. Either way, the example stood.

Now that he was sober, Sir Darius's terrible secret had begun to prey upon him ever more hungrily, in his waking hours as well as during his recurring dreams of the naked figure of Scandal in the pure white country house, and the growing conviction that he himself was a pariah such as those of whom he wrote, or ought to be, and might yet become one if his great Lie became known, lent his work a passion that made his sentences blaze from the page. He was an isolated old gentleman by this time. Even the consolations of Freemasonry were no longer available; the order's Indian membership had drifted away after the end of Empire, and Sir Darius had long since ceased to participate in such threadbare encounters as continued to take place in a new lodge as shabbily paltry as the old lodge had been grand. (Lately he had been remembering his estranged friend, brother Mason and erstwhile squash partner Homi Catrack, and had even suggested to his wife that they should ask the fellow over and renew the old association; whereupon Lady Spenta had to remind him gently that Catrack was dead, sensationally gunned down with his paramour in their love nest by a cuckolded naval officer some three years previously. The case had filled the newspapers for months, but Sir Darius had somehow failed to notice.)

The invitation to England offered an end to this shadow life of his, in which he flitted through the background of events in which he took no part. "And there is Methwold too," he said to Lady Spenta, brightening. "What times we'll have! The grouse moors! The Athenaeum! English honey! What larks!"

Lady Spenta bit her lip. Sir Darius's Anglophilia had intensified with the passage of the years. He frequently praised "U.K." for the grace of its withdrawal from Empire, and also for the "pluck" with which that war-battered nation had rebuilt itself. (No mention was made of Marshall Aid.) India, by contrast, he constantly chided for its "stasis," its "backwardness." He wrote innumerable letters to the newspapers deriding the Five-Year Plans. "What use are steel mills if we sink into ignorance of our natures?" he would thunder. "The greatness of Britain stands squarely upon the Three Concepts . . ." These letters were not published, but he continued to write them. In the end Lady Spenta did not bother to have them posted, but destroyed them privately, without hurting his feelings.

Why did William Methwold no longer write? Sir Darius frequently asked this question, without guessing that Lady Spenta could answer the question if she chose to do so. "Perhaps it is because of my research," Sir Darius wondered. "Possibly he is still squeamish about the old stigma attached to the field. He is a public servant, of course, and must be careful. No matter! When we dine together I will put him straight."

"Go if you must. I will not go with you," Lady Spenta told her husband. Not knowing how to warn him of the humiliation that awaited him in his beloved England, she chose not to witness his destruction. He left on a BOAC Super Constellation, wearing a courtroom shirt of Egyptian cotton with stiffly starched collar and cuffs, and a three-piece suit of finest worsted, with a fob chain glinting upon his belly. Lady Spenta saw on his face the look of tragic innocence worn by goats on their way to the slaughterhouse. She had written to Lord Methwold begging him "if possible, to be kind."

Methwold was not kind. In spite of Sir Darius's urgent letters, and Lady Spenta's own private pleas, he neither met his old friend at Heathrow Airport, nor sent anyone to meet him, nor invited him to stay, nor offered to put him up at his club. Lady Spenta had taken the precaution of asking Dolly Kalamanja to send her husband Patangbaz to the airport, and it was Pat's jolly round face that greeted Sir Darius in the crude arrivals shed (the airport was still under construction at that time, and facilities for passengers were substantially worse than those at Bombay's Santa Cruz). Sir Darius looked haggard and dishevelled at the end of his gruelling journey and equally gruelling interrogation by immigration officials who were bewilderingly unimpressed by his explanations, his credentials or even his knighthood, news of which they treated with extreme scepticism. His repeated references to the eminent Lord Methwold elicited only hollow laughter. After several hours of questioning, Sir Darius was finally released into England, a confused and somewhat punctured man.

Pat Kalamanja's Wembley home was a spacious suburban mansion in red brick equipped with fake white pilasters and columns to give it a more classically impressive air. Kalamanja himself was affable, good-natured, anxious to do the right thing by the father of his future son-in-law, and extremely busy, so that while Sir Darius was given the run of the house he saw his host for no more than a few snatched meals. During these brief encounters Sir Darius was terse and preoccupied. At breakfast, Pat Kalamanja, a business tycoon down to his well-pared fingernails and a man uneasy with small talk, did his best to put his guest at ease. "Nawab of Pataudi! What a cricketer! Blanchflower's Hotspurs! Hell of a football team!" At dinner, he offered political commentary. In the forthcoming American elections, Mr. Kalamanja strongly favoured Richard M. Nixon, because of that gentleman's "plain speaking" to the Russki leader Khrushchev during a visit to a model kitchen in a Moscow trade fair. "Kennedy? Too pretty; means too tricky, what do you say?" But Sir Darius's thoughts were elsewhere.

He spent the empty days telephoning his friend Methwold without reaching him, sending reply-paid telegrams to which no reply was given, and even, on one occasion, making the long journey by bus and Tube train to the door of the Methwold mansion in Campden Hill Square, to leave a long and injured letter of reproach. Finally Lord Methwold did get in touch. A terse note arrived at Wembley, inviting Sir Darius to walk with him, the next morning, in the grounds of Middle Temple, "of which you no doubt have many memories you may possibly wish to re-live."

It was enough. Sir Darius Xerxes Cama understood everything. All spirit left him, and he deflated completely. Mr. Kalamanja, returning home in the evening, found a darkened living room and his guest slumped in a chair beside a cold fire with an empty bottle of Johnnie Walker rolling at his feet. He feared the worst until Sir Darius moaned loudly in his sleep, the moan of a soul caught in the burning pincers of a demon. In his dream Sir Darius was surrendering to Scandal's embrace. He felt his body catch fire as he was consumed by his disgrace and shame, and screamed out at the top of his voice. Patangbaz Kalamanja rushed forward and hugged him. He awoke red-eyed and shivering, pushed good-hearted Pat aside and rushed from the room. The next morning, a crumpled and haunted figure, he asked Kalamanja if his travel agency could get him on an earlier flight home. He offered no explanation and his host did not know him well enough to ask for one. Sir Darius flew back to Bombay without meeting William Methwold, without delivering his paper on the Fourth Function, and without any remaining ambition in life except one—to die in peace—which he would also fail to fulfil. On his return he unearthed his proudest possessions from the Godrej steel filing cabinet where they had lain under lock and key for half a lifetime, the precious letters patent pertaining to his knighthood, and returned them to the British Consulate in

Bombay. His story was over. He shut himself up in his library with a bottle, and waited for the end.

WE LEAVE home not only to make room for ourselves but to avoid the sight of our elders running out of steam. We don't want to see the consequences of their natures and histories catching up with them and beating them, the closing of the trap of life. Feet of clay will cripple us, too, in our turn. Life's bruises demythologise us all. The earth gapes. It can wait. There's plenty of time.

TWO VISIONS broke my family: my mother Ameer's vision of the "scrapers," the giant concrete-and-steel exclamations that destroyed forever the quieter syntax of the old city of Bombay; and my father's fantasy of a cinema. It was Vina Apsara's great misfortune to put down roots in us, and to idealize my parents as the joint architects of a storybook happy home, just as our little clan started to come apart. "Rai," she once said to me, "you're a lucky bastard, but also a sweetheart, because you don't mind sharing your luck."

Luck runs out. My parents had fallen off their pedestals well before their early demises. Easy to list their faults. My father's great weakness was gambling, in the indulgence of which he took heavy losses. By 1960 these had moved beyond the mere forfeit of small mountains of matchsticks and grown into debts as sizeable but less easily redeemed. He lost at cards, he lost on the horses, he lost at dice, and he had fallen, too, into the clutches of a "private bookmaker" who called himself Raja Jua, "for Chance is the King of all, from our Betters to the Best," and who permitted serious Bombay gamblers to bet on whatever they chose: the outcome of a murder trial, the likelihood of an Indian invasion of Goa, the number of clouds that might cross the western sky in a day, the crucial first week's gross of a new movie, the size of a dancer's breasts. Even the ancient rain game, the *barsaat-ka-satta,* a bet on when the rains would come and how much would fall, was a gamble against which Raja Jua, the prince of bookmakers, would give odds. Bombay has always been a high rollers' town. However, my innocent father, V. V. Merchant, was not so much the roller as the rolled.

As for my mother: her cynicism, once just a pose, an idealist's armour, her defence against the corruption that was all around her, had itself corroded her youthful principles. I accuse her of being willing to destroy what was beautiful for the sake of what was profitable, and to rename these categories "yesterday" and "tomorrow." She was at the forefront of the builders' lobby that was working flat out to scupper the "second city" project for a New Bombay across the harbour in favour of more immediately lucrative land reclamation schemes at Nariman Point and—yes!—at Cuffe Parade as well. It was the proposed Cuffe Parade redevelopment that horrified Vivvy Merchant. All his life my father had faced the internal struggle between his love for the history and glories of the old Bombay and his professional involvement in the creation of the city's future. The prospect of the destruction of the most beautiful stretch of seafront in the city drove him into permanent, but unfortunately silent, opposition to his wife. Silent, because Ameer was still a woman who could brook no criticism. The merest hint that she might be acting improperly would have been enough to induce a storm of weeping and a quarrel that would not end until he abased himself and agreed that he had utterly and cruelly wronged her, and that her injured innocence fully justified her high dudgeon and copious tears. V.V. Merchant, unable to talk to her about his grave concerns, was obliged, instead, to follow the dictates of his nature, and dig.

He could dig in people as easily as in sand. Digging into me, as I grew, he found out one of my secrets. "This photography of yours," he said, speaking for once in short, clear words, "no doubt it is very much liked by pretty young girls?" And I was too inhibited to reply, Yes, Father, but that isn't the point. Your Paillard Bolex, your Rolleiflex and Leica, your collection of the works of Dayal and Haseler: those are my inspirations and spurs. And photography, too, is a kind of digging. I said none of that, though it would have made him proud to hear it. Instead I quipped, "Yeah, that's it, Daddy-o." He winced faintly, smiled a vague smile and turned away.

But when he dug in my mother, he didn't turn away. He went on until he dug up what would ruin her; and thus destroyed himself.

And that whitest of white elephants, the Orpheum cinema, into which he sank the business's capital with a wanton zeal that even Ameer Merchant was unable to restrain—wasn't that, in its suicidal way, an answer to his wife and her cartel of futurist vandals? In his vision of the theatre, he saw it as a Deco temple for the 1960s, at once a tribute to the city's golden period and a money-spinning Mecca for our movie-crazy city's host of "fillum" fans. But this, too, was a gamble that went badly wrong. Building costs spiralled upwards, the borrowing requirement got out of control, and the dishonesty of sub-contractors resulted in the use of materials and fittings well below specification. Rival cinema bosses bribed municipal inspectors to quibble over approvals and tie up the project in red tape. Ameer, her attention elsewhere, left the Orpheum to Vivvy; unwisely, as it turned out. In the end, Vivvy's gambling debts obliged him to offer the deeds to the new cinema as collateral to Raja Jua. He did not know, at that time, the name of the man for whom this Jua worked.

ON MY thirteenth birthday my father gave me a pretty serious German camera, a Voigtländer Vito CL, with a built-in light meter and a hot-shoe port for a flash gun, and the first photographs I took were of Vina Apsara, singing. She was better than Radio Ceylon. Most evenings, we'd gather round and she'd let fly with that perfect voice, which grew bigger and richer by the week, by turns dirty-knowledgeable and angel-pure. That voice which had started on its road to immortality. To listen to Carly Simon sing "Bridge Over Troubled Water" is to understand how much Guinevere Garfunkel brought to the table in that partnership. So it was in the great days of VTO. There are bands that are hit machines, bands that earn the respect of the music crowd, bands that fill stadiums, bands that drip sex; transcendent bands and ephemeral, boy bands and girl bands, gimmick bands and inept bands, beach and driving bands, summer and winter bands, bands to make love by and bands that make you memorize the words to every song they play. Most bands are awful, and if there are aliens from other galaxies monitoring our radio and tv waves, they're probably being driven crazy by the din. And in the whole half-century-long history of rock music there is a small number of bands, a number so small you could count to it without running out of fingers, who steal into your heart and become a part of how you see the world, how you tell and understand the truth, even when you're old and deaf and foolish. On your deathbed you'll hear them sing to you as you drift down the tunnel towards the light: Shh . . . Sha-sha . . . Sha-la-la-la-la . . . Shang-a-lang, shang-a-lang . . . Sh-boom . . . Shoop . . . Shoop . . . Shh. It's all over now.

VTO was one of those bands. And Ormus had the vision, but Vina had the voice, and it was the voice that did it, it's always the voice; the beat catches your attention and the melody makes you remember but it's the voice against which you're defenceless, the unholy cantor, the profane muezzin, the siren call that knows its way directly to the rhythm center, the soul. Never mind what kind of music. Never mind what kind of voice. When you hear it, the real thing, you're done for, trust me on this. Finito, unless you're tied like Odysseus to the mast of your ship, with clay stopping up your ears. That goose of yours? It's fried.

I THINK, now, that it was Vina's singing that was holding us together in those days. She was our rock, not the other way around. While V.V. Merchant plunged into debt, and also, silently, investigated his wife, assembling a thick dossier on her illegal manipulation of the city's decision makers—while, in short, a time bomb was ticking beneath our lives—Vina sang to us, reminding us of love.

O fierce intensity of childhood seeing! As children we're all photographers, needing no cameras, burning images into memories. I remember our neighbours on Cuffe Parade, their pretensions, their happy and unhappy marriages, their quarrels, their motor cars, their sunglasses, their handbags, their discoloured smiles, their kindnesses, their dogs. I remember the weekends with their odd, imported pastimes. My parents playing golf at the Willingdon, my father doing his best to lose to my mother in order to preserve her good mood. I remember a couple of Navjotes spent guzzling food served on the leaves of plantain trees, several Holis drenched in colour, and at least one visit to the giant prayer maidan on Big Eid, which sticks in the mind because it was so rare. I think my father just wanted me to appreciate what

I was missing and why. I remember my friend sweet Neelam Nath, who grew up to die with her children in the Air-India crash off the Irish coast. I remember Jimmy King with his pasty complexion and spiky black fringe; he died young, suddenly, at school. All the classroom doors and windows were closed so that we couldn't see his father driving into the quadrangle to take his son's body home. I remember a long, skinny boy clambering across the rocks at Scandal Point with his friends. He looked through me as if I weren't there. Gold Flake posters, the Royal Barber Shop, the pungent mingled smells of putrefaction and hope. Forget Mumbai. I remember Bombay.

Then they gave me a camera, a mechanical eye to replace the mind's eye, and after that, much of what I remember is what the camera managed to snatch out of time. No longer a memoirist but a voyeur, I remember photographs.

Here's one. It's Vina's sixteenth birthday, and we're at the Gaylord restaurant on Vir Nariman Road, eating chicken Kiev. My mother and father both wear unfamiliar expressions. He looks angry, she seems distracted, vague. Vina, by contrast, glows. All the light in the photograph seems to have been sucked towards her. We are shadowy bodies revolving around her sun. Ormus Cama sits beside her, like a dog begging to be fed. Half of me is in the picture too. I asked a waiter to take the photo but he didn't frame it right. It doesn't matter. I remember what I looked like. I looked the way you look when you're about to lose the thing that matters most.

On the ring finger of Vina's right hand was a glowing moonstone, her birthday gift from Ormus. She had already slept with the ring under her pillow for a week, to test it out before agreeing to accept it, and her dreams had been so erotic that she had awoken each night in the small hours, trembling with happiness and drenched in yellow sweat.

Ormus is asking permission to take Vina to a "concert." V.V. and Ameer are avoiding each other's eyes, skirting the edges of a fight. "The Five Pennies," Ormus says. "Take Umeed also," says Ameer, waving a hand. Vina looks daggers. They pierce my thirteen-year-old breast.

After the success of the Danny Kaye biopic *The Five Pennies,* its subject, the real-life bandleader Red Nichols, had come to Bombay on tour with a new, reformed bunch of Five. Jazz, stimulated by the weekend-morning jam-session brunches, was still hot in town, and a big crowd gathered. I've got the photographs to prove it, but I can't remember where the concert was. Azad Maidan, Cross Maidan, the Cooperage, or somewhere else. Out of doors, anyhow. I remember a raised stage in the open air. Because my mother had sent me along, Ormus brought Virus as well. The four of us got there early and stood near the front. I was disappointed when the Pennies appeared, because Red Nichols was only a little fellow, and his hair was short and white, not a bit like Danny Kaye's flowing carroty locks. Then he picked up his horn and blew. Trad jazz. I liked it, once in a while, I'll confess. But then Vina always said I had bad taste.

That Five Pennies concert is famous for what happened at the very end of an average sort of set that had failed to get anyone's pulse going. After less than wild applause had died down, the crimson-tuxedoed quintet made ready to go into their encore. "The Saints," what else, but no sooner had Red Nichols named the tune than a member of the audience vaulted on to the stage, waving an Indian wooden flute and grinning his goofy, but also infectious, grin.

"Oh, my God," shouted Ormus Cama, and leapt up on stage after his brother.

"Wait for me," yelled Vina, radiance bursting from her as she followed the Cama boys towards her own inescapable destiny; and that made three invaders. Me, I'm a coward. I stayed in the crowd and took photographs.

Click. Red Nichols's horrified face. He has been warned about India, its huge crowds that can turn, in an instant, into murderous mobs. Had he been resuscitated by Danny Kaye, only to die by being trampled under-foot in Bombay? *Click.* Virus Cama's smile works its magic, and the old bandleader's horror is replaced by a look of amused indulgence. *Click.* What the hey. Let the dumb guy play. And you, both of you? What do you do? *Click.* Vina Apsara steps up to the microphone. "We sing."

Oh when the sun (oh when the sun)
begin to shine (begin to shine).

Ardaviraf Cama's playing was undoubtedly skilful, but the music came out of his flute sounding inappropriate; it was a sound in a different currency, an anna trying to be a penny, but it didn't matter, partly because he was happy enough tootling away, and partly because the crafty Nichols had turned off his mike, so if you weren't in the first couple of rows you couldn't hear him at all; but mostly because the minute Ormus and Vina opened their mouths and began to sing, everybody just stopped thinking about anything else. When they had finished, the audience was cheering wildly, and Nichols paid them the compliment of saying they were so good that he didn't mind being upstaged.

THE CONCERT was over, the crowd was drifting away, but I stood rooted to the spot, taking photographs. The world was cracking. Ormus and Vina were deep in conversation with the musicians, who were packing up their instruments and shouting at the local stagehands to watch what they were doing. My heart was breaking. While Ormus and Vina chatted to the jazzmen, their hands and bodies were talking to each other. Click, click. I can see you, you two. Click. Peekaboo! Do you know I'm doing this? Are you letting me watch, is that it, even though I'm getting the goods on you, in here, in my little German box of wonders? You don't care any more, is that it? You want it all out in the open. Click. And what about me, Vina? I'll grow up too. He waited for you. Why wouldn't you wait for me? I want to be in that number!

From the start my place was in a corner of their lives, in the shadow of their achievements. Yet I will always believe I deserved better. And there was a time when I almost had it. Not just Vina's body, but her attention. Almost.

The musicians were piling their equipment into a small bus. An invitation had been extended and accepted, and it didn't include me. Ormus came over to chase me off: Ormus rampant, full of sex and music.

"Okay, Rai," quoth he, officiously. "Go with Ardaviraf now, okay? Virus'll get you home." Who do you think you are? I wanted to shout. Do you think I am a baby, to be seen home by the village idiot? But he was already walking away, he was embracing Vina, swinging her off her feet, kissing her, kissing her.

The sky was falling. Virus Cama bared his teeth at me, smiling his idiot smile.

THEY MADE love that night in Nichols's suite in the Taj Hotel, a stone's throw from the Cama residence. The great cornet player found himself another room and sent up a lovers' feast, and also the messages that had started to arrive for them, which were sent to the band because nobody knew how else to contact the two singers. There were offers to perform all over town, starting at the hotel itself. But as Vina was proud of recounting, the food and drink was not touched, nor were the letters opened until morning. They had better things to do.

The details of the deflowering of Vina Apsara by Ormus Cama are a matter of public record, placed there long ago by Vina herself, so there's no need to dwell on the exact degree of discomfort (considerable), or on Ormus's compensating expertise as a seducer of virgins (a few years after the event, Vina proudly named and numbered Ormus's previous conquests, thus unleashing a pandemic of scandals throughout Bombay society), or on their early difficulties (he was too gentle for her, too reverent, which annoyed her and made her too aggressive, and too physically rough, for his taste), or on their equally early successes (his caressing of the tiny hollow at the base of her spine, his exploration with the tip of his tongue of the edges of her nostrils, his slow sucking of her closed eyes, the head of his penis pressing into her navel, his finger moving along her perineum, her legs around his neck, her buttocks moving against his sex, her generous mouth, and above all her discovery of the extreme sensitivity, unusual in a man, of his nipples: as you observe, I have not forgotten one single jot or tittle of the lubricious catalogue). Suffice to say that the deed—the deeds—were done; that the lovers did not return to their own beds that night; so that on this occasion joy came at night, and it was the morning that was dark and full of sorrow.

The willingness of Vina Apsara to talk publicly about private matters—her catastrophic childhood, her love affairs, her sexual preferences, her abortions—was as important as her talent, perhaps even more important, in the creation of the gigantic, even oppressively symbolic figure she became.

For two generations of women she was something like a megaphone, broadcasting their common secrets to the world. Some felt liberated, others exposed; all commenced to hang upon her every word. (Men, too, were both divided and enthralled, many desiring her greatly, some affecting to find her whorish and repulsive; many loving her for her music, others hating her for the same reason—for whatever elicits great love will invariably call forth hatred also; many fearing her for her mouth, some celebrating her and claiming that she had liberated them as well.) But because she frequently changed her mind, abandoning fervently held positions in favour of their opposites, to which she then also adhered with a flaming certainty that brooked no argument, many women had begun, by the time of the earthquake in Mexico, to see her as a traitor to the very attitudes with which she had helped to set them free.

If she had not died, she might have sunk into a cranky, ignored old age, out of step in a way that was merely wrong- or pig- or muddle-headed, whereas once she had defiantly, triumphantly, been the only one in the parade marching in step, until the other marchers took their lead from her. However, eccentric irrelevance was a fate she was spared. Instead, her death unleashed the full power of the symbol she had constructed. Power, like love, most fully reveals its dimensions only when it is irrevocably lost.

WHENEVER I think of these events, the Saints start marching through my brain. I picture Ormus and Vina waking in bloodied sheets, held fast in each other's arms. I see them opening the unopened messages and allowing themselves to begin to dream about their professional future as well as the future of their love. I see them dressing, saying their farewells to the American musicians and catching a yellow-and-black taxicab to Cuffe Parade, ready to face the music. And throughout this sequence, there's Red Nichols's cornet playing, or maybe it's Louis Armstrong's trumpet I'm hearing. Oh, when the band begin to play. Oh, when the band begin to play.

The first cloud is about to appear on the horizon. Ormus is speaking important words. "Marry me." He takes the moonstone ring off her right hand and tries to slip it on to her engagement finger. "Marry me right away."

Vina grows tense, resists the moving of the ring. No, she will not marry him. She refuses, turns him down flat, doesn't even need time to think about it. But she does not resist the ring, she accepts it, can't stop looking at it. (The taxi driver, inquisitive, Sikh, is all ears.) "Why not?" Ormus's howl is piteous, even a little pathetic. Vina gives the driver more to enjoy than he could have hoped for. "You are the only man I will ever love," she promises Ormus. "But do you seriously suppose you're also the only guy I will ever fuck?"

(A trumpet—it's definitely Satchmo—comes blaring in. Armstrong's instrument is the golden horn of experience, the trump of worldly wisdom. It laughs—*wuah, wuah*—at the worst that life throws up. It's heard it all before.)

There must be somewhere better than this. It's what we all thought in our different ways. For Sir Darius Xerxes Cama, "somewhere better" was England, but England turned against him, and left him shipwrecked, marooned. For Lady Spenta, the good place was the place of pure illumination, where dwell Ahura Mazda and his angels and the blessed; but that place was far off, and Bombay increasingly felt to her like a labyrinth without an exit. For Ormus Cama, "better" meant abroad, but the choice of that destiny meant the severing of all family ties. For Vina Apsara, the right place was always the one she wasn't in. Always in the wrong place, in a condition of perpetual loss, she could (she did) unaccountably take flight and disappear; and then discover that the new place she'd reached was just as wrong as the place she'd left.

For Ameer Merchant, my cosmopolitan mother, the better place was the city she was going to build. V.V. Merchant, true provincial that he was, was tormented by the idea that the good place had existed, we had possessed and occupied it, and now it was being destroyed, and in its obliteration his beloved wife was profoundly implicated.

IT WAS the year of divisions, 1960. The year the state of Bombay was cut in half, and while new Gujarat was left to its own devices, we Bombayites were informed that our city was now the capital of Maharashtra. Many of us found this hard to take. Collectively, we began to live in a private Bombay that floated a little way out to sea and held itself apart from the rest of the country; while, individually, each of us became our own Bombay. You can't just keep dividing and slicing—India-Pakistan, Maharashtra-Gujarat—without the effects being felt at the level of the family unit, the loving couple, the hidden soul. Everything starts shifting, changing, getting partitioned, separated by frontiers, splitting, re-splitting, coming apart. Centrifugal forces begin to pull harder than their centripetal opposites. Gravity dies. People fly off into space.

I RETURNED to Cuffe Parade on foot after the Five Pennies concert, having with some difficulty shaken off Virus, to find our home transformed into a war zone: or, more exactly, into a pit of dreadful loss. My parents circled the living-room rug like wrestlers, or as if the Isfahani rug were no longer covering a solid floor of mahogany boards but had become a flimsy cloth flung over a bubbling abyss. Glaring red-eyed at each other, they were facing something worse than the loss of the future, worse than the loss of the past. It was the loss of their love.

Piloo Doodhwala had come to call during my absence: not the over-blown Piloo reclining on a cloud of satraps, whom you have already encountered, but a quieter Piloo, accompanied by a single male associate whom he introduced as Sisodia, a business-suited man in his late thirties, astonishingly small, very heavily bespectacled and balding. He had a terrible stammer and a bulging leather attaché case, out of which he now produced a folder concerning the Cuffe Parade development plan, among whose sponsors, listed on the cover of the dossier, was Mrs. Ameer Merchant of Merchant & Merchant (Pvt.) Ltd. As V. V. Merchant had begun to learn by digging, Ameer had joined forces with Piloo's people to push the scheme through. On a coffee table, Piloo's aide spread out a copy of the official survey map of Cuffe Parade. Many of the villa plots were coloured green for "go." Several were covered in green and white stripes, meaning "under negotiation." Only a very few were coloured red. One of these was Villa Thracia, our home. "Your goodwife has already ist ist stated her con consent to the sus sus sale," explained Mr. Sisodia. "All relevant dada documents are hee hee here. As property is technically under your goo goodname, it will be neck neck necessary for you to sign. Just here," he added, pointing, and holding out a Sheaffer fountain pen.

Vivvy Merchant looked at his wife. Her eyes were stone.

"The scheme is fantastic," she said. "The opportunity is incredible."

Piloo leaned forward in his seat. "Lots of cash," he explained in confidential tones. "Plenty phor all."

My mild father spoke mildly, but his thoughts were not mild. "I knew something was up," he said. "But it has gone much further than I guessed. I take it the city is in your pocket. Land use regulations waived, building height regulations to be flouted with impunity."

"Phixed," nodded Piloo, amiably. "No trouble at all."

Mr. Sisodia rolled out a second chart, the plan of the proposed development. A substantial land reclamation scheme was proposed. "More Cuffe," quipped Piloo, "phor our Parade." But Vivvy was looking elsewhere. "The promenade," he said. "Must be sacriphiced, alas," said Piloo, twisting his mouth downwards in a gesture of regret. "And the mangrove forest," Vivvy wondered. Piloo began to sound a little tetchy. "Sir, we are not building tree houses here, isn't it?"

Vivvy opened his mouth. "Bephore you rephuse," said Piloo, holding up a hand for silence, "consider, please, the phollowing."

Mr. Sisodia rose, went to the front door and let in a second aide, who had evidently been asked to wait outside for his cue. When he entered the living room, V.V. Merchant gasped and seemed visibly to diminish.

The second aide was Raja Jua, the king of bookies. He, too, carried a leather attaché case. From it he now produced a folder containing a full record of my father's debts and all the papers relating to the Orpheum cinema, which he passed to the first aide. "Out of his ha ha high pup pup personal esteem for your lay lady why wife," said Mr. Sisodia, "and to avoid all agra agra aggravations, Pilooji is disposed to dismiss these bag bag bagatelles. Development pot potential runs into sue sue super crores. These outstanding ma ma matters are petty. Only sigh sigh sign the agreement of iss

iss sale for Villa Thracia, and all dead dead debts will be wiped clean."

"The deeds to the Orpheum," Ameer said. "How could you do it?"

"And our home," V.V. replied. "How could *you*?"

Piloo's face darkened. "If I was a king phrom the time of the great heroes," he said, "I would challenge you to one more gamble. Win it, and the slate is wiped clean. Lose, and I take your lady wife." He smiled. His teeth glittered in the lamplight. "But I am only a humble man," he said. "So I will settle phor your honour, and your home. Also, Mrs. Merchant agrees to appoint Mr. Sisodia as your cinema in-charge. Good phiscal practice must be restored in our partnership. Mowies are Sisodia's second passion, but money is his phirst."

V. V. Merchant rose to his feet. "I agree to nothing," he said in his mild way. "Now get out." Ameer also rose, but her manner was very different. "What do you mean, get out?" she shouted. "We must just lose everything, everything I have built, we must be cleaned out, because of your weaknesses? Lose the cinema, lose control of the company, lose the biggest capital opportunity of the last twenty years and live in poverty until we have to sell the house anyway, just to eat? Is that what you want?"

"I am sorry," said V.V. Merchant. "I will not sign."

There must be somewhere better. Oh, most lethal of ideas! For Piloo Doodhwala was the only one of us who accepted the condition of life as it was, as a given. He did not fritter away his energies on deranged utopian fantasies. How then could he fail to emerge as the big winner? Our lives lay at his mercy, at his feet. How could it ever have been otherwise?

Piloo slaughtered more than goats. He made big killings in many fields. My life has taken a different route, but I have never forgotten the lesson he taught my father—the lesson my parents' catastrophe taught *me*—while, elsewhere in Bombay, Vina and Ormus were making endless love.

Things are what they are.

ALL EVENING, all night, my parents fought. I lay awake in my room unblinking as a lizard and listened to their duelling broken hearts. At dawn my father went to bed but Ameer continued to circle the living room like a spoon in a bowl, stirring up the most poisonous of all rages, the wrath churned in the body by the thrashings of dying love. And then Vina and Ormus walked in, and Ameer, possessed by her rage, rounded upon her young ward.

I am unable in all decency to write down the abuses heaped by my mother upon both the lovers, but particularly on Vina. She screamed at her for three hours and twenty-one minutes without appearing to draw breath, pouring out over the young girl what was meant for Vivvy. When she was done she staggered out of the house, exhausted, and collapsed into her beloved old Packard. It bore her away like a runaway horse. A moment later my hollow-faced father lurched out to the Buick. He, too, drove off so erratically—in the opposite direction to Ameer—that I feared for his life. But neither of them suffered the irrelevance of a traffic accident. They had already been in a near-fatal wreck before leaving home.

Insults are mysteries. What seems to the bystander to be the cruellest, most destructive sledgehammer of an assault, *whore! slut! tart!*, can leave its target undamaged, while an apparently lesser gibe, *thank god you're not my child,* can fatally penetrate the finest suits of armour, *you're nothing to me, you're less than the dirt on the soles of my shoes,* and strike directly at the heart. If I offer no exhaustive catalogue of my mother's harsh remarks, it is also because I am unable to judge their several effects. Was it this phrase or that phrase, this blow or that lash? Was it the mere fact of the tirade, or the cumulative effect of that vitriolic tour de force which left both Ameer and Vina physically drained, like fighters who have wrestled each other to a standstill?

Vina Apsara, a young person who had seen too much, whose trust in the world had been horribly eroded, had slowly allowed herself to believe, during her years at Villa Thracia, that she might be able to stand confidently upon the solid ground of our love. Our love as well as Ormus's. Therefore she in her turn had fallen in love not only with us but with our preoccupations, our city, and our country too, to which she had begun to half believe she might be able, in her own way, to belong. And what my mother did that day pulled away the Isfahani rug of Vina's trust in love itself, and revealed the abyss below.

Vina stood still, no more than semi-conscious, with the palms of her hands facing forward, questioning, expecting no answers, like the survivor of a massacre staring into the face of death. Ormus took her face between the palms of his hands. Very slowly she swayed back and away from his touch. At that moment his great love must have seemed to her like a great trap. To fall into it would be to make possible her utter annihilation at some point in the future, when he would turn on her with a sneer on his face and hatred in his voice. No more risks, her face said. This stops, right now.

VILLA THRACIA, my beautiful childhood home, burned to the ground three days later. Whoever was responsible took care not to commit murder. No doubt the house was watched until the arsonist was certain it was empty, and then it was thoroughly torched. One by one we returned and assembled on the promenade, to stand with bowed heads while black snow fell all around.

Vina Apsara, however, did not return.

You will forgive me a small lump in the throat as I say farewell to Villa Thracia. It was one of the smaller bungalow-villas on the old Edwardian Cuffe Parade, but ours was only a small family, and it had suited us very well. There was half-timbering around the front-facing casement windows, but the rest of the place was brick, trimmed here and there with stone. Red tiled gables stood over them, and over the front door too, making a quaint little porch. Up above was the house's somewhat pompous—or let us say *confident*—defining feature, a square, centrally positioned neoclassical turret, complete with pilasters and pediments on all four sides. This supported a little dome of scalloped green ceramic tiles, with a rather self-aggrandising mini-spire on top. In this ornate upper chamber my parents had lain during their long happy married years. "It's like sleeping in a bell tower," my mother used to say, and my father would reply, squeezing her hand, "And, my dearest, you indubitably are the tower's belle."

Up in smoke it went. Stripped of possessions, memories and happiness, we thought of the touch of falling ashes on our cheeks as our home's farewell caress. Eyewitnesses to the blaze reported that the fire itself had loved the dying house, hugging it tightly, so that for a few instants Villa Thracia seemed to have been re-created in flame. Then smoke, black, unfeeling smoke, took over, the illusion was destroyed, and darkness covered all.

The destruction of your childhood home—a villa, a city—is like the death of a parent: an orphaning. A tombstone "scraper" stands upon the site of this forgotten cremation. A tombstone city stands upon the graveyard of the lost.

WHERE ONCE stood "Dil Kush," Dolly Kalamanja's lavish three-story mansion on Ridge Road, Malabar Hill, that old-world masterpiece, all galleries and verandahs and light, with its marbled halls, its hurriedly acquired collection of paintings by Souza, Zogoiby and Hussain, and above all its mature tropical gardens boasting some of the oldest tamarind, jackfruit and plane trees in the city, and some of the finest bougainvillaea creeper too, you would now find neither trees nor creepers, neither grace nor space. Sitting like a squat missile on its launch pad, the skyscraper Everest Vilas fills that territory with its grey, discolouring concrete and is unlikely to yield possession any time soon. Everest Vilas is twenty-nine storeys high, but mercifully those are stories I do not need to tell. The phantom past is still standing on Ridge Road whenever I take a look. "Dil Kush" lives, as does the day when Villa Thracia burned and Dolly kindly insisted on giving us shelter under her ample, low-pitched roof.

Ormus arrived, at once exhausted and frenzied. It was late at night, but nobody was going to sleep. Vina was still missing. Ormus had searched high and low for her, rushing around all their favourite haunts, until he began to vomit from the stress. Finally, spent, disoriented, he staggered into "Dil Kush," and such was his shaky, giddy, rudderless wretchedness that Ameer Merchant—who was, it must be said, beginning to be eaten alive by remorse—buttoned her lip. Convinced that Vina had died in the fire, that she'd been turned to smoke and blown away, bereft Ormus spoke of following her beyond the grave. Life had lost all value; death at least had this merit, that it was the only experience he and his beloved could now share. He spoke ominously of self-immolation. It was my father, alarmed by the young man's state of mind, who comforted him. "Keep an open mind," said V.V. Merchant, though the words sounded hollow to us all. "No pertinent evidence of her perishing has as yet been obtained."

Persis Kalamanja, I must say, was looking a little shifty, which at the time I put down to the evident ambiguity of her position; for we could all work out that her hopes of marrying Ormus had received an undeniable, if horrible, fillip. Saintly as she was, Persis could not have failed to wonder about the future: might not her own joyful beginning rise from the ashes of Vina's tragic end? And then, being the tender-hearted young woman she was, she would have worked furiously to suppress such vile imaginings (which were rendered yet more vile by the sensation of delicious anticipation they released in her breast). She lowered her eyes and scrupulously supported my father's position. Vina might be not dead but merely delinquent. She laid her hand on Ormus's; he jerked his away, glaring savagely. With trembling lip she backed off and left him to his fears.

WHO LIT the fire?

The morning brought news, and two C.I.D. officers, the insufferably preening Detective Inspector Sohrab and the contrastingly self-effacing Detective Constable Rustam. These gentlemen informed us that as a result of interviews with neighbours and public-spirited passers-by who had contacted the police, the time of the fire's beginning had been definitively fixed at one p.m. Unfortunately, said D.I. Sohrab, "no miscreants were witnessed absconding from the site." A thorough search of the charred ruins of Villa Thracia had now been completed, and luckily no corpses had been found. (When Ormus heard that Vina had not been burned to death, he looked so happy that my mother had to remind him sternly that a great tragedy had nevertheless occurred.)

The three live-in household servants, cook, bearer and hamal, had all been located. They had been hiding out in the nearby colony of Koli fisherfolk, terrified both of the fire and of being held responsible for it. The police did not, however, believe that the fire was the domestics' fault. Their stories checked out, even though it was a little unusual for all three of them to have been running household errands at the time in question, leaving the villa unattended. Still, there was "clear evidence of an arson attack," Inspector Sohrab said keenly, "though details must be withheld for the nonce." Slowly we realized that we were under suspicion of having burned down our own home. Oleaginously, Sohrab now suggested that the firm of Merchant & Merchant was in alleged financial difficulties; that Shri Merchant himself had reportedly accrued gambling debts. Insurance claims could be beneficial, wasn't it so? My father was outraged at these "foul imputations." "Enquire of those who stand to benefit," he instructed the C.I.D. wallahs, with an unwonted edge to his voice. "Visit Shri Doodhwala and his cronies, and you will be in far greater propinquity to the luciferous rogues."

The cops left, but the doubts remained. The awful truth is that my tempestuous mother half suspected my father of the crime, and even my gentle father had begun to harbour suspicions of his own regarding Ameer. For three days, since their quarrel, my parents had lived apart: she at Villa Thracia, he with friends in Colaba. The fire had brought them together again, if only for my sake. Awkwardly, to keep up appearances, they were sharing one of Dolly's spacious guest bedrooms. But the atmosphere between them was icy.

I was in the room next door, and at night, once again, I could hear them hiss and fight. Ameer was angry enough with her husband to insinuate that he had tried to murder her, and all of us, in our beds. He pointed out mildly that the fire had started in broad daylight, at a time when she was unlikely to have been sleeping. She snorted contemptuously at so nitpicking a reply. V.V., for his part, wondered if she had turned arsonist in order to force his hand. "Is it possible that you would go to such reprehensible extremes in pursuit of those barbarous 'Cuffescrapers'?" At which Ameer shrieked, so that the whole night-time house could hear, "Oh God, look what filthy *galis* he's giving me now!"

Alas, the Piloo faction had indeed won the day in the battle against my father's intransigence. Now that Villa Thracia was gone, V.V. dejectedly gave in and sold Piloo, for a far lower price than the one he had initially refused, the plot of land on which our burned husk of a villa stood like a memorial to the death of idealism. The huge Doodhwala development project moved a step closer to success. The monster edifices of his imagination would bestride the city like the Martian spaceships in *The War of the Worlds.* In cases involving the pursuit of such very large pots of gold, a little firebuggery is not so very unusual.

But Piloo Doodhwala was an influential man. Influence, according to the astrologers, is an ethereal fluid emanating from the stars, which affects the actions of mere mortals such as we. Let us say, then, that Piloo uncorked his ethereal fluids—for he possessed influence of more than one variety—and let them freely flow down, from the highest echelons of the Bombay C.I.D. to the humble detectives assigned to the case. Within a matter of days, these officers announced that they had "conclusively eliminated" him from their investigations. When my father expressed astonishment, Inspector Sohrab told him with some asperity, "You should be grateful. You personally and your goodwife also have generously been included in the said elimination."

The investigation had been "redirected along more profitable avenues of inquiry." These concerned the vanished U.S. citizen, Miss Nissa Shetty alias Vina Apsara. Inquiries at Santa Cruz airport had established that Miss Apsara exited Bombay within hours of the fire, on a TWA aircraft travelling to London and New York. Her unexplained flight was deemed to be of the highest significance. Further detective work, in collaboration with Scotland Yard via the Interpol network, revealed that Miss Apsara's plane ticket had been purchased in pounds sterling in the U.K., and that the issuing agency was Mr. P. Kalamanja's London-based Kalatours outfit. Mr. Kalamanja himself had paid Miss Apsara's fare.

Mrs. Dolly Kalamanja was a small woman wearing big jewellery, a new-rich grande dame who believed in "putting on a show." Her hair was the blue of steel and its style was modelled on the Queen of England's, with those distinctive Ionic squirls adorning the temples. Her bust too—a single, solid bolster without hint of undulations, stretching across her chest like a sleeping policeman, a speed bump prominent enough to slow down anyone unwise enough to make too fast an approach—was reminiscent of Elizabeth II's. She was strong-willed, more conservative than most of Bombay's broad-minded Parsi community, and her high voice was in the habit of being obeyed. Much of what she felt about her own life was formulaic, which did not prevent the emotions from being felt strongly. Thus her husband Patangbaz Kalamanja was her "rock," and her daughter Persis, her "pride and joy." The news of Pat's involvement in the escape to "foreign parts" of a suspected arsonist hit her hard. She reeled. The universe seemed to lose shape and meaning. The earth trembled. The "rock" wobbled, cracked. Persis helped her mother to a chair, and she fell into it with her head "in a whirl," fanning herself with a hankie.

The grand formal drawing room at "Dil Kush" was as well appointed, with its teak sideboards and mirrors in extravagant geometric shapes and overstuffed Biedermeier sofas and priceless Deco lamps and genuine tigerskin rugs and bad oil paintings (and, to be fair, some good ones), as the saloon of a great ocean liner: the *Titanic,* perhaps. Certainly it felt to baffled Dolly like the deck of a badly holed ship. In her "condition," the room seemed to tilt and start sliding slowly towards some dreadful netherworld.

"How did that girl get to my Pat?" she wailed, faintly. "Just now I'll book a call to U.K. and box his blooming ears!"

It was like a scene from a Poirot story. We were all standing or sitting around the room, watching Dolly's melodramatic conniption. Persis was pouring her a glass of water, and the C.I.D.'s finest were positioned on a tigerskin, well satisfied with the impact of their news. But neither cocky Sohrab nor dumb Rustam could have been expecting what followed, which was not the threatened telephone call to Patangbaz in Wembley. For as it happened, there was no need to trouble the international operator. Persis Kalamanja sat at her mother's feet, massaging them with her hands, looked directly and without wavering into the eyes of Ormus Cama, and confessed.

Not only confessed, but gave Vina Apsara an unbreakable alibi.

WHEN THE impossible becomes a necessity, it can sometimes be achieved. Hours after Ameer Merchant's tirade had destroyed her faith in the reality of love, Vina called Persis and asked to meet her at (where else?) the Rhythm Center record store. Her uncharacteristically faltering manner persuaded Persis to set aside her reservations, and she agreed.

And at the store they went into a listening booth, pretending to check out the sound-track album of the year's big musical hit, Gordon MacRae and Shirley Jones in Rodgers and Hammerstein's *South Pacific.* And while Miss Jones sang about washing some man out of her hair, Vina—Vina in a frightening, cracked-mirror, off-centre mood that Persis had never seen in her before—threw herself upon her rival's mercy for much the same reason. I have to go, she said, and don't ask me to talk about it because I won't, and don't think I'll change my mind because I won't. And you have to help me, because there's nobody else, and because you can, and because you're so fucking sweet that you won't tell me to fuck off, and anyway, because you want to. You want to in the worst way.

Then she talked about it, anyway. They're fucking with me, she said, they think they can put their feelings inside me and then just rip them out, it's like they're Martians or something, I've got to get away. Persis asked, who. Shut the fuck up, Vina snapped, I said I didn't want to talk.

And more of the same, much more, through "Bali H'ai" and "Happy Talk" and so on. Can you pay, Persis asked her, and she answered I'll get the money, but you have to go ahead and fix up the ticket right now, I mean *now,* and I'm good for it, I'll get it to you somehow—*she was begging openly, winging it, dangling at the end of her rope,* Persis said boldly in the drawing room at "Dil Kush," *god knows how she got that way but somebody had to catch her, so I reached out my hand, I helped her, that's all. And besides, she was right,* she added, staring on and on into Ormus Cama's bewildered face, begging for help, in her own way, as shamelessly, as desperately, as Vina had begged her. Asking for the smallest of words, the faintest reassuring movement of the eyebrow, or perhaps, just possibly, the miraculous comfort of his smile. Asking to be told, yes, now you have a chance.

She was quite right. I did want to. So I did.

Persis had called her father, and Pat Kalamanja had never been able to say no to his little girl; it's for a friend, she said, it's too complicated, she said. Okay, forget it, it's fixed, he gave in, I'll send through the PTA today, so you can pick the ticket at the airline bureau tomorrow, or day after, latest. So you see, Persis said to Inspector Sohrab, you mustn't blame him, he knew nothing, it was me.

PTA is passenger ticket advice, Persis explained. You pay at one end, the ticket gets issued at the other. And I never expected her to have the cash, I knew Daddy would eat the bill anyway when he knew why I wanted the ticket, but she showed up here before noon on the day of the fire with two fat suitcases and a pillowcase full of jewels, and I knew where she got the jewellery from, Ameer auntie, don't think I had the slightest intention of holding on to it, but then all this started, this C.I.D. *tamasha,* and I got scared, I didn't know what to say, so I kept my trap shut, but I've opened it now, please excuse delay. She was with me all the time after that. I took her to the airport and put her on the plane myself and she's gone, and I hope she never comes back.

She may be a thief, said honest Persis, but she didn't start any fire.

The interrogation of Persis Kalamanja by Messrs. Sohrab and Rustam took place behind closed doors in a private room of her family home, lasted several hours, often grew heated, and failed to shake her testimony to the slightest degree. She did, however, fill in the story's blanks. It transpired that Pat Kalamanja had forked out only for a ticket as far as London, not the United States. At Persis's request, he had good-heartedly met Vina off the plane and taken her home to Wembley, because she had nowhere else to go. The next morning she had borrowed a small quantity of English currency from him, left her bags and gone into central London alone. She did not return that night, and agitated Pat was on the verge of calling the police when she walked in the following morning, offered no account of her absence, returned his money in full—the money for her ticket as well as the borrowed cash—and told him she was "all set," called a taxi, refused to allow Pat to help her with her bags, muttered a cursory thank-you and disappeared. Her present whereabouts remained unknown.

Soon after Persis was questioned, Vina Apsara was formally declared to be "no longer under suspicion of arson." Nor was Ameer Merchant prepared to accuse her of theft, because as Persis's story unfolded my mother's remorseful agonies had intensified sharply. She knew that Vina's flight was her doing, that she was the assassin of the runaway girl's joy, and although Ameer was a mistress of the flinty exterior, I could see through her dikes and embankments to the great flood tide of grief behind. Mourning the loss of a girl whom she had, in her own way, truly loved, Ameer cared little for her lost baubles. Vina's removal of jewels from Villa Thracia had resulted, after all, in the preservation and return of at least some of the family treasures. And if she had left the country with her suitcases bulging with Ameer's finest slinky sequinned dresses and dripping with the rest of my mother's diamond rings and emerald earrings and pearl necklaces, which no doubt she had sold in London to raise cash, Ameer waved it all away, what of it, she shrugged, the poor child is more than welcome, for if she had not pinched them, they would have been consumed by fire. Then my mother retired to her room, to weep long and hard for Vina, and for herself and her own departed happiness as well.

Thus Persis Kalamanja not only helped Vina to leave Bombay, as she wished, but also saved her from being wrongfully accused of a crime she did not commit. The police did not break Persis down, and I will not suggest here that the alibi she gave Vina was anything but the whole, the nothing-but-the truth.

When she was worried, she could twist her beautiful mouth until it looked as if it was being wrung by a dhobi. The effect was almost unbearably erotic. In those days there was a whole generation of young men hoping she would twist her mouth in their direction. But the man at whom she was twisting it now, twisting it with all her heart, as she emerged from the police interrogation to face the questions in his eyes, was utterly unmoved. This was her reward for helping Vina: that Ormus Cama completed, at that moment, the process of wiping her off his personal map and out of the history of his life. He looked at her with open hatred; then with contempt; then with indifference; then as if he no longer remembered who she was. He left "Dil Kush" as if withdrawing from a stranger's house into which he had stumbled by mistake. And Persis became "poor Persis" then, and "poor Persis" she remained for the rest of her old maid's life.

Nobody was ever charged with the crime of burning down Villa Thracia. The C.I.D.'s heroes, Sohrab and Rustam, concluded that "criminal intervention" was "off the agenda" and withdrew from the case. Many Bombay properties had old and dangerous wiring systems, and it was easy enough, finally, to believe in an electrical fault as the blaze's probable cause.

Easy enough, especially when the influence kept on flowing down from the top, until all possible suspects were, in the satisfied words of Piloo's aide Sisodia, "Foo fool fully Exxon Exxon exonerated."

DISORIENTATION IS loss of the East. Ask any navigator: the east is what you sail by. Lose the east and you lose your bearings, your certainties, your knowledge of what is and what may be, perhaps even your life. Where was that star you followed to that manger? That's right. The east orients. That's the official version. The language says so, and you should never argue with the language.

But let's just suppose. What if the whole deal—orientation, knowing where you are, and so on—what if it's all a scam? What if all of it—home, kinship, the whole enchilada—is just the biggest, most truly global, and centuries-oldest piece of brainwashing? Suppose that it's only when you dare to let go that your real life begins? When you're whirling free of the mother ship, when you cut your ropes, slip your chain, step off the map, go absent without leave, scram, vamoose, whatever: suppose that it's then, and only then, that you're actually free to act! To lead the life nobody tells you how to live, or when, or why. In which nobody orders you to go forth and die for them, or for god, or comes to get you because you broke one of the rules, or because you're one of those people who are, for reasons which unfortunately you can't be given, simply not allowed. Suppose you've got to go through the feeling of being lost, into the chaos and beyond; you've got to accept the loneliness, the wild panic of losing your moorings, the vertiginous terror of the horizon spinning round and round like the edge of a coin tossed in the air.

You won't do it. Most of you won't do it. The world's head laundry is pretty good at washing brains: Don't jump off that cliff don't walk through that door don't step into that waterfall don't take that chance don't step across that line don't ruffle my sensitivities I'm warning you now don't make me mad you're doing it you're making me mad. You won't have a chance you haven't got a prayer you're finished you're history you're less than nothing, you're dead to me, dead to your whole family your nation your race, everything you ought to love more than life and listen to like your master's voice and follow blindly and bow down before and worship and obey; you're dead, you hear me, forget about it, you stupid bastard, I don't even know your name.

But just imagine you did it. You stepped off the edge of the earth, or through the fatal waterfall, and there it was: the magic valley at the end of the universe, the blessed kingdom of the air. Great music everywhere. You breathe the music, in and out, it's your element now. It feels better than "belonging" in your lungs.

Vina was the first one of us to do it. Ormus jumped second, and I, as usual, brought up the rear. And we can argue all night about why, did we jump or were we pushed, but you can't deny we all did it. We three kings of Disorient were.

And I'm the only one who lived to tell the tale.

We Merchants moved into rented accommodation in the Camas' apartment block on Apollo Bunder, separate flats for my mother and father, and me like a yo-yo between the pair of them, learning independence, still playing my cards close to the chest, growing up. In those days Ormus Cama and I were closer than we ever managed before or since, on account of our common loss. I guess we could each tolerate the other's need for Vina because she wasn't around either of us. There wasn't a day when we didn't both spend most of our time thinking about her, and the same questions were in both our hearts. Why had she abandoned us? Wasn't she ours, hadn't we loved her? Ormus had the better claim, as always. He had won her in a bet, he had earned her by waiting through the long self-denying years. And now she was gone, into that immense underworld made up of all the things and places and people we did not know. "I'm going to find her," Ormus repeatedly swore. "No limit to where I'll go. To the ends of the earth, Rai. And even beyond." Yes, yes, I thought, but what if she doesn't want you? What if you were just her Indian fling, her bit of curry powder? What if you're her past, and at the end of your long quest you locate her in a penthouse or trailer park and she slams the door in your face?

Was Ormus ready to plunge even into this inferno, the underworld of doubt? I didn't ask him; and because I was young, it took me a long time to understand that the hell-fires of uncertainty were already burning him up.

Back then it wasn't easy to travel if all you had was an Indian passport. Inside this passport some bureaucrat would laboriously inscribe the few countries you were actually allowed to travel to, most of them countries that had never crossed your mind as possible destinations. All the rest—certainly all the interesting places—were off limits unless you got special permission, and then they would be added to the passport's handwritten list by another bureaucrat, with the same handwriting as the first. And after that there was the problem of foreign exchange. There wasn't any: that was the problem. There was a national shortage of dollars and pounds sterling and other negotiable currencies, so you certainly couldn't have any, and you couldn't travel unless you had some, and if you did buy some at extortionate rates on the black market, you might be called upon to explain how the stuff got into your hands, which would make it even more costly, because of the additional expense of the shut-up money, the bribe.

I offer this brief lesson in nostalgia economics to explain why Ormus wasn't on the first plane in pursuit of his great love. Darius Xerxes Cama—plain Mr. these days—was mostly in his cups, and after his own shaming experience of rejection, by England in general and William Methwold in particular, was unapproachable on the subject of transcontinental travel. Mrs. Spenta Cama (the loss of her title still smarted) flatly refused to buy her least favoured son even the cheapest ticket on a cut-price Arab airline, or the smallest acceptable number (one hundred) of under-the-counter "black pounds." "Chit of a girl is not worth ten pice," she declared flatly. "Just see that beautiful Persis at last, why can't you. Poor girl loves you to pieces. Let the blinkers fall from your eyes once and for all."

But Ormus was blinkered for life. In the next few years I had ample opportunity to observe his character at close quarters, and beneath his brilliant, shifting surface, the mazy, chameleon personality that made every girl he met want to pin him down; beneath his alternately concealing and revealing nature, now open as an invitation, now closed as tight as a trap, now needing, now pushing away, beneath all the improvised melodies of himself, there was this unaltered, unvarying beat. Vina, Vina. He was a slave to that rhythm, for good.

Let me make one thing clear: he wasn't faithful to her absent self, to her memory. He did not withdraw from society and light a nightly candle at her deserter's shrine. No, sir. Instead, he sought her in other women, sought her furiously and inexhaustibly, searching for an inflection of her voice in this beauty, a toss of her hair in another's flowing locks. Most women offered only disappointments. At the end of these encounters he often found even the ritual courtesies of the situation beyond him and would confess the true nature of his quest, and sometimes the real woman who had disappointed him would have the generosity to listen to him speak of the departed shadow woman, for hour after hour, until the dawn, when he would fall silent and slip away. A few women came close to satisfying him, because in certain lights, if they said very little and lay just so; or if, once he had placed a lace handkerchief or a mask over their faces, their now-anonymous bodies held some echo of hers, a breast, a curve of the thigh, a movement of the neck; then, ah, then he could delude himself for fifteen or twenty seconds that she had returned. But inevitably they would turn, they would speak lovingly to him or arch their bare, strong backs, the light would change, the mask would drop away, the illusion would be destroyed, and he would abandon them where they lay. In spite of maudlin confessions and casual cruelties, however, the young women who showed up at his performances (for he had begun to sing professionally) continued to seek these more private, and almost invariably wounding, audiences.

Nor was his search confined to young hipsters. The catalogue of his substitute loves during these years reads like a cross section of the female population of the city: women of all ages, all walks of life, thin women and fat women, tall women and short, noisy and quiet, gentle and rough, united only in this: that some shard of Vina Apsara dwelt in them, or was believed to do so by the distraught lover she had left behind. Housewives, secretaries, building-site workers, pavement dwellers, sweatshop labourers, domestic servants, whores . . . he hardly seemed to need sleep. By day and by night he would rove the streets, looking for her, the woman who was nowhere, trying to draw her out of the women who were everywhere, finding some fragment to hold on to, some wisp of her to clutch at, in the hope that this *nuage* might at least cause her to visit him in his dreams.

Such was his first pursuit of her. To me it felt almost necrophiliac, vampiric. He was sucking the lifeblood out of living women to keep alive the phantom of the Departed. Often, after a conquest, he would confide in me. Then felt I like Dunyazade, Scheherazade's sister, sitting at the foot of the queen's sleepless bed while she told tall stories to save her life: he would tell me every detail—somehow failing to give the impression that he was boasting—and I, dazed and aroused in equal measure by his passions and descriptions, might on occasion murmur, "Maybe you ought to get over her. Maybe she isn't coming back." Then he would shake his head with its lengthening mane of hair, and shout, "Get thee behind me, Satan. Seek not to come between the lover and his love." Which made me laugh; as it was not meant to do.

What a figure he cut in public! He glittered, he shone. Every room he entered took its shape from his position in it. His smile was a magnet, his frown a crushing defeat. His days "on the loaf" were over. No more hanging around girls'-school gates. He was singing most nights now, playing every instrument in sight, and the girls were flocking to him. The city's hotels and clubs, even the Hindi movie playback producers, were vying for his services. He played the field, signing no contract, committing himself to nobody exclusively, and was hot enough to get away with it. The main attraction of the city's Sunday morning brunches, where, largely thanks to him, jazz was giving way to rock 'n' roll, his gyrations caused the city's demoiselles to swoon. Their mothers, while disapproving strongly, could not take their eyes off him, either. Anybody from the Bombay of those days would remember the young Ormus Cama. His name, his face, became part of the definition of the city in that departed heyday. Mr. Ormus Cama, our women's guiding star.

In conversation, particularly when he leaned close in to some young lovely in big bangs and a spreading pink skirt, his intensity was almost frightening in its sexual power. Celebrate the physical, he would hiss, for we are flesh and blood. What pleases the flesh is good, what warms the blood is fine. The body, not the spirit. Concentrate on that. How does that feel? Yes, it felt good to me too. And that? Oh, yes, baby, my blood too. It's hot.

Our selves, not our souls . . . He spread his erotic gospel with a kind of innocence, a kind of messianic purity, that used to drive me wild. It was the greatest act in town. I did my best to copy it as I moved through my teens, and even my poor mimic version brought fair results with the girls of my generation, but often they'd laugh in my face. Most times, as a matter of fact. I'd count myself lucky to get anywhere with one girl in ten. Which I have in common, as I have since learned, with the male species in general. Rejection is the norm. Knowing this, we long for acceptance all the more. We aren't holding the cards in this game. If we have the knack of it, we learn finesse. . . . Ormus, though, he was an artist, he held the ace of trumps: viz., sincerity. He would take me along to his jam sessions and even to some of his nocturnal songfests (I had two parents vying for my love and favours, so it was easy to twist them round my little finger and get permissions which might otherwise have been refused), and after he finished singing I would watch the maestro at work, sitting in a booth or at a table, with some young female hanging on his every word. I watched him with an almost fanatical attention, determined not to miss the small unwary moment, the tiniest of off-guard instants, when his mask slipped, when he revealed to his disciple-spy that it was just a performance, a calculated series of effects, a fraud.

The moment never came. It was because he meant it, meant it from the depths of his being, that he won followers, fans, hearts, lovers; that he won the game. That Dionysiac credo of his, reject the spirit and trust the flesh, with which he had once wooed Vina, was now knocking half the city for six.

There was only one woman he would not attempt to seduce, and that was Persis Kalamanja. Maybe this was her punishment for having helped Vina get away from him, that she would never taste even a night of his fabled delights; or perhaps it was something else, a mark of his high opinion of her, an indication that had it not been for Vina Apsara, she would indeed have stood a chance.

But Vina existed, and so "poor Persis" was erased.

THE PRIVATE Ormus, the one I was privileged to observe at Apollo Bunder, was very different from this public love god. The bruise on his eyelid itched. Often his old darkness would descend upon him, and he would lie motionless for hours at a time, turning upon that inward eye that saw such strange apocalyptic sights. He no longer spoke much of Gayomart, but I knew his dead twin was in there, fleeing endlessly down some descending labyrinth of the mind, at the end of which not only music waited, but also danger, monsters, death. I knew it because Ormus still came back out of the "Cama obscura" with batches of new songs. And maybe he was going in deeper, taking more risks, or perhaps Gayo was coming back towards him and singing right into his ear, because now Ormus was bringing back more than vowel sequences or misheard, nonsensical lines (though sometimes, for example when he first played me a number called "Da Doo Ron Ron," it was hard to tell the difference). He was being given whole songs now. Songs from the future. Songs with names that meant nothing in 1962 and 1963. "Eve of Destruction." "I Got You, Babe." "Like a Rolling Stone."

Ormus liked to compose his own songs up on the flat roof of the apartment block, and spent eternities up there, lost within himself, searching for the points at which his inner life intersected the life of the greater world outside, and calling those points of intersection "songs." Just once he let me photograph him while he worked, picking away at a guitar laid on his lap across his crossed legs, eyes shut, gone. My Voigtländer camera had escaped the Villa Thracia fire because I had become inseparable from it and had taken it with me to school. I had read in a book called *Photography for Beginners* that a true photographer was never parted from the tool of his trade, and had taken the advice to heart. Ormus liked my attitude, found it "serious," he said, and in spite of my store of jealousy regarding Vina I was always anxious for his good words, so I puffed up horribly when he praised me. His personal nickname for me, in those days, was "Juicy." "My friend Juicy Rai," he'd introduce me—just sixteen in 1963—to his louche club-world set. "You never heard anyone like him. Always seeing photographs—three strangers in a bus queue all lifting their legs at the same time like in a dance routine, or people waving from the deck of a departing steamer, and one of the waving arms is a gorilla's—and then he hollers out, Juicy this? Juicy that? And of course nobody did see it but him, but what do you know, it turns up on his film. Young Juicy," he'd slap me on the back, and his female partners would bestow upon me their most groin-melting, glamorous looks. "Fastest shot in the East." At which I, humiliatingly, youthfully, would blush.

So in November 1963 he let me photograph him while he worked. A lot of the songs he was writing then were of the protest type, idealistic, strong. In the matter of worthiness, which so often exercised my private thoughts, Ormus was of the party that believed there was more wrong with the world in general than its ordinary citizens. In this he was like my mother; except that she, disillusioned, had decided she couldn't beat the world's corruption and had joined forces with it instead. Ormus Cama had not given up on the perfectibility of man and of his social groupings as well. That day on the roof, however, eyes closed, talking to himself, he sounded puzzled. "This isn't how things should be," he'd murmur every few minutes. "Everything's off the rails. Sometimes a little off, sometimes a lot. But things should be different. Just . . . different."

It became a song, in the end: "It Shouldn't Be This Way." But watching him, making myself invisible so that I didn't inhibit him, moving around the roof on cat's paws, I had the strange sense that he wasn't speaking figuratively. Just as Ormus could surprise by the depth of his sincerity, so also his literalness could catch one off guard. I felt the hairs on the back of my neck begin to rise. The muscles in my stomach knotted. "Things aren't like this," he kept repeating. "It shouldn't be this way." As if he had access to some other plane of existence, some parallel, "right" universe, and had sensed that our time had somehow been put out of joint. Such was his vehemence that I found myself believing him, believing, for example, in the possibility of that other life in which Vina had never left and we were making our lives together, all three of us, ascending together to the stars. Then he shook his head, and the spell broke. He opened his eyes, grinning ruefully. As if he knew his thoughts had infected mine. As if he knew his power. "Better get on with it," he said. "Make do with what there is."

Later, as I drifted off to sleep in my room, Ormus's rooftop torment came back to haunt me: his sudden possession by the idea that, like a runaway freight train, the world had veered sideways off its proper track and was now banging about, out of control, upon a great iron web of switched points. In my pre-sleep drowsiness, it was a notion that unnerved me; for if the world itself were metamorphosing unpredictably, then nothing could be relied upon any more. What could one trust? How to find moorings, foundations, fixed points, in a broken, altered time? I came awake fast and hard, with my heart pounding. It's okay. It's okay. Only a waking dream.

The world is what it is.

I thought then that Ormus's doubts about reality might be a kind of revenge of the spirit, an irruption, into a life dedicated to the actual and the sensual, of the irrational, the incorporeal. He, who had rejected the unknowable, was being plagued by the unknown.

THE DAY after the President of the United States had that narrow escape in Dallas, Texas, and we were all becoming familiar with the names of the would-be assassins, Oswald, whose rifle jammed, and Steel, who was overpowered on some kind of grassy knoll by a genuine hero, a middle-aged amateur cameraman called Zapruder, who saw the killer's gun and hit him over the head with an 8 mm ciné camera . . . on that extraordinary day, Ormus Cama had a different name to conjure with, because he arrived at the Regal Café, Colaba, to be informed that among the audience for his late-night set would be a party from the United States of America, including Mr. Yul Singh himself. Even then most music-loving metropolitan Indians had heard of Yul Singh, the blind Indian record producer who founded Colchis Records in New York City in 1948 with a ten-thousand-dollar loan from his optician. After Colchis struck gold by playing "race music," rhythm and blues, to white radio audiences, that optician, Tommy J. Eckleburg, briefly became a Manhattan celebrity himself. He even showed up with Yul Singh on the talk-show promo circuit.

"So why does a blind man need an optician, Yul?"

"Optimism, Johnny. Optimism."

"And why does an optician need a blind man, T.J.?"

"Don't go insulting my good friend now, Mr. C. He's differently sighted is all."

When Ormus arrived at the Regal and was told about the Yul Singh party, he frowned hard and began to complain of a terrible headache. He took pills and lay down in his dressing room with an ice pack on his head, and I sat beside him, massaging his temples. "Yul *Singh,*" he kept repeating. "*Yul* Singh."

"The top banana," I said, proud of my newly acquired knowledge. "Aretha, Ray, the Beatles. Everybody." Ormus winced, as if the pain in his head had intensified.

"What's the matter?" I asked. "Pills not working?"

"There's no such man," he whispered. "He doesn't fucking exist."

That was ridiculous. "You're hallucinating," I told him. "You'll be telling me next there's no Jesse Garon Parker." He took the point, and covered his face with his hands. I heard a snatch of song.

It's not supposed to be this way
it's not supposed to be this day
it's not supposed to be this night
but you're not here to put it right

and you're not here to hold me tight
it shouldn't be this way.

Then his head seemed to clear; the pills had kicked in. He sat up on his couch.

"What's wrong with me?" he said. "This is no time to be cracking up."

"Break a leg," I told him, and he went out to play.

AT THE end of the set, which, in honour of the visiting Americans, Ormus had dedicated to President Kennedy's survival, I was with him in his tiny dressing room, along with three young women (no room for more). Ormus was stripped to the waist, towelling himself down, to the delight of the ladies. Then Yul Singh knocked at the door. Ormus shooed the women out but told me I could stay.

"Kid brother?" Yul Singh asked, and Ormus grinned. "Something like that."

Singh was a piece of work. He was wearing the most beautiful blue silk suit I had ever seen, his shirts bore his personal monogram, his two-tone shoes made my feet ache with envy. He was fortyish, small, dark, goateed, and his sunglasses—the work, no doubt, of that ocular couturier *par excellence,* Dr. T.J. Eckleburg—were made to fit the curve of his head, so that you never could catch a glimpse of those sightless eyes, no matter how much you craned your curious neck. In his hand was a white cane, made of pure ivory, with a silver head.

"Okay, listen to me," he said: straight to the point. "I don't come to Bombay to find acts, okay? I come to see my mother. Who god bless her she's over seventy now but still rides a horse. You don't need to know that. So, I heard your music, and what, you think I don't know anything, who the fuck are you trying to kid?"

All this spoken through teeth glittering in the most courteous of smiles. I had never seen Ormus so discomfited. "I don't understand, Mr. Singh," he said, suddenly sounding very young. "You didn't like my performance?"

"Who cares what I like? I told you, I'm off duty. My mother's out there. She heard you, I heard you, the whole town heard you. What is it, a kind of tribute act, right? I'll give you this, you've got those songs down, and the phrasing, you could be those guys. So, okay. I'm not interested. You're doing it to get women, pocket money, what? You get women? Is that what you're looking for?"

"Just one woman," Ormus said faintly, shocked into honesty.

That made Singh stop and cock his head. "She ran out on you, huh. You were singing these cockamamie tribute numbers, and she'd had enough."

Ormus pulled the shreds of his dignity around him. "I get the point, Mr. Singh, thank you for your honesty. I wasn't singing my own songs today. Another night, maybe I'll give them a try." Singh smacked his cane on the bare floor. "Did I say I was finished? I'll tell you when I'm finished, and I won't be finished until you tell me, boy, where you got hold of that last number you sang, what bootlegging motherfucker stole it for you, that's what I said when you started singing, you see what you made me do, you made me swear in front of my white-haired mother, I hate to do that. She was knitting, it made her drop a stitch. You don't need to know that."

The last song had been a tender ballad, slow, full of longing: a song for Vina, I thought, one of Ormus's rooftop compositions, written while dreaming of lost love. But I was wrong. The name of the song was "Yesterday."

"I heard it," Ormus said, lamely, and Yul Singh rammed the tip of his cane into the floor once more. "Impossible, okay?" he said. "That song, we aren't putting it out until next year. We haven't even recorded it yet. There isn't even a fucking demo. The guy just wrote it, he just played it to me on his fucking piano in London, okay, and then I fly to Bombay to see my sweet old mother who god bless her I've now left out there for many minutes wondering why is her son swearing in front of her, you understand what I'm saying, this is not right. It shouldn't be this way."

Ormus was silent, stopped in his tracks. How could he say, I have a dead twin, I follow him in my dreams, he sings, I listen, and these days I'm getting better at hearing the words? Getting better all the time?

Yul Singh stood. "Let me tell you two things. One, if you ever sing that song again, I'll have lawyers on you tighter than a straitjacket and your balls will be on my table beside my cornflakes in a little china bowl. Two, I never swear. Never. I'm famous for my clean tongue. Therefore comprehend, please, my distress."

He was going through the door. I caught a glimpse of two burly aides in tuxes. He turned for a parting shot.

"I didn't say you didn't have talent. Did I say that? I don't believe so. You have talent. Maybe great talent. What you don't have is material, except what you stole, beats me how and you aren't going to say. What you also don't have is a band, because those guys in pink jackets with their big-band haircuts are definitely going nowhere except back home on the bus. Further, motivation. This it seems to me you are also short on. When you've got material you think it's up to snuff, when you've got an act you think it'll travel, don't come and see me. When you've got motivation, that's different, if someday you get it, but maybe you won't, which don't worry I won't be waiting. Maybe if you find that girl, yeah. Find her and she'll be the making of you. I owe everything personally to my own lovely wife who unfortunately she's not accompanying me on this trip. You don't need to know that. Good night."

"So he doesn't exist," I said to Ormus. "That's lucky, then."

Ormus looked like he'd been hit by lightning. "It's all wrong," he mumbled stupidly. "But maybe this is how it has to be."

CHAPTER SEVEN

More Than Love

I must confess that I never completely accepted the passport/foreign exchange explanation of Ormus's non-pursuit of Vina. Where there's a will, etc., I couldn't help thinking; so when Yul Singh shrewdly queried the singer's motivation, I realized he'd put his finger on the problem and was only saying aloud what I already knew. Such was Ormus's outward confidence, however—his sexual swagger, his ease with his body and voice, his charm—that I had allowed myself to believe (more exactly, I had kidded myself that I believed) that those private inwardnesses of his, and even those panicky outbursts about errors in reality, could be ascribed to his intense artistic sensibility, which drew him inexorably towards what Browning calls the dangerous edge of things.

"The honest thief, the tender murderer." Interesting as such paradoxes undoubtedly are, Ormus Cama sought an edge more dangerous by far, an edge in the mind, beyond which he pursued his dead brother, returning with prophetic music but risking, each time, that he might not return at all. It was unsurprising, I thought with teenage omniscience, that such journeys into the unknown should take their toll, and leave the voyager moody and erratic. In short, I believed Ormus Cama to be a little touched in the head, knocked off balance by loss, as separated twins (and jilted lovers) sometimes are. The surviving male Camas were, all of them in their various ways, a couple of annas short of the full rupee; Ormus, neither homicidal nor mute nor sunk in a whisky stupor of defeat and shame, was both gifted and charismatic, and his strangeness only increased the attraction. So there were many ways for me to set aside my early doubts, to stop articulating, even to myself, the obvious insight that Vina's sudden desertion, immediately after their long-postponed and profoundly satisfying first (and only) night of love, had badly damaged Ormus's sense of himself, had left him holed below the waterline, listing in the water, bailing furiously and trying not to drown. Now that Yul Singh's clear-sightedness had opened my own eyes, I could see the thick, paralysing fog of fear enveloping Ormus Cama, the sense of deep inadequacy revealed by his Bombay Casanova act, his unstoppable Don Juanism. If Aphrodite had resigned from Olympus, if Venus had announced that her job wasn't worth doing any longer, it could not have hit Ormus harder than Vina Apsara's disillusionment with love. He too had lost confidence, and faith in the very idea of Vina, the idea of there being an eternal and perfect partner whom he might perfectly and eternally love and by whom he might in his turn be rendered perfect and eternal. "I'll follow her to the ends of the earth," he boasted, but he wouldn't even go as far as the airport.

He had begun to fear what he desired most. On the greatest day of his professional life he developed a migraine, and then failed to perform a single song of his own to the celebrated producer sitting beside his knitting mother in the audience. Instead, he sang his Gayo ditties, those cover versions of the well-known hits of the day which he had so uselessly heard long before, in dreams; and so he was mistaken by the producer for a novelty act, a provincial echo of the big-city action, a hick. It was the same with Vina; he'd lost his nerve. The fear that she might no longer love him—that she might, indeed, slam that trailer door in his face—had grown stronger than his love, kept him at home.

IN THE thirteen months after Yul Singh's exposure of his secret timorousness, Ormus Cama's loss of nerve gradually became apparent to everyone. Until that day the house musicians at the various clubs and coffeehouses, such as the Pink Flamingoes backing combo at the Regal Café, had treated Ormus like a demi-god, one of those mythological heroes whose fate it is to end up twinkling in the heavens. After the boss of Colchis Records gave him the thumbs-down, however, the musicians of Bombay wasted no time in letting Ormus Cama know that it was no good his putting on airs any more, he might think he was the Mod God (a title—more alliterative than accurate—which he'd been given by a critic), but as far as they were concerned he was no better than they were, just the singer with the band, and singers were two a penny, so he'd better watch his step. And to complete his discomfiture, he also lost what we used to call "the knack."

The first women to reject his advances, the starlets Fadia Wadia and Tipple Billimoria, briefly became famous in the city's café society as the bubble bursters of Ormus's lady-killer reputation. Within weeks of those first refusals, however, the whole of "Ormie's Army" had deserted him. Only Persis Kalamanja remained, magnificently waiting in ardent solitude in her mother's Malabar Hill mansion. But that was a phone call Ormus Cama never made. To call Persis would be to admit he was finished. It would be like calling a tower of silence to rent space on the vulture-crowded roof. Persis Kalamanja, infinitely patient Persis, who bore no malice towards any human being, Persis the beautiful, every mother's ideal daughter and most men's dream of a bride, had been transformed by Ormus's tormented fancy into an avatar of the Angel of Death.

He became an increasingly forlorn, frayed figure during the course of that year, and still he made no effort to go in search of Vina. Even Mrs. Spenta Cama, who had never succeeded in loving her youngest child and had opposed with all her force Ormus's obsession with the under-age Vina, found herself saying, with a kind of irritation, "What do you think she's going to do after all this time? Plop down the chimney on Christmas Day, all tied up with ribbon and a card?"

THE CAMA apartment boasted no chimney; the family was not in the habit of celebrating Christmas; Vina Apsara did not come to call, with or without gift wrapping. But someone did return. And after that, Christmas Day was still nothing for Camas to celebrate, but it was also impossible to forget.

CYRUS CAMA broke out of jail that Christmas Eve, disguised as a Syriac priest, having convinced a guard that he was a great seer whose murdering days were behind him and who would be of far greater value to the nation as a free man, spreading his unique message around the land. He emerged into a nation in dire need of guidance. Jawaharlal Nehru was dead. His successor, Indira Gandhi, was little more than a pawn in the hands of the Congress kingmakers, Shastri, Morarji Desai and Kamaraj. A fanatical gang of political bully boys, Mumbai's Axis, was on the verge of seizing control of Bombay, and Hindu nationalism was sweeping the country. There was a general feeling that things were going too fast, that the national railway train was roaring ahead without a driver, and that the decision to drop international tariff barriers and deregulate the economy had been too hastily taken. "Maybe in twenty years' time, when we are stronger," said an *Indian Express* editorial, "but why now? Where's the fire?"

On the night of Cyrus's escape, his twin brother Ardaviraf woke up suddenly, shuddering, as if something evil had moved lightly along his spine. He remained in that position, sitting up in bed, shivering, until he was discovered by his mother, who wrapped him in blankets and fed him chicken soup until the colour returned to his cheeks. "It's like he saw a ghost," Spenta said on the phone to Dolly Kalamanja, whose briskly matter-of-fact pooh-poohing of all paranormal gibberish always made the mystically inclined Spenta secretly feel a good deal better. "Poor fellow," clucked Dolly sympathetically. "Devil knows what foolish notions course through that boy's head."

The next morning brought news of Cyrus's escape, and Spenta gave Virus a long look, but he only grinned his innocent grin and turned away. Spenta Cama was gripped by an undefined fear. She knew it was no good discussing the alarming development with her increasingly withdrawn husband. Instead, she called her closest ally. "What won't my Khusro do this time," she wailed at Dolly. "What shame won't he now bring down on my head?" But Dolly Kalamanja, who knew her friend well, heard some deeper terror beneath Spenta's lamentations, a fear which had driven Spenta to talk openly about a subject whose very existence she had never before liked to admit. Dolly was no longer an innocent arriviste, and had found out about jailed Cyrus some while back. Such was her fondness for Spenta, and her own good nature (which she had passed on to Persis), that she had never once raised the topic. "If mum is the word Spenta wants," she had told Persis, "then mum's what she'll get from me."

The two women had a busy programme that day. There was a Kalamanja "charitea" at Dolly's place, followed by a special fund-raising fashion show, or Xtraordinary Xmas Xtravaganza, at the Orpheum cinema, and after that a round of hospital visits. "Come over early," Dolly advised Spenta. "Get your mind off it. Masses to plan." Mrs. Spenta Cama, plagued by anxiety, scurried gratefully across to Malabar Hill at once, and plunged into good works with energy and relief.

Ormus, too, would say afterwards that he had left home feeling nervous and on edge, but then in those hard days he often was. He shrugged off the feeling and went to work. He had been booked, that evening, to croon supper-club material at the Cosmic Dancer Hotel on Marine Drive, whose restaurant had been given a Christmas theme by the addition of much cotton wool and a few plastic trees. Ormus was forced to dress up in a red outfit with a white beard and sing a selection ranging from "White Christmas" to Eartha Kitt's "Santa Baby," even though this last song was so clearly written to be sung only by a woman. It was a B-list booking that said much about his declining reputation.

Sometimes it is necessary to touch bottom in order to know which way is up; to go a long distance down the wrong road before you know the right way. Ormus Cama had been allowing himself slowly to sink, crippled by a terrible, lassitudinous inertia that bore a marked resemblance to his father's. On the night of Darius's murder, however, Ormus Cama at last saw himself plain. At the end of his set at the Cosmic Dancer Hotel, those two purgatorial hours spent singing old songs through a Santa Claus beard, he listened to the sparse, uninterested applause and began to laugh. He removed his beard and Father Christmas hat and laughed until the tears streamed down his face. Afterwards many Bombayites would claim to have been present at Ormus Cama's last show in the city, enough people to fill the Wankhede Stadium several times over, and the accounts they gave of his farewell remarks were many and various. He was said to have spoken angrily, or humbly, or arrogantly, or in French. He was accused of having harangued the audience about the future of popular music, or berated them for their inattention, or begged them to give him one more chance, at which he had been booed from the stage. Some said he had made a political speech, attacking the assembled B-list fat cats for their corruption and greed; or that he had blasphemed, not only against Christmas and the Christians, but against all gods and rites—"charades"—of worship. According to these hordes of self-styled witnesses, he had been magnificent or pathetic, a hero or a clown.

The truth was that he couldn't stop laughing, and the only thing he said wasn't addressed to anyone present. "Shit, Vina," he said, holding his sides. "I'm sorry it took me so long to understand."

MEANWHILE, BACK at the Apollo Bunder apartment, Gieve the butler had served dinner to Darius and Ardaviraf Cama and then retired to the servants' quarters, where he found, to his amazement, that all the resident domestics had run off, except for the cook, who was in the process of leaving. "And where do you think you're going?" Gieve asked this fellow, who just shook his head and exited at top speed via the servants' outside staircase, a clanking cast-iron spiral fixed to the rear of the building. It is plain that Gieve himself felt no warning pangs of terror, because he lay down on his cot as usual and was soon asleep.

Mr. Darius Cama spent the last hours of his life alone in his beloved library, fuddled by old age, mythology and booze. He had become obsessed by the notion that the Greek figures of the Titans Prometheus, "forethought," and his brother Epimetheus, "afterthought," the sons of the "First Father," Uranus, might have been derived from the Puranic heroes Pramanthu and Manthu, and that the swastika, that ancient Indian fire symbol, could also be connected to Prometheus's symbolic rôle as the thief of Olympic fire for the benefit of his creation, mankind. The Nazis had stolen the swastika and defiled it—as the Nazi connection had sullied the entire field—and the old gentleman scholar hoped in his muddled fashion that these, his last researches, might in some small way redeem both the swastika and the study of Aryan myth from the terrible deformation to which history had subjected them. However, he was unable to think clearly enough to follow his arguments through. His notes wandered from the point, digressing from Prometheus and Epimetheus to their youngest uncle, Cronus, who took a cruel sickle and cut off his father's balls. The last words Darius Xerxes Cama wrote slid away from scholarship entirely to reveal all his confusion and pain. *No need to cut off my balls,* he wrote. *Did it all by myself,* and then his head fell forward and rested upon his papers, and he slept.

SPENTA CAME home late and went quietly to her room; Ormus, wreathed in radiance, returned an hour before dawn, singing without restraint, and switched on a great blaze of chandeliers and standard lamps. Exhausted Spenta in her room saw no lights, heard no songs and did not awake. Blinking rapidly, as if he were emerging into the light after years spent hiding from the world in a darkened attic, Ormus retired, having spent the night prowling the city streets, laughing, calling out Vina's name, drunk on nothing but excitement, burning with need. He entered his room noisily, fell down on to his bed and passed out fully clothed. The apartment slept, innocent of the tragedy within its walls.

Morning came, rapid and intolerant, the way morning is in the tropics. As usual it was the city that woke Spenta with its shrugging, careless noise of shouts and engines and bicycle bells. Crows sat on the windowsills, bold as brass, and cawed her out of bed. But in spite of all this noise, it was a silence that dragged Spenta upright, a silence where there should have been sound. A part of the morning orchestra was missing: there were no household noises. Spenta, pulling a floaty chiffon peignoir over her nightdress, went forth into the apartment, where she found neither the sweeper woman and her daughter, squatting with their brooms, nor the hamal, busy with the dusting and polishing. The kitchen was empty. Gieve was nowhere to be found. She called aloud: *"Arré, koi hai?"* No answer. Such laziness was unforgivable. Spenta stormed through the kitchen towards the servants' quarters, grim of face, determined to give her indolent household the rough edge of her tongue;

and came back an instant later, running, with one hand over her mouth as if she were stifling a scream. She flung open the door to Ardaviraf Cama's bedroom. He was asleep, snoring beatifically. Then she went into Ormus's quarters. He tossed blearily and grunted. Darius's bedchamber was empty. Spenta went towards the library, then came to a standstill outside the closed double doors, as though she could not bear to open them because she was unprepared for the sight she would then be required to see. With a hand on each doorknob, she leaned forward, until her forehead was pressing painfully against the shining mahogany; and she wept.

It is said that after an anointed king passed away, his soul took refuge in the body of a crow. It may also be that the name of Cronus, who killed his father, derived from the Greek word for crow and not, as is more often thought, from the word for time. And it is a fact that when Spenta opened the library door, a single crow was sitting on her husband's desk, right beside his uncaring head. When it saw Spenta, it cawed loudly, took flight in a panicky circle, colliding twice with the leather spines of old books, and then made its escape through the room's high windows, which had—unusually—been left wide open, even though the air conditioner was on. Spenta Cama gently laid the back of her right hand against her husband's cheek. Which was cold.

DARIUS XERXES Cama and his manservant Gieve had both died of suffocation, which was the murderous "trademark" of Cyrus the Pillowman. The time of death was fixed at around ten-thirty in the evening. The butler had resisted his murderer energetically. There were traces of blood—possibly the killer's—under his long fingernails. Darius did not seem to have resisted at all. His face was calm, nor were there any signs of a struggle. It was as if he had given up his life's breath gladly, as if he were happy to yield it up to his own son.

Good mythology makes bad detective work. The Greeks would have us believe that the First Father was murdered by his youngest son at the instigation of the First Mother, Gaia, Mother Earth herself. But at the time of the Cama killings, Ormus had been singing to a room full of unimpressed diners, and Spenta had been caressing the hands of mortally ill patients at the Lying-In Hospital.

Inspector Sohrab of the Bombay C.I.D., arching a disapproving eyebrow, noted his surprise at having occasion to interview Camas, Kalamanjas and (as near neighbours who might have seen something significant) Merchants too, so relatively soon after the mysterious fire at Cuffe Parade. However, there could be no doubt that the prime suspect in the present case was the psychopathic escaped killer Khusro alias Cyrus Cama, whose blood was of the same type as the stuff under the dead butler's nails. The motive for the murders was of minor significance in the case of "crazies," who could, as Inspector Sohrab pointed out, "do anything you can think of at the drop of a hat." It was his best guess that Gieve had been killed first, just to get him out of the way. Darius Xerxes Cama had been the real target, perhaps—"just a wild surmise, see"—because Cyrus resented having been first banished from his home, chastised by his teachers more or less at his parents' request, and then legally disowned. Sohrab and Rustam looked at Spenta Cama with open hostility. "Lucky you were out," said Inspector Sohrab viciously, "or you too may have received your deserts."

Some side issues had resolved themselves. The domestic staff had all returned, shuffling and surly, claiming that as Christians they had simply been attending Midnight Mass at the Cathedral and had then gone to visit their family members in the city's outlying suburbs. It was Christmas, after all, and they had been determined to observe it even if their heartless employers had refused to give them the night off. Gieve had not been a Christian. There was nothing else to explain.

There were only two matters, according to Sohrab and Rustam, that still required clarification. Firstly, on the same night as the double killing at Apollo Bunder a person answering closely to the description of the said psychopathic killer Khusro Cama had been seen leaving the scene of a murder by asphyxiation in the city of Lucknow, halfway across the sub-continent. And secondly, the profile of the blood under the dead Gieve's fingernails also corresponded precisely to that of Khusro's twin, the speechless Ardaviraf

Cama, on whose forearms there were undeniable scratches, deep enough to have drawn blood.

Virus sat in a corner of the library, his eyes fixed upon the desk at which his father had been found. His feet were up on the chair, and his arms were locked around his knees, and he was rocking slowly back and forth. Sohrab questioned him, badgered him, cajoled him, threatened him, all to no avail. Virus said nothing. "Leave the boy alone," Spenta Cama shouted at the C.I.D. inspector at last. "Can't you see he is grieving? Can't you smell how we are all stinking with misery? Go away and do your job, and when you catch," and here she broke into tears, "when you find my other boy, you keep him safe and sound."

On New Year's Day, 1965, Cyrus Cama walked up to the main gate of Tihar Jail and surrendered. Under interrogation, he denied all knowledge of the murder in Lucknow (for which another man was eventually arrested and hanged, protesting his innocence to his last breath). However, he freely confessed to the parricide, and confirmed that the death of the manservant had been—and here he quoted Auden—a "necessary murder." He pointed to the gouges on his arms, wounds far more severe than Virus's scratches, categorically denied that they were self-inflicted, and gave a description of the double crime, so detailed and so closely in line with the known facts and forensic evidence as to terminate all discussion. He was returned to solitary confinement in the jail's maximum-security psychiatric wing, and it was decreed that the teams of prison officers who guarded him should be changed "with high frequency," so that no other poor sucker could ever fall under Cyrus's passionate, erudite, fanatical, lethal spell.

After the fire at Villa Thracia, Persis Kalamanja's alibi had freed Vina from suspicion. Now it was Cyrus Cama's turn to exonerate his brother. All these alibis, all these alternative story lines, that we must abandon! The story, for example, in which our seafront home was destroyed by Vina's revenge; in which the fire inside that much-abused child burst out and consumed my childhood too. And the even stranger story of how Virus Cama, his mysterious mind somehow linked to his twin brother's, carried out the Apollo Bunder murders for him; of how Cyrus could be in two places at once and know, thanks to the unfathomable communication between identical twins, every detail of the murders he forced his silent brother to commit. These stories float, now, in the limbo of lost possibilities. We simply have no grounds for believing them to be true.

And yet, and yet. After her husband's murder Spenta Cama never went to sleep without locking her bedroom door. Nor did Ormus join his dumb brother, whose smile was as sweet as ever, for any more sessions at the family piano.

Impossible stories, stories with No Entry signs on them, change our lives, and our minds, as often as the authorized versions, the stories we are expected to trust, upon which we are asked, or told, to build our judgements, and our lives.

NINE FEET from wing tip to wing tip, the vultures hover over the *dokhma,* the Tower of Silence, in the gardens of the *Doongerwadi* on Malabar Hill. Their circling reminds Ormus of the fly-past of aircraft at the funerals of the great. *Between the Parsi and the vulture there exists the great binding intimacy of last things. For us there is no rush. We have our whole lives to wait, I for you, you for me. Each knows the other will keep his appointment.*

We pass through rooms lined with portraits of our famous dead and come to the long funeral hall. Here is the priest and here is the sandalwood man and here is the fire which is the representation of god but is not god. Here are the pallbearers, the nassasalars. *Here is my brother, Ardaviraf the silent. Holding a white scarf between us, we lead the procession into the gardens where the towers stand. There are plenty of birds today, thirty birds, like the thirty in Attar's great poem who made the journey to the Simurg and became the god they sought. The thirty vultures joining together and becoming Vulture. That is the kind of thought my father might have thought, the kind of connection he might have made. You must know who comes to see you today, O vulture, I must explain him to you, in silence, accompanied by my brother of silence, before the silent towers.*

He was a distant father, but we had no other. He was disappointed in us. We were not what he had hoped for. We were less than his dreams. But he praised you, vulture, for your rational, scientific mind. He praised our last meeting, in which the cycle of life is renewed. And on his desk, among the notes he had been working on when he died, he spoke thus of you:

Prometheus chained to a pillar in the high Caucasus, with Zeus's vulture gnawing at his liver all day long. By night the liver regenerates. Unending punishment of pain. The vulture of Prometheus seen as proof of the vindictiveness of Z. With each bite it shows us why we should turn aside from gods & take the rational path. The gods lie, accuse us falsely. (Re: Prometheus, some trumped-up business about a secret love affair with P. Athene.) The gods are whimsical, irrational, divine. For the crime of being ourselves they turn us into rocks, spiders, plants. The agony inflicted by the mordant v. is nothing less than the agony of reason. Joyful agony. It shows Prometheus who he is, how he should live, why the gods are wrong, why he is right. Vulture, we are in your debt. And forever joined to you by ties of our lives' blood. Which may be more powerful than love.

Prometheus the creator of mankind, who saved us from Zeus's wrath by warning Deucalion to build an ark against the Flood. Prometheus father of science & knowledge, who gave us fire and received the vulture in return. What is Titanic in us, let us seek. What is Olympian, let us expunge. I am my father's son. I had thought myself free of him, self-made, but that was vanity. Death shows us the power of blood.

I am my father's son. The punishment of Prometheus I take upon myself. O Promethean vulture of reason, help my father find his way to his deserved rest.

Spenta Cama sent news of Darius's passing to his old friend Lord Methwold, who had continued to write to her with surprising frequency. By return of post she received a long letter of condolence, which spoke of Darius in the warmest terms, much regretted the gulf that had grown up between them, and invited Spenta and her sons to England. "Though it is winter here, yet these different skies, these unfamiliar surroundings, may by virtue of that very difference help to soothe, if not assuage, your pain." On receiving this letter Spenta Cama had a number of thoughts more or less at once: that she was not in as much pain as she had expected; that after the years of Darius's decline, his death felt almost like blessed relief, not least—as the absence of struggle had hinted—to himself; that having refused for half a lifetime to share her husband's English dream, she now found that the prospect of an English winter was filling her with excitement, anticipation, even joy; and that it would be very nice to see William Methwold again after all these years, very nice indeed.

And then there was the problem of money. Darius had died a poor man, and Ormus Cama's income—on which the household had relied to a far greater extent than his disapproving mother had been prepared to admit—had declined sharply. In recent months Spenta had sold off a few "trinkets and baubles" to help maintain standards. Her money worries had etched themselves deeply on her formerly unlined brow and thus come to the attention of Dolly Kalamanja, who had not been so graceless as to speak of them openly. Instead, like a true friend, she had found disingenuous excuses for sending Spenta "little gifties"—silk sari lengths, baskets of laddoos, hot-tiffin carriers laden with the latest international cuisine from the celebrated "Dil Kush" kitchens—in short, the bare necessities of life. For her part, Spenta received the presents lightly, as if they were no more than the trivial evidences of a good friendship, and made sure that she, in her turn, sent Dolly the occasional gift of love: a small ivory carving from the secret treasure chest she kept under her bed, or a novel filched from Darius's library.

Thus Spenta was able to accept her friend's largesse without losing face. But she was practised enough in the codes of polite society to know that her financial situation would soon be the talk of the town, for what Dolly could perceive and keep to herself, less loving eyes would also see soon enough, and less respectful tongues would feel no compulsion to be discreet. Widowhood had only served to underline the crisis by revealing to Spenta the extent of Darius's debts. It seemed inevitable that the Apollo Bunder apartment would have to be sold and the family would be forced to move into humbler accommodation, joining the swelling ranks of distressed Parsi gentlefolk whose extreme indigence was a phenomenon of the age and another mark of the passing of the Empire upon which they had gambled and lost.

Into this growing crisis Lord Methwold's letter of invitation dropped like a blessing from her guardian angels. Spenta hugged it to her bosom and giggled, most improperly for one so recently bereaved. An interested male party with a fortune is a boon to the spirits. *Lady Methwold,* Spenta murmured, and then had the decency to blush, and think of her sons.

Naturally, there was no way of leaving helpless Ardaviraf behind, but once they were in England, Lord Methwold would know what to do for the best; and as for Ormus, that loafer, that immoral nightclub singer who had turned out so poorly, she did not feel able—for she was an honest woman—to decamp without telling him that he had also been invited. When she did tell him, she made it very plain that she was not expecting him to accept Lord Methwold's invitation and would quite understand if he decided his life must take a different, more "bohemian" course. (With what delicate disdain she articulated that word "bohemian"!) In short, she went as close as her nature allowed to telling him he was not wanted on the voyage. To her horror, however, Ormus Cama accepted, with what looked very like elation. "It's high time I got out of this two-bit town," he said. "So, if it's okay, I'll tag along for the ride."

SPENTA CAMA left Bombay at the end of January 1965, accompanied by her sons. None of the three ever returned to India. By the end of the year Spenta had become Lady Methwold. At Methwold's insistence, Virus Cama had been placed in a sanatorium where he would receive the finest care, and also twice-weekly flute lessons from a professional flautist of Indian extraction. As for Ormus, he had vanished into the rest of his life, about which there will be a great deal to say hereafter. The newlyweds Spenta and Methwold were left to their own devices, as was only right. Spenta's new husband was full of remorse for his cold-shouldering of Darius in the matter of the faked legal qualifications. "In his way he was a giant," Methwold said. "But a giant out of time. The age of giants has gone, and we mortals grow careless of the few that remain. But the two of us can hold hands through this long winter, and remember."

These words were spoken on the broad, frosty parterre of an ample residence in the Home Counties, of which Spenta was the new châtelaine: a white Palladian mansion set upon a hill above the winding Thames. White curtains blew at the French windows of the orangery. There was a fountain crawling with gods.

It was the mansion of Darius Cama's dreams.

DEATH IS more than love or is it. Art is more than love or is it. Love is more than death and art, or not. This is the subject. This is the subject. This is it.

What deflects us from the subject is loss. Of those we love, of the Orient, of hope, of our place in the book. Loss is more than love or is it. More than death or is it. More than art, or not. Darius Cama's "fourth function" added, to the tripartite system of Indo-European culture (religious sovereignty, physical force, fertility), the necessary additional concept of the existential outsider, the separated man, the banished divorcé, the expelled schoolboy, the cashiered officer, the legal alien, the uprooted wanderer, the out-of-step marcher, the rebel, the transgressor, the outlaw, the anathematized thinker, the crucified revolutionary, the lost soul.

The only people who see the whole picture are the ones who step out of the frame. If he was right then this is the subject also. If he was wrong, then the lost are merely lost. Stepping out of the frame, they simply cease to exist.

I am writing here about the end of something, not just the end of a phase of my life but the end of my connection with a country, my country of origin as we say now, my home country I was brought up to say, India. I am trying to say goodbye, goodbye again, goodbye a quarter century after I physically left. This ending is oddly positioned, coming as it does in the middle of my story, but without it the second half of my life could not have happened as it did. Also, it takes time to come to terms with the truth: that what's over is over. Because as it happens I didn't go of my own free will. As it happens I was driven out, like a dog. I had to run for my life.

SMALL EARTHQUAKES were recorded in several parts of India during the late 1960s and early 1970s; nothing serious, no loss of life and minimal damage to property, but enough to make us sleep a little less easily in our beds. One shook the Golden Temple in the Sikh holy city of Amritsar in the Punjab, another rattled teeth in the small southern town of Sriperumbudur. A third scared the children of Nellie in Assam. Finally, the picturesque waters of a Kashmiri lake, high Shishnag, that cold mirror in the sky, began to roil and spume.

Geology as metaphor. There were plenty of rishis and mahagurus, and even political columnists and editorial writers, who were prepared—eager!—to link these tremors with the great public events of those years, such as Mrs. Gandhi's emergence as a formidable leader, "Mrs. Mover-and-Shaker," and her victory over Pakistan in the great War of 1965, which lasted exactly twenty-two days and was fought on two fronts simultaneously, in Kashmir (the "Kashquake") and in Bangladesh (the "Banglashake"). "Old Order Cracks Up," cried the pundits, and, once the allegations about Mrs. G.'s electoral malpractices began, "Dark Rumbles Shake Gandhi Administration."

I, however, did not need geology to explain the upheavals in my immediate circle. I, Umeed Merchant, a.k.a. Rai, turned eighteen in the year of the War. Ormus had gone, and Vina was a fading memory, and I was shuttling between my estranged parents' apartments along with the household servants, because they shared the domestic help as well as me, and when I was angry with them, and at that age one is often angry, I would say that I felt as if I were just another one of their underpaid employees. Then my mother's inoperable brain tumour was diagnosed and within weeks she just died, click, as if somebody had turned out her light, and left me burdened with whole volumes of gentler sentences that I had left unsaid. She was fifty-one years old.

The evening after we buried my mother, my father and I drove out to take a look at Cuffe Parade. The long process of levelling and reclamation was almost complete. The villas, promenade and mangrove forest were long gone, and the sea had retreated before the power of the great machines. An immense brown expanse of land stretched before us, an almost blank slate upon which history was only just beginning to write. The huge dusty space was broken up, articulated, by metal fencing, and large signs forbidding various activities, and the concrete and steel foundations of the first tall buildings; also pile drivers, steamrollers, trucks, wheelbarrows, cranes. And though the day's work was over, we could still see clumps of workers in the near and middle distance, men were leaning against concrete stumps out of which steel rods twisted like the branches of trees created by some botanical Frankenstein, women with hitched-up saris were holding their earth-carrying metal bowls against their hips and smoking beedis under the No Smoking signs, laughing harshly out of grim gap-toothed faces which knew that life was nothing to laugh about.

This was not the emptiness of the desert but a desert of the spirit, I thought.

"No," said my father, reading my mind. "It is an empty canvas, primed and waiting for the intervention of the artist's hand. Your mother was a visionary. Here, from this propagatory enclave—seedbed wrested from seabed—her Ozymandian colossi will rise, and the mighty will look upon Bombay and despair." He was speaking of his rival, the only one who could have parted two people who loved each other so deeply, and in that moment I did not know whether to hate the city that had torn them apart or to take my lead from V.V.'s desperate generosity in his time of inconsolable grief, his compassionate irony, and forgive Bombay as he forgave it, and also pity it as he did, in the name of that dear, lost love. I thought of sand castles and ice cream and tunelessness and puns, and I thought anew of Vina, in whom there was more of Ameer Merchant than could now be found anywhere else on earth.

It had grown dark, and the evening bugs were biting me to bits. "Let's go," I said, but he didn't hear me. It was my turn to read his mind. She became cynical, he was thinking, she made a pact with the devil, and the devil sent a monster into her head and bore her away. "That isn't it," I said. "It wasn't anything to do with that. You don't believe in the devil, anyway. It was just a stupid disease." He snapped out of his reverie with such a wretchedness upon him that I embraced him. I was six or seven inches taller than him by this time and his scrawny head with its wild wisps of grey hair lay against my chest and he sobbed. The lights of the city—Malabar Hill far away, the Queen's Necklace of

Marine Drive curving towards us—hung around us like a noose.

Back then I was partial to science fiction novels. There was a European novel, Polish, I think, about a planet that could bring people's thoughts to life. Think of your dead wife, and there she is in your bed. Think of a monster, and it will crawl into your brain, through your ear. That sort of thing.

Lights like a noose. These were words that came to mind as my father wept on my breast. I should have been more careful with my thoughts. I should have stayed with him that night, but I wanted to be alone, I wanted to sit and stand and walk in Ameer Merchant's rooms and breathe in the past, before it changed for ever. I should have wondered why he told me to turn off the fan as I left him sitting on his bed in his stripey nightsuit. No moon, and stenchy air. I should have stayed with him. The darkness of the city fell around him like a noose.

Some people can sleep under a moving fan and some just can't. Ormus Cama could turn the room upside down and rest under his fan like a man at a mechanical oasis. Vina, however, once told me she could never get rid of the idea that the damned thing would come loose and fly at her while she slept. She had nightmares of decapitation by those whirling blades. Personally, I always liked my fan. I would set the control at minimum and lie back with that slow familiar disturbance of air rolling softly over my skin. The disturbance that calmed. It made me dream of lying stretched out at the edge of an equatorial ocean, lapped by tides warmer than blood. My father was the opposite. "Doesn't matter how hot it is," Vivvy Merchant said. "The dratted downdraft induces a cold and tremulous sensation. Shivers my timbers, in sum."

Because I knew this about him, I turned off the fan without argument and left him by himself, left him to choose between the living and the dead, which was an easy choice, I guess, when Ameer was among the ranks of the expired, while the cohorts of the extant included only me. Love is more than death, or is it. There are those who say that the songsmith Orpheus was a coward because he refused to die for love, because instead of joining Eurydice in the afterlife he tried to drag her back to the life before; which was against nature, and so failed. Judged by this standard, my father was a braver man than the Thracian lyre player, for in his pursuit of Ameer he sought no special privileges from the guardians of the hereafter, he requested no return tickets from the monsters at the gates. But Eurydice and Orpheus were childless, and my parents were not.

I am the one who has to live with the choice my father made.

O Nissy Poe with your pendant mother in the goats' shed in Virginia long ago. Vina, we are linked by the thing we have seen, by the burden we have to bear. They didn't want to see us growing up. They didn't love us enough to wait. Suppose we hadn't turned out okay? Suppose we needed them? Suppose a thousand things and a thing.

Murder is a crime of violence against the murdered person. Suicide is a crime of violence against those who remain alive.

THE SERVANTS woke me early and took me to his bedroom. They clustered in the doorway, wide-eyed, driven half mad by what they saw, like Goya figures at a witches' sabbath, goggling in fascinated terror at the Goat. V.V. Merchant was hanging from the ceiling fan. Lights like a noose. He had used the flex from a standard lamp to fashion the instrument of his ending. He was rotating slowly, turning in the breeze. This is what got to me, broke through my reserve, prevented me from suppressing my feelings and casting a cold eye on the event: that somebody had come in here and switched on the fan. "Who did it?" I shrieked. "Who turned the damn thing on?"

"Sahib, it was hot, sahib," said the Goya figures. "Sahib, and there is the question of the smell."

HE HAD never really believed in their separation, always hoped to win her back. One day she would wake up, he imagined, and wonder why he wasn't in the bed beside her, she would see the error of her ways. That mattered, her seeing the error of her ways, because the Ameer he wanted back was the woman he'd married, not the cynical Mammon worshipper who had joined forces with Piloo Doodhwala. His own grievous fault caused him much daily torment. In his determination to break his gambling addiction, he had gone so far as to ask for my help. What he wanted was for me to become his bookmaker, and so I opened a book. When the cardplaying bug bit him, we played cards. Evening after evening of matchstick poker. I would make entries in the book each time we played, and kept an exact tally of his matchstick losses, which were, as ever, heavy. As for the racetrack, he managed to keep away from it, except on gymkhana days when families were welcome. Then I would accompany him, having made sure he was carrying no money, and instead of making bets we would take photographs of the horses he fancied. If he backed a winner we kept the photograph and pasted it into the book alongside a note of the odds; if not, we ripped it up and hurled it into a trash can as if it were a useless betting slip from the Tote. However, details of these "losses" were also entered in the book of his withdrawal from addiction. When he wanted to bet on the weather, I took the bet. He would see two flies on a windowpane and want to bet on which of them would take off first. As he went about town he would often get into disputes about cricket scores, movie credits, the authorship of songs, and instead of betting real money, he would ring me, and I would enter the bet in the book, afterwards adding a note saying whether he was right or wrong. In this way, very slowly, he had cured himself. The fantasy bets in my little copybook—which was yellow and bore, on the cover, the legend *Globe Copy* and a picture of a saturnine ringed planet—gradually weaned him off the real thing. Each month there were fewer entries for me to make, until at last there came a month in which I was not required to make any entries at all. He took the book and showed it to Ameer. "It's over," he said. "Why not give Piloo the bum's rush and we can resume?"

"You're right about one thing," she told him. "It's over, that's for sure." Two weeks later the tumour made its appearance. Six weeks after that she was dead.

Sometimes it's just over and you can't make it all right. Justification by works: an overrated idea. There are the dumpers and there are the dumped, and if you fall into the latter category no amount of fantasy gambling can save you.

In my life I have done my share of dumping (mostly women) and have not often been the spurned party. Except, of course, that my father—for whom Ameer's last rejection was perhaps even more painful than her death—strung himself up and left me dangling. Thus making himself both dumper and dumpee. Except, also, that Vina always turned away from me whenever her love of Ormus, her addiction to him, her Ormus habit, required her attention.

But even Ormus Cama had to learn what it felt like to be cast out, fourth functional, dispensable; to be exiled beyond an unbreachable pale.

CHAPTER EIGHT

The Decisive Moment

Let us now praise unjustly neglected men. The first permanent photograph was taken in 1826, in Paris, by Joseph Nicéphore Niépce, but his place in our collective memory has been usurped by his later collaborator, Louis Daguerre, who sold their invention, their magic box, the "caméra," to the French government after Niépce's death. It must therefore be stated without equivocation that the celebrated daguerreotype plates could not have been created without Niépce's scientific knowledge, which far exceeded that of his partner. Nor was the art of photography Niépce's only child; for he was also the creator of the mighty pyréolophore, or combustion engine. Truly, a father of the New.

What was it like, that First Photograph, forerunner of the Age of the Image? Technically: a direct positive image on a treated pewter plate, requiring many long hours of exposure time. Its subject: nothing more elevated than the view from the Nicéphorean workroom window. Walls, sloping roofs, a tower wearing a conical hat, and open countryside beyond. All is dull, still, dim. No hint here that this is the first quiet note of what will become a thundering symphony, or it may be more honest to say a deafening cacophony. But (I switch metaphors in my excitement) a floodgate has been opened, an unstoppable torrent of pictures is to follow, haunting and forgettable, hideous and beautiful, pornographic and revelatory, pictures that will create the very idea of the Modern, that will overpower language itself, and cover and distort and define the earth, like water, like gossip, like democracy.

Niépce, I bow my head to you. Great Nicéphore, I doff my beret. If Daguerre—like the Titan Epimetheus—was the one who opened this Pandoran box, unleashing the ceaseless click and snap, the interminable flash and sprocket of photography, still it was you, great Anarch!, who stole the gods' gift of permanent vision, of the transformation of sight into memory, of the actual into the eternal—that is, the gift of immortality—and bestowed it upon mankind. Where are you now, O Titanic seer, Prometheus of film? If the gods have punished you, if you're chained to a pillar high up on an Alp while a vulture munches your guts, take comfort in the news. This just in: the gods are dead, but photography is alive & kicking. Olympus? Pah! It's just a camera now.

PHOTOGRAPHY IS my way of understanding the world.

When my mother died I photographed her, cold in bed. Her profile was shockingly gaunt, but still beautiful. Brightly lit against a darkness, with shadows gathering great scoops from her cheeks, she resembled an Egyptian queen. I thought of the female pharaoh Hatshepsut, whom Vina also mirrored, and then it hit me. *My mother looked like Vina;* or, as Vina might have looked, had she grown old and died in her bed. When I made eight-by-ten prints of the photograph I liked best, I wrote "Hat Cheap Suit" on the back with a thick black marking pen.

When my father died I took his picture before they cut him down. I asked to be left alone with him and used a roll of film. Most of the shots avoided his face. I was more interested in the way the shadows fell across his dangling body, and the shadow he himself cast in the early light, a long shadow for a smallish man.

I thought of these acts as respectful.

After they were gone I walked the streets of the city they had both loved in their different, irreconcilable ways. Though that love had often oppressed and stifled me, I now wanted it for myself, wanted to have my parents back by loving what they loved and so becoming what they had been. And photography was my means of gaining an education in their love. So I photographed the workers at the Cuffe Parade development site as they walked with perfect, nonchalant balance along the beam of a crane a hundred feet above ground. I seized for myself the maelstrom of straw baskets at Crawford Market, and took possession, too, of the inert figures who were everywhere, sleeping on the hard pillows of the sidewalks, their faces turned towards urinous walls, beneath the lurid movie posters of buxom goddesses with sofa-cushion lips. I photographed political slogans on *art dekho* buildings, and children grinning out through the toe of the giant Old Woman's Shoe. It was easy to be a lazy photographer in Bombay. It was easy to take an interesting picture and almost impossible to take a good one. The city seethed, gathered to stare, turned its back and didn't care. By showing me everything it told me nothing. Wherever I pointed my camera—*Juicy that? Juicy* that?—I seemed to glimpse something worth having, but usually it was just something excessive: too colourful, too grotesque, too apt. The city was expressionistic, it screamed at you, but it wore a domino mask. There were whores, tightrope walkers, transsexuals, movie stars, cripples, billionaires, all of them exhibitionists, all of them obscure. There was the thrilling, appalling infinity of the crowd at Churchgate Station in the morning, but that same infinity made the crowd unknowable; there were the fish being sorted on the pier at the Sassoon dock, but all the activity showed me nothing: it was just activity. Lunch runners carried the city's tiffin boxes to their destinations, but the boxes guarded their mystery. There was too much money, too much poverty, too much nakedness, too much disguise, too much anger, too much vermilion, too much purple. There were too many dashed hopes and narrowed minds. There was far, far too much light.

I began to look at the darkness instead. This led me towards the use of illusion. I composed pictures with sharply delineated areas of light and dark, composed them with such manic care that the light area of one image corresponded precisely to the blackness in another. In the darkroom I had set up for myself in my father's old apartment I blended these images. The composite pictures that resulted were sometimes dazzling in their mixed perspectives, often confused, sometimes unreadable. I preferred the composite darknesses. For a time I began to shoot deliberately into the dark, picking human life out of lightlessness, delineating it with as little light as I could get away with.

I decided not to go to college but to concentrate on my photographs. I also wanted to move. I could not bear to go on living in those two separate sets of rooms under the same roof, within the schizoid structure of my parents' fatal unhappiness. Then the much larger Cama apartment was put up for sale by the firm of Cox's & King's, acting as local agents for the new Lady Methwold, who had no plans to return. I got hold of the keys and went to take a look. I shut the door behind me and for a while I did not turn on any lights, but allowed the darkness to take what shape it chose. As my eyes adjusted, I saw soft Himalayas of dust-sheeted furniture ribbed faintly with the sly light that had sidled in between the closed imperfect shutters. In the library I stood beside the shrouded bodies of Darius's desk and chair and peered at the shelves of naked, staring books. It was the books that at first glance seemed dead, like withered leaves. The furniture, beneath the winter of the white dust sheets, looked as if it were simply waiting for the return of spring. I was intrigued to note that the apartment did not trouble me; not even this room in which a world had ended retained any power to move. I had seen other such rooms. I pointed my camera, and working very quickly, feeling an eagerness take hold of me, I took several shots.

After I moved into the apartment, however, it was the books that came to life and spoke to me. Darius's lifetime of learning was of no long-term interest to his sons, for all Ormus Cama's noble funeral thoughts and Cyrus's high, if warped, intelligence; so it—the library, the old man's unquiet shade—adopted me instead. On an impulse I bought it along with the apartment, and began to read.

For a while I became a photographer of exits. It isn't easy to take photographs of strangers' funerals. People get annoyed. Yet it interested me that Indian funeral practices dealt so openly, so directly, with the physicality of the corpse. The body on the pyre or on the *dokhma,* or in its close-sewn Muslim shroud. Christians were the only community to conceal their dead in boxes. I didn't know what it meant, but I knew how it looked. Coffins forbade intimacy. In my stolen photographs—for the photographer must be a thief, he must steal instants of other people's time to make his own tiny eternities—it was this intimacy I sought, the closeness of the living and the dead. The secretary staring through eyes made garish with grief at the body of his great master dressed in fire. The son standing in an open grave, holding his father's shrouded head in his cupped hand, laying it tenderly upon deep earth.

Sandalwood plays its perfumed part in all these rites. Sandalwood chips in the Muslim bier, in the Parsi fire, on the Hindu pyre. The odour of death is an intimacy too far. But a camera cannot smell. Dispensing with nosegays, it can stick its nose as far in as it is permitted to go, it can intrude. Often I had to turn on my heels and run, pursued by insults and stones. Murderer! Assassin! the mourners shouted after me, as if I were responsible for the death they mourned. And there was a truth in the insults. A photographer shoots. Like a gunman standing by a little gate in a prime minister's garden, like an assassin in a hotel lobby, he must line up a clear shot, he must try not to miss. He has a target, and there are crosshairs in his eyepiece. He wants light from his subjects, he takes their light and their darkness too, which is to say, their lives. Yet I also thought of these pictures, these forbidden images, as gestures of respect. The camera's respect has nothing to do with seriousness, sanctimony, privacy, or even taste. It has to do with attention. It has to do with clarity, of the actual, of the imagined. And there is also the issue of honesty, a virtue which everyone routinely extols and recommends, until it is directed, in all its uncushioned force, at themselves.

Honesty is not the best policy in life. Only, perhaps, in art.

Deaths are not the only exits, of course, and in my new rôle as exit photographer I sought also to document more quotidian departures. At the airport, spying upon the sorrows of parting, I sought out the single dry-eyed member of a weeping throng. Outside the city's cinemas I examined the faces of audiences emerging from dreams into the pungency of the real, with the illusion still hanging in their eyes. I tried to find narratives, mysteries, in the come and go at the doors of great hotels. After a time I no longer knew why I was doing these things, and it was at this point, I believe, that the pictures started to improve, because they were no longer about myself. I had learned the secret of becoming invisible, of disappearing into the work.

Invisibility was simply extraordinary. Now, when I went in search of exits, I could walk right up to the edge of a grave and photograph an argument between those who wanted flowers scattered over the body and those who argued that the religion permitted no such effete indulgences—or I might eavesdrop on a quayside family quarrel at the docks in order to capture the moment when the newlywed young daughter of old parents, a girl who had refused an arranged marriage and insisted on a "love match," stormed away from her disapproving mother and boarded the waiting steamer, clinging to her awkwardly grinning, weak-moustachioed disaster of a husband, and set out into her new life carrying the burden of a remorse she would never be able to shed—or I might sidle into any of the secret moments we hide from the world, a last kiss before parting, a last piss before starting, and snap happily away. I was too excited by my power to be scrupulous about its use. The inhibited photographer should set down his camera, I thought, and never work again.

As MY parents' sole heir, I had become a young gentleman of means. The family business, Merchant & Merchant, with its thick folder of architectural contracts and its important interest in the Cuffe Parade and Nariman Point developments, I sold for a handsome sum to the consortium of developers headed by Piloo Doodhwala. The Orpheum cinema, now flourishing under new management, I likewise disposed of to the glinting Mr. Sisodia, who had already leased a lot in Film City and founded the Orpheum movie studios that would make his reputation and fortune. "Or or always welcome at the awfu awfu Orpheum," Mr. Sisodia assured me as I signed the papers. But I had washed my hands of my parents' work. In these old stories, I sought no further part. I snapped Sisodia's picture—thick black glasses, cadaverous teeth, Methwold-hairless head, ruthless, charming, insincere, every inch the embryonic movie mogul—and quickly took my leave.

BY THE start of the 1970s the city's air had become badly polluted, and public commentators, ready as ever to allegorize, called it a sign of the filth in the national atmosphere.

The city's doctors noted an alarming rise in migraine sufferers, and the oculists revealed that many patients had started complaining of double vision, though they couldn't remember bumping their heads, and there was no other evidence of concussion. Wherever you went you saw men and women standing in the street scratching their heads, frowning. There was a growing general sense of disorder, of things being out of kilter, off the rails. *It shouldn't be this way.*

Bombay had become Mumbai, by order of its rulers, the MA party, of which, it unsurprisingly emerged, Shri Piloo Doodhwala was a principal benefactor and power broker. I dropped in on Persis Kalamanja to complain about the new name. "And what are we supposed to call Trombay, then? 'Trumbai'? And how about the Back Bay? 'Backbai'? And what's to be done with Bollywood? I suppose it's 'Mollywood' now." But Persis had a bad headache and didn't laugh. "Something's going to happen," she said seriously. "I can feel the ground beginning to shift."

PERSIS HAD turned thirty. Her beauty, which had reached its full womanly bloom, had also become oddly asexual, neutered, in my opinion, by her development of an enigmatic little smile which I found almost insufferably pious. My sarcastic carpings aside, however, her saintly personality and the zeal with which she had joined her mother in a heavy programme of good works had earned her much respect all over town, while her continued celibacy, at first the subject of giggles and whispers, then a cause for pity, nowadays engendered in most of us a kind of unholy awe. There was something otherworldly about Persis these days, and I was not surprised when her mystical side, which lies beneath all our surfaces like a fault, began to manifest itself, and she took to making gloomy predictions of the future. She sat dressed in simple homespun amid the splendours of "Dil Kush" and foretold doom, and if she was our Cassandra, then maybe—just maybe—Bombay was about to fall, like Troy.

Ours was an unlikely intimacy, a friendship of opposites, born of loss. After Vina and Ormus had gone, Persis and I gravitated towards each other, like disciples after the departure of their masters, like echoes of a silenced sound. But as the years passed we became each other's bad habit. I disapproved of her self-denying saint act. No more old maid, go get laid, I would tell her in my best social-butterfly manner; enough with the soup kitchens, get into some hot water of your own. For her part, she scolded me for my many undoubted failings, and in this unexpected way we grew fond, even inordinately fond, of each other. She never gave the slightest sign of wanting anything from me other than platonic, brother and sister friendship, and fortunately that madonna rictus of hers, her smile like a holy sword, had chopped off my own desire at the root.

It was the day of the kite festival. The rooftops were already filling up with children and adults, launching their technicolor diamonds into the air. I had arrived at "Dil Kush" with my own selection of kites and *manja* reels, including the kite fighters' special battle thread, black gut dipped in a suspension full of tiny shards of broken glass. *Kala manja.* How did a family that must have originally got its name by selling such a ferocious weapon, the H-bomb of the kite world, produce a namby-pamby like you, I asked Persis, who was in an uncharacteristically foul humour today, too sour even to smile her infuriating smile. "I guess I just looked past the dirty kites to the pure heavens above," she snapped, meaning it. She was worried about something, more worried than she was willing to admit.

Dolly Kalamanja came into the room with her house guest, a tall, sloping Frenchman in his sixties, wearing an absurd trilby pulled down so low it all but touched his nose. He was armed with a small Leica pocket camera, and eager for the roof. "Persis, come, no," cried Dolly. "Don't just sit on and miss the fun." But Persis shook her head mutinously. We left her by herself and made our ascent.

Kite dogfights raged overhead. I hurled my warriors into the fray and slew my foes, one, two, three. In the crowded sky it was impossible to be sure whose kite attacked, whose fell. They became unidentified flying objects. One stopped thinking of them as having owners. They were their own masters, kites-errant, duelling to the death.

Dolly had half introduced me to the Frenchman on the stairs to the roof, calling him simply "our Mr. H.," showing off her bit of French. *"Notre très cher Monsieur Ach.'"* I noticed with some annoyance that he hardly ever looked up at the sky, and paid no attention whatsoever to my victories. The rooftops—flat or sloping, ridged or domed, and all crowded with people—held his attention entirely. He took small steps, this way, that way, until he settled. Then, frozen in a half stoop, he waited, Leica at the ready. His patience, his stillness, was inhuman, predatory. I understood that I was watching a master of invisibility at work, an artist, an occultist. He would dissolve while I watched him, he became simply not-there, an absence, until the little scene he was stalking satisfied him, and then, click, he would fire off a single shot and re-materialize. He must indeed be a master marksman, I thought, to need no more than one. Then he would make his little dance of steps again, settle again, vanish again, click, and so on. Watching him, I lost my favourite kite. Someone else's *kala manja* cut me down. I didn't care. I had seen enough to know the Frenchman's name.

At that moment the earthquake began. My first thought, when I felt the tremor, was that this was an impossibility, a piece of make-believe, a mistake, because we did not have earthquakes in Bombay. In those years when many parts of the country had begun to shake, Bombayites had prided themselves on being quake-free. Good communal relations and good solid ground, we boasted. No fault lines under our town. But now Piloo Doodhwala's MA boys were stoking the fires of discord, and the city had begun to shake.

It was what Persis had foretold. There could be no denying that she had developed some sort of sixth sense, some preternatural sensitivity to the treacheries of life. In China they were predicting earthquakes by watching the behaviour of cattle, sheep and goats. In Bombay, apparently, one now needed only to keep Persis Kalamanja under observation.

The truth is that it was not a bad earthquake, low on the scale and of short duration. But there was widespread damage, because the city was unprepared. Many shanties, hutments, *jopadpatti* lean-to shacks and slum dwellings fell, as well as three tenement *chawls* and a couple of derelict villas on Cumballa Hill. Cracks appeared in large structures, including the façade of the Orpheum cinema, and in roads and underground drains, and there was much smashed furniture and glass. There were fires. The sea wall at Hornby

Vellard broke and for the first time in more than a century the tides swept in through the Great Breach, and the Mahalaxmi racetrack and the Willingdon Club's golf course were both swamped under a foot of briny water until the damage was repaired. When the sea retreated it left behind its mysteries: unknown fishes, lost children, pirate flags.

An unspecified number of construction workers and kite fighters fell to their deaths. A dozen or so citizens were crushed beneath falling masonry. The tram lines twisted madly up from the roads, and after that they were ripped up for good. For three days the city seemed hardly to move. Offices remained closed, the monstrous traffic jams vanished, pedestrians were few and far between. In the open spaces, however, crowds gathered, huddling far from the buildings, but casting anxious glances, too, at the earth of the maidans, as if it had become an adversary, sly, malign.

In the months that followed, as Mrs. Gandhi's dictatorial Emergency tightened its grip, the national mood grew sombre and fearful. But the worst excesses of the Emergency occurred elsewhere; in Bombay it was the earthquake that people remembered, the earthquake that gave us the shock that shook our confidence in who we were and how we had chosen to live. An op-ed columnist of the local edition of *The Times of India* went so far as to wonder if the country might literally be breaking apart. "Long aeons ago," he reminded us, "India made a tryst with destiny, breaking away from the mighty southern proto-continent of Gondwanaland and linking her destiny to the northern landmass of Laurasia. The Himalaya mountains are the evidence of that coming together; they are the kiss that joined us to our fate. Is it a kiss that failed? Are these new movements of the earth the prelude to a titanic divorce? Will the Himalayas begin, very slowly, to shrink?" Eight hundred words of questions without answers, of traumatized predictions that India would become the "new Atlantis" as the waters of the Bay of Bengal and the Arabian Sea closed over the Deccan plateau. The paper's publication of so panicky a text indicated the depth of local concern.

ON THE roof, during the few, but impossibly elongated, seconds of the quake, the great French photographer M. Henri

Hulot turned his camera perversely towards the sky. All over town terrified kite flyers had let go of their controlling reels. The heavens were full of dying kites, kites nosediving towards the earth, kites being smashed in mid-air by collisions with other kites, kites being torn to shreds by the boiling winds and by the Dionysiac madness of their sudden freedom, that fatal liberty acquired in the midst of catastrophe and then stolen away again, almost at once, by the inexorable gravitational pull of the cracking earth below. Click, went the Leica. The result is the famous image "Earthquake 1971," in which the tearing mid-air explosion of a single kite tells us everything about the unseen mayhem below. The air becomes a metaphor for the earth.

"Dil Kush" was a solidly constructed mansion, its foundations driven deep into the living rock, and so it trembled but did not break. One of the water tanks on the roof did split, however, and I pulled Hulot away from the path of the gushing water, which he gave no sign of having seen. Dolly Kalamanja was already running downstairs, shouting out her daughter's name. The Frenchman thanked me courteously, touching his hat, then tapping his camera with a self-deprecating shrug.

Downstairs, Persis sat sobbing amid broken glass, inconsolable, like a homespun princess surrounded by opulent jewels, like a lonely woman amid the ruins of her memories. The earthquake had shaken up feelings which she had tried to bury long before, and now they were pouring out of her, like water from a burst tank. Dolly flapped helplessly around her with a large handkerchief, mopping at her face. Persis brushed her mother away as if she were a moth.

"Everybody leaves," she wailed. "They all go away and we're left here to wither and die by ourselves. No wonder the whole place cracks to bits and falls down, it's all shrivelled up and old and on its own."

M. Hulot, clearing his throat, extending an arm, not knowing whether to touch her or not, allowed his fingers to flutter helplessly by her shoulder. A second moth, which she was too polite to swat. He essayed gallantry. "Mademoiselle, I assure you, the only rotten fruit here is imported from France."

She laughed, a little crazily. "You are wrong, monsieur.

You may be over sixty, but me, I am five thousand years old, five thousand years of stagnation and decay, and now I am going to pieces and everyone is going away." She whirled towards me then, and glared savagely. "You, why don't you also go? He has been trying to leave for years," she snarled at the alarmed Hulot, with sudden, shocking vehemence. "Always photoing exits. What are all these ways out but rehearsals for his own? All he wants is to run away to his beloved Europe, his Amrika, but as yet he hasn't found the guts."

"You take photographs?" Hulot asked me. I nodded, dumbly. I could never have imagined that I could have a chance to discuss my obsession with such a figure. Now that the chance had come it was impossible to take it, because Persis Kalamanja was on fire.

"Living in that place of dead men, dumb men, killers and evacuees," Persis jeered in a loud, unsteady voice. "What for? To be their lost shadow, their last camp follower, like one of those club bearers or ancient fogeys who are sitting waiting for the British to return?"

"This is a lot to deduce from a change of address," I said, trying to make light of her hostility, of the thing that had burst out of her depths and attacked me for the crime of not being another man; of living in his home and not being he.

"You were born with everything," she raged, having moved beyond all restraint, "and you're throwing it away. Family business, everything. Next you will throw us away also. Of course! You are leaving, but you are so confused you don't know it. Walking the city streets with your stupid camera, thinking you're saying hullo when really it's one long goodbye. Arré, you're mixed up about everything, Umeed, I'm sorry. You want so much to be loved but you don't know how to let people love you. What do you want, hein? Plenty-women-lots-of-money? White birdies, black chickies, pounds sterling, U.S. greenbacks? Will that satisfy you? Is it what you're looking for?"

Even as she said the unsayable, the unforgivable, I was unsaying her words, forgiving her, because I knew I was taking another man's beating. I was struck by the fact that the questions she was hurling at me were such close variants of what Yul Singh had asked Ormus Cama years before. And as she asked it I knew that my answer was the same as his. It was an answer I couldn't bring myself to give her, but she saw it on my face anyway, and snorted with contempt.

"Always second in line," she said. "And if you never get her? Then what?"

I had no answer. Fortunately, as things turned out, I didn't need one.

M. HULOT asked to see my work, and we made our escape. I drove him through the chaos of the city—the fallen trees, the collapsed balconies like soldiers' chevron stripes, the demented birds, the screaming—to what was now my apartment. He spoke uninhibitedly about his own technique; about the "pre-composition" of an image in the imagination, and then the intense stillness, the waiting for the decisive moment. He mentioned Bergson's idea of the self as "pure duration," *no longer situated under the sign of the permanence of the* cogito, *but in the intuition of the duration.* "Like a Japanese artist," he said. "An hour of being there before the empty canvas, learning the void, and then three seconds of strokes, *paf! paf!*, like swordsmanship, very exact. You want to go to the West," he said. "But I have learned most from the East."

I was surprised that a man as unassuming, as determinedly everyday as he, should speak so much about magic, about the "soul of the real," an oxymoron that reminded me of Darius Cama's "miracle of reason." "It was Balzac," Hulot said, "who told Nadar that photographs stripped away the subject's personality. The idea of the camera has always been closely related to the older, but parallel, idea of ghosts. The still camera, yes, and the film camera even more so."

There was a film he greatly admired, he said: *Ugetsu,* by the Japanese master Mizoguchi. A poor man is taken up by a great lady, kept in style and offered unimaginable delights, but she is a phantom. "It is easy for a film to convince us of this proposition so improbable, because on the screen, all are equally wraithlike, equally irreal." A more recent film, *Les Carabiniers* by Jean-Luc Godard, proved Balzac's point by extension. "Two young country boys go off to war, promising their girls that when they return they will bring back all the wonders of the world. They return, penniless, with nothing more than a battered suitcase to show for their adventures. But the girls do not excuse them, they want their promised wonders. The soldiers open the suitcase, and *voilà!* The Statue of Liberty, the Taj Mahal, the Sphinx, I don't know what other things beyond any price. The girls are completely satisfy; their beaux have kept their word. Afterwards the soldiers are killed: a machine gun in a cellar. What remains of them is the treasure they brought home. The wonders of the world.

"Picture postcards," he laughed. "The souls of things."

IN THE former library of Sir Darius Xerxes Cama, upon the same table at which Darius and William Methwold had pursued their studies, I spread out my portfolio for Hulot. The chandelier lay in pieces on the floor, and books had tumbled from the shelves. To keep myself busy while Hulot examined my pictures, I began to pick up the fallen volumes. I had been reading my way through the old texts and commentaries. The books in Greek and Sanskrit were beyond me, I readily admit, but the ones I could read had captured me, drawing me into their cosmos of savage divinity, of destiny that could be neither diluted nor avoided, but only heroically endured, because one's fate and one's nature were not separate things, only different words for the same phenomenon.

"Have you looked at the past?"

At first, lost in the contemplation of the fallen books, I didn't understand the Frenchman's question. Then in a rush I began to jabber about my father's photograph collection, about Haseler and Dayal. I was aware of how provincial I must sound, so, like an over-enthusiastic schoolboy, I dropped the more cosmopolitan names of Niépce and Talbot, of the daguerreotype and the calotype. I referred to Nadar's portraits, Muybridge's horses, Atget's Paris, Man Ray's surrealism; to *Life* magazine and *Picture Post.*

"Are you really so serious a young man?" he teased me, gravely. "Did you never see any dirty postcards or look for porno magazines?"

That made me blush, but then he became serious and changed my life, or rather allowed me to believe what I had not until then really dared to believe: that I could have the life I most desired. “You have understood something about attention and surprise,” he said. “Something of the double self of the photographer, the ruthless *tant-pis* killer and the giver of immortality also. But there is a danger of mannerism, what do you think.”

Of course, thank you, maestro. Mannerism, yes, a great danger, a terrible thing, I will be on my guard against it in future, maestro, be assured of it. Thank you. Attention, surprise. Exactly. These will be my watchwords. Have no fear.

He turned away from my babbling to look out of the high windows towards the Gateway, and changed the subject. “Your friend Persis is like many remarkable people I have met in Asia,” he said. “Her prediction of the tremor. Extraordinary, yes? It is perhaps her asceticism that has enabled her, that has opened her to such things. She is a seer without a camera, an *illuminée* of the decisive moment. It is quite normal after such a feat prodigious that there should be some uncontrollable emotional release.” He swung round to see how his statement had gone down, and caught me in the act of pulling a face. He roared with laughter. “Oho, you don’t like that,” he observed.

An answer was expected, and so, even though I had no explanation for Persis’s astonishing prescience, I took a sternly rationalist line. “Excuse me, monsieur, but hereabouts we are plagued by godness masquerading as goodness. The supernatural level is our lifetime detention centre. And every so often our deep spiritualism leads us to massacre one another like wild beasts. Excuse me, but some of us aren’t falling for it, some of us are trying to break free into the real.”

“Good,” he said, mildly. “Good. Find your enemy. When you know what you’re against you have taken the first step to discovering what you’re for.”

He made as if to go. I offered him my services as a driver, but he declined them. He wanted to stalk the shaken city for the images he was pre-composing in his mind. As he left, he gave me his card. “Call me when you come,” he said. “Maybe I am able to be of a little help.”

M. HULOT had told me ghost stories: the spectre of a Japanese woman, the postcards of the dead *carabiniers*. Images on film were the ghosts in the machine. Three days after the earthquake, I saw a ghost of my own; not a photograph, but a genuine apparition, a revenant from the past. I was at home at Apollo Bunder, participating in the great clear-up of broken glass and tumbled books. The phones weren't working and there were power outages—"load shedding"—during the hottest hours of the day. I was sweating and short-tempered and not at all prepared for a loud banging on the apartment's front door. I opened up with a scowl on my face and found myself facing the phantom of Vina Apsara, which looked as shocked as I.

"This isn't right," she said, clutching her brow, as if she had a headache. "This isn't supposed to be you."

It seemed that ghosts could grow up. She was ten years older than when I'd last seen her: a ravishing twenty-six. Her hair exploded from her head in a huge halo of frizz (it was the first Afro I'd ever seen), and she wore the wised-up, not remotely innocent, expression that was mandatory for the "alternative" women of the period, especially singers who were politically involved. But Vina was always good at putting out mixed signals. As well as the single black glove of the black American radicals, she had painted the *Om* symbol in scarlet on her right cheek and wore an English dress from a boutique called The Witch Flies High, one of the dark wisps of Indianized occult-chic couture characteristic of the period, which very approximately covered a part of her long and outrageous body. Her dark skin had a burnished quality to it: a heightening. I did not know it then, but it was the gleam created by the brilliant gaze of the public eye, the first rough licks of the tigerish tongue of fame.

"You're years too late for him," I said, a little too cruelly. "Nobody waits for ever, not even for you."

She pushed past me into the apartment, as if it belonged to her. Knowing she came from nowhere, had nothing but what she made of herself, she had learned to treat the whole world as her possession, and I, like the rest of the planet, meekly acquiesced, and acknowledged her dominion over me and mine.

"What a train wreck," she said, surveying the smashed apartment. "Did anybody get out of this alive?"

Her delivery was unimpressed-tough-broad, but her voice

trembled briefly. That was when I understood that the earthquake had jolted Vina into the realization that she was still tied to Ormus, that he was still the only man for her, and the fear that he might be dead or injured had overridden all the uncertainties that had driven her away and led her to create her hard-boiled persona. The earthquake hurled her on to a plane and brought her back to Bombay, to Ormus's door; only it wasn't his door any longer. Other upheavals had placed me in his space. I made her coffee, and slowly, as if rediscovering an old habit, she stopped striking attitudes and metamorphosed back into the girl I had known and, yes, damn it, loved.

She had completed her apprenticeship in the coffee bars and clubs of London, from beatnik folk dives like Jumpy's to the bubbling psychedelia of Middle Earth and UFO, and then moved to New York. There, she went down a blind alley to Folkville, where she shared star billing with Joan Baez but felt alien and ill at ease. She then disgusted and lost her folkie fans by moving into the "mainstream" and doing a season in a sequinned fishtail dress (as it happens, one of the outfits she had stolen from my mother), opening for the Supremes at the Copacabana, because she wanted to be the first brown woman supporting the first black women to play that exalted and conservative gig. Also because she wanted to upstage Diana Ross; which she did. After that she changed direction again, becoming an early pioneer of the trail that led from the Wrong End Café to Sam's Pleasure Island and Amos Voight's Slaughterhouse, where the worlds of art, film and music met and fucked, while Voight mildly, ruthlessly, watched.

She was becoming notorious as an unashamed exhibitionist—a reputation that her largely absent Witch dress did nothing to disprove. To wear such a garment in Bombay could be dangerous, but Vina didn't care. She was an ornery loudmouth too. She appeared regularly on the covers of underground magazines, those new cracks in the media façade caused by the Western youthquake. By pouring out her rage and passion in those journals of narcotic typography, and posing pneumatically for their porno-liberal pix, she became one of the first sacred monsters of the counterculture, an aggressive iconoclast, half genius, half egomaniac, who lost no opportunity to roar and suck and boo and preen and demolish and cheerlead and revolutionise and innovate and flash and boast and scold. The truth is that this noisy-noisome, pestilential-pest act of hers had set her singing career back. Nowadays such fuck-you, in-your-face aggression would be merely conventional, almost necessary for the wannabe rockette; but in those days such battles had not yet been won. People could still be, and often were, insulted and shocked. You could shoot yourself in the foot.

So while her marvellous voice ensured her a full slate of bookings, her bad mouth lost her many of them. The Copacabana engagement, for example, was terminated after one week, when she casually referred to her stuffed-shirt audience as "dead Kennedys." The United States, still at war both with itself and in Indochina, had been plunged into deep mourning by the freak double killing of President Bobby Kennedy and his elder brother and predecessor, ex-President Jack, both slain by a single bullet fired by a delusional Palestinian gunman. This was the so-called magic bullet which bounced around the lobby of the Ambassador Hotel, L.A., whining like a demented hornet, and ended up scoring an appalling double hit. In that grief-charged atmosphere, when hundreds of thousands of Americans reported sledgehammer migraine headaches and violent dizzy spells, and people stood dazed on street corners murmuring "It shouldn't be this way," Vina was probably lucky that her gibe only lost her a job. She could have been run out of town on a rail. She could have been lynched.

Once, casually, she had married and divorced, and the list of her lovers was long. Interestingly, though she liked to hint at bisexuality, the list was exclusively male. Professionally unconventional Vina was a traditionalist in this area, at least, though her promiscuity was extreme even by the standards of the times.

When Vina arrived on my doorstep, her celebrity as a singer had not spread outside a medium-size circle of cognoscenti; she had belatedly been signed to a recording contract by Yul Singh's Colchis label, but thus far word of her talents had not travelled back east. Nor was her mouthy notoriety locally known. Distraught, anonymous, she stretched out on one of my sofas and smoked a joint. I am ashamed to say that I had never previously been offered what I still quaintly called a "reefer," and its effect on me was rapid and potent. I lay down beside her, and she drew close. We stayed like that for a long time, allowing the distant past to make its connection with the present, letting the silence erase the intervening years. It grew dark. The power was back, but I switched on no lights.

"I'm not too young any more, am I," I said at last.

"No," she said, kissing my chest. "Am I too old?"

AFTER WE made love—in the bed in which Ormus Cama had been conceived—she wept, then slept, then awoke to weep again. Like many women of the time, she had used abortion as a supplementary birth control technique, and the fourth time—she had recently learned—had left her barren. Unable to have children, and following her normal practice of drawing universal conclusions from her own idiosyncratic experience, she had responded by developing a great polemic against Western birth control methods, a jeremiad against the scientific manipulation of women's bodies for men's pleasure, which hit a number of bull's-eyes and then turned into a cockeyed eulogy of the wisdom of the more "natural" habits of the women of the East. At some point during that night, when I confess my mind was on other matters, she muttered that her main reason for returning had been her desire to go out into the villages and learn the secrets of natural birth control from the women of India. This remark, made in profound seriousness, had the effect of making me laugh. No doubt it was the residual effect of the hashish, but I laughed until the tears ran down my face. "And when you've finished praising them for being so sophisticated about rhythm and withdrawal and all," I cackled, "they'll ask you if you can spare a diaphragm, and a few rubbers too." By the time I had finished making this observation, Vina was fully dressed, operatically choleric and on her way out.

"That isn't why you came, anyway," I giggled loudly. "I'm sorry you had a wasted trip." She threw something fragile at me from the doorway, but I was used to broken pottery and glassware. "You're a low-life runt, Rai," she snarled. I didn't know then about her penchant for this type of behaviour, the easy conquests followed by the vicious scorn. It seemed to me that, once again, I was taking someone else's knocks, being punished for occupying another man's space.

I sobered up once she'd gone. When a woman who obsesses you hands down harsh judgements, they go deep. And when the chance to make those judgements come true offers itself, maybe you take them, maybe you live down to her low opinion of you and spend the rest of your life with the no-longer-deniable accusation stabbing you in the heart.

AFTER ONE night with Ormus Cama, Vina flew away for a decade. After one night with me, she took off again. One measly night, and then poof! Do you see why she felt like a phantom to me, why her visit felt like that of the ghostly sisters in *The Manuscript Found at Saragossa,* who can make love to the hero only in his dreams? And yet this night, at the end of which she went away almost before she had arrived, changed everything. It was the night Persis's prophecy came true, and I, too, came unstuck from India and began to drift away.

Withdrawal, the method of prophylaxis favoured in the Indian villages, which has done so much to control the exploding Indian population, was subsequently recommended by Vina Apsara to her American and European sisters in a series of controversial interventions. I am at least able to confirm that she herself remained a devotee, if not entirely a mistress, of the art.

THE OFFICIAL version of Vina's one-night-only return engagement in Bombay, when she neither sang nor shot her mouth off but merely rekindled an old flame, then poured cold water all over him and flew off again, leaving him drenched and quaking, was somewhat different. All her life, the story she told everyone, perhaps even Ormus Cama, was that when she heard the news of the Bombay earthquake she had indeed rushed to the airport, possessed by the sudden realization of her undimmed love for a man she had not seen for ten long years. "Just my luck," she would say. "Most romantic thing I ever did, and he wasn't even there."

But the thirty-six-hour trip had not been wasted. By a

stroke of good fortune, she had been able to meet in her hotel suite with that great honorary Indian Mother Teresa, a true saint, who had endorsed Vina's views wholeheartedly. A meeting with leading Indian feminists had also been arranged. These impressive women told her about the rumoured plans of Mr. Sanjay Gandhi to force sterilisation upon an unwilling population. Vina launched a pre-emptive strike against this atrocity in the making. "Once again Western technology and medicine go hand in hand with tyranny and oppression," she said in a celebrated press conference. "We must not let this man conquer Indian women's wombs." In those days the West's love affair with Indian mysticism was at its height, so her statements gained widespread support.

To return to the personal, to the love story the whole world was happy to hear a thousand times and a time, the tale of the birth of the immortal VTO: At the end of her brief stay (Vina would say), she had been granted a kind of miracle. Just before leaving for the new Sahar International Airport, having a few minutes to waste, she had turned on the radio and twiddled the knob, looking for the Voice of America wavelength. All of a sudden she heard a familiar voice. "My heart stopped, except that it also went crazy, like a horse," she'd explain, in a charming self-contradiction, which she would usually follow with another. "I couldn't bear for the song to finish, but I also needed it to stop at once, so I could hear what the DJ said." The song was called "Beneath Her Feet," one half of a double-A-side release (the flip, which was driving the disc towards #1, was called "It Shouldn't Be This Way"). The band was named Rhythm Center, on Colchis.

"Ridiculous, huh?" she told a thousand and one journalists over the years. "After all that time it turned out we were signed to the same label. I guess we both owe Mr. Yul Singh a great big thank-you."

Persis complained of having been erased from the record by Ormus; I could say the same of Vina's treatment of me. But in truth it was different between us. True, I couldn't cure myself of her, and that was the same as what Persis felt for Ormus. But Ormus had forgotten Persis Kalamanja; whereas Vina, whatever she said or didn't say, kept coming back to wherever I was to be found. I was her favourite thorn; she couldn't get me out from under her skin.

MAYBE SHE really did hear Ormus on the radio. I'll buy into that, what the hell, I like fairy tales too. She heard him sing his great love song to her, heard him clean across the world, and felt a loop in time closing, felt herself slip back a decade, moving towards a crossroads she had reached once before; or, like a railway train, approaching an old familiar set of points. Last time she had gone one way. Now she could switch tracks and skip across into the alternative future she had foolishly denied herself. Picture her in the Taj Hotel, looking across Bombay harbour, hearing her lover's song. She looks sixteen again. She is under the spell of the music. And this time she chooses love.

AND NOW I must sing the last song of India that will ever pass my lips; I must quit my old stamping grounds once and for all. Here's an irony worth a shake of the head or a rueful grin: that the severance of my connection with the country of my birth should come to pass at the point of my deepest intimacy with it, my broadest knowledge, my most genuine feelings of belonging. For whatever Persis thought, my years as a photographer had opened my eyes to the old place, and my heart as well. I had started by searching for what my parents had seen in it, but soon I began to see it for myself, to make my own portrait, my own selection from the overwhelming abundance that was everywhere on offer. After a period of feeling an odd, alienated disconnection, feeling it as something not chosen but simply *so,* I was seeing my way, through the camera lens, of being a "proper" Indian. Yet it was the thing I most rejoiced in, my photographer's craft, that ensured my banishment. For a while this created problems for me of value, of defining right thought, right action. I didn't know which way was up any more: what was ground, what sky. The two seemed equally insubstantial to me.

Do you remember Piloo's goats? It is a long time since I left them to their own devices. Now, however, I must return to those spectral animals. It is a goat song that I must sing.

At the time of the earthquake, all manner of bizarre

rumours were in the air. Those about Mrs. Gandhi—her electoral fraud, which could very well lead to the Allahabad High Court barring her from holding public office—were so sensational that they fully occupied most people's attention. Would the Prime Minister resign, or try to cling to power? The unthinkable was becoming thinkable. At every dinner table, every water well, every *dhaba* and street corner in the country, people argued over the issue's rights and wrongs. New rumours spread every day. In Bombay, the earthquake raised the general hysteria level to an even higher pitch. In such a climate, it has to be said, nobody was very interested in goats.

The day after Vina's disorienting flying visit, however, I was telephoned by Anita Dharkar, a bright young editor at the *Illustrated Weekly,* which had published individual pictures and photo-essays of mine from time to time. "So, wanna hear the red-hot scuttlebutt on Piloo?" she enquired. She knew of my loathing for the man who had wrecked my parents' marriage. Find your enemy, Henri Hulot had advised. I knew who my enemy was. I just didn't know what I could do to harm him; not until shrewd Anita made her call.

(I must reveal that between Anita and myself there was, well, something. A light occasional thing between colleagues, but with enough substance to it to make me disguise the confusion within me that Vina's visit had left behind. My old gift for playing the cards close to my chest came in useful. I don't think Anita suspected anything was up.)

"Piloo? Did the earthquake gobble him up?" I asked, optimistically. "Or is he climbing into Mrs. G.'s back pocket like every other cheap crook around?"

"How much do you know about his goat farms?" asked Anita, ignoring me.

Officially, Piloo was out of the milk industry now, having given in gracefully to his competitors at the Exwyzee Milk Colony. Instead, he had gone into the mutton-and-wool business in a big way. "Why don't you just turn them into meat and coats?" a petulant young Vina had once asked him. Well, so he had. His ranches were spread across rural Maharashtra and Madhya Pradesh from the baking lowlands of the

Godavari River valley to the slopes of the many hill ranges of central India, from the Harishandra range, the Ajanta plateau and the Ellora hills to the Sirpur hills and Satmala plateau in the east, and the Miraj hills near Sangli in the south. Fearlessly, he had established large herds near the bandit-infested gulches of Madhya Pradesh, and Andhra Pradesh as well. He was now one of the national goat industry's largest employers, and his famously high standards of hygiene and quality control had won nationwide awards, and entitled him, as well as the standard fodder subsidies, calculated per head of livestock, to the substantial tax rebates and improvement grants available to such enlightened rural entrepreneurs.

"Enough," I answered Anita. "But why do you care? You're vegetarian, and allergic to mohair too." I liked Anita. I liked her looks, which were lavish, and her singing voice, which was the best I'd heard since Vina's. I liked the gleam of her dark, naked body, its black light, its definition, its boldness. I liked, too, that she appreciated my pictures and championed them inside the *Weekly,* where there were certain opponents.

"Suppose I told you," Anita was saying, "that those goats don't exist?"

THE CREATIVE imagination possessed by a great scam artist is of a high order; one can't help but admire. What surrealist boldness he displays in the conception of his deceits; what high-wire daring, what mastery of illusion in their execution! The flim-flam maestro is a superman for our times, disdaining norms, scorning convention, soaring far beyond the gravitational pull of plausibility, shucking off the puritan naturalism that would hold most ordinary mortals back. And if in the end he comes unstuck, if his ruses fail like the melting wings of Icarus, then we love him all the more for revealing his human frailty, for falling fatally to earth. In his moment of failure he deepens our love and renders it eternal.

We have been privileged, in India, to observe at close quarters some of the very best—the best of the best—members of the trickster hall of fame. As a result, we are not easily impressed, we demand the highest levels of performance from our public crooks. We have seen too much, yet we still want to be made to laugh and shake our heads in disbelief; we rely upon the scamster to rekindle a sense of wonder dulled by the excess of our daily lives.

Since Piloo's pioneering work, we have marvelled at the People's Car scam of the later 1970s (huge sums of public money disappeared from a project headed by Sanjay G.), the Swedish Cannons scam of the 1980s (huge sums of public money went astray from an international arms deal that besmirched the reputation of Rajiv G.), and the Stock Exchange scam of the 1990s (strenuous efforts were made to fix the movements of certain key stocks, using, naturally, huge sums of public money). Yet when students of the topic gather together—that is to say, whenever and wherever two or more Indians meet for coffee and a chat—they will generally agree that the Great Goat Scam gets their vote for the all-comers gold-medal position. Just as *Citizen Kane* is always chosen in movie polls as the best film of all time, and VTO's *Quakershaker (How the Earth Learned to Rock & Roll)* invariably beats *Sgt. Pepper* into second place in the voting for best ever album; just as *Hamlet* is Best Play and Pelé is Best Football Player and Michael Jordan is the Hoop Dreamboat and Joe DiMaggio is forever Best American, even if he needed the famous line in the famous song explained to him, he thought he was being sent up, didn't understand the reverence in which he was held, so also Piloo Doodhwala is unshakeably ensconced as India's Scambaba Deluxe.

And the fellow who put him up there was me.

Fodder fraud does not, at first glance, look as romantic a diddle as gun-running commissions or manipulating the investment market. Goats, after all, famously eat anything, so the subventions to farmers are necessarily small: on the order of one hundred rupees per goat per annum, or around three dollars a head. Goat feed = chicken feed, you may scornfully conclude. Not much scope there for one of the great confidence tricks of all time. Doubter, be reassured. Mistake not flamboyance for genius, or glistering garbage for gold. It was the very smallness of the sums involved that enabled Piloo to set up his glorious scheme, the sheer banality of the project that protected it from public scrutiny for so many years. For while one hundred chips is a mere bagatelle, it is, nevertheless, one hundred chips in your pocket, as long as your goat is of the Non-Existent type. And because the Non-Existent Goat breeds faster, and requires less attention, or indeed space, than any other variety, what is to stop the energetic goat farmer from increasing the quantity of his livestock at high speed, almost ad infinitum? For the Non-Existent Goat never falls ill, never lets you down, never dies unless it is required to do so, and—uniquely—multiplies at the precise rate stipulated by its owner. Truly, the most obliging and likeable of goats, it makes no noise, nor is there any shit to shovel.

The scale of the Great Goat Scam was almost beyond comprehension. Piloo Doodhwala was the proud owner of one hundred million wholly fictitious goats, goats of the highest quality, the softness of whose wool had passed into legend, whose flesh was a byword for tenderness. The flexibility of the Non-Existent Goat allowed him to defy the received wisdom of centuries of goat husbandry. Deep in the heart of central India he achieved the incredible feat of rearing top-quality cashmere goats—who were conventionally thought to need high mountain pastures—in the heat of the plains. Nor had communal issues restricted him. His meat goats could be raised by vegetarians, whose work with these magical creatures involved no loss of caste. It was an operation of immense beauty, requiring no work at all, except for the effort of maintaining the fiction of the goats' Existence. The financial outlay required to ensure the silence of thousands upon thousands of villagers and government inspectors and other officials, and to pay off the border bandits, was very considerable, but entirely within tolerable limits if considered as a percentage of the enterprise's turnover, and it was, after all (see above), cushioned by tax breaks and capital subsidies to boot.

One hundred times one hundred million is ten billion rupees, one hundred thousand crores. Two hundred million pounds sterling. Three hundred million dollars per annum, free of taxes. Hush money and protection money payments, annual salaries to the villagers employed to tend the Non-Existents, and miscellaneous expenses added up to less than five percent of this exquisite sum and represented nothing worse than a tiny mole, a sort of financial beauty spot, upon the immortally lovely face of this magnificent scam, which Piloo operated without hindrance—indeed, with the enthusiastic support of many of Maharashtra's greatest figures—for almost fifteen years.

Three hundred million times fifteen is four and a half billion dollars. One and a half million crores of rupees. Less expenses, certainly. Let's not exaggerate. Call it four billion dollars, net.

I WENT in to the office to discuss the brief. Anita Dharkar had a satirical spread in mind. On the left, Piloo's deserted "ranches"; on the right, a more typical goat farming operation. "Presenting Piloo's Invisible Goats," she extemporised, enjoying herself. "Here you see them, not being seen. Unlike these Ordinary Goats, which, as you can see, you can see."

I, who had boasted about my talent for invisibility, was commissioned to photograph these phantoms, Doodhwala's "ghoasts." Anita wanted Piloo's magic herds on film. "Piloo is not only protected by corruption," she said, becoming serious. "Also, there is the infinite indifference of India. *Chalta-hai,* isn't it? So it goes. We expect our Piloos to get up to tricks, and we shrug and turn away. Only if you get the pictures proving the case beyond all doubt will we be able to make anything happen."

She had acquired a full list of all Piloo's registered goat-rearing facilities. "How'd you do that?" I asked, impressed. But she was too savvy to betray a source, even to me. "Truth will out," she said. "In the end, there's always an honest Injun somewhere, if you can find him. Even in Inja."

"Or maybe," I said, less idealistically, "there's someone Piloo forgot to buy."

"Or maybe," Anita took up the thread, "it's just in the nature of secrets to come out, because the only way to keep a secret is not to tell anybody, which is why I'm not answering your disgraceful question about my informant. And Piloo's secret was shared by too many people. The wonder is it didn't leak years ago. Piloo must've been paying damn, damn well."

"Or maybe," I responded, "your source is a kind of

patriot. People are always complaining, right?, that India is too busy aping the West. But here is our very own special talent; we should celebrate it. About scams we don't need to learn a thing. We can teach. Listen, I'm sort of proud of Piloo. I hate the bastard, but he has done a beautiful thing."

"Sure," said Anita. "So let's try to give him what he deserves. The Padmashri, even the Bharat Ratna. No; these honours are not big enough. How about a pair of official portraits, front view, side view, wearing stripey outfit, and holding a card with name and serial number also, if poss?"

It sounded good to me. "Just get the photos, Rai, okay?" she said, and walked out of the room.

SHE DIDN'T tell me about the other photographer, the one she'd sent before me, the one who hadn't returned: not because she was anxious to avoid alarming me, but because she knew I would be offended at being her second choice, She wanted to come with me, too; she had it all planned out. We would fly to Aurangabad, acting like newlyweds on honeymoon, not a camera in sight. For verisimilitude and other reasons, we would check in at the Rambagh Palace Hotel and make love all night. To keep up the honeymoon cover story—for we were going into Piloo country, where any doorman, any *chaprassi,* could be a stool pigeon—we would go to Ajanta and stand in the darkness of the caves while a guide switched a light on and off and the Buddhist masterpieces appeared and vanished. The bodhisattvas, the pink elephants, the half-clad women with their hourglass figures and perfect globes of breasts. Anita's body was the equal of any fresco and the offer was an attractive one, but I left Bombay without telling her and plunged into the hard heart of India, intent upon doing what I had laughed at Vina for wanting to do, what city dwellers almost never do in India. I would enter rural India. Not to learn about rhythm or withdrawal, but to get old Piloo's goat.

After that strange, jangling single night with Vina, it did me good to get away. *Of course I never set any fire. You think I burned your house down? Did your mother think so? Gee, thanks. I may have been a thief, but I wasn't crazy.* She had wanted to meet my mother, to offer restitution. New jewellery for old. But it was too late for things like that. The rifts in our world could not be mended. What was burned could not be unburned, what was broken could not be fixed. A dead mother, a father rotating slowly and reeking of bitter perfume as his bedroom fan turned. Strange fruit. I tried to imagine how Ameer Merchant might have reacted to Vina's return. I think she would simply have opened her arms and taken Vina right back into her heart.

To think about those days again—Ameer, V.V., the fire, the lost love, the wasted chances—was upsetting. The size of the countryside, its stark unsentimental lines, its obduracy: these things did me good. To be moving within its great dusty sweep, its lack of interest, helped restore a sense of proportion; it put one in one's place. I drove my Jeep—laden with supplies of dry and tinned food, jerry cans of petrol and of water, spare tyres, my favourite hiking boots (the ones with the secrets in their heels) and even a small tent—into the far east of Maharashtra. I was in Piloo's empire, looking for the back door.

Always the back-door man.

A journey to the centre of the earth. The air grew hotter with every mile, the wind seemed to blaze more fiercely on my cheeks. The local bugs seemed larger and hungrier than their city cousins, and I was, as usual, lunch. The road never emptied: bikes, horse-drawn carts, burst pipes, the blare of buses and trucks. People, people. Roadside saints in plaster. Men in a circle at dawn pissing on an ancient monument, some dead king's tomb. Running dogs, lounging cattle, exploded rubber tyres prominent among the piles of detritus that were everywhere, like the future. Groups of youths with orange headbands and flags. Politics painted on passing walls. Tea stalls. Monkeys, camels, performing bears on a leash. A man who pressed your trousers while you waited. Ochre smoke from factory chimneys. Accidents. *Bed On Roof Rs 2/=*. Prostitutes. The omnipresence of gods. Boys in cheap rayon bush shirts. Everywhere around me, life was striving, pullulating. The roaches, the beasts of burden, the enervated parrots, fought for food, shelter, the right to see another day of life. The young men with their oiled hair strutted and preened like skinny gladiators, while the old watched their children suspiciously, waiting to be abandoned, to be shouldered aside, tossed into some ditch. This was life in its pure form, life seeking no more than to remain alive. In the universe of the road, the survival instinct was the only law, the hustle the only game in town, the game you played until you dropped. To be here was to understand why Piloo Doodhwala was popular. The Great Goat Scam was the life of the road writ large. It was a mega-hustle which freed his people from the daily hustles that drove them into early graves. He was a miracle man, a prophet. It would not be easy to bring him down.

MY PLAN—more a notion than a strategy, really—was to get as far off the beaten track as possible. I had seen from Anita's list that many of Piloo's ghost farms were located in the most remote parts of the state, in highly inhospitable territory, with a communications infrastructure that was poor to non-existent. Any farmer of Actually Existing Goats would have had the greatest difficulty, and would also have incurred inordinate and crippling expenses, in simply bringing his herds to the slaughterhouse or shearing shed. Non-Existent Goats caused no such problems, naturally, and the inaccessibility of the "ranches" made the true nature of Piloo's operation easier to conceal. I was gambling on the over-confidence of his minions in these far-flung places. A photographer from the *Illustrated Weekly* would be the last person on earth they'd expect to see.

At that time, a much ballyhooed Trans-India Auto Rally was taking place, and it was my intention to pose as a lost driver in need of food, water, rest and guidance. This would, I hoped, buy me a few hours of time in the company of Piloo's phantoms. Then it would be up to my powers of photographic invisibility to seize the opportunity. Dusty, exhausted, I turned my Jeep off the main highway on to ever smaller and more broken roads, and headed for the hills.

After travelling for two days I came to a river, a trickle down the centre of a dry, rocky bed. There was a peasant passing, as there always is, with a stick over one shoulder and a water pot hanging from each end of the stick. I asked him the river's name, and when he answered "Wainganga," I had the odd feeling of having taken a wrong turning out of the real world, of having slipped somehow into fiction. As if I had accidentally crossed the border of Maharashtra not into Madhya Pradesh but into a parallel, magic land. In contemporary India those hills ahead of me, a low range with jungled ravines, would have been the Seoni range, but in the magic sphere I had entered they were still called, in the old fashion, Seeonee. In their jungles I might chance upon legendary beasts, talking animals who never were, created by a writer who put them in this faraway wilderness without ever seeing it with his own eyes: a panther and a bear and a tiger and a jackal and an elephant and monkeys and a snake. And on the hills' high ridges I might at any moment glimpse the mythic figure of a human boy, a Non-Existent Boy, a figment, a man-cub dancing with wolves.

Now Chil the Kite brings home the night
That Mang the Bat sets free.

I had reached my destination. A deeply rutted dirt path led off the country road towards Piloo Doodhwala's mysteries. Still in the grip of my curious mood of unreality, I drove towards my fate.

THE SHEER unchartedness of rural India in its most profound depths never failed to amaze. You turned off the road on to the rural tracks and at once felt as the earth's early navigators must have done; like a Cabot or Magellan of the land.

Here the polyphonic reality of the road disappeared and was replaced by silences, mutenesses as vast as the land. Here was a wordless truth, one that came before language, a being, not a becoming. No cartographer had fully mapped these endless spaces. There were villages buried in the backlands that never knew about the British Empire, villagers to whom the names of the nation's leaders and founding fathers would mean nothing, even though Wardha, where the Mahatma founded his ashram, was only a hundred-odd miles away. To journey down some of these tracks was to travel back in time for over a thousand years.

City dwellers were constantly told that village India was the "real" India, a space of timelessness and gods, of moral certainties and natural laws, of the eternal fixities of caste and faith, gender and class, landowner and sharecropper and bonded labourer and serf. Such statements were made as if the real were solid, immutable, tangible. Whereas the most obvious lesson of travelling between the city and the village, between the crowded street and the open field, was that reality shifted. Where the plates of different realities met, there were shudders and rifts. Chasms opened. A man could lose his life.

I am writing about a journey into the heart of the country but it's just another way of saying goodbye. I'm taking the long way round to the exit because I can't agree with myself to let go, to be done with it, to turn away towards my new life, just to settle for that fortunate existence. Lucky me: America.

But it's also because my life hinges on what happened out there, on the banks of the Wainganga River, within sight of the Seeonee hills. That was the decisive moment that created the secret image which I have never revealed to anyone, the hidden self-portrait, the ghost in my machine.

Nowadays I can behave, most of the time, as if it never happened. I'm a happy man, I can throw sticks for my dog on an American beach and let the turn-ups on my stone-grey chinos get wet in the Atlantic tides, but sometimes in the night I wake and the past is hanging there in front of me, rotating slowly, and all around me the jungle beasts are growling, the fire grows dim, and they are closing in.

Vina: I promised you I would open my heart, I swore that nothing would be spared. So I must find the courage to reveal this also, this terrible thing I know about myself. I must confess it and stand defenceless before the court of anyone who can be bothered to judge. If anyone remains. You know the old song. Even the President of the United States sometimes must stand naked.

Or I washed my hands in muddy waters, I washed my hands but they wouldn't come clean.

AT A certain point I left the Jeep behind, off the track, and proceeded on foot. As I crept towards my goal I felt an excitement—no, it was more than a mere kick, it was fulfilment—which left me in no doubt that I had discovered what I wanted most. More than money, more than fame, maybe even more than love.

To look with one's own eyes into the eyes of the truth,

and stare it down. To see what was *thus,* and show it *so.* To strip away the veils and turn the thunderous racket of revelation into the pure silence of the image and so possess it, to put the world's secret wonders in your suitcase and go home from the war to your once-in-a-lifetime woman, or even to the picture editor you slept with twice a week.

But this world was not rackety. Its stillness was unnatural, it was much more than country hush. I had entered the territory of the four-billion-dollar phantom goat, and the goat is, of course, an ancient avatar of the devil. Allow me to concede that in that occult silence I felt a little scared and far from help.

The herds are shut in byre and hut
For loosed till dawn are we.

There was a cluster of buildings ahead. Huts and byres, but where were the villagers' herds? Yet more silence burst from Piloo's scam sheds, eloquent as a lion's roar. I reached into the patch pocket on my right trouser leg and felt the reassuring presence of the slim little Leica which I'd bought myself in honour of my encounter with the great Henri Hulot. Then men carrying field implements rose up all around me, seeming to burst from the very earth, and that, as far as photography was concerned, was that.

They had seen me coming a mile off, which didn't in itself matter too much. In my long and various professional life, I have bribed and sweet-talked my way past the roadblocks of regional warlords in Angola and former Yugoslavia, I have found routes in and out of twenty-seven different revolutions and major wars. The security cordons at the Milan and Paris fashion collections, the concentric circles of armed and unarmed aides guarding the route to the man or woman of real power, the maître d's at the leading Manhattan restaurants, pah! I snap my fingers under their collective nose. Even on that early adventure, rookie that I was, I felt confident of my ability to hoodwink these back-of-beyond yokels and then get the goods on their little livestock swindle.

Unless, of course, they weren't yokels. Unless they were members of one of the feared gangs of killer bandits who roamed these invisible parts. Unless Piloo was actually using the bandits to police his operation. Unless they murdered me there and then and left my body for the vultures and carrion crows.

MY CAPTORS and I turned out to have no language in common. They spoke a local dialect that made no sense at all to me. However, conversation quickly became redundant. After they had removed my cameras and rolls of film and the keys to my Jeep and robbed me of all my money, they took me to the place of imaginary goats. Here I met the other journalist, the one of whose existence I had previously been unaware. He was waiting for me in one of the byres, hanging from a low beam, rotating slowly in the hot draughts of wind, and dressed very like myself. The same patch pockets on his trousers, the same hiking boots. The same empty camera bag at his feet. He had been dead for much too long, and even as I started vomiting I understood that my yarn about the Trans-India Rally was probably not going to be believed.

Why didn't they string me up right away? I don't know. Boredom, probably. There's not much to do out there in the boondocks when you don't even have real goats to fuck. You've got to spread out your pleasures. The anticipation is more than half the fun. Crocodiles do the same thing. They keep their quarry half alive for days sometimes, saving them for later. So I'm told.

Boredom and laziness saved my life. These husbanders of fictive billies and nannies were people who had made their illicit living for one and a half decades by doing nothing at all. If they were bandits (which I increasingly doubted), they were bandits who had lost their edge. Many of them were stout, soft-bodied, which was rarely true of peasants and dacoits. Corruption had both fattened their bodies and eroded their spirits. They bound me and abandoned me, left me retching emptily on account of the stench of my dead colleague, and at the mercy also of the one zillion crawling things to whom a dead body is the occasion for a grand inter-species reunion.

At night the phantom goatherds got drunk in another hut, and the loud noises of their carousing stopped only when they were all unconscious. I managed to free myself of the badly tied ropes around my arms and legs, and after a few moments more I made my escape. The Jeep was where I'd left it, looted but with enough gas in the tank to get me to a town. I managed to hot-wire it and drove away as fast as the surface would permit. I did not turn on the headlights. Fortunately there was a bright-yellow gibbous moon to light my way.

"Thank god," Anita Dharkar said, when I reached a telephone and reversed the charges and woke her up. "Thank god." I was so angry she'd said such a thing that I shouted abuse at her down the phone. Fear, danger, panic, flight, stress: these things have odd, displaced consequences.

Thank god? No, no, *no.* Let's not invent anything as cruel, vicious, vengeful, intolerant, unloving, immoral and arrogant as god just to explain a stroke of dumb, undeserved luck. I don't need some multi-limbed Cosmic Dancer or white-bearded Ineffable, some virgin-raping metamorphic Thunderbolt Hurler or world-destroying flood and fire Maniac, to take the credit for saving my skin. Nobody saved the other fellow, did they? Nobody saved the Indochinese or the Angkorans or the Kennedys or the Jews.

"I know the list," she said. I was calming down. "Yeah, well," I said, awkwardly. "I just needed to make the point."

The photographs I brought back to Bombay created a great sensation, though considered purely from the aesthetic viewpoint they were as dull and uninspired as the First Photo itself, that ancient monochrome view of walls and roofs as seen from the studio window of Joseph Nicéphore Niépce. They were pictures of emptiness, of corrals and pastures, byres and sheds, in which no animals could be seen; of fences, doors, fields, stalls. Photographs of absences. But tell-tale Doodhwala Industries stencils were visible everywhere, on wooden walls and fence posts and on the occasional vehicle: a cart, a truck. Just as the banality of goat fodder had enabled Piloo to construct his mighty fraud, so the banality of these images, what one might call their *decisive voiding,* served to deconstruct the swindle. Within weeks of their publication, a major fraud squad investigation was in progress, and within three months warrants were issued for the arrest of Piloo Doodhwala, most of the "magnificentourage," and several dozen lesser associates across two states.

The bizarre character of the scandal attracted international attention. The photographs were widely re-published, and as a result I received a brief handwritten note from M. Hulot, offering his congratulations on my "scoop de foudre" and inviting me to join the world-famous Nebuchadnezzar photographers' agency, which he had founded in the year of my birth, along with the American Bobby Flow, "Chip" Boleyn from England and a second French photographer, Paul Willy. It was as if Zeus had tapped me on the shoulder and asked me to join him and the other naked, omnipotent pranksters on top of their storied hill.

It was the beginning of the life I have led ever since, the first day, one might say, of my life as a man. And yet, as the attentive reader will already have divined, something was badly amiss.

It is time, after all these years, to answer certain questions.

Rai—here's the first question—*how does a man shoot a roll of film while bound hand and foot? How does a man film a "goat farm" which he has never visited (for the pictures clearly showed images of at least two separate establishments in different parts of the country)? Most puzzlingly of all, how does a man take photographs after his camera equipment has been removed?*

I could say there was another loaded camera hidden in the Jeep, taped under the offside rear wheel arch, and the murderous bastards missed it. I could say I was goaded into passionate, dangerous action by the experience of spending a day retching and gagging in the company of a hanged man, who wore the same clothes and boots as myself, whose swollen, blackened face might have—or so it seemed to me, in my torment—borne more than a passing resemblance to my own. I did it for him, I could tell you, for my murdered, stinking companion, *mon semblable, mon frère.* I did it for the dead twin I did not know I had.

I became careful, circumspect. I found a hiding place during the night from which I could work by day. I became invisible, motionless, invincible. I got the pictures. Here they are. The bastards went to jail, okay? Can I do anything else for you? Anything else you want to know? What's that? What did you say?

Why didn't you buy more film?

Oh, for crying out loud. They robbed me. I was broke.

And then Anita came, and brought you home.

Right. Right.

So, when did you go to the second location, far away in the Miraj hills?

Later. I went later. What's your problem?

In that case, why didn't you take more film?

What, you think it was easy to get those photos? Just to get five or six images would have been a sort of miracle. This was one full roll.

> *Tell us about the boots, Rai. Talk about the hiking boots.*
> Stop it. Shut up. I can't.
> *Oh, but you must.*

Okay: the thing you could do with these special, imported hiking boots: if you slightly loosened a screw at the base of the heel, you could twist the whole heel section round to reveal a small cavity. A cavity just about large enough to hold a roll of film. I'd used the trick a few times, for example when photographing Mumbai's Axis rallies. As a matter of fact, I'd used it this time. When I left my Jeep to go "ghoast"-busting, I had a spare film in each heel.

The hanged man and I were alone for a long time. His feet swung not far from my revolted nose and yes I wondered about the heels of his boots yes when I got the ropes off I made myself approach him yes in spite of his pong like the end of the world and the biting insects yes and the rawness of my throat and my eyes sore from bulging as I puked I took hold of his heels one after the other yes I twisted the left heel it came up empty but the right heel did the right thing the film just plopped down in my hand yes and I put an unused film in its place from my own boot yes and I could feel his body all perfume and my heart was going like mad and I made my escape with Piloo's fate and my own golden future in my hand yes and to hell with everything I said yes because it might as well be me as another so yes I will yes I did yes.

I've seen that film now, *Ugetsu Monogatari,* the Japanese picture Hulot praised so highly. I must have seen it a dozen times. It's not only a ghost story; there's a sub-plot. A poor man wants to be a great samurai warrior. One day he sees a famous fighter being killed. Afterwards he boasts that he is the one who bested the hero. It makes his reputation. For a while.

I never actually said the photographs were mine. I just processed them and handed the results to Anita at the *Weekly* offices and allowed everyone else to give me the credit; which I took. Which isn't quite the same thing as boasting.

Who am I kidding?

There. Now I've removed my mask, and you can see what I really am. In this quaking, unreliable time, I have built my house—morally speaking—upon shifting Indian sands. *Terra infirma.*

Piloo Doodhwala had his scam; and as you see, I had mine. He made four billion dollars. I just made my name.

I brought the film out, but it hadn't been shot by me. It would never have seen the light of day if I hadn't found it, but it wasn't my work. Piloo might never have been arraigned, might never have been sent to jail, might have gone on earning his goaty billions for the rest of his life, if not for me. But the photographs weren't mine. It was over a quarter of a century ago, and since then I've earned my spurs, I deserve my goddamn reputation, I've worked for everything I've got. But the pictures that made my name, that brought me to the world's attention? They weren't mine, they weren't mine, they weren't mine.

Too human for the Wolf Pack, too vulpine for Man, Mowgli in the Seeonee hills resolved to hunt alone. Not a bad resolve for a photographer. After my experiences by the banks of the Wainganga, I made the Man Cub's vow my own.

ANOTHER BITTER pill: the Piloo exposé jailed him, but instead of ruining him, it actually made him bigger. The size of the pro-Piloo demonstrations in the rural areas of Maharashtra and Madhya Pradesh alarmed and impressed the Bombay and Delhi power élite. Prosecuting Piloo began to be described as an act of vengeance by the "English medium" liberal élite against a true man of the masses, a son of the soil. The moment he was jailed he announced his intention to run for public office, and his campaign quickly became unstoppable. The Bombay jailkhana became Piloo's royal court. His cell was furnished like a throne room, and banquets were brought in daily by Golmatol and his daughters. Mighty figures came to visit and offer obeisance. Mumbai's Axis grandees supported Piloo's bid for mayor, and within six months of being jailed he had been elected to the post. A pardon was sought for him and swiftly granted by the President of India, acting on the urgent advice of the increasingly powerful Sanjay Gandhi, a shoo-in for the next Indian Premier. A general election was called, and the Indira Congress, in association with its new Hindu nationalist allies across the country, including Mumbai's Axis in Bombay and Maharashtra, swept back to power. Emergency rule was ended. No longer necessary: the electorate had endorsed tyranny and corruption. *Chalta hai.*

So it goes.

MUCH OF this, the apotheosis of Piloo, the total victory of Pilooist values over everything in India that I had slowly come to love, happened after I had gone. Listen: once I received the invitation from Nebuchadnezzar I'd have left anyway, but I'd have kept my links to the old country, like Hulot himself I'd have made it one of my subjects, because there it was inside me, colonizing every cell, an addiction so deep it could not be destroyed without killing the addict too; or so I naïvely believed. What happened instead was that Anita Dharkar was beaten and raped in her own home in the middle of the night the weekend after Piloo went to jail, and her assailants, who hadn't even bothered to hide their faces, told her to be sure and tell me that I was their next port of call, only in my case they didn't intend to be so gentle and considerate.

"Is there somewhere you can go?" she asked. I wanted to go to her, but she told me not to come round on any account, her family was looking after her, she would be fine. I knew she would not be fine. "You should leave the country," she said. "Things will get much worse before they get better." I asked her if she would come with me. Her voice was thick-lipped, juddering, broken, and her body, I didn't know how to think about what had been done to her body. But she would not leave. "They have finished with me now," she said. "So, no problem." She meant that India was still the only place on earth to which she could imagine herself belonging, corrupt and crooked and heartless and violent as it was. She belonged, and optimism and hope were still not dead in her in spite of her appalling violation. She could not define herself, could not give herself any meaning, except here, where her roots had gone too deep and spread too wide.

Something required me to leave. Something else required her to stay. In my story, which is also that of Ormus Cama and Vina Apsara, Anita Dharkar, poignant, lovely, sweetly singing Anita who was defiled for the crime of possessing integrity, Anita the photo editor, heroine and patriot, is a boat against the current, moving determinedly in the opposite direction to the tale.

Her dream was of an India which would deserve her, which would show that it had been right for her to remain. There are noble women who remain married to coarse wife-beaters for similar reasons. They see the good in their bad men.

And of course there was somewhere I could go. I locked up my home, dismissed the servants and went to see Persis. *Get me a ticket, Persis. Fix it with your airline contacts that I can travel under a false name. Don't ask me why, Persis. You don't want to know. Persis, I'm going, as you always said I would. Thank you. I'm sorry. Goodbye.*

Persis, gentle gatekeeper of our lives. Who stood by the river that separates the worlds and helped us to cross, but could not do so herself.

EVEN AFTER the assault on Anita, it did not occur to me, when I left my Apollo Bunder apartment, that I was going for good, that I would never again set foot in those rooms; nor on that street, to brush off Virus Cama's troop of urchins; nor in that city, to witness its surge towards the skies; nor in any part of India, though it remained a part of me, as essential as a limb. India, where my parents lay buried, and the smells were the smells of home. I was heading full of anticipation towards a new life, the life I wanted, but I had no sense of having burned my boats. Sure, I'd go back. Things would cool down. Piloo, now rising, would take a tumble soon enough. Nobody remembered anything, anyway, and to return as a big-deal Nebu Agency photographer would ensure me open-arms treatment and the widest possible access. Of course it would. Real life was not like an earthquake. Rifts might appear, but most of them mended, after a fashion. It's not as if some science fiction chasm had appeared, so wide that there was no way across. It was just end-of-part-one, start-of-part-two, is all.

But Pilooism won the day, Pilooism and Sanjayism, its Delhi twin. Delhi and Bombay used to hate each other. Bombay-wallahs sneered at the way Delhi people licked the arse of power, then turned it round and sucked its indifferent cock. Delhi-ites derided Bombay's money-grubbing glitzy materialism. This new alliance united the dark side of both. The corruption of money and the corruption of power, united in a super-corruption that no opponent could withstand. I never foresaw that; but Lady Spenta Cama had intuited it long ago.

The best in our natures is drowning in the worst.

Nothing could touch those two. The law couldn't damage Piloo, and Sanjay, too, led a charmed life. Even when his light aircraft stalled in mid-air while he was looping the loop like a fool over his mother's official residence, he managed to survive the emergency landing. Oh, the utter Caligulan barbarity of India during the consulship of those terrible twins! The beatings, the bullyings, the jailings, the flailings, the burnings, the bannings, the buyings, the sellings, the shamelessness, the shamelessness, the shame.

I know it's different now. The quadruple assassination. I know. People will say I've been away too long, I don't understand the situation, it's not as I say it is, it never was, it was better in some ways, and in others, worse.

But I'll tell you how it feels, after all these years. It feels like an ending in the middle pathway of my life. A necessary ending, without which the second half would have been impossible. Freedom, then? Not exactly. Not quite a liberation, no. It feels like a divorce. In this particular divorce I was the party who didn't want the marriage to break up. I was the one who sat around waiting, telling myself, it'll be okay, she'll think better of it, she'll come back to me and all manner of thing shall be well. But she never came back. And now we're all older, it's too late, the links didn't break, they just wore away years ago. At the end of a marriage the moment comes when you have to turn away from your wife, from the unbearably beautiful memory of the way you were, and turn towards the rest of your life. That's me at this point in this story. Once again, I'm the dumpee.

AND so farewell, my country. Don't worry; I won't come knocking at your door. I won't phone you in the middle of the night and hang up when you reply. I won't follow you down the street when you step out with some other guy. My home is burned, my parents dead, and those I loved have mostly gone away. Those whom I still love I must leave behind for good.

I go—I hunt—alone.

India, I have swum in your warm waters and run laughing in your high mountain meadows. Oh, why must everything I say end up sounding like a *filmi gana,* a goddamn cheap Bollywood song? Very well then: I have walked your filthy streets, India, I have ached in my bones from the illnesses engendered by your germs. I have eaten your independent salt and drunk your nauseatingly sugary roadside tea. For many years your malaria mosquitoes would bite me wherever I went, and in deserts and summers around the world I was stung by cool Kashmiri bees. India, my *terra infirma,* my maelstrom, my cornucopia, my crowd. India, my too-muchness, my everything at once, my Hug-me, my fable, my mother, my father and my first great truth. It may be that I am not worthy of you, for I have been imperfect, I confess. I may not comprehend what you are becoming, what perhaps you already are, but I am old enough to say that this new self of yours is an entity I no longer want, or need, to understand.

India, fount of my imagination, source of my savagery, breaker of my heart.

Goodbye.

CHAPTER NINE

Membrane

One universe shrinks, another expands. Ormus Cama in the middle 1960s quits Bombay for England, restored to himself, feeling his true nature flowing back into his veins. As the plane lifts from his native soil, so his heart lifts also, he sheds his old skin without a second thought, crosses that frontier as if it didn't exist, like a shape-shifter, like a snake. His fellow steerage passengers cocoon themselves in uninterest, they sit jammed up against the lives of strangers but pretend they notice nothing in order to maintain the fiction that they are not themselves observed. Ormus's unleashed personality is unable to contain itself within such demure fictions. His self has taken wing. It overflows its bounds. He stares openly and long at the other travellers, memorising them, these are the people who are going with me to the New World, and he even speaks to them, smiling his disarming smile.

Welcome aboard the *Mayflower,* he greets them, seizing their hands as they pass his seat, the terrified uncomprehending peasants from remote inland villages on their way to desert kingdoms, the perspiration-sprinkled executives in cheap suits, the frowning chaperones of a veiled young bride fainting in a pink *gharara* with too much gold braid, the unwary young student on his way to a miserable four years in an English boarding school, and the children. There are children everywhere, children running in the aisles imitating aircraft to the dismay of the cabin staff; or standing up on their seats grave-eyed and motionless, showing a more than adult understanding of the importance of this momentous day; or screaming like strapped-down lunatics at their fastened seat belts; children dressed in spectacularly lumpy woollen jumpers in functional grey and navy blue, their very garments proclaiming their alienation from the new homes they have never seen, trumpeting the difficulty they will have in adjusting to life in those lightless northern climes.

We are the Pilgrim Children, Ormus thinks. Where the first foot falls, let us call it Bombay Rock. Boom chickaboom, chickaboom boom.

He himself has dressed carefully for the journey, arraying his body in the casual wear of America: the Yankees baseball cap, the white Beat Generation T-shirt with the ragged cutaway sleeves, the Mickey Mouse watch. There is a touch of Europe too, in the black hipster jeans which he literally charmed off the legs of an Italian tourist at the Gateway, a susceptible youth, one of the first longhaired Westerners to arrive in India in search of beaches and enlightenment, and no match for Ormus Cama's astonishing powers of persuasion, which left him bare-legged and dumbfounded with his right fist full of money and Ormus's gift of a neatly folded lungi hanging over his bemused left arm.

England may be my immediate destination but it is not my goal, Ormus's clothes announce, old England cannot hold me, it may pretend to be swinging but I know it's just plain hanged. Not funky but defunct. History moves on. Nowadays England is ersatz America, America's delayed echo, America driving on the left. Sure, Jesse Garon Parker was white American trash who wanted to sing like a black boy, but the Beatles, for goodness' sake, the Beatles are white English trash trying to sing like American *girls*. Crystals Ronettes Shirelles Chantels Chiffons Vandellas Marvelettes, why not wear some spangly dresses, boys, why not get some beehive hairdos instead of those loveable moptops and have the sex change operations too, go the whole way, do it right.

These reflections before even setting foot in England or America or any place except the land where he was born, which he is leaving for good, without regrets, without a backward glance: I want to be in America, America where everyone's like me, because everyone comes from somewhere else. All those histories, persecutions, massacres, piracies, slaveries; all those secret ceremonies, hanged witches, weeping wooden virgins and horned unyielding gods; all that yearning, hope, greed, excess, the whole lot adding up to a fabulous noisy historyless self-inventing citizenry of jumbles and confusions; all those variform manglings of English adding up to the livingest English in the world; and above everything else, all that smuggled-in music. The drums of Africa that once beat out messages across a giant landscape in which even the trees made music, for example when they absorbed water after a drought, listen and you'll hear them, yikitaka yikitaka yikitak. The Polish dances, the Italian weddings, the zorba-zithering Greeks. The drunken rhythm of the salsa saints. The cool heart music that heals our aching souls, and the hot democratic music that leaves a hole in the beat and makes our pants want to get up and dance. But it's this boy from Bombay who will complete the American story, who will take the music and throw it up in the air and the way it falls will inspire a generation, two generations, three. Yay, America. Play it as it lays.

While he is required to remain seated he occupies his narrow chair as if it were a throne, managing somehow in that confined space to lounge, to give the impression of consummate, even royal, ease. In the countries below him other kings are going about their business. The King of Afghanistan is acting as tourist guide to well-heeled travellers while blocks of hashish bearing government seals of quality and grade are sold in the high-street stores of his capital city; the Shah of Iran makes love to his wife, whose moans of pleasure mingle with the screams of the vanished thousands in the torture chambers of SAVAK; the Queen of England dines with the Lion of Judah; the King of Egypt lies dying. (And so, in America, a magic land that is swinging slowly but surely towards the top of Ormus's personal Faraway Tree, does Nat "King" Cole.)

And the earth continues, unpredictably, wrongly, to move.

Not everybody is happy to be going West. Virus Cama is sitting bolt upright between his mother and brother, can sense the distance between himself and jailed Cyrus growing, and as the bond of their twinship stretches so his dumb face seems to distend with grief. The pink bride is crying softly behind her veil, ignored by her sweat-stained bodyguards. And Spenta Cama on a wing and a prayer is flying in a state of extreme tension, keeping her fingers crossed, heading for her blind date with William Methwold, the one great gamble on which her future depends.

Ormus closes his eyes and drifts languidly away from consciousness towards turbid airplane sleep. Down the Las Vegas corridors of his mind he chases the dragon, the wisp of smoky nothing that is also Gayomart his dead twin. The past is dropping away from him. Vina has escaped from his yesterdays and is now waiting up ahead, she is his only future. Quake me, Ormus Cama, murmuring down towards sleep, asks of Fate. Rock me like a baby in the bosom of music. Shake me till I rattle, shake me but don't break me, and roll me, roll me, roll me, like thunder, like a stone.

THIS WHEN they're flying over what's that down there, the Bosphorus is it, or the Golden Horn, or are they the same place, Istanbul, Byzantium, whatever: drugged by flight, detached from the indifferent earth, he feels a certain resistance in the air. Something fighting back against the aircraft's forward movement. As if there's a stretchy translucent membrane across the sky, an ectoplasmic barrier, a Wall. And are there ghostly border guards armed with thunderbolts watching from high pillars of cloud, and might they open fire. But there's nothing for it now, this is the onliest high road into the West, so onward, drive those dogies onward. But it's so springy, this invisible restriction, it keeps pushing the airplane back, boeing!, boeing!, until at last the *Mayflower* breaks through, it's through! Sunlight bounces off the wing into his bleary eye. And as he passes that unseen frontier he sees the tear in the sky, and for a terror-stricken instant glimpses miracles through the gash, visions for which he can find no words, the mysteries at the heart of things, Eleusinian, unspeakable, bright. He intuits that every bone in his body is being irradiated by something pouring through the sky-rip, a mutation is occurring at the level of the cell, of the gene, of the particle. The person who arrives won't be the one who left, or not quite. He has crossed a time zone, moved from the eternal past of early life into the constant now of adulthood, the tense of presence, which will become a different kind of preterite, the past of absence, when he dies.

The visionary moment takes him by surprise, unnerves him. After a few seconds the opening vanishes and there's nothing out there except the cloud columns, the jet streams, the anachronistic, remnant moon, and infinity, spreading. He feels his fingers tremble, there's a biochemical quiver moving through his body, it's the way you feel when somebody slaps your face or impugns your honour or just leans drunkenly into you and calls you an asshole, it's the way you feel when you feel insulted. He does not want this charismatic experience, wants the world to be real, to be what it is and no more, but he knows that he has always been prone to slipping off the edge of things. And now that he has taken flight, the miraculous has assailed him, has surged through the fractured sky and anointed him with magic. A mantle of sunlight settles on his shoulders. Get away from me, he protests. Just let me sing my songs. His right hand, its fingers still unsteady, touches his mother's left; and clasps.

Spenta, shocked by Ormus's unexpected words, unable to avoid the conclusion that they are meant for her, is perplexed by his apparently contradictory capture of her jewelled hand. Physical displays of affection between Spenta and Ormus are uncharacteristic, infrequent. The mother finds herself feeling light-headed, and begins to blush like a young girl. She turns to look at her son, and at once her stomach whirls, as if the plane had dropped a few thousand feet through a hole in the air. Sunlight is falling on Ormus, and she feels there is another light emanating from within him now, a radiance of his own, rhyming with the sun's. Spenta who has walked with angels most of her life looks on her child as if for the first time. This is the son whom she tried to dissuade from accompanying her to England, the last-born flesh of her flesh, whose blood bonds she would have been prepared to cut loose. Remorse consumes her. My goodness, she thinks, my son is already more than a man, he's more than halfway to being a young god, and it's no thanks to me. With unpractised awkwardness she covers his hand with her other hand and asks, Something on your mind, Ormie? Is there maybe something I can do for you? He shakes his head absently, but she insists, driven on by her sudden guilt: Anything, there must be some little service.

As if awakening from sleep, he says, Mother, you must let me go.

Get away from me. So he was saying goodbye after all, she thinks, and foolish tears blub out: What are you saying, Ormie, have I not been, she can't finish the sentence, because she knows the answer, which is No. A good mother? No, no.

Ashamed, she turns her face away. She is sitting between her sons. Ardaviraf Cama sits straight-backed in the window seat, oblivious, silent, smiling his serene smile. That faint empty rictus of idiot joy. We are crossing a bridge in the air, Spenta understands. We, too, are travellers between the worlds, we who have died to our old world to be reborn in the new, and this parabola of air is our Chinvat Bridge. Having embarked, we have no option but to go forward on that soul's journey in which we will be shown what is best, and worst, in human nature. In our own.

Determinedly, she turns back to implore Ormus: Take some money, at least.

He agrees to accept five hundred pounds. Five hundred pounds is a lot of money, you can live on it for six months or more if you're careful. He takes it because he knows that he is the one giving the gift. It is her liberty, not his, that is the subject of this transaction. He is already free. Now she is buying her freedom from him, and he is permitting her to do so. The price is more than fair.

He has passed through the membrane. His new life begins.

EUROPE UNROLLS below him like a magic rug, and delivers up an unexpected Cleopatra. A young Indian woman materialises, a stranger, squatting by his aisle seat. Her long hair is worn loose over a long shirt and black tights, the uniform of the arty metropolitan beatnik. Her self-presentation is intimate, sultry. Here I am, darling, she says, surprised to see me? He confesses that yes, he is indeed a tad taken aback. Don't tease me, she cries, making a moue. You weren't so reticent in the hotel room, when you were playing fast and loose with my oiled and perfumed body while the waves at high tide, the aroused and moonlit sea, drowned our noisy cries. You crashed against me like the ocean et cetera. You told me I was the most beautiful girl in the world, at the height of your passion you swore I was the only one for you et cetera et cetera, so how can you be surprised that I'm on this flight as per arrangement, and now we can live happily ever after in jolly old London Town et cetera et cetera et cetera.

He has a good memory, but he does not remember her. She tells him the name of the hotel and the number of the room and then he is sure it isn't true. He has not forgotten—how could he forget?—wearing a Father Christmas outfit at the Cosmic Dancer on Marine Drive, but he never took a room there, with or without sea view. The woman has perched herself on the arm of his seat. I would watch you sleep and even your breath was music, she reminisces. I would bend over your body, my nakedness a beat away from yours and so on, and I felt your melody waft against my skin and so forth. I would inhale your lazy odours and drink the rhythms of your dreams. And so on and so forth. And so often. Once while you slept I held a knife against your throat. Spenta, who has heard every word—every passenger within six rows has heard every word—looks out of sorts, pulling her grumpy bulldog face. Ormus remains calm, begins to let the stranger down gently. Clearly a mistake has been made.

A second woman, older, bespectacled, sari-clad, flustered, comes bustling up, speaks sharply to the first: Maria, how can you bother the gentleman so? You're too intelligent, you should have better sense. Go back to your seat at once! Yes, miss, says the beatnik, demurely. Then swiftly she kisses Ormus on the mouth, thrusting a quick, long tongue between his astonished lips. I will be every woman you have ever wanted, of every shape, of every race, of every wild proclivity et cetera, she whispers. I will be your secret heart's unspeakable desires. Just going, miss, she adds in a different, placatory voice, and retreats. As she passes down the aisle she sings out, over her unembarrassed shoulder, Look for me in your dreams and so on. And send for me when it's time.

Passengers mutter and grouch. She waves lightly, and is gone.

The older woman lingers. Mr. Cama, she says, awkward

but resolute, would you allow me to ask you a couple of personal questions, pardon the intrusion?

She introduces herself as the young woman's former teacher at Sophia College: My most brilliant student, it is all so stupid. Such expressiveness in that child, words fail me. But there is a mental problem, what a tragedy, it drives me mad. . . . She says she is taking her protégée on a tour of London galleries and shows. Such strong creativity in the girl, she sighs, but alas, she makes things up.

Taking a breath, she makes her enquiry. Mr. Cama, she has heard you singing, and now she is singing only of you. But her love story. It is important to establish. Do you know her from back home? From where we are from?

She speaks as if her Bombay, her India, were somehow different from mine, Ormus thinks, but lets it pass. Maybe she came to a show, he tells her, but no, I don't know her from a hole in the ground.

These things happen, he tells the lady in the sari. He is as yet only a small-time entertainer, a tiny bulb in the blinding light show of fame, but even for him this isn't the first such encounter. There was a Russian girl, the daughter of a Bombay-based consular official, who sent him seventeen numbered letters in English, each accompanied by a poem in Russian. One letter a day, until on the eighteenth day there was no poem and a melancholy awakening. *Now I know you do not love me, so I will be sending my virginal yearnings to great poet Mr. A. Voznesensky instead.* In the plane to London the sari-clad teacher nods: You can see that I had to ask. I never knew what to think. What a fixation! So much detail, I thought how could it be a fantasy, but of course it could not be true. Don't be angry. You must be furious. Only have pity. When a gifted child is damaged it is all our loss, isn't it? No, never mind, it's nothing to do with you. We are not a part of your world. Thanking you all the same.

Ormus delays her with questions of his own.

The teacher looks shifty. Yes, unfortunately it has been going on for some time, she confirms. Apparently the two of you have a love nest in Worli, but of course you don't have it. And she says you want to marry her but she wants to be free of ties, even though she is bound to you in far deeper ways than any ordinary married persons can comprehend, it is a marriage of mythological proportions and when you die you will take up residence in the stars et cetera. But of course you do not want this, she has been drawn into your penumbra and it has become more real than her own. It is not real. I mean it is real for you but not for her.

Once again, the odd locutions. There is mystery here.

She has written poetry, the teacher bursts out, painted paintings, learned the words to the songs that you have sung. Her room a shrine to your not existing love. You should understand that the paintings are good paintings, the poems are not without talent, her singing voice is strong and it can additionally be sweet. Maybe once you said a friendly word to her after a show. Maybe one day you smiled and touched her hand. And when we got on to the plane you said Welcome to the *Mayflower*. That was unwise, it would have been better not to say it. And the *Mayflower* is not the name of this plane. The name of the plane is *Wainganga*. Oh, it doesn't matter what the name is.

And her name is Maria, Ormus asks. He twists round in his seat, trying to see where she's sitting. The teacher shakes her head. No need for names-shames, she says, leaving. A sick stranger and her friend, you must be happy with that. Why names? You'll never talk to us again.

But as he watches the teacher scurry down the aisle, Ormus hears Gayomart whispering in his ear: The obsessed young woman's name is not an irrelevance. She's not from the past. She's the future.

MR. JOHN Mullens Standish XII, the radio pirate, known as Mull, Ormus Cama tells me (years later, in the period we have both come to think of as A.V., that is to say, After Vina), I would call the first man of genuine consequence to take me under his wing, an entrepreneur of real acumen, exceptional leadership qualities, a certain ruthless charm, a deep thinker, the first honourable gent I encountered on my journey West, and what was he? A common buccaneer, a desperado, a man facing possible arrest at Heathrow Airport an hour or two after our meeting. This, however, troubled me not in the slightest. Quite the contrary. Ever since boyhood, I'd had a head full of criminals of the sea. Captain Blood, Captain

Morgan, Blackbeard, the Barbary Corsairs, Captain Kidd. The great Brynner, with hair and a moustache, as Jean Lafitte in Quinn and DeMille's movie about the Battle of New Orleans. The novels of Rafael Sabatini, the feats of the Elizabethan privateers. Nor was I limited to storybook stuff. You, Rai, with your darker perspective, there's too much of the world's horror in your eye, so you don't see. How to relish the seafaring criminals of our own childhood coastline. Yet there they were, all the time, plying their trade right under our noses. Looking out to sea from Cuffe Parade or Apollo Bunder, we—you and I!—we saw the Arab dhows, the dirty little engine-driven fishing launches. Silhouettes on the horizon, red sails in the sunset. Carrying who knows what booty to who knew where—

Save this guff for the magazines, I interrupt. Narcotics smuggling is not so romantic, that's the truth. Criminal mafias, ditto.

He ignores me, lost in rhetoric: And if the pirate Drake hadn't beaten the Armada, and the Spanish had conquered India instead of the British? You'd have liked that, I guess? (Such moments, when Sir Darius Xerxes Cama's Anglophile xenophobia emerges from his son's mouth, are genuinely spooky.)

British, Spanish, what's the difference? I cry, to provoke him.

Well, he rises to the bait, if you'd . . . then he sees my game, restrains himself and grins ruefully. Anyway, he shrugs, when Standish approached me, it seemed as if Jason himself was inviting me aboard the *Argo* to join the quest for the Golden Fleece. And all I had to do was play music.

THEY ARE already in German airspace when the stewardess—Ormus, perhaps excusably in view of the date and his own Bombay English, still thinks of her as an air hostess—summons Mr. Cama into first class. Mull Standish rises to welcome him: tall, Bostonian, not yet fifty but already silvery and patrician, reeking of old money, dressed in Savile Row silk and Lobb leather. Don't be fooled by appearances, he greets Ormus, handing him a Scotch and soda without troubling to ask, adding: It's mostly phoney. You'll find I'm pretty much a rogue.

I caught your Santa act, he mentions further, twinkling. On an earlier visit. That was some exit you made.

Ormus shrugs, is unamused by the happenstance of it: the Cosmic Dancer Hotel again. As if Nataraja, the old Lord of the Dance, were out there somewhere, choreographing the steps of his petty human destiny. I was going through a bad time, he snaps. I'm better now. He doesn't add that the excitement of England, as it approaches, is flooding through him, as if he were a drain-blocked Bombay street in the monsoon. Standish, a big man, sees it, anyway: Ormus's aroused condition, his readiness for whatever may come. His so to speak protagony. You're the vigorous type, he notes. Good. We have that in common, for a start.

Standish's own vigour is so great that it seems he might burst out of his suit and shoes at any moment, like Tarzan in the City, like the Hulk. This is a person who has business with the world, who expects events to fall in with his plans. An actor and a maker. His highly manicured nails, his equally well attended hair, speak of a certain *amour propre.* Near the end of this long plane flight he looks daisy-fresh. That takes some doing. That takes an exercise of will.

Is there something I can do for you?

Ormus's question actually makes Standish applaud. You're in even more of a hurry than I'd hoped, the older man congratulates the younger. And here I am thinking it's the East that's timeless, and us transatlantic rats who can't stop racing to Hell and back again.

No, Ormus answers. Actually it's the West that's exotic, fabulous, unreal. We underworlders . . . He realizes that Standish isn't listening. Don't go chippy on me, Mr. Cama, the American says: distantly, even idly. We may be working together for some time, and we're going to have to be able to speak our minds, any way we choose. Even a pirate can cleave to his First Amendment rights, as I hope you will allow. (The twinkle is back in his eyes.)

He's a Cambridge man—Cambridge, England; two years of graduate school. In his day he was a brilliant Chinese scholar, with dreams of setting up an academic institution of his own once he was through studying. Things have not worked out as he hoped. An early marriage to a woman in the rag trade failed, though not before it produced two sons, who stayed in England with his angry, resentful ex-wife when he went back across the Atlantic. For a time he taught Chinese at Amherst College. Then, frustrated at failing to gain the rapid advancement he expected, he made a curious, flamboyant decision. He would drive long-haul trucks across America for a few years, work his ass off, save money, start his dreamed-of Chinese school. From teacher to Teamster: a metamorphosis that represented the first stage of his true coming to be, his American way. He lit out, without illusions or regrets.

He quotes Sal Paradise by heart: *So began the part of my life you could call my life on the road. Before that I'd often dreamed of going West to see the country, always vaguely planning and never taking off.* For two years, maybe three, time was kind of stretchy then, you never knew how long things were taking, I crisscrossed America, carrying its produce to those who needed it, who were addicted to it as badly as any junkie, or had been told they needed it so often that they became addicted to the telling. A heavily fatigued speedhead, blissed out on distance and music and harsh, hungry freedom. Of course I never saved any money at all, spent it right away on women and substances, and most of all I spent it at Vegas, where the big wheels kept taking me, the spinning roulette wheels of my monster trucks.

Standish is away with his thoughts. Ormus, sipping Scotch, understands that a full opening of the self is being offered here, an absolute honesty, offered at once and without restraints as the proof of the soliloquist's bona fides. Listening, Ormus closes his eyes for an instant, and there is his own Vegas, that blaze of light through which his dead brother ducks and dives. So they have Las Vegas in common too.

Like Byron, like Talleyrand . . . I do not hesitate, Ormus Cama tells me A.V., to compare Mull Standish to such men; for he often made the comparison himself, and these days, a person's self-description is quickly adopted by all and sundry—Clown Prince, Comeback Kid, Sister of Mercy, Honest John—so why deny Standish his chosen similes? . . . like Joyce's Nausicaä, Gertie MacDowell, the American has a club foot. The Lobb shoes have to be specially built to accommodate and support it. In the matter of sexual attraction, it is well known that neither Talleyrand nor Byron was adversely affected by his damaged limb. However, in the younger days about which he has chosen to tell Ormus, Mull Standish was still more of a Gertie: his foot crippled his self-belief. Then, while he was losing his stash in an early round of the World Championship of Poker, he was approached by a young man, who spoke appreciatively of his physical beauty and offered him a substantial sum of money to accompany him to a suite at the Tropicana. Standish, feeling broke, absurd and flattered, agreed, and the encounter changed his life.

This was the beginning of my voyage across a frontier I'd thought forever closed to me. (His voice is languorous now, his body stretches out and grows dreamy with remembered joy.) Through that slash in the iron curtain between hetero-sex and homosex, I saw a vision of sublimity. After that, I gave up the trucks, and for a passage of years I stayed in Vegas, as a working male.

Prostitution taught him he was beautiful and desired, it allowed him to dream, to construct the Mull Standish who would dare to enter the zeitgeist and shake it all about. From Las Vegas to New York's Forty-second Street was a predictable next step, and it was here that he became the beneficiary of a classic only-in-America moment. A limousine pulled up; its window motored open; out leaned that self-same young man, the trick from the Tropicana, his transforming angel. *Jesus. I've been looking for you for months. Jesus Christ.* It turned out that Mr. Tropicana had come *(a)* into his inheritance, and *(b)* to the conclusion that Mull Standish was his one true love. As a token of this love he gave Mull a brownstone apartment building in St. Mark's. In a trice the midnight cowboy was transformed into a member of the propertied classes, a respectable member of the Greater Gotham Business Guild of gay businessmen, and a pillar of the community. Thereafter Standish rapidly parlayed his early, lucky break into the beginnings of a jaw-dropping real estate portfolio, thanks to his continuing, long-term relationship with the Tropicana Kid—let's call him Sam—and, therefore, honorary membership of the inner circle of one of New York's true First Families, the great construction dynasties, the master builders, the high grammarians of the city's present tense.

Mayors, bankers, movie stars, basketball stars, representatives, Mull Standish says, and it is the first time Ormus hears a note of boastfulness in his voice, These people have been, let us say, frequently at my disposal.

America is not so unlike India, after all.

Why aren't you there now? Ormus has perspicacity of his own. There is a hidden dimension here, a side to the tale that has not been disclosed. Mull Standish raises a glass, acknowledging the question's shrewdness. I have certain issues with the IRS, he confesses. Corners were cut. There was a degree of clumsiness. It suits me to be in England for a time. England, where it's still illegal to be queer. As for India, I go there for my spiritual needs. I see this is a remark of which you do not approve. What shall I say? You have lived in the wood all your life and so you cannot see the trees. To provide the planet with good air to breathe, we have been given the Amazon rain forest. To provide for the planet's soul, there is India. One goes there as one goes to the bank, to refill the pocketbook of the psyche. Excuse the vulgar money-oriented metaphor. I have a refined act but I am not at bottom the refined type. Leopardskin briefs under the sober suit. Lycanthropic tendencies at the time of the full moon. A certain loucherie. In spite of which I have my spiritual hunger, the needs of my soul.

The stewardess tells me you've been calling this plane the *Mayflower,* it has pleased you to make that joke. Did you know that Standish is a famous *Mayflower* name? I guess nobody reads Longfellow any more, especially in Bombay. Still, it's a poem of more than a thousand lines, a long and vile thing. Miles Standish, a professional soldier, suffering from soldierly inarticulacy, wishes to marry a certain Puritan maiden, Priscilla Mullens or Molines, and makes what you might call the Cyrano error, sending his friend John Alden to plead his cause because the cat had gotten his tongue and wouldn't let go. Young Alden, a cooper, a signatory of the Mayflower Compact, the founder of Plymouth Colony, a man of fortunate looks and pleasing manner, is unfortunately much in love with the same damsel, and yet in friendship's name agrees to do as he is bid. Well! Mistress Molines or Mullens, she hears him out, then looks him squarely, forwardly in the eye and asks, Why don't you speak for yourself, John? Tedious hundreds of lines later they are married, and the gruff old soldier, my vanquished—and distant—ancestor, is left to make the best of it. I tell you this because, though I'm no Puritan, Mistress Priscilla's words are now my motto. I ask nothing on others' behalf, but am shameless and inexorable in my own interest. As now, this minute, in making my approach to you.

Ormus reddens, and Standish, seeing his embarrassment, laughs. No, not sex, he reassures him. Piracy on the high seas.

ENGLAND RUSHES towards them, then stops. Air traffic congestion, even in 1965. Unable to make their approach, they circle in the sky. Down below them, the pirate navy has assembled, an invasion is in progress. Here is a decommissioned old passenger ferry, flying the Jolly Roger, moored in the North Sea. The *Frederica.* Here's another, the *Georgia,* anchored off the Essex coast, near Frinton. Look down at the Thames Estuary: those three tiny dots, see them?, are also part of this cutthroat fleet. Ormus, tired, exhilarated, is in an airplane state of mind; hollow, unreal, a condition in which it's hard to keep a grip on things. Mull Standish seems utterly unfazed, and is talking, now, about childhood:

There was a heavy glass ball that used to sit on the windowsill of my bedroom. My father would turn it to catch and refract light. There were bubbles in it, like galaxies, like dreams. The small things of our earliest days move us, and we don't know we don't know why. Now that I've started this pirate fleet thing, I keep seeing that ball. Maybe it's innocence, freedom, I couldn't say. Maybe it's about a transparent world: you can see through it to the light. Maybe it's just a ball of glass, but somehow it's moving me, it's making me do this.

It occurs to Ormus as Standish talks on that he's giving too many reasons for doing what he is doing: over-explaining what is, after all, a nakedly commercial enterprise, news of which has already reached India. At a brilliant moment in British music, British radio is deadly dull. Restrictions on "needle time" mean that when you want the latest hit records—John Lennon singing "Satisfaction," the Kinks' "Pretty Woman," or "My Generation," by the new supergroup High Numbers, who changed their name from The Who and immediately made the big time—all you get is Joe Loss or Victor Sylvester, music for dead people. But because commercial radio isn't illegal if it's not land based, the pirate ships have come to give the kids what they want. Needle time and adverts. Hello pop pickers this is Radio Freddie broadcasting on 199 . . . this is Radio Gaga . . . this is the Big M. The pirates aim their sounds at Britain and the country surrenders. And Mull Standish is the Lord High Desperadio: the music brigands' king.

Reasons go on pouring out of him. Maybe he's in England because, to be absolutely frank, things with his lover, Sam Tropicana, are no longer what they were, the bloom is off. Or maybe he just plain got bored with the construction industry, all those hard hats and girders, all those empty rooms for other lives to fill. Or maybe it's the fault of the CIA, because, yes, they approached him on several occasions, a Chinese-language expert is assumed to be top-grade spy material, so they try and sign you up before the Yellow Peril gets to you and turns you to the dark side, and the second time he refused them—a man called Michael Baxter or Baxter Michaels had made the approach right in the foyer of the Sherry Netherland—he was accused of having an attitude and threatened with the confiscation of his passport. *I crossed some line when that happened, it changed America for me, and it became possible to leave.* And then, of course, it's surprising he's taken so long to get round to mentioning it, there's the war, America is at war. Ballot boxes have been stuffed full of votes for President Kennedy, war is always good for sitting presidents, his numbers are up from the tight squeeze against Nixon in 1960, he's got four more years of power and priapism at Pennsylvania Avenue, and now it's the voters, the young generation of soldier electors out there in jungled, swamped, incomprehensible Indochina, who are being stuffed into boxes in shocking quantities and being sent home to various addresses less exalted than JFK's. Their numbers, too, are up.

Mull Standish is against the war, but that's not exactly what he wants to say. He wants to say—his eyes are gleaming now, and the energy pours from him with redoubled, frightening force—that the war has turned him on to its consequent music, because in this dark time it's the rock music that represents the country's most profound artistic engagement with the death of its children, not just the music of peace and psychotropic drugs but the music of rage and horror and despair. Also of youth, youth surviving in spite of everything, in spite of the children's crusade that's blowing it apart. (A mine, a sniper, a knife in the night: childhood's bitter end.)

That's when I really fell in love with rock, Standish is off and rolling, because I admired so much what it was doing, the humane democratic spirit-food fullness of its response. It was not just saying fuck you, Uncle Sam, or give peace a chance, or I feel like I'm fixin' to die, or even making patriotic noises, zap zap zappin' the Cong. Rather, it was making love in a combat zone, insisting on the remembrance of beauty and innocence in a time of death and guilt; it privileged life over death and asked life to take its chance, let's dance, honey honey, in the street, on the phone, and we'll have fun fun fun on the eve of destruction.

His manner has changed completely, from patrician Bostonian to eager-beaver muso peacenik, and Ormus, watching the transformation, begins to see who he really is. Never mind all his explanations, the truth is he's just another one of us chameleons, just another looking-glass transformer. Not only an incarnation of Jason the Argonaut but also perhaps of Proteus, the metamorphic Old Man of the Sea. And once we've learned how to change our skins, we Proteans, sometimes we can't stop, we career between selves, lane-hopping wildly, trying not to run off the road and crash. Mull Standish, too, is a slip-slider, Ormus understands: a shape-shifter, a man who knows what it's like to wake up as a giant bug. That's why he picked me out, he can see we're of the same tribe, the same sub-species of the human race. Like aliens on a strange planet we can recognize each other in any crowd. At present we have adopted human form, here on the third rock from the sun.

Standish, this new, exhilarated, high-as-a-kite Standish, says: I came to England to get away from a country at war. One month after I arrived, the new Labour government decided to join forces with the Americans and ship its own kids out to die. Things here stopped being theoretical.

British boys and girls, too, started being mailed home in small packages. I couldn't believe it, as an American I felt *responsible,* as if I'd flouted quarantine regulations and imported a deadly epidemic, I felt like a flea carrier. A plague dog. This development was not as per programme. In a spin, I flew out to India, which is what I do when I need to regain equilibrium. That's when I looked in at your big moment at the Cosmic Dancer, by the way.

After Bombay, Standish had gone to sit at the feet of a teenage mahaguru in Bangalore, and then up to Dharmsala to spend time at the Buddhist Shugden temple. *Again*—I find myself thinking when Ormus tells me the story—*again the curious possessive fascination of the hedonistic West with the ascetic East. The arch-disciples of linearity, of the myth of progress want, from the Orient, only its fabled unchangingness, its myth of eternity.* It was the god-boy who came through. He's an old soul in a young body, Mull says reverentially, a Tantric Master in his final incarnation. I confessed everything to that wise child, my alienation, my guilt, my despair, and he smiled his pure smile and said, The music is the glass is the glass ball. Let it shine.

I understood then that the limit on needle time was the enemy, the censor. The limit was General Waste-More-Land's broadcasting ally, General Haig's whore. Enough with big bands and men in white tuxes with bow ties pretending nothing was going on. I mean come *on.* A nation at war deserves to hear the music that's going *mano a mano* with the war machine, that's sticking flowers down its gun barrels and baring its breasts to the missiles. The soldiers are singing these songs as they die. But this is not the way soldiers used to sing, marching into battle bellowing hymns, kidding themselves they had god on their side; these aren't patriotic-bullshit, get-yourself-up-for-it songs. These kids are using singing, instead, as an affirmation of what's natural and true, singing against the unnatural lie of the war. Using song as a banner of their doomed youth. Not *morituri te salutant,* but *morituri* say up yours, Jack, those about to die give you the fucking finger. That's why I got the ships.

He slumps back in his seat, almost talked out. He has sold up a chunk of his American real estate holdings to purchase, equip and staff up these barely seaworthy little boats. A complete encirclement of England and Scotland is envisaged, seagoing conditions permitting. Now we're blasting the material at them round the clock, he says, Hendrix and Joplin and Zappa, making war on war. Certainly, the loveable moptops too. Also the Lovin' Spoonful, Love, Mr. James Brown feelin like a sex machine, Carly Simon and Guinevere Garfunkel feelin groovy et cetera. My one regret is that we can't moor a boat on the Thames, right outside the Houses of Parliament, mount giant speakers on the deck and blow those complacent bastards right out of their murderous seats. But never say die; this project, too, is in development. So what do you say? Are you with us or withered? There or square?

HE HAD me badly off balance, just the way he wanted me, Ormus tells me, A.V.: I was ripe for adventure, and he'd taken me by storm.

The pilot announces the flight's clearance to land. The air hostess approaches, asks Ormus to resume his own seat. Ormus, rising to go, asks Mull Standish, Why me?

Call it a hunch, he replies, No, let's say inspiration. I flatter myself that I am a judge of men. Something about the way you tore off the Santa beard that night. Something about you struck me, strikes me, as, ah, ah.

Piratical? Ormus suggests.

Emblematic, Mull Standish finds the word, with what looks suspiciously like the makings of a blush mounting above the semi-stiff collar of his Turnbull & Asser shirt. I asked around a little, you know. Seems you're capable of generating a following. People look to you. Maybe you'll get 'em listening to us.

But I'm trying to be a singer, not a DJ on a cold, wet boat, Ormus makes his last, wavering stand. His imagination has been captured, and Standish knows it.

You will be, Standish promises. As a matter of fact you already are, and a good one, might I add. Yes, sir. At this very moment—hark at you—I could swear you're singing right now. Yes. I can hear your song.

AS THE plane touches down, Ormus Cama's head starts pounding. There is something about this England in which he has just arrived. There are things he cannot trust. There's a rip, once again, in the surface of the real. Uncertainty pours down on him, its dark radiance opens his eyes. As his foot alights upon Heathrow, he succumbs to the illusion that nothing is solid, nothing exists except the precise piece of concrete his foot now rests upon. The homecoming passengers notice none of this, they stride confidently forward through the familiar, the quotidian, but the new arrivals look fearfully at the deliquescent land. They seem to be splashing through what should be solid ground. As his own feet move gingerly forward, he feels small pieces of England solidify beneath them. His footprints are the only fixed points in his universe. He checks out Virus: who is untroubled, serene. As for Spenta Cama, her eyes are fixed on the crowd of waving greeters high above. Trying to pick out a familiar face, she has no time to look down. Never look down, Ormus thinks. That way you won't see the danger, you won't plunge through the deceptive softness of the apparent into the burning abyss below.

Everything must be made real, step by step, he tells himself. This is a mirage, a ghost world, which becomes real only beneath our magic touch, our loving footfall, our kiss. We have to imagine it into being, from the ground up.

But he will spend his early days on the sea, within sight of land, which will remain just out of reach but which will listen, as though hypnotized, to his seductive, imagining voice.

BEYOND THE barrier, William Methwold and Mull Standish are waiting, two large pinkish thumbs sticking out of a rackety Indian crowd, the land children running at top speed to greet their cousins from the air, outpacing the astonishingly stentorian shouts of the older women in their heavy-framed spectacles and wine-dark overcoats worn over brilliant saris, and the bellowed rebukes of the older men with jutting lower lips and jangling car keys. The younger women, not in fact demure, group together to perform demureness; they lower their eyelids, whisper, simper. The younger men, not in reality half as backslapping and juvenile as they seem, likewise gather in clutches, their arms around one another's shoulders, to yell and joke, giggle and nudge. Ormus, emerging into England, finds himself momentarily, dizzyingly, back in India, hearing an echo of home. Nostalgia tugs at him for an instant. He jerks himself free of it. There's new music in the air.

Out of the migrant throng, this new way of being British, the two white men rise like Alps. Methwold is a walking antique, with mottled skin blotched over his hairless unwigged dome, making his baldness look like a map of the moon, with its dry seas of shadow and tranquillity, its veiny lines, its pocks. Limp fleshfolds flap above the collar that has grown too large for his neck. He walks with a stick, and he looks, Spenta is happy to note, as pleased to see her as she is to see (indeed, to recognize) him. As for Mull Standish, he has evidently evaded arrest. Perhaps the IRS isn't as hot on his trail as he fears; and as for his pirate ships, technically they are breaking no law, though the state's lawyers are working overtime to come up with pretexts on which they can be closed down.

The Camas pause. They are at their crossroads. Their futures tug them apart.

Okay, then, Ormus says to his mother.

Okay, then, in a muffled voice she replies.

Okay, then, Ormus punches Virus on the shoulder.

Virus makes a tiny sideways motion of the head.

Okay, see you, then, Ormus repeats. Nobody is touching him, but he feels himself held. He pulls against the force field, turns a shoulder and tugs hard.

Okay, see you, then. Spenta seems incapable of offering more than echoes, is herself becoming no more than a member of that crowd of echoes bouncing around them, fading, fading.

Ormus goes towards Standish, parts from his mother without looking back. Though his last image of her is a trembling lip and a lace kerchief at the corner of an eye, still in the rear-view mirror of his mind he can see her looking grateful. He can see her future shining like a diamond on her brow, the great mansion, the silver thread of river, the green and pleasant land. Though he abhors the countryside, he is happy for her. She has given him what she has been able to give, though she could never love him. It has been less than enough by ordinary standards, but he is prepared to call it sufficient. In a way it is this lack of emotional enthusiasm, this absence of unconditional love, that has prepared him for his great future, has gotten him on to the runway, so to speak, like a jet aircraft, ready to fly. And she herself is husband hunting now. She's a fishing fleet of one. Best for her to arrive as unencumbered as possible. Virus grins mutely at her side at the approaching English milord, but Ormus makes himself scarce. Spenta, preparing her smile for Methwold, has no time for a sentimental farewell. Mother and son go their ways: she into the arms of an old England, he into the new country that's in the process of being born. Destiny summons them both, breaking their family ties.

Music in the air, from a crackly transistor. Soft brushes coax a whispered beat from a drum, a big bass line is laid down, a high riff screams from an invisible clarinet. All that's needed is for a singer to grab some of that stuff and go for broke. Here she comes, her bluesy coloratura spiralling over and around the jazzy rhythm of the tune. Vina! It sounds like her voice, drowned in crackles and arrivals-lounge ruckus as it is, but high, strong, who else could it be. As she will one day hear him on a Bombay radio, so today, at the beginning of his journey back into her heart, he thinks he hears her, and even when, after their reunion, she promises him it couldn't have been, she didn't have a recording contract back in '65, he refuses to accept his mistake. The long-haul terminal was a chamber of echoes that day, and that's how he heard her voice, an echo returning from the future to summon up his love.

He is clear about his purpose: by his labours to make himself worthy of her again. And when he's ready he'll find her, he'll make her real by touching her kissing her caressing her, and she'll do the same for him. Vina I'll be the ground beneath your feet and you, in this happy ending, will be all the earth I need.

He walks towards her, away from his mother, into the music.

THE RAPID disenchantment of Ormus Cama with his fantasy of the West, which will be the making of him as an artist and almost the unmaking of him as a man, begins the instant he lays eyes on Radio Freddie, that seven-hundred-ton rust bucket, pitching uncertainly, like a super-annuated rodeo rider, upon the saddle of the sea. His heart sinks. His imagined journey from periphery to centre has never included the low, dank northern flats of Lincolnshire, nor this biting, sou'westered journey out from shore. He feels "out of land," the landlubber's version of fish-out-of-water. Briefly he wants out, but there's nowhere to go, no other course but the one on which he's set. Indentured Indian labourers arriving in Mauritius and erasing from their Bhojpuri vocabularies such words as "return" or "hope" would have felt, in Ormus's shoes, no less enslaved.

By contrast, Standish, erect at the prow of the motor launch that is transporting him to his kingdom, aquiline of profile, silver hair streaming, looks exalted, haloed. A man with a mission is a dangerous man, Ormus thinks, feeling for the first time in their admittedly brief acquaintance a jolt of something resembling fear. Then Standish turns his head, gleaming with anticipation, points. There they are, he shouts. Look at them, Hook and Smee. The two Tweedles. They hate me, naturally; as you will soon discover. (This in an odd voice pitched halfway between tragedy and pride.) Mr. Nathaniel Hawthorne Crossley and Mr. Waldo Emerson Crossley, he finishes, raising an arm in salute, Your new colleagues. My sons.

The men standing at the *Frederica*'s rail do not return his greeting.

HAWTHORNE CROSSLEY—greatcoated, long-silk-scarved, corduroy-jeaned, the sole of one shoe coming loose—has inherited his father's looks and volubility. He uses his mother's surname, but he's Standish translated into English, filled up with alcohol and spite, and aged twenty-four or -five. Hail Standish, he mocks, as Ormus follows Mull aboard Radio Freddie, Hail the pioneer hero, maker of charts, conqueror of nations. So must the empire builders have looked in their prime, eh, Waldorf? My baby brother, he explains to Ormus. Not named as Mr. Standish would have you believe in honour of a great philosopher but after a fucking salad, as eaten by his presently divorced parents on the night he was conceived.

Rheumy-eyed Waldo, smaller, fuzzy-headed, leather-jacketed, Lennon-bespectacled, his mother's boy, beams, nods, sneezes. In his personal universe Hawthorne is a blazing star.

Hail Standish, Waldo eagerly agrees.

Think of stout Cortez in the Keats poem, only it was really Balboa, gazing at the Pacific, Hawthorne exhorts. Consider Clive of India on the battlefield at Plassey, Captain Cook sailing into Sydney harbour. The Islamic conquerors bursting out of Arabia to face the might of Persia, only to find the once mighty superpower rotten and decayed. They blew it away like sand. It's what Standish hopes to do to the BBC Light Programme.

Why isn't one of you in the studio? Mull Standish fondly interjects.

Because we decided to play the whole fucking Floyd album, Hawthorne answers, every last bubble and shriek. So we've got hours. We reckoned we could trust Eno to flip the disc while we greeted the aged parent. He takes an uncorked bottle of bourbon from his greatcoat pocket. Mull Standish takes it from him, wipes off the neck, prepares to drink.

Robert Johnson was poisoned by a theatre owner who suspected Johnson of fucking his chick, muses Hawthorne, thoughtfully, Sonny Boy Williamson tried to save him, knocked away the bottle he was going to drink from. Don't ever drink from an open bottle, he said. You never know what's in it. Johnson didn't like the advice. Don't ever knock a whisky bottle away from me, he said, and drank from another open bottle, and bango! End of story.

Mull Standish drinks, hands back the bottle, introduces Ormus.

Aha, the Indian nightingale!, says Hawthorne. (It is raining now, a fine icy drizzle that inserts itself between the men and their clothes, between Ormus and his happiness, between the father and his sons.) The bulbul of Bombay! He found you, then. About fucking time. And now you're his Koh-i-noor diamond, the fucking jewel in his arse. A little on the old side for the work, I'd have thought. All I can say is I hope you wash your mouth before applying it to my fucking microphone.

Hawthorne, *Jesus Christ.* Standish's voice is low and dangerous, and the younger man's tongue stumbles, dries.

But it's too late, the cat's out of the bag. Why me? Ormus had asked, and Standish had replied, Call it inspiration. But of course it had nothing to do with inspiration. It's love.

Bareheaded in the rain, Mull Standish, exposed, shamed, confesses and apologizes to Ormus Cama: I have been less than frank. I asked around about you, I told you that. I should have admitted that my personal feelings were in fact engaged. The eagerness. The eagerness of my enquiries. I suppressed that information, which was culpably wrong. However, you have my one thousand per cent guarantee that it won't become a problem between us. . . . Hawthorne snorts with mirthless laughter. Runny-nosed Waldo, not to be outdone, snorts too. Mucus explodes from his nose, like a glutinous flag. He wipes it off his face with the back of his chilblained hand.

Ormus is hearing echoes again. In Hawthorne Crossley he sees Vina reborn, Vina in her childhood incarnation of Nissy Poe, in whose family history there are poignant parallels to the tale of this smart-mouthed, bitter child of a broken home. He sees, too, that Mull Standish's long autobiographical reminiscence about his lover, "Sam Tropicana," who pursued him for months, then found him and changed his life, was a parable, a tale told in code, its real meaning being: *This is what I can do for you. It's true: I hunted you, you have been the quarry of my own obsessive love. But now I can change your life, it is my turn to give as once I was given, to be the bringer of good things as once they were brought to me. I want nothing from you except that you permit me to be your Santa Claus.*

I want nothing from you, Mull Standish is saying, miserably. For you, however, I want very much indeed.

Let me out of here, Ormus Cama demands, and Mull Standish, who has abruptly run out of all his words, can do nothing but drip in the rain and extend, in a profound, involuntary gesture, both of his trembling, supplicant arms. Their palms are upturned, and empty.

Hawthorne Crossley relents. Oh, stay. Will you stay, for fucksake. Stay for the same reason we do: viz., that here there's booze and music, no dope, alas, because the law keeps boarding us to see if there's the tiniest chance of fucking us up, but really the only thing to be afraid of is that one of these fine days the sea god might decide to open up his great gob and swallow us down. Whereas out there—he gestures vaguely with the emptying bottle of Beam towards the land—out there it's just too fucking terrifying for words.

Out there there's kinky bishops, Waldo elucidates. And dodgy Scotch eggs and takeaway chop suey and bent coppers and voodoo dolls and napalm. There's anabolic steroids and cows and anti-personnel strikes north of the DMZ. And Bideford Parva and Piddletrenthide and Ashby-de-la-Zouch and country people in wellies and the Mekong delta where wellies aren't much use and Tet which isn't a place but a date, like Christmas, that's out there too. There's Arsenal F.C. and Ringo marries his hairdresser and Harold Wilson and Russians walking in space. And axe murderers and mother-rapers and father-rapers.

The draft as well, Hawthorne concedes, belching, We're all blowing in *that* wind. What we're hoping is, if we do this long enough, and throw in a spot of littering and creating a nuisance on the side, we may be thought not moral enough to be in the army. If we're lucky we might be not moral enough to blow up women and children and such. We might even be not moral enough to die.

Like Arlo Guthrie, explains Waldo, swaying. (They've finished the bottle of Beam.) Meanwhile, out there, the wrong people are escaping bullets. King Jigme Wangchuk of Bhutan escapes assassination attempt. A machine-gun attempt on the Shah of Iran's life fails. President Sukarno survives a communist coup.

Race riots in Watts, Hawthorne picks up the thread, Edward Heath elected Tory leader. Two charged with Moors murders. Churchill dead. Albert Schweitzer dead. T. S. Eliot dead. Stan Laurel dead. The British believe in God but prefer tv, polls prove. China has the A-bomb. India and Pakistan on brink of war. And England swings like a fucking pendulum do. It scares me to fucking death and back again.

Stay, repeats Waldo, showing his teeth and offering a bottle of sherry, Harveys Bristol Cream. Best we can do at the moment. Welcome to wonderful 199.

Ormus takes the bottle. And who's Eno? he asks. The third Stooge?

You don't have to worry about Eno, Hawthorne shrugs.

Eno's a prince. A man among men. A needle in a haystack. Eno's the business. He's OK.

It's raining harder. Mull Standish makes as if to go. His sons ignore him.

His real name's Enoch, Hawthorne says, turning his soaked back on his father. He dropped the *ch* because he understandably didn't want a racist handle, what with him being a person of tint. It's as if you were a person of Jewishness who got named Hitler by accident and decided to be a Hit instead. Or if your name was unfortunately Stalin and you shortened it to Star.

Mao's a tough one, says Waldo. But you could always answer to Dong.

Hawthorne confides, Actually, he's called Eno because e knows how all this fucking equipment works and we don't have a clue.

Or, Waldo offers, because e no say very much.

Or, Hawthorne continues, because he takes a lot of fruit salts, poor love. It's his third-world digestion. Anyway, when you get to know him you call him Ali. Eno Barber, Ali Barber. I expect that's a joke you'll find funny. I expect that's a joke with a cultural reference that isn't too fucking tough for you to pick up.

He doesn't get it, Waldo pouts. He hasn't had halfway enough to drink, he says.

Hawthorne leans in on Ormus, blasting him with a fog of whisky breath. Listen, Mowgli, he says, not without aggression, you're our fucking guest here, see. How d'you expect to understand the fucking host culture if you insist on remaining teetotal, if you obstinately refuse to fucking integrate in this obstinate fucking Paki obstinate bastard way?

Maybe he's too good for us, Waldo ponders. Too good for Harveys Bristol Cream. Too good for the finest British sherry our father's money can buy.

Mull Standish, with the help of the motor-launch captain, leaves the *Frederica*. Now that you boys have started getting on so well, he says, I'm sure the station will just go from strength to strength.

God save the Queen, Hawthorne Crossley salutes his father extravagantly, And he probably ought to keep an eye on that Elizabeth Windsor as well.

* * *

In Ormus Cama's classic rock 'n' roll belter "Ooh Tar Baby"—an encrypted remembrance of his English years, sung in the sour-sour, down-and-dirty cool-cat growl that became his abiding gift to the male singers of the New York underground—the Tar Baby is England itself. England kidnaps people, he says in interviews, when, on his comeback tour, late in his career, he breaks the habit of a lifetime and consents to a few journalistic encounters. England seizes hold, he says, and won't let go. It's uncanny. You arrive for whatever reason, just passing through en route to the rest of your life, but watch out, or you'll get stuck for years. That old Tar Baby, you can greet her courteously but she won't give you the time of day, you can speak to her as nice as pie but she won't act polite, 'til finally you're so ticked off that you bust her in the mouth, and then, too late!, you're held fast. Once you attack her you're in her thrall. It's a strange kind of love, what I call stuck love, but you can't get away. You're only some dumb rabbit anyhow, how smart can you be to be punching out that sticky old sister, if you know what I mean. So you're hanging there, and you can't help yourself, you're beginning to think in a way she's cute, but then you start worrying that maybe in the bushes there's that hungry fox, lying low and saying nothing and waiting for his supper.

Ooh Tar Baby yeah you got me stuck on you. Ooh Tar Baby and I can't get loose it's true. Come on Tar Baby won't you hold me tight, we can stick together all through the night. Ooh Tar Baby and maybe I'm in love with you.

CHAPTER TEN

Season of the Witch

At first the music is the only thing he can get a grip on. Mull Standish XII, who chooses the playlists for all his boats, has a good ear and sure instincts. As he becomes familiar with these lists, Ormus privately concedes that his premature dismissal of cisatlantic rock music was way off beam. This is the golden age of British rock 'n' roll. After Sinatra and Parker, this is the third revolution.

Mull visits each boat once in every two-week period. (The terms of employment for DJs aboard Radio Freddie are also based on a fourteen-day rotation, two weeks on, two weeks off.) He arrives with a clattering canvas bag of the latest platters and announces the musical marching orders for the next fortnight: push this, spotlight that, play this one once in a while but only because we can't not play it, listen to this one, you guys, this kid's going to be vast. There is a sense of an audience building, and the terrestrial bosses are definitely getting nervous. You can tell this is so because the frequency of the drug-squad raids is increasing. In Ormus's first shift they are boarded twice, the boat is turned upside down, its human cargo is strip-searched, there is a good deal of sneering and shoving, and finally they are left alone again.

My fucking rectum's getting so habituated to being probed by these rozzers' rubber-gloved fingers, announces Hawthorne, it's beginning to fucking like it.

Waldo gravely assents. Probably something in the genes.

Ormus, however, finds it hard to see the funny side. Naked and innocent before the officers of the law, suffering their jolly rogerings, he shakes with rage and shame. This is an England his father never knew, at whose existence he could not have guessed.

Except during the police searches, Cap'n Pugwash (not

his real name) and the crew of the *Frederica* have little time for the broadcasting staff. Their quarters are separate, and few words are exchanged. The raids, however, are forging a curious bond between the two camps. The bluebottles' stings act as a unifying force. The invasions, the gibes, transcend the gulfs of world-view and class between the mariners and the radio upstarts. After one raid Pugwash himself—a stubbly, beer-bellied grouch with an appropriately piratical moustache—unbends so far as to say to Hawthorne Crossley, *You keep at it, mate, yeah? You give 'em what bleeding for.* Then, gradually, the surly standoff resumes.

Such are the shock troops of Mull Standish's conquering navy, the navy of peace and music, to whom all England must—according to the chief pirate's strategy—inevitably succumb. In spite of his new-found admiration for the music, Ormus is finding it hard to get a handle on England. Water slurps beneath his feet. Everything shifts. He is told that the kids are crazy for Freddie, but the England he sees on the horizon is a low dark shape below a low grey sky, distantly mooing with uninterest.

Drunkenly, clumsily, the station gets through the days and nights. The weather is continuously dreadful: rain, wind, more wind, more rain. The *Frederica* pitches and rolls. Waldo Crossley is frequently sick, and not always over the side. Somehow, a minimum level of hygiene is maintained, so that the health inspectors, when they make their raids, are unable to close the show down, and leave angry and frustrated. Ormus, learning the art of gonzo broadcasting, comes to see that Eno, the person of tint, is the key. Eno dresses in immaculate whites and sports a cream Borsalino hat, and he is a world unto himself, wanting nothing to do with DJs or crew. He appears not to eat or drink or sleep or (in spite of the Crossleys' fruit-salts slur) even shit or piss. In the ship's studio he keeps things moving from his position behind a desk that looks like an electric hedgehog, bristling with switches. That's where he stays, on the far side of his glass window, Ali Barber in Aladdin's cave, and there's a large sign on the wall behind him saying *Know Your Place.* Eno believes in apartheid, Hawthorne explains, and that means you too. You know that in South Africa the blacks hate the Indians more than they hate the whites.

He's from South Africa, then? Ormus surmises.

Waldo shakes his head gravely. No. Stockwell.

THE MUSIC is extraordinary. Keening slow-hand guitar playing, the old wise voices of ridiculously young blues rockers, the hard-edged raunch 'n' roll women and the soft ethereal crystal-voiced maidens, the screaming feedback swirls of psychedelia, the ballads of war and love, the hallucinated visions of the great troubadours. By clinging to the music Ormus can keep a hold on what's real. The music tells him truths he finds he already knows. The music is a great wild bird calling out to the bird of the same species that lies hidden in his own throat, in the egg of his Adam's apple, hatching, nearing its time.

Ormus, Hawthorne and Waldo set up a sleep rota. They crowd into the confined studio space two at a time, Ormus and Hawthorne, Hawthorne and Waldo, Waldo and Ormus. Time stretches endlessly before them, the land drifts off like a fantasy, and cocooned as they are in rain and alcohol it's easy for them to imagine they're talking to themselves. What goes out over the air in between songs: their interior monologues, the fatigue-and-whisky-polluted streams of their wrecked consciousness.

Ormus, during one night shift, in the small hours when the monsters crawl, notices that his co-jockey Waldo has fallen asleep. Whispering, as if speaking privately to his beloved, he calls out across the skies for Vina. Eno, impassive in his booth, offers no comment. He is lost in electricity, devoted to the maintenance of the signal, dedicated to purity of sound. Perhaps he isn't even listening to Ormus's cry, just hearing the level and timbre of it, throwing his switches, watching his gauges, the flickering of illuminated needles reflected in his eyes.

Are you there, my love, Ormus murmurs. Oh my long-lost love. You did not trust me and I was wounded, proud, I let you go away. Now I must prove myself worthy, I must perform labours, pursue quests, shoulder the burdensome world.

Mull Standish sends an urgent message via the ship's radio. The first mate, who is also the radio operator, transcribes the text, and Cap'n Pugwash—who has been tuning in to Ormus's soliloquy—is sufficiently moved (he's a big lump-in-throat softy, really) to bring Standish's message personally to Eno, who flattens the paper against the glass window. This is an inspiration, Ormus reads. Who is she? Is she real? Did you make her up? Certainly you mustn't find her too soon. Keep it going. Instalments every night. This will build the audience like nothing else. The lovesick floating romeo sings to his unheeding love. You want a singing career? You just found the door. This will give you profile, saliency, share of mind. This will make your make your name.

Vina Apsara has not heard Ormus's appeal. She's in America and doesn't know he's floating off the coast of England, damp and yearning, and calling out her name.

Nobody tells her. It isn't time.

THE MIGRAINES come. They're getting worse. Sometimes he is unable to sleep at all during his allotted hours. He picks up one of the paperbacks abandoned in his cabin—it must be Mull Standish who brought them aboard in the hope of pushing a little culture into his sons, who have promptly tossed them into the spare cabin, the one they never enter, the one that's now Ormus's little hole of privacy. Books by famous American writers, Sal Paradise's odes to wanderlust, Nathan Zuckerman's *Carnovsky,* science fiction by Kilgore Trout, a playscript—*Von Trenck*—by Charlie Citrine, who would go on to write the hit movie *Caldofreddo.* The poetry of John Shade. Also Europeans: Dedalus, Matzerath. The one and only *Don Quixote* by the immortal Pierre Ménard. F. Alexander's *A Clockwork Orange.*

Here's the year's hit fantasy-thriller, *The Watergate Affair,* in which the future President Nixon (President Nixon! that's how wild a fantasy it is) has to leave office after trying to bug the Democrats' offices, an accusation that's finally proved true, in a wildly implausible twist, when it turns out that Nixon also bugged himself, ha ha ha, the things these guys think of to make us laugh.

But every time he picks up one of these books his brain swirls and thumps, and he is forced to put them down unread. His head bursts with confusions and when he closes his eyes he finds that behind his eyelids his dead twin Gayo has changed his behaviour. Gayomart no longer runs away but comes towards, stands up close, staring at Ormus like a man gazing into a mirror. You're a changed man, Gayomart Cama grins. Maybe that's Gayomart out there and you're in here now, trapped in unreality. Maybe now I'm dreaming you. Ormus is appalled by the hostility in Gayomart's glittering grin. Why do you hate me, he asks. Why do you think, his brother replies. I'm the one who died.

To keep Gayo away he must keep his eyes open. He is so tired that he has to use his fingers to push the heavy lids apart. He switches on the monitor in his tiny cabin and tries to concentrate on the brothers Crossley doing their shift.

IF YOU'RE listening, Antoinette Corinth, you witchy insomniac, and I know you're listening because you always are, then this one's for you. This one comes to you from Hawthorne with love. And Waldo would add his personal salutations but alas at present he's being somewhat indisposed in the bin. This one is to honour your genius, O queen of the black arts, princess of the pentangle, Baroness Samedi, priestess of Wicca, adept of the secrets of the Great Pyramid, dispenser of all good things, dressmaker extraordinaire, O Mother who gave us suck. We took your name and you at once let it go, espousing, instead, the noble Corinthian tradition. Mother forgive us for we are royally arseholed. Forgive us Mother for we have taken the shilling of him what done you wrong. As you have surmounted your bitterness towards him, as you have found it in your mighty soul to transcend your most righteous anger, so also let us not come into your bad books, if that's at all possible, because we really needed the spondulicks the cash the moolah the bread the bread. Forgive us Mother for we are soldiers of the Queen our Father and this is wonderful 199, Radio Freddie, and for all you night owls and our own dear Mum here's Manfred Mann to promise us that god is on our side.

Listening to Hawthorne's tirade, Ormus Cama is reminded of Sanjay Gandhi's legendary resentment of his mother Indira for abandoning his father Feroze. Mull Standish is Indira metamorphosed, he thinks, Indira who was powerless against her savage son, who endowed Sanjay with a lifetime's supply of rage.

Is there a god? wonders Waldo Crossley between Manfred Mann and the Searchers. Biggish question. Take your time.

If there's no god, why do men have nipples, Hawthorne ripostes between the Searchers and the Temptations.

On the other hand, if there's no god, it does explain why we have to have Peter, Paul and Mary, reasons Waldo persuasively, between the Temptations and the Righteous Brothers.

If there's no god, who left the tap running up there? Hawthorne roars at the end of "Unchained Melody," thumping the studio table. Check*mate,* I *think.*

The Miracles begin to sing. It goes on raining.

AT THE end of the first fortnight, the Crossley brothers bring Ormus Cama home to mother, where he is to take up residence in the spare room. Home is a maisonette above their mother's clothes shop in a red-brick row-house backwater at the wrong end of Chelsea, past too many kinks in the King's Road, tucked away between the gasworks and Wandsworth Bridge Road; yet time seems to eddy and swirl around this spot, it knows the difference between size and mass. Only the truly massive can push it around. Here, in limbo, time has located a mighty gravitational force, an omnivorous black hole.

Vina once came here. She bought a flimsy frock.

The boutique—a new word that will not last—is called The Witch Flies High and it is already legendary: that is, the arbiters of these matters have agreed that it is one of the enclaves by which the zeitgeist—another fashionable word that will fall from favour—will come in time to be defined. The kiss of posterity is deemed to have blessed The Witch already. She pulls the city into her gravitational field, shapes the moment to her will. Within its event horizon, the laws of the universe cease to apply. Darkness reigns. Antoinette Corinth is the only law.

Mick Jagger is rumoured to wear the dresses, those brief concoctions of velvet and lace. John Lennon's white limo stops outside once a week and a chauffeur takes away whole racks of clothes for the great man and his wife to try on. German photographers with stone-faced models arrive to use The Witch's windows as backdrops for their fashion spreads. The boutique has famous painted windows, featuring the Wicked Witch of the West from the land of Oz. She flies over Emerald City, cackling. Her smoking broom does sign writing in the sky. *Surrender Dorothy.* (The ignorant and unfashionable mistake this for the name of the shop. Such persons are invariably refused admission. Antoinette Corinth loathes Dorothy Gale, her dog and all inhabitants of Kansas, Kansas-as-metaphor, flat, empty, uncool. Antoinette Corinth is Miss Gulch.)

Antoinette lounges in the boutique's doorway, illuminated by a yellow tungsten street lamp, an ample woman wearing a groin-length black lace mini-dress with matching shawl and talking to a waistcoated dandy who turns out to be a celebrated society couturier, and her first backer, Tommy Gin. She permits her sons to peck her on the cheek, ignores Ormus's polite greeting. Gin, too, cuts him dead. Ormus follows Hawthorne and Waldo into The Witch.

Inside, it's pitch dark. You go through a heavy bead curtain and are instantly blinded. The air is heavy with incense and patchouli oil and with, too, the aroma of substances forbidden aboard Radio Freddie. Psychedelic music terrorizes your eardrums. After a time you become aware of a low purple glow, in which you can make out a few motionless shapes. These are probably clothes, probably for sale. You don't like to ask. The Witch is a scary place.

In the depths of the boutique is a dimly discernible presence. This is She. She runs the shop, and makes Twiggy look like a teenager with a puppy-fat problem. She is very pale, probably because she spends her life sitting in the dark. Her lips are shiny black. She also wears a black mini-dress, but hers is velvet, not lace. This is her urban vampire look. (Her other style, black smocks worn with smudged black eyes, is described by Antoinette Corinth as "dead baby.") She stands knock-kneed and pigeon-toed after the fashion of the period, her feet forming a tiny ferocious T. She wears immense silver knuckle-duster rings and a black flower in her hair. Half love child, half zombie, She is a sign of the times.

Ormus attempts charm, introduces himself, mentions his recent arrival in England, says some words about his first stint aboard Radio Freddie, and at this point, faced with the glint of her basilisk eyes in the purple haze, runs out of words and sputters to a halt.

Talk radio's over, she says, Dialogue's dead.

This is stunning information. In five words the neo-Kantian, Bakhtinian definition of human nature—that we change each other constantly through dialogue, through intersubjectivity, the creative interplay of our several incompletenesses—is laid to rest. The essentially Apollonian universe of communication shrivels beneath the contemptuous force of She's Dionysiac post-verbalism. Before Ormus can absorb so revolutionary a change, however, Tommy Gin comes into the store at speed, pursued by a hooting Antoinette Corinth. Listen, man, I'm sorry, man, Gin expostulates, clasping both of Ormus Cama's hands, It's the Witch, man, she likes her joke. I mean, you're Indian, I love India. The Maharishi, man. And the Buddha, and Lord Krishna. Beautiful.

And Ravi Shankar, offers Ormus, trying to be friendly. But Tommy Gin has run out of Indians and can only nod furiously. Right, right, he nods, beaming.

Right, Ormus Cama concurs.

But what I'm saying—Gin returns to his embarrassed apology—is, back there, man, I laid a heavy trip on you, but it's only because she's always shitting with people's heads, I mean, if you can believe it, she told me you were *Jewish.* You can dig that, man, you can see how that would, yeah. But you're not, man, you're just not. Oh, wow.

Hey, Indian guy, shouts Antoinette Corinth, waving a joint in a long cigarette holder. Perhaps you should teach me a few of your whatchoumacallit rope tricks. You seem to have tied the Queen up in knots, unless I'm *very* much mistaken.

Ormus Cama faced with Gin and Antoinette has the sense of having come into the presence of malignity. Gin doesn't count: he's a nasty pinprick, a squib. But from Antoinette Corinth there pours a barely disguised and vengeful malevolence. This is not that wise woman free of all bitterness eulogized by her sons over the pirate airwaves. This is a woman of such palpable vindictiveness that, even though he has no reason to believe he is the target of her venom, Ormus feels physically endangered. He begins, involuntarily, to back away, and bumps into something hard in the dark. A rack of dresses falls to the floor, hangers clattering.

Hah! Hah! (Antoinette Corinth's laugh is a heavy smoker's retch.) The little dear. He's simply terrified. Ormus, baby. Welcome to Unfold Road.

* * *

MULL STANDISH telephones that evening: Everything fine? She acting OK? And before Ormus can answer: Your musical future. I'm working on it. My plans are close to firmed up. Did you know the Georgie Fame record couldn't get played on the BBC, and now, thanks to us, it's a top three hit? That's a big step. It proves the pirates' power. And the next proof is you. Because if we can do it with an unknown, then we're really calling the shots. We need to talk material. We need to talk musicians. We need to talk, period. Don't ask me when. I'm on it. I'm way ahead of you. I'm already there. Be prepared.

There can be no doubting, in retrospect, that Mull Standish was in love with Ormus Cama: in pie-eyed, adolescent, moon-calf love. But he was also a man of quality, a person of character, and he kept his word. Never in all the years of their partnership did he sexually importune the artist whom he helped to build into a world superstar. Without Mull Standish—who put the band together, provided the instruments, booked the recording studios at his own cost and acted as his own promo man—there would certainly have been no Rhythm Center. And without Rhythm Center, there would have been no VTO.

That night on the phone, his first night at the maisonette over The Witch, Ormus remains sceptical: What do you want from me? he wants to know.

Mull Standish's voice wavers fractionally, loses much of its rich timbre. My sons, he says, faltering. Put in a good word for me with my sons.

Which isn't easy. Released from the captivity of Radio Freddie, Hawthorne and Waldo Crossley are busily opening the doors of perception. In their mother's lair—zodiac on the ceiling, astrolabes, Ching sticks, fliers advertising Tibetan overtone chanting, cat, broomstick, the works—they lie semi-conscious, blissing out, with Mummy's help.

They do like their lump sugar, Antoinette Corinth beams. After two weeks, their poor tongues were just hanging out. And you, my Oriental prince? One lump or two?

In spite of a life spent in the allegedly exotic East, Ormus is not accustomed to meeting witches. Awkwardly cross-legged on an Afghan rug, he shifts his weight from haunch to haunch and declines the offered drug. Squinting through Antoinette's chosen darkness, he registers the caged parrot, the Mexican chac-mool, the Brazilian samba drums. Books about the old religions of human sacrifice and blood. A sorceress with Latin accents. Ormus begins to finds it hard to take her seriously. This is an act, isn't it, a posture, a game. In this "culture," people have time for games. Maybe they never get past games. A "culture" of grown-up children.

Germs on a slide.

Antoinette notes Ormus's interest in her paraphernalia, senses his scepticism, launches into a long self-justifying oration. "People are looking for something better. An alternative. And here's this simply immense body of forbidden knowledge, absolutely coherent, fantastically erudite, the hidden learning of the entire human race, and all placed beyond the respectable pale. Why? Well, obviously. Because they don't want us to have access to the power. The *nuclear* power of the secret arts."

That's some of it. Now Ormus begins to see and hear her more clearly. She sounds like a demagogue: self-righteous, a True Believer. She sounds like somebody covering up, using the half-digested rhetoric of the age's lunatic fringe to lend colour to a life story of whose painful banality she is perhaps afraid. What is she, anyway? A tailor who got lucky in trade, but was unlucky in love. Two grown sons and an empty bed. It seems to Ormus that she infantilises her children, that feeding them hallucinogens is her way of keeping them babyish, helpless, dependent; of keeping them hers. In the grip of a sudden wave of nauseous revulsion against the spirit of the age, Ormus finds Antoinette Corinth hard to like: clutchy, a self-dramatist, shrill.

He asks if it's permitted to use the drums. She is disappearing down the smoke rings of her mind, and waves, vaguely. Softly, eagerly, the silky twisting rhythms flow from his fingertips. It is as if the drums have been yearning to speak to him, and he to them. Finally, he thinks: at long last, here are friends.

Fucking Paradise, grunts Antoinette Corinth, and passes out. Ormus doesn't care; he is lost in the samba, the carnival under his flying, beating hands.

Long after he has gone to bed on the floor below her he

hears her wake and crash around upstairs. He hears odd chanting, the chinking of finger cymbals, a woman's voice howling at the moon.

THIS ENGLAND, addled by mysticism, mesmerised by the miraculous, the psychotropic, in love with alien gods, has begun to horrify him. This England is a disaster area, the old are destroying the young by sending them to die in distant fields, and in response the young are destroying themselves. He is having an essentially conservative response not only to the war but also to the countervailing laissez-faire of the age, a response that will intensify as he learns more about the place. A revolt against the damage, the waste, the self-inflicted wounds, the bedspread jackets, the swallowing of various forms of gibberish that has replaced the exercise of intelligence, the susceptibility to gurus and other phoney leaders, the flight from reason, the descent into an inferno of privilege.

In time he will write songs about this disaster area, songs that excoriate a generation lost in space, songs bursting with a savage indignation that will make them, by one of the ironic inversions of the culture, into anthems for the very people he is attacking. The dying, drifting, broken generation, which has told itself a great lie—that it represents hope and beauty—will hear the truth in Ormus Cama's earthquake songs; will look in those cruel mirrors and see themselves. Ormus Cama will find his Western voice, in the words of M. Henri Hulot, by understanding what he is against. And, in the form of Vina, his one and only love, who he's for.

When Sir Darius Xerxes Cama returned from his spirit-destroying trip to England he was interrogated about that country by his butler, Gieve, who had heard certain lies which he knew were too absurd to be true; but he needed Darius to confirm their falsehood:

They say, sir, that in U.K., if a man does not have a job, the government gives him money. If he does not have a house, the government gives him a pukka residence, not a *jopadpatti* shack on the pavement but a solid construction. If he or his family are sick, the government pays for the hospital. If he can't send his children to school, the government sends them free. And when he is old and useless, the government gives the good-for-nothing cash money every week for the rest of his life.

The idea that a government might behave in such a way seemed to offend Gieve's sense of the natural order. When Darius confirmed the approximate accuracy of the assertions, the butler couldn't stand it. He smacked his brow, shook his head, couldn't speak for a moment. Then he said, "In this case, sir, *why is anyone in U.K. ever unhappy*?"

Why is anyone unhappy in this privileged corner of the globe? Yes, OK, the war, Ormus concedes. But does that excuse everything? Does it mean people can pour themselves down a drain and call it peace? Does it mean people can untie the strings of the world—*and hark, what discord follows*—and call it freedom?

His horror, his sense of foreboding, of wrongness and impending doom—cracks in the world, abysses, the four horsemen, all the anachronistic apparatus of millenarian eschatology—is increased by the knowledge of his own involuntary gift of visions, the holes in the real that manifest themselves to show him another reality, which he resists, though it beckons him to enter; for entry would feel—he knows this—very like insanity. Can it be this visionary madness, the thing he most fears within himself, that's most in tune with his new world?

SHE COMES to him near the end of the night, matter-of-factly joins him on his mattress, without emotion, under some sort of narcotic influence. Their sex, performed in the red-rimmed, bad-breath hours after the cold dawn, is unconvincing, bony, brief; dry frottage, like a duty. Like sex's end: an old married couple's last parched congress. Exhaustion claims them, and they sleep. In two weeks he'll go back to the ship, and if somebody else sleeps here, She may also come to him, sleepwalking.

In the sky above them, Major Ed White is walking in space. He has stepped out of the frame. For fourteen minutes he is the ultimate outsider, the only sentient creature hanging above the Earth, outside the Gemini 4 spacecraft. Ecstatic, he has to be coaxed back into Gemini by his co-astronaut, his space twin.

There is a horse on tv called Mister Ed and Ormus Cama drifting towards sleep allows himself to confuse the two. First centaur in space. Or Pegasus, the last of the winged horses, returning to our corrupt, post-classical times.

She takes him to a club called UFO to satisfy people's need to believe in space creatures other than Major or even Mister Ed. Coloured oils squeezed between glass slides pulse to the music. Hairy heads nod in time, like windscreen poodles. There is much pungent smoke. What is he doing here in this wasted dark when Vina is somewhere else, waiting. Or not waiting. While beside him, concealed in inarticulacy, She doodles on a napkin, decorating the word "unfold." Her calligraphy finds the name of the club in the name of the street. *UnFOld Road.*

Even here, underground, he feels like the Gemini astronaut, floating, above, outside, watching. Bursting with ecstasy. Waiting to become.

BY DAY he walks the city streets, looking for other Englands, older Englands, making them real. He eschews narcotic assistance. He is high on the place itself, its brilliant, familiar strangeness. To be utterly lost amidst buildings you recognize, to know nothing about a cityscape of which you have carried around, for years, what you thought to be an ample and sufficient storehouse of images, is a delirious enough experience. No funny cigarettes required. On the loaf, elated by the great dirty river, the grimy sunsets, Ormus Cama loses his heart, without warning, to the smell of fresh, leavened, white bread.

There was leavened bread in Bombay, but it was sorry fare: dry, crumbling, tasteless, unleavened bread's paler, unluckier relation. It wasn't "real." "Real" bread was the chapati, or phulka, served piping hot; the tandoori nan and its sweeter Frontier variant, the Peshawari nan; and for luxury, the reshmi roti, the shirmal, the paratha. Compared to these aristocrats, the leavened white loaves of Ormus's childhood seemed to merit the description which Shaw's immortal dustman, Alfred Doolittle, dreamed up for people like himself: they were, in truth, the undeserving poor. They were nothing like the lavish loaves sitting plump and enticing, and for sale, in the windows of the capital's many bakeries—the ABC chain, the Chelsea Bakery itself. Ormus Cama plunges into this new world, betraying, without a backward glance, the fabled breads of home.

Whenever he passes a bakery, he feels compelled to enter. The daily purchase and consumption of quantities of bread is, in a way, his first wholeheartedly erotic encounter with London life. Ah, the soft pillowy mattressiness of it. The well-sprung bounciness of it between his teeth. Hard crust and soft centre: the sensuality of that perfect textural contrast. O White Crusty loaves of 1965, both sliced and unsliced! O small and large Tins, Danish Bloomers, flour-dusted Baps! O bread of heaven, bread of leaven, feed me till I want no more! In the whorehouses of the bakeries Ormus pays without a murmur for his encounters with the amorality of the loaf. It's anybody's, but once coin of the realm has been exchanged, these swallowed morsels, these love bites, are his and his alone. East is East, thinks Ormus Cama; ah, but yeast is West.

Standish has bought him a guitar. His pockets stuffed with fresh bread rolls, Ormus sits in parks and makes technical experiments, looking for the new voice that will match his new being, in this new world. What develops at first differs from the driving hard-rock delivery which he originally favoured, and to which he will always, when the spirit moves him, return. This new voice, however, is sweeter, higher, and the songs it sings have longer lines and more complex melodies that cross over and under one another, lifting and circling, like dancers. Mull Standish will choose to record one of these songs: "She (The Death of Conversation)."

(Tabla drums, rakataka takatak. A bouncing guitar. Horns. Waa whup-whup waa, waa whup-whup waa. A full, lush sound, nothing like the screech and thunder characteristic of the period. It sounds new. So does this voice, speaking in unexplained personal references, but somehow including the listener in its private world. A girl lies down in darkness, she asks why am I right on the floor, why am I right on the floor here, when the rest of my life is so wrong. I need a carnival costume, I want my day in the sunlight, don't want to be a black cat in a back catalogue.)

Ormus has fully regained his touch with the ladies.

Arrested by his beauty, by the grace of his long-striding walk, they sweep him off the city streets. The doors of the lonely city open wide. Sometimes he owns up to being the new boy on Radio Freddie, and feels the first astonishing cat-lappings, the addictive caresses, of Western fame.

Soon it begins to feel like a long time ago that he was Indian, with family ties, with roots. In the white heat of the present tense these things have shrivelled and died. Race itself seems less of a fixed point than before. He finds that to these new eyes he looks indeterminate. He has already passed for Jewish, and now as he is noticed by the girls on their scooters and motorbikes, the girls in their bubble cars and Minis, the girls in their false eyelashes and high boots, as they screech to a halt and offer him a ride, he is taken for an Italian, a Spaniard, a Romany, a Frenchman, a Latin American, a "Red" Indian, a Greek. He is none of these, but he denies nothing; during these brief, casual encounters he adopts the protective colouring of how others see him. If asked a direct question he always tells the truth, but it embarrasses him more and more that people, young women particularly, find his true identity so sexually attractive for such phoney, Ginnish reasons. *Oh, that's so spiritual,* they say, slipping out of their clothes. *So spiritual,* galloping him like a horse. *Spiritual,* wagging at him doggy fashion. Mortified, he finds these invitations impossible to refuse. The spiritual Indian, uprising, carnally conquers the West.

Here, he is at the frontier of the skin. Mull Standish meets him for coffee at the Café Braque in Chelsea. We aren't going to conceal anything, Standish announces. We just aren't going to make a big deal out of it, or you'll be stuck in the ethnic ghetto for keeps. We're also going to lie about your age. Pushing thirty is no time to start a career in this business. This here is electric babyland.

Eating his way through plateful after cottony plateful of Wonderloaf and butter—brought to the table with growing irritability and scorn by the Braque's immortally surly waiters—Ormus ponders the link between deracination and success, and persuades himself that the taking of a stage name is not a dishonourable act. Who ever heard of Issur Danielovitch, not to mention Marian Montgomery, Archibald Leach, Bernie Schwartz, Stanley Jefferson, Allen

Konigsberg, Betty Joan Perske, Camille Javal, Greta Gustafsson, Diana Fluck, Frances Gumm, or poor dear Julia Jean Mildred Frances Turner, before they changed their names. Erté, Hergé, Ellery Queen, Weegee . . . The whole history of the pseudonym justifies him. Yet in the end he finds he can't do it. He will remain Ormus Cama. This is his compromise: that the band will not bear his name, though the musicians Standish has assembled are a job lot of sessions artistes. He names this, his first outfit, after the site of his first meeting with Vina. Rhythm Center. "She," by Rhythm Center. I like it like it, Mull Standish says, sipping coffee, tapping his cane. Yes that yes that grooves.

Thank Christ, Standish adds. I thought you were going to call it White Bread.

Only when it's too late will Ormus discover that Standish has issued a false biography of his new star, inventing a melting-pot, patchwork-quilt, rainbow-coalition tale of mixed genes, elaborating on the years of struggle in odd dives in European cities, everywhere but Hamburg (to avoid the Beatles comparison). The poverty, the despair, the overcoming, the making of the finished article. When he does find out, he confronts an unrepentant Standish, who lays down the law: The truth won't play. This, however, is a résumé with legs. Long legs. *Fabulous* legs. Sing the songs, sonny, and let Uncle Mull take care of business.

Later in his career, Ormus Cama will be attacked, often and viciously, for denying his origins. By then, however, Mull Standish will be dead.

STANDISH ASKS after the boys, and his demeanour alters. The bullish man of the world gives way to a more vulnerable and hesitant persona. What do they say? he probes, wincing slightly, his arms coming up a little way off the table, crossed, as if bracing for a blow. What do they say about me? She's been poisoning them for two decades, turning their thoughts against me. Are they safe with her? God knows. She's crazy, you know, you'll have spotted that. Which cuts no ice with them. She's the parent in place, while I, I have no defence. I left, I deserted them, I changed my what's the new word orientation. My pointing towards the East. I can't help that. But I'm here now, I want to be a, a good one, a real one, but maybe it's too late, maybe I can't.

Father, Ormus says. The word you're avoiding.

So they hate me, right. You can tell me, I can take it. No; lie.

Ormus recounts a conversation with Antoinette Corinth. This may surprise you but I want them to like him, she said. It's up to him to build the bridge, God knows he's starting late, but yes, I can see he's finally decided to try. OK. I want them to be close to their father. I want them even to love him, I want him to have the pleasure of his sons' love, I want him to love their love so profoundly that he can't do without it, I want that, even for him, why would I not want it?

He shakes his head, can't believe it. She said that?

She said, It's what I'm waiting for, Ormus recalls.

What does that mean?

In the sense of hoping for, I suppose. (Ormus is trying to be even-handed, trying not to take sides.) Maybe you're seeing phantoms where none exist. Maybe she just has a more generous side than you're willing to allow.

Yeah. And maybe the moon is made of cheese, Standish surrenders to sarcasm. Hey, look. Up in the sky, above the Pheasantry. Wasn't that a flying pig?

LAND, WATER, water, land. Time drips, floats, stretches, shrinks, passes. The story of the first record by Rhythm Center, its pirate provenance, Standish going from store to store around the country, begging, cajoling, threatening, begging some more: all this is well known. The song does well but not astoundingly well. Ormus's nocturnal apostrophising of his lost love is catching on faster than his music. But Vina isn't there. She lies over the ocean, she's singing with Diana Ross at the Rainbow Room, she's hanging out with Amos Voight and so on, and she hears nothing from her lovesick swain.

There is the war and the protest against the war. A generation is learning how to march, how to riot, it is inventing the chants that turn groups of kids into armies that have the power to frighten the state. What do we want when do we want it. One two three four, two four six eight. Ho ho ho.

The non-war news also feels high, spaced out, out of joint.

In Spain a group of aristocrats has been unable to leave the grand salon of the urban mansion in which they recently enjoyed a sumptuous banquet. Nothing impedes them, yet they do not leave. At the gates of the compound in which the mansion stands, a similar invisible impediment prevents anyone from entering. Gawpers, the mansion's domestic staff, the emergency services, press at the open gate but do not pass through. There is talk of a divine curse. Some claim to have heard the beating wings of the angel Azrael overhead. His dark shadow passes like a cloud.

A Polish patriot, Zbigniew Cybulski, has been murdered in a back yard, amid sheets blowing from washing lines. Blood spread across a white sheet held against his midriff. A battered tin mug that fell from his hand has become a symbol of resistance. No: it is a holy relic, worthy of worship. Bow down.

An American girl in Paris is becoming an object of reverence. There are those who call her the reincarnation of the armoured virgin, St. Joan. A cult is in the process of being born.

These are not secular times. In the sphere of the secular all is bombs and death. Against which, it seems, sex and music may not be bulwarks enough.

A great movie star has tragically died. She was in love with two friends, who told her that her face, her smile, put them in mind of an ancient carving. They quarrelled over her. At length, after lunch in a small café, she took one of the friends for a ride in her car and deliberately drove straight off the end of a washed-out bridge, into the water. Both of them were killed. The other man, still seated at the café table, watched his beloved and his friend vanish for ever.

Not long before dying, the actress made a hit record, accompanying herself on acoustic guitar. Now the record is played constantly, the first French song to zoom up the British charts, paving the way for Françoise Hardy and others. Ormus, whose French is poor, strains to understand the lyrics.

Everyone to his taste, turning, turning, in the whirlpool of life?

Is that it?

* * *

ON BOARD the *Frederica,* Ormus Cama notices that the sign on the wall in Eno's cubicle has changed. *Keep your distance.* After that he makes a point of checking, and the changes continue. One week the sign says, *Don't get too close.* Another, *Mend no fences.* Another, *Love not that ye be not loved.* Another, *Fight that sweet tooth. Save more than your teeth.* One message is long and in blank verse:

May the gods save me from becoming
a stateless refugee!
Dragging out an intolerable life
in desperate helplessness!
That is the most pitiful of all griefs;
death is better.

Ali's cracking up, Hawthorne Crossley says, Must be the sleep deprivation.

Must be the hat, Waldo opines, Or is he, by any chance, illegal?

If he was illegal they'd have closed us down by now, Hawthorne reasons.

Ormus says nothing when he sees the long text. He understands that Eno is sending a message directly to him. He feels the hot sting of its criticism and tries to catch the engineer's eye. But Eno seems far away.

Many years will pass before Ormus Cama learns that the author of the long text is not Eno Barber but Euripides. The shorter texts, however, are Eno's own.

Mind your backs. Mind your heads. And these messages? Who are they for?

At The Witch, too, Ormus is receiving messages. She still sometimes comes to his bed when the whim takes her. Dialogue being over, they do not speak. They greet, fuck, part in silence: the copulation of ghosts. But sometimes she, too, leaves him notes. Some are melancholy, opaque. *If music could cure sorrow it would be precious. But no one thought of using songs and stringed instruments to banish the bitterness and pain of life.* Most of the notes, however, are about Antoinette, whose dominant personality seems entirely to have subjugated She's. Antoinette's hard life and times. Disowned by her wealthy family for marrying the club-footed

Standish, and then abandoned by the bastard with two small children and no income, she dragged herself out of the gutter by her own talents and round-the-clock work. *She is a frightening woman; no one who makes an enemy of her will carry off an easy victory.*

The notes are confused. Sometimes they are fearful of Antoinette's rage, at other times they praise her generous love. Towards Tommy Gin, with his vain tousle of carefully teased red hair, his floral waistcoats, his preening, his bigotry, She's scribblings are unreservedly hostile. *He thinks he invented her, he thinks he invented everything, the clothes, the music, the attitude, the protest marches, the peace sign, the women's movement, Black is Beautiful, the drugs, the books, the magazines, the whole generation. I guess none of us would have anything in our heads if not for him, but in fact he's not important, just an evil little shit who knows how to get himself noticed, but she's a real artist, she doesn't go in for all that crap, she creates beauty from the depths of her wounded soul, and you wait and see, she'll break off with him any day now, she'll cut him out completely, the Witch doesn't need a Wizard, and once she's dumped him he'll just shrivel and die like a vampire in the sun.* It seems that silent She has a lot of words locked up inside her, after all. Apollo is in there. Behind the black Dionysiac clouds enveloping this young woman, the sun god is struggling to release his light. It doesn't take Ormus long to understand that She is deeply in love with her boss. Men may come and men may go but the two dark ladies, the large flamboyant one upstairs and the small wasted one sitting in the purple dark below, are in it for the duration.

Distracted by this realization, Ormus perhaps fails to grasp what he is being told, on land by She, at sea by Eno Barber. That there is danger here, coming steadily closer. That the earth is beginning to tremble. Like most protagonists he is deaf to the warnings of the chorus. Even when he dreams a terrible dream—the boys tumbling down the maisonette stairs with the tops of their heads exploded, standing open like burst cans of beans—he attaches no weight to the portent. He is trying to keep a lid on his visionary tendency, in this milieu of cabbalistic nonsense he is making an effort to shun omens and keep a grip on the actual, to concentrate on the music and stand firm upon the dailiness of English life.

To hold on to the elation, the joy he brought with him, the idea of renewal.

His thoughts turn more and more towards Vina. The Vina that exists only in his imagination, whom he knows more intimately than any living being, is being confronted on the stage of that same imagination by another Vina, her adult self, her unknown twin. Life has happened to her and turned her into a stranger. New life, and the eternal haunting of the past. The dead family, the slaughtered goats, the murdering mother hanged in the loafing shed. Piloo, Chickaboom, those too, but above all the dead, pendant mother, and Nissy sitting with her, calling nobody, fearing that this present foretells her future. The dangling ankles, the long bare calves are the image of her own.

Ormus's old fears creep back; he imagines Vina looking him blankly in the eye, saying, *No, that's the past,* and walking off into some alien sunset, leaving his life emptied of meaning. But such dark fancies fail to overpower him. He is filled with light, radiant with possibility. He hit bottom at the Cosmic Dancer and it showed him the way up. Now he is soaring towards the skies, none of his argosies shall fail, and at the appropriate moment he will find her, take her hand, and they will fly together over the bright glow of Metropolis at night. Like fairies, like long-tailed comets. Like stars. That's his story, the one he's written for himself, to which reality has no option but to conform.

But at present he's caught up in another story. They say another galaxy is presently invading the Milky Way, swirling its otherness into our familiar neighbourhood, bringing its story into ours. It's small, we're (relatively) big; we'll pull it to pieces, destroy its suns, rip its atoms up. So long, small galaxy, goodbye baby and amen.

Ormus's story and the story of The Witch Flies High are swirled together now. Which will pull the other apart?

Even worse: will they turn out to be the same story after all?

I'VE BEEN thinking about what you might call the Medea issue. A witchy lady, Ms. Corinth, undeniably; with sons, and a deserter father too. Can't deny the similarities, especially as Antoinette has chosen to play them up, abandoning "Crossley" for "Corinth." What is she trying to do, scare people? Or just Mull Standish? Is she genuinely capable of tragedy, of going so far beyond the frontiers of motherhood and sanity that her deeds acquire the stature of destiny? Is she *fated*? Ormus, who at first found her malevolent, has come to think of her as half posturing phoney, half lunatic-fringista, more insubstantial than shady, a designer witch, using numerology to help her pick her lovers, using occult signs not to conjure devils but only to decorate the busts of her nightmare-black baby-doll dresses. Unlike the note-writers—She, Eno—he isn't buying. And the two silent scribblers, after all, are individuals whose own dysfunctionality erodes their credibility as analysts. Ormus Cama, finally, cannot believe that he has walked on to the stage of some fearsome contemporary goat song. Antoinette Corinth cannot, will not, be responsible for his fate.

We underestimate our fellow humans because we underestimate ourselves. They—we—are capable of being much more than we seem. Many of us are able to answer life's darkest questions. We just don't know if we can come up with the answers to the riddles until we're asked.

There will be a tragedy. Antoinette Corinth will not be held responsible.

MULL STANDISH perseveres with his wooing of his children, and Hawthorne and Waldo slowly respond. As the cycles of their pirate world accumulate into a year, then two, his sons' bantering treatment of him acquires a quality of genuine affection. There are loving gestures: an arm around a shoulder, a playful, filial punch to the cheek that opens out, at the last instant, into a brief stroking gesture of the fingertips. The needs of blood draw them close. The day comes when one of them—Waldo, inevitably, the less defended personality of the pair—accidentally calls Standish "Dad," and even though Hawthorne subjects him to prolonged abuse for this gaffe, Standish is moved to tears. And Hawthorne isn't really cross. "Dad" feels like the right word, even to him. After all these years.

Adversity helps, of course. Laws are being passed that

will close the pirates down. The weather, which once scattered and wrecked the Spanish Armada, has not dealt kindly with Standish's pirate fleet. These are old tubs, and they leak. Batter them with storms and they threaten to break. There are growing problems of insurance, and the boats are, beyond a doubt, dangerous.

There is a new terrestrial station, Radio 1. It steals many of Standish's most talented broadcasters. His ships begin to shut up shop, one by one. Soon there is only Radio Freddie, the first to start broadcasting and the last to remain.

The *Frederica,* rusting, knows her time of rest cannot be far removed.

RHYTHM CENTER, Ormus's first band, has had a series of small successes, making the Fifty, seeming never to reach the modest plenty of the Forty. In part the failure to make a real breakthrough is because the band plays no live gigs, it being Standish's view that the club audience wouldn't "buy" them. His strategy is to keep it mysterious, build a cult, an underground groundswell. There are also the difficulties associated with recording on a small independent label, Standish's own Mayflower franchise: the distribution problems, the limited promotional budgets. The death is reported of the American DJ Alan Freed, who has finally drunk himself into an early grave after giving currency to the word "payola," that's pay plus Victrola. Freed is dead but the practice of accepting bribes to play records is not, and Mull Standish may be rich but he can't go up against the big boys in this bidding war. His pirates will play Rhythm Center's 45s but the other pirates won't. And the BBC, well, nobody ever proved a corruption charge against the BBC, but Ormus hasn't made their playlist, either. In spite of his reasonable success. The BBC makes its own decisions, it isn't led by the common herd. What, they should let the kids decide what they put on the air? *Please.*

Outside England, forget it, no dice. No pay, no play. Vina is in America but Ormus's voice is trapped on the other side of the Atlantic. She can't hear his plea.

The songs themselves are the real problem. Something unreconciled in the writing. There are too many people inside Ormus, a whole band is gathered within his frontiers, playing different instruments, creating different music, and he hasn't yet discovered how to bring them under control: the lover yearning for his vanished love, swooning for Vina into the North Sea night; and the dreaming eavesdropper following his dead twin brother who sings him the songs of the future; and the simple rock 'n' roller in love with a banging-heartbeat beat; and the impish comic penning ironic faux-country odes to bread; and the angry moralist railing against the addle-brained age, its fakeola, its fuddled death wish; and finally, the reluctant visionary who is given glimpses of another possible universe, glimpses he would prefer not to see.

He hasn't fully grasped how to make of multiplicity an accumulating strength rather than a frittery weakness. How the many selves can be, in song, a single multitude. Not a cacophony but an orchestra, a choir, a dazzling plural voice. He worries, as Standish does, about being too old; hasn't understood that this can be set aside, rendered irrelevant. In short, he is still trying to settle on the one true line to follow. Still looking for ground to stand on, for the hard centre of his art.

THE CRUCIAL change comes, as all true Ormus fans will readily know, in mid-1967, in a recording studio in a Bayswater backwater, behind the Whiteleys department store. The story of the recording of Ormus Cama's song "It Shouldn't Be This Way," and of the subsequent three-year delay in its commercial release, has been told so often that it barely needs repeating. The popularly known version of the event is broadly true, and even if it weren't, the advice of the Wild West newspaper editor is well worth taking.

If the facts don't fit the legend, print the legend.

Mull Standish is waiting by the mixing desk when Ormus arrives, looking grim. Okay, I'm ready, he says. Get rid of the musicians.

Standish stiffens, grows very still. All of them? he asks.

Every last one, assents Ormus, flopping down on a squashy corner seating unit and closing his eyes. And wake me when they've gone, he adds.

Now Rhythm Center is Ormus and only Ormus. He's alone in the studio with guitars, keyboards, drums, horns, woodwinds, a big bass, an early Moog synthesizer. He sits down behind the drums and starts to play.

What, you're going to play them all, the sound mixer wants to know. What am I supposed to do, I'm on four-track here.

(Who is this guy, he means. This is the real world here, feller; sixteen-track, thirty-two-track, forty-eight-track recording tape, that's fantasyland, it's the future, and this in front of me it's just a mixing desk, ain't got no time machine.)

We'll just have to bounce the tracks down as we go, Ormus snarls. Something's got into him today. It's not a good idea to argue.

Bounce them down, the engineer says. Sure, why not.

Bouncing down is what you do when you need to keep tracks free. You mix together two tracks and transfer the mixed sound to a third track. Then you can re-use the first two tracks to record two more parts of the music and you bounce these down to the free fourth track. Now you've got two tracks containing mixes of two tracks each. If you've still got a lot of parts to record, you can bounce these two tracks down into one, giving you a single track with four parts on it and three free tracks.

And so on.

The problem is that once you've done this you can never separate the tracks again. The mix you make is what you're stuck with. You can't pull the music apart and play with it any more. You're making final, irrevocable decisions as you go. It's a recipe for disaster, unless the person doing it is a genius.

Ormus Cama is a genius.

Each time he lays down a track—he can play every instrument in the studio better than the sessions guys he's just fired—he comes into the booth, lies down on the seating unit, closes his eyes. The sound mixer moves his slides, turns his dials, and Ormus directs him until the music coming out of the speakers is the secret music in his head. Pull these up, push those back, he says. Bring this in here, fade that away there. Okay, it's okay. That's it. Don't change a thing. Go.

You're sure, now, the mixer says. Because this is it. No turning back.

Bouncey bouncey, Ormus grins, and the mixer laughs and sings back at him.

And like a rubber ball I come bouncing back to you.

The sound grows, becomes fat, exciting. The mixer's a big unfazeable guy, he's getting paid, what's to worry. He's good at what he does, he's worked with everyone, he doesn't get impressed. But look at this, his shoulders are going, boom, to the music, dip, to the beat. This Indian bloke running in and out of the studio, blowing a horn, mixing it in, bouncing it down, then strings, then a bubbling electro beat, he's got the ear, he's got the chops.

Bouncey bouncey!

It's time to sing. *But you're not here to put it right, And you're not here to hold me tight. It shouldn't be this way.*

When it's done, the mixer stands up and holds out a huge paw. I wish you all the best with your song, he says. I've had a good day today.

Ormus stands toe-to-toe with Mull Standish. The rage is still on him.

So, he asks, quietly, furiously. Am I ready or what?

Standish nods. You're ready.

BUT THIS famous scene is the aftermath of a scene people don't talk about:

On the last night of Radio Freddie, at the emotional closing-down ceremony aboard the erstwhile ferryboat, Cap'n Pugwash and his fellow pirates are moved to tears on behalf of their beloved rusting tub. Listen, Pugwash keens, as if speaking by the bedside of a dying lover, you lot are only going off the air, but she's going off the water, the poor old girl. Yes, it's the knacker's yard for the *Frederica,* and nothing to be done about it but drink.

Much is imbibed. Eno Barber sits behind his glass window with a bottle of rum. The sign on the wall behind him reads, *Go away.* Hawthorne and Waldo sing schoolboy rugby songs. This amazing loss of cool passes unnoticed in the general stupor, and actually endears them to the Pugwash bunch, which joins in lustily. Dinah Dinah show us your leg, a yard above your knee. If I were the marrying kind which thank the Lord I'm not sir. Ugly, boastful, male, ultimately innocent songs.

Ormus confronts Mull on deck. They're both drunk. Mull steadies himself against the movement of the boat by putting a hand on Ormus's shoulder. The singer pushes it away, and Mull staggers briefly, then gathers himself. You bastard, Ormus tells his friend, you've been holding me back. Two fucking years. What am I supposed to do? How long am I supposed to wait? Optimism is the fuel of art, and ecstasy, and elation, and the supply of these commodities is not endless. Maybe you don't want me to make it. You want me to stay small-time, not even a has-been but a never-was, beholden to you, a hanger-on, a fly in your goddamn web.

Mull Standish keeps his temper. It's true, he says, mildly. I haven't pushed you as I might. My small indie label, et cetera. You call that holding you back, then okay, I held you back. I'm holding you back because if I let you go now you'll fail, you'll fall to earth. You haven't found the courage to fly. Maybe you won't. The problem is not technical. You're worried about wings? Look on your shoulders. There they are. The problem, pal, is not wings but balls. Maybe you're just a no-balls eunuch and you'll sleep on a mattress at The Witch for the rest of your eunuch life.

The boat sways and so do they. Ormus Càma is being given a great gift. Words are being said which will oblige him to face the issue of himself.

Whatever you want to say about yourself is fine with me, Standish says. You say you've got a dead twin in your head who's listening to the chart-toppers of tomorrow, I could care less. You talk about visions, baby, I say follow that star all the way to Bethlehem and check out the kid in the manger. The trouble is you're running away from it all, there's too much of you missing from your music. You're phoning it in. People notice. I tell you what, just fuck off, why don't you. What I see is potential that is not being realized. This as an investor I do not care for. What I know is that music comes out of the self, the self as given, the self in itself. *Le soi en soi.* The silk in silk, as we used to say in my punning Francophone youth.

Standish is breathing heavily now. His entire being is crackling at the edges of his body. St. Elmo's fire; like that. Because he loves this man, he's straining at his physical frontiers to show him the way. Is it Vina you need, he roars.

Then find her. Don't whine into a radio mike on a broken-down boat. Find her and sing her your songs. What's the most dangerous thing you can do? Do it. Where's the nearest edge? Jump off it. Enough already! I've said my piece. When you're ready, if you're ever ready, give me a call.

Loud singing explodes from the cabin. I'll come again, you'll come again, we'll both come again together. We'll be all right in the middle of the night, coming again together.

A WEEK passes and then Ormus calls.

Set it up. I'm ready. Set it up.

And later, at the end of the recording session, when they have the precious tape, they're standing toe-to-toe, uncertain whether to fight or kiss.

What I want the music to say is that I don't have to choose, Ormus finally speaks up. I need it to show that I don't have to be this guy or that guy, the fellow from over there or the fellow from here, the person within me that I call my twin, or whoever's out there in whatever it is I get flashes of beyond the sky; or just the man standing in front of you right now. I'll be all of them, I can do that. Here comes everybody, right? That's where it came from, the idea of playing all the instruments. It was to prove that point. You were wrong when you said the problem wasn't technical. The solutions to the problems of art are always technical. Meaning is technical. So is heart.

Technically, then, says Mull Standish, I shouldn't lay a hand on you, because I promised, but now you've made me a happy man, would you allow me a hug?

THE RELEASE of this song will bring Vina Apsara back to him at last. It will mark the beginning of their almost frighteningly totemic celebrity. And it will not happen for over three years.

The happiness of Mull Standish (with Ormus, with his sons) is what Antoinette has been waiting for. What she means by this, and whether she is to blame for what is soon to follow, the reader must presently judge.

A few weeks go by. Then, in the maisonette above The Witch:

It must be a Saturday, and it's only around noon, so naturally nobody is up, and the shop's shut. The doorbell—the maisonette's bell, not the shop's—rings for such a long time that, leaving She semi-conscious on the mattress, her face dusted lightly with ash, Ormus struggles into a pair of red crushed-velvet flares and staggers downstairs to the door.

On the doorstep is an alien: a man in business suit and matching moustache, with a briefcase in one hand and, in the other, a copy of a glossy magazine open at the page on which a model is wearing one of The Witch's latest offerings.

Good afternoon, says the alien, in excellent English. I have a chain of shops in Yorkshire and Lancashire . . .

She, naked beneath a hopelessly inadequate dressing gown, cigarette dripping from her lips, weaves down the stairs with a hand in her hair. The alien turns puce and his eyes start sliding around. Ormus retreats.

Yeah? enquires She.

Good afternoon, the alien tries again, although his English is giving him difficulty all of a sudden. I have a chain of shops in Yorkshire and Lancashire selling ladies' fashions, and I am most interested in this particular garment as featured here. With whom would I speak with a view to placing a first order for six dozen items, with an option to repeat?

It is the biggest order The Witch has ever had. Halfway up the stairs now, the imposing, black-and-gold-caftanned figure of Antoinette Corinth materialises. Impossible to know her thoughts. Ormus fancies he feels a tingle in the air, the sense of having arrived at a turning point. The alien waits patiently while She considers matters. Then, with great deliberation, the manageress nods a few times, slowly. Fashionably.

We're closed, man, she says, and shuts the door.

Antoinette Corinth comes down and kisses She on the mouth. After which, still in Antoinette's arms, She turns to Ormus and, most unusually, speaks further words.

A fucking artist, she says. This beautiful woman.

At this point the doorbell rings again. She turns and goes back upstairs, this time with Antoinette. She is plainly not planning to return to Ormus's humble mattress. The cushions and silks, the exotic markings and draperies of

Antoinette's lair await her. Ormus stands and looks at the closed door.

Again, the bell. He opens the door.

On the doorstep, holding a wickerwork hamper that contains a selection of the finest leavened breads money can buy, is the overlord of the Colchis label, the blind recording angel himself, Yul Singh; and behind him, a limousine half as long as the street.

You see, Mr. Cama. You see before you. Now that you're ready, which I have to say I congratulate you, I didn't expect it, but I heard your tape from your man Mr. Standish who allow me to say you found yourself a good one there, and having ears to hear I have heard what I have heard, so as it turns out it was not required for you to seek me out, which as I remember I advised you on no account to do. As things transpire which I don't mind saying it's a funny old world, and so Mr. Cama with your permission it is I who have come to you.

"LORELEI," FROM the first VTO album, the self-titled *VTO* (Colchis, 1971):

Certain shapes pursue me, I cannot shake them from my heel. Certain people haunt me, in their faces I will find the things I feel. Uncertain fate it daunts me, but I'm gonna have to live with that raw deal. No authority's vested in me, on what's good or bad or make-believe or even real. But I'm just saying what I see, because the truth can set you free, and even if it hasn't done too much for me, well, I still hope it will.

And I can feel your love, Lorelei. Yes, I can feel your love pour on me. Oh I can feel your love, Lorelei.

IN THE summer of 1967, Ormus takes a drive in the country one weekend afternoon with his good friends Hawthorne and Waldo Crossley, in Hawthorne's Mini Cooper S (with Radford conversion), to celebrate his recording contract with Colchis Records. Antoinette Corinth, in an unusual display of maternal affection, insists on packing them a picnic lunch. A thermos of tea, and sandwiches.

I'm so delighted for you, she says to Ormus, magnanimously. And what with your success and the boys taking to him at last, I'm glad for Mull as well. I can't imagine he's ever been happier. Not a cloud on his horizon. Blue skies ahead as far as the eye can see. Bye, darlings, darlings. Have a lovely day.

At first things go swimmingly. They pass a troupe of white-faced mimes in a park playing slow-motion tennis without a ball, and they stop for a while, sipping tea from the hot thermos, to watch the intensely contested game. Their topics of conversation are diverse. They touch on the suicide of the Beatles' manager, Brian Epstein; and the American race riots; and Cassius Clay's refusal to fight in Indochina, the stripping of his title and his transformation into Muhammad Ali; and even the *musique concrète* of Stockhausen. But mostly they talk about driving down to the anti-war music festival taking place at Woburn Abbey, in spite of the widespread fear of violence. Troops as well as armed and mounted police have massed on the outskirts of the Woburn estate, and government spokesmen are warning the musicians and the crowd to avoid inflammatory or seditious behaviour. In response, many musicians have vowed to be as seditious as possible. There are rumours of possible gas attacks, even of the use of automatic weapons.

(The national mood is so ugly that when a daily newspaper, reacting to the growing hippie phenomenon but failing to connect its message of peace to the overwhelming fact of the war, describes the season as a "summer of love," it comes across as a risible piece of government propaganda.)

However, the catastrophe, when it comes, has nothing to do with the protest movement or the forces ranged against it. Ormus Cama is a known opponent of the Wilson government's decision to involve British troops in Indochina—*why do Labour leaders always have to prove they have the balls for war?*—but he is not stopped at any army barricade, nor is he the subject of a charge of mounties.

What happens is apolitical: a traffic accident.

Hawthorne Crossley is behind the wheel, perhaps driving too fast, certainly losing concentration and seemingly overtired and erratic; and in a sleepy English village off the M1 the Mini Cooper collides with a large heavy-goods vehicle carrying a weighty and odorous cargo of agricultural fertiliser. Hawthorne Crossley is killed outright, Waldo suffers head injuries which cause irreparable damage to his brain, while Ormus, in the back of the car, is also gravely injured. Ordure covers everything. The emergency services have to dig down to them through a little hill of excrement. A rendezvous with a truckload of shit: it would be funny, if it were not so unfunny.

ORMUS IS in the back seat of the car. He closes his eyes for an instant because alternative universes have begun to spiral out from his eyeballs in rainbow-coloured corkscrews of otherness that fill him with terror, and because he does not know about the impurities in the thermos of tea he thinks he's producing the hallucination all by himself. So he clenches his lids against the twin exfoliating beanstalks of the vision and when he opens them again all the world is truck. The improbably loud drag of metal against metal. The ticking of the seconds slowed down until they sound like the doomy muffled beats of a funeral drum. When you hit a big truck in a small vehicle, he remembers from somewhere, the greatest danger is that you will be sucked underneath it and decapitated or at least crushed. Heavy metal with its wall of sound goes on sliding past. They bounce off the truck's rear wheel arch, spin, hit something else, a house or a tree, and stop. Nobody's wearing a seat belt. Ormus, tumbling dreadfully in the confined space of the car, glimpses rag-doll Waldo lolling in the front passenger seat with his mouth open; and then the driver, Hawthorne Crossley, floats into view, heading wide-eyed for the windscreen. Hawthorne exhales violently, like a madman's laugh, *hahaaa,* and Ormus sees a little white cloud fly out of his mouth and hang there for a moment, like a speech bubble; and disperse. Then like an underwater swimmer reaching the surface Hawthorne's head breaks the windscreen and passes through it and that's that. When Ormus is able to remember things he will remember this as the moment he saw Hawthorne's life leave his body, and what does that mean, does it mean there is a spirit after all, a soul that's in the flesh but not of it, a ghost in the soft machine. That will be a thing for him to wrestle with at another time, but right now all wrestling has to stop, because something hard has punched him, like a fist, in the left eye.

Time accelerates as they decelerate. Fertiliser pours down. He nothing knows.

THIS IS what is reported. The casualties are taken to a nearby cottage hospital. Ormus's American manager, a "hobbling, Svengali-like figure," Mr. Mull Standish, arrives soon afterwards, together with the record company boss Yul Singh, expensively accoutred in a navy-blue suit, Ray Charles shades and black leather gloves, and accompanied, Piloo Doodhwala fashion, by an entourage of aides and bodyguards. Standish, utterly demolished by the fate of his sons, sobs helplessly by their hospital beds; it's reportedly Yul Singh's team of Sikhs who spirit the singer away through a back exit, in spite of his serious wounds and fractures, and remove him to a secret location where he will be given private care. Ormus is reported to be holed up in a village in the Welsh borders, or in the Scottish highlands, or suburban Essex. There are sightings in Paris and Switzerland; in Venice (the masked carnival) and Rio de Janeiro (where he dances, again in the carnival, amid the small-breasted and ample-buttocked women beloved of Brazilian men); in Flagstaff, Arizona, and don't forget Winona—he's getting his kicks on Route 66. He is said to be horribly disfigured; it is rumoured that his vocal cords have been severed; a "definitive" investigation in a Sunday newspaper reveals that he has given up his life as a musician for ever, converted to Islam and joined an obscure sect of devotees—the "Cats of Allah"—based, improbably, in the heart of the Jewish community of Hampstead Garden Suburb. The most persistent rumour is that he is lying, deeply comatose, in a top-secret intensive care unit, isolated in a glass case like Snow White asleep in her coffin.

For three and a quarter years, Ormus will remain in sequestration, far from the public eye. Neither his record label, Colchis, nor his personal representatives at Mull Standish's Mayflower Management offices, will issue any statements.

Stories circulate, and there's no point in arguing with them. Parts of them are accurate enough, except for the bizarre worldwide sightings of the suddenly invisible man, whose disappearance—there is no escape from these bitter ironies—propels him from third-rate popster status to a condition of considerable renown. The longer he stays invisible, the greater grows his fame. A cult develops, whose adherents believe that Ormus Cama will awake to lead them out of these troubled times, beyond our vale of tears to redemption. Reissues of his Mayflower records, as well as bootleg recordings of his early Bombay performances, begin to circulate and sell; a legend grows. People, being people, begin to speak cynically of a publicity stunt. Yul Singh is well known as a wily bird, and Standish, though less known, is no less wily.

The coma story, however, is true. Ormus is not dead but sleeping.

The speculation grows so intense that the human dimension of the tragedy is almost completely obliterated. The people involved cease to be thought of as living, feeling beings; they become abstract, pieces in a riddle, a heartless game. They become empty vessels into which public speculation can be poured.

Certain facts do not come to light. Yul Singh and his inner circle at Colchis work to suppress them, and ironically the cloud of conjectures actually helps.

In the bloodstream of the Crossley brothers, and that of Ormus Cama too, doctors have found dangerously high levels of the hallucinogen lysergic acid diethylamide 25. These medical reports do not become public knowledge, however. Nor does any police action follow from them.

In the wreckage of the Mini Cooper, a thermos flask has been found. Somehow, this flask is not retained in police possession, or subjected to any kind of examination by the authorities. For some reason it is given into the hands of a "family friend." The friend never resurfaces. Nor does the flask.

There is therefore no proof that there was any sugar in the tea.

A MAN'S worth reveals itself in the hour of his greatest adversity. What is our value when the chips are down? Do we merely flatter to deceive, or are we the real thing, the stuff of alchemists' dreams? These, too, are questions to which most of us, mercifully, are never required to supply answers.

The rising of Mull Standish to the occasion of tragedy, though unsurprising to those who know him, is nonetheless an example to all. Emerging dry-eyed from his cottage-hospital grief, he dedicates himself to the welfare of the living. In the weeks that follow, the fevered energy with which he locates and hires the finest available treatment for Waldo is a marvel to behold. Waldo will recover from his physical injuries. For several years after that he will benefit from the attention of a team of specialists thanks to whose efforts he will be able to resume a limited, but surprisingly contented, existence in the world.

Yul Singh's men follow Standish's orders. Ormus Cama is taken to a white house on a hill overlooking the Thames, a house at whose open French windows white curtains blow in the breeze, to be cared for by his mother. Thus one rift in the world at least is on the way to being healed. Spenta receives her broken child with loud cries of self-reproach, spends a rapid fortune to set up a state-of-the-art sanatorium in the sunny and spacious old orangery, and resolves to nurse Ormus back to health with her own hands, positioning herself constantly by his bedside, although exhaustion obliges her, from time to time, to snatch a few hours' sleep. Lord Methwold is recently dead, peacefully, in his sleep, deceased without issue, and his wife is the sole—and uncontested—beneficiary of his impressive will. This country mansion is now hers; also the town house at Campden Hill Square, the healthy bank accounts, the substantial holdings in gilts and blue-chip equities. A real stash, in sum. The former Lady Spenta Cama has received the news of her good fortune as an admonition from god. To be suddenly rich in worldly goods is to understand the nature of her deeper impoverishment. Of her three sons, one is in jail for murder, a second has been despatched (oh, callous mother!) to a nursing home, so as not to trouble her aged spouse. The youngest has long been estranged from her, thinking himself unloved; now he's badly hurt. She, who believes herself devout, has failed in her soul's duty.

Secretly, away from the failing Methwold, she has been tuning in to Radio Freddie, keeping in touch with her son through his work. The station's closure has been hard to bear: it is a second parting, a second rupture. Her letter to

Ormus, maudlin and full of apologies, addressed to him in care of the pirate station, arrives in Standish's hand on the day of the singer's ill-fated car journey. So it is Standish whose intervention returns Ormus to the bosom of his family. (Virus Cama is home too, liberated from his captivity by his stepfather's demise.)

This service nobly performed, Mull Standish returns to London, to Wandsworth Crematorium, for it is time to burn his son.

AT THE crematorium, he leans on his cane, closes his eyes, at once sees the great fire-jets billow around the young man's body, cleansing him of himself. Though he is an American and has lived an intensely American life, Mull does not weep. Opens his eyes. Antoinette Corinth and She, their arms around each other, are dabbing at kohl-blurred faces under their black lace veils. More than dialogue is dead now. Standish closes his eyes again and sees Waldo Crossley's future. Waldo, made foolish by the accident, smiles sweetly at autumn leaves as he spears them upon a blustery parterre. Above which, looking down at him from the windows of a large white house, is Ormus's mother. Who wishes nothing more than to make eternal reparation for a lifetime of poor mothering. Who will care for Waldo as if he too were her beloved child.

It's over. No more weeping. Standish moves across the aisle to speak quietly to his ex-wife. It's my belief that this is your work, he says, mildly. I didn't think you could do it, but now I'm sure you did. I can't imagine how great the burden of your hatred must be. I can't conceive of carrying so much poison in your heart for so very long. The killing of your children to spite their father. It's like something out of a book.

You loved them and they came to love you. Her voice is ice. Her teeth glitter maliciously. That is what gives me the greatest comfort, and pleasure.

Murderess, he says. Infanticide. May the gods blast your life, he says.

She turns on him. They were disturbed boys ever since you abandoned them. For years now they've been doing whatever it takes to escape the truth. Namely, that their faggot father fucked off fast. When they were kids they'd eat a can of boot polish if they thought it would bring them an hour's escape. They'd drink cough medicine by the quart. Glue, pills, bloody plastic-bag erections, that's what was happening, so Mull, don't you fucking start with me. Then you showed up like god almighty, gave them a job, finally decided to love the little bastards. That *really* drove them to drink and everything else. Needle time. Or hadn't you noticed. But then you close down the station, you take it away from them, and you even let the poor runts see that you love some other shitbag more than them. You just don't get it. You never did get it. They were terrified of you, terrified that you were about to fuck off again. Out of their heads with fear. That just after they started loving you, you'd high-tail it with your Indian prince.

He will not let her see him tremble; controls himself; accuses her again.

You prepared the picnic, he says. You planned to kill them all.

Or, she counters, they put the stuff in there themselves. To die and take your lover boy with them. Poor darlings. They couldn't even get that right.

Mull Standish waits alone for the ashes. Hawthorne's ashes are his own life. Decisions must be made: to be or not to be. You face up to life, you give it your best shot, you approach it with all the openness and humanity you have, and you get this. One boy in a fake Greek urn, the other a shell without a self. This isn't what was supposed to happen.

He enfolds the urn in his arms and kisses and kisses it. This is my beloved son in whom I am well pleased.

THE SMALL galaxy that is passing through the larger galaxy of my story is being torn apart, destroyed. Antoinette Corinth and She close down The Witch and leave for the Pacific coast of Mexico, dressed in fiery tropical colours, exchanging dark silence for brilliant light and noise. No charges are contemplated against them. It is for each of us to decide which truth we choose to follow: the truth of tragedy, of story, Standish's Medean truth, or Antoinette's accusatory version, or the more sober truth of the Law. Innocent till proved guilty, and so on.

Either way, it's not much good to Hawthorne and Waldo.

Soon after the women's departure there is a fire in Unfold Road and the store burns down. Arson is suspected but not proven, and after a delay the insurance companies pay up. Mr. Tommy Gin, as the principal backer, receives the lion's share of the payout, but a cheque of appreciable size is sent to the beautiful seaside resort of Zopilote in the Mexican province of Oaxaca, on the Golfo de Tehuantepec. The cheque is cashed, but no further news of Antoinette Corinth and her companion, She, is received. They have, for the moment, vanished into an impenetrable elsewhere, into which this story cannot go.

Certain patterns recur, seem inescapable. Fire, death, uncertainty. The carpet whipped out from under us to reveal a chasm where the floor should have been.

Disorientation. Loss of the East.

DURING THE later stages of the so-called lost years, after his emergence from the long coma, Ormus Cama will for a time keep an occasional journal, a haphazard thing littered with automatic writing, crazytalk, "poetry," visions, conversations with the dead, and many ideas for songs.

In one of the earliest entries, he will describe a hallucination experienced in the back seat of the fateful Mini Cooper, in all probability just before the encounter with the fertiliser truck:

The top of my head was open, just blown apart as if by an explosion, and he climbed out and ran away. Now he doesn't come to see me any more, because why would he, he's free, he's not running through the corridors and staircases of the casino looking for a way out, he's escaped, he's out there somewhere. If you meet him, remember he's not me. He just looks that way. He's not me.

And this is another early entry:

Vina I know you better now. My darling I have met your lethal mother. I have faced her other, and survived.

CHAPTER ELEVEN

Higher Love

In the early days, before the orangery sanatorium is ready, Ormus is placed in Spenta's own bed, attached to drips and monitors. This part of the house is old and flaky, like the England out of which it was born. A fine rain of plaster dust settles slowly on Ormus's cheeks. Spenta at his bedside brushes the pale flecks away with a paisley-patterned silk cloth. Virus Cama, back home again, sits with his hands resting softly on his knees in a corner of the master bedroom, on a carved folding chair in black teak, a chair that was once used by a travelling Collector in what is now Maharashtra and Madhya Pradesh, on his journeys along the Wainganga and into the Seeonee hills. Spenta regards her broken sons, Sleep and Silence, bows her head, and resolves for the one hundred and first time to make it up to these lost boys, to heal them with belated love. It is not, must not be, too late for redemption: theirs and her own. She prays to her angels but they no longer answer. Her sons are her only angels now.

But Cyrus, she mourns dumbly. For Cyrus, it is too late.

Memorabilia of British India are all around. A mirror-work *chhatri* hangs over a long-armed recliner chair. Company school pictures, hand-coloured Daniell engravings. A silver tea service, a stone godhead, photographs of great days spent shooting birds and beasts, a tiger rug, stone boxes with silver *bidri* inlay work, an *itr*-seller's perfume chest, a harmonium, carpets, cloths. A framed letter from Morgan Forster describing oddly echoing caves in the side of a scrubby hill.

The Indian nurse arrives.

It is only some while later, after Spenta has remembered who she is and where she has seen her before, that they realize nobody can recall letting her in. She seems to materialize from nowhere, hovering solicitously behind Spenta and Standish, wearing a pristine starchy uniform in pale blue and white, with a small watch pinned at her breast. The agency sent me, she says vaguely, busying herself with sheets and towels and reading the chart hooked over the foot of the comatose singer's bed. Spenta and Standish are at a low ebb. Exhaustion and shock have taken their toll, so that even when Virus Cama gets up from his Collector's chair to tug worriedly at his mother's sleeve Spenta just shrugs him off and slumps down with her head in her hands. Standish, too, is on the point of collapse, having barely slept since the catastrophe. The Indian nurse turns down the lights in the master bedroom and takes charge with a competence that brooks no argument. She is a good-looking girl, well spoken, knowledgeable about the leading families of Bombay society. She tells Spenta about her time with the Sisters of Maria Gratiaplena, though, she hastens to add, she herself is no nun. It is perhaps because of this reference that Spenta, whose thoughts are much abstracted, begins to call the newcomer Maria, a name to which she readily answers. Rest, Maria says, and Standish and Spenta troop meekly out, followed by Virus Cama, who keeps looking over his shoulder at the nurse and shaking his greying head.

When she is alone with sleeping Ormus, the nurse begins to talk to him in a voice full of smoke and longing. At last, my love. Though it is not our beautiful little nook in Worli, still it will do, for wherever you lie, that place is my palace and so on, whatever bed contains your body is my only desired resting place et cetera, and even when you die my love I will follow you into your grave, into it and beyond, et cetera et cetera et cetera.

Then she goes on to remind the unconscious man of their past lovemaking, the many wonderful things they have done together, those supreme proofs of their passion, athleticism and flexibility, to say nothing of the sensual powers of certain natural oils. Her long oration is an erotic masterwork that would be lost to posterity were it not for the Grundig tape deck which Mull Standish has installed beneath Ormus's bed just in case he should return briefly to consciousness and say something, anything, during his manager's and his mother's simultaneous absence from the room. Ormus stays silent, but the thin brown tape phlegmatically absorbs everything Maria has to say, eavesdropping on her intimacies just as those other, fictitious tapes listened in on the imaginary "President Nixon" in the novel *The Watergate Affair.* And at a certain point she moves on from reminiscence to action, she describes to the unknowing Ormus in explicit detail how she plans to rouse him from his slumbers by arousing his carnal desires, there is a clink of glass containers, then the slippery sounds of oil-slathered hands moving across one another and applying themselves to the sleeping figure.

The sound quality on the tape is good. Anyone listening to it can easily picture Maria as she climbs on to the bed (mattress noises), and because the human imagination all too easily runs away with its suppositions, I must move on quickly to the clearly recorded sound of a door flying open, and the horrified voices of Spenta and Standish as they burst in, Spenta having finally summoned up the memory of the nympho on the plane to London.

They order the Indian nurse to get off, get dressed and get out, because how dare she, is she so wholly lacking in the faintest scrap of decency, they will see her disbarred from nursing duties, she should cover her breasts at once, yes, and her pudenda too, and above all she should stop laughing, stop it this minute, this is no laughing matter, in five seconds' time they are going to send for the police.

Her laughter fills the tape as she leaves the room.

Ormus remains asleep; dormant and, in spite of all Maria's ministrations—so the story goes—still soft.

SHE KEEPS showing up. Ormus is moved to the new facility in the orangery and the next night she's there. Spenta goes to the toilet for a minute and returns to find Maria, naked except for a black veil, bending over Ormus's exposed sex, the movements of her ample mouth half concealed by gauze. She really is very beautiful, very wanton and very mad, Spenta thinks, but that doesn't explain how the girl got inside. Spenta gives orders for a constant vigil to be maintained, a guard is posted, dogs are unleashed in the nocturnal grounds. Still Maria finds a way in. One night Standish is on duty, reading the latest Yossarian to help him through the night, and in spite of the writer's comic genius he nods off for, he thinks, no more than a couple of minutes. When he awakes he is startled to find her there, fully materialized, oiled, veiled and naked, in spite of the hounds and the locked grilles and the beam-operated alarm system: and this time she is actually straddling Ormus, bouncing vigorously up and down, riding his soft cock horse. You'll never keep me away from him, she crows. I am his destiny, his private need and so on. That woman (she means Vina) can never give him what he wants, but I know what he desires better than he, I give it to him before he knows he's going to ask for it et cetera. I come from his secret world.

Who are you, Standish demands, blinking. He is heavy with sleep, and he's also wearing his reading glasses, so that everything more than nine inches away looks blurry and unreal.

As he tries to focus on her, she disappears. A crack seems to open in the air itself, and she steps through it and is gone.

The human capacity for rationalization is a thing of wonder. It enables us to disbelieve the evidence of our own eyes. Since what Standish has fuzzily seen is impossible, he concludes that he has not seen it. She must have slipped out the door while he was still dozy, he concludes. He gets up and looks, but she's gone. Standish notes the further failure of the security system and suspects an inside job. The crazy girl is probably buying the favours of some staff member, a gardener, a handyman. Someone is smuggling her in and being rewarded, no doubt, with some of that sexual action with which she makes so free. It must be looked into. Meanwhile, no real harm done. Standish returns to his book.

Peacefully, Ormus sleeps on.

MULL STANDISH, a contemporary man, looks for answers in the everyday. Spenta just as naturally turns towards the paranormal, fears a haunting and summons Parsi priests from London and the local Anglican vicar. Fire ceremonies and exorcisms are sonorously performed. After these rites there are periods, often very extended, when the Indian woman fails to manifest herself. For these absences, as for her presences, no explanation is given; Spenta, however, gives the credit to the servants of Ahura Mazda and the Christian God.

Then Maria appears again, and the whole cleansing ritual is renewed.

There are days when Spenta feels mortally afraid. Deserted by angels, she fears she and her family may now have fallen prey to demons. At such moments she looks to Mull Standish for comfort. Always immaculately groomed, expensively tricked out in silk-collared camel coat or raffishly cigar-chewing in mink, Standish in these agonizing times still stands foursquare on the unsteady earth, a well-planted man, a tree that has no plans to fall any time soon. His calm tones, his gravitas, his sleek hair: these things reassure Spenta, and a gleam comes into her eye, though she is seven years his senior and can have no realistic expectations. Still, she pays greater attention to her appearance, she lowers her eyelashes, she flirts. Standish, noting the advent of an unrequitable love, has grown fond enough of Spenta to let her dream.

For all his apparent solidity these are years of misfortune for Mull Standish. The sudden collapse of a Newark office block for which one of his U.S. subsidiaries supplied cooling systems has been followed by a more general erosion of confidence in his construction business. Due to the end of his liaison with "Sam Tropicana," his erstwhile lover's family is determinedly putting the poor mouth on him, and New York's City Hall has started frowning on his projects and tenders. The IRS irregularities have been squared, but only after the payment of arrears plus a punitive fine. In Britain the end of the pirate phase has done more than financial harm; it has removed some essential excitement from his life. He has wound up his record label and makes his bread and butter, nowadays, from investments in rental property shrewdly acquired during the pirates' boom years.

Naturally, like any dynamic entrepreneur, and there can be no doubt of the rightness of that description, he continues to have his schemes and dreams. Hippies in Sloane Square sell yo-yos that light up as they rise and fall. He has a piece of this action, also in much else that is gimcrack and union-jacked and over-priced and sold in Carnaby Street. His gift for what marketing men call gap analysis has led him to launch a listings service, *Where It's At,* which begins as a poor folded sheet guiding the young to pleasures both mainstream and "alternative" and quickly grows into a money-spinning weekly magazine. For ordinary mortals, this slate of activities would be proof of robust health, and robustness is the quality Standish—still, in his early fifties, an indefatigable powerhouse of a fellow—works hardest to project. However, he is a man with a broken heart. If he is to be compared to a great tree, then there is something decaying at its core. One day, without warning, it may suddenly fall. Only then will passers-by be able to see the sickness, and understand.

When he walks with Waldo Crossley in the grounds of Methwold's riverside estate, congratulating his son on the skill with which he has learned to spear leaves and other detritus, flattering him on the way he looks in the Methwold livery, and being rewarded by Waldo's tear-jerkingly wide, happy, brainless smile—or when he keeps vigil by Ormus Cama's bedside, seeing in the comatose singer the shadow of his own dead Hawthorne—then Standish's back is straighter than ever, his jaw firmer, his eye less moist. But he has been poleaxed and no mistake. The danger is that if Ormus fails to awake, Standish may also fall into some final sleep. Their fates are joined. As the months and years go by, and Standish loses hope of an awakening, little threads of his cloak of discipline begin to fray. There's a tic, sometimes, in the corner of an eye. There are days when a few stray hairs elude his formerly omnipotent brush. When he stands, Spenta notices the first signs of a stoop.

If I was a little younger, she says, taking his arm while they walk on the parterre one late afternoon, I might give you a run for your money.

He hears the loneliness, the echo of a woman standing in the empty room of her future, and decides he has no alternative but to be truthful.

I am one of those, he says, almost tongue-tied for once, for whom the love of women was never really the point.

Wonderful, she claps her hands. I also can see no point in such activity at our age. But companionship, isn't it? That we can offer each other as twilight falls.

At which Mull Standish finds himself at a loss for words.

* * *

ABRUPTLY, MARIA stops coming, perhaps despairing of Ormus's prospects. Neither Spenta nor Standish says so, but both think her absence a bad omen.

They begin to speak of the unspeakable: of the life support. For more than three years, Ormus Cama has needed monitors, drips, plasma. There have been moments when respiratory equipment has been necessary. His muscles have atrophied, he is weaker than a baby, and without the machines, the nursing staff, the orderlies, he could not possibly survive. Spenta asks Standish the unaskable.

What do you think, honestly, will he wake up.

And Standish is no longer able to offer a convincing Yes in reply.

It would be possible to arrange a mishap, he says. A power cut, plus a failure of the back-up generator. Or a tube might accidentally fall out of the sleeping man's nose, or a life-giving needle drop from a vein. It might be, what's the word, stumbles Standish. Merciful.

I still believe, Spenta obstinately wails. In I don't know what, a miracle. In blessings from above. In, what to call it, higher love.

WHEN COLCHIS Records releases the double-A-side 45 "Beneath Her Feet" b/w "It Shouldn't Be This Way" by the defunct band Rhythm Center, it is intended as a farewell gesture, a surrender to the inevitable. Ever since the accident Standish has been adamant: Ormus will recover, at that point he will resume his career, and until then it would be both macabre and bad business to put out any discs.

Yul Singh has gone along with this in his equivocal way.

If this is your wish Mr. Standish which I'm offering no opinion then so be it, it's your call. You change your mind you come and see me. The industry moves on at high speed, you don't need to be told, so we'll see about it as and when. God willing I'm still in this seat, maybe I can help you out.

The time comes when Standish and Spenta agree that they want Ormus to sing again, to sing one last time before the machinery ceases to support his life and he departs. Standish asks Yul Singh to set the music free; which request, for all his tough talk and caveats, the ferocious Colchis overlord—understanding that the request is a kind of death sentence—is unable to deny. Whereupon, to everyone's amazement, the record is a hit. And Vina Apsara in a Bombay hotel room hears Ormus singing, and flies back into his life: and saves it.

HERE SHE is at his bedside, whispering into his ear. Here is Spenta, not knowing whether to fear her as another revenant demon, or to grieve with her for their mutual loss, or to hope. Here is Mull Standish holding his breath. Here, hovering like vultures, are a doctor, a nurse, an orderly.

In the doorway, hat in hand, is blind Yul Singh.

Ormus, she whispers. Ormus, it's me.

At which he opens his eyes; it's as simple as that. His mouth trembles. She bends down to hear him.

The doctor swoops, shoulders her aside. Excuse, please. We must establish the degree of damage. Turning to Ormus with a glitter of bedside teeth, he asks: Who am I?

A drug dealer.

The voice surprises everyone by its strength, its sardonic note. The doctor points to Yul Singh in the doorway. And he, who is he?

A commissar.

Then the orderly, carrying clean sheets and towels.

He isn't important.

And how about you, the doctor asks. Do you know who you are. Do you know what you want.

Vina, he calls. She comes close, takes his hand. *Yes,* he answers. *Now I know.*

HOW SHALL we sing of the coming together of long-parted lovers, separated by foolish mistrust for a sad decade, reunited at last by music? Shall we say (for in song we are set free from surly pedantry, and may hymn the soaring spirit, rather than the crumpled letter, of the truth): they ran singing through fields of asphodel and drank the nectar of the gods, and their kissing was as beauteous as the evening horizon, where the earth first touches and then becomes the sky? Shall we liken his sweeping caresses to the movement of the winds across the surface of the sea, now raging, now tender, and her arched responses, so eager, so potent, to the surging ocean waves? Shall we go so far as to speak of love divine, all loves excelling, and conclude that there must be a Great Lover looking down upon us from on high, to whose unconditional passion and openness of heart this earthly pair holds up its shining mirror?

No, this is a story of a deep but unstable love, one of breakages and reunions; a love of endless overcoming, defined by the obstacles it must surmount, beyond which greater travails lie. A hurdler's love. The forking, fissured paths of uncertainty, the twisting mazes of suspicion and betrayal, the plunging low road of death itself: along these ways it goes. This is a human love.

Let Vina speak. He in fact died that day, did you know that, she reveals, lying unclothed and overwhelming across my big brass bed one steaming summer's day in the middle 1980s in New York. That's right, she says with a twist of the mouth, he always did have fantastic timing. I come all the way across the world to find him and that's when the bastard decides to cash in his chips. For one hundred and fifty seconds he genuinely checked out, kicked the bucket, bought the farm. Ormus the flatliner. He went down that tunnel towards the light. Then he turned right round and came on back. Afterwards he told me it was on account of me?, he heard my voice calling behind him?, he looked back, and it absolutely saved his life. Blip blippety blip not-fade-away on the monitor screen, the flatline starts jumping, oh doctor, doctor, he's alive, it's a blessing a miracle, he's come back to us, heavens to Betsy, praise the Lawd. Dead for two minutes but in the third minute he rose again from the dead.

He didn't come back to us, Vina boasts, he came back to me. Didn't wake up until I made my appearance, what was the point, right, because I wasn't there. They'd always said there was nothing wrong with him, levels of electrical activity in the brain were normal, the strong probability being that there wasn't any lasting damage, he was just perfect and dandy?, except that he wasn't awake. No, Lady Methwold, there's no explanation, in these cases they either wake up or they don't and that's the whole of it. He could sleep for years, the rest of his life, or he could open his eyes tomorrow. Or in twenty years' time, not knowing he's missed a day, those awakenings are the most difficult, they look at their hands and scream what's this disease that's shrivelling up my skin, you have to judge the moment when you show them a mirror?, and it's a delicate judgement, believe me, there is the danger of suicide.

Vina repeats, proudly: He waited for me, sleeping, all those long years. Nothing in life was interesting any more unless I was by his side. Then I showed up and jeepers if those peepers didn't pop open right on cue. If that's not love then I don't know what. Which doesn't mean I didn't give him a hard time later on. But that's because he's a man.

A hole has appeared in downtown Mexico City, a chasm thirty metres across. It has swallowed buses, kiosks, children. For years water has been sucked out of the swampy sub-soil to sate the thirsty city, and this is the underworld's revenge. The fabric of the surface is being unwoven from below. Right here in Manhattan the buildings themselves are beginning to stagger. Just a few blocks north of my brass bed, there's a brownstone that's started shedding bricks. A net has been erected to protect pedestrians. People have always jumped off buildings in New York, but this is something new. This building is jumping off itself.

The papers are full of such new catastrophes but Vina wants to talk about old ones. In these years of their semi-retirement she has started coming to me more and more often, and as she removes her clothes she can't help showing some resentment of the great Ormus Cama, of the prominence given to his talent in the burgeoning histories of the VTO phenomenon. This is the price I have to pay for enjoying her favours: this ceaseless Ormusic, her personal obsessive Camamania. She comes to me to let off summer steam. If I were to object, she'd stop coming. Sex is never the point with Vina. Sex is trivial, like blowing your nose. She comes to me because I know her story. She's here to write new paragraphs: to complain. That, for Vina, is intimacy. That amuses and arouses her. Vina on the bed, stretching, turning, torments me, knowing I am happy—or at least willing—to be thus tormented. She is forty years old, and fabulous.

So let's never forget I was the one who fetched him out of the underworld, she boasts, like that Hindu goddess?, what's her name, Mousie.

Rati, I correct her.

Yeah, right. Rati who saved Kama the god of love. When the god of love opened his eyes, by the way, the left eyeball was almost colourless. The doctors blamed a blow received in the car accident and regretted that as the pupil was "stuck" in its fully dilated state and could no longer contract?, the eye would see very little, and blurrily. But I told the doctors it wasn't the accident. He looked down the tunnel and the light poured into his eye. One-eyed death at the tunnel's end glaring at Ormus Cama. He's lucky the other eye survived.

(And the left eye saw plenty, anyway. It saw too deeply, too far, too much.)

I don't interrupt. When Vina starts with her fanciful mysteries, all you can do is lie back and wait for her to lose interest, which never takes too long. Here she is, back again at the story of Kama and Rati. Anyhow, without me he'd be stir-fry, baby, she says, referring to the negative effects of Lord Shiva's thunderbolt on the errant love god of Hinduism. Without me he'd be nothing, he'd be ash.

Thus Vina on the great love of her life. When he awoke, I was his mirror, she says. He saw himself in my eyes and liked what he saw. And lived.

When I want to provoke her, when the monologue about Ormus finally gets my goat, I raise the subject of Maria the phantom nymphomaniac. I do it by conjuring up the old show tune from *West Side Story.* Maria, I start humming, and at once Vina stiffens; her skin actually heats up—I feel her temperature rising—and her eyes begin to boil. Then she disguises her jealousy by transforming it into outrageous behaviour. Do you want me to show you, she asks, savagely. Shall I perform upon you those unnatural acts. Hers, the so-called spectre's. You be Ormus, lie back and close your eyes just like you always wanted, and I'll be her, the slavering succubus. Would you like that, Rai, hey. You'd love it, am I right. Her terrible rising voice, caught halfway between a tear and a shriek, makes my ear whistle.

Keep it down, I say, a little frightened by this undressed ignoble savagery. Vina, come on. I don't need this and neither do you.

But perhaps she does need it, she feels injured by the very

existence of this Other, it offends her. Other-hatred is for Vina the mirror image of self-love.

The young Indian woman, no longer posing as a nurse but still answering to the name of Maria, starts coming to Ormus again, the first manifestation being a few days after Vina awakens him from his big sleep. She is discreet, however; Vina's presence guarantees Maria's absence, as if this were a condition of her appearances, a law of her fantastic realm. Ormus begins both to dread and to desire solitude because of these secret visits.

Fearing quick rejection, Maria has evolved a new strategy of volubility. Instead of tearing off her clothes and jumping on him, she seduces him with talk, fast, interesting talk, and he listens, because ever since he re-opened his pale left eye he has started seeing things he can't understand, things he needs to understand. It's as if his two eyes are looking into slightly different worlds, or rather two variations of the same world, almost the same and yet utterly separate. Double vision: he gets a lot of headaches.

Your eyes have been opened now, Maria murmurs, massaging his temples. He lets her do it. Now I can come to you like this, it's so much easier, whenever I want. Your eye knows, it remembers. Worli, the Cosmic Dancer, our life in the otherworld. These places feel like dreams et cetera, but they are places you have been and so on. I know it's hard for you. You have to live here for now. I understand. You have to blot certain things out to retain your ability to function and so forth. As for her, she's not good enough for you, but even this I can bear. I will never leave you. This is what you were sent to do. You slipped into your mother's womb behind your dead brother and they believed you belonged to them. Your songs will change this world. This is your fate. You will open their eyes and they will follow you towards the light et cetera et cetera. Your time has come to shine. All your dreams are on their way. See how they shine.

Is it possible that such an otherworld exists, he marvels.

And if it exists, he wonders privately, might it not also be possible that in that otherworld this strange girl might still be considered insane?

Her visits to his bedroom are necessarily brief. He is weak, convalescent, rarely left alone. She talks fast, continues to restrain her passions, seeking to present herself as an intelligent and educated person, a person worthy of his love.

Realities are in conflict, she tells him. Your right eye, your left eye, stare into different versions and so on. At such a moment the frontier between right and wrong action also dissolves. I myself have suspended moral judgement and live according to the more profound imperatives of my appetites et cetera.

He closes his left eye, experimentally. Maria disappears, as if someone had thrown a switch.

On her next visit she complains about her abrupt dismissal, insists on being treated with respect. I am here for you in any way you want, she says, but I don't care to be treated meanly and so forth. Just be a little polite.

What she wants to talk about most is earthquakes. There are going to be more of these, she prophesies. There are always earthquakes, Ormus answers. Yes, she says, but these are different. Two worlds in collision. Only one can survive and so on. In the end this world will crumble and fall et cetera and we will be together at home for ever and I will make you mad with joy et cetera et cetera et cetera as you must already know.

When she is not with him, she says, she visits past and present earthquake zones, in China, northern California, Japan, Tajikistan and elsewhere; all those places where the fabric of the earth has put itself in question. To Ormus, there is something ghoulish about this hobby, and about the lyricism with which she describes these high tragedies. She speaks of the earth beginning to sing, and rocking people's houses as if they were swinging cradles. The earth's pounding lullaby, not soothing but turbulent, coaxing human beings and their creations towards not sleep but death. She has spent a lot of time in Turkey, travelling to remote regions—Tochangri, Van—and India, too, gives her plenty to talk about: the devastation of Dharmsala and Palampur in the century's early years, and the narrow escape in Simla of Lady Curzon, the Viceroy's wife, who was just missed by a chimney that fell into her bedroom; also the Monghyr earthquake of 1934, when sulfurous mud and water bubbled up from great apertures in the earth like proofs of the existence of Hell, and Captain Barnard's Flying Circus was hired by the local authorities to overfly the area and assess the damage.

The great cracks in the streets of Orléansville, Algeria, the tidal wave that engulfed Agadir, the tidal wave that drowned Messina, the collapse of Managua and the escape of Howard Hughes, the Tokyo-Yokohama catastrophe of 1933, the endemic instability of Iran, and the strange behaviour of Sir J. A. Sweetenham, British governor of Jamaica, who refused the aid of the American navy after much of Kingston was flattened in the year 1907: about all these she painstakingly informs her bewildered beloved, in rather too much gruesomely relished detail.

Underlying all earthquakes is the idea of Fault, she says. The earth has many faults, of course. Literally millions have been mapped et cetera. But human Faults cause earthquakes too. What is coming is a judgement.

Now I know she's mad, Ormus thinks, but holds his tongue.

Earthquakes, Maria eagerly explains, are the means by which the earth punishes itself and its population for its wrongnesses. In spite of her disavowals of universal morality, she becomes, when she gets carried away, quite a tub-thumping fire-and-brimstone damnation preacher, bringing Ormus her hot gospel. She looks back to a utopian golden age in which there were no quakes, for the world was at peace, there were no conflicting versions, the earth lacked its present tragic quality of irreconcilability. The lithosphere itself, she argues, was originally intact but has been gradually deformed by movements in the planet's slowly convecting interior and so on. This hot, cauldron-like interior may be called the earth's original sin, its First Fault, and earthquakes are its consequences. Too late now to contemplate any return to that original state of balance, of grace. Too late to reconcile the earth with itself. We must brace ourselves for the tectonic movements, the slippages, the tsunamis, the landslides, the rocking, rolling cities et cetera et cetera, the smashing of the real. We must prepare for shocks, for the fragmentation of the planet as it goes to war with itself, for the endgames of the self-contradictory earth.

Human Faults cause earthquakes too. Maria on subsequent visits returns to her wildest notion. It is her view that there are certain individuals in whom the irreconcilability of being is made apparent, in whom the contradictoriness of the real rages like thermonuclear war; and such is the gravitational force of these individuals that space and time are dragged towards them and deformed. There are rifts, tears, slippages, incompatibilities. It is not that they are responsible for deforming the universe, but that they are the instruments through whose agency that growing deformity is clearly and terrifyingly unveiled.

It is her view that Ormus Cama is such an individual.

She says nothing about Vina in this regard.

She has talked enough. Now she has other plans, and advances upon him. He is in bed, too weak to resist her, and she knows she has aroused his interest. This time he will not refuse.

Ormus closes his eye.

IT'S ALMOST fourteen years since our first night of love back in old Bombay and still Vina lies unclothed on our hot bed without so much as a sheet to cover her. Another sleeping beauty waiting for her prince (not me, not me) to come.

In the middle 1970s I photographed a great Russian ballet dancer who had defected from the Kirov in France, running towards a group of soldiers and shouting, *Help to me, help for me,* in broken English, pursued by KGB goons. *Help by me, help with me.* Soon after his escape he ended up, as we all end up, in Manhattan, and found his way to my studio wrapped in furs, like a high-stepping big-mouthed bear. I stood him on a white sheet in front of an old eight-by-ten plate camera. He was certainly the loveliest creature he had ever seen, the most gorgeous by a long long way, and so with the help of (not very much) white wine I persuaded him to remove first his furs and then more and more of his clothes, until at length he was triumphantly nude, and delighted to be so. I told him to let his head hang down and allow his arms to hang loosely. Then he should slowly raise his head, and as he did so he should also bring his arms up and out from his body, and that was the shape I wanted, he should hold that, the exposure was a full second long and the plate camera's depth of field was also a problem. He did as I asked and as his strong animal's head rose I saw that the eyes were closed, he was lost in a rhapsody of self-love, which was so profound that synchronously with the rising of his arms he also raised, for my camera's unhoped-for benefit, a long and glisteningly happy erection.

Love by me. Love with me, to me, for me. Love of me.

Vina's self-love is not less than this.

Here are some things she actually sings to me, in vengeful retribution for my humming that teasing Bernstein tune and raising the forbidden subject of Maria, her alternative-reality rival. Rai—this part's the spoken intro—you think you're such a fuckin' star. Let me tell you who you really are. (Now comes the song.) You are ass and I like class. I like diamonds, you are glass. You brown mouse, I like black rats. You boy pussy but I like tom cats. Just because you got this dance, don't think you stand a fuckin' chance.

(End of song.)

Rai, you are burger and I have steak at home. You are not what I want, never were, never will be. But I'm a hungry woman. *I want more than what I want.*

Do you know what you want, they asked Ormus, twice: once when he awoke from the big sleep, once later. They never asked me but if they had I'd have had the answer down pat. I learned it from a good teacher, the toughest in the world.

THERE IS a wind in the willows, and perhaps that is a water rat scurrying to his hole. It is a balmy day, soft-breezed, and oarsmen are on the water in lazy sculls and heaving eights. Flags flutter from passing pleasure craft. Beneath taut sails young men *en matelot* lean and strain. Aboard the motor launches all is relaxation. Brass-buttoned blazers, white duck trousers, the long bare legs of pretty girls. An ack-ack popping of corks. Quails' eggs, and smoked salmon on brown bread. The river people wave to one another as they go, and if that is really Jesus Christ wearing a straw boater in that punt, then he too is welcome, he too deserves this moment of blessed beauty, this storybook English peace.

The war seems very far away.

Spenta walks down a path to the river, past a slope of bluebells and Waldo Crossley picking up leaves and an oak where once that old bastard Castlereagh liked to take his ease. He killed himself while staying here, slit his throat from ear to ear, they say, and emerged from his toilette bleeding to death from this second, lethal smile. In spite of the dead man's ghost, this walk is Spenta's favourite journey, along her mile and a half of shore, and it has become her custom to talk to her first husband while she takes the air.

How you would've loved it, Darius, to have guardianship of these historic moments, this riverbank, and oh, Darius, to feel this bliss. Life has vanquished death and even the furniture celebrates. The gloomy old leather chesterfields are shining and the whiskered ancestors posing in their frock coats and whatnot have stopped looking grim and have cracked out in smiles.

Our son has come back to us and all the world's in bloom. To this place, Darius, the country's grandees would come to let their hair down, believing themselves beyond inspection and above criticism. Lord Methwold was an unbuttoned host and here, in his prime, he offered recherché pleasures to the great. But the old roué Lord Methwold grew lonely and tired and took a widowed Parsi bride. After that the grandees found the house unsuitable for their preferred sports and the carnival moved on. None of those funny goings-on under my roof, Darius, I can promise you that.

But tell me: is a third marriage proof of lax morals? Especially if for example with a younger man? Even if the gentleman concerned has no interest in um?

By taking Darius around with her, by pleasing his shade and seeking his approval, she assuages a certain guilt. She now possesses what he yearned for above all things: a place in England, perhaps even in Englishness. I resisted it all your life, Darius, so you never had it, and now I've got it instead. If I walk these fields with you, if I tell you the stories of the house and make them yours as well as mine, will you forgive me, my true husband, my love. You see what a poor woman I have been. Everyone must forgive me. You and my sons.

Praise God. Our son Ormus has come back.

Darius, he's awake, but we'll lose him soon. He didn't come back for us. My little Ormie. My little shrimpy boy.

* * *

WILL YOU look at this shit, Vina scoffs from the parterre, looking down on Spenta and the shining Thames. Ormus is walking again, slowly, resting an arm on her shoulder. He who moved so beautifully now staggers like a drunk puppet. It's a museum, Vina says. Ye old world. For a boy like you, a place like this is living death. No wonder you got stuck in that coma?, but you're out of it now?, and at your age it's time you finally high-tailed it out of the British Empire.

There are butterflies, songbirds, wildflowers. There are onion-domed gazebos in the woods. Vina, voluble, impatient, makes this well-kept, carefully manicured or tidily unkempt country estate sound like the jungle, like some grass-hut Africa. I mean let's go, Ormus. I'm like out of here. Sail away with me.

That's a song about being tricked into slavery, he objects. It's about deceptions and lies. It's ironic.

England's the trick, she says. You're an American, she says. You always were.

He begins to sing about the ways in which America is unlike Africa. America, which is mercifully free of lions, tigers, murderous black mambas. It's the first time since the coma that he's raised his voice in song.

Sonny Terry and Brownie McGhee covered it, she says, turning away from him so he can't see the tears standing in her eyes. You've got to hear them. Newman may have written it but those guys made it hurt.

She gets rid of the throat lump and returns feverishly to the attack: Ormus you got stuck here, but it was an accident, and man, you're not stuck any more. You can either stay and I don't know immigrunt the rest of your life away, and let's not forget immigratitude, that's expected too, along with immigrovelling?, or you can cross the mighty ocean and leap into that old hot pot. You get to be an American just by wanting, and by becoming an American you add to the kinds of American it's possible to be, that's in general I'm talking about?, okay?, and New York City in particular. However you get through your day in New York City, well then that's a New York kind of day, and if you're a Bombay singer singing the Bombay bop or a voodoo cab driver with zombies on the brain or a bomber from Montana or an Islamist beardo from Queens, then whatever's going through your head?, well that's a New York state of mind.

Of course there are Americans you'll never be, she goes on, Boston Brahmins, slave owners' sons from Yoknapatawpha, or those sad sacks on the daytime confession shows, fat men in check shirts sitting with fat women showing too much thigh, wearing their naked subtitles and baring their clumsy souls. Just because they do not remember their history?, it doesn't mean Americans don't have it or they're not doomed to repeat it. You'll never have that stuff, that's for sure. But you don't need it. You'll say things all wrong but they'll at once become American ways of saying things. You won't know shit but it'll right away become an American type of ignorance. Not belonging, that's an old American tradition, see?, that's the American way. You'll never be a child in a haunted Virginia hollow, Ormus, or see your mama swinging in a barn, but that's cool, you've got horror stories of your own. And you don't have to do it?, but if you want to you can pretend, you can start arguing in bars about the Yankees' pitching rotation or stressing over the Mets, you can play remember-when, that's as in remember-when the Brooklyn Dodgers or Runyon's Broadway or the Village in the fifties or the birth of the blues. It's like you have a leg sawn off and you still feel it twitch?, only it's the opposite?, you can start feeling the twitching of legs you never had, and guess what, if you pretend long enough, then baby it becomes a good old American pretend, you can walk on those pretend legs without even crutches and they'll carry you wherever you're going, because what do you know, half the country's faking it just like you, and the other half isn't, but there's no way to tell who's which. So you get your strength back, Ormus, hear what I'm saying, and then you take up thy bed and you don't just walk, you fuckin' fly out of here. With me. America starts today.

Whoo-ee, she thinks, exhausted and astonished by the vehemence of her propaganda. *Whoo.* Well bang that drum, wrap me in the flag and call me Martha. But if I don't get him out of here pronto, I'm the one, because who can breathe this air, that'll suffocate to death.

* * *

VINA HAS been at war with Spenta since the moment she arrived. Mother and lover circle Ormus in his bed, as if they were prizefighters and he the referee.

All this technology, Vina smacks at the array of medical equipment. It may be good for fixing your teeth but it understands nothing, it explains nothing, and that's why it achieved nothing.

The finest money could buy. It kept him alive, Spenta plaintively replies, not knowing why she's sounding so apologetic, unable to get off the defensive.

Imbalances in the doshas, Vina diagnoses. They disrupted the flow of his prana life-energy force?, and impeded the body's fire. Impeded agni leads to the production of ama. Toxins. We must concentrate on panchakarma: on purging him. Focus on his feces, urine, sweat. The three malas are the key.

What are you saying, Spenta says. These words.

It's your culture, Vina gibes. The world's greatest and oldest holistic system. You don't know this? The five basic elements, earth, water, air, fire, ether?

Oh, ayurveda, Spenta sounds relieved. Yes, daughter, I know many of you youngsters are interested in these old ideas again, but this was never our Zoroastrian way. I personally like Ormus's deceased father put my trust in the finest Western care. Developed, like you, darling, over here only, in the West.

I'll plan it all out, Vina says, ignoring her. He'll need masseurs, herbal remedies. I'll teach him yoga as he gets stronger. Breathing exercises too. And a strict vegetarian diet, okay.

Meat is good for muscle, protests Spenta. And fish for brain. Surely it would be best to leave such matters under professional doctors' care. It must be so, that experts' régime affords best hope of recovery.

Did the doctors wake him up, okay? Vina spits at her. Did the experts have that expertise? Okay. Time somebody started paying attention to what works.

Maybe, daughter—I don't know—maybe you're right—

Rasayana, Vina firmly prescribes. It'll make a younger man of him.

Means what, child?

Sunbathing, Vina says. And herbs yoga meditation. And chanting.

Chanting, Spenta repeats, helplessly. Why not. He always loved to sing.

This is not a battle over medical treatment, but an intergenerational war of possession, and Spenta, who believes that she has already lost, has no weapons with which to fight. Unexpectedly, however, heavy artillery is offered. Big, shambling, baggy Patangbaz Kalamanja in a loose dark suit comes to call with bad news. Dolly is dead: of a thrombosis that worked its way to her generous and unsuspecting heart.

That earthquake shook something loose in her, opines Pat, his usual good-natured smile stretched by grief into a kind of snarl. Her own blood turned against her and became her killer, isn't it.

He gave the impression he was describing a murder in the family, and that was plainly how he felt. He blamed himself, of course. All these years I have foregrounded business interests and neglected the little lady, he mourned, looking like a lovelorn panda. She had Persis, but her damnfool husband sat on in Wembley, preferring to be a boss. Now she has gone! What good is Dollytone to me without my Dolly's own dear tones?

The Wembley place has been put on the market. Typically, Pat has nothing but good words for the country he is leaving. Britain is best, he says firmly. But Persis, now, she is my only home.

They are on the stone terrace overlooking the formal parterre, and Vina comes out to join them. Pat Kalamanja is rattled by the arrival of the woman whose charms defeated those of his own beloved daughter. He stiffens when introduced. Vina offers routine condolences, then, unable to check her impulses, asks whether the late Dolly lived and ate according to the principles of vegetarianism and traditional medicine; and adds, foot in mouth, that had she done so with due rigour and attention she might not have succumbed to the blood clot that stopped her heart.

The sight of a choleric Patangbaz Kalamanja, beet red of face, arms flailing, is rare indeed; yet this is the surprising Pat who rounds on Vina and lets fly. Who are you to speak of old learning? he cries. Some cheap singer, isn't it? Yet this same ayurveda you praise is expressly opposed—diametrically and inalienably opposed—to your brand of debauched activities. Music, drugs, television, sexual aggression, exciting movies, pornography, personal stereos, booze, cigarettes, the physical arousal of bodily rubbing in nightclubs and discothèques. This degraded material fills your personal environment, isn't it? Yet what are such stimuli but just the things which our learning names unnecessary and harmful? You have the cheek to speak of vegetables when your whole life is an abomination?

Just as rare as angry Pat is the spectacle of a flushed, nearly speechless Vina. I am an entertainer, yes, she says, shaking her head as if she's been punched. But surely?, as a manufacturer of radios et cetera?, you wouldn't . . .

Your self craves excitement to fill an emptiness born of insecurity, Pat Kalamanja rages. It is an addictive personality that goes for such low-life materials. Probably you have unfulfilled desires from a past life.

Pat, be calm now. (Spenta feels obliged to intervene on her rival's side.)

It is the bad times, roars the Dollytone tycoon. Kalyug, the age of destruction! Now we see the downward mutation of the species and also of knowledge itself. The universe proceeds by mirror images, and each set of imitations and replicas is less than that which it copies. Even in my beloved Persis I see only my Dolly's echo. Charles Darwin! Evolution! Just a sham, isn't it? A sham and a shame.

What a thing to say about your daughter, Vina objects, rallying.

You shut off! Pat Kalamanja roars. Leave India's sacred knowledge within India's national boundaries! What is knowledge? It is the Mind of Vishwaroop, the Cosmic Entity. It is the software of universal consciousness. Keep out of it, you, you, *virus*.

Come away, coaxes Spenta, taking her friend's elbow. Vina is not the right target for your wrath. Fate has dealt you a cruel blow and you must strive to understand it. It is not a time to indulge.

Patangbaz subsides, panting. He is no longer the god of anger but once more a stooped widower, coming apart at the seams. You should return home also, he advises Spenta as they move away from the stunned Vina. What is here for you now?

Darius is here, she answers. I am living in his Garden of Eden and he is happily by my side. We walk and talk. It's like this.

Everywhere there are women sitting alone because of men who will not return, says Pat Kalamanja, thinking of Persis. And men also, he adds, longing for women who have gone. Life is a broken radio and there are no good songs.

Go to Persis, says Spenta, kissing him on the cheek. Cling to love while you can. At least he has his daughter, she thinks. As for herself, a vegetarian immoralist, whose determination to succeed will now be twice as great, is planning to make off with her son.

IT'S BEEN ten years, more than ten. Red Nichols is dead and the Five Pennies aren't worth a nickel. When Ormus and Vina speak of love, they may be chasing phantoms. But though the body metamorphoses, it also remembers. They remember each other's moves, each other's need and smell and touch, each other's extremeness.

There's forgetting, too. Her return, his awakening: they feel like they've journeyed to a city they've both visited in dreams. Everything's familiar, there is much that tugs at the heart, but they don't know their way around. And there are whole neighbourhoods they've never seen.

They set out to learn each other again.

I've been alone, she says. Even when there was a man in my bed; maybe particularly then. You don't know, she says. You truly have no notion. A woman alone in this assassin's business, this thief's murderer's rapist's business. Sometimes you don't get paid. And after they steal your money they bootleg your work, they dirty your reputation, they call you whore.

You don't want to know what I have done. I have danced in a G-string in dirty Midwest dives. Bums in Atlantic City bars have put their hands on me, but I always knew I was a queen in exile, I had that in me?, the waiting?, the knowing my kingdom would come. One day, I knew, the poor would beg me for money and I would say, no dice, jack, I did my hustling, go do yours. People. Always hitting you up, always hitching a ride.

He says, weakly, you sound like you've lived a hundred years.

Two hundred, she says. My heart broke open and history fell in. That, and the future too. I go back a century to ugly Ma Rainey preaching Trust No Man, and forward a century to some space kitty floating weightless round the moon and singing to a stadium in the sky. I sat at the feet of Memphis Minnie, who's only just alive?, a fat balloon in a wheelchair now, she stopped crying just long enough to boast how she out-guitared Broonzy and to teach me the Minnie-Jitis. And what Holiday said about herself you know to be true of me. I was a woman when I was sixteen. Now I'm old as money, old as gold. Now I'm old as love.

He staggers in the gardens, struggling for his lost strength, his storied grace.

I want my man, she croons. I want my man. I don't want a skinny man, and I don't want a fat, and I don't want a man who cares about such things as that. And I don't want him angry, and I don't want him mean, and I don't want him sugar sweet or cute or peachy keen. And I found my man. I found my man.

The blues is just another name for not having any place, she sings. The blues is looking down at planet earth when you're stuck in outer space. Now that I've found you baby I can leave the blues behind. I can put my arms around you and ease my troubled mind. Rock and roll, she lets fly with the full force of her voice. My baby taught me how to rock and roll. I was half, he made me whole, if he's the bridge I'll pay his toll. Rock and roll. My baby taught me how to rock and roll.

To restore his energy she gives him aloe vera juice to drink and teaches him yogic breathing. What worries her most are his vibrations. She makes him spread his hand out flat on a board and hangs a crystal pendant over it. At once the crystal begins to swing insanely around, describing intricate patterns in the air, as if in the grip of a force field of unimaginable strength. She gasps and catches at it, even though she's not supposed to. I had to, she explains, it was about to shatter to bits. It couldn't take the violence of what you're putting out. I don't know what you've got inside you?, but it's stronger than a nuclear bomb.

* * *

THREE OF us went west from Bombay. Of the three, it was Vina, for whom it was a return journey, who first got caught up in the gnaw and churning of the western world's spiritual hunger, its chasms of uncertainty, and turned turtle: a tough shell over insides full of mush. Vina the radical, the word-hooligan, the outlaw, the woman on the edge: open her up and you found crystals and ether, you found someone who longed to be a disciple and be shewn the straight path. Which was a part of Ormus's power over her, and India's too. As for me, she found me anomalous, oxymoronic, an accusation she might profitably have levelled at herself (but never did). Rai, the un-Indian Indian, the easterner without a spiritual side: she needed to conquer me, to show me the truth about myself, which in her forcefully expressed view I was busily denying. So she kept coming back to me, bouncing between Ormus's bed and mine.

Also, of course, she liked illicit sex. *I want more than what I want.*

WHEN HE was strong enough to make love it was our turn, his and mine, to circle round the bed, Vina remembers. (I'm in bed myself by this time, and I've had a bellyful of Vina's Ormusings but I can't shut her up, nobody ever could.) Like stringed magnets, she says. Like dancers at a masked ball, only undressed.

Vina, for petesake. It's late.

Okay, but we did. At that moment which should have been a happy time, you know?, after everything?, we both you could say all of a sudden got to the point, a.k.a. our little deficiency in the department of trust.

Now why would that be an issue between you, I wonder, applying my lips to her moderately interested nipple. Why would the two of you mmff have anything to discuss ffwp in that region whatsoever. Is that mmhm mmhm nice.

Which murmured sarcasms, as I should have known, provoke a Vina tirade. Their unspoken sub-text—you were the broken promise, lady, the one who walked out on him, and as your presence within my bedroom walls goes some distance to proving, infidelity's your middle name—brings her bolt upright in bed, pushing angry hands into the depths of her hair as if in search of a weapon. Vina can do five minutes—*twenty* minutes—on almost any topic under the sun, and I am now given, with many added expletives, which I shall delete, her impromptu but impressively polished riff on trust, argued as is her custom from the general—trust as an aspect of modernity, its possibility and necessity created by our release from the tribe into the self—to the particular, namely, that which existed or did not exist between herself and Ormus; and, peripherally, me.

The allegedly permanent breakdown of trust between men and women: it's a long time since this began to sound unoriginal, even though it has to be admitted she has a right to the subject, as one of the first women to make it her own, and to keep shouting until it became everybody else's. Scarcely more interesting is her argument that women no longer see men purely as individuals, but think of them as repositories and products of the ignoble history of their sex. But then comes a neat twist. If men are not entirely individuals (and nor are women), then they can't be held fully responsible for their actions, since responsibility is a concept that can exist only in the context of the modern idea of the auto-determinant self. As products of history, as mere culturally generated automata, we're excluded from trusting and being trusted, because trust can exist only where responsibility can be—is—taken.

Professor Vina. I seem to remember she did end up holding some sort of honorary chair in one of the newer disciplines at a small, chic liberal-arts college in Annandale-on-Hudson. I certainly remember her amazing years as a lecture tourist. (This was after VTO stopped performing in public and before she attempted that final, fatal solo comeback.) She went on the college circuit with her "chautauquas," a word she stole from Robert Pirsig's Zen best-seller and re-cycled to describe her otherwise impossible to categorize stand-up evenings mixing ideological harangues, comic cabaret turns, autobiographical self-exposure and overpowering songs. The original, authentic chautauqua was a Native American talk-gathering, but Vina was never big on discussion or, indeed, on authenticity, which she held to be a pernicious notion that needed "deconstruction." Her chautauquas were really improvised monologues, whose closest cousins were the oral narrative sessions of the great Indian storytellers, actually existing Indians from actually existing India, as she liked to say, pulling rank over the Red kind and meaning it, although it was a part of her magic, the thing that made her the colossal figure she became, that—publicly, at any rate—no Native Americans ever took offence.

I remember, I photographed, the rapt upturned faces of the worshipful college young listening to this grand survivor of the heroic age who prowled the stage attired in wildly eclectic ethnic symbols, mojos, caftans, quetzal feathers, classical breastplates, tika marks, and held forth in shockingly explicit detail about her own life, its highs and lows, its sexual adventures and political encounters (sometimes these strands became deliciously entwined, as for example in her account of a long weekend in the private lodge of a Caribbean dictator with too much beard and not enough chin). Without warning, she'd electrify her young audiences by surging out of anecdote into heart-stopping *a capella* renderings of gospel songs, blues standards, jazz-scat Ella music, soft bossa nova shuffles and rock anthems, all in that voice, Our Mistress's Voice, her true gift to us all, an instrument that was, literally, too good for this world. Literally, to die for.

On stage or in my bed, Professor Vina was one of Vina's most awesome alter egos, it was some performance, but even as I listened quietly to the battlefield thunder of her arguments, I found myself noticing the cracks and rifts she was trying to cover up, the divisions in her soul, and thinking that Maria the disappearing nympho had a point when she spoke of our inner irreconcilability, the tectonic contradictoriness that has gotten into us all and has commenced to rip us to pieces like the unstable earth itself.

Professor Vina and Crystal Vina, Holy Vina and Profane Vina, Junkie Vina and Veggie Vina, Women's Vina and Vina the Sex Machine, Barren-Childless-Tragic Vina and Traumatized-Childhood-Tragedy Vina, Leader Vina who blazed a trail for a generation of women and Disciple Vina who came to think of Ormus as the One she had always sought. She was all of these and more, and everything she was, she pitched uncompromisingly high. There was no Self-Effacing Vina to set against Vina of the Screamingly Stretched Extremes.

That's why people loved her, remember: for making herself the exaggerated avatar of their own jumbled selves, but pushed to the edge or, better, driven to the heights: of talent and articulacy and outrageousness and promiscuity and self-destructiveness and intellect and passion and life. Higher Vina, engendering in the multitude a reciprocally higher, though entirely earthly, love.

As for the particular, the matter of trust between Ormus Cama and herself, an issue in which I myself have been a significant if ultimately peripheral factor, Vina uses her cockeyed theories of the externally determined self to bring in a not-guilty verdict on her many infidelities and desertions. The girl can't help it, that's what her position comes down to, when you strip away all the long words. What's in her nature is just there, generated by history or genes or sexual politics, it doesn't finally matter which. It's as if Olive Oyl were to usurp the catchphrase of Popeye the Sailor Man. *I yam what I yam an' that's what I yam.* It's like all the justifications of infidelity which men have used since time began.

Take it or leave it, she said; and Ormus took it—irresistible Ormus, for love of whom so many women pined, for whom the saintly beauty Persis Kalamanja had sacrificed all her hopes of joy.

Can there be a great love without trust?

Sho' thing, Rai, honey, she says, doing her panther stretch and ghetto drawl, sho' nuff they can. An' Ormus and me, we is the ever-livin' proof.

(*Ever-living,* I find myself thinking. *Vina, don't tempt fate.*)

Aloud I say, You know, Vina, I don't really get it. I never have. The way you two are together. How does that work exactly?

She laughs. Higher love, she answers. Love on a higher level. Just think of it like that. Like, exaltation.

She's relaxing now, having talked herself back into a good mood. When she isn't spaced out or blazing mad she can take a joke. Where was I, she says, settling back, her head on my stomach. Oh, right. We were circling the bed. He was out of the orangery by then?, I should mention that. Adios to that goddamn glass box. Instead this dusty bedroom full of disapproving clubmen frowning off the walls and above them if you believe plaster copies of classical friezes. And on Corinthian pedestals, marble busts. Persons in togas with laurel wreaths sitting on their ears. It's the seventies and the world's falling apart?, but we're given the fucking Parthenon to sleep in. The curtains by the way you would otherwise find only in old movie theatres, that dark sea of cloth, I expected them at some point to lift?, and for there to be I don't know trailers, commercials, our feature presentation. But okay, guess what?, the main attraction was us.

When Vina settles in for one of these all-night marathons, once she's started running on her personal movie screen a selection from her library of personal lifetime classics—and it might turn out to be a double or even triple bill—you just pass the popcorn and diet cola and go with the sleep option, having no other. Sleep for me has not for many years been a thing to look forward to. There are pictures in my head too, and at most of them I'd rather not take a second look.

I have much to say about myself, I have my own stories to tell. Mostly they'll wait. (While the gods are occupying centre stage, we mortals must hang about in the wings. But after the stars have finished all their tragic dying, the extras come on stage—it's the end of the big banquet scene—and we get to eat up all the fucking food.) But the pictures are here now. I can't put them back in their box.

A photographer has a second portfolio that he can't show because he never got the images on to film. If he's a photo-journalist many of these pictures visit him in dreams and ruin his fitful nights. Bobby Flow, the control-freak genius of the Nebuchadnezzar Agency, had three words that he said taught you all you needed to be good at the job. *Get up close.* Which he brilliantly did until somebody blew his head off in a swamp in Indochina, that being an occupational hazard. And the other one is when they don't blow your head off, because then it fills up with the actually existing world, the big picture of the world as it is when somebody peels the skin off. Flayed. Red in tooth and claw.

Earthrise re-shot as a bleeding broken skull hanging in exploding space.

I got up close enough times, too many, and I have my battle tales, my tall stories, like everyone else. Photographs taken while sheltering from bullets behind the dead bodies of other photographers. Wall-eyed toothless lunatics with Uzis shoving their guns' noses into my stomach, and even, once, into my mouth. The day I was pushed up against an ochre wall and made the subject of a mock execution, a Slav warlord's little joke. Listen: it's nothing. I seek neither to brag nor to complain. I went because it was my thing, my need. Some go because it's their need to die, some to see death, some to boast when they get back alive. (Everyone's a philosopher.) I could say guilt's got nothing to do with it, that film removed from a dead man's shoe is ancient history, but I'd be lying. That is, up to a point I'd be lying, because while I admit, okay, sure, every time I stand up in front of a screaming child with a bazooka I'm trying to prove I deserve to be there, I have the right to be carrying that camera, that accreditation—if you want ten-cent Lucy van Pelt psychoanalysis, there it is. What really interests and scares me is that the drive goes deeper than that, deeper even than the picture of a man hanging from a slowly rotating fan.

Something in me wants the dreadful, wants to stare down the human race's worst-case scenarios.

I need to know that evil exists and how to recognize it if I pass it in the street. I need it not to be abstract; to understand it by feeling its effect on me, the corrosion, the burn. Once in a chemistry exam I dropped concentrated acid on my hand, and the speed with which the brown stain spread across my skin was even more frightening than the acid itself. Science-fictional speed. But the point is I recovered, I'm fine, my hand works. Does this sound like self-justification? That every time I come away from my chicken game against evil, it's like proving at least to myself that the bad guys still lose a few, they can even have a really long loser streak?

It does?

Okay, so I'm just a violence junkie and one day I'll OD. Like Bobby Flow. Hulot's the clever one. He gave up taking pictures and paints watercolours instead. His paintings are truly dreadful, the worst type of *petit-maître* banality. He has discovered sentimentality and good taste in his old age and these two elderly nursemaids will keep him alive.

I don't need to tell you where I've been. You know already. This Southeast Asian swamp burning with eerie napalm fire, that casual pile of heads by the side of a dusty African road, this terrorist attack on a Mideast market square, that Latin American village mourning its busload of land-mined kids. Sure you do. You've seen my work. We all do this work. It's what's wanted.

AND WHEN I can't stand hell any more I change my clothes, I put on some of the best casualwear Seventh Avenue has to offer, head for the studio and drop in on pussy heaven: fashion photography, when you can make beautiful women in expensive clothes behave as if they were in a war zone. They stare, leap, spin, gasp, duck, arch, jerk. I've seen machine-gun fire take a body that way.

That's not all I do with them. It depends on the girl. Some of them are calm and I go with that, I create seas of calm around them, oceans of light and shadow. I drown them in peace until it scares them, and then they come alive. Others know something of my more brutal work and want to show me how real they are, how much they know of harshness, of the street. The contrast between harshness and couture usually works, until it becomes a cliché. Then for a while I go with beauty, piling beauty on beauty, making it overwhelming, almost indecent, like a ravishment.

So that, too, ends up being an assault.

And there's portraiture, though I'm not always as lucky as I was with the erection guy. And there's advertising. And there is more private, essayistic work, but maybe I'll save that for another day. I'm tired. The pictures are coming. The pictures you haven't seen, the ones that come at night.

In the beginning was the tribe, clustering around the fire, a single multi-bodied collective entity standing back-to-back against the enemy, which was the rest of everything-that-was. Then for a little while we broke away, we got names and individuality and privacy and big ideas, and that started a wider fracturing, because if we could do it—us, the planet kings, the gobblers with the lock on the food chain, the guys in the catbird seat—if we could cut ourselves loose, then so could everything else, so could event and space and time and description and fact, so could reality itself. Well, we weren't expecting to be followed, we didn't realize we were starting anything, and it looks like it's scared us so profoundly, this fracturing, this tumbling of walls, this forgodsake freedom, that at top speed we're rushing back into our skins and war paint, postmodern into premodern, back to the future. That's what I see when I'm a camera: the battle lines, the corrals, the stockades, the pales, the secret handshakes, the insignia, the uniforms, the lingo, the closing in, the shallow graves, the high priests, the non-negotiable currencies, the junk, the booze, the fifty-year-old ten-year-olds, the blood-dimm'd tide, the slouching towards Bethlehem, the suspicion, the loathing, the closed shutters, the pre-judgements, the scorn, the hunger, the thirst, the cheap lives, the cheap shots, the anathemas, the minefields, the demons, the demonized, the führers, the warriors, the veils, the mutilations, the no-man's-land, the paranoias, the dead, the dead.

Professor Vina's rhetoric: here's where it leads.

Can you hear in my voice that I'm angry? Good. I've been reading a book about anger. It says that anger is evidence of our idealism. Something has gone wrong, but we "know," in our rage, that things could be different. *It shouldn't be this way.* Anger as an inarticulate theory of justice, which, when you act it out, is called revenge. (Alternatively of course I'm just another choleric snappeur, warped by life, by endlessly playing second fiddle to the main event. This is the clickista's indispensable but somehow low-grade work: second-fiddling while Rome burns. . . . And here, in bed, with Vina? No difference. Ormus Cama is in the seat reserved for the first violin.)

When Vina is angry with me, she remembers the rage of my mother, Ameer Merchant, which drove her away from us, away from love. This is why I forgive her the vindictive remarks. I know I'm standing in for Ameer when Vina lets fly, and I can't help thinking she's sort of entitled.

When I'm angry with her, I remember my mother too. I remember Ameer taking Vina under her wing, teaching her, oiling and brushing her, kohling and hennaing her, pouring herself into that brilliant damaged girl. I remember my own unresolved quarrel with my mother, my broken-home anger, my accusations, the pain I heaped on her own bitter unhappiness. I look at Vina and see Ameer in her. Once, I showed her the pictures I'd taken of my mother on the day of her death. I wanted to see if Vina saw it: the likeness.

She saw it right away. Hat Cheap Suit, she said. But she wasn't thinking of the female pharaoh, and nor was I. She was thinking, *this is me. This is a picture of the future, an image of my own death.*

And as things turned out she was almost right; because when she died, there were no deathbed photos. There wasn't a deathbed, or a body to take a picture of.

My mother's photograph was almost all we had.

VINA'S STILL talking, and all at once she's uncertain, now that she's arriving at the point of the story she wants my full attention, but my consciousness is slipping away, I'm all in, done for, crashing.

Rai?

Mmhm?

It's as if we were both watching—for something, you know—in each other, that is—it's like what you do?, when you're taking a photograph?, and sometimes you wait and wait and it doesn't come, but when it comes, you've got it?, bang?, one shot and it's yours? What's that called? Rai? What's that called?

Unhnh.

So that's what happened. All the pretence just slipped away?, all the injury?, all the past?, and we just, just. Clicked. The decisive moment. That's it. *Click.*

Hynhnyhnm.

By the way, his bruise vanished, she's saying, but her voice is fading out. The birthmark on his eyelid. Did you know that? He hasn't got it any more.

I don't care. I'm asleep.

CHAPTER TWELVE

Transformer

In a pool of light on the red-eye to New York there's a sleepless Hispanic kid, baleful of eye, wrestling grimly with a new kind of science fiction plaything. It's some sort of motor car, but he's not interested in playing vroom-vroom, he's pulling the car apart. Its fins swivel, its tires swing out until they're at right angles to the folding table, its body hinges and opens like an anatomy model. Dazzlingly, startling the brain, it unfolds, exfoliates, deconstructs itself and then clicks together in new, unforeseeable configurations. The boy is finding it difficult to grasp the last secrets of this metamorphic riddle. More than once he slams it down on the table, where it lies unfinished, trapped in an unreadable transitional phase. The noise wakes up the masked sleepers around him, and transfers the boy's own annoyance to these adult others. Finally the dozing man in the aisle seat, his father probably, pushes back his sleep mask and with swift irritable hairy hands shows the boy the gimmick of the toy, and then all at once the car has vanished, and what's standing there instead, rearing up on metallic hind legs, is a big little monster, a grotesque techno-being, some sort of fierce robot thing brandishing lurid, finny ray guns in outsize gauntleted fists. The twentieth century—the car—has been supplanted by this visitor from a dystopic future.

The child begins to play. Boom! Boom! The robot annihilates the seat in front, the armrests, many passengers. In a while the boy falls asleep, cradling the monster in his arms, not at all alarmed by the idea that the commonplace machinery of the present contains the secrets of such apocalyptic tomorrows, that we could transform our quotidian roadsters, our unassuming station wagons, our bourgeois sedans, into fearsome war machines if we could but learn the trick.

Boom! Boom! The boy dreams of destroying the world.

Ormus Cama, watching from across the aisle, is caught up in a fantastic fiction of his own; except that it's no fiction. There is a world other than ours and it's bursting through our own continuum's flimsy defenses. If things get much worse the entire fabric of reality could collapse. These are the extraordinary thoughts he's having, trembling intimations of the end of things, and there's one accompanying puzzle: How come he's the only one who can see the vision? An event on this cosmic scale? Is everybody sleepwalking? Don't they even care?

The northern lights hang around the aircraft, blowing in the solar wind like giant golden curtains—like answers—but Ormus isn't interested, he's lost in his questions. What, Vina asks, struck by the hunted look on him. What. She's bewildered by what he's doing with his eyes, he's closing first one, then the other, winking into the night sky over Greenland like an old lecher making a pass.

Ormus, come on, you're scaring me.

You wouldn't believe me anyway.

I believed you before, didn't I? Gayomart, remember? The songs in your head.

That's right. That's right, back then you were the one who did.

Well then. *What.*

So he confesses the truth which he himself finds beyond belief: that ever since she awoke him from his long beauty sleep he's been living in—or rather with—two worlds at once. He tries to describe to her what he first saw on the flight to London, the gash in the real. Is it like a hole?, like a black or some other color hole?, in the sky?, she struggles to picture it. No, he says, and clutches at the billowing aurora for help. Imagine if this, he says, waving an arm, this, us, where we are, all of it, if it was all a movie on a screen and we were in it, a huge screen like at a drive-in or just hanging in space like a curtain, and then suppose there were slashes in the screen, a mad knifeman ran into the cinema and hacked at that curtain, so now there are these great rips going right across everything, across you, across the window, across the wing out there, across the stars, and you can see that behind the screen there's a whole other set of things going on, maybe another whole I don't know level, or maybe another movie screen with another movie playing, and there are people in that movie looking the other way through the rips and maybe seeing us. And beyond that movie another movie and another and another until who can guess.

There are things he doesn't tell her at this time. He doesn't say, some people seem to have found a slip-sliding method of moving between the worlds. He doesn't say, there's this woman, I don't have any way of stopping her, she shows up whenever she feels like it. He doesn't speak the name Maria.

There's an in-flight movie playing in the next sector of the plane, where the insomniacs are seated. Vina can see the small screen hanging in the darkness a way off. A Scottish doctor keeps turning into a twisted monster and back again. It's that remake, she recognizes it, of the old horror picture, Dr. whatever and Mr. right. Looks like a dud. Even the insomniacs haven't lasted the course. The film's images float silently over the airborne cargo of sleepers, dreaming towards America. Vina is on the edge of her seat. She feels elated, panicky, confused all at once, and flounders for the right thing to say. Where's your bruise, she eventually asks, touching his left eyelid gently. What happened to that, your magic bruise. You had an accident and lost a contusion?, that's what?, illogical.

He's gone, Ormus says. His expression is terrible to behold. Gayomart. He burst out of my head and vanished. I'm alone in here now. He's free.

No bruise but his eyes are different colors.

There's more, he says. The bruise has faded, but now the blind eye's the one that's seeing things. If I close it, the manifestation goes away. At least it goes away most of the time. Sometimes it's so powerful I can even see it with both eyes shut. But shutting the eye is maybe ninety-five percent effective. Then if I close my right eye and it's just the left one that's open it's like dying. Everything disappears and only the otherness is left. As if I'm standing in a snowstorm and looking through windows into another place and in that place, I don't know how to explain this, I'm not even sure if I exist.

He does not add, but then there is Maria.

He sounds wired, screechy. He is saying things that cannot be. I've been thinking, he offers shakily. I was wondering, maybe an eye patch.

Voices, she asks, do you hear voices. What are they saying to you, is there any message. Maybe you should be listening for that, a communication, something important for you to pass on.

This would be a good moment to mention the nocturnal visitor, but Ormus sidesteps it. You aren't freaking out, he notes with admiration. There are those who would run screaming. I'm crazy, raving, don't you think so, most people would. I was in a coma for more than a thousand and one nights, maybe I came out doolally which in case you aren't aware is madness from India. Homegrown, the local brand. Deolali. The heat there drove the British soldiers off their heads. But what, you don't think I'm boiling mad, you think it's possible.

I always knew there was something beyond, she says, letting him rest his head on her bosom in the pressurized dark. I always knew it even when you or Rai made fun. What, this dump was all we got?, no higher-rent accommodations to aspire to?, impossible. But I don't know. You took some pretty hard hits in that crash, so it could be—and I'm not a doctor, okay—double vision, some neural hallucination, the brain can do that?, or maybe it's true, you're looking into another whole thing. I always was the open-minded one. I'm expecting aliens to vacuum me up any day now. Or again, yeah, maybe you're nuts. Which also makes no difference. Have you noticed how many people are nuts? I'm beginning to think it's everyone?, only most of them haven't noticed. In which case sanity isn't the crucial issue. The crucial issue is what do I think of you, and I already answered that by taking an earlier plane, the one from Bombay. You called, I answered. And then I called to you and you opened your eyes. Two-way radio. What do you want, a neon sign? I feel the earth move under my feet. This can't be love I get no dizzy spell. Read my lips. I already made my choice.

There's no message, he says.

It's not paradise, he says. It's not so very unlike here. What I catch glimpses of through the shredding—and I'm starting to see more clearly—I'd call them variations, moving like shadows behind the stories we know. This doesn't have to be supernature, it doesn't have to be god. It could be just—don't ask me—physics, okay? It could be some physics beyond our present capacity to comprehend. It could just be I found a way of stepping outside the picture. There's a Pop Art dance pattern piece by Amos Voight, he says. An Arthur Murray School affair with outlines and arrows, left foot right foot, you get up on to it and follow the steps. Except in this case at a certain moment all your weight's on the foot you're supposed to move. So the pattern doesn't work, it's a joke, a trap. Unless you take a foot off it, change your weight and continue. You have to break the rules, deny the frame story, smash the frame. There's this Russian word, he says. *Vnenakhodimost.* Outsideness. It could be I found the outsideness of what we're inside. The way out from the carnival grounds, the secret turnstile. The route through the looking glass. The technique for jumping the points, from one track to the other. Universes like parallel bars, or tv channels. Maybe there are people who can swing from bar to bar, people who can if you understand me channel-hop. Zappers. Maybe I'm a zapper myself, he says. Exercising a kind of remote control.

Remote controls for tv sets were new then. They were just beginning to be used as similes and metaphors.

What's it like, she wants to know. The other world.

I told you, he answers, feeling the onset of the weary blues. The same only different. John Kennedy got shot eight years ago. Don't laugh, Nixon's President. East Pakistan recently seceded from the union. Refugees, guerrillas, genocide, all of that. And the British aren't in Indochina, imagine that; but the war's there all right, even if the places have different names. I don't know how many universes there are but probably that damn war's in every one. And Dow Chemicals and napalm bombs. *Two, four, six, eight, no more naphthene palmitate*—they've got another name for that too, but it burns little girls' skins the same way. Naptate.

He says, there's a ton of singers in sequins and eyeliner, but no trace of Zoo Harrison or Jerry Apple or Icon or The Clouds, and Lou Reed's a *man.* There's Hollywood but they never heard of Elrond Hubbard or Norma Desmond, and

Charles Manson's a mass murderer, and Allen Konigsberg never directed a picture and Guido Anselmi doesn't exist. Nor do Dedalus or Caulfield or Jim Dixon, by the way, they never wrote any books, and the classics are different too.

Vina's eyes have been growing wider, she's been emitting suppressed little giggles of disbelief, she can't help it.

The Garden of Forking Paths, he says, naming her favorite nineteenth-century novel, the interminable masterwork of the Chinese genius, the former governor of Yunnan province, Ts'ui Pên.

What about it? Don't tell me they don't . . .

(She's actually angry: this is the last straw, her face says.)

No such book, he says, and she slams fist into palm.

Damn it, Ormus, and then she controls herself, doesn't let her thoughts slip past her lips: *This is a joke, right. Or else you're really mad.*

He reads her mind anyway. All my life, he says—and there's despair dragging at his voice, distorting the way it sounds—it's been the empire of the senses for me. What you can touch and taste and smell and hear and see. All my speeches in praise of the actual, of what is and persists, and no time for the airy-fairy. And now here in spite of it all are fairies from the fucking ether. All that is solid melts into fucking air. What am I supposed to do?

Make it sing, she says. Write it with all your heart and gift and hold on to the hooks, the catchy lyrics, the tunes. Fly me to that moon.

He sings other men's soft, muffled odes into her consoling breast. You are my sunshine. I'm a king bee. Hold me tight.

Music will save us, she comforts him. That, and, and.

Love, he says. The word you want is love.

Yeah that was it, she grins, caressing his cheek. I knew that.

Will you marry me?

No.

Why the fuck not?

Because you're an insane person, asshole. Go to sleep.

THE WORLD is irreconcilable, it doesn't add up, but if we cannot agree with ourselves that it does, we can't make judgements or choices. We can't live.

When Ormus Cama saw his vision, he revealed himself to be a true prophet, and I say this as a dyed-in-the-wool unbeliever. I mean: he was genuinely ahead of his time. We've all caught up now. He isn't here to see them, but the contradictions in the real have become so glaring, so inescapable, that we're all learning to take them in our stride. We go to bed thinking—just a random example—that Mr. N—— M—— or Mr. G—— A—— is a notorious terrorist, and wake up hailing him as the savior of his people. One day the islanders inhabiting a particular cold wet lump of godforsaken rock are vile devil worshippers swigging blood and sacrificing babies, the next day it's as if nothing of the sort ever occurred. The leaders of whole countries vanish as if they never were, they're miraculously erased from the record, and then they pop up again as talk show hosts or pizza pluggers, and lo!, they're back in the history books again.

Certain illnesses sweep across large communities, and then we learn that no such illnesses ever existed. Men and women recover memories of having been sexually abused as children. Whoosh, no they don't, their parents are reinstated as the most loving and laudable people you could imagine. Genocide occurs; no it doesn't. Nuclear waste contaminates large swathes of entire continents, and we all learn words like "half-life." But in a flash all the contamination has gone, the sheep aren't ticking, you can happily eat your lamb chops.

The maps are wrong. Frontiers snake across disputed territory, bending and cracking. A road no longer goes where it went yesterday. A lake vanishes. Mountains rise and fall. Well-known books acquire different endings. Color bursts out of black-and-white movies. Art is a hoax. Style is substance. The dead are embarrassing. There are no dead.

You're a sports fan but the rules are different every time you watch. You've got a job! No you don't! That woman powdered the President's johnson! In her dreams—she's a celebrated fantasist! You're a sex god! You're a sex pest! She's to die for! She's a slut! You don't have cancer! April Fool, yes you do! That good man in Nigeria is a murderer! That murderer in Algeria is a good man! That psycho killer is an American patriot! That American psycho is a patriot killer! And is that Pol Pot dying in the Angkoran jungle, or merely Nol Not?

These things are bad for you: sex, high-rise buildings, chocolate, lack of exercise, dictatorship, racism! No, *au contraire!* Celibacy damages the brain, high-rise buildings bring us closer to God, tests show that a bar of chocolate a day significantly improves children's academic performance, exercise kills, tyranny is just a part of our culture so I'll thank you to keep your cultural-imperialist ideas off my fucking fiefdom, and as for racism, let's not get all preachy about this, it's better out in the open than under some grubby carpet. That extremist is a moderate! That universal right is culturally specific! This circumcised woman is culturally happy! That Aboriginal whistlecockery is culturally barbaric! Pictures don't lie! This image has been faked! Free the press! Ban nosy journalists! The novel is dead! Honor is dead! God is dead! Aargh, they're all alive, and they're coming after us! That star is rising! No, she's falling! We dined at nine! We dined at eight! You were on time! No, you were late! East is West! Up is down! Yes is No! In is Out! Lies are Truth! Hate is Love! Two and two makes five! And everything is for the best, in this best of all possible worlds.

Music will save us, and love. When reality bites, and it bites me almost every day, I need Ormus's music, his take. Here it is in my hand, shining like a National guitar: "Song of Everything"'s the track I'm choosing, the first song he wrote in America, at Tempe Harbor, within days of his arrival. I'm sitting here at the end of time with my good friend Mira Celano—and there's a lot to tell you about *her* later in the program—so, Mira, this one's for you.

Everything you thought you knew: it's not true. And everything you knew you said, was all in your head. And everything you did and everywhere you went, well you never ever did that and you were not sent. I think you'll find we're trapped in someone else's mind. Yes I think you'll find we're trapped in someone else's mind. And it's only make-believe but we can't leave it behind.

Everything you think you see: it can't be. There's just me. Darling there's just me, just me.

* * *

In a time of constant transformation, beatitude is the joy that comes with belief, with certainty. The beatific bathe in almighty love, wear smug grins and play their harps and acoustic guitars. Safe in their cocoon from the storms of metamorphosis, the blessed give thanks for their unchangingness and ignore the leg irons biting into their ankles. It's eternal bliss, but nix nix, you can keep that jailhouse cell. The Beats and their Generation were wrong. Beatitude is the prisoner's surrender to his chains.

Happiness, now, that's something else again. Happiness is human, not divine, and the pursuit of happiness is what we might call love. This love, earthly love, is a truce between metamorphs, a temporary agreement not to shape-shift while kissing or holding hands. Love is a beach towel spread over shifting sands. Love is intimate democracy, a compact that insists on renewals, and you can be voted out overnight, however big your majority. It's fragile, precarious, and it's all we can get without selling our souls to one party or the other. It's what we can have while remaining free. This is what Vina Apsara meant when she spoke of a love without trust. All treaties can be broken, all promises end up as lies. Sign nothing, make no promises. Make a provisional reconciliation, a fragile peace. If you're lucky it might last five days; or fifty years.

I offer all this—the airplane terror and doubt, my own post facto musings, his lyrics (which some British professor calls poetry, but then there's always a professor; to me, set down on the page without their music, they seem kind of spavined, even hamstrung)—so that you can have a sense of the amazing realizations to which Ormus Cama was quickly coming. He'd been given a second chance at life, a second act in a country whose citizens' lives famously don't have second acts, and he had concluded that he'd been allowed back for a purpose. Chosen. He was struggling for other language, language that didn't imply an allower, a chooser, but the inertia in language is hard to resist, the inexorable advancing weight of its accumulated history. And all this had filled him up with new music. He was bursting with the stuff, and now that we know the stuff he was bursting with, the image of his arrival in America—that pale man in his mid-thirties with haunted eyes, still gaunt-faced and dressed in crummy bluejeans—feels like a hinge moment, around which turned so much that would become our shared experience, part of the way we saw and constructed ourselves.

ORMUS CAMA sees the mighty pincushion of Manhattan puncturing the haze of the high dawn air and begins to smile the smile of a man who has just discovered that his favorite fiction turns out to be no lie. As the plane banks and drops he recalls my father Vivvy Merchant's love of Queen Catherine of Braganza, through whom Bombay and New York are forever yoked together. But this recollection fades almost at once: because from the start it was the cloud-scrapers of the isle of the Manhattoes that pricked Ormus's heart, he shared my mother's dream of conquering the sky, and never itched for the thronged streets of Queens, its bazaars bustling with the polyglot traffic of the world. Vina, on the other hand, Vina whom Ameer Merchant loved, never ceased to be a street urchin in her heart, even when immense celebrity forced her into its glittering cage. But New York, for Ormus, was from the beginning a doorman, an express elevator and a view. You could say it was Malabar Hill.

THE CITY is temporarily withheld, however: in the words of Langston Hughes, a dream deferred. Yul Singh has arranged everything—documents, permissions, limousine—and has placed one of his country residences, for the purpose of "decompression," of effecting a "soft landing," at the disposal of the "lovebirds." This it's a hell of a place which I say so myself, the winery there makes a powerful Pinot Noir, you two should take time out, drink some wine, think about the future, which okay you're not so young Ormus but the old guys are doing okay, you catch my drift, there's potential, and with Vina beside you she's a doll I don't have to tell you and that voice of hers like a fuckin' steamer horn pardon my French, it could work, no promises, it's down to the material which I don't have to tell you you should get to work on right away, but what the hey, take thirty-six hours, take two days, you wouldn't believe the line of talent at my door, longer every day, you know what I'm saying, forget about it.

Ormus receives this welcoming monologue (in which Yul Singh's tongue is shown not to be as clean as he once claimed) on the car phone in the back of a black-windowed stretch driven by one of the legendary tribe of Colchis factotums, those Americanized heavies of Punjabi descent who are Yul's bodyguards and chauffeurs, bouncers and valets, accountants and lawyers, strategists and enforcers, publicists and A&R men; who dress in identical black Valentino suits and molded shades; and who are universally known, though never in their imposing short-fused presences, as Yul's Sikh jokes. Will Singh, Kant Singh, Gota Singh, Beta Singh, Day Singh, Wee Singh, Singh Singh, and so on. If these are not their real names then everyone has long forgotten what those prosaic handles might have been. Ormus and Vina's present companion is the aforementioned Will. I'll be taking you as far as the helipad, he says, barely turning his head. Mr. Yul's personal Sikorsky will take care of your onward journey today.

No point resisting. Give in gracefully. Ormus and Vina settle back into the deep leather upholstery. Where is this honeymoon lodge, Ormus idly asks.

Sir the Finger Lakes area sir. Does that make any sense to you?

Vina sits up. It does to me. Where's it near to?

Yes ma'am, it's located at the southern tip of Lake Chickasauga. Heart of the state wine-growing region. Ma'am, this would be in the neighborhood of a little town, maybe you're familiar with it, by the name of Chickaboom.

Captivity in Egypt, Vina moans, closing her eyes. Even the Israelites didn't have to return once they'd got away.

Excuse me? Ma'am? You lost me there?

No, nothing. Thank you.

Yes ma'am.

THE HOUSE at Tempe Harbor, in wood painted pale gray with white trimmings and the sort of ornate carved "lacework" more typically glimpsed through the tropical palm fronds and bougainvillea creepers of Key West, is in fact the creation of a perverse Floridan millionaire of Swiss-German origin, Manny Raabe, who escaped in old age from effete Southern warmth (and occasional hurricanes) into these bracingly nostalgic northern latitudes, and promptly died of the cold. Yul Singh has since put in an underfloor heating system and installed numerous extra chimneys and fireplaces. It's a mighty place, with two slated mansard roofs conceived on the grand scale, like Swiss Alps. Singh keeps it hot, and stuffed with parakeets and tropical plants: as if rebuking the late Raabe for his folly. There's a sauna. The chef—Kitchen Singh—is under instructions to concentrate on a strongly spiced sub-continental cuisine. Tempe Harbor has been transformed by its new owner into a shrine to heat. Which if you don't care for it I apologize, Yul Singh is on the phone the moment the chopper sets down, but if you buy a haunted house you should it's my opinion make it unattractive to the ghost.

There's no trace of a ghost but they're not the only guests. Another pair of "lovebirds" is in residence, the art-house-movie director Otto Wing and his newlywed bride, a long, gummy Nordic beauty called Ifredis, who insists on skipping naked across the midnight lawn to go skinny-dipping in Lake Chickasauga's cold black water, pursued by the scholarly, bespectacled body of her similarly nude husband, who can be heard shrieking out the *An die Freude* as the water hits his genitalia. Joy, shrieks Wing in German. Joy, thou lovely spark of God, daughter of Elysium.

There's a lot of shrieking, as it happens. Wing and Ifredis can't get enough of each other and fuck uninhibitedly whenever and wherever the spirit moves them, and it moves them all the time and all over the place. Ormus and Vina witness the lovers' passion again and again, in the mansion's many living rooms, in the lakeside gazebo, on the pool table, the tennis court, the deck.

These people, says Vina, slightly put out. They make us look like virgins.

When they're not fucking and shrieking, Wing and Ifredis are sleeping, or eating quantities of cheese and drinking orange juice by the quart. (They appear to have their own food supplies, and usually forgo Kitchen Singh's lavish banquets. They generate all the heat they can handle without his culinary aid.)

Their conversation, such as it is, touches mostly on Jesus Christ. Ifredis is a hundred-and-ten-percenter, a girl who holds nothing back. She goes in for religion with the same naked, cold-water zeal as she evidences in her shrieking sex bouts. Swiftly identifying the weak point, the wavering heathen, she pursues Ormus into the hot tub in the spa wing and interrogates him with pitying wonder dripping from her wide blue eyes. So is it really true you no god at all have? I guess not, says Ormus, unwilling to discuss his new visionary condition. There follows a long sorrowing silence, until Ormus understands that reciprocity is required of him. Oh, right, he mutters. Er, how about you?

Ifredis whoops, a long orgasmic sound. Uhh, she purrs. I just love Christ Jesus. Wing arrives, leans on the side of the tub and kisses her deeply, as if drinking at a spring, then emerges from her mouth to offer this thought. I adore in this woman her directness, he says. Her lack of irony. At the point we have reached in the century it is important to eschew all ironic communication. Now is it time to speak directly to avoid a chance of misunderstanding. In all circumstances to prioritize such avoidances.

His bride is tugging at his sleeve. Otto, she pleads, making a rubbery moue. Otto, I want to sit on your arm. She rises like a steaming Venus from the tub and they scamper off. Her English is not good, Otto sings out at Ormus over his departing shoulder. To avoid misunderstanding I should explain that at her present vocabularial level she makes occasionally a confusion of the limbs.

If one were of a paranoid disposition (and these are paranoid days) one might suppose that Yul Singh has engineered this long weekend with great deliberation: that even from distant Park Avenue Yul Singh the blind puppeteer is pulling his guests' strings, the way George Bernard Shaw up there on his godlike cloud manipulates his Higgins and Eliza marionettes on the cover of the original *My Fair Lady* cast recording.

Every detail of life at Tempe Harbor, after all, bears witness to the long reach of the mogul's influence. Even in his absence, Cool Yul is a hands-on host. There are the unpredictable but frequent phone calls to both guests and staff, there is the meticulous attention to detail: the vegetarian menu for Vina, the doctor in residence in case Ormus's health should suddenly deteriorate. The décor is a curious mixture of European high good taste and Indo-American flaunt-it brashness: antique Louis Quinze chairs imported from France and reupholstered in monogrammed powder-blue silk. YSL. The monogram (for Yul Singh Lahori, his rarely used full name) is ubiquitous: on most of the furnishings, on the specially rolled in-house cigars and cigarettes, on the silver cufflinks presented as keepsakes by the housekeeper Clea Singh to all male guests, and even on each thick square of the personalized toilet paper rolls and the house range of TH condoms, sanitary napkins and tampons discreetly positioned, according to gender, in the his-and-hers bathrooms that are a feature of each guest suite. Framed gold and platinum records line the walls; also portraits of the great man—who bears more than a passing resemblance to the actor Vincent Price, that smooth nocturnal prince of the fanged classes—and of his aristocratically etiolated and long-suffering French wife Marie-Pierre d'Illiers. Who I must personally admit is my symbolic ideal, my immortal tea cake, who when I taste her lips I remember everything important in life, Yul Singh confides to Ormus on the phone. Okay, so you want to ask now about my, don't bother to pretend you don't know this, on the surface contradictory and also extremely public liaisons with as they say a string of young beauties, he goes on. The famous disarming grin, the helpless spreading of the arms, come across to Ormus even down the telephone. Alas, Singh confesses, quite unabashed—his Indian reticence supplanted by this adopted American confessional style—memory is a great quality, also possessing considerable erotic force, by the way, which strictly speaking you don't need to know that, it's a private matter between myself and the lady, nevertheless as I was saying remembrance is tops, but sometimes by way of contrast it is even better to forget.

Yul is a ruthless visionary, an amoral schemer. Might it not be a part of his grand design to throw cold water over Ormus and Vina's grand renewed passion, by offering them, in the form of Wing and Ifredis, an admonitory pair of Vargas caricatures of themselves? Happiness writes white, Montherlant said, and Yul Singh, an educated man for all his down-market posturing, is able to take a smart tip. Lovebirds bill and coo and don't get much work done. A little trouble in paradise might well be worth stirring up.

And the Jesus-freak material? Just adds an extra piquancy to the sauce.

Is this scripted dialogue and action? Are these *actors*?

Probe a little more deeply into the Tempe Harbor episode, and further reverberations can be felt. YSL is a lifelong philanderer who nevertheless loves, honors and can never get away from his utterly admirable and evidently *complaisante* wife. In Vina, perhaps, he has already discerned a sexual adventuress as daring as he, a woman in search of an anchor, of solid ground from which to make her nocturnal leaps into the unknown. Ormus—Yul Singh has intuited—must be once again that anchor, the still center of her turning wheel. If he's the rock she can be the roll. This will fuel his music and her singing, both; for art must be made secretly, in quiet places, while the singing voice needs to soar into open space and seek the adulation of the crowd. Yul Singh has his own visionary blind eyes, which can see into possible futureworlds, enabling him to bet heavily on them, even, sometimes, to bring them into being. This is what he has seen: that Ormus and Vina's genius, their future, their ability to become what they have it in themselves to be, depends on the engendering and perpetuation of special forms of pain. The noisy pain of the compulsive wanderer and the dumb pain of the one who's left.

Wing and Ifredis need neither sleep nor food except for their secret cheese. They are found fucking on the kitchen table, and under the living room rug. The whoops and shrieks grow louder, longer, somehow less human, by the hour. Vina and Ormus feel swamped, stalled, by this pornographic operetta. They are rendered temporarily incapable not of desire but of its physical (and vocal) expression. Like a couple of maiden aunts, they sip drinks on Tempe Harbor's farthest-flung terraces, and disapprove.

Up early on the third morning, Vina finds a dead stag lying in the reeds at the lake's edge: not shot, just deceased. Its head is half under water; antlers break the surface like hard weeds. Insects buzz their requiem. The legs are stiff, like a giant toy's. More specifically, it occurs to her, like the legs of a wooden horse. For some reason she cannot at once identify this unbidden thought makes her cry. Huge sobs burst from her; after a few of these, the memory follows. Of, outside the long-vanished Egypt cigar store, a wooden charioteer and his horse. *A one-horse town and the one horse was made of wood.* Vina summons a house limo—driven by Limo Singh, as the turbaned and uniformed chauffeur informs her without a tic of the irony forbidden by the avant-gardist Otto Wing—and, abandoning Ormus to the screaming lovers of Tempe Harbor, is driven at speed into Chickaboom.

Later, searching the grounds for her, Ormus wears his new eye patch in burgundy-colored velvet (run up for him by Clea the obliging housekeeper) and, with his single available eye, spots the stag, roped to a small tractor, being removed from the water by the chief gardener, Lawn Singh. For an instant he thinks it's Vina. Then his good eye mocks his pounding heart. Four legs not two, hooves not feet. Don't tell Vina you made *that* mistake.

He goes indoors, still oppressed by the residue of fear, the jangly biochemicals coursing through his veins. He makes for the music room—it's soundproofed, you can't hear Otto and Ifredis in there—and sits down at the Yamaha baby grand. You see a dead animal, you think it's the woman you love. You can't trust your eyes. You can't trust *her.* There's music pouring out of his fingertips.

Everything you think you see, he sings. *It can't be.*

And if Yul Singh—Machiavelli, Rasputin, he's never minded what people call him as long as the artistes keep signing on and the customers keep buying—is indeed watching his anguished guest through blind eyes from his Shavian cloud up there in the cloudless sky, he will certainly, at this point, be breaking into the widest of self-satisfied smiles.

THE CIGAR store's gone but it's a small town and Egiptus is an uncommon name. It doesn't take much more than an hour of asking around to learn that the old man choked on a bone years ago but the woman is still just about alive, though emphysema should ensure it won't be for much longer. Mrs. Pharaoh, one old-timer called her in a bar. Now Limo Singh is driving down a long straight country road between vines and corn. There's a red silo and one of those newfangled windmills. It's hot when the wind lets up but the wind isn't letting up today, it bites and plans to go on biting.

The road begins to bend and narrow, loses its confidence, becomes uncertain, sputters into sidetracks, with the wind blowing up a dust cloud to blur things even further, and then in a back-road graveyard of machinery, a place that's lost definition and grown jowly like a plain man's ageing jawline, they find the rusting Winnebago, standing at the edge of a cluster of wrecked and cannibalized automobiles and tractors, surrounded by tall grass so it looks like it's hiding.

She's in a trailer, Vina thinks, but there's no movie to follow. The limo stops and she keeps sitting for a few moments, feeling the loop of time close, and feeling, too, the advent of an unexpected sentiment beyond anger and revenge.

Compassion.

She gets out of the limo and walks through the scrap yard. The trailer door opens. A small gray spike of a head sticks out and starts hollering furiously, with intervals for lung-sick gasps.

What you looking at lady I ain't no fucking sight to be seen. I ain't no local curio you can check out just because you read about me in a fucking guidebook. I should charge admission. What is this. Somebody send you up here? You got business with me or did you just come up here in your fancy vehicle to gloat at folks who didn't have your luck?

A fit of wheezing. Vina just stands there.

Do I know you?

Vina takes off her shades. The old woman looks like she's been hit.

Oh, no, Mrs. Pharaoh says. No thank *you*. That's the past.

She slams the trailer door in Vina's face.

Vina stands there.

The door opens an inch.

You hear me I got no comment at this time. You got no entitlement coming here and invading my constitutional right of privacy. To come accusing me. I ain't in your law court missy I'm in my personal fucking place of residence on my personal patch of mangy fucking grass and I ain't in your court of law. You and your flunkey here you're trespassing and maybe I'll call the cops on you. You think because I can't fucking breathe.

The door swings open. The widow Egiptus is holding on to the handle and, with her spare hand, catching at her chest. She sounds like: a mule. Like: death.

Vina waits.

I didn't do right by you, the woman gasps. That's what you think. To you I'm dirt. I took a young life already damaged and treated it like shit. Well looky here how things worked out. You end up in the big time and I end up in the fucking long grass. You don't reckon maybe you owe me for that. You don't reckon maybe I gave you the kick in the butt that put you on your road, and the survival equipment that took care of you on that journey. Look at you, you look like some tough bitch. Meaning, thanks to me. So don't you come here and fucking stand there like judgement day and hand down your verdict. You took my strength and left me to fucking die. Can't you see I'm dying in front of your face. What do you care. You'll go and I'll go on dying behind your fucking back. Maybe they won't find my body for weeks, not until it's blowed up like a airship and stinking up the county like a bad conscience. It ain't your verdict I got to worry about it's another whole fucking court entirely. Another whole sentence. Jesus.

Mrs. Egiptus shuts the Winnebago door once again and Vina listens to the noises of emphysema in its advanced stage. She turns to Limo Singh. I've had all I can handle for now, she says. Give her the address. Invite her to dinner at eight and tell her it'll be informal, she doesn't need to put on her glass slippers and satin gown. I'll wait in the goddamn car.

Thus Cinderella invites her wicked stepmother to the ball.

PRE-DINNER DRINKS and drugs—champagne, cocaine—on the lawn at Tempe Harbor. Which by the way all I ask is you indulge in the conventional manner, through the nose, Yul Singh stipulates in a series of firm telephone calls to his guests. We got a vogue now for rear-end insertion, excuse my frankness, there's a fellow calls himself Rock Bottom, one of Voight's celebrated superstars, maybe you're acquainted with him but in my frank opinion he's the one to blame. Which it's a free country he can do as he pleases but I'm a little old-fashioned, I don't care for my guests feeding their assholes in front of the hired help.

Mrs. Pharaoh—Marion, the widow Egiptus—comes in like gangbusters, concealing her considerable unease behind a barrage of obscenity; getting her retaliation in first. Her spotless floral-printed dress hangs loose on her emaciated birdy frame. Otto Wing, campily entranced, raises his nose from a small mirror and peers at this ancient apparition.

Wow, Vina invited a bag lady, he announces loudly.

So you're rich now, Marion Egiptus says to Vina right there in the entrance vestibule. You're up here with your rich buddies having yourself a high old time. Sure, I know what that means. A shift in the fucking balance of power. I'm done for and you made good. This is America, money gives you rights. You get the right to haul me out here and shame me, and your friend Mr. Asswipe gets to insult me right into my fucking face. That's okay. I know the score. How's this for a deal. Gimme twenty bucks and I'll apologize right now for how I treated you way back when and for twenty more I'll forget what a twisted little whore you always were. For fifty bucks I'll kneel down and kiss your rich foot and I'll suck your black pussy why not for an even hundred. Your four-eyed friend here, I'll cut him in too. Bag lady, huh. I could show him some fancy action. Put a bag over my head, professor, cut a hole for my mouth, and for two hundred bucks I'll give you what not even Mary Magdalene let alone no naked fucking under-age foreign whore could dream up. But sit down to dinner with you stinking scum? You don't got the money could make me do a thing like that.

I like this woman, enthuses bespectacled Otto Wing. So lacking in circumlocution, and her offer also is intriguing. To have intimate relations with a person who stands at the very gates of eternity. This has possibilities.

But the blasphemy, Otto, Ifredis objects, We must loudly to such language exception take. Her evening dress leaves little to the imagination, and she pushes it even further off the shoulders to attract and hold his attention; which works. Holy flagrant youth triumphs over bad-mouthed blasphemous age.

And the pit of eternal fire will surely open beneath her foots before so long, Ifredis victoriously predicts. Also by the way lady I am not under-age and if you care to know it one hell of a performer in the bag.

Sack, Otto corrects her lovingly, running a hand down her exposed back. One hell of a performer in the sack.

Whatever, darling. I am confuse in my words because just now there is overmuch speech of bags.

Vina takes wheezing Marion Egiptus by the arm and more or less drags the unwilling old woman down to the lakeside, to the same spot where the dead stag fell. Okay, Marion, she says, you're right and you're wrong. You're right I drove out to your trailer to put you down, I wanted some kind of closure?, after all these years of refusing even to speak your name I wanted you to know I made it anyway, I wanted your goddamn envy. But about my inviting your ass up here to jerk you around you're wrong. You're so goddamn fucked up, when I saw that it made me want to help you, so I'll do what I can, doctors, medical bills, whatever.

You're offering money?

Yeah. Yeah, I'm offering cash. And you don't even get to vacuum my cunt.

Okay, I'll take it, the old woman says quickly. How much?

Not as much as you think, Vina shrugs, coming clean. All this isn't mine. I'm just the singer and this, it's the label's.

Marion Egiptus cackles, bringing on a coughing fit. Water streams from her eyes. When she recovers, leaning against Vina, she says, Shit, honey, I knew *that.* When you're real rich, not pretend rich which is about your level, you don't care to make war or peace with the past. Baby, you leave it behind. You're *gone.*

For an instant, the widow Egiptus goes on leaning against Vina's side.

I'm glad I didn't leave you behind, Vina says. Their hands touch.

Marion pulls away. Yeah, she snarls. But once you've handed over the money you won't have to carry me on your fucking back no more. Don't think you're doing nothing for me. You're buying your personal freedom is all.

Well, okay, Vina concedes, maybe so. Nobody wants to be a slave.

MARIA'S AT Tempe Harbor too. No locked door can keep her out. She sets off no alarms. She arrives whenever Vina briefly leaves Ormus to his own devices, and she's all done talking, she is physically insistent once again, even urgent, a phantom soul sister of the erotomaniac Ifredis Wing. Her body feels real enough, and she is strong. She grips his wrists and forces him back on to his bed. Still, Ormus resists. He thinks of Vina, and Maria's power ebbs. Her grip fails. A force drains out of her.

You can't help it, she says disconsolately, stepping away. You're stuck in this stupid place, this dirty fork in the true path. This uncertain earth, its troubled water, its belching fires, its poisoned air et cetera. Its wrongness. No wonder it creates these pernicious side effects. You're polluted, poor darling, you're sick of some psychotropical disease and so forth, and you think what you feel is love.

Strangely, Maria's coming and going is no longer entirely unrestricted. It's as though, by coming into his presence through his pale, blinded, other-sighted eye, she has been deprived of her old means of arrival and departure. It seems that now that she has become a part of his vision, of his seeing, he can control her appearances. She can no longer materialize and then vanish simply by turning sideways, as if there were a slot in the middle of nothing. She can't mail herself in and out of this world like a letter; not any more.

So Clea's eye patch makes possible what no security system can manage. Ormus resolves to keep his left eye patched and in darkness.

Vina is all he sees and all he wants to see.

EVEN WITH the eye patch in place Ormus Cama has been finding that America defies credibility. In the hall outside his and Vina's suite there is a drinks machine that eats paper money. This astonishes him. Paper is incapable of the simple mechanical feats which are the limits of his scientific imagination. Electronics—scanners, printed circuits, yes/no pathways—these mysteries are beyond his ken, as secret as the mysteries of the ancient Greeks. The paper-triggered automaton is the gatekeeper of a new world of miracles and confusions, a world where the door knobs turn the wrong way and the power switches are upside down.

It is evident from the daily newspapers that the world beyond the frontiers of the United States (except for Indochina) has practically ceased to exist. The rest of the planet is perceived here as essentially fictional, and what is most distressing about the war in Indochina is that this basically imaginary country is depriving American youngsters of their very real lives, to which they have constitutionally guaranteed rights. This is a disturbance in the natural order, and protests are intensifying. On tv, helmeted, shielded figures bearing arms are seen marching across college campuses, reclaiming the God-given right of Americans to kill or maim their own youngsters before the Indochinese get a chance to do so.

Tv is new to Ormus Cama and it has further wonders to reveal.

There are many advertisements for anti-personnel devices ingeniously and variously disguised as edible foodstuffs and designed to turn the stomachs and digestive tracts of the American people into savage, heaving battlegrounds. These alternate with promo films for a wide range of chemical remedies, each claiming to be the only reliable way of restoring intestinal peace. In between the commercials he gets word of the death of Louis Armstrong whom once he loved in the film of *The Five Pennies* and in other films too. He glimpses many families—including a family of talentless musicians—being laughed at in their own homes by invisible strangers who seem easily amused. There is word of foo fighters—flying saucers—landing in the wide open spaces of the Midwest. An old man, an actor whose chief gift is his inability to remember anything he is told for more than fifteen minutes, is running for governor in California and is routinely referred to as an exemplary American.

The music, however, makes him feel at home. In the soundproofed music room he listens with excitement and pleasure to the *200 Motels* album by Uncle Meat, a live tape of the already legendary tour performances by Zoo Harrison's Caledonia Soul Orchestra, Eddie Kendricks singing "Just My Imagination," the Plastic Ono Band's "Imagine."

However, when he hears some kid moaning about the end of rock 'n' roll, Ormus gets angry. Died? The music is just getting born. Vina is its mother and he's the father, and anyone who thinks otherwise should get out of their high-speed road.

In his heart of hearts he knows why he's really angry. He's fifteen years late for the party. These should have been his years, and instead they belong to others. Time's running out. Every day there's one day less to seize.

He's up at the house now, watching Vina down below, by the lake, talking to Mrs. Pharaoh and stuffing dollar bills into the dying woman's shabby purse. He shakes off the miasmic state induced by Maria's visits, and is overcome by a rush of great love for the woman who has renewed his life. How extraordinary she is, how much she has had to combat, to overcome. He must marry her at once. She must stop making her joking refusals and agree to marry him without delay, perhaps even here, at Tempe Harbor. Yes, that would be perfect! By confronting the woman who was not good to her in her younger days, she has laid a ghost to rest. Yul Singh exorcised the ghost of old Manny Raabe by the use of heat. Vina has chased her phantoms away by looking them in the face, and giving up her revenge. Her business with the past is done. To be married at this moment would turn a page.

His desire for Vina swells and overflows. Hers is the only love that can—that *will*—unite his broken vision, make him whole. As his are the only arms that can hold her together after all her struggles, all her pain.

There is a field of cosmos wildflowers by the lake. It's the perfect spot.

He glows with love. Soon it will be his wedding day.

IF SHE hadn't made that final settlement of accounts with Mrs. Marion Egiptus of Chickaboom, N.Y.—if her childhood suffering had not been assuaged by an adult cash transaction—then Vina Apsara might just have been raw and vulnerable enough to entertain Ormus's renewed proposals. If Otto and Ifredis Wing had not raced up to her on the lawn, passing the departing Mrs. Egiptus, and proposed a little ménage à trois, or, if she insisted on including her solemn and preoccupied gentleman friend, à quatre, then Vina might not have been so thoroughly consumed by disgust, might not have transferred her contempt for the Wings' post-marital antics to the institution of matrimony itself.

But these things have been done and cannot be undone. And so it is that Ormus, approaching her at the water's edge in the last light of day, with a bunch of wildflowers in his hand and a heart full of love, finds her in viperish mood.

WE'VE GOT to get out of this place, I mean right now, Vina seethes at her fatuously smiling beau, who's come a-romancing only to find his beloved transformed into a hissing harpy. Her former foster mother's soured anger has ignited her own formidable rage. Ormus, Jesus *Christ.* What are we doing?, we must be crazy?, we should be setting fire to this nightmare palazzo instead of acting like Cool Yul's private harem. His eunuchs and what's the word concubines. We should be burning it to the fucking ground. For this we left England? If this is the twentieth century, baby, we should be making urgent plans to exit permanently into some other epoch. Run, comrade, the old world is behind you, the students said in Paris, '68. Down with a world where the guarantee that we won't die of starvation has been purchased with the guarantee that we will die of boredom! Victory will be for those who know how to create disorder without loving it! Come *on,* Ormus. What's the project, right? Are we going to tear down the asylum or just move in here to some fucking padded cell and I don't know begin to *babble*?

I came out just now, he says—knowing it's the wrong time, not able to help himself, sensing that things are about to slip away from him again, that his wildflower wedding has vanished down a fork in reality along which he won't be able to follow it—I came to ask you to marry me.

I already done tol' you, honey, she answers, the cornpone accent only just taking the edge off the rebuff. I ain't the marryin' kind. I'm jus' the girl who cain't say yes.

She won't do it. Can't bring herself to. She loves him, she loves him to hell and back, but she won't put it in writing and sign her name to it. Freed from the nagging pain of her childhood memories, she refuses this new captivity. She offers him the conventional anti-nuptial radicalism of the time. Monogamy is a manacle, fidelity is a chain. A revolutionary not a wifey will she be. A changer of the world not of diapers she'll become.

He isn't listening. High purpose has descended upon him. If you won't marry me now, then I want to know when you will, he demands, with a stubbornness so deep that it has metamorphosed into something else, into, perhaps, destiny. And the force of his wanting it is so palpable that Vina—who loves him with her life, who knows his love is the equal of hers, who can't trust either his love or her own for five minutes at a time—takes the demand seriously. Name the day, he blazes. As far in the future as you want. Your one hundred and first birthday if you want. But name it and hold to it and I'll never ask you again until that day comes. Give me your unsinkable word and it will keep me afloat all my life. Just name the fucking day.

She's twenty-seven years old, and if there's one thing she's learned it's that nothing stays the same for five minutes, not even your goddamn name. So this demand for an immutable day, it's a storybook device, it's some retro Knights-of-the-Round-Table Camelot-and-chivalry deal. A courtly love revival. He's asking her to mortgage the future, but in the future she'll be someone else again, she'll have changed a dozen times, and nobody can expect your unknown future self to be bound by the mistakes and promises of youth. It's like selling the moon. You can sell it if you're able to find a buyer but only a fool would expect you to deliver. Make the fucking promise, she thinks, and after that it's *caveat emptor.* Let the buyer beware.

Okay, she says. Okay, already, keep your rug on. Ah, ten years from now, she says, how's that. (Thinking, ten years is an impossible eternity. In ten years, the music business being what it is, and taking her own volatile temperament and tempestuous life history into account, she could be mad or dead. Or thirty-seven, which feels worse. In ten years the light dying around them this evening will be fifty-eight thousand six hundred and fifty-seven billion miles from here and she might be pretty far away herself. Ten years is never-never land, you turn right at a star and go straight on till morning. No rules apply. Besides, behind her back, rabbits rabbits, she's crossing her treacherous fingers.)

Ten years from today? From right now?

(He's being serious. Jesus. Never mind, he'll get over it, it'll be fine.)

Sure, Ormie. Ten years, the clock's running, three, two, one, go.

Then he tells her his side of the bargain.

WAITING FOR her, briefly possessing her, then losing her: this has been his lot. He waited for her to come of age, there was a single night of love, and then at once she vanished. He fell, he rose again, he strove to become worthy of her, to perform great labors, to solve the riddle of her departure, he set himself after many vicissitudes back upon his true course, and then a chance accident felled him once more; suspended his animation. She returned and worked a miracle, which was undeniably a miracle of love, and then for a few moments they were together, while he healed. But in spite of her continued avowals of their love, of hers, she refuses to offer him the fixity that is only natural and which, in his bizarre two-eyed condition, he needs. He finds that the waiting—another ten years, as she has specified—is preferable to her daily vagaries, her whims. The waiting is at least solid, it has a beginning, a middle and an end, he can lean his weight against it knowing it will not step away at the last instant and let him fall. But in waiting there is no inbetweenness, no acceptably nuanced position, no half measures or relativity theory. As there is none in love. One either loves, or waits for love, or banishes love for good. That is the full range of possible choices. As she has chosen waiting, so he chooses now to amplify what waiting means.

For ten years, until she is thirty-seven years old and he has turned forty-four, he will not touch or be touched by her. Not so much as a clasping of hands or a caress upon the cheek will he offer or permit. What he suffered for love when she was under-age he will suffer again now that they are both in their prime. She has made a promise and he has no doubt that she will honor it. She should also be clear that he will honor his. These promises will be their substitutes for marriage vows. This non-performance, this empty vessel—this suspended absence, swinging hammock fashion between the twin poles of their stark choices—will be the bed of their *grand amour.*

To put it another way: for ten years, it will be strictly business between them. Stricter than business; for this is not a parting, not a divorce agreement, but a lovers' pact, that ends in a long-delayed but much-desired tryst. It ends in for ever. Therefore he submits himself to the rules of love. Though he will not *lay a finger* on her for her stipulated decade, he enters freely and without coercion into a condition of celibacy. He will not share with any other woman what he cannot share with his beloved.

All this he swears.

Ten years from now, the time of denial will end and they will enter into joy.

THE LOVE of God, as Otto and Ifredis, the beatifically beating Wings of desire, have abundantly proved, need not hinder your sex drive. Alas, mortal love all too easily gets in its own way.

A RUSSIAN man goes into a car showroom and is approached by a sales representative. There's no car actually on display in the showroom, they unfortunately don't have any showroom models at present, but, the salesman explains, we have photographs, and certainly, sir, I'll be happy to take your order. The customer quickly signs the purchase papers and asks, How soon can I have it? In two years from now, the salesman replies—Okay. But will it come in the morning or the afternoon?—I'm sorry, sir, I don't think you understood, I said it'll take two *years*.—Yes, that's right, but in two years' time, will it be the afternoon or, preferably, the morning?—This is ridiculous, sir, what can it possibly matter?—Well, you see, I've got the plumber coming in the afternoon.

This is a post-communist joke. I place it here anachronistically, around eighteen years ahead of its time, because it's a parable about people who, like Ormus Cama and Vina Apsara, are obliged by circumstances to take a long view. Whether these two, the loves of each other's lives, whose gift of loving is exceeded only by their talent for erecting mighty obstacles to that love, are the creators of their circumstances, or destiny's fools, I leave to others to decide.

* * *

VINA CAN'T bear it. *Not this again, your fucking heroic oaths.* She rails, implores. He's throwing away what is wonderful between them in the name of an archaic convention. He must reconsider. He must come to bed at once.

You could have said ten days, he points out. You could have said ten minutes. The length of the engagement was your choice, its nature is mine.

Stopped in her tracks, almost panting in her desperation, Vina faces the crisis of her life. And, as always, when tenderness fails her, as she believes it always has failed her and always will, she has recourse to ferocity.

Fine, she says. Have it your way. Strictly business. Deal.

For ten years, he reminds her. Your word is your bond.

And you can live like a monk if you want?, she snaps her exit line, but don't expect this little lady to follow your lead.

When she's out of sight, Ormus Cama takes off his eye patch and the otherness streams in. He reels, then gathers himself. Little by little, he must learn to see double without growing dizzy and losing his balance. He will have, if not love, then whole sight. That, and music.

FROM THE moment their pact is made, that devil's contract that will make neither of them happy, there's no stopping them. At the epicenter of the American earthquake that is VTO lies this very Oriental disorientation. Abstinence: it becomes their rocket fuel, and flies them to the stars.

CHAPTER THIRTEEN

On Pleasure Island

A journey to the center of the earth. (Cab fare from Vina's place, $4 with tip.)

First stop, just around the corner from the center of the earth, is the artist Amos Voight's studio, alias Slaughterhouse-22. Amos was born Wojtyla, and years later, when the Polish Pope comes along, Amos in his great old age will seriously announce he's suing John Paul II for nomenclatural plagiarism.

At the Slaughterhouse, amid the printmaking and photography, small billionaires hang out in corners like gargoyles eager for rain, watching the curvy girls with the thick dicks go in and out of the movie studio. Amos never forgets a billionaire, never ignores them for longer than is enjoyable, so they're happy. At this moment Amos is holding forth to Vina about his dead friend Eric, who has been found naked in an empty bathtub in a seedy apartment on the Upper West Side. Like David's Marat, killed by tragic heroin, Voight says in that unsparing voice like a woman's sigh. It's too bad, he says. At least when the Lizard King went, his bath was full. Vina puts her arms round him, holds him. I took a ride up there, he says. It was horrible. $11 with tip.

To cheer him up, Vina takes Voight over to the center of the earth for champagne and orange juice and a steak sandwich ($36.93 including taxes). It's just a couple of blocks away. Its name is Sam's Pleasure Island, and there's no Sam, never was one, but if pleasure is your pleasure then you've come to the right place.

(Even those who never come to such places derive a form of perverse satisfaction, vicarious, perhaps malign, from knowing that they exist, that an essential part of America's contract with her citizens is being fulfilled. The pursuit of happiness; and of death.)

Oh, gee, says Amos, entering. I love New York. It's full of people still doing stuff they gave up years ago.

Lou's singing. *Wagon Wheel.* Boy, she's hot. Look, here are Rémy Auxerre and Marco Sangria, nobody knows more about music than Marco and Rémy. What do you say, boys, asks Amos, do you like what she's doing now.

Rémy answers, We must free our soul from the everyday and open it to *influxus mentium superiorum,* the influence of higher minds. To this end, our tools are vacantness and alienation. When influence finds our reason unoccupied, it shows it something of universal knowledge.

Oh, good, that means he likes it, Amos says to Vina.

How can you tell, she asks.

But it's so easy, because he's Martinican, you know, says Amos. It's that great French bullshit, he does it nearly as well as the French. People dance differently in different towns, most of us adapt, but not our Rémy. I love that, it's so great, so confident and empty, don't you think.

I want you to meet Ormus?, Vina says. We're now a band.

Just don't ask me to produce your album, Amos says. (He's really down tonight.) Just ask some other sucker, okay.

Nobody's asking you for anything. Vina smacks him playfully on the head, and his thatch of hair flies out like a soft explosion. Be nice now, Amos. You're on the Island.

Here's Ormus, wearing his eye patch, looking even gloomier than Voight.

I'll tell you what we've got in common, apart from almost having the same name, Amos confides, slipping an arm through his. We both came back from the dead. You had that crash, and somebody shot me, can you believe it, a woman, so butch. I wasn't supposed to make it but I just thought I would.

You old fraud, Vina scolds him. You know everything about everyone. You just pretend you're an ignorant blinking little mole just out of his hole.

Like a mole in the ground I will root this mountain down, says Ormus.

Oh, gee, a Negro spiritual, Voight snaps, deliberately invoking the archaic term in the age of Black is Beautiful.

Suddenly direct, he peers at Ormus. Colored cels wash their faces in red and purple light. What color are you, anyway, it's so hard to tell these days, he demands, sharp as a rebuke. You know what they say about Vina. They say she's a brown girl trying to be black, which is just plain snippy and so unfair to a girl with naturally frizzy hair and a liking for trouble. Now I'm clear what color *she* is, but I am not fully briefed on the pigmentary orientation of Parsi males, so I guess I'll have to ask you straight out.

Do I have to be a color, Ormus mutters, coloring. Can't we get beyond, finally, I mean can't we get under our skins.

Aw, spoilsport, couldn't you even be lime green or something? green is nice. (Here Voight turns to the nearest femme of a group of sequinned gender illusionists.) And you, my dear, what color are you.

Oh, I guess velvet, honey, is that a color.

Sure, velvet, that counts; how about your pal.

Her? She's Gemini.

Voight turns back to Ormus. You see, here at Sam's they have every shade and variety of color in the book. Do you know Anatole Broyard, by the way? He's got the greatest trick. Every day when he enters the subway in Brooklyn he's black, but by the time he shows up for work at *The New Yorker* he's pure white. And did you ever hear of Jean Toomer? The most important writer of the Negro Renaissance. His book *Cane,* you know, way back in 1923, Waldo Frank called it a harbinger of the South's literary maturity, of its emergence from the obsession put upon its mind by the unending racial crisis. The dawn of direct and unafraid creation, that's what I believe he said. Seems to me you'd like that old book.

Ormus is tempted into unwariness. I've got an idea for a song, he offers. *At the frontier of the skin wild dogs patrol.*

You sure would've liked Toomer, Voight reiterates mildly. A light-skinned man like you. He disappeared, you know. The rumor was he'd crossed the color line. Arna Bontemps used to say that didn't mean he got away from the racial problem. The invisible cloak didn't get him out of the jam everyone else was in.

Excuse me, Ormus says, I don't want to spoil your evening but I'm tired, my head hurts, good night.

Ouch, Amos says, watching Ormus's back as it flounces off. Ooh, that hurt.

He's cheerful now. He squeezes Vina's arm. This was so good an idea, darling. This is so fun.

AT THE heart of Sam's Pleasure Island is the court of the Yul King. Sit, if you're so lucky, beside Yul Singh in his choice booth—blind Yul with his trademark Manhattan on the rocks and his thick Cohiba cigar—and sooner or later the whole world will pass by and pay homage. Nobody can out-dress, out-drink, out-smoke or out-cool the Yul. Vina slides in next to the man. Amos is on her left.

Everybody's in tonight, Yul grins. Which check it out check it out.

Here are the Vampire Lesbians of Sodom. Darlin', they say, we're all born naked; the rest is just a drag.

Here is a giant fat man, naked except for the zippered bondage hood on his head. Look, he's got his cock on backwards; it's poking out between the soft billow of his ass.

Here are Angel Dust and Nutcracker Sweet, two of Voight's own fabulous porno actresses, I call them all horses, he says, because every few weeks they get carried out to the glue factory, they end up on some brown envelope or ten-cent stamp or something. I guess at least they get to be licked again, one last time.

Here's Lou, she's finished her set. Isn't she gorgeous? There's her new squeeze, Laurie. What a hunk.

Here's the guy to see if you just got into town and you want to know where the party is and who to fuck later.

Here's the woman who was the last person on earth to see the guy who strangled himself with a noose, trying to get an erection for her, imagine how low her self-esteem must be, poor baby.

Here are the guys who set fire to money.

Here are penis-ironers, testicle-boilers, shit-eaters, penis-boilers, testicle-eaters. Over there is the world Spermathon Queen, who encountered one hundred and one men, four at a time, in a non-stop seven-and-a-half-hour megafuck. She's still in touch with all one hundred and one partners and refers to them as her Dalmatians. Naturally, her personal icon is the fur-loving Cruella de Vil.

Here's the earth mother who adopted nineteen babies from different international trouble spots. But when the trouble dies down she trades the babies in for needier kids from the new hot zones. (Every time I cover a war I wonder which orphaned tot will end up at her place, and who'll be out on the street.)

Here's Ifredis Wing. Her whole life is an act of worship, and she gives it all back to Jesus. Here's a brother with a crown of thorns on his head; he should get together with that poor girl. Otto's vamoosed already, he's now into Buddhism, he's flown to Dharmsala with a shaven-headed chick who's recognized as some sort of actual saint but she's also a martial arts maven so go carefully, Mr. Wing.

Here are more believers. They believe in the Divine Mother Goddess-Ma in her concrete high-rise in Düsseldorf. They believe in going for the burn. They believe in the name of God written in the seeds of a watermelon. They believe in the wise ones flying towards them in a comet's tail. They believe in rock 'n' roll. They believe reason and psychology are crutches you use until you find wisdom. Then, when you've found it, you throw away those crutches and dance. They believe they're the sane ones and it's everybody else that's crazy. They believe in Pleasure and its island. They do not believe the rumor about this island: that if you stay long enough, it'll make a donkey of you.

Hey, the space gods are in tonight. There's the guitar hero who was born on an asteroid in the general vicinity of Mars. There's Sun Ra, another alien. There's the thin Limey who used to work as a UFO spotter after he fell to earth.

And there's Neil. Neil from the Silver Spaceships. Neil, the living proof that there's rock 'n' roll on other planets.

Everybody. The whole Western world.

Voight is remorseless tonight. Isn't Ormus Cama the boy that sings about frontiers, he asks Yul, about going to the edge and crossing over? Well, dear, dear. He hardly got across the welcome mat tonight.

It can't be the edge as well as the center, says Vina, refusing to rise to the bait.

Sure it can, my pretty, says Yul Singh. Take a look around. Sure it can.

* * *

WAR-WEARY, divided, their belief in the mighty eagle's global ascendancy damaged by the humiliating withdrawal of U.S. personnel from Indochina, Americans find they want what Ormus Cama has to say. The helicopters circle over the Saigon embassy like angels of judgement; the living cling to them and beg for salvation. The dead have already been judged, and found guilty, by defeat. Limb-shorn veterans retreat psychotically into forests and mountain fastnesses, to dream of rice paddies and King Cong rising out of the water right in front of their screaming faces, here comes a chopper to chop off your head. You can get the boys out of the war but you can't get the war out of the boys. In this bereft moment, rudderless America is unusually open to the paradoxes of Ormus's songs; open, in fact, to paradox itself, and its non-identical twin ambiguity too. The U.S. Army (and its rock songs) went into one East and came out with a bloody nose. Now Ormus's music has arrived like an affirmation from another East to enter the musical heart of Americanness, to flow into the river of dreams; but it's driven by the democratic conviction, retained by Ormus from the days when Gayomart sang the future into his ears, that the music is his as well, born not just in the U.S.A. but in his own heart, long ago and far away. Just as England can no longer lay exclusive claim to the English language, so America is no longer the sole owner of rock 'n' roll: that is Ormus's unstated sub-text (Vina, always the loudmouth, the thrower-down of gauntlets, will come out with it soon enough, and put a few patriotic noses out of joint).

The story of the ten-year engagement and of Ormus's consequent oath of celibacy spreads quickly; and this, too, makes Ormus and Vina irresistible. The new band takes off almost at once, and the force of its ascending shakes the land. Starting as oddities, they grow quickly into giants. At once conqueror and celebrant, Ormus storms the citadels of rock, and Vina's voice, as Yul Singh foresaw, is his weapon. Her voice is the servant of his melodies; his singing the servant of her voice. And while Vina's is the exceptional instrument, capable of affecting the hairs on the back of your neck as it swoops and dives, Ormus's lower, gentler harmonies perfectly offset her pyrotechnics, and the two voices, when they blend, create a magical third, more Righteous than the

Righteous Brothers, Everlier than the Everlys, Supremer than the Supremes. It's a perfect marriage. Ormus and Vina, put asunder by vows, are joined together in song. *V-T-Ohh!* America, disoriented, seeking a new voice, succumbs to theirs. Young Americans, in search of new frontiers, board VTO's Orient express.

That part of the American soul which is presently in retreat finds comfort in the new stars' restatements of the great American musical truths, the foot-tapper tempi that start out walking and then find the dance hidden in the walk; the placing of the beats that tug at our bodies; the speak-to-me rhythm and blues. And that America which by losing certitude has newly opened itself to the external world responds to the un-American sounds Ormus adds to his tracks: the sexiness of the Cuban horns, the mind-bending patterns of the Brazilian drums, the Chilean woodwinds moaning like the winds of oppression, the African male voice choruses like trees swaying in freedom's breeze, the grand old ladies of Algerian music with their yearning squawks and ululations, the holy passion of the Pakistani *qawwals.* Too much of the people's music settles for too little, Ormus says on the occasion of the issue of the self-titled first album (the one with the burgundy-colored velvet eye patch on the sleeve). It offers the people crumbs when they should have banquets.

He wants to work with what he calls the full orchestra, meaning not stiffs in tuxes but the full range of musical emotional intellectual yes and moral possibility, he wants this music to be capable of saying anything to anyone, but above all meaning something to someone. He's started to speak in this big new voice, and the someones out there are listening.

Angry America, too, is listening hard: the America of loss, the America that's taken a beating and doesn't fully understand how, or what it's done to deserve this pain (this America is looking not at the Indochinese dead but only at its own). This raging America responds to Ormus's wrath, because he's a very angry man, angry with Vina, himself and the cruel destiny thanks to which the decade of his high triumph has been rendered meaningless by the emptiness of his bed.

It responds in two ways. Only one of these is appreciative. Beneath the America that opens itself to VTO, there's another country that turns against him, that sets its jaw and closes its mind.

Ormus and Vina begin to acquire powerful enemies.

Someone should shut those uppity bigmouths once 'n' f'r all.

Melancholy and chastity make sublimation possible, according to the fifteenth-century Florentine Marsilio Ficino, and it's sublimation that sets free the *furor divinus.* First in the Peace Ballads of Ormus Cama, then in his legendary quake album, *Quakershaker,* fury is evident in every chord, every bar, every line, fury deep-drawn like black water from a poisoned well. Whether it be divine or earthly *furor* is a matter of some considerable dispute.

If Ficino believed that our music is composed by our lives, the contemporary Czech Milan Kundera thinks, contrariwise, that our lives are composed like music. "Without realizing it, the individual composes his life according to the laws of beauty, even in times of the greatest distress." To stand the old principle of good design on its elegant head: in our functioning we follow the dictates of our need for form.

BRAVO, ORMUS. I've got to hand it to the guy. Bearing a satchel full of hard-won images of the fall of Saigon I come trudging home with a lifetime supply of nightmares to the sweet-dream needlework merchants and powdered-happiness pashas clustered on the stoops of the brownstones of St. Mark's, and lo! there on the corner newsstand is our Ormie, already notoriously publicity shy, hitting a three-run homer, adorning the covers in the same week of *Rolling Stone* (with Vina), *Newsweek* (Vina's reduced to an inset) and *Time* (not a trace of Vina to be seen). Not only has he pushed the war news on to the inside pages but he's also marginalized one of the great beauties of the age, who is rapidly becoming one of the most famous women in the world. Some recluse! Some publicity! He must've really touched a nerve. Two quick albums, *VTO* and *Peace Ballads*—in those days before the omnipotence of videos and marketing, musicians put out records a whole lot more often—one, two!, and he's sitting on top of the world.

They made peace in the other world too. (Baby I've got

one of my own.) Ain't no better than it is for you. (Good to know we're not alone.) Well the war is over and the battle's through. (But I can't reach you on the phone.)

I call your number but you ain't home. I call your number but you ain't home. Seems I made this long journey just to wait on my own. It's been a long journey home. A long journey home.

VTO's *Peace Ballads* defies the injunctions of the post-ironical cinéaste Otto Wing. "Picking up the Pieces," "(You Brought Me) Peace Without Love," "Long Journey Home," "Might As Well Live": it's easy enough to hear the bitter, disabused ironies in many of Ormus's songs. But the music he's come up with is jauntily, almost perversely up-tempo. The overall effect is oddly affirmative, even anthemic, and for many young people these jaundiced, dystopic tracks become unlikely, adult anthems of relief, a new beginning, release. On my own block I can hear the young dope peddlers—Nicely-Nicely Johnson, Harry the Horse, Sky Masterson, Big Julie, Nathan Detroit—whistling Ormus Cama's material. Peace without love: they are marketing this very product, the guaranteed top-grade genuine article, by the ounce. It's the only racket; always was. And when you run out of peace juice, bliss pills or sweet treats for your veins, you are always welcome to return to Happy Valley here and get yourself another tasty helping, as long as you are in possession of the requisite spondulicks. Which, the dealers at least would argue, is more than can be said for love.

Americans buy the *Ballads* by the wagonload, but the album's anti-war message causes a few subterranean rumbles. Agencies who see it as their rôle to protect the country from fifth columnists, from being *destabilized,* start taking a discreet interest. Yul Singh receives a polite phone call on his unlisted private line from a voice that calls itself Michael Baxter when it says hello and Baxter Michaels when it signs off. A warning shot across the bows. A word to the wise. We have some concern about certain lyrical content. There is naturally no question of infringing any individual's First Amendment rights, but the songwriter if we understand it correctly is not a U.S. citizen. A guest who wishes to remain welcome is not well advised to piss on his host's best rug.

Yul Singh summons Ormus and Vina to his suite of

offices near Columbus Circle and then suggests a walk in the park. Ordinarily New Yorkers pride themselves on ignoring the fame of the famous but the exceptional success of *Peace Ballads* necessitates exceptional measures. For Ormus, an old hippie Afghan jacket, large round-lensed purple shades, a fright wig. Vina is harder to disguise. Her height, her Afro shock, her attitude, defy concealment. After much haggling she agrees to wear a floppy wide-brimmed felt hat in bright scarlet, because it matches her long Italian leather coat. Yul Singh refuses as usual to use a white stick, leans, instead, on Will Singh's iron forearm. Half a dozen more Singhs follow at a discreet distance, in case of crowd trouble. In the park, emboldened by foliage, Cool Yul passes on the content of the feds' phone call. Vina snorts her disdain, declines to take the threat seriously—*Everybody's got a fed on their tail right now, from Dr. Nina to Winston O'Boogie, it's like a fashion statement?*—and goes off at one of her zany tangents. What do they know, nobody ever gets rock lyrics right, anyway. For years I thought Hendrix was a faggot. You know, 'scuse me while I kiss this guy. And what *was* that about my feet begin to crumble. I used to admire the surrealism of rock lyrics?, the wild non sequiturs. Then I realized it was just my fucking ears.

Ormus, Yul Singh says quietly, these are what can I tell you sensitive times, people are touchy, skinless, you may be giving them too much truth. I'm just saying which it's a matter for you, okay, but you should keep under control your crazier sentiments and if I may say so also her many unscripted remarks.

That'll be the day, Vina snaps, flinging down her hat and shades and striding off fast through the dappled sunlight, a giantess at war. She turns heads, but the thunderclouds around her look too dangerous; people leave her alone.

There's no follow-up. Somebody's decided to let this one go. The attack on Ormus comes fifteen months later, after the earthquake songs.

THE CULTURE needs a vacuum to rush into, it is an amorphousness in search of shapes. Ormus and Vina's suspended love, that divine absence which we can fill with our fantasies, becomes the center of our lives. The city seems to organize itself around them, as if they are the principle, the pure Platonic essence, that makes sense of the rest.

I flatter myself that here I use the word "we" to describe a collectivity of which I am not a part.

They live separately. She's in a third-floor loft downtown, all the way west on Canal, a large space rescued from post-industrial decay in a building with brutalist common parts that satisfy some instinct of hers for roughness, though the loft itself is eminently creature-comfortable. She fills it with fish tanks for dumb company and whole walls of hi-fi equipment to shut out the noise of the West Side Highway and the no doubt even louder roar of Ormus's absence, which sounds constantly in her ear like the ocean in a shell. He's in a vast empty apartment uptown in the old Rhodopé Building, a classic-period Art Deco landmark; cocooned in space, looking east across the reservoir. Whole rooms contain nothing except a piano, a guitar, a few cushions. A fortune invested in soundproofing and air-purification systems. Ormus still wears his eye patch when he's out and about, and always when he's performing, as an aid to concentration, but here in this luxury padded cell he gives free rein to his craziness, his double vision: he rides it hard, busts it like a bronc. He shuts out the world and hears the music of the spheres. Though he is sworn to celibacy, he lets Maria come.

Their audiences, their arenas expand. The music gets louder. He goes on stage wearing earplugs but there's already damage to his hearing. Vina has her ocean-roar; in his case it's a ringing noise like a faraway alarm. This is the last sound he hears at night, the first that penetrates his consciousness each morning. Sometimes he mistakes it for air knocking in underfloor pipes or the wind whistling through a cracked pane of glass. *The ringing noise is my life,* he writes in his journal. *It's just another thing I can't escape.*

After a tense initial period during which they sometimes see each other in the evenings, with painfully awkward results, they agree to meet only to rehearse with the other band members, to discuss their finances and to perform. They are never alone together any more, they never eat a meal or take in a movie in each other's company, never phone each other, never go dancing, never feed animals in the zoo, never touch. Like divorced couples, they avoid each other's gaze. Yet mysteriously they continue to say they are both deeply, irreversibly, for-ever-and-a-day in love.

What can this mean?

It means that they are with each other constantly even while they are apart. When she stands in the shower she imagines him on the other side of the glass door, watching the water run down her body, pressing his lips to the steamy glass. She puts her own lips to the inside of the door, closes her eyes, imagines him waiting for her. The water becomes his hands, and her own hands run down her body, searching for and often becoming his touch. And when he lies in his bed he convinces himself there's a warm hollow in the mattress beside him, as if she has just left the room; he closes his eyes and she returns, she comes close. Their curled bodies are a pair of question marks at the end of the puzzling sentence of the day.

When he writes a line he always wonders what she'll think of it, he hears her goddess's voice take his music and hurl it into the sky, to hang there like a shining star. And when she eats, alone or with others, she never fails to think of his carnivorous habits, his high daily intake of red meat cooked medium rare, and a look of exasperated affection crosses her face, a look which (if she is not alone) she uncharacteristically declines to explain.

Her decision to live her private life in public embarrasses and even humiliates a man as private as Ormus has become; yet he wonders every day at the raw courage of her engagement with the world, of her willingness to walk naked in its streets in the service of what she thinks of as the truth. In response to her blabbering mouth, his own reserve grows around him like a wall. She beats her fists against it, as she does against his famous oath; but she also thinks of his choices, as she thinks of him, with a respect that she accords to no one else.

Entering the same room, they crackle with the electricity of their solitary loving. They quarrel, of course. What he thinks of as his commitment to monogamy, she calls his growing absolutism. She accuses him of tyranny, which he calls fidelity. It is her nature that separates them, he replies. Her determined infidelity, her refusal to value what is of value, namely the love of a good man, himself. What he calls infidelity, she calls freedom. What looks to him like promiscuity, she provocatively renames democracy. These arguments go nowhere; like, perhaps, all lovers' quarrels, though they cannot be ended, defused, as other lovers' quarrels are: by oblivion's kiss.

Everything is remembered.

And they can kiss only while they sleep; only in their dreams.

VINA CONTINUES to reveal everything to everyone all the time. The more intimate the detail the surer it is to see the light of day. When they go on stage Ormus stands with his back to the audience, facing his fellow musicians like a conductor, Karajan with a Stratocaster, while she yells out a number to the audience, which everyone knows by now is the number of days that have passed since she and Ormus last had sex. She announces the names of her latest stopgap lovers, her Reichian belief in the healing powers of orgone energy and multiple orgasms, and the precise nature of her sexual preferences.

(Domination, bondage, aggression alternating with submissiveness, punishment, surrender: long before her eighties imitators she was bringing out into the open the flimsy repetitive secrets of our forbidden hearts, flaunting beneath the intense weight of stage lighting what had previously skulked around in the dark; demolishing—by inhabiting—taboos. For this she was predictably called the pornographer of the phonograph, the stereotypist of the stereo, by those who did not care to notice what was staring everyone in the face, namely her colossal and growing need for him, that need which she shouted to the whole planet in order to belittle and thus survive it, which hit her with redoubled intensity every morning of her life—her heart's seismic scale, like the Richter, proceeded by doublings—and forced her into ever greater extremes of compensatory behavior, loudmouthings, promiscuity, drugs. Namely that there was only one person in all the world whom she was trying to offend: no matter how large the audience, how outrageously suggestive her performance, her true purpose was profoundly intimate, and her true audience numbered one.

Or perhaps, if I may be permitted a flash of vanity, two.

I say this because she, the queen of over-exposure, never exposed me.)

The arch-enemy of the hidden, she keeps me secret until the end. About our long afternoons on my outsize brass bed, Ormus will never learn as long as she lives. Why? Because I'm not nothing to her is why. We have *duration,* a present and a future, is why. Because a cat may look at a queen and maybe, just maybe, sometimes the queen looks right back at that hungry young tom.

Her casual amours, which she makes public, are rendered insignificant by being named. None of them lasts long, anyway: a few weeks, a couple of months at best. My love affair with her—or call it half a love affair, because half of the two of us was in love—will last for almost eighteen years.

Gayomart Cama skipped out of Ormus's head and disappeared. The great man lost a twin brother, but (without knowing it) gained me. I'm his true Other, his living shadow self. I have shared his girl. She doesn't tell him because this would matter to him. This would tear him apart. The people with whom you share a history: these are the people who can leave you shipwrecked and drowning.

This is how Vina will one day leave both of us.

If the Other cannot be named, the shadow self must also, by definition, be selfless. She gives me no rights over her, comes and goes as she pleases, summons and banishes me at her pharaonic whim. It's not for me to mind about her cavalcade of playmates; certainly not to be jealous of Ormus himself. Yet each new sexual revelation comes as what I'm learning to call a *zetz* in the *kishkes.* And the fact of Ormus, of the love that can neither be nor cease to be, is a knife slowly twisted in the heart. She makes public sport of his celibacy; I'm counting differently. Every day that passes is one day closer to his goal, the day when he'll ask her to keep her promise.

There's only one man for me, and I can't have him, she shouts to the crowds. Listen and I'll sing you his beautiful songs instead.

He keeps his back to the audience. He can't show them his pain.

THE BREAKDOWN of boundaries, what Erwin Panofsky called decompartmentalization, gave rise during the Renaissance to the modern idea of the genius. The fifteenth-century manifestos and treatises of Alberti, Leonardo and Cennini leave us in no doubt that this decompartmentalization is intimately connected to the urbanization of artistic sensibility, or, rather, to the artist's conquest of the city. The Renaissance artist is no longer a worker bee, a mere craftsman dancing to a patron's tune, but polymathic, a master of anatomy, philosophy, mythography, the laws of seeing and perception; an adept of the arcana of deep sight, able to penetrate the very essences of things. The achievements of modern artists, Alberti proclaimed, prove that the modern world is not exhausted. By crossing boundaries, uniting many kinds of knowledge, technical and intellectual, high and low, the modern artist legitimizes the whole project of society.

Such is genius! Leonardo, Michelangelo: they claim kinship, even equality, with the gods. The opposed destinies of immortality and destruction are theirs.

As for Ormus, at first, upon his helicoptered arrival in Manhattan, he enters a condition of worship, marveling at this new Rome, open-mouthed and slack-jawed, as did Alberti in Florence in the 1430s. Every chord he plays will be a paean to the sky-high city, he promises himself. If it can conquer the heights, so too will he.

He should have been my mother's son. I should have been his dad's.

One might suggest simply that Ormus Cama's worship of the city has quickly been reciprocated; it has become the city's worship of him. And where this city leads, this Rome, all the world's cities quickly follow.

Alas, this is an over-simplification. If Ormus lands in Manhattan as a provincial with stars in his eyes, circumstances quickly sour his joy. The rusting decadence of the city at ground level, its shoulder-barging vulgarity, its third-world feel (the poverty, the traffic, the slo-mo dereliction of the winos and the cracked-glass dereliction of too many of the buildings, the unplanned vistas of urban blight, the ugly street furniture), and the bizarreries to which Vina initially insists on exposing him, at such boho meccas as Sam's Pleasure Island and the Slaughterhouse, these things fuel his celebrated moral disgust. Groovy Manhattan is plainly no better than Swinging London. He retreats into high-rise heaven and watches the city float in space. This celestial Manhattan is what he loves. Against this backcloth of noble silence he will set his pet sounds.

He, too, is screaming inside. His agony will emerge as music.

GIVE ME *a copper and I'll tell you a golden story.* Thus, according to Pliny, did the oral storytellers of old preface their fantastic tales of men transformed into beasts and back again, of visions and magic: tales told not in plain language but adorned with every kind of extravagant embellishment and curlicue, flamboyant, filled with the love of pyrotechnics and display. When writers adopted the mannerisms of these storytellers it was, says Robert Graves, because they "found that the popular tale gave them a wider field for their descriptions of contemporary morals and manners, punctuated by philosophical asides, than any more respectable literary form."

What hope can I, a mere journeyman shutterbug, a harvester of quotidian images from the abundance of what is, have of literary respectability? Like Lucius Apuleius of Madaura, a Moroccan colonial of Greek ancestry aspiring to the ranks of the Latin colossi of Rome, I should (belatedly) excuse my (post)colonial clumsinesses and hope that you are not put off by the oddness of my tale. Just as Apuleius did not fully "Romanize" his language and style, thinking it better to find an idiolect that permitted him to express himself in the fashion of his Greek ancestors, so also I . . . but look here, there is an important difference between myself and the author of *The Transformations of Lucius*, better known as *The Golden Ass*. Yes, you will say, there is the small matter of talent, and you'll hear no argument from me on that score; but I'm driving at something else: viz., that while Apuleius happily admits to the fictionality of his fiction, I continue to insist that what I tell you is true. In his work he makes an easy separation between the realms of fancy and of fact; in my own poor effort, I am trying to set down the true-life account of the life of a man who saw, long before the rest of us, the artificiality of such a separation; who witnessed the demolition of that iron curtain with his own eyes and courageously went forth to dance on its remains.

Thus:

WHEN HE is by himself in his gigantic empty apartment Ormus removes his eye patch and the double vision returns. He looks into the heart of the otherness, the streaming. The barriers between the world of dreams and the waking world, between the spheres of the actual and the imagined, are breaking down. There is a progression. Something is changing. Instead of the gashes through which he formerly saw these visions, the windows to the other quiddity now have blurry edges. Sometimes they grow very large; it's difficult to tell where this world ends and that begins. His apartment here looks exactly like his apartment there.

The frontiers are softening. The time may not be far off when they disappear entirely. This notion, which ought to excite him, instead fills him with terrible dread. If the forking paths are coming together, if a point of confluence is ahead, what does this mean for life on the earth he knows? If such a decompartmentalization were to occur, and all verities suddenly failed, could we survive the force of the event? Ought we to be building bunkers, arming ourselves, donning badges that identify us as fellow members of this reality and not the feared (perhaps soon the hated) other?

If each of us has alternative existences in the other continuum, which of our possibilities will live on, which will disappear?

If we are all twins, which twin must die?

ONCE SHE is convinced of the immutability of his self-denying oath, the wraithish Maria visits him less often. When she does come she's usually sulky, protesting Ormus's use of the eye patch to shut her out, to say nothing of the oath itself. She doesn't stay long, but never fails to remind him of what he's missing.

He notices that she often arrives out of breath, perspiring. She seems tired. Is it possible that as the two whatnesses join and meld it's getting harder for her to slide back and forth in her unsettlingly supernatural way? Could it be that when the blending is complete, the two worlds will obey the same natural laws, and Maria will have to enter and leave through the door just like anyone else?

If so, will there be an apartment—her apartment—awaiting him in Bombay? Will the Cosmic Dancer Hotel possess, in its ledgers, a record of the suite they booked for that supposed night of passion long ago?

How will he ever know fact from fiction again?

The headache begins. He replaces the eye patch and lies back on his bed.

That's enough for now.

It's not up to you no more, you can't choose if it's peace or war, just can't make choices any more, your nightmare has come true; and when the day becomes the night, and when you don't know wrong from right, or blind from sight or who to fight, don't tell me you feel blue.

For Jack and Jill will tumble down, the king will lose his hollow crown, the jesters all are leaving town, the queen has lost her shoe; the cat has lost his fiddling stick, so Jack be nimble, Jack be quick, as all the clocks refuse to tick, the end of history is in view.

The earth begins to rock and roll, its music dooms your mortal soul, and there's nothing baby nothing you can do. 'Cause it's not up to it's not up to it's not up to you.

The earthquake songs of Ormus Cama are rants in praise of the approach of chaos, paradoxically composed by an artist working at the highest levels of musical sophistication. The songs are about the collapse of all walls, boundaries, restraints. They describe worlds in collision, two universes tearing into each other, striving to become one, destroying each other in the effort. Dreams invade the day, while waking's humdrums beat in our dreams.

Some of the songs are intricate tapestries of driving, woven sound. In other pieces, however, Ormus with great deliberation abandons the juggling fantasies that come to him naturally and adopts a bare, discordant manner, demanding of Vina a raucous aggression to which she adds a terrifying intensity of her own. This is something entirely new in Ormus: this purposive disharmony. This is celibate misery speaking, the Miltonic pain of unconsummated love.

Untwisting all the chains that tie / the hidden soul of harmony.

Many of these raw songs are jeremiads addressed directly to Vina, so that when she sings them it's weirdly disorienting because he's putting into her mouth—that is, she's spitting out of her mouth—the words he needs to say to her. He isn't reclusive in his art. Music is his nakedness. This excites us. Watching them on stage, listening to them on our records and tapes, we can see and hear the tension in their strangely obstructed love. Their huge, rotten love, which they insist on denying themselves for so long, so long. It makes them the only lovers whose news we can't wait to hear.

Sung in Vina's swooping, belting voice, certain songs release something primal, even animal, in the listener. Though their message could be called nihilistic, their musical clothing is potent enough to captivate the world's disenfranchised, idolatrous young. Ormus, his own youthful excesses forgotten, a sensualist rendered simon-pure by a mighty promise of abstinence, a devotee of the flesh transformed into a preacher of the spirit by his horror at the profligacy with which the New World squanders its privileges, now berates his admirers for their wantonness, for the licentious debauchery of their ways; and though from the virtuous heights of his chastity he thunders about a generation mired in hedonism, lost in the archipelagoes of indulgence and desire, the objects of his fury love him for his wrath. Prophesying doom, he is the best beloved of the allegedly doomed. Vina in her magic voice sings Ormus's musical anathemas, and the anathematized young of the Western world are enchanted. They rush out to their rhythm centers and buy.

Whenever the *Quakershaker* songs are performed a wildness bursts out of the audience. There is a loud howling as of wolves. As floodlights rake the crowd, they reveal abandoned, Dionysiac scenes. The fans, possessed by the music, tear at their garments, at one another, at the air. Young women's arms snake upwards, entwined, their hands moving like wings. They sit astride their lovers' shoulders. The men's faces are turned inwards, towards their partners' splayed and naked groins, and there is much snuffling and slavering and many porcine grunts. When the crowd roars it is like a lion and beneath the roar there is sometimes heard a hissing, as of serpents.

There are disappearances. Young people fail to return home and are eventually marked down as runaways. There is loose talk of bestial metamorphoses: snakes in the urban gutters, wild pigs in city parks, strange birds with fabulous plumages perching on skyscrapers like gargoyles, or angels.

The laws of the universe may be changing. Such transformations may—incredibly, horrifyingly—become normal.

We may be losing our grip on our humanity. When we finally let go, what's to stop us from turning into dinosaurs, saber-toothed tigers, jackals, hyenas, wolves?

What's to stop us from sliding, as darkness falls and (as in the Orphic hymn to Night) *terrible necessity rules over all*?

THERE IS much conservative condemnation of the new supergroup and its adherents, who are variously censured as neurotics, parasites, plunderers, libertines and cheats. At a concert in Toronto a thinly perspiring police chief with glasses like side-view mirrors warns Vina about certain explicit gestures she has been making during performances. *Keep it clean. No funny stuff. No grabbing yourself, okay?* Seeing that there's a tv camera present Vina gives the hapless police chief five minutes on the First Amendment and artistic freedom, and when she gets on stage she grabs herself so hard and so often there's a danger she might come off in her own hands. The police chief, faced with the likelihood of a riot, fails to intervene.

The cult of VTO—its adherents have started calling themselves New Quakers, a case of the wild stealing a name from the mild—grows larger every day, fueled by the rhapsodic exegeses of Ormus's lyrics and Vina's singing provided, in a series of landmark critiques, by the keepers of the flame of rock music, the Italian-American Marco Sangria and the Francophone Martinican Rémy Auxerre.

It is a characteristic of rock music that it drives otherwise reasonable men to rapture, to excess. Even by the gushing standards of music journalism, however, Marco and Rémy are extreme. They have access to levels of rhapsody that make them the envy of their peers.

Literally, Sangria screams, Vina Apsara's voice *is music;*

music in its most profound essentials. The relationship of Vina and Ormus expresses the tension between wisdom and eloquence. And the intervals of the Ormic guitar may well be, *mathematically speaking,* the structural basis not only of the whole universe but of the human soul as well. When we explore our inner space, as both Buddhists and sub-atomic physicists agree, we find a microcosm there which is identical with the macrocosmos: Ormus's music reveals to our hearts the identity of the little and the large.

It spreads the music of the soul to our other limbs, and so, when we dance, we dance the dance not of the body but of the soul.

Rémy amplifies these claims in his own esoteric way.

This is the struggle of the great musician, Rémy writes: that he seeks not only to sing Apollo's pure, clean song but also to move to Dionysus's dirty rhythm. The reconciliation of the conflict between the Apollonian and the Dionysiac we may call *harmonia.* Where reason and light meet madness and darkness, where science meets art and peace meets battle; where the adult meets the child, where life faces death and scorns it, make your music there.

The singer uses the frenzy of the gods, Rémy says. The frontier between the empires of Apollo and Dionysus breaks down under the pressure of this divine fury. There are four levels of *furor divinus.* Poetic *furor* calms the soul, sacerdotal *furor* prepares the spirit for exaltation, prophetic *furor* lifts us to the level of the angels, erotic *furor* unites the soul with God. Ormus's music possesses them all in the highest degree.

There are two great spirits, Rémy writes: Spiritus Humanus, that links body and soul, and Spiritus Mundi, linking the sublunary and translunary worlds. These *lunatic* terms are Auxerre's version of Ormus's doctrine of the two realities, world and otherworld. *In VTO's music these two spirits are united.* This, Rémy concedes modestly, is perhaps a grand unified theory of the soul: at certain unimaginably high levels of heat and compression—that is to say, genius—we and the cosmos are one. Ormus Cama is the proof incarnate of this theory.

Starving for soul food, the stadium-filling legions swallow large gobbets of the above effusions. What really excites them, however, is catastrophe: Marco Sangria's line-by-line, image-by-image exposition of Ormus's eschatological world-view. *The Quake is coming, the Big One that will swallow us all. Dance to the music, for tomorrow, suckers, we die.*

Eschatology and gossip: the uranium and plutonium of the late twentieth century. Vina has made the story of her life, and Ormus's, into the world's soap opera. Such is the frisson engendered by the famous celibacy oath that half the world's women line up to offer Ormus what they hope will be irresistible temptation. These appled Eves are not unlike male bar-room boasters who back their improbable charms against the resistances of all forbidden women—movie stars, lesbians, their best friends' wives. Ormus, holding himself aloof from all blandishments, even engenders violence in some women who think it unreasonable of him to deny himself, who espy in his rejection of them an insult to red-blooded women everywhere. Threats are received, and the policing of VTO concerts, as well as security at the Rhodopé Building, is stepped up as a result. Such bacchic fury is one part of the temper of the times.

Vina has her own booth at Sam's these days. There, surrounded by lovers and disciples—Marco, Rémy, whoever's in town—she holds forth. She has wisdom of her own to impart, and wants the world to know her views on, for example, the latest quasi-sciences. Biofeedback and cognitive behavioral therapy, orthomolecularism and macrobiotics. She praises the beneficial effects of Jamaica dogwood, of cabbage rubbed against the skin, of the therapeutic use of sound waves. While her crusading vegetarianism prevents her from drinking the blood of lizards and bats, she graciously concedes that the beneficial effects of such beverages have been proven beyond much doubt.

Her diet book and her health and fitness régime will become worldwide best-sellers. Later, she will successfully pioneer the celebrity exercise video and license a range of organic vegetarian meals, which, under the name Vina's VegeTable®, will also succeed. (In the commercials, healthy young consumers make the tripartite gesture of her rock fans, the two-finger peace V, the time-out T with its connotations of sporty leisure, and the approbatory thumb-and-forefinger O. *VegeTable Organics* is what we are asked to believe the sign language recommends, but that's just standard adland doublespeak.)

She is the woman most cited by the world's young women as their rôle model.

She clenches her fist against racial injustice and sings from political platforms and amid charred buildings in the aftermath of racial troubles in the American South and West. Owing to her majestic bearing, her golden voice and, above all, her renown, nobody questions her right to sing out for American blacks. She, too, has crossed the color line: not away from, but towards.

She is a fiery, witty speaker on behalf of women's rights and against the sloppy *imperium* of men. This lays her open to attack by one segment of the women's movement. How is it, these sisters want to know, that this outsize, free-spirited female is so obsessed by the clearly obsolete male member, so anachronistically in need of penetration, that she actually boasts in public about her "conquests"? Is she not, as completely as the self-incriminating chauvinist Norman Mailer, a prisoner of sex?

Why does she sing only Ormus's songs?

Why doesn't she lend her voice to the artistic vision of today's women? Why doesn't she write her own material?

Can she be free if she's just the instrument of one man's art?

Such debate—passionate, informed, ideologue—is also a part of the turbulent spirit of the age. Vina ignores her critics and sails on, a great galleon in search of fabled treasure. She is the *Argo,* and Ormus sails in her. Music itself is the Golden Fleece they seek.

Breaking their own rule about not seeing each other outside work, simultaneously overcome by need, on a whim they drive to the Nevada desert and use the four-wheel drive to write their names in the sand, so big, Vina tells Ormus, that they'll be able to identify us from the moon, like the Wall of China. After that they start calling themselves the Chinese Wall. When Vina explains to a journalist back in New York what the joke means, it backfires, they are accused of arrogance, even of attacking religion, because being Vina she adds that they wrote their names over an area bigger than any church. *You can't see no churches from the moon.* That remark, added to the Black Power salutes she's been giving lately and the perceived anti-establishment contents of Ormus's lyrics, is enough. The long-delayed assault against them is launched. Vina's an American citizen, born in the U.S.A., so she gets unprovoked police visits in the middle of the night, when she is "invited" down to the precinct house to be grilled about her political associations with Yippies, Panthers, assorted unionists and leftists, and Amos Voight's crowd of weirdo undesirables. She gets drug raids (all unsuccessful; she's not that stupid), and the IRS turns her finances over as if they were rocks beneath which all sorts of poisonous snakes must lurk. Ormus, a foreigner, gets the Immigration and Naturalization Service. In March 1973 he is ordered by an immigration judge to leave the country within sixty days. The reason given is that he was once involved in a fatal car accident and though he was not the driver samples of his blood taken at the time revealed the presence in his veins of an illegal narcotic substance. When this is announced in court, Ormus understands he's up against power on a scale he's never encountered before, a power so great it can undo the good work of Mull Standish and Yul Singh and make public what has lain hidden for six long years.

(I say again: back then certain battles had not been won. It was still possible for the future to lose to the past, for pleasure and beauty to be defeated by piety and iron. One war ends, another begins. The human race is never really at peace.)

Nevertheless, discovering the tip of what will prove to be a broad stubborn streak, Ormus appeals. *America is a place to live in,* he tells the press in a rare news conference on the steps of the court. *I don't want to just scoot in and then duck out with the loot.*

There's not much chance of his scooting anywhere, to tell the truth. He's with three bulging, glitter-toothed lawyers, and Mull Standish, pushing sixty but still sleek, still looking like a contender, and Vina, who has chosen today to wear a molded golden breastplate over black T-shirt and leggings, putting Ormus, the classicist's son, in mind of Pallas Athene girded for battle, a Pallas Athene with knuckle-duster rings and movie-star shades. They're surrounded by seven identically sunglassed Singhs, then by a second circle, of the NYPD's finest, who with linked arms and many menaces hold back not only the press corps but also the thrashing, ululating New Quakers, at whose extreme fringes lurk hairy charismatics with much the same psychiatric profiles as the self-impalers at the heart of Shiite Muharram processions: denizens of the psychotropics of Capricorn, the lands of the sacrificed goat.

Why don't you marry him, a reporter asks Vina, in her face, straight out. (This is New York.) If you marry him, it's over. He'll at once have the right to stay.

He should have that right, anyway, Vina answers, by reason of the gift he brings. He improved this town just by showing up.

Why don't *you* marry *her,* the same reporter then asks Ormus, as if Vina hasn't spoken. Hey, why take the long road when there's a short cut, right.

We have a bargain, Ormus answers, meaning the ten-year oath. There are disbelieving titters from the press corps when he spells it out for them. Ormus scowls, clams up. *I gave my word.*

Standish responds swiftly to the darkening mood; raps his cane on the step. (The British formality of his dress imposes itself on the crowd: against the three-piece Savile Row suit, the Jermyn Street shirt, the mother-of-pearl buttons, the tailored shoes, the Aquascutum loden coat, what chance do jeans and sneakers really have?) Okay, that's it, ladies and gents. Show's over for today. Thank you for your interest and attention. Officer, can we get some help here, let's move it to the limo right now.

GETTING STANDISH back into full managerial harness was Vina's idea. Putting distance—the whole Atlantic Ocean—between him and the band had originally been her strategy too. Like many confident, talented people she saw no need to give a non-creative person a piece of the cake if she didn't have to; she could handle Colchis Records. Sure she could. She already had her solo deal, she'd held out for plenty (multi-record options, generous recording funds), she reckoned she knew her way around the insalubrious parts of Contract City as well as its glamorous, brightly lit boulevards—the mugger-shadowed back streets of small print as well as the shining royalty marquees—so now that Boss Yul was taking on VTO, she would negotiate that contract too.

After signing, she had begun to have her doubts. Record sales were huge, way up in the superstar bracket, multi-millions of units were being shifted, but the amounts paid into their bank balances were shockingly small. On her say-so Ormus had bought that white elephant of an apartment on the Upper West Side, and all his bank accounts were fiercely in the red. Ormus—always the more trusting one—left the business end to Vina and the lawyers and accountants she employed. At financial meetings he often actually fell asleep until Vina shook him and put a pen in his hand, whereupon he signed on whatever dotted line was indicated. Now she feared he might have done well to stay awake. She did not share her doubts with him but admitted that, if only to provide an objective second opinion, she wanted Mull Standish back on the team.

At first, to be honest, she confessed to Ormus, I was a little jealous?, because he's so in love with you?, pretty pathetic, huh. Of me, I mean. But we need somebody in between us and Mr. Yul Singh. We need cushioning, distance. It'll improve our bargaining power.

This was after the *Peace Ballads,* at around the time when YSL started to crack the whip about her political utterances et cetera. So when Vina went so far as to wonder whether they were being fleeced—golden fleeced, she called it—by Cool Yul, Ormus suspected a personal, nonbusiness agenda. He wanted to protest, Yul has been pretty good to us so far, but he saw the look in Vina's eye and didn't argue. Besides, he'd been missing Mull Standish himself.

Standish had remained in England, unable to tear himself away from poor pickle-brained Waldo picking up leaves in Spenta Methwold's gardens. However, his continued presence was misinterpreted by Spenta as a sign of his long-term interest in her own forlorn offer of companionship, and there followed a slow, melancholy comedy of misunderstandings played out in a form of Noh theater, or as stylized dumb-show tableaux: neither did Spenta speak her own hopes nor could Mull Standish find the words to dash them; and Virus Cama watched everything but said nothing, while Waldo was now capable of only the simplest, most innocent insights about the birds and the bees and the flowers and the trees and the sky up above. Standish felt trapped between his gratitude to Spenta, for giving Waldo a semblance of a place in life, and his solicitude for her; things had been allowed to go too far, and the truth—that she had given her ageing heart to one who could never take it—would only humiliate her now. In this strangulated environment he felt energy flow out of him. He began to think the unthinkable: that life might after all be no more than a defeat.

Vina's telephone call came like a blood transfusion. At once he set in motion his long-prepared fast-track plan to divest himself of all his British enterprises, even his much-admired listings magazine, which had beaten off an upstart rival to maintain its grip on the market, with spin-offs successfully launched in Manchester, Liverpool, Birmingham and Glasgow. As for Spenta, he now had a face-saving way of leaving her. When he told her of his imminent departure her chin shook for just an instant. Then, reconciling herself in that moment to her fate, she said, Of course go. I will look after our two injured children. We are a sort of accidental family, after all, isn't it; a family of damage and loss.

Mull Standish bowed his head and withdrew.

In New York, facing the full horror of the Vina-negotiated contracts, he became once more his capacious, potent self. He insisted on absolute control, no arguments, and fired all the band's advisers five minutes after he finished reading himself in. Then he called Ormus and Vina to a crisis meeting in his reopened midtown office suite. Right now it was just a secretary and a Xerox machine, but expansion plans were at an advanced stage. It's a catastrophe, of course, he said, drumming his fingertips on the table. Only one more album under firm contract and eight more optioned. That means they can dump you whenever they like but you can't walk away from them or change the deal. Just eleven percent of suggested retail list price, for crying out loud, less three points for the producer, and will you look at these numbers on free goods and promo. Let me spell it out for you. One cassette of *Peace Ballads* has slapped on it an SRLP of, let's keep it in round numbers, seven dollars. Never mind what it's discounted at in the stores, this is what all the figures are based on. Then you take twenty percent off for packaging, that gives you a royalty base of five sixty. At eleven percent that's a royalty of sixty-two cents per cassette sold. But now you subtract twenty-one cents for Mr. Producer, which I take it is none other than our friend Mr. Singh, and then hello, we have this completely off-the-wall twenty percent for assorted freebies, so you can kiss goodbye to one fifth of what's left. That leaves just thirty-two point eight cents, out of which you've got to pay the other band members, LaBeef and the Baths, one percent each, generous to a fault, so that costs you another twenty-one cents. The pair of you are left with exactly eleven point eight cents per cassette, split two ways, but first you deduct the quarter of a million in recording costs and the full hundred and fifty thou for independent promotion—*one hundred percent of the total,* and you *signed*?—off the top of that, and what do you know, here's a thirty-five-percent reserve against returns. So what's it sold, six million units, call that one hundred thousand dollars each, maximum, and by the time you've paid your taxes you'll see maybe fifty-five percent of it, but that's only if you've got a good accountant, which is not the case. I'm guessing fifty thousand with taxes paid, bottom line, and that's on a mega-megahit. You *children.* And meanwhile you're spending money like it's going out of style, million-dollar apartments, fancy electronic toys, I bet your gigs lose money too, I haven't even started on Ormus's pathetic writing deal, and you're wondering why the numbers are red. Jesus Christ.

So what do we do now, Vina asked in an unfamiliar, deferential voice. I mean, are we permanently fucked? How do we play it?

Standish sat back in his chair and grinned. We start playing sneaky bridge, he said. We finesse.

YUL SINGH's trans- and inter-continental movements make him a hard man to pin down. He owns a Napa Valley winery, a secret Arizona hideaway ranch, a Caribbean island and great stashes of classical-period sculptures in bank vaults in, allegedly, Toronto, Boston and Savannah. It is said he visits these vaults alone, at night, to fondle his winged marble Nikes and full-breasted Aphrodites in subterranean chambers with two-foot-thick walls of steel. He has mistresses and protégés, schemes and assignations, and always plays the cards close to his chest. He also owns cows. Sixty-six million dollars' worth of Holstein dairy cattle, a sizeable proportion of the entire Massachusetts herd. Cows are sacred, mystic, he tells people when they ask why. Also, business is doubleplus good.

For reasons nobody understands he has studied and now conforms to the arcana of maximum security, booking himself on several flights leaving at the same time for different destinations, using assumed names, avoiding predictability. You're just a high-rolling record-industry honcho, for goodness' sake, Standish scoffs to his face at their first meeting at Colchis, in a room full of circular platinum and gold. What, you're acting now like Carlos or Arafat?

To which Yul replies: Listen, Standish, no offense, I like you but you're behind the game, which the fact is it's signed sealed and delivered, your artists are bound and gagged on my personal sacrificial altar, am I making myself clear, I own them, the devil didn't own Faust the way I have these babies, they're mine.

Standish has good ears, close to the ground, contacts from his old days as one of the great builders of the city, and when Yul Singh unsurprisingly gives him the brush-off, he puts these eavesdroppers back on the active roster. I want him to know he is no longer playing pattycake, he tells Ormus and Vina, he has to understand that the negotiation has entered the major leagues. For this I need inside material. He does not add that the first news he has received from his paid listeners is that he himself might be in need of security, his old jilted lover Sam Tropicana has heard he's back in town and certain explicit threats have been made, certain red-faced fulminations have been overheard both in the somber upscale setting of the exclusive Knickerbocker Club and also in the more unbuttoned environment of the sidewalk outside Catania's pizza place in Belmont in the Bronx, near D'Auria Brothers Pork Store and Our Lady of

Mount Carmel on 187th Street. There is no getting round the fact that Sam Tropicana is now one large *fromage* but Standish declines to panic.

Forget about it, it's the past, he tells his ears. Time flows only one way and I don't believe in yesterday.

Finally the team comes up with the goods, and when Yul Singh holding Will's arm walks into the auction rooms in San Narciso, Calif.—the oldest building in town, actually pre-dating World War II—he is greeted in a cold lobby of gleaming redwood floorboards and the smell of wax and paper by Mull Standish tapping his cane. You what the fuck, inquires Yul inelegantly, genuinely discomfited. I guess your smoke screens weren't all they should be, YSL, grins Standish, I assume heads will have to roll.

So you're here for what, Yul demands, recovering fast.

First let me tell you why *you're* here, says Mull. Turns out you're interested in conspiracies, underground organizations, militias, the whole right-wing paranoid-America thing. Who knows why. You're here to bid for the memorabilia of some defunct immigrant cabal, used to go around writing DEATH on people's walls. Don't Ever Antagonize The Horn. They had a trumpet logo. Nice.

You're out of your depth, okay, Yul argues, his equilibrium restored. Lemme tell you the laws of the universe. The law according to Disney: Nobody fucks with the mouse. Which in my version, with the louse: that's me. The law according to Sir Isaac Newton: to every action an equal and opposite reaction. But that was way back, before television, and in Britain too. I say, no sir, that reaction's gonna be unequal if I got anything to do with it. You fuck with me, I fuck you two times and your kid sister too. Don't antagonize the horn, you got that right, did you know I played clarinet. So here's the deal. The law of laws. Heads Yul wins, tails you'll lose.

Nice talking to you, says Standish, and exits: slow, deliberate, like a matador turning his back on the bull. Contempt wins many bullfights. Sometimes, however, it gets you gored in the back.

THE LEGAL war between the two best-dressed men in the music universe, the legendary head of Colchis Records and the manager of the all-powerful VTO group, rocks the business. It is fought with weapons that cannot be described in English, on an esoteric legal battleground that might as well be made of moon cheese. Standish hires a team of Indian lawyers and launches against Colchis whole armadas of suits, entire arsenals of writs. The record company replies in kind. They are like battling spiders and VTO's music is the fly snared in their webs of sticky string.

Vina asks Standish, Couldn't we just somehow I don't know settle?

No, he answers.

Ormus says, This is never going to end, is it.

Yes, he replies.

Look, he says. What's happening here is we're trying to win a war we've already lost. He has your signatures, all we have is nuisance value. And if we're a big enough nuisance for long enough, if we tie up enough funds because they're under litigation, then in the end he'll come to our table and deal.

That's all? Vina asks, disappointed. That's all you've got?

That, and Indian lawyers, says Standish, deadpan. The maestros of the law's delays. *Jarndyce* v. *Jarndyce* is a stroll in the park for these guys. These are marathon runners, and Yul knows it. These are the gold medalists of stall.

But what if, Ormus begins, and Standish stops him.

This is the high road, the way in through the front door, he says. Maybe there's also a low road, a back-door entry. This, don't ask me. Maybe never, but anyway not now.

The *Quakershaker* album—self-produced in Muscle Shoals and Montserrat by Ormus; Yul Singh never enters the studio—sells over twenty million units and every penny of the money's tied up in court. Yul Singh invites Standish (who has been advancing living expenses to Vina and Ormus out of his own pocket) to come into the New York office when he's back from a trip to Europe, and *just talk.* The week before this meeting's due date, the authorities' attack against Ormus and Vina is launched.

Mull Standish is of the party that holds that there is no such thing as coincidence. He hires yet more lawyers, both Indian and non-, but behind the scenes he's the one orchestrating the defense. The greater the difficulties, the greater grows his energy, the more precise his focus. He arranges solidarity concerts at the Fillmores, East and West. Dylan, Lennon, Joplin, Joni, Country Joe and the Fish turn up to sing for Ormus. As character witnesses, Mayor Lindsay, Dick Cavett and Leonard Woodcock, president of the United Auto Workers union, speak to Ormus's integrity and value. A suit is filed demanding the government's case records and asking that the immigration service's ruling be overturned. There is also the appeal before the immigration board itself.

In July 1974 the appeal is lost. Once again Ormus is given sixty days to go, or be deported by force.

During those war years, there are no new VTO records. Ormus retreats into the Rhodopé Building and if he's writing he's not telling anyone, not even Standish, not even Vina. Between Vina and Standish, both in love with Ormus Cama, a surprising intimacy forms, a friendship based in part on Ormus's denial of his body to them both, in part on their joint relish for the fray. She accompanies Standish to meetings of the gay businessmen's Greater Gotham Business League, joins in their lobbying of politicians on the subject of the recent increase in attacks on the gay community, and gains the League's support for Ormus's cause. Standish and Vina become a formidable pair of lobbyists. They brief Jack Anderson, whose Report then reveals both that the drug in Ormus's blood at the time of the Crossley accident had been administered in a spiked drink without his prior knowledge, and also that over one hundred aliens with worse drug records than Ormus's have been allowed to remain in the U.S.A. This in turn persuades a New York congressman called Koch to introduce a bill designed to allow the U.S. attorney general to grant residency to Ormus Cama. The tide, very slowly, turns.

In October 1975 the deportation order is overturned by the U.S. Court of Appeals, and a year later, Ormus receives permanent residence status. Once again, there is something like solid ground beneath his feet.

The celebrations are short-lived, however, like an opening-night party that dies when some killjoy comes in waving the *Times* critic's fatal panning of the show. Like the laughter dying on Macbeth's lips at the appearance of what Yul Singh once memorably called Banquet's Ghost. Now Singh himself is the specter at the feast. Openly dismayed by Ormus's victory, he hardens his own resolve. He meets with Standish and simply says, No deal. Then he digs in for a war of attrition, calculating that he can starve Vina and Ormus out. It's their money that's tied up, after all. He has plenty of access to funds elsewhere.

When it becomes plain that long litigious years stretch ahead, Standish begins to lobby Colchis's distributors, WEC, arguing that as the deadlock has taken the world's #1 band out of distribution, they, the distributors, are being hit in the pocket by Yul Singh's intransigence, his czarish refusal to come to the table like a reasonable man.

Ormus Cama is a tough cookie, he points out. He will sing for quarters on the sidewalk if he has to, but he will not be enslaved. Did they see the *Rolling Stone* cover, by the way, the one with Ormus and Vina naked and in chains? How worth it was that?

He gets a fair hearing, but Yul Singh is a big man, and can soak up a lot of pressure. It will be five more years before the battle ends. By 1980 Mull Standish has used up most of his personal fortune, and defeat has become a real possibility. By 1980 he has played all his cards.

Then the back door opens, and the low road to success is revealed.

AT THE nadir of the struggle against Colchis, Ormus has a bread oven installed in his apartment and spends his days baking his beloved loaves—crusty white, granary brown, flour-dusted buns—and discourages all callers. This is his way of going into retreat. On an impulse, Standish and Vina decide to head for a retreat of their own: Dharmsala in the Pir Panjal range, the place of exile of Tenzin Gyatso, the fourteenth Dalai Lama and, in Standish's opinion, the truest man in the world. Vina calls Ormus to tell him the news of their imminent departure. He speaks only of bread.

India is still there. India abides, and is the third thing that binds Vina and Standish together. Delhi is hot. It is blazing with discontents in the aftermath of the assault on the Sikh extremists who were cornered, and made their last stand, in Amritsar's Golden Temple. (This was the so-called Wagahwalé gang of terrorists, named after the egg-bald Man Singh

Wagahwalé, a small bearded man deformed by the memory of the slaughter of his family during the Partition massacres and now fatally in love, like so many small, bald, bearded men around the world, with the fantasy of a micro-state to call his own, a little stockade in which to wall himself up and call it freedom.) The terrorists are dead now, but the sacrilege of the Indian Army's assault on Sikhism's holy of holies still reverberates. Reprisals are feared, and then counter-reprisals, and so on, the familiar sorry spiral. This is not the India Vina and Standish want. They make haste for the Himalayan foothills.

Indians—or let's say plains Indians—behave like children when they see snow, which seems like a substance from another world. The towering mountains, the lack of pretension of the wooden buildings, the people who seem free of all but the simplest worldly ambitions, the thin clear air as pure as a choirboy's soaring treble, the cold and, above all, the snow: these things render the most sophisticated urbanites open to what they would not normally value. The sound of small bells, the scent of saffron, slowness, contemplation, peace.

(In those days there was also Kashmir. The peace of Kashmir is shattered now, perhaps for ever—no, nothing is for ever—but Dharmsala remains.)

Vina once again finds herself playing second fiddle in the company of Mull Standish, and oddly doesn't mind. The origins of Tibetan Buddhism in the teachings of the Indian Mahayana masters, the formation of the different sects, the ascendancy of the Yellow Hats, the doctrine of the four noble truths: on these and other matters Standish is a fountainhead of information. Vina imbibes. Years ago, Standish met the Dalai Lama himself, and formed at that time a particular attachment to the deity Dorje Shugden, who, it is said, spoke to Gyatso through a monk in a trance state and told him the secret route by which he escaped from Tibet's Chinese conquerors and made his way to India.

Dorje Shugden has three red eyes and breathes out lightning. But he is one of the Protectors, wrathful as he looks.

On this trip there is unfortunately no question of an audience with the High Lama, who is abroad, but Standish plans to perform ritual devotions to Shugden. He, too, is a man looking for a way.

He asks Vina Apsara if she'd like to be a part of this.

Okay, Vina says. Why not. I came this far.

Then we'll be *vajra* brother and *vajra* sister, Standish tells her. *Vajra* is the unbreakable thing, a bolt of lightning, a diamond. It's the strongest bond, as strong as a tie of blood.

But at the doors of the down-at-heel Shugden temple Otto Wing is waiting for them with bad news. Shaven-headed and robed, every inch the true believer, the most faithful of the faithful, his heavy black-rimmed glasses the only remnant of the Otto who frolicked with Ifredis Wing in Tempe Harbor a lifetime ago, he informs Standish through pursed, disapproving lips that the Dalai Lama has broken with Dorje Shugden. These days he preaches against the deity, discourages his worship. He says that the Shugden cult detracts from the Buddha himself. To seek external help from such spirits is to turn away from the Buddha, which is disgraceful. You must not pray here, he instructs the shaken Standish. The road to the four noble truths no longer passes through this place.

Tense, embattled Shugden monks admit he's telling the truth. There is division in Paradise. Tibetan Buddhism has always been somewhat sectarian, and one of those divides has started to widen. Standish is so upset that he refuses to stay. Otto Wing flaps around, insisting that they all meditate together, but Standish brushes him off. *We're out of here.* Meaning: I no longer belong. Even in this haven I can find no peace.

No sooner have they slogged up into the mountains than they must take the slow buses and trains back down into the city heat. Vina goes along with this, because what she sees on Standish's face is an alienation that fills her with fear for him. This man has fought so hard and lost so much: children, illusions, money. She worries that he may not survive this latest blow.

They arrive in Delhi, to find the city in uproar. A quadruple assassination, by Sikh bodyguards, has resulted in the deaths of Indira Gandhi, both her sons, and the increasingly powerful political figure of Shri Piloo Doodhwala. Dreadful reprisals are being visited upon the city's Sikh population. The air is full of atrocity. Vina and Mull check in at the old

Ashoka and sit together, stunned, not knowing what to do for the best. Then there is a knock on the door. A cockaded hotel employee hands Standish a thick, dog-eared file tied up in quantities of thin, hairy rope. The file was left at reception by a man who did not, however, leave his name. No description of the man is initially available. After much coaxing, the hotel front desk eventually concedes the slight possibility that the courier was wearing the saffron and burgundy robes of a Tibetan monk. Also seen briefly in the hotel lobby that day were members of the disbanded "magnificentourage" of Piloo Doodhwala, perhaps even—though this is unconfirmed—the great man's grieving wife, Golmatol Doodhwala herself.

In that overheated time it is easy for Vina, and even perhaps Standish, to believe in almost any rumor, any possibility; even that the package comes not from any mortal source but from a deity, which perhaps feels, in the hour of its own fall from grace, some kinship with the plight of VTO; that Shugden the Protector has in his wisdom sent them this priceless gift.

Inside the package is irrefutable documentary proof—in the form of facsimiles of signed documents, checks, etc., all duly notarized as true copies—that the celebrated Non-Resident Indian Mr. Yul Singh, the very same Yul Singh who has been taking such an interest in American underground cults and cells, Yul Singh the consummate rock 'n' roller, who has always presented himself to the whole world as the ultimate cosmopolitan, wholly secularized and Westernized, Boss Yul, Coolest of the Cool, YSL himself, has been for many years a secret zealot, a purchaser of guns and bombs, in short one of the financial mainstays of the terrorist fringe of the Sikh nationalist movement—of, in fact, the Wagahwalé cult, whose leaders were so recently murdered in Amritsar, and who have just exacted, for that assault, a terrible retribution, wrought from beyond the grave.

Is this new twist part of Piloo's posthumous revenge against *his* murderers?

Vina and Standish sit in air-conditioned coolness and contemplate this gift which India, greatest of all gods from the machine, has just dropped into their astonished laps. Outside, just a couple of miles down the road, the revenge slaughter of innocent Sikhs is being carried out by bloodthirsty mobs led by officials of the governing party.

Mull Standish, ordinarily the most fastidious, most thoughtful of men, is so carried away by what he has been given that he makes an observation which, in the circumstances, could be said to be in extremely poor taste.

The more I see of the West, he says, the more I realize that the best things in life come from the East.

WHEN A great tree falls in the forest, there's money to be made from the sale of firewood. After Standish, back in New York, mails Yul Singh selected photocopies of the material in his possession—at his home address, for the sake of discretion—the record company boss invites him over to Park Avenue for a drink, and meets him at the elevator without a trace of rancor. You got me fair and square, he admits right off. I call that good work. I always told those kids they got a good one in you. A man wears many masks, few people strip him down to the bone. The criminal and the detective, the blackmailer and the mark, these are close connections which there's not many marriages more intimate. These are bonds of steel.

Vajra bonds, Standish thinks. Thunderbolts and rocks.

My wife reads the mail for me here at home, Yul Singh adds, which I don't have to tell you means I made a full breast of it all, so she's fully up to speed. He leads Standish into a vast room with much on the walls that is of interest to this India-loving man: an elephant's silver caparison, stretched and framed; small bronze Natarajas; Gandhara heads. Marie-Pierre d'Illiers is at the far end of the room, standing very still with a long flute of champagne in her hand. Her dark hair drawn tightly back, hanging in a chignon at the nape of her long and now slightly scrawny neck. She is tall, thin, utterly possessed, utterly unforgiving. She makes Standish feel like what he probably is: a blackmailer and, which is worse, the burglar of all her joy. I have for you just one question, Monsieur Standish, she says in faintly accented English. You and your charges will be owed now an immense sum of money, but truly immense; wealth beyond dreams. (*Question* and *immense* are spoken as French words.) So what I ask is this: If a good price can be made, will you buy my cows? I always detested that we were in the dairy trade, but in the end I grew fond of my Holsteins. I am sure you will be suited to the business ideally. The milking and so on.

There is a brief touch of hands between the blind husband and the all-seeing wife. At that moment, with her use of the past tense tolling in his ears as if it were a death knell, Standish understands what Yul Singh has told his wife about his future intentions, and what she has promised him in return.

Please, this way, Yul Singh shepherds him to a table covered in papers. The documents are retrospective, the terms are now at the outer edge of what is earned by any performer in the world, and there is favored-nation status. Please take your time and make any changes you care to make.

When the reading is done Standish takes out his pen and signs many times. Yul Singh's signature is already there.

He rises to go.

There is no possibility, Marie-Pierre d'Illiers murmurs, of an accommodation being arrived at regarding these documents?

The bull is on its knees waiting for the coup de grâce.

No, Mull Standish says. I am sorry. You must understand that I have simply been used in this matter, by a principal whose identity I don't know. If I do not move, the principal will surely bring these papers to light by another means. So, I can't help you. But as to the dairy herd, yes, if the price is right, we're interested.

He leaves them there, in long shot, at the far end of the great chamber of their lives, sipping Cristal champagne as if it were poison. Hemlock, Standish thinks, and then the elevator door closes and he's going down.

THEIR DEATH (too many sleeping pills) is announced the next day. The obituaries are as large and as fulsome as any great star's. News of the end of VTO's dispute with the Colchis label is withheld for two weeks, as a mark of respect for the genius of the music man who has died.

The Sikh documents, interestingly, are not released into the public domain, even though Yul Singh, in a farewell message to the Colchis board, has sketched out their contents to explain his actions. The interests of the label are not served by making this final missive more widely known. Standish chooses not to say what he knows, and nobody comes forward in his place. Death has apparently satisfied the principal. Yul Singh is not pursued beyond the grave.

At Sam's Pleasure Island, Cool Yul's booth is left unoccupied for one full month, guarded against the incursion of the crass and ignorant by a formidable phalanx of Singhs. During this month, the Pleasure Island staff make sure that a Manhattan on the rocks and a thick Cohiba cigar are always waiting at Yul's absent elbow.

After that, however, the city's life moves on.

CHAPTER FOURTEEN

The Whole Catastrophe

More sadness, before joy. Mull Standish does not live to enjoy his great victory for long. The night before his 1981 disappearance he's working late at the office and makes midnight telephone calls to both Ormus and Vina to read them the riot act. Standish who never spoke up for himself hectors them both about their love, the pending, freeze-frame love which blots out his own. The ten years are almost up, he says, and it's time you both stopped acting like fools. To Ormus he says, that you were not able to return my feelings for you is of small concern to anyone but me, and I can handle it, thanks. (No, he couldn't, not really, but he carried his grief stoically, like the English gentleman he wasn't; he had acquired the stiff upper lip that went with the Savile Row tailoring he liked.) But that the two of you should squander what's left of the immense fortune of your love, he scolds, having already wasted so much time, that would be a thing I could not forgive. To Vina he adds, The suspense is killing me. Will you, won't you, will you, won't you. I say join the goddamn dance. And let me say that if you don't the disappointment might kill me too, and if it does and if there's light at the end of that famous tunnel maybe I'll come back and shine it in your eyes. If I have to haunt you into doing the right thing I'll find me a white sheet and howl.

The next day the richness of his life is reduced to the thin finality of a crime scene: a wrecked office, broken windows, an absence. Some, not much, blood on the carpet: a nose-bleed, perhaps. A broken cane. Unexpectedly, there is what looks like a suicide note, in an open notebook on his desk. *Suicides are most frequent in the spring. When the world is falling in love, your own lovelessness hits you hardest.* Why would a man write such a note, then trash his office, punch himself in the nose, break his walking stick and vanish without trace? This isn't a suicide note, Vina tells the police, it's a diary entry. He was just talking to us about love on the phone and I guess it made him sad. But this was not a man to take his own life. This was a great fighter, a person who overcame.

This version is, after some initial hesitation, accepted as the most probable. The event is classified as abduction, and murder is suspected. Suspicion focuses on a certain jilted lover, but no hard evidence comes to light, nobody sends anyone a fish wrapped in the morning paper, no charges are ever laid. Nor is Standish's body found. Time must pass before he is legally declared dead and Waldo Crossley, Spenta's simpleton gardener, becomes a seriously wealthy man.

(When Spenta Methwold in a white mansion high above the rural Thames hears the news of Standish's disappearance she bundles Ardaviraf and Waldo into the back of her Mercedes and drives aimlessly for three hours through the surrounding country lanes. Spenta is an old woman these days, there are cataracts in both eyes, so it's like driving in blinkers, half blinded by a lifetime's accumulated tears, the stalactites of grief. In the local village of Fawcett, Bucks., she ignores a Give Way sign and is hit simultaneously from both sides by surprised farmers' wives in Mitsubishi 4WDs. It's a slow-motion accident, nobody is really hurt, but Spenta's car doors won't open. Without apology or complaint she drives to the nearest garage and the three of them wait patiently while mechanics cut them free. She goes home with Waldo and Virus in a mini-cab and when she reaches her front door she tells Virus and Waldo that this was her last journey, she is no longer interested in the world beyond her doors. *I will just sit on and think of the departed and you, our sons, will take care of me.* Then she calls her doctor and cancels the planned operation to remove the cataracts. Blinkered sight, tunnel vision, is all she now requires. The big picture is no longer a thing she wishes to see.)

STANDISH HAS gone all right. Ormus and Vina at a high window watch spring dance across the park. Here we are without family or tribe, having lost our greatest ally, he says. Now it's just you and me and the jungle. Can we stand together against whatever comes at us, the worst and the best of things? Will you? he asks her. Will you keep your word?

Yes, she says. I'll marry you, I'll spend the rest of my life with you, and you know I will love you. But don't ask me for high fidelity. I'm a lo-fi kind of girl.

There's a silence. Ormus Cama's shoulders drop in lovesick, dumb surrender. Just don't tell me, he says. I just don't want to know.

I LIKE to remember Vina Apsara the way she was in those last years, the years of her marriage and greatest happiness, when she became the world's most dreamed about woman, not just America's Sweetheart like Mary Pickford long ago but the beloved of the whole aching planet. Vina in her thirtysomething prime striding down Second Avenue, wafting past the aromas of Thai, Indochinese and Indian food, the tie-dyed clothes, the African adornments and basketry. Her Afro had long departed, though her long hair would never escape frizziness, and her fist-clenching days were over. Her old fist-clenching buddies were Republicans now, successful community fat cats or gimcrack entrepreneurs whose designs for erotic bluejeans—with built-in penis pouches flapping absurdly beside the zipper—started to bomb the day they left the drawing board. What's gone is gone, Vina would say without regret of the old days, adding the half-complaining admission that, try as she might, and even taking into account her youthful troubles with Marion Egiptus, even allowing for her years of harassment by taxmen and policemen, she had never had to endure one hundredth of the racial abuse and hardship that came the way of her African-American friends. *Face it, Rai, we're just not the target here.* That's right, I confirmed, and didn't need to add that celebrity has a way of washing whiter too.

Nobody understood the workings of fame, upside and downside, better than Vina. Those were the days when the first crossover stars were making their way through the firmament: O.J., Magic, people whose talent made people color-blind, race-blind, history-blind. VTO was a high member of that élite, which Ormus always took in his stride, as if it were the most natural and proper thing in the world. He had taken to quoting biologists, geneticists. Human beings are just about identical, he'd say. The race difference, even the gender difference, in the eyes of science it's just the teeniest-tiniest fraction of what we are. Percentagewise, it really doesn't signify. But life at the frontier of the skin always made Vina uneasy. She still sometimes had nightmares about her mother and stepfather persuading a Virginia head teacher that her daughter wasn't no Negro, she was half Indian, not no redskin Pocahontas neither but Indian from faraway India itself, India of elephants and princes and the famous Taj Mahal, which pedigree naturally excused her from local bigotries and entitled her to ride on the yellow bus to the white kids' school. Vina also dreamed of lynch mobs, of burning crosses. If such horror was happening to anyone, anywhere, it might yet someday happen to her.

I remember Vina on fire with the dark flame of her adult beauty, flaunting on her ring finger another man's sparkler and platinum band, and, on her right hand, a cherished moonstone too. I truly believe she never knew how it tore me up when, using me as her confessor while lying in my arms, she told me about herself and Ormus, sparing nothing. Now that they were married she had somewhat reined in her public tongue and kept from the insatiable world a few at least of the privacies of her marriage bed, but she did need to talk to someone, and for all her liberation theology she was a woman without close women friends. I was her secret, to whom she told her secrets. I was what she had.

By the early 1980s I had moved a few blocks north, joining forces with three other photographers—Mack Schnabel, Aimé-Césaire Basquiat, Johnny Chow, all of them former Nebuchadnezzar hands who had quit, rebelling against the agency's worsening habit of treating its lensmen like dogs on a short leash—to buy an old whale of a building on a leafy stretch of East Fifth Street between Second Avenue and the Bowery, just across from the *Voice* offices on Cooper Square. This was an immense defunct dance and music space called the Orpheum, a name which, by conjuring up memories of my parents' cinema in Bombay, brought a lump to my throat and left me no option but to buy my share of what was then little more than a crumbling shell. Its purchase and renovation cost me more than I'd ever planned to spend on mere accommodation, but we'd got in on the ground floor of the property boom, so a big paper profit was quickly made, though by that time none of us would have thought of selling. We of the vagabond shoes, all four of us lifetime globe-trotters, had the strange, sure feeling that we had found our true home in the belly of our NoHo whale. I'd ended up with the vast top floor and a studio and terrace on the roof above. In addition, its ownership shared by the group, there was a cavernous double-volume former auditorium that could serve as giant studio, soundstage or exhibition gallery.

In the front lobby, carved into a stone wall, was a Latin motto. *Venus significat humanitatem.* It is love that is the sign of our humanity. This was a sentiment with which we were all prepared to live.

It was perfect. So this is what they feel like, I thought: roots. Not the ones we're born with, can't help having, but the ones we put down in our own chosen soil, the you could say radical selections we make for ourselves. Not bad. Not bad at all. I began to think about staying home more, but on the other hand I had a motive for travel which the three rebels didn't. I traveled, in part, to get away from Vina's absences. To get away from the brass bed she wasn't in, the empty bed which tormented me with memories of the times when she did turn up, usually unannounced, to remind me why I'd never married, and make our wretched liaison feel (almost) worth the pain.

Vina had moved uptown, into Ormus's Rhodopé Building super-apartment, now expanded with their limitless unblocked funds into a complex of four apartments, "to give ourselves space." Missing her old Canal Street haunts, she compensated by plunging into the property market. She started buying up historic houses all over the East Coast, sometimes sight unseen. I'd just look at the map and it would feel right? Also, she told me, I consulted numerologists sometimes. This is how she was right to the end, a strange mixture of high intelligence and the superstitious nonsense of her times. She loved the Orpheum, loved sunbathing naked beneath the winking spire of the Chrysler Building and, in the opposite direction, the giant gray henge of the World Trade Center. Nearer to home, a dark water tower stood watch over her on Martian legs. Like a rocket, she'd fantasize. Look across town. A whole fleet of rockets standing on the rooftops. They're preparing to leave, to grab our water, blast the city to smithereens and take off, leaving us to die of thirst in our ruined urban desert. Vina was interested in Armageddon. Velikovsky's crank best-seller *Worlds in Collision* and its sequel *Ages in Chaos,* with their theory of "cosmic catastrophism," the new eschatological fiction by John Wilson, the ponderous old Cold War movie *Fail-Safe,* were all favorites. You could see why she liked *The Lord of the Rings.* This offered the end of a world too, but, unusually, it was a sort of happy ending.

Across the street from the Orpheum was a little coffee-and-vegetarianism store run by New York Buddhists. The coffee was good, the vegetarianism praiseworthy, but ever since her return from Dharmsala the omnipresent downtown tinkle of Buddhism had started to get Vina's goat. She was all in favor of noble truths but she was not comfortable with the way the Buddha, a wealthy and powerful prince who renounced power and wealth to gain enlightenment as a mendicant sage, now attracted followers among the wealthiest and most powerful class in the wealthiest and most powerful city in the wealthiest and most powerful nation on earth. The kids in the store were sweet and by no means were they zillionaires but they weren't carrying begging bowls or sleeping rough either, and their fellow Buddhists among the ranks of America's élite seemed to have an original definition of the simple life, of the Path. Vina was not sure how much renunciation was going on, but if the Dalai Lama wanted it, she said, and if the Constitution allowed?, with those backers he'd have a shot at President, or at least Mayor of New York. She had his campaign music all prepared. *Hello Dalai. Lama-Lama-Ding-Dong.* If you lost your sense of humor and pushed her into a corner she'd admit she was on the High Lama's side in his struggle against the Chinese, who wouldn't be, but she'd be annoyed at being forced into the admission. Most of the time she preferred to be sardonically out of line, out of step. To sound harsher than she was. Which fooled nobody, strangely enough. People saw through her tough-guy routine, even liked her for it, and the cruder her formulations, the harder she tried to be this radical alienated individual, the more profoundly she was loved.

India still called to her, and she couldn't understand my decision not to return. You and Ormus, she shook her head, just my luck to pick the two men in the world who turned their back on the old place. What?, I should go alone? Just me and a bunch of security guards?

Listen, I told her (her frankness lending added force to my own confessional promptings), the day doesn't pass when I don't think of India, when I don't remember childhood scenes: Dara Singh wrestling in an open-air stadium, Tony Brent singing, Sherpa Tenzing waving from the back of an open car outside Kamala Nehru Park. The movie *Mughal-e-Azam* bursting into color for the big dance number. The legendary dancer Anarkali strutting her stuff. The non-stop sensory assault of that country without a middle register, that continuum entirely composed of extremes. Sure I remember it. It's the past, my past.

But the tie is broken. There are conversations going on every day in India, conversations we'd be dragged into, that we no longer wish to have, that we can't stomach the thought of repeating even one more time, tired arguments about authenticity, religion, sensitivities, cultural purity and the corrupting effects of foreign travel.

We, she marveled. I suppose you think you're speaking for Ormus too.

Yes, I said. What do you think "Tongue Twistin'" was about, anyway?

("Tongue Twistin'" is, on the surface, one of Ormus's lighter efforts, cast as a simple song of teenage disappointment, a verse of yearning followed by a verse of disillusion. I like the way she walk and I even like the way she smell. Yeah and I like the way she talk and I really want to ring her bell. Now I know she's kinda crazy and a little too much, but I'm hopin' for the strokin' of her lovin' touch, and I'm really not insistin', but if we were tongue twistin', what a twistin' good time it'd be. The love story doesn't work out, alas: She don't like where I'm livin' so she don't care 'bout the way I feel. You know I had a lot of givin' but she told me that I was unreal. I tried to paint her picture but I had no luck, I tried to write her story but she said it sucked. Now I'm tired of her resistin', gonna go tongue twistin', with someone who wants to twist with me.)

In our weariness, Vina, I think we were always as one; as we are in our love for you, which is to say our love of the joy of life itself, which you embody. *Vina significat humanitatem.* That's the truth. It's you.

Well, that speech deserves a reward, she murmured, curling a hand around my head and drawing me down to where she lay, nude and splendid, beneath the blind skyscrapers and the all-seeing sky. Hug me, she ordered, and I did.

A kind of India happens everywhere, that's the truth too; everywhere is terrible and wonder-filled and overwhelming if you open your senses to the actual's pulsating beat. There are beggars now on London streets. If Bombay is full of amputees, then what, here in New York, of the many mutilations of the soul to be seen on every street corner, in the subway, in City Hall? There are war-wounded here too, but I speak now of the losers in the war of the city itself, the metropolis's casualties, with bomb craters in their eyes. So lead us not into exotica and deliver us from nostalgia. For Dara Singh read Hulk Hogan, say Tony Bennett instead of Tony Brent, and *The Wizard of Oz* makes a more powerful transition into color than anything in the Bollywood canon. Goodbye to India's hoofers, Vijayantimala, Madhuri Dickshit, so long. I'll take Kelly. I'll take Michael Jackson and Paula Abdul and Rogers and Astaire.

But if I'm honest I still smell, each night, the sweet jasmine-scented ozone of the Arabian Sea, I still recall my parents' love of their *art dekho* city and of each other. They held hands when they thought I wasn't looking. But of course I was always looking. I still am.

THE PARTY girl and the recluse, the loudmouth and the silent one, the promiscuous and the marrying kind: I never really believed they'd tie the knot, but they did, and right on schedule too. Vina's friend Amos Voight used to tell people that the celebrated ten-year engagement was just those kids' crazy game, a flirtation that acknowledged their mutual attraction but also resigned itself to the failure between them of trust, which left them no foundation on which to build any sort of marriage. Also, he'd say, it's just *so* good for business. The publicity, darlings, you couldn't buy it. Voight's philosophy of life was that you didn't read your clippings, you weighed them, and as long as your publicity was putting on weight, why then everything was just dandy. And it was true that as a publicity stunt the suspended love affair took some beating. Even during the band's long recording silence the unusual bond between Ormus and Vina kept them in or near the forefront of people's minds.

The contemporary public has had a long training in Voightian cynicism; it no longer believes what it's told. It's convinced there's a sub-text beneath every text, a hidden agenda behind the overt one, an otherworld running parallel to the world. Because Vina shoved her promiscuity under people's noses, celebrated and satirized it, there were many who didn't believe it was "real." These citizens also openly queried Ormus's faithful restraint. The less scrupulous newspapers and magazines assigned their finest muckrakers to the case, and even put professional gumshoes on Ormus's tail to see who he was secretly sneaking around with, but they all came up empty. The desire to debunk the extraordinary, the urge to chop off its feet until it fits within the confines of the acceptable, is sired by envy on inadequacy. Most of us, on arriving at the notorious inn of Polypemon Procrustes in Corydallus, Attica, would find that the bed we were offered was far larger than ourselves. In the middle of the night he would seize us and stretch us screaming on the rack until we fit. Many of us who are racked by the knowledge of our smallness begrudge the few true heroes their great size.

Ormus, Vina and I: three of us came West and passed through the transforming membrane in the sky. Ormus, the youthful proselytizer of the here and now, the sensualist, the great lover, the material man, the poet of the actual, saw visions of the otherworld and was transformed into an oracle, a ten-year monk and an Art Deco–rated recluse. As for me, I must say at last that I passed through a membrane too. I became a foreigner. For all my advantages and privileges of birth, for all my professional aptitude, I was turned by the fact of leaving my place of origin into an honorary member of the ranks of the earth's dispossessed. Indochina helped, of course, unforgettable Indochina with its forgotten yellow dead, click, and the firestorm of bombing in neighboring

Angkor that gave birth to a life-devouring beast, the Khmer, click, which walked like an evil phoenix out of the flames to declare war on spectacles, tooth fillings, words, numbers and time. (And on cameras too. That was my narrowest escape, needing much luck as well my old trick of invisibility. Khmer-sympathizing insects saw through my cloaking devices and assaulted me, and for weeks afterwards I was laid up with malaria as well as soul-sickness on Cheung Chau island in Hong Kong harbor, but I was mightily relieved to settle for that, and for a slow convalescence eating waterfront fish and noodles.)

Over the years I saw the hand of Mighty America fall hard on the back yards of the world, click, not the helping hand-across-the-sea extended to America's friends but the fist which he-that-is-Mighty hammers on the green table of your country to tell you what he wants and when he wants it, i.e. right now, buster, assume the position, this means you. I came back from click the Angkoran slaughterhouse Tuol Sleng, after which I didn't find amusing any more the name of Amos Voight's studio; from click sickening Timor only to learn that officially, according to the word from Might Central at Foggy Bottom, there was no such place on the face of the earth; from Iran '79 where click the Puppet King forced his people into the arms of a revolution click that ate them alive; click from blasted Beirut; click from the revolution-speckled bananarama of Central America. I came home like Godard's soldiers bearing photographs of the dark wonders of the world, all my clicked body heaps and skull mountains and land-mined school buses and score-settling murderers and famines and full-blooded genocides, and when I opened my cheap suitcase to prove I'd kept my promise my sweetheart wasn't around, but there were photo editors who asked me, Mr. Merchant, do you love America? Ray—is that some kind of alias, Ray?—Ray, to what extent are you a communist stooge?

Our lives tear us in half. Ormus Cama the reluctant mystic, the surviving twin, lost the double in his head and discovered instead a doubling in the whole of existence. His two eyes, seeing different whatnesses, made his head and heart ache. Something of the same sort was my fate regarding this thing, America. Because the America in which I led my well-off, green-carded life, Orpheum-America in which love is the sign of our humanity, America below Fourteenth Street, loosey-goosey and free as air, gave me more of a sense of belonging than I'd ever felt back home. Also, with the dream America everyone carries round in his head, America the Beautiful, Langston Hughes's country that never existed but needed to exist—with that, like everyone else, I was thoroughly in love. But ask the rest of the world what America meant and with one voice the rest of the world answered back, Might, it means Might. A power so great that it shapes our daily lives even though it barely knows we exist, it couldn't point to us on a map. America is no finger-snapping bopster. It's a fist.

This, too, was like seeing double. This was where my heartaches began.

In combat zones there is no structure, the form of things changes all the time. Safety, danger, control, panic, these and other labels constantly attach and detach themselves from places and people. When you emerge from such a space it stays with you, its otherness randomly imposes itself on the apparent stability of your peaceful home-town streets. What-if becomes the truth, you imagine buildings exploding in Gramercy Park, you see craters appear in the middle of Washington Square, and women carrying shopping bags drop dead on Delancey Street, bee-stung by sniper fire. You take pictures of your small patch of Manhattan and ghost images begin to appear in them, negative phantoms of the distant dead. Double exposure: like Kirlian photography, it becomes a new kind of truth.

I'D STARTED getting into quarrels, even into fights. Yes, in bars, with strangers, that too, fights about nothing. Me. I heard myself boring and bullying in a thick drunk's voice I barely recognized but I couldn't stop myself. As if the violence I'd seen had ignited some answering violence deep within me. The fires at my center ascending through faults in my personality to pour out through the volcanoes of my eyes, my lips. One evening not long after Standish's disappearance I escorted Vina to Xenon, then to 54. Ormus hated those places, so I could act as Vina's walker without arousing his suspicions. She on the other hand couldn't leave the clubs alone, it was an addiction, and anyway Vina never cared about what people might think. She wore black but it didn't look much like mourning dress; there wasn't quite enough of it for that. Well, anyhow, at 54 there was this slick-haired guy who made some wisecrack about it being too soon after Mull's last exit . . . oh, never mind. Vina pulled me away just in time. She said what I was experiencing was male anger, gender-based, *because you're losing control.* Meaning, men were. That felt like a shot so wide of the mark I didn't even know where to look to retrieve the arrow, so I started bitching about Ormus instead. These otherworld songs of his, I said, shouting over the music, what does he think he's doing, offering people a promised land or what. It makes me mad, I said, because even though if you listen to the small print he's just saying it's different, not better, that isn't what the kids are hearing. Who hears the lyrics properly anyway, you said it yourself. Those fucking New Quaker lunatics, you think they're hearing right? They're aching for doomsday, praying for the end, bring on the *dies irae,* the day of wrath, because then the fucking kingdom will come. I can't fucking stand it. Will you guys please stop.

That was when she told me. We're doing it, she shouted. We're getting married. I hope you'll cool down long enough to come.

The music had stopped, and she'd yelled into the sudden silence. It was quite an announcement. Everybody in the joint started applauding and Vina just grinned and took her bows. In the end, having no option, I clapped too.

SOMETHING UNEXPECTED was happening in the music world, the younger bands were failing, the glitter litter had lost its shine and the kids were looking to the older guys. As if the human race were to turn away from the present evolutionary moment and commence to reverence the dinosaurs who came before. It was disgraceful, in a way, but being older was getting to be an advantage. Ormus Cama was forty-four years old and this was working in his favor. The same age as the music, people kept repeating, the same age as the music, like a mantra, as if it meant anything, as if music didn't cross frontiers of time as well as space. To be the same age as the music was suddenly to know it all, like the ancient Delta blues brothers, like Old Adam himself. Wisdom was the hot commodity now, and Ormus had that, the wisdom of the recluse, of the Delphic oracle, of, oh, let's say Brian Wilson of the Beach Boys. And in addition, in the eyes of the record-buying public he possessed something which was not to be found in Delphi or the California surf: viz., the wisdom of the East.

VTO had a hit record again, and what a record it was, a jam-packed carnival of a double album, *Doctor Love and the Whole Catastrophe.* That was a phrase Ormus liked, he'd read or heard it someplace and it stuck. He used to say that music could be either about almost nothing, one tiny strand of sound plucked like a silver hair from the head of the Muse, or about everything there was, all of it, *tutti tutti,* life, marriage, otherworlds, earthquakes, uncertainties, warnings, rebukes, journeys, dreams, love, the whole ball of wax, the full nine yards, the whole catastrophe. The new album was a rich mosaic of all these: love songs and jeremiads, heart-stopping odes and visions of doom. It couldn't miss.

On the sleeve he and Vina posed in the fig-leafed nude, like classical statues wearing shades. Like mythical lovers, Cupid and Psyche, Orpheus and Eurydice, Venus and Adonis. Or a modern pair. He was Doctor Love and she, in this reading, was the Whole Catastrophe. This sleeve was afterwards called a prophecy of death by the same people who believed Paul McCartney was dead because he was the only one walking barefoot across the zebra crossing on *Abbey Road,* the people who insisted that if you put your stereo needle on the grooves in the reject-zone of *Sgt. Pepper* and then turned the platter anti-clockwise with your finger you'd hear John Lennon saying *I will fuck you like a superman.* The world of popular music—the fans as well as the artistes—sometimes seemed to be populated exclusively by people with troubled minds.

Vina and Ormus were finally allowing themselves just to be in love, and their flowering happiness was the damnedest thing. Soon after their marriage they paid for full pages of advertising space in the world's press to say how they felt: an idea that must have been Vina's. Much of the text sounded like her work too. This is what they told the world: that they had learned to love each other fully, trusting each other totally, through their dreams. They had discovered that each was dreaming of the other, every single night, *and they were the same dreams. We were actually, in reality, but without knowing it, leaving our bodies to enter the other's dream. Our spirits made love and taught our waking bodies to trust.*

So their wet dreams had got them through ten years, that was how I saw it. They, however, now had rather loftier ideas about the power of love, and of music, *which is the sound of love.*

Love is the relationship between levels of reality.

Love produces harmony and is the ruler of the arts. As artists we seek to achieve, in our art, a state of love.

Love is the attempt to impose order on chaos, meaning on absurdity.

It is inventive, double-natured, holding the keys to everything.

There is love in the cosmos.

Love was born before, and is more potent than, the laws of nature.

Love raises us above the limitations of our bodies and gives us free will.

We assert the love of man for his fellows.

We assert love as a cosmic force, bringing about creation.

We transform constantly and we remain constant. Music is the bridge between our worlds. Music liberates and unifies.

We are filled with the madness of love, which leads the mind beyond understanding towards a vision of beauty and joy.

Songs are love's enchantment. They are everyday magic. The Sirens' song drew men to their deaths. Calypso's song kept Odysseus enchanted by her side. No man can resist the song of Aphrodite, or of Persuasion, her singing witch.

Songs enchant away our pain.

May we, who are full of desire, always have song, sweet song, sweeter than any drug.

Love is harmony. Harmony is love.

(We dedicate this record to the memory of our friend and savior, Mullens Standish the loving pirate. May your skull and crossbones always fly high.)

* * *

THE MUSIC was their real lovemaking. So much has been said and written about Vina's big-mouth attitude, but what I want to hear is more about the way she used that big mouth in song, along with those lungs, that brain. I want to hear about that voice-of-the-century voice. How she improved her phrasing by studying film of violinists—Heifetz, Menuhin, Grappelli—and, impressed by the bowing that created an apparently continuous sound (all teeth and no gaps was the way she put it), how she set out to sing the same way. To sing like a violin. To give herself that famous long-line fluidity she also studied the way horn players breathe, and spent hours improving her lungs by swimming underwater laps at her health club. Then she just stood up and let rip with (in the bad old days) a bottle of bourbon in her hand and it was as if she'd been born that way. The art that conceals art: the most flamboyant rock star in the world was a devotee of the philosophy of artistic discretion. Never let 'em see how you do it, that was her creed. She once said to me: What do they want to know, how? That's not for them to know. It's my job to do it and theirs to applaud.

The atom-splitter Oppenheimer, on beholding the power of his brainchild the Bomb, quoted the Bhagavad Gita. *I am become Death, the Destroyer of Worlds.* Death's magic mushroom, born of the marriage of fissile materials. In the eight years between Ormus and Vina's marriage and her untimely end, there were some harsh, carping voices, notably those of their erstwhile admirers Rémy Auxerre and Marco Sangria, who alleged that both leading members of VTO were highly unstable personalities, permanently on the verge of coming apart, and that if they weren't super-rich rock stars they'd be in the funny farm. I say only that if they were fissile, then at least the energy released by their union—love's own Manhattan Project—was a brightness rather than a darkness, a source of pleasure, not pain, an aspect of Life-the-Creator rather than the Destroyer, Death.

You must imagine me gritting my teeth as I write this.

Love made them irresistible, unforgettable. As performers, as people, deferral's end and the relief of consummation rendered them, if I may be permitted the pun, consummate. When they walked into rooms, hand in hand and glowing, people fell silent, in awe. They had been perfected by love. And there was plenty to spare. The long-dammed torrent of their joy poured over anyone within range, drowning strangers in unlooked-for happiness. Their stage act had been reinvented completely. Ormus turned round to face the audience. Legs planted wide apart, golden guitar sparkling in his hand, tall, thin, his face like a monument to his long wait and belated triumph, the golden eye patch adding to the power of the persona, lending it piratical overtones, he represented the danger and realism of the music as well as its underlying hope. Unfortunately, owing to his damaged, whistling eardrums, he needed protection against the decibels the band was pumping out, and so a soundproofed glass case had to be constructed for him, complete with air-conditioning and floor pedals which controlled and varied the sounds of his weeping guitar. At the focal point of the stage, brilliantly lit, was this object out of space opera or fairy tale, and Ormus Cama, who had once lain comatose in the glass coffin of a converted orangery, now sang and played, fully conscious, inside another glass box.

While he stood still, encased in glass, Vina ran and leapt, pranced and whirled, a super-fit, super-charged Vina, a Vina who was taking care of business and of herself. If he was Being, she was Becoming, and behind them the rhythm section laid down a succession of righteous laws; the drums beat their message to the skies.

And around and about them—perhaps to deflect attention from his own enforced static rôle—Ormus began to devise great spectacles, hyperbolic feats of showmanship that showed him to be a Bombay lad at heart, turning naturally to the mythic vulgarity of the Bollywood musical. Yes, showtime; science fiction dystopias, fabulated dragonworlds, seraglio visions featuring platoons of harem-panted, rhinestoned-naveled belly dancers, black-magic rings of fire o'ertowered by Baron Samedi inflatables, and the whole multiple-image videorama which is now the staple fare of stadium rock but in those days gave people the kind of shock Bob Dylan did when he went electric. (What could once be achieved by plugging a guitar into the wall now requires a military operation. We are not as easily shockable, not as innocent as we were.)

The addition of showmanship, of spectacle, gained VTO new legions of admirers. They entered that zone of celebrity in which everything except celebrity ceases to signify. Camamania, Vinamania were in full swooning, screaming swing, but some early exegetes jumped off the bus. Sangria and Auxerre attacked VTO for having betrayed their old fans, for selling out. Perspiration instead of inspiration, light shows instead of enlightenment, greed instead of need, wrote Marco Sangria, accusing the band of becoming little more than the biggest stick of bubble gum on earth. Ormus, that golden eye patch, that giant glass earmuff, Sangria scoffed: why not just put your whole head in a fucking bag?

Later, when Vina and Ormus "went political," organizing the Rock the World charity concerts, meeting world leaders to demand action on global famine, protesting the cynicism of international oil companies in Africa, joining the campaign for third-world debt relief, demonstrating against health hazards at nuclear processing plants, documenting the growing invasion of personal privacy in America by the spreading tentacles of the secret state, highlighting the abuse of human rights in China, proselytizing the vegetarian message, the same commentators who had abused them for their superficiality now berated them for pomposity, for stepping out of their playpen to argue with the grown-ups.

Ormus Cama's second full-page press advertisement, *What Is the Whole Catastrophe?*, in which he publicly expressed his fear that some sort of apocalypse might be imminent, some sort of science fiction encounter between variant and incompatible versions of the world, was the last straw.

To be given the world as a toy must be pleasant, Rémy Auxerre wrote. But then one must have a certain aptitude for playing the world's big games. To be given the world as a stage is also a great privilege, he added. But on the world's stage there are only a few heroes and many babbling fools.

In a way they had ceased to be real. To Auxerre and Sangria, they had become little more than signs of the times, lacking true autonomy, to be decoded according to one's own inclination and need. Marco Sangria, whose most profound conviction was that the truth of the twentieth century is a secret truth, the century's history a secret history of antichrists and outcasts, announced that the VTO super-phenomenon was now too one-dimensionally *overt,* too vulgarly *apparent.* Their success was therefore a metaphor of the flatness, the one-dimensionality, of the culture. It was a rebuke to its own fans. The Martinican Auxerre, champion of racial and cultural admixture, of the *Creolization of the soul,* made it his task to expose Ormus and Vina—Vina, the honorary Panther!—as deracinated, even Tomist. After long researches he published a thousand-page hatchet job bringing all Ormus's family's skeletons out of their closets, the colonialist Anglophilia and examination fraud of Sir Darius Xerxes Cama, the braining of Ardaviraf, Cyrus the serial killer, Spenta playing the British milady by the Thames; and Vina's too, her murderer-suicide mother, her "willingness" to travel on school buses from which black kids were banned, and so on. From this work we learned that Marion Egiptus had "died in poverty" without so much as a phone call from the little girl she raised, but we did not learn of Vina's youthful miseries in Chickaboom, N.Y., or that she had paid all Marion's medical bills for years. We learned, too, that Vina's father, the disgraced Indian lawyer and ex-butcher Shetty, having filed for bankruptcy many years previously, was now a bum, a panhandler, living rough in an insalubrious quarter of Miami. *What sort of debased beings are these,* Auxerre demanded, *these great lovers who can love only themselves, but spurn their own family, their own people?*

One skeleton was not dragged out of the shadows to dance its hideous bone-clicking dance in the public eye.

One year and one day after their marriage, Vina had returned to my bed. Not often, not for long, but she came back. She came back to me.

I'LL TELL you why those poison-pen attacks flopped, Vina murmured in my arms. It's because everybody loves a lover. I'm a lover; everybody loves me.

Then what are you doing here, I asked.

It's that Amos dance pattern, she said. If you want to solve the riddle, you've got to step out of the frame.

But that was just a clever answer. There were others. One of these was that Vina wanted to save me. Look at your life, Rai, where you go, what you do. You dive with your camera into the cesspit of the human race, so obviously you think we're all made of shit. Then back home with the flat-chested knickerless clothes-ponies, that's hardly an improvement, is it. Those girls only open their mouths for one reason and it's not to fucking eat or speak. Look at your pathetic life. There was that girl who loved you, you left her behind, what was her name. (She knew the name. This scolding was a ritual. She wanted to make me say it.) Anita, I said. Anita Dharkar. She chose to stay home.

Did you ask her, Vina demanded. Even if you did, you didn't do it properly, your heart wasn't in it. Now I'm going to tell you a thing about your life. Your life is dirt. You're more like Ormus than you know only he's all cleanness and light and you're all mud and darkness. If you're the best on offer, we should all give up right now.

Thanks, Vina, I love you too, I murmured, more shaken than I cared to show.

Yet when I'm with you I feel you're part of something, some lifestream?, she went on. I think that's what each of us is, a part of some larger river, and no matter how muddy and poisoned any individual bit of the river might be, you can still pick up the sense of that larger flow, that great and generous water. This is the life and death business I'm talking about, Rai. You're a heathen, you pretend there's no life afterwards, but I'm telling you you're a part of something right here and now and what that is, whatever it is, it's good, it's better than just you on your own?, only you're just rolling along, you don't even know the name of the river of yourself.

Stop now, I said, it's Wednesday, on Wednesday I put out the garbage.

The way I saw it, my uninterest in her mystical side nagged at her, she needed to conquer that resistance, and that's one of the things that kept her coming back. But in the end the ordinary physical things, the man-woman things are primary. We were good together, end of story. Even though she was an old married lady now I allowed her to think she didn't have to be. I asked nothing, but gave what she needed. With me she was single again. She was free.

Oh, one more thing: Ormus, her one true love, was beginning to scare her.

About VTO's victory over the Sangria-Auxerre assault, however, she was spot on. In those days there were more women fronting bands and making solo careers. Some of them were angry because men and love had not been good to them, many of them had eating disorders, others were deranged on account of things that happened to them as children, *touch me daddy don't touch me, hug me mama don't hug me, love me daddy won't you leave me alone, love me mama wanna be on my own. You know that I remember too much. So I don't know what to do with your Tender Touch.* Still others were super-cool smooth operators with an empty thing in their eyes. Marco Sangria's angry sister Madonna, also now an influential critic, was already saying that gender, the body, was the only subject. Once upon a time the Crystals sang *he hit me and I'm glad.* Now it was *hit me and I'll break your fucking jaw.* (This was an improvement, evidently.)

In the middle of all this misery Vina, uniquely, looked like—she *was*—singing out of pure happiness. That single fact made our hearts soar, even when she was delivering Ormus's most jaundiced lyrics. The joy in her singing showed us there was nothing we could not overcome, no river too deep, no mountain too high. It made her the world's beloved.

(On this occasion, I use the words "we" and "our" to denote a collectivity of which I was certainly a part, as deliriously infatuated as any front-row fan.)

It began to be seen as her band. Ormus produced the records, dreamed up the shows with the design team, wrote the songs, and looked on stage like a small craggy god down from Rock Olympus, but he was encased in glass, which distanced him, made him abstract. He became more of a concept, an animatronic special effect, than an object for our dreams and desires. Also, we could tell he was a control freak. Those ten years of waiting, they hadn't been natural. This mythic monogamy of his, this excess of determination, there was something domineering about it, something obdurate that would not be denied. We could see how she might react against so possessive a love. How, even loving him, even adoring him, she might run to find room for herself.

So it was mainly Vina for us, Vina the Voice, Vina whose non-stop motion on stage was like a message saying Ormie, baby, Ormie, my only boy, I love you my darling but you can't tie me down. You can marry me but you can't catch me; if I'm the blithe spirit, you're the genie in the bottle. You can run the show but I can run. Yes, it was Vina we wanted, Vina of the horribly injured childhood who instead of whining on about it in a million interviews just shrugged her shoulders and made nothing of it at all, Vina who without ever asking for or expecting our sympathy told us about her abortions and barrenness and consequent grief, and thereby earned our love; Vina who took books by both Mary Daly and Enid Blyton with her when she went on tour, Vina of the thousand fads and cults who could look right into the future President's face and ask him how it felt to be named after a woman's pubic hair.

I WILL tell you now what I have not sufficiently expressed throughout this long saga: the thing with Vina, being her spare prick, coming off the bench for a few minutes per game, this was hard for me. There was too much time and room for my imagination to work. I imagined their lovemaking so often, and in such *Kama Sutra* variety, that I would break out in a rash. I actually would: whether of heat or fury I cannot say. Only a foreign war, a fresh batch of photographic models just off the plane from Texas, or a cold shower could bring my temperature down, restore to normalcy the beating of my heart.

I tried to make myself believe that the marriage with Ormus wouldn't last. When she told me that she had reached an understanding with him, that he would turn a blind or at least a patched eye to her *amours* as long as she didn't flaunt them in a crass and obvious way, at first I felt a spurt of hot joy because she had gone to such risky trouble to make room in her life for me. Later, in the shower, where sometimes when her absence became too painful I'd ask my soaped hands to play her part, just as her hands had understudied Ormus during his decade of non-performance, I felt my reactions becoming more complex. It was, I thought, as if I were a clause in their marriage. A sleeping partner in their merger. This doomed me to play second fiddle forever; it was in the contract. My rising anger informed me of a truth I had thoroughly suppressed: viz., that I still entertained hopes of having her all to myself.

Often I practiced feeling contempt for glass-boxed, reclusive Ormus. What sort of man would consent to become the *mari complaisant* of as major a beauty, a presence, as Vina Apsara? To which my mirror replied: And what sort would agree to take the droppings from another man's table, the leavings from his bed? There was a malicious and probably untrue story about the novelist Graham Greene according to which his mistress's husband would position himself on the sidewalk outside the apartment block in which the author of *The Quiet American* resided, and at the top of his voice shout abuse into the warm night air: *Salaud! Crapaud!* To which Greene, when asked about the story, allegedly replied merely that as his apartment was on an upper floor he would not have heard the cries, and so unfortunately he could not confirm or deny the tale.

Salaud! Crapaud! In my case, it was I, Vina's bit on the side, who felt the urge to hurl abuse. I, who with my photojournalist's khaki hat on prided myself on my ability to blend into the background, to disappear, quickly came to loathe my invisibility in the story of Vina, the erasure from the public record of the great matter of my heart. But the more Vina and I were seen in public together, hiding in plain view, the less people were inclined to gossip. The blatantness of our association proved its innocence, yes, even to Ormus. Or so he always maintained.

One day in the Orwellian year of 1984—a time to dispense with doublespeak, to tear down the dreadful Ministries of Truth and Love—I could bear the situation no longer and rushed over to the Rhodopé Building, hot for certainty. In my hand was an envelope containing a set of photographs of Vina, nude photographs taken by me in the immediate aftermath of passion. She, who found it so hard to trust or to be trustworthy, had trusted me to make and keep private such explosive images as these; but it was the trustless marriage she preferred to her stolen hours with me. And as my behavior amply demonstrated, she would have done better not to trust me, either.

The point was that even Ormus Cama could not fail to understand what the pictures proclaimed: that for many years I had enjoyed the favors of his beloved wife. He must surely name his weapons. Prussian sabers, baseball bats, pistols at dawn by the Bethesda Fountain, I was ready for anything. For, as Vina would say, closure. I roared red-misted into the Rhodopé lobby, where I was restrained by a uniformed doorman.

It was Vina's father, the ex-lawyer, ex-butcher Shetty, now over seventy but looking ten years younger. His dreadful life had not marked him. Hearty, even jovial, he took what it dished out and stayed upright. Vina had hired a small army to find him after the newspaper article about his plight. When they unearthed him she'd flown to Florida for the big reconciliation scene and offered him whatever he wanted: retirement, a place of his own in the Keys, maybe, and of course a healthy allowance, but all that he had turned down flat. I'm the type that prefers to be in harness, he told her. Get me something where I can die with my boots on. Now he was installed in this new job, delighted with the uniform, beaming at the world. Cool in summer, warm in winter, a nodding acquaintance with the city's finest, he said. At my age and with my track record it's better than I could have hoped. India, forget about it. (His Indian linguistic education, which had stressed the importance of precise enunciation, made a strange match with his freewheeling U.S. idiom.) India, it's gone for all of us. I'll take Manhattan.

In my confrontational fury I hadn't remembered it might be Doorman Shetty's shift, but there he was, fit and ready and eager to please. Hey, Mr. Rai, sir, how is it hanging, what do you say, can I be of any assistance.

I just stood there holding my envelope, determination draining from me. Should I call upstairs, Mr. Rai? You want a ride in the elevator? Or just delivering a letter for Mr. Ormus or my daughter, can I get that for you, no problemo? Sure thing, leave it to me, it's my job.

Never mind, I said, exiting. Just a mistake.

He called after me, raising a cheery hand. Missing you already, Mr. Rai, you come back now, do you hear?

A terrible din was heard from the street outside; a junk band had showed up. Shetty's mood darkened. Charging past me, he confronted a group of youngsters playing a kitchen sink, a shopping cart, a dustbin, a wheelbarrow, buckets and, perhaps in VTO's honor, a strange chimeran fudge of a stringed noisemaker they called a guisitar, put together from the scraps of two wrecked instruments.

What do you call this, Shetty wanted to know. Where do you get off.

We're the Mall, said a red-eyed, goateed youth, asserting his leadership over his rag-haired, trembling tribe. (Not just a junk band but a band in search of junk, I noted silently.) We offer this serenade, he proclaimed, to the rock gods living in the sky. In the face of the radical uncertainty of the age we make odes to materialism, paradoxically utilizing items of no value to society. We celebrate donut culture, it's sweet and it tastes good but there's a void at the heart?

Get away from my canopy, Shetty commanded. Do it now.

There is no arguing with the authority of the New York doorman. The Mall obediently packed up and skulked away. Then, like an avatar of the Age of Greed, the leader turned back, shivering slightly, to glare at Mr. Shetty. When we're big, mister, I mean when we're monster big, I'm gonna come back here 'n' fucking buy this fucking building, and then it's your ass, baby, you have been warned.

My threat, the envelope I bore, was just as empty, I understood. Vina was right to trust me after all. I couldn't do it. I couldn't risk her withdrawal from my life. I too was an addict, hopelessly far gone, and she was my candy girl.

It occurred to me that in the field of love and desire Vina was just behaving like a man; showing herself capable, like most men, of loving wholeheartedly and simultaneously—halfheartedly—betraying that love without guilt, without any sense of contradiction. She was capable not so much of a division of attention as of multiplying herself, until there was enough Vina to go round. We, Ormus and I, we were her women: he, the loyal wife standing by her philandering husband, settling for him in spite of his roving eye, his wanderlust; and I, the simultaneously wanton and long-suffering mistress, taking what I could get. That way round, it made perfect sense.

I REMEMBER her hands, long-fingered, quick, chopping her beloved vegetables as if she were the high priestess of a pagan cult, matter-of-factly getting through the day's quota of sacrificial offerings to the gods. I remember her hunger for information, the way her bright, half-educated mind latched on to the many information-heavy intelligences her fame and beauty brought her in contact with (newspaper and tv bosses, Hollywood studio heads, rocket scientists, heavy hitters from Morgan Guaranty and D.C.) and how she pumped these sources for all she was worth, as if facts would save her life. I remember her fear of disease and early death.

Vina was a quick study, and by the time Mull Standish departed she was no longer the arrogant flake who had landed herself and Ormus in Contract Hell. Under his tutelage she had become a sharp businesswoman, as formidable as many of the big wheels for whose brains she showed an exaggerated respect they usually didn't deserve. She managed the stocks and bonds, the real estate, the growing art collection, the bakeries, the Santa Barbara winery, the cows. Ormus's fabled love of bread had led Standish naturally into this market; now Vina ensured that the high standards of the Camaloaf franchise were maintained from coast to coast. The bread was already an established brand; but few people thought of Vina Apsara and Ormus Cama as being amongst the finest viticulturists in California, to say nothing of the biggest dairy farmers in the northeastern United States, but that's what they had become. The winery thrived and the already huge herds of Holsteins acquired by Standish from the Singh estate had become even larger, their milk and cheese ubiquitously available. From goats to cows, Vina told me. Seems I can't help being on the udder side.

This in spite of the fact that during this period she had gone not only vegetarian but fully macrobiotic. No wine, definitely no dairy products. Occasionally, as a treat, she allowed herself a handful of those small Japanese dried fish. It was always interesting to me that she could make such a separation: that business, in spite of everything, was still business. Mull Standish had been an influential teacher.

Nowadays she was the worldly one, while Ormus's obsession with catastrophe had rendered him meditative, inward, strange. So, for example, it was Vina who decided for sound fiscal as well as strong sentimental reasons to buy Yul Singh's old Tempe Harbor place when it, like the cattle, was offered to the band cheaply by the estate lawyers, who informed her that it was the wish of the deceased that they be given first refusal at the most advantageous terms. (This was Yul's way of making a posthumous peace. He did not insult them by leaving them the property outright, as a gift. That would be to claim a friendship that had not existed for years. It was a finely judged decision. It showed respect.)

It was also Vina who decided to employ the Singhs. The new management at Colchis was dispensing with their services without explanation, and a deputation comprising Ormus and Vina's first chauffeur, Will, and Clea the châtelaine of Tempe Harbor, seamstress of Ormus's first eye patch, arrived at the VTO offices to plead the retinue's cause. Stripped of his black Valentino suit and sunglasses, no longer obliged to play the heavy, Will in jeans and white shirt turned out to be a hesitantly articulate young man. Clea was the same tiny, decent old lady she'd seemed at Tempe, only more worried. These were ordinary people sucked into the realm of the extraordinary and fighting back, playing their one and only card. Rumors had reached their ears of Yul's covert activities, they said, and they had, with some justice, concluded that they were being punished for their former boss's misdeeds. Just as innocent Sikhs in India were slaughtered after the Quadruple Assassination—the many suffering on account of the actions of the few—so the Colchis Singhs, too, had become the victims of American jitteriness. If Yul Singh had been a terrorist financier, then, in the view of the label, all his fellow Sikhs were tarred with the same brush. Yet we are not such people, madam, said Clea with simple dignity. We are persons of ability, willing and able to serve, and we ask you to grant our good wish.

Vina took on the whole entourage on the spot.

In 1987 Amos Voight died, Sam's Pleasure Island closed its doors for good, an era seemed to be ending, and Ormus Cama completed fifty years on earth. Turning fifty seemed to hit Ormus hard. His excursions from the Rhodopé complex had become few and far between, though once in a while Vina dragged him to a downtown music venue, accompanied by a clutch of Singhs, to hear a hot new act. These were disappointments more often than not, though just lately a young Irish quartet, Vox Pop, had impressed them as a possible start-up act. Mostly, however, their forays into Musicworld served only to confirm that the old order was, improbably enough, refusing to fade. The times were not a-changing. Lennon, Dylan, Phil Ramone, Richards, these old men were still the giants along with VTO themselves, while the likes of Trex, Sigue Spangell, Karmadogma and the Glam had been little more than blips.

Even Runt, the new rejectionism, all snarl and spittle, hadn't interested Ormus and, after a brief flare of scandal and attention, hadn't lasted. How could it, Ormus shrugged, you can't start a revolution in a clothes shop. Runt had been the brainchild of the resurfacing Antoinette Corinth, Tommy Gin and She, the Three Witches, Ormus Cama called them. Back in London, they had indeed dreamed up the angry new sci-fi look—rubber, slashed fabrics, bondage thongs, body piercing, the maquillage and attitude of android replicants on the run from exterminating blade runners—at their new Fulham Road store, and then invented a rock group to sell it. Inevitably they showed up in New York, acting as if they were the tastemakers supreme of London society, come to Manhattan to wreak a little British havoc. She, at Antoinette's bidding, did Daryl Hannah backflips in a distressed-leather miniskirt down the length of the bar at 44. No knickers, of course, darlings, Antoinette redundantly pointed out at the top of her voice. We call it Runt 'n' Cunt. New York gave them their fifteen minutes and forgot them. Their band, the Swindlers, the supposed shock troops of the new wave, fizzled in the face of American *pudeur* and ended up fatally shooting each other—and Corinth and Gin—in a suite at the Chelsea Hotel. She alone survived, having jumped ship five minutes before the fight that ended the revolution. She ran shrieking through the lobby wearing rubber and black lace, disappeared into the city night and never bothered to come back for her other clothes.

I remembered She's old loathing of Tommy Gin and wondered if this might have played a part in the shootings. But She had vanished for ever, and the question went unanswered. The Swindlers' violent stupidity was thought to be explanation enough.

Ormus barely responded to the news of Antoinette Corinth's death. This woman had in all probability tried to kill him once, had caused a car accident that deprived him of years of his life, but he seemed beyond resentment. He was thinking about the coming cataclysm.

THEY HAD been married in the Rhodopé Building looking out at the glory of the park. They honeymooned in that same private universe and needed nothing more, neither Venice nor the Hatshepsut Temple nor an island in the sun. And on the morning after his marriage Ormus Cama woke up and opened his pale eye and the otherworld was not there. The dark eye saw the world as it was, this joyous new world in which Vina lay beside him in his very own bed, and the other, accident-injured (accident-*opened*) eye saw nothing, or little more than a blur. The vision of doubleness had faded and he could not summon it back.

The years passed and the otherworld did not return, Maria no longer came to see him, and with the passage of time he began to have his doubts about its existence; it began to feel like a trick of the mind, a mistake. It was like waking from a dream; into happiness.

For a time he was tempted to let it go, to consign it to the realm of fantasy. To settle for joy, for the long-awaited arrival of completeness, of perfection: what a temptation! *I once was lost but now I'm found, was blind but now I see.* But the truth nagged at him, it wouldn't set him free. It's real, he told himself. It has turned away from me and hidden its face, but what is so, is so.

If the lost otherworld be likened to a Whale, then Ormus Cama had become its Ahab. He hunted it as a madman hunts his doom. On plane flights he stared out of the window searching for the slashes in the real. He went on wearing eye patches of various colors and fabrics because to admit that they weren't necessary was also to surrender to the fantasy that the otherworld didn't exist.

His music changed. In the eighties, as well as his VTO work he wrote long abstract pieces called *Sounds of the Otherworld,* which could not by any stretch be thought of as rock 'n' roll. He hired Carnegie Hall and a bunch of classically trained musicians and was greeted with derision for his pains, but he persisted, and a few people began to mention these new works with respect.

The longer the otherworld remained hidden, the more fearful he became.

Like Ahab, he knew that his whale had *sounded,* but he was determined to be near the great cetacean at its next rising. When sounding, a whale may plunge down through the waters, fathom after fathom, at bewilderingly high speed. There in the depths of the black water it may bide its time, then shoot upwards and smash through the surface of the sea, bursting upon the empire of the air as if it were the end of the world.

This was Ormus's greatest fear. In 1984 he published his thoughts in the international press and was immediately written off as another rock 'n' roll nut.

My greatest concern is that I feel the fragility of the fabric of our space and time, he wrote. *I feel its growing attenuation. Maybe it's running out of steam, coming to its predestined close. Perhaps it will fall away like a shell and the great granite truth of the otherworld will stand revealed in its place.*

Maybe the otherworld is the next world, not in a supernatural sense, not in the sense of an afterlife, but just the world that will succeed our own. (I am still convinced that when our scientific knowledge is greater, we will be able to explain such phenomena as these without recourse to superstition. It is simply a new aspect of the real.)

Maybe our own world is no more than a vision in some other accidental individual's damaged eye.

I don't know what I'm saying. I do know there is a danger of an ending, of a ceasing to be. I do know we can't trust our damaged earth. There is another cosmos hidden from us, sounding. When it bursts into our presence it may blow us away, as if we had never been.

We are aboard the whaleboats of the Pequod, *awaiting the final coming of the whale. As a man of peace, I am not shouting "Man the harpoons!" But I do say we must brace ourselves for the shock.*

As A matter of fact there was a Parsi aboard Melville's storied ship, and his rôle was that of the weird sisters in Macbeth: to prophesy Ahab's doom. *Neither hearse nor coffin can be thine,* he said. In the story I have to tell, the prophecy does not fit Ormus. But it fits Vina like a glove.

Call me Ishmael.

* * *

For all her fearsome competence, Vina didn't know how to deal with Ormus's deepening obsessions. I was her safety valve, her light relief. If you believe, she despaired, he wants me to get the mayor to agree to give us an acre of the park, a field for cows to graze in. That way, he says, when the earthquakes come, we'll get an early warning. He says everybody has to play music non-stop and there should be daily love festivals in major city centers everywhere because all we have to fall back on is harmony, all we have to protect us is the power of music and love.

That, and Ermintrude the cow, I observed.

I don't know what to do, she said. I don't know what to fucking think.

I remember her despair. I remember promising myself at that moment, I will break this crazy marriage if it's the last thing I do. If it's the last fucking thing, I will set this lovely woman free.

She still fought her daily bout against self-doubt and existential uncertainty, the universal bogeys of the age. Once when she was young, she told me, her mother took her to the state fair. There was a special kind of Ferris wheel with cages around the seats and a lever you could pull that would permit your little capsule to spin right over, turning you head over heels while the wheel took you up and around. Of course you could lock it off if you wanted and have the normal ride, but the bored little rat-toothed runt of an attendant didn't bother to tell them a damn thing about that, so when they started tumbling they both thought something had gone dreadfully wrong and they were about to die. Those five screaming minutes in the moving cage still returned to Vina in dreams. Now I know what it's like to be inside a laundromat appliance, she joked, but what she was talking about wasn't funny. She was talking about being out of control of your little bit of world, of being betrayed by what you counted on. She was talking about panic and the fragility of being and the skull beneath the skin. She was saying she was married to a lunatic and she loved him and couldn't handle it and didn't know what was going to happen, how it would end. She was afraid of death: his, her own. It's always there, death, in a Ferris wheel, in a loafing shed for goats. In a bedroom where something heavy swings from a slowly rotating ceiling fan. It's like a paparazzo waiting in the shadow. Smile, honey. Smile for the Reaper. Say *Die.*

In 1987, if you recall, Democratic presidential candidate Gary Stanton withdrew from the race for the nomination after the re-emergence of an old girlie scandal involving sex and death on Wasque Beach, Martha's Vineyard. Several of the smaller countries of Western Europe—Illyria, Arcadia, Midgard, Gramarye—voted against economic and political union, fearing it would result in a diminution of particularity, of idiosyncrasy, of national character. The Olympic 100-meter sprint was won by a Canadian man who was afterwards disgraced and erased from history. All official photographs of the event were retouched and videotapes were computer-doctored to show only the runners who finished second, third and fourth. There were bursts of unusually bad weather—blamed by the more meteorologically challenged Californians on a Hispanic handyman named Elvis Niño, who got beaten up in the street by irate Orange County residents—and there was also big trouble on the world's money markets, where the great fictionists behind the long-running *Currency* sitcom were having trouble with their creative processes.

But for millions of music-lovers 1987 would be remembered as the last great year of VTO. (Even the new leader of Angkor, the composer of over eighty songs, all of which dutifully topped the local charts, named Ormus and Vina as his "#1 Inspirational Lights" and invited them to play in Phnom Penh, an invitation which they were unable for pressure-of-work reasons to accept.) The year culminated in the huge free Concert in the Park at the end of the summer. After that they gave up performing in public—that is, Ormus retreated from view, he went home to bake bread, and the others had no choice but to accept his decision.

Goodbye, VTO, wrote Madonna Sangria. Once you made the city lights burn brighter, cars go faster, love taste sweeter. Once you lit the violence of our alleys like a Vermeer and turned the metropolis into our lyric dream. Then, guys, you turned into a pile of garbage I wouldn't throw at a f∗cking cat.

Vina was upset about Ormus's unilateral *fiat*—at forty-three she was nowhere near ready to quit—but for external consumption she maintained full solidarity with her husband. In spite of all my urgings to run away with me, she stood by her man, declaring to anyone who would listen that their love was as strong as ever, that she looked forward to the exciting new phase of their careers which would shortly dawn.

THE THREE other band members broke off all relations with the Camas and announced the formation of a breakaway shadow band called OTV, which failed to make any impression on the record-buying public, especially after Vina cruelly revealed that on *Doctor Love and the Whole Catastrophe* and other albums, including "live" albums, the entire rhythm guitar part played by the breakaway band's new frontperson, a stone-faced blonde named Simone Bath, had been replaced in the studio by jobbing axemen, because poor Simone's performance just hadn't been up to the mark.

Meanwhile, forty was proving as difficult a hurdle for me as fifty was for Ormus. Without success, I'd tried everything I could think of to prise Vina away from her increasingly cryptic partner. Don't start with me, Rai, she'd say. I don't come to you for a hard time. I can get plenty of that without leaving home. So much for the perfect love match, I thought, but I buttoned my lip and turned to lighter pleasures. Which failed these days to induce in me the old delirious joy. I had committed the back-door man's cardinal sin of hoping for more than was my right or due. I wanted the front-door key.

To console myself, and of course to provoke Vina, I turned to other women. I even got in touch with Anita Dharkar in Bombay, because I thought it might usefully provoke Vina if I took her tip and rekindled this old flame; but television had captured Anita as I never could. The Indian videocassette information and music services that were the forerunners of the imminent satellite invasion had made her a star. She had a weekly "Lite News" hour and a music show and, reborn as "Neata Darker," had become an icon of the Westernized—and the rapidly Westernizing—urban Indian young. She sent me promo shots of herself got up *à la* rock chick and I found myself mourning the serious, patriotic journalist I used to know.

There was no continuity in human lives any more, I thought. Nineteen eighty-seven was the year of *The Last Emperor,* the Bertolucci movie that proposed that a human being—Pu Yi, the eponymous Emperor—could genuinely and sincerely change his nature so completely that, having been born the god-king of China, he could end up happily accepting his lot as a humble Chauncey of a gardener, and be a better person for it. A case of communist brainwashing, perhaps, dryly wondered Pauline Kael, but maybe it wasn't. Maybe we just jump tracks more easily than we think. And (I'm back on the subject of Anita now) maybe rock 'n' roll helps you do it better.

That year, to put distance between myself and Vina, I went back to Indochina to take the pictures which were afterwards published in my book *The Trojan Horse.* My idea was that the war in Indochina hadn't ended at the time of the ignominious U.S. withdrawal. They'd left a wooden horse standing at the gates, and when the Indochinese accepted the gift, the real warriors of America—the big corporations, the sports culture of basketball and baseball, and of course rock 'n' roll—came swarming out of its belly and overran the place. Now, in Ho Chi Minh City and Hanoi, too, America stood revealed as the real victor. Indochina became just another consumer-serf of (and supplier of cheap labor to) Americana International. Almost every young Indochinese person wanted to eat, dress, bop and profit in the good old American way. MTV, Nike, McWorld. Where soldiers had failed, U.S. values—that is, greenbacks, set to music—had triumphed. This, I photographed. I do not need to say that the pictures went down big. This (with the exception of the sweatshop material) was news that many Americans wanted to hear. Even the old-time anti-war demonstrators were pleased. To my eye, the pictures contained large dollops of ambiguity, of tension. They were, I suppose, ironic. The irony, however, was largely lost on many who praised them. What's irony when you can celebrate this new Cultural Revolution? Let the music play. Let freedom ring. Hail, hail, rock 'n' roll.

Timeo Danaos et dona ferentes. Discontinuity, the forgetting of the past: this is the wooden horse at the gates of Troy. Whose occupants burned, are burning, will surely burn the topless towers of Ilium. Yet I myself am a discontinuous being, not what I was meant to be, no longer what I was. So I must believe—and in this I have truly become an American, inventing myself anew to make a new world in the company of other altered lives—that there is thrilling gain in this metamorphic destiny, as well as aching loss.

On the subject of forgetting: after my return I briefly became involved with Ifredis Wing, who was now trying to be a photographer herself and arrived at the Orpheum as Johnny Chow's assistant. Chow lived on the first floor and Ifredis gradually worked her way up, via Schnabel and Basquiat, to the penthouse, and me. She still had the sexual appetite of a nympho rabbit—Vina, who else, had given me a detailed account of the shenanigans at Tempe Harbor—and her looks had, if anything, improved. Her blond hair now worn boyishly, spikily short, her body still womanly and long. But as a photographic assistant she was a total bust, on account of her terrible memory, which led to a number of film-processing disasters that none of us found funny. It's one thing to laugh about living in an amnesiac culture and quite another to have an amnesiac labeling your rolls of exposed film.

I'm sorry, I no remembrance have, she apologized when I screamed infra-red murder at her in the developing room. But this also means, she added, brightening, that I will not your discourteous words tomorrow morning remember, after I have slept on your arm.

Otto, by the way, had moved on from Buddhism to supercapitalism, had married a billionairess fifteen years his senior and was now a prominent figure both in Hollywood and on the Eurotrash party circuit. He no longer made art movies, having turned his attention to seventy-million-dollar action flicks instead. He had become the unquestioned master of what were known in the biz as *whammies:* the climactic set pieces, full of explosions and derring-do, on which such films thrived. (I once saw him on tv, being interviewed at the Cannes festival and shrugging off critical drubbings to explain his new cinematic philosophy: *First act, lots of whammies. Second act, better whammies. Third act, nothing—but—whammies!*)

For a time, I found myself strongly attracted to memoryless Ifredis Wing, who bore no mortal person any malice, reserving her wrath entirely for god. In the aftermath of her desertion by Otto she had entirely lost her faith. Once the god-squaddie supreme, she was now possessed of the zeal of the apostate and came on like an atheistic stormtrooper. Devotees of Indian mahagurus, Scientologist movie stars, Japanese cultists, British sports reporters repackaged as the Risen Christ, American gun-lobby crazies bunkered down in the desert with charismatic prophet-leaders telling them who to make babies with and how often: Ifredis spent a lot of her non-fucking time soliloquizing on the follies of such as these. The great world religions took a trouncing too, and I have to say I found all this pretty enjoyable. It wasn't often I met someone more thoroughly disenchanted with the world's credulity than myself. Plus, she really was wonderful in bed. Sometimes she lazily played at adolescent sex, all finger-fucks and blow-jobs; more often she just came at you like Octopussy, all arms and legs and whoops-a-daisy. Either way was fine with me.

It fizzled; she drifted away, as I knew she would. Nothing really went wrong between us, but then there really was nothing between us to go wrong. We were both filling in dead time, and one day she woke up and looked at me and had forgotten who I was. I went to take a shower and didn't hear her go.

AFTER MY return from Indochina, I began to rethink my work. Journalism and its sneering sidekick, cynicism, no longer seemed enough. In a way I envied Ormus Cama his madness. That vision of a literally disintegrating world held together, saved and redeemed by the twin powers of music and love, was perhaps not to be so easily derided. I envied its off-the-wall coherence, its controlling overview. Also, I confess, I was in the market for redemption myself. Something had to stop me dreaming about a dead man's shoe, about a heel that twisted sideways to reveal a roll of film that would change its finder's life. I had left so much behind, but that memory never seemed surplus to requirements. No matter how light I traveled, it was always there, in the pockets of my dreams.

These were days of guilty uncertainty. Ormus had found his way of dealing with the zeitgeist. Even that dreadful junk band, what did they call themselves, the Mall: they had a plan. My way seemed to have fizzled out in a dead end. With Vina, with myself, I was getting nowhere.

My fellow "Orphics" on East Fifth Street had all abandoned photo-journalism for good, and the eagerness with which they were pursuing other interests aroused my envy, an emotion that's always reliable as a guide to the secret heart, *le secret-coeur,* as Hulot's Nebuchadnezzar partner Bobby Flow used to call it in his broad Yankee Franglais: that is to say, our deep neediness, the substitute in a climate of godlessness for the bleeding heart of Christ. Aimé-Césaire Basquiat, our beautiful young shaven-bodied Francophone, was using an old eight-by-ten plate camera, long exposures and gorgeous high-definition lighting to give a lapidary, Renaissance-classical look to a sequence of formal head-shot portraits and, more contentiously, to classically composed scenes of what were, to me, utterly stupefying sexual practices. The content of these out-there photographs made me feel like an innocent country boy who knew nothing of the world's true diversity, who in spite of staring into the maw of horror had never begun to guess what ancient impulses were really swimming in our lightless, hidden depths. It was Basquiat's simple idea to bring these things out of the dark into his sumptuous light and thus change our idea of what beauty is.

His third project was a sort of photographic reply to his namesake Césaire's celebrated poetic affirmation of *négritude,* the *Cahier d'un retour au pays natal.* Basquiat, who had left Martinique as a baby and defiantly stayed away ever since, was slowly creating a photo-essay—*Cahier d'un exit*—about exile, about rootless slip-sliders like himself, photographing them as if they were beautiful aliens floating an inch off the ground, as if they were blessed as well as cursed. Sometimes the three projects blended into one, and I was startled one day to see a powerful portrait of Basquiat's fellow Martinican Rémy Auxerre, haloed in light and ingesting, in extreme close-up, what was all too evidently Basquiat's own cock, an organ we all knew well because of its owner's penchant for nudity.

It's easy to say—and after his early death, all wasted body, wizened skin and frightened eyes, there were many who were quick to say it—that Basquiat was on a fast road to nowhere. But what I remember was the exaltation on his face each day. That was a room to which I also desperately wanted to find the key.

Johnny Chow and Mack Schnabel were involved in less edgy but equally rewarding careers: fashion and advertising work to support the high Manhattan society life they both adored, and more personal photo-essays for the good of the soul. Schnabel—a small man with a huge hawk's head and more than his share of nocturnal demons—would go to Italy twice a year for the Milan collections. Afterwards he headed off to Rome and took eye-popping pictures of the half-mummified, decayed, skeletal bodies in the catacombs. From that he progressed to taking pictures of civilian cadavers on a regular basis, fascinated by death's democracy. Violent death didn't interest him any more; just the fact itself, our shared inheritance, James's distinguished thing. The young and the old are the same age when they're dead, he'd say. They're *as old as it gets*. Other differences vanished also. Klansman and bluesman, Hamas fundamentalist and Jewish settler, Afrikaner and Sowetan, Indian and Pakistani, town mouse and country mouse, the farmer and the cowman, Mr. Tomayto and Ms. Tomahto, there they were, side by side on the slabs of his photographs, stripped of their frontiers, equalized for all time. To this continuing portfolio he gave the grandly Shakespearean title *Golden Lads and Girls,* who, you'll recall (*Cymbeline,* act IV, scene 2), all must, / As chimney sweepers, come to dust.

As for all-action Chow, that driven, gambling-crazy roadrunner who called himself the ideal New Yorker *because I'm like the city, man, I don't fucking sleep:* he was busy with his fifteen-year study *Queens,* a portrait of the polyglot borough. But he was at least as proud of the advertising photographs he took for Heinz. Multi-cultural street life, man, that's already rich, he told me. It's got texture, depth, does half your job for you. You got any idea what it takes to make interesting the surface of a cream of mushroom soup? Now that's a challenge.

One day Basquiat (fully dressed) came up to see me and

wanted to hang out and play some music. Rummaging through my vinyl he came up with an oldie, *Exile on Main Street,* and put it on the deck. Rai, deed you evair see that tour movie, *Cocksuckair Blues,* they got Robair Fronk to make eet as well as thees covair, he wanted to know. Otherwise I can get eet, I know a man, we can run eet for ourselves some evening, que penses-tu.

Listening to "Sweet Virginia," the druggy music of another age, a strange, mouthy admixture of South London and the American South, I found myself staring at the album's collagist sleeve, its strips of film featuring a funeral (civilians and soldiers saluting a hearse), snapshots of faces both famous and not, a newspaper front page, a scrap of handwritten lyric, the repeated image of the road. The crudely hand-lettered credits. *Amyl Nitrate: marimbas. Clydie King, Vanetta, plus friend: background vocal. Bill Plummer: uprite bass.* The music inspired only nostalgia but the photographs still had plenty to say. Yes, Robert Frank, I thought. This was the sign I'd been waiting for.

Cocksucker Blues was okay, messy and of its unappetizing moment, but I was still primarily a stills man, and what really spoke to me was Mabou. In 1970, after separating from Mary Frank, Robert Frank bought a house in Mabou, Nova Scotia, with the artist June Leaf. The raw, strong work he made there was, is, a demonstration of how far a photograph can stretch, how much it can include, once it gives up the idea of including it all, once it accepts that it isn't going to break on through to some universal truth. A human eye, disembodied, floats against a high-contrast seascape. Words as well as images hang pegged and drying on a windblown clothesline. There are many photographs shot through glass on which words have been scrawled or else the words are written right across the image itself. *No Fear* over a typewriter with, once again, the ubiquitous sea. *Hold Still Keep Going.* Against that stark flat mournful landscape articulated by poles and frames the fading name of his dead daughter. *For Andrea who died. I think of Andrea every day. Look Out For Hope.* Pigs' carcasses. Hospitals. Cold. Ice. Packing cases. Nothing cropped, nothing aligned. Photographs like torn images in broken glass. A woman, I think it's June Leaf, lies on sand, full of joy. I had looked at these pictures before but never seen them. Now they led me to discard much of what I'd thought, they gave me what I wanted: a way of starting again.

Looking at the Mabou pictures, I remembered these lines of Virginia Woolf: A masterpiece is not the result of a sudden inspiration but the product of a lifetime of thought. Henri Hulot, my first master, had been a great believer in the sudden inspiration, the decisive moment that reveals an underlying harmony. Frank wasn't, and had probably put together his *Black White and Things* as an answer to Hulot's thesis, much as *Catch-18* is an answer to *The Naked and the Dead.* I realized I had been pursuing the unattainable, looking at atrocities in search of capital-A Atrocity, searching in so many deaths for Death. Now I decided to abandon universals and harmony to absolutists like Hulot and Ormus and concentrate on the inexhaustible happenstance of life.

I decided that nothing was forbidden. I was re-learning the imagination's alphabet and so it was okay to play with all the toys.

For some reason (I really don't think this needs to be spelled out) I became interested in double exposures. I constructed story sequences in which beautiful, often naked young men and women—Basquiat's perennial nudity had had its effect on me—were attended by see-through wraiths: a mother standing like the Christ of the Andes, arms spread wide, atop a skyscraper, a father hanging from a ceiling fan, a dream lover, a second self. As I opened myself to the language of dreams I was shown, and tried to re-create, images whose meaning was obscure, whose obscurity excited me. A man at a desk was visited by a phantom horse which put its hooves over his eyes. A naked man in an empty room talked to a white-masked version of himself. (This with sentences of text, scrawled by myself at the foot of each frame of the sequence: *Do you know who you are? Do you know what you want?*) To my surprise I found that much of the imagery that came to me had religious overtones: a double-exposure sequence describing a dying woman's out-of-the-body experience, another sequence in which a man suddenly explodes into pure light: first his head, then his body and clothes. I allowed myself the supernatural, the transcendent, because, I told myself, our love of metaphor is pre-religious, born of our need to express what is inexpressible, our dreams of otherness, of more. Religion came and imprisoned the angels in aspic, tied our winged beauty to a tree, nailed our freedom to the ground. In these sequences I tried to reclaim the sense of the miraculous without having to bend the knee before any god. The god of the imagination is the imagination. The law of the imagination is, whatever works. The law of the imagination is not universal truth, but the work's truth, fought for and won.

I invented an alter ego for myself, an enigmatic Mitteleuropean photographer, named Moosbrugger after the murderer in Musil, prowling the streets of New York looking for echoes in this New World of Vienna, of Budapest, of Prague. This pseudo-photographer photographed the love affairs of gargoyles, the Arthurian adventures of the great population of statuary living high above the city streets. The statues came to life, loved, fought, lived according to their personal codes. They were like the knights of Charlemagne, as well as the American pioneers. Moosbrugger's statue-work was some of my favorite stuff.

I worked with reflections, glass, shadows. Using mirrors, I became skilled at scale distortion. I learned how to hold the galaxy in the palm of a man's hand, and what happened if you placed mirror images inside other mirror images and photographs inside photographs, dizzying the eye, until the last image was crushed in a fist. First to create an illusion, then to show that it *is* an illusion, then finally to destroy the illusion: this, I began to see, was honesty.

One day I developed a roll of film and there was the ghost image of a woman I didn't know superimposed on several of the shots. I couldn't work it out. On this occasion I was certain I had not run the film through the camera twice, and anyway I didn't recognize the woman's silhouette. True, it was not unlike Vina's body, but it wasn't Vina's body. It was a stranger, moving through a space that was and was not mine.

As if I had penetrated a membrane and touched an otherworld.

That night while I slept the woman showed up in my dreams and told me her name. She said a little too contemptuously for my liking that she could read me as if I were a book. She said if she wanted to she could close me and put me back on her shelf and then my story would never finish, it would stop dead in the middle of a sentence. I was lying naked in bed and she leaned over me, murmuring threats. I tried to argue back. I told her the inside of a book is there whether you read it or not. Even if nobody ever reads it, it's there, doing its work. That's enough, I said. Being there is what counts.

She hissed, do you remember when we were lovers? Do you remember our wonderful first night of love? No, she said, you don't even remember me, do you, you bastard. Fuck you. I'm going. Maybe I'll never come back.

I woke up sweating and alone. Maria, I thought. I just met a girl called Maria.

I BEGAN to take pictures of infidelity: my apartment just before Vina entered the frame, or just after she left it. The rumpled bed of guilty passion. The water on the tiled floor by the shower. Used glasses. Half-eaten food. After a time Vina agreed to participate in the sequence. Her masked face. Her anonymous, naked body moving rapidly out of shot. Her extended arms, stretching towards the forbidden. These photographs brought us a new kind of closeness, and as she gave more and more of herself to the work, becoming more collaborator than subject, so I began superstitiously to fear the power of crazy Ormus's eye-patched, shamanic eye. Some days I could swear I could feel it roving the cosmos like a searchlight, like Robert Frank's eye at Mabou, like the cloud-razored moon in *Un Chien Andalou.* Like the eye of the Dark Lord Sauron searching for the Ring.

Thus I became an autobiographer, using whatever came to hand, drawings, stories, crayons, surrealism, Vina, texts. Realism isn't a set of rules, it's an intention, I pontificated at an amused, unusually tolerant Vina. The world isn't realistic any more, what are we going to do about that? Think of a photograph of people who never change, leading their grooved lives with if they're lucky a bit of bedroom psychodrama: *that's* the fantasy. A battlefield on which you don't see the undercurrents of history doesn't show enough of the truth. A battlefield on which you don't see so to speak angels and devils, the so to speak gods with their super-weapons, and the let's say ghosts. Somehow to show the metaphoric beneath the actual, driving what happens, making things so.

And how do you propose to photograph an undercurrent, she asked.

I don't know, I grinned. I guess start by looking in the right places.

You're changing, she told me. Don't stop?, I like it. I like it really a lot.

WE WERE all changing. The change in Ormus, his sleep-masked retreat into locked and darkened rooms for days on end, his worsening migraines, his sobbing fits, his shrieks, these things gave rise to a great turbulence within Vina, tore her apart, made her feel helpless, alienated her, made her sit outside his locked door pleading to be let in. When she was let in she would attend at his darkened bedside for days on end, holding his hand, nursing him, while he thrashed like a great fish out of water and screamed about the imminent catastrophe. Doctors were brought to him, sedatives were prescribed. The condition of his mind was not good. Vina came to me more often now, fleeing the melodrama at the Rhodopé Building, leaving Ormus to be cared for by the infinitely patient Clea and the Singhs. She said, His breakdown leaves a hole where our relationship used to be. I still love him, you know, love's a mystery, right, but there's nothing between us any more. He's off in outer space or the fifth dimension, watching out for the end of the world. Sometimes I think he isn't coming back.

She knew she had to resume an independent life, to find her own new way. Gradually she became an enthusiastic participant in the alternative art scene, working with indie film-makers, performance artists, dancers. Meanwhile she was writing her own songs for the first time, trying them out on me, jamming with her many A-list music-world friends. She made surprise appearances at small downtown music venues with a scratch band and was pleased by the reception she got. By the fall of 1988 she had an album, *Vina,* and was planning to go on the road. Not America or Europe to start with, she told me. I don't think I'm ready. Just a small tour of Latin America for a start?, the music is pretty much influenced by those guys anyway. Brazil, Mexico, just a toe in the water.

I want to remember her the way she was then, surging into her mid-forties full of beauty and courage, alone and scared but heading back out there, looking for her life. I want to remember that in those days before the tour she at last admitted what I'd waited my whole life to hear, namely that I had become a factor, a problem. I was no longer an occasional snack, a side dish. No longer containable. For too long it had been a case of Ormus and Vina sailing along with Rai clinging to the side of their racing yacht. It had been their story; now, at long last, it was mine too. Mine, at last.

She said she was disoriented, confused, she needed time to think, all of that. Yes, she was thinking of leaving him. She couldn't bear to be there any more. She couldn't bear to leave him. She couldn't stay.

She said, You don't know how alike you are, you two, except that he's going down for the third time and you're coming up for air.

She said, I have to get away. I'm going on this tour. I have to think.

I'll come with you, why don't I, I said. I could be your official tour photographer. All I'd ask is total access. You know? Total.

No, don't come.

I can't let you go. Vina, after all this. We're this close. I have to come.

Jesus, Jesus. I don't know. Okay, come. No, don't come. Come. Don't come. Come. Don't come. Don't come. Don't come. Come.

I'll come, then.

No. *Don't.*

WE SHOULD have listened to Ormus. It wasn't just the great San Francisco earthquake of 1984: the 1980s had been a bad time for the whole faulty earth. In October 1980 twenty thousand people were killed by a 7.3-Richter event in El Asnam, Algeria, a quake so severe that it broke many local seismologists' measuring instruments. Three thousand people died in southern Italy a month later. In October 1983 a quake hit Hasankale village in eastern Turkey (two thousand dead); in September 1985 the Mexico City authorities were forced to use the baseball stadium as a morgue (over two thousand dead). A medium-size event wrecked San Salvador in August 1986, and then, two years later, a mysterious rash of quakes broke out along various international frontiers. A 6.7-Richter whopper rocked the India-Nepal border in August 1988 (over five hundred dead), and just three months later a thousand people died, this time on the China-Burma line. One month after that, a force of 6.9 on the Richter scale devastated the Armenian-Turkish border. The town of Spitak, with a population of fifty thousand, was totally destroyed; eighty percent of the buildings in Leninakan (a city with a population of three hundred thousand souls) tumbled down; one hundred thousand people died, and Gorbachev paid a visit to the scene. When, in January 1989, two villages in a border area of Tajikistan were buried by landslides and mudslides (one thousand people dead, also many thousand head of cattle), the so-called "borderline fault" phenomenon began to attract worldwide attention. *Is the world coming apart at the seams?* was the question asked by a cover story in *Time*, and even though the official, seismological answer was a resounding No, I began, for the first time, to wonder what Ormus Cama was seeing in his delirium. If dogs and pigs and cattle could feel quakes before our measuring instruments, was it possible that a human being could predict them months, years, in advance?

YEAH, BUT if we'd listened to Ormus, what then? Like all Cassandras, he was short on remedies. In the end such prophecy is useless. You just have to live your life, make your choices, move forward until you can't.

In February 1989 Vina Apsara and her new band flew to Mexico for a series of arena concerts. Without telling her, I caught a flight to Mexico City too. I had her itinerary, the list of her hotels and so on. This time I would not let her escape.

CHAPTER FIFTEEN

Beneath Her Feet

When I show up at the Cattlemen's Club in downtown Mexico City she shocks me, trumps my ace, by beginning instantly, abundantly, to weep. She's slumped in a deep armchair and the liquid level in the bottle beside her confirms what I already know from the papers, i.e. that the first gig didn't go too well. Her band is still learning to play together, the papers say, and she looked oddly ill at ease on stage without Ormus there for reassurance, Ormus Cama in his glass box. They find things to praise, her beauty and so on, but she knows when she's being panned. She sniffs and snorts; the tears make it impossible for me to judge accurately the condition of her nose. How far do I have to run to get away from you, Rai, unfairly she sobs, fuck you, how deep a hole do I have to dig. Large men move menacingly in my direction but she waves them irritatedly away.

I call it the Cattlemen's Club because its fat-cat confidence is a Latin American echo of the establishment in *Dallas,* the soap not the city, where men in big hats clutched bourbon-and-branch and bitched about the price of oil. But this joint makes *Dallas* look like the boondocks, like any place where two roads cross and then make a low fast run for the horizon. It's a mighty stone-clad pyramid set on the upper floors of a shining high-rise near the Zócalo and it looks like all the extinguished peoples of the region have been exhumed to construct it: Olmecs, Zapotecs, Mayas, Toltecs, Mixtecs, Purépechas, Aztecs. It is a temple, in its monied way: a place of power with added settees and liveried waiters. You suspect the covert presence of altars, of knife-wielding priests. Vina, the sacrifice *du jour,* has been given a suite of rooms, where publicists and journalists and photographers and hangers-on and heavies come and go. To get past security I have to send in my card. She keeps me waiting just long enough for me to start worrying about a humiliating rejection. Then I am led into her presence to be greeted by her waterworks display, also the shocking red hair, and the strange thing is that my mouth is dry, my heart's pounding, I'm actually scared. I have come naked into this conference chamber, with, to paraphrase James Caan in *The Godfather,* nothing but my dick in my hand. I've got only my dumb love to offer, this love that is finally after all the second-fiddle decades insisting on taking over the orchestra. Take me or leave me, that's what I've come to say, knowing that if she doesn't want me I'm defenseless, a cap-in-hand schoolboy without even an apple for a bribe.

Meanwhile, this being one of the earth's buggier zones, I'm being bitten all over, scratching at my neck like Toshiro Mifune's scummy samurai (but without the sword skills). I'm in a nightmare. It's the beginning of the last act of the play and I've walked out on stage and there are no lines in my head, no prompter hissing from his box by the footlights. Vina, I say. She puts a finger across her lips, dries her eyes, waves me into a chair. Not that, she says. Let's talk about something else. In these last Mexican days it's a command she often gives.

She wants to tell me about the hot political scandal that's flaring up now, the President's brother who is on the run after embezzling the equivalent of eighty-four million U.S. dollars, there isn't a country prepared to give him asylum, not even Cuba, so he circles the globe like a ship carrying nuclear waste, unable to find a port. *And this is supposed to be the new, clean régime!* (The name of Piloo Doodhwala is on both our lips, so there is no need for it to be spoken.) She wants to talk also about the Argentinian footballer, Achilles Hector, who has been kidnapped by the revolutionists in the south. His amazing name, Greek and Trojan?, winner and loser?, a double hero, she says. His captors gave deadlines. They threatened to cut off his toes, one by one, if their demands were not met. But the deadlines passed, and so far no toe in the mail. The revolutionists are also football fanatics. It's a question of which of their passions will prevail.

She wants to talk about the villa on the Pacific coast, the one she stayed in for the first three days of her Mexican sojourn, to which she will shortly return. The Villa Huracán outside Aparajitos, caught between the jungle and the sea. From the jungle comes the singing of the obscene bird of night, perhaps Lowry's *Trogon ambiguus ambiguus,* his wonderful ambiguous bird. Deep in the ocean echoes the roar of the *huracán,* the god of storms. The villa is actually not a villa at all but a row of pink-washed edifices—"rooms"—topped with *palapas,* high cones of thatch. It is jointly owned by the shockingly young new Colchis boss, Mo Mallick, and a Hollywood heavy hitter named Kahn. The death of Yul Singh and the retirement of VTO, his biggest act, has holed Colchis badly, but Mallick has pushed his leaking boat out for Vina on this tour, gambling that she can make it without Ormus. Hence the offer of the Huracán. Hence, also, one reason for Vina's present depression. She has been heavily backed to come through and it looks as if she may not be able to deliver the required goods. Mallick, at twenty-eight already a Vegas high roller, can take a hit if he has to, like any player at the big tables he knows the money isn't the point, it's just a way of keeping score. But he cares about the score. To win the big ones gets to be a matter of pride. To lose? Let's talk about something else.

The other guests, she wants to tell me, were a famous Chilean novelist and his much younger, and strikingly attractive, Irish-American wife. There was a breakfast terrace halfway down the cliffside, where fruit and tortillas and champagne arrived in a picnic hamper that rattled through the air on ropes and pulleys. *El desayunismo magical,* the novelist called it. The Irish-American wife spoke of her close involvement with the republican movement "back home," that is to say in Ulster, whose bitter earth she had never trodden, telling of her fund-raising efforts and the profound commitment with which the republican leadership was working for peace. Meanwhile the novelist ate and drank heartily, refused to comment on the Irish question and pronounced himself too frail to descend any further. *Sea level will have to do without me.* He sat on the terrace in an old polo shirt and khaki shorts. Vina kept him company while the entertainment executives gamboled at the ocean's edge below, competing for the attention of the young Boston-Irish aristocrat-revolutionary wife, splashing around her in the shallows like great lumbering hounds, all eagerness and dangling tongues. Speaking of dangling, Vina on the breakfast terrace observed that the writer's legs were wide apart and he wasn't wearing any underwear. His balls were big and smooth and pink, the same pink as the villa walls, and his cock was big and gray, the dull gray of the stone slab on which he sat with the ocean at his rear. I couldn't stop looking, Vina tells me, not bad for seventy-five, I thought. Afterwards I asked Mallick if the old gent had been trying to impress me, I mean, was this flirting?, or what?—but Mallick said no, he does it all the time, it's just innocent display. That's how I think of the Huracán now, she quips gaily. As a sacred place, the place where innocence is displayed.

She doesn't know how to make the choice I am obliging her to make.

She is brittle, over-bright, stretched.

She wants to talk about anything on earth except love.

Vina, I say again. She glares at me, furious now. This is one thirsty city, she says. The sub-soil water levels are falling alarmingly?, and any day now the place will just subside, just drop out of sight. Now that's what I call falling-down drunk. And then there's the Pope, I'm supposed to follow *his* act, how's that for lousy timing.

The Pope has just played Mexico City and he even talked about rock 'n' roll. *Yes, my children, the answer is indeed blowing in the wind, not in the wind of godless desolation but in the harmonious breeze that fills the sails of the ship of faith and blows its passengers all the way to heaven.* Vina, who couldn't match his audiences but knows that VTO could probably have given him a run for his money, has to console herself by sneering at the over-extended metaphor and by retailing the latest papal gossip. His curt anger towards worker-priests, liberation theology, all that jazz. And there's this story doing the rounds about his driver, she says. No, not the chauffeur of the Popemobile. I mean his driver back in the old days when he was plain Cardinal Wojtyla? Apparently this driver had been with him for years, and when it was time to elect a new Pope the two of them drove down from Cracow in some little beat-up Polish pollution-wagon. What a road movie, right?, the future Pope and his workingman sidekick strikin' out for glory. Anyway, they get to the Vatican, the driver waits and waits, the smoke goes up, *habemus Papam,* and finally he hears the news, it's his good buddy, his road pal, his boss. Then a messenger comes to see him. Drive the car back to Cracow and then find yourself another job, says the messenger. Your ass is fired.

I've seen her in all kinds of moods before, but never so desperate. She's flying to Guadalajara in the morning—Guadalajara, where Pancho Villa shot the clock and stopped time, she says—and she knows the show isn't right, her life isn't right, and she doesn't know how to fix either one. She looks at my face and all she sees there is *leave him, Vina, come live with me and be my love,* and she can't handle that at present, *let's talk about something else,* she starts cracking Orpheus jokes. This is an old riff of hers, one she first laid down when she heard I was moving into an Orpheum; me, Rai, scion of the clan with the worst voices in Indian musical history. You should change the name, she said, out of respect you should name it after a different fucking god. Maybe Morpheus, the god of sleep. I played along: How about Metamorpheus, god of change. It went downhill from there. We came up with Endomorpheus and Ectomorpheus, the twinned gods of body type. Waldorpheus Astorpheus, god of hotels. Motorpheus, the biker god. Hans Castorpheus, the magic mountaineer. Shortpheus, god of anger. Conpheus, the head-scratching, puzzled god.

She wants to talk about gods because death-worshipping Mexico has startled her. Compared to the deities they've got here, she says, Apollo's just a theater, Poseidon's an adventure, Hermes is a fucking silk scarf.

She comes to a halt, looks at me. Vina doesn't often implore, but I see that right now she needs me to take up the chit-chat baton and run with it. She needs me not to force her to face what must be faced. Mutely, she pleads for compassion; even for mercy.

Incredible violence is the gods' stock-in-trade, I therefore commence obligingly to improvise. Rape, murder, terrible revenges. You go to them with open arms, but these are fatal embraces. The old gods, Hindu Norse Greek, laid down no moral laws, requiring nothing of us except worship. Reverence, the deified Herakles tells Philoctetes in Sophocles' play, is what Olympus digs above all else. On the surface this sounds preferable to the newer guys, no sermons on the mount, no Islamic how-to manuals, but watch out, there's an elephant trap. To revere the gods is to fear their wrath and therefore to seek constantly to propitiate them. Natural disasters are proofs of the gods' displeasure, because the world is our fault. Therefore incessant expiations. Therefore human sacrifice, et cetera.

That's what I love about you, Vina says, relief and gratitude concealed beneath her sardonic accents. Wind you up and you'll run off at the mouth for a good half hour; which allows a girl to tune out and get some rest.

It is at this point that I mention earthquakes.

Which isn't so surprising, given our location in notoriously quake-prone Mexico, not to mention the subject of VTO's biggest hit album and Ormus Cama's recent warnings about the coming apocalypse. I am not a superstitious man or, as I hope I have made plain, a religious one. I do not believe that by speaking of earthquakes I called down on our heads the anger of the gods. But for the record I note the fact that I so spoke.

Also, to be precise: not on my head. On Vina's.

Earthquakes, I point out, have always made men eager to placate the gods. After the great Lisbon earthquake of November 1, 1755—that catastrophe which Voltaire saw as an irrefutable argument for the tragic view of life and against Leibnizian optimism—the locals decided on a propitiatory auto-da-fé. The celebrated philosopher Pangloss was hanged (the more conventionally approved bonfire wouldn't light). His associate, Herr Candide of Thunder-ten-tronckh, a name like an occult incantation, likely to provoke earthquakes where none had previously occurred, was flogged rhythmically and for a long while upon his bloodied buttocks. Immediately after this auto-da-fé there was an even bigger earthquake, and that part of the city which remained standing instantly fell down. That's the trouble with human sacrifice, the heroin of the gods. It's highly addictive. And who will save us from deities with major habits to feed?

So god's a junkie now, Vina says.

The gods, I correct her. Monotheism sucks, like all

despotisms. The species is naturally, democratically polytheistic, apart from that evolutionary élite which has dispensed with the divine requirement entirely. You instinctively want the gods to be many because you are One.

And the stories, she says, her mood improving. She's just kidding around now, shooting the breeze, getting her mind off her troubles. I've managed to put a faint smile back on her face. What about the stories, she repeats. Does a damned heathen such as you not even find pleasure there?

When we stop believing in the gods we can start believing in their stories, I retort. There are of course no such things as miracles, but if there were and so tomorrow we woke up to find no more believers on earth, no more devout Christians, Muslims, Hindus, Jews, why then, sure, the beauty of the stories would be a thing we could focus on because they wouldn't be dangerous any more, they would become capable of compelling the only belief that leads to truth, that is, the willing, disbelieving belief of the reader in the well-told tale.

The myths, you may have noticed, require their protagonists to be stupid. To walk blithely into mortal danger, blind to the most obvious traps.

(All this and probably more, I permit myself to say. I have not spoken like this, so exhaustively, so unrestrainedly, in a long time. And I repeat, I do not believe in hubris, the crime of thumbing your nose at the gods, and therefore I also do not believe in the coming of Nemesis. But I have sworn to tell everything and so I must also say that before what happened happened I made these, in the eyes of believers, no doubt injudicious remarks.)

Let's go to my hotel room and get fucked up, Vina briskly proposes. A snort of soma, a sip of ambrosia. Sure, I'm up for that. Lead on, my queen. It occurs to me, not for the first time, that I am in the position of a mortal man petitioning a so to speak goddess for love. Vina and Adonis: like that. I am aware that humans do not usually come well out of these encounters.

But the non-existent gods, too, can fall.

HER STYLE, these days, is late-eighties ultraglamour; no more hippie (or radical) chic. Très movie star, with an extra shock 'n' roll twist of outrageousness. Tyler, Gaultier, Alaïa, Léger, Wang, but most often Santo Medusa: his all-in-one technicolor-beaded catsuits, his shocking-pink *smokings* worn double-breasted over a shirtless torso, his chain-mail mini-dresses slit to the waist. Vina and Tina, people say, are slugging it out for the ageless-diva crown.

This is the hotel room. This is the woman I love. These are some of the last moments of her life on earth, her life above ground. Every stupid thing she says, every crack she makes, every heart she breaks, these are things I will forever hug to myself, to save them from the *barranco,* the abyss. This is the CD she plays: *Raindogs,* the honky-tonk blues as reinvented and growled out by Lee Baby Simms. She starts singing along with Simms, low and slow, and the hair rises on my neck. *Will I see you again / on a downtown train.* The walls seem to be swaying to the music. It's like Valéry, I remark. *Le roc marche, et trébuche; et chaque pierre fée / se sent un poids nouveau qui vers l'azur délire!* Valerie who, she shrugs, not caring, lost in music and smoke.

She's on her way to Guadalajara, the city where time stops. To Guadalajara and beyond.

This is us, making love. She always made love as if it were for the last time, that was how she did everything, how she led her life; but for us, though neither of us knows it, this in fact is the last time. The last time for these breasts. The breasts of Helen of Troy were so astonishing that when she bared them to her husband at the fall of Troy, Menelaus was unable to do her harm. The sword fell from his nerveless hand. This is the woman I love and these are her breasts. I run this tape over and over in my head. Did you show the earthquake your breasts, Vina, did you bare them to the god of storms, why didn't you, if you did you might, you surely would, have survived.

These are the breasts of the woman I love. I place my nose between them and inhale their pungency, their ripeness. I place my cock between them and feel their swollen caress.

This is Vina, talky as always after sex. She wants to beef about the problem of age for female singers: Diana, Joni, Tina, Nina, herself. Look at Sinatra, she says. He can hardly stand up, there are notes he can't even dream about any more, and somebody should kill that animal sitting on his head, but he's a guy, therefore these are not career problems. (Yes, she puts herself up there with the Voice. She's a Voice too. She has no false modesty. She knows her artistic worth. Tina and me, she says, we're re-writing the book. Not Fade Away, that's the new title, honey. We're telling you how it's gonna be.)

She's on to the younger generation, its inadequacies, its complaints. Here's Madonna Sangria again, still obsessing in *Rolling Stone* about the female body. Not its uses but its abuses. Not sex but gender. Will you listen to the low-grade grumpiness in this grouchy kid, Vina growls, talking mostly to herself. Man, we had high octane. We had *rage*. To whine about guys?, to complain about mom 'n' pop?, just wasn't in it. We had the generals and the universe to fight. *My boyfriend left me, men are assholes?* Give me a break. I'll take the good-time girls any day. Bop she bop. She bop she-waddywaddy. (She's singing now.) *She's so fine . . .*

Bullshit, she snarls abruptly. She's wasted and more than half asleep but she's arguing with herself. Always was a man pulling our strings. Ike Turner Berry Gordy Phil Spector Ormus Cama. Ike Spector Berry Turner. A man is for power and a woman is for pain. I'll say it again. Orpheus lives, Eurydice dies, right?

Yeah, but you're Orpheus too, I start to tell her. It's your voice that's making the enchanted stones of the city rise deliriously into the blue, that causes the city's banks of electrical images to dance. *Oraia phone,* the best voice, we all know to be yours, not his. And meanwhile he's the one sinking into his otherworld-underworld, and who's going to rescue him, I bite my tongue because this is the opposite of the line I have flown south to pursue: *Who if not you.* Instead I say, It's time men like him started rescuing themselves.

And I go on, Anyway, Orpheus dies too. And having said it, I want to rip out my tongue. Wrong, wrong! But what's said is said.

Vina's sitting up in bed now, stone sober and suddenly, illogically, mad as hell. You think you can walk in his shoes, she says. You think you can sleep in his hollow. In your dreams, Rai baby. Never in a million. You came all this way to tell me you want him dead?, maybe you'll want me dead too, if I don't bow down before your will, before your fucking *dick.* You came down here to murder love and call the murder love.

No, that's not it, I say uselessly. Dionysiac Vina has risen up in wrath, goddess of pleasure and destruction. Go, she orders, and miserably I obey.

The next day in Guadalajara—I've followed her there too, but I'm on my own, barred from backstage, unable to reach her by hook or crook or carrier pigeon—I wander wretchedly, with my thoughts *shooting out all over the place,* as Moses Herzog says. There's a woman bishop now in the U.S.A., maybe I could call her, she could probably get through to Vina and I don't know somehow on a sisterly basis intercede. Stroessner's out in Paraguay, a coup, but the day they announce a world shortage of dictators will be a cold day in Hell. I see where they executed the Sikhs who carried out the Quadruple Assassination. Say hi to Cool Yul for me, guys, maybe he's not so cool no more, not where he's at.

You're changing, she said to me. Don't stop.

Metamorphosis, this is what I need to explain to her, is what supplants our need for the divine. This is what we can perform, our human magic. I'm talking now not about the ordinary, quotidian changes that are the stuff of modern life (in which, as someone said, only the temporary is contemporary); nor even about the adaptive, chameleon natures which have become so common during our migrant century; but about a deeper, more shocking capacity, which kicks in only under extreme pressure. When we are faced with the Immense. At such a hinge moment we can occasionally mutate into another, final form, a *form beyond metamorphosis.* A new fixed thing.

Three of us passed through a membrane in the sky and were transformed by the experience. That's true. But what is also true is that those transformations were not at that time completed. It would perhaps be more accurate to say that we entered a transit zone: the condition of transformation. A transitional phase in which we might have been trapped for ever, which only the imperative force of the Immense can force towards completion.

The Immense has shown its face to Ormus Cama. He has become the agent of that revelation. For him, whatever the consequences, there can be no going back.

For Vina and myself—this is what I need her to understand—the Immense has taken the form of our lifelong, intermittent but inescapable love. Thus, if she will only leave Ormus for me, our lives will change entirely, we will both be altered in astonishing ways, but the new form which then emerges—she and I, together, in love—this will last for ever. For ever and a fucking day.

Putting the screws on her? You bet. I repeat: only under extreme pressure can we change into that which it is in our most profound nature to become. Lichas, hurled into the waters by Herakles, drained of life by fear, turned into a rock. Turned *for ever* into a rock, you can go and sit on it—on him—right now, in the Euboean Gulf, not far from Thermopylae.

This is what people get wrong about transformation. We're not all shallow proteans, forever shifting shape. We're not science fiction. It's like when coal becomes diamond. It doesn't afterwards retain the possibility of change. Squeeze it as hard as you like, it won't turn into a rubber ball, or a Quattro Stagione pizza, or a self-portrait by Rembrandt. It's *done*.

Scientists get angry when laymen misunderstand, for example, the uncertainty principle. In an age of great uncertainties it is easy to mistake science for banality, to believe that Heisenberg is merely saying, gee, guys, we just can't be sure of anything, it's all so darn *uncertain*, but isn't that, like, *beautiful*? Whereas actually he's telling us the exact opposite: that if you know what you're doing you can pin down the exact quantum of uncertainty in any experiment, any process. To knowledge and mystery we can now ascribe percentage points. A principle of uncertainty is also a measure of certainty. It's not a lament about shifting sands but a gauge of the solidity of the ground.

By the same token, as we say in Hug-me, I get annoyed when people misunderstand change. We're not talking about the goddamn *I Ching* here. We're talking about the deepest stirrings of our essential natures, of our secret hearts. Metamorphosis isn't whimsy. It's revelation.

In various bars around the Plaza de Armas, the Calzada Independencia Sur, the Calle de Mariachis, I'm learning to tell the difference between tequilas. Sauza, Ángel, Cuervo, the three big distilleries. For me it's between Sauza and Ángel, but then maybe I haven't tasted enough of the other guy's wares, hey, camarero, hit me again, hombre, muy pronto. The white tequila is the cheap hooch; then there's reposado, that's three months old; but for the good stuff you should stick with the tres generaciones, the name's an exaggeration but six to twelve years of ageing are well worth the wait. At some point I check out Orozco's *Man in Flames* mural. He's a national institution now, a major brand name, but back in the thirties he had to flee to America, where he made his reputation, the familiar story, you've got to leave home and get the gringos to love you before you get the time of day in your old neighborhood. Five minutes later, usually, you're called a sell-out, but Orozco is still in favor, lucky man.

She has made her choice and I'm not it. She has chosen not to change.

I wonder with the help of the three generations of the Ángel distillery how to make it through the rest of my life. I am only forty-two years old. Shit, she's older than I am, what is this, have all the under-forty women in the world written me off? I don't know. I guess if you drink down all these generations you get to be incredibly old. Three more generations, please, camarero. Here they come, begat begat begat. That's better. The women look younger all the time. The busboy's sprouting wings.

If I had a soul I would sell it now and gain my heart's desire. And another three generations, sir waiter, if you will.

Señor I think perhaps it is already sufficient. Where is your hotel. If you wish it, I will call for you a taxi.

ON FEBRUARY 13, 1989, the last but one night of her life (we have been here before), the legendary popular singer Vina Apsara chooses the good-for-nothing greaseball playboy Raúl Páramo, a man given to the wearing of personal jewelry, to be the agent of my sexual humiliation. I'm waiting for her in the hotel lobby when she sweeps in, half naked, already oncefucked, in the arms of this pathetic nonentity who is grinning as dementedly as a village idiot who has won the lottery and whose doom, as things turn out, is even closer than her own. She pauses right in front of me, tongue-twistin', clutching at him not three feet from where I stand. She is making her point. *You're nothing in my life, Rai, you mean even less than this punk, so do me a favor, fuck off and die.*

I, however, have received from the lady a lifetime's instruction in the art of waiting for whatever scraps of herself she may care to throw in my direction. Surrendering the torn remnants of my pride, I bribe the floor security officer and am therefore allowed to spend the night in the corridor outside her suite, sitting on a small folding stool—every photographer has one, along with a nose for trouble and a light stepladder—and preparing to throw myself at her feet and beg to be allowed back into some dirty back room of her life.

As Vina once sat outside tormented Ormus's locked door, waiting to be let in, so that she could care for him, so I now wait for her. We are one another's echoes. We are the ringing in one another's ears.

Now it's noon on Valentine's Day. We have been here before. Here is Vina in the hotel corridor, panicky and uncertain, locked out of her suite, in flight from her dying lover; and here is doglike Rai, her faithful retainer, ready as ever to offer his abject, panting services.

We have been here before. It's two hours later and a helicopter is flying over blue agave. My brief exile is at an end; her feelings dictated by her needs, Vina again sees me as an essential ally, at present her onliest help and stay. I am a rock, like Lichas hurled into the sea. And a rock feels no pain.

We pass her retinue on the road below. *Of all you bastards he's the only one I can trust.* Vina, who thinks of trust as a prison, has declared her trust in me.

She's badly jolted by the Raúl Páramo business. In my headphones I hear the nostalgic sound of Hug-me, the argot of our youth. It's been a long time. Afterwards, remembering, I will be powerfully moved by the thought that Vina near her end circled back to our beginning. Of course the private language was useful, to shield our talk from the headphoned ears of the pilot and co-pilot, but for that purpose even English would probably have sufficed. She went further than she needed, resurrecting old Bombay in the hot dry Mexican air. Remembering, I can't help thinking of her decision as an earnest of our intimacy; as a promise of things to come.

We have been here before. We know that this promise won't, can't, be kept.

She is a worried woman: the police, Páramo, the drugs. She is even—astonishingly—concerned about me. Can I ever forgive her awful behavior et cetera, sometimes she just lashes out and hurts the people she cares for most, and how strong I was to still be there for her?, not to walk away?, to give her another chance. But can she please please take a rain check in the matter of love, because right now she can't think straight?, the tour, everything?, she owes it to me to wait until her head is clear. Rai, you've waited this long, honey, you can wait *do-teen* more days.

In the language of love's childhood I hear the words that thrill my still-besotted adult heart. Okay, I'll wait, I say. I'll hang on, Vina, but not for long.

Hug me honey honey hug me. Hang on Sloopy, come on come on.

The fierce heat of the day, the cheering crowd in the football field, the two silver Bentleys of Don Ángel Cruz, the frightened animals, the mariachis, and Vina singing: *Trionfi Amore,* the last song anyone ever heard her sing.

. . . il cor tormenta
Al fin diventa
Felicità.

Then the earthquake. I take up my cameras and shoot, and for me there are no more sounds, only the silence of event, the silence of the photographic image.

Tequila! We have been here before.

In the time of Voltaire it was believed that underground seams of sulfur connected the sites of earthquakes. Sulfur, with its stench of Hell.

FACED WITH the blazing magnificence of the everyday, the artist is both humbled and provoked. There are photographs now of events on an unimaginable scale: the death of stars, the birth of galaxies, soup-stirrings near the dawn of Time. Bright crowds of suns gather in the wildernesses of the sky. Magellanic clouds of glory, heavenly Pisan towers set in a celestial Campo dei Miracoli, lean across the frame. When we look at these images, there is, yes, legitimate wonderment at our own lengthening reach and grasp. But it would be vain indeed to praise our puny handiwork—the mastery of the Hubble wielders, the computer enhancers, the colorizers, all the true-life-fantasist counterparts of Hollywood's techno-wizards and imagineers—when the universe is putting on so utterly unanswerable a show. Before the majesty of being, what is there to do but hang our heads?

This is irksome. This, naturally, pisses us off.

There is that within us which believes us worthy of the stars. Turn right on this forking path and you find god; turn left and there is art, its uncowed ambition, its glorious irreverent over-reach. In our hearts we believe—we *know*—that our images are capable of being the equals of their subjects. Our creations can go the distance with Creation; more than that, our imagining—our imagemaking—is an indispensable part of the great work of *making real.* Yes, I will even assert as much as that. (Usually I make such assertions when I'm alone in the sealed privacy of the bathroom, but today all bathroom truths must come out to play.)

For example: nobody has yet successfully photographed the gashes in the cosmos which, if Ormus Cama is to be believed, are responsible for the present rash of catastrophes. To get such a picture would be to effect a profound reality shift, a first-magnitude change in our understanding of what is.

However, there is a new picture of an earthquake on the sun. It made all the world's front pages in full, enhanced color. The earthquake looks like a heat bubble exploding through the surface of a hot thick golden porridge. But the seismic solar porridge ripples we see are apparently more than seven Everests high—over forty miles.

If we didn't have the photograph the news of the earthquake would lack felt reality. As it is, every newspaper reader on the planet is now asking the same tremulous question.

Is the sun in trouble too?

Thus, a photograph can create the meaning of an event.

Sometimes even when it's a fake.

In my last photograph of Vina the ground beneath her feet is cracked like crazy paving and there's liquid everywhere. She's standing on a slab of street that's tilting to the right; she's bending left to compensate. Her arms are spread wide, her hair's flying, the expression on her face is halfway between anger and fear. Behind her the world is out of focus. There is a sense of eruptions all around her lurching body: great releases of water, terror, fire, tequila, dust. This last Vina is calamity incarnate, a woman *in extremis,* who is also by chance one of the most famous women in the world.

After the disappearance of Vina Apsara at the Villa Huracán, my earthquake picture will join that small stock of photographic images—Monroe's flying skirt, the burning girl in Indochina, Earthrise—which actually *become experiences,* part of the collective memory of the human race. Like every photographer, I have hoped to end my days with my name attached to a few powerful images, but the Vina picture will outstrip even my most ambitious, self-glorifying aspirations. *The Lady Vanishes,* as it will come to be known, will surely be my bitter posterity. If I am remembered at all, it can only be for this. So in one sense at least, Vina and I will be joined together for ever, in spite of everything, a consummation for which I've wished, all my life, even more devoutly than I've wished for professional success. Yes, we're linked for all time, beyond hope, beyond life: metamorphosed by the Immense into the Eternal. But I was wrong about the nature of the metamorphic force working its marvels upon us. In our case, it was not love but death.

Be careful what you wish for.

At the beginning of my life in photography I was guilty of an inglorious fraud: a dead man's pictures were passed off as my own. Ever since then—as I have sometimes admitted to myself, though at other points I have temporarily managed to suppress the memory of that twisted boot heel, of the other hanged man in my life—I have needed whatever is the godless equivalent of redemption; call it self-respect. Here's an irony: when at last I do create one of the iconic images of the age, I can only wish I hadn't, I at once and for ever concede that she, the subject, was of a worth far greater than any photo I could take of her; I cannot bear to be left with this single mute reflection of her infinite variety.

You can have the fucking photo. I want her back.

Also, because the picture will first appear alongside news reports of what I keep calling her disappearance because I'm finding it hard to use the other word, it will be permanently associated in the public mind with that final moment of terror. This is how people are. Even though we all know there could not have been a photographer present at Vina's end, we accept the authenticity of the image without much trouble. My picture of Vina in a heaving Tequila street mutates under the pressure of the world's need for last things, under the pressure of this global manifestation of the Immense, into a portrait of the star at the moment of her, say it, death.

So it's a sort of unintentional fake. Another fraud. And though I will try to set the record straight, telling the story of the photograph over and over again, nobody will really be listening. They will already know all they need to know. *The Lady Vanishes.* The world has made up its mind.

WE HAVE been here before.

This is a helicopter, hovering just above the broken ground. This is the woman I love, calling to me through the open door. *I'm going, then.* And I'm shouting back, I can't go. *What?* Go. *Fuck you.* What? *Goodbye, Hope.*

And this is what people are saying when they aren't saying what they mean.

I'm going, then. (Come with me, please, I need you, I can't believe you won't come with me.) I can't go. (My darling, I want never to let you out of my sight again, but goddamn it, you kick me around, you know that?, do you want to see the bruises?, and just this once I'm not putting you first. I'll be there soon enough, this time you can wait for me. If you want me, you'll wait. That's right, a test. Yeah. Maybe it really is.) *What? (You bastard?, you think you can hold out on me? Oh Jesus, Rai, don't play games, not now, not today.)* Go. (Okay, no games. I love you forever and beyond. But this is my work. I'll be there sooner than blinking. Go. I'm right behind you. I love you. Go.)

Fuck you. (I never wanted you to come to Mexico in the first place fuck you but you came anyway fuck you I guess that proves something yeah but I hurt you anyway I was mad I was wrong fuck you and then you helped me fuck you that really churned me up fuck you so I trusted you I really trusted you fuck you then the earth moved and you abandoned me fuck you you took your photographs I could have been dying I could have been broken and dying but you had your work to do fuck you and now you won't come with me fuck you now when I finally worked out that I need you fuck you I want you fuck you maybe I love you I do love you fuck you Rai I love you fuck you. I do.)

What? (What???)

Goodbye, Hope. (Goodbye for a moment, you bastard, but after this I'm never letting you out of my sight. The next time I see you will be the beginning of the rest of our lives.)

Every night for years, I replayed that shouted dialogue in my head, and now I think this may be what it means. Maybe *Goodbye* really was the never-to-be-completed beginning of *Hello*. I hope so, I hope so. Even though it's a meaning that makes the loss weigh more heavily and the pain harder to bear.

WHAT THE pilot says on Televisa: Señora, we took her over the mountains to the seacoast and everywhere below us was a destruction to break the heart. Our thoughts were urgent for our own families, it is true, but we discharged our duty to the end. Our calls ahead to the Villa Huracán were not fulfilled, the telephone was out of service, but the famous personage she insisted on going forward with the arrangement, always she was saying faster, can you not get there in a faster time. For her, to whom what man could say no, we have made our best effort, and when we come to El Huracán it appears she has been blessed with fortune, all is intact, in all our broken motherland this one corner has remained whole to receive herself. As was our pre-arranged plan we land on the sand at the foot of the cliff and she will climb up to Huracán. But on the beach is nobody to carry her baggages which you can easily imagine are plentiful for she is a fashionable one. Of course we can carry the bags, no problem, but understand sirs we are concerned for the machine and also, I confess it, there is a great desire to see once more my wife and sons in Acatlán. Also the personage she is insistent and is a personage of much force of expression, you comprehend, and so it is in compliance with her own desire that her baggages are reposed on the first step of the escalinata to the height and we say our farewells and that is the finish of it.—Excuse, please?—But naturally we were concerned for her safety. It is why we have made two circles over the establishment and have not departed until we have seen him, the other individual who was there.—No, regrettably, other than the distinguished lady personage on the sand we cannot identify any other person. However we have no way left her unattended. That is a scurrilous imputation. The situation at El Huracán at that point is still normal. By the time we leave no misadventure of any type is to be observed.

The Colchis boss Mo Mallick talks to Larry King on CNN. His shoulder-length blond hair, his earnest glasses, his fabulous profile. Excerpts: Sure, Larry, we were scared, I can admit that, who wouldn't be. . . . The house has, or I guess that should be had, that's still so hard to say, it *had* its own generator, so we had some quantity of power, but the phones, the water, that stuff was all down, for the whole coastline as it transpired, I'm telling you these were major heaves. . . . And I had guests, Larry, Chile's probably greatest living writer and his lovely American wife, these were responsibilities also, and what can I say, it simply never occurred to me that she'd make the trip, you know what I mean?, it wasn't the moment for a few super days by the old Pacific sea. Listen, the staff were out of there, I mean like bats out of, not meaning any disrespect, I understand how they felt, I'd probably have done the same myself, but they were *gone*. And I'm like, how quickly can I get myself and my guests to a place of safety, wherever that is, you know? Like, we've been lucky so far but don't push it. . . . It didn't cross my mind for a minute that she would just set herself down, with no plan for an exit, no direction home, you know?, on the *bleep*ing, excuse me, beach.—Excuse me?—Oh, the pilot said he saw . . . ?—No, Larry, I can't say who that would be. The staff are all accounted for, I believe, and my guests and myself, ditto. If there was somebody hanging around there, poor bastard, it's news to me. Maybe a looter, I don't want to be pejorative here, it would be the same way in California, no question, but uncertain times kind of bring forth thieves. I guess he paid a high price, huh.

The seismic moment of an earthquake is measured by multiplying its area (the length of the fault times the width), the amount of slip, and the stiffness of the local rock. The strength of an earthquake is usually characterized by using the logarithm of moment—known as the *magnitude*—rather than the moment itself. Thus all earthquakes, small to large, are ranked from one to nine, each unit of magnitude representing a tenfold increase in strength. A quake of the ninth magnitude is one billion times more powerful than a first-magnitude shock. This system of measurement is named after the American seismologist Charles Richter. Additionally, the intensity of an earthquake, defined as an index of its destructive effect, is classified from I to XII on the so-called Modified Mercalli scale. The monster quake that hits the Pacific coast of Mexico in the early evening of February 14, obliterating the Villa Huracán, the nearby hamlet of Aparajitos, the towns of Puerto Vallarta to the south and of Mazatlán to the north, and much else besides, measures a full nine on the Richter scale, which is to say: as bad as it gets. Also, XII on the Modified Mercalli, meaning complete destruction. Seismologists report the creation of a gigantic new fault, approximately one thousand kilometers long and one hundred kilometers wide, and running more or less exactly along the coastline. The worst earthquakes occur in subduction zones, where tectonic plates collide and one plate is pushed beneath the other. In 1960 a quake with an eight point five magnitude smashed up a big chunk of Chile. For the international seismological community, the 1989 Aparajitos quake signals the sudden, devastating extension to the north of that mighty subterranean war, the crunching encounter of the great plates. It is a major event in the geological history of the earth. A rift along the eternal frontier between the dry land and the sea.

Another possibility, of course, is that it is the first great calamity to be caused by the collision of worlds described by Ormus Cama in his much-derided worldwide bulletin; the beginning of an unimaginable end.

* * *

SHE IS alone when it happens. Perhaps she stands on the breakfast terrace beneath a giant fresno ash, drinking a margarita made with tres generaciones tequila, thinking about an old novelist's exposed genitalia, or about Ormus Cama and his eye patch, his headaches, his prophecies. Or about the future; about me. Imagining her, I have again shrouded her in photographic silence. If the birds shriek, if the wind suddenly howls in the trees, if, as on Prospero's isle, the jungle behind El Huracán is filled with noises, I know nothing of these. A tempest is coming, but I am not interested in spells or usurpations.

Or, she is not alone. Some Caliban emerges from the jungle to reclaim his birthright. She is menaced. Or, she is not menaced. She struggles. No, there is no struggle. There is no Other. The pilot lied to seem more responsible than he was, to save face; that's all. The Other is a phantom, a figment. She is alone, with a margarita in her hand, there is a beautiful sunset. In her last minutes she is bathed in the beauty of the world. Perhaps she sings. I want to think of her singing, against the orange and purple sky.

Though I hear nothing else, yet can I hear her heroic voice raised in song.

Then the ground simply opens and eats her, like a mouth.

A great sweep of Pacific coastline is similarly, simultaneously, devoured. The slip of the earthquake is eleven meters: huge. The ocean boils in and fills the gash in the earth, the tear in reality. Water, earth, fire belch high into the sky. The deaths, the *disappearances,* are measured in the tens, the hundreds of thousands.

The earth closes over her body, bites, chews, swallows, and she's gone.

I CANNOT rightly organize my thoughts.—*I fear I am not in my perfect mind.*—O, she's rubble, and at the bottom of th'abyss!—Vina, the joy of life, the sign of our humanity—disappeared!, in this century of the disappeared, of disappearance—so many people missing from the record—the human race offers the earth god its greatest prize, Vina!!, and the deity, instead of being satisfied, feels its appetite whetted beyond all endurance and restraint, and gulps down a hundred thousand more—Ormus, she's lost to us both, crushed in that muddy embrace—you said it, Ormus, they're your words, the earth learns to rock 'n' roll—Madman, shall I blame you or embrace you?—by singing it, did you will it into being?—Then can you sing her back to life, for yourself, for me?

This was the woman for the love of whom
more lamentation burst out from one lyre
than from the throats of all lamenting women
since the world began. Whose mourning
made a world—brought all things back again,
the forests, valleys, roads and villages;
their cattle, fields and streams; a world
like ours
circled by sun and spanned by stars like ours—
but set quite differently within
those other heavens. So beloved was she.

The scale of the emergency dwarfs individual tragedies. So many dead, so much damage both structural and infrastructural, such a hammer blow to the country's soul, and more: to the human race's sense of ease upon the earth. Roads, bridges, airstrips, whole mountains lie in ruins, or beneath the encroaching sea. A gargantuan relief operation is under way, and access to the devastated area, for all but military and relief-agency personnel, is denied. A few television news crews and stills photographers are given accreditation and taken in and around by army helicopters. International aid requires pictures. We can be of use. My Nebuchadnezzar Agency card—I never did get around to quitting formally—gets me a ride.

So I am deep in the heart of ruination when the Vina photograph goes boffo on the planet's front pages; when she becomes the face of the catastrophe. I am looking at scenes out of Bosch—the decapitated heads of children hanging from the branches of broken trees, women's naked legs sticking vertically upwards, like twin swords, out of "solid" rock—scenes that trouble even a war photographer's stomach. I have no awareness of having helped to create a myth. Even when the colonel in charge of press operations goes out of his way to arrange an over-flight of the site of the vanished Villa Huracán, I understand nothing. He is pandering to the Western world's cult of celebrity, I think. He's probably right: it's good for a few extra column inches, which, translated into dollars, makes this part of the itinerary a real money spinner. As pictures go, this one's no different from the others: the torn land, the intruding ocean, the uprooted trees. Standard disaster imagery, not a palapa or swimming pool or dead starlet to be seen. I am thinking these hard-bitten thoughts when unexpectedly I fall apart. I weep in my bucket seat until the thick marrow-snot comes down my nose. I weep like a howling dog on the grave of his fallen mistress. In the end one of the tv-crew sound engineers asks me to shut the fuck up, I'm louder than the rotor blades, my misery is wrecking the goddamn shot.

These fallen boulders are her tombstone, this brokenness her grave. I shout her name aloud. Vina, Vina.

When we land, back at the Guadalajara army strip, the colonel, a man my own age, comes up to me. You knew her, I think?—Yes, I say.—Then is it your picture? He takes out his wallet and there, folded up, is teetering Vina in the tequila-flooded street. I stare at the badly reproduced image on the worn and smudgy newsprint, while the wind tries to tear it from my hands. Señor, it is a sad time for you, the colonel says, and for sure I have much respect for your personal grief, but please, you can give me on this picture your amiable autograph?

Dazed, I sign my name.

Ormus Cama arrives in Guadalajara in a black linen suit and matching velvet eye patch, leaning on big Will Singh and tiny, antique Clea, with a phalanx of other Singhs to defend him from the world. He has taken two floors of the giant Hyatt on the Plaza del Sol in the modern, yanqui-style Zona Rosa: one entire floor for himself, the other for the Singhs. Clea comes looking for me in my humbler old-town abode. Please come, she says. In all the world it is you only he wishes to see.

Clea's grave, narrow face seems overly burdened by its cargo: a pair of outsize spectacles with clear plastic frames and lenses so thick that, without them, she must be all but blind. I can't guess at her age; she could be anywhere from sixty to a hundred. At her efficiency, her iron loyalty to

Ormus, her indefatigability on his behalf, there is no need to guess.

It's been a long time, I say. (Meaning, what can I say to this bereaved and damaged heart? I, of all people. Should I tell him the truth? Where does honesty end and cruelty begin? What matters more: my need to be known as her lover, or his need not to know? Let him live in ignorance. He's got enough to worry about, what with the imminent end of the world and all.)

Clea is pursing her lips, smoothing her long, belted skirt, faintly shaking her head. My answer has not met with her approval.

Once you were friends, she says, as if that settles it. Meekly, I follow her down to the waiting limousine.

Ormus's floor of the Hyatt is like the *Marie Celeste:* uncannily still. A five-star ghost town at the top of the city. He has had it redecorated in accordance with his minimalist tastes. Almost all the furniture has been removed, all of the pictures and ornaments, and many of the doors. White sheets cover the walls, and the carpets too. There is a small sign by the elevator asking that shoes be removed. This is an unshod, segregated world.

I pad about the soft moonscape in my socks, looking for the great man. At length I hear the sound of an acoustic guitar emanating from a room which still boasts a door. It's an old song, but I know it at once, even though the words are new.

All my life, I worshipped her. Her golden voice, her beauty's beat. How she made us feel, how she made me real, and the ground beneath her feet.

And now I can't be sure of anything, black is white, and cold is heat; for what I worshipped stole my love away, it was the ground beneath her feet.

She was my ground, my favorite sound, my country road, my city street, my sky above, my only love, and the ground beneath my feet.

Go lightly down your darkened way, go lightly underground, I'll be down there in another day, I won't rest until you're found.

Let me love you true, let me rescue you, let me lead you to where two roads meet. O come back above, where there's only love, and the ground's beneath your feet.

Maybe in the otherworld she isn't dead, I'll have to look for her there, he says, seeing me standing flummoxed and trembling in the doorway. So this supposed alternative reality of his has become a version of Rilke's mourning-created world, a lamentation-cosmos *like ours, but set quite differently within those other heavens.* A world of grief made real by song, by art. Whatever. I shake myself out of the music's spell. She's dead, and these fancies are of no use to me.

She was right to trust in nothing, I say aloud. Even the ground betrayed her. Yet, trusting nothing, she was prepared to gamble on love, and that was heroic, nothing less. I stop there, not specifying: love of whom, or how many. Let it be.

He's sitting cross-legged on the floor of the empty room with a twelve-string country guitar across his knees. He looks terrible; his hair is almost white, and thinning. His skin is gray and ill. There was never any surplus weight on him, but he has lost a lot of pounds. He looks old. He is just fifty-two.

Was it you, he asks, without looking at me. At the villa, the other person, was that you. The photograph, et cetera. I need to know.

No, I say. The picture was before. I wasn't there till later, with the press corps.

A silence. He nods, slowly, twice. Okay. This, he accepts.

I always knew there were others, an other, he says, dull-voiced, still staring at the guitar strings. At my request she provided no details. All she said was, he was completely unlike me.

(I remember something else she said. *The two of you are more alike than you know. Only he's going down . . . and you're on the way up.*)

All she said, Ormus goes on, is it was a physical attraction, whereas what we had was the whole thing: love. (His mouth twists, bitterly. So, as it happens, does mine.) This was simultaneously hurtful, because obviously I was not fulfilling her needs, and comforting, because it told me she would stay. But now they're saying in the papers that the other person, whoever he was, looked exactly like me. In fact for a minute there they thought it was me, they called to ask if I'd been in Mexico. Clea and the office had to deal with that. It's pretty funny, right. I first heard about her death because people wanted to know if I was a corpse myself.

It's just speculation, I say. As far as I know there's no trace of any other person, let alone any description of him. Or her. It's just garbage in the papers.

When she was alive I managed not to care about him, he says. Now I need to know who he was. He's my gateway to her, you can understand that. To her underworld, her other reality. He, whoever he is, can help me find her. He can bring her back. Shall I tell you who I think it is?

My heart bangs. Who, I ask.

Gayo, he replies. Gayomart, my twin, who escaped from my head. It makes perfect sense, don't you see. She was fucking both of us, she needed to know both sides of that story. And maybe he died with her, but maybe he's still out there. I have to know which.

I see now that he really is not sane. His is a consciousness that surfaces intermittently, between long, damaging hibernations, and is no longer capable of seeing things as they are beyond his shrouded walls. You're wrong, I tell him. This is useless, stupid. Just sing your song, Ormus, sing it and say goodbye.

You don't get it, he says, looking me in the eye for the first time. The mystery of her life is now as horrible as the fact of her death. You were her friend, Rai. I know we drifted apart but she always liked you. Help me.

It's time to leave. I shrug and shake my head.

No.

He calls after me as I'm leaving. *The earthquake site,* he wants to know. *Was it flimsy?* That makes me stop and turn. It was a wreck, if that's what you mean, I tell him. As if you took a picture of beauty and then systematically broke everything in the picture. It was like that.

He's shaking his head. It's thinning out all over, he says. I don't think it can survive, it's not strong enough. So these places where it just gives out, where it rips, they must be almost translucent. You saw it, didn't you see it? The flimsiness. The weakness of it all.

I saw a catastrophe, I say. I saw the place she died.

ORMUS WILL use all his considerable resources to pursue Vina's phantom lover. He will employ detective agencies, and rewards will be offered. When this becomes known in

New York, that is to say, everywhere, people begin to laugh behind their hands. He is making himself ridiculous, and doesn't care.

On more than one occasion (as I afterwards learn from Clea Singh) the detectives he hires point their fingers in my direction. When this happens, Ormus just laughs, fires them and hires new investigators.

He believes he can see through the surface of things to another truth below, but remains incapable of seeing what's right under his nose.

ORMUS AND I have one thing in common. We're both trying to cling to the reality of the woman we loved, to preserve and deepen her memory. And yes, we both yearn for resurrection, for her impossible return from the dead: our Vina, just as she was. Our wishes, however, are ceasing to signify. Vina in death is assailed by a second seismic force, which swallows her up all over again. Which swallows her up and regurgitates her in a thousand thousand hideous pieces.

This force also goes by the name of love.

CHAPTER SIXTEEN

Vina Divina

That she was loved, of course I always knew. The facts about her public persona were not in doubt: that people in countries she had never visited cherished her for the beauty of her voice; that millions of males desired her body and dreamed of it at night; that women of all ages admired and were grateful for her outspokenness, her fearlessness, her musicianship; that when she campaigned against famine, or for the alleviation of the third world's burden of debt, or on behalf of various environmental and vegetarian agencies, the world's leaders, expecting to patronize her, to pat her on the backside and ignore her demands, were first impressed, then seduced and finally coerced into significant concessions by her quickness of intellect, her determination, her grasp; that she was intensely famous, fabulously photogenic, overwhelmingly sexy and great good fun; and that she was the first superstar of the age of confession, who, by her willingness to bare her scars, to live her private life in public, to talk about her wounds, her mistakes, her faults, found a direct line to the world's ashamed unconfident heart, so that, extraordinary and powerful and successful as she was, she came to be seen as an ordinary woman writ large, flawed yet worthy, strong and weak, self-reliant and needy. She was a rock goddess of the golden age, but she was, improbably, also one of us.

To know all this was nevertheless to be entirely unprepared for the scale of the worldwide response to her death. She was, after all, "only a singer," and not even a Callas or a Sutherland but merely a "low-culture" popular entertainer whose rock group, VTO, had been disbanded for almost two years. Her attempted comeback had hardly been a triumph, her solo record had sold acceptably but not well. These were the signs of a falling star. Given her fame, it was predictable that press, radio and television coverage of her demise would be heavy; that there would be small gatherings of grieving fans; that tears, many of them crocodile, would be freely or opportunistically shed; that there would be a number of determinedly jaundiced, professionally against-the-flow voices seeking to tarnish and diminish her memory; even that scandals hitherto concealed might come to light. But any more extreme reaction would be entirely without precedent. Retrospectives, tribute albums, charitable donations, a surge in back-catalog record sales, a memorial concert or two, and then on to the next business: these were the characteristic stages, the ordained rites of such a passage.

Dead Vina, however, had a surprise up her sleeve for us all.

This posthumous goddess, this underground post-Vina, queen of the Underworld, supplanting dread Persephone on her throne, grew into something simply overwhelming. Alive, and at her peak, she had been a beloved figure, even an icon, an electrifying performer and a charismatic loudmouth, but that was about the size of it, let's not get carried away. Dying when the world shook, by her death she shook the world, and was quickly raised, like a fallen Caesar, to the ranks of the divine.

AFTER THE great earthquake of '89, the footballer Achilles Hector is immediately released unharmed by his captors, thus becoming possibly the only person to benefit from the appalling tragedy. He tells a press conference that he feels as though he is beginning a new life, that having come so close to death it is as if this regained freedom were his afterlife, and our mortal earth Paradise itself. For these incautious words he is predictably condemned by Church leaders and ignominiously obliged to withdraw his happy, hyperbolic remarks.

Meanwhile, the astonishing afterlife of Vina Apsara is rapidly spiraling beyond the power of any authority, spiritual or temporal, to censure or control.

ALL OVER the world, when the news of her death breaks, people pour into the streets, whatever their local hour, pushed out of their homes by a force they can't yet name. It's not the news of the earthquake that galvanizes them, not the myriad Mexican dead they're mourning, it's just her. It's hard to mourn for strangers except conventionally, routinely; the true mourners of the hundred thousand casualties are themselves among the dead. But Vina is not a stranger. The crowds know her, and over and over again, in the streets of Yokohama, Darwin, Montevideo, Calcutta, Stockholm, Newcastle, Los Angeles, people are heard describing her death as a personal bereavement, a death in the family. By her dying she has momentarily re-invented their sense of a larger kinship, of their membership in the family of mankind.

On the front lines of the world's armed conflicts, amid the noxious fumes of ancient hatreds, men and women gather in cratered roads and sniper alleys, and embrace. It was always Ormus Cama's hope that it might be possible for human beings—for himself—to transcend the frontier of the skin, not to cross the color line but to rub it out; Vina had been skeptical, questioning his universalist premises, but in death she has indeed transcended all frontiers: of race, skin, religion, language, history, nation, class. In some countries there are generals and clerics who, alarmed by the Vina phenomenon, by its otherness and globality, seek to shut it down, issuing commands and threats. These prove useless. Inspissated women in sexually segregated societies cast off their veils, the soldiers of oppression lay down their guns, the members of racially disadvantaged peoples burst out from their ghettos, their townships, their slums, the rusty iron curtain is torn. Vina has blown down the walls, and this has made her dangerous. The love of her muddied radiance has spread deep into the territories of the repressed. Defying the authorities, dancing in front of their tanks, linking arms before the faltering rifles, the mourners move to her phantom beat, looking increasingly like celebrants, and even seem prepared to embrace martyrdom in her name. Dead Vina is changing the world. The crowds of love are on the move.

The standard model of the universe tells us that after the big bang, matter was not evenly distributed through the new cosmos. There was clumping, and from these aggregates of matter were born the galaxies and stars. Likewise, as the human race explodes out of doors, it clumps. The favored centers of congregation are not the high places of the world; not the palaces, parliaments, houses of worship or great squares. At first people seek out the low milieux of music, the dance halls, the record stores, the clubs. But these addresses prove unsuitable: not enough room. The crowds begin, instead, to gravitate to stadiums, arenas, parks, maidans—the major venues. Shea Stadium, Candlestick Park, Soldier's Field, San Siro, Bernabeu, Wembley, Munich's Olympic Stadium, Rio's fabulous Maracanà. Even the old Altamont speedway is thronged. In Bombay where she never performed professionally—there was just that one moment on stage with the Five Pennies more than a quarter of a century ago—the Wankhede is full. In Tokyo, Sydney, Johannesburg, Beijing, Teheran, they gather in great numbers and simply wait.

After a slow, even hostile start, the world's authorities are forced into grudging compliance. Days of public mourning are announced, services of remembrance are proposed. The gathered crowds have no interest in this belated reaction of the high and mighty. From their governments they demand only food, water and toilet facilities, and these begin to be provided.

In the packed stadiums, the sound systems offer her music to the crowds. This gift is accepted. Where possible, videotapes of her performances are played on stadium screens. In many countries, national sporting programs are suspended, cinemas and theaters are closed, restaurants stand empty. In all the world, or so it seems, there is only this single, uniting event: the miracle of the stadiums, the people gathered to share their loss. If her death was the death of all the world's joy, this life after death is like that joy reborn and multiplied.

In many stadiums the crowds call for stages to be constructed, and they duly are. Individual men and women walk up on to these stages and begin to declaim. They talk simply, personally but selflessly, about where they were when they first heard her music, and what it has meant in their lives, at their weddings, their children's births, the deaths of their lovers; in solitude and fellowship, on special days and everydays, in their dotage and their youth.

As if for the first time, the importance of this music—her music, and the music of which she has been part—is made manifest as people, motivated by her living-dead memory, find their voices and speak awkward or eloquent words of love. Music—Vina's voice, singing Ormus's melodies—surges round the world, crossing all frontiers, belonging everywhere and nowhere, and its rhythm is the rhythm of life. And Ormus singing his "Song for Vina" answers her. Disembodied, or rather embodied in song, their love hangs in the air, its story no longer limited by corporeal or temporal constraints. This love is music now.

Immortal, I think. Their immortal story, in which my own love's mortal tale is nowhere to be heard.

HERE IS a Gary Larson cartoon of Vina and Jesse Garon Parker, the grotesquely Vegas-rhinestoned Fat Jesse of his latter, pill-popping, burgerizing days. They're alone in a motel room, looking out at the world through the slats of a venetian blind. What's this supposed to be, the dressing room of the undead? A zombie transit zone on the Far Side? Ha ha ha.

The lords of information have been caught napping by the unexpected gigantism of the death and after-death of Vina Apsara, but within hours the greatest media operation of the century is well under way, dwarfing the Olympic games, the Cannes Film Festival, the Academy Awards, the Royal Wedding, the World Cup. Video packages are wrapped, sound is bitten. A global struggle begins, whose prize is something beyond even audience share or advertising revenue. Meaning itself is the prize. Overnight, the meaning of Vina's death has become the most important subject on earth.

Vina significat humanitatem.

Here is Madonna Sangria, speaking of women's pain as men's only access to an understanding of the transcendent—*she died that men might learn how to feel*—and expatiating, also, upon sublimation. *Now that she is safely dead they can say how much they lusted after her, without upsetting their wives.* (Madonna Sangria, who latterly reviled Vina and her music, is now, guiltily, reconstituting herself as the keeper of the flame.)

Here is a female music fan from Japan, a futuristically fashionable young beauty in a Planet of the Apes designer outfit, calling Vina Apsara the great love of her life; no man or ape could ever come as close as this woman she never met.

Here is a fast-mouthed Italian woman admitting Vina to the pantheon of the century's female heroes, and as the true genius of VTO, whose voice could bring about miracles. Ormus Cama? Pah! A parasite. A leech.

Here is a fat Englishwoman, last of the Runts, stuck in her tongue-stud-and-leather time warp, boasting mendaciously of the time she told Vina she was too old to rock. Move over, grandma, and tell grandpa Cama the news.

Here is a great American intellectual's essay, "Death as Metaphor," in which she argues that Vina's life, not her death, was the liberating force; that death is merely death and should be seen as such: as the revenge of the inevitable upon the new.

Here is a recently ordained woman priest, deducing that the Vina phenomenon reveals the world's spiritual hunger, its need for soul food. She invites the stadium crowds to congregate each Sunday in their neighborhood church, *as Vina would very likely have wished.*

Here are Islamist women wearing birdcage shrouds. In their emphatic opinion this madness about a single immoral female reveals the moral bankruptcy and coming annihilation of the decadent and godless Western world.

Vina, who was driven from home to home, is claimed by the places that drove her out: rural Virginia, upstate New York. India claims her, because of her paternal bloodline; England, because it's where her singing career began; Manhattan, because all that is mythic on today's earth is a citizen of New York.

Here is a cultural-studies guru, Primo Uomo, repeating for the one millionth time the oft-iterated idea that Vina has become the patron divinity of the age of uncertainty, the goddess with the feet of clay.

Here are two British psychoanalysts. This one, the young lazy-eyed hunky one, author of *Winking, Nibbling and Licking* and *Sex: The Morning After,* speaks in awed tones of a mammoth spontaneous act of group therapy. That one, a grumpy codger of the old school, is haughtily contemptuous, criticizing the way in which the Vina event privileges raw sentimentality over reason, so that now we can no longer think, only feel. This one calls the phenomenon populist-democratic. That one fears it may be crypto-fascist, the origin of a new kind of intolerant mob.

Here are literary critics and drama critics. The literary critics are divided; the lisping old warhorse Alfred Fiedler Malcolm quotes Marlowe's Faustus—*Then will I headlong run into the earth: Earth, gape! O, no, it will not harbor me!*—and tries to build a complex theory about great celebrity being a Promethean theft of divine fire, whose price is this posthumous hell-on-earth in which the dead woman is actually rendered incapable of dying, and is constantly renewed, like the liver of Prometheus, to be devoured by insatiable vultures calling themselves devotees. This is eternal torment masquerading as eternal love, he says. Let the lady rest in peace. He is rudely ridiculed by the two young turks on the panel, Nick Carraway and Jay Gatsby, who mock his arrant élitism and offer a spirited defense of the place of rock music in society, though they are also fashionably scornful of the low quality of language used by the speakers in the stadiums, their repetitiveness, the use of doggerel rhyming and tabloid cliché, the worrying prevalence of received ideas about the afterlife (Vina living forever, in the stars, in our hearts, in every flower, in every new-born child). These ideas, Gatsby says sharply, are not very cutting-edge; not very rock 'n' roll.

The drama panel is divided too. There is praise for the spontaneous, improvisatory, street-theater rawness of the phenomenon, but the British participants bemoan the inordinate length of the global mourning, the French regret the absence of a firm directing hand, the Americans are concerned about its lack of leading players or a viable second act. All the theater people unite, however, to complain that their views are receiving insufficient attention, that they are as usual being treated as the poor relations, the beggars at the feast.

Here are tv biopic-film producers, advertising for lookalikes. Here are the open casting calls. Here are the lines of hopefuls, stretching round various blocks.

Here is Rémy Auxerre, calling the size of the phenomenon a product of the *feedback loop.* In the days before globalized mass communication, he argues, an event could occur, pass its peak and fade away before most people on earth were even aware of it. Now, however, the initial purity of what happens is almost instantly replaced by its televisualization. Once it's been on tv, people are no longer acting, but *performing.* Not simply grieving, but *performing grief.* Not creating a phenomenon out of their raw unmediated desires, but rushing to be part of a phenomenon they have seen on tv. This loop is now so tight that it's almost impossible to separate the sound from the echo, the event from the media response to it. From what Rémy insists on calling the *immediatization of history.*

Here are two wild-haired New Quakers, a paranoiac and a mystic, probably both Gary Larson fans, denying her death. . . . Where's the body? Just show me the body, okay? She's not dead, somebody wanted her out of the way is all, we should be storming the Pentagon, the United Nations, you know? . . . No, she's free, man, only we are not worthy of her, we have to purify ourselves, and at the hour of our cleanness she will cometh again, dig, maybe from a spaceship?, maybe from a chariot of the gods?, to liberate us. Like Buddha Jesus, man, she liveth.

Television.

BACK AT the Orpheum in the winter cold, alone and bereft, I hug myself and shiver while my white breath hangs in the air. I'm sitting out on the roof in my hat and coat with my hands over my cold-stung ears, trying to conjure up Vina sunbathing naked in the height of summer, Vina stretching her body and turning to me with a lazy faithless smile. But it's too cold, and anyway the racket is everywhere, there's no escape from the war of meanings, the white air is full of words. *Diachronically speaking, this is an event in history, to be understood within time, as a phenomenon with certain linear antecedents, social, cultural, political. Synchronically, however, all versions of it exist simultaneously, collectively forming a contemporary statement about art and life . . . its importance lies in the random meaninglessness of the death . . . her radical absence is a void or an abyss into which a tide of meanings can pour . . . she has become an empty receptacle, an arena of discourse, and we can invent her in our own image, as once we invented god . . . no possibility of the phenomenon fizzling any time soon because the phase of exploitation has now set in, the shirts bearing the last photograph, the commemorative coins, the mugs, the tackiness, her old schoolmates selling their stories, her army of casual lovers, her entourage, her friends . . . these are multiplier effects, she's caught in an echo chamber and the noise bounces round and round, getting boomier, fuzzier, less distinct . . . it's just noise now . . . and imagine, if she had lived, the dying of her flame, her slow descent towards non-fame, towards nothing . . . that really would have been an ending, a tumble into the Underworld, and the worst part is she would still have been alive. Maybe it's better this way. For ever young, right? Well, young-looking, anyway. Pretty fucking fantastic for a woman of her years.*

I find myself rising to my feet, bellowing formlessly, waving my arms at the blind sky, with cold tears freezing on my face. As if my rooftop's a Tower of Silence and Vina's living memory lies here, naked, beneath the circling vultures, helpless and unguarded except for me.

After forty days the crowds vacate the stadiums, in response to Ormus Cama's direct appeal, and slowly the surface regularity of the planet's daily life resumes. On Ormus's behalf, the Singhs are frequently in court, seeking to protect the "Vina property" from crass exploitation. The new Vina look-alike Quakette, a doll that sings a stupid song until its stand first begins to vibrate, then cracks open and gulps her down, is a particular target. It seems that all the cascading emotion of the Vina phenomenon will end in the slave market of capital. One minute she's a goddess, and the next she's *property.*

ONCE AGAIN, I'm underestimating her. It is true that commercial interests will do their damnedest to possess and use her, that her face will continue to appear on magazine covers, that there will be video games and CD-ROMs and instant biographies and bootleg tapes and cynical speculation about her possible survival and every kind of Internet chat-room baloney. It is also true that her own "side"—her record label and, in the rôle of her management and business team, Ormus and the Singhs—will capitalize on the Vina Effect too, putting her face on the milk, the bread, the wine, as well as the vegetarian meals and records.

(I once read a story about a woman who loathed her lazy slob of a husband. When he died she had him cremated and put his ashes in an hourglass, which she set on her mantelpiece with the words, *At last, you bastard, you're going to do some work.* Ormus's love for Vina is not in doubt, but he, too, is sending her ghost out to do business for the family firm.)

All this is true. But what will become evident during the course of the year is that something like an earthquake is building within people, that in countries all over the globe Vina's adoring constituency has acquired a taste for collective action and radical change. Instability, the modern condition, no longer frightens them; it now feels like possibility. This is Vina's true legacy, not the acres of mawkish commentary or the bad-taste dolls.

And the heaving earth, too, has more changes in store.

THIS IS the way I remember it.

That whole first year after she died, I was badly off balance, not knowing what to do for the best, where to put my own distress, how to continue. I kept recalling a day on Juhu Beach, and a girl in a Stars-and-Stripes swimsuit badmouthing everything in sight. That was the day I drew my picture of the world as I wanted it to be, the picture I inhabited from that day on, until the day she died. Now it felt like somebody had snatched the picture out of my hands and ripped it to bits.

When you have no picture of the world, you don't know how to make choices—material, inconsequential or moral. You don't know which way is up, or if you're coming or going, or how many beans make five.

(Nineteen eighty-nine was also the year everybody else's picture broke, the year we were all plunged into an unframed limbo: the formless future. I'm aware of these facts. But that's politics and seismology, and I'll come to it later. I'm talking now about what happened to me.)

I'd wake up thinking she was in the room, and then lie in

the dark, shaking. I'd see shadows move in the corners of my eyes and they were her too. Once I rang her private phone line at the Rhodopé and she answered after the first ring. *Hello. I can't come to the phone right now. Please leave a message and I'll get back to you as soon as I can.* I understood that Ormus had not been able to make himself erase her voice. After that I called the number a dozen or more times a day. Often, when I rang, the line was busy. I wondered how many other lost souls were pushing buttons on their phones, just to hear those two dozen words. Then I thought that perhaps there was just one other caller. Ormus Cama, like me, needed repeatedly to hear his dead wife's last recording.

I'll get back to you as soon as I can, a promise I needed her to keep. But what was the message I should leave? What was the communication that would bring her back from the dead?

Briefly, I felt my heart go out to Ormus Cama, my rival in love. Now my rival for nobody's hand. In the midst of that ocean of "love," here were these two shipwrecked lovers, Ormus and Rai, unable to open their hearts to each other, unable to help each other, making stupid telephone calls to the dead from their sinking rafts.

One year after her death, somebody erased the tape—I'm guessing it was Clea Singh, trying to haul Ormus out of his despondent slough—and that day I wept again, as if Vina had just that moment been gobbled up by the hungry earth.

Of all the things said and written about her, the comments that made most sense to me were the ones about death being just death, the arguments against interpretation. Don't make her a metaphor. Just let her rest in peace. I wanted to fight against the billowing firestorm of meanings, I wanted to put on my fireman's hat and turn a hose on the flames. Meanings beamed down from the satellite-crowded skies, meanings like amorphous aliens, putting out pseudopods like suction pads and sucking at her corpse. At one point I tried to construct a text of my own, some nonsense about the heroism of rejecting interpretation, the abrasive but desirable embrace of absurdity. But I got bogged down in ethics. How to live a moral life in an absurd universe, and so on. I didn't want to opt for quietism, to say it was better simply to cultivate one's garden. Something in me retained a desire for engagement with the world. I tore the piece up and spent my days leafing through my portfolio of Vina pix and, until the tape was wiped, calling her on the phone.

DURING THAT first year, noting that I had largely ceased to go out, that when I wanted to eat I would order in, that most of this food was liquid, and that my long-term cleaner had quit because the place was getting to be like a slum, my fellow Orpheum residents took it upon themselves to "save me." Johnny Chow came to advise, gravely, that I was paying too much attention to death. That was a laugh. Sugar Ray Robinson, Lucille Ball, the Ayatollah Khomeini, Laurence Olivier, R. D. Laing, Irving Berlin, Ferdinand Marcos, Bette Davis, Vladimir Horowitz, "La Pasionaria," Sakharov, Beckett *and* Vina, in one year, I pointed out thickly: it's Armageddon out there. Never a great debater, Chow withdrew, shaking his elegant head. Mack Schnabel suggested I make a selection of my Vina pictures and then hold a show in the building's gallery space. That was a tough one. Would such an exhibit look like a dignified personal tribute or just another case of an opportunist schmo jumping on the unstoppable Vina bandwagon? I couldn't make up my mind. Anyway, it was a while before I got round to finalizing the selection. Most days I suffered from blurred, or even double vision. Clarity was not my strongest point in those unhappy months.

Basquiat came up to talk to me about girls, which was sweetly conventional of him, considering his own astonishing preferences. Fantastique weemain are beursteeng out all ovair, he wanted me to know. Aftair so long, it ees no good to be alone 'ere weez your fantômes.

Fantômes is correct, I told him. There's a beautiful woman who keeps getting into my pictures, I don't know how. I photograph an empty room, my bathroom, maybe, I'm spending a lot of time in my bathroom, and when I develop the roll she's looking at me out of a mirror. No, it's not Vina, it's someone else completely. A haunting stranger. So you see that now there are two.

This dooble expozhair idée of yours, he said. Eet ees gone too far, I theenk.

Finally they approached me as a group to read me some

loving version of the riot act. Say yes to life, clean up your act, take a minute to smell the roses, the usual formulae. I must admit they made quite an effort. They got the place into some sort of shape, cleaned out the drinks cupboard and the bathroom cabinet, dragged me down the street for a shave and a haircut, and threw a party in my apartment, featuring all the most desirable unattached women they knew (and this, given our profession, was a great many). I understood what was being done for me and why. Mostly friendship, yes, and for that I was and remain profoundly grateful. But there was also the other side of the coin. People don't like being around despair. Our tolerance for the truly hopeless, for those who are irremediably broken by life, is strictly limited. The sob stories we like are the ones that end before we're bored. I understood that I had good and true friends in these three men, that it was all for one and one for all and these were my musketeers. I also saw that I needed to behave better for their sakes. I had become their nagging toothache, their dose of gut-rot, their ulcer. I needed to get better before they decided to cure themselves of me.

If friendship is a fuel, the supply of it is not endless.

In the middle of my so-called coming-out party, I looked over at Aimé-Césaire and saw the mark of death on him, and the party began suddenly to seem like a wake for that beautiful man who, like Finnegan in the song, was sitting up gaily and enjoying his own farewell do. I knew about Schnabel also, that since his punishing divorce he continued to be at war with his ex-wife Molly, who had successfully obtained court orders preventing him from going within a mile of his two kids, and who visited Mack's father on his deathbed to tell him, falsely, that Mack was a heroin addict, guilty of both violence towards and sexual abuse of the boys. Johnny Chow had his own saga of catastrophes, mostly connected with gambling. Were these people from whom I was prepared to take advice?

Yes, I said to myself. Better a whore than a nun, better a wounded soldier than someone who never heard the crump of the guns.

At that moment I saw Johnny Chow forcing his way through the crowd of revellers, grinning demonically, with Vina Apsara on his arm.

* * *

I'D HEARD about the impersonation craze, the Vina supper-club/cabaret look-alikes, the underground, heavy-metal and reggae Vinas, the rap Vinas, the Vina drag queens, the Vina transsexuals, the Vina hookers on the Vegas Strip, the Vina strippers outnumbering the Marilyns and Long Tall Texans on amateur nights around these infinitely varied United States, the porno-Vinas on the adult cable channels and closed-circuit hotel tvs, the hardcore under-the-counter blue-video-Vinas, and the innocent biannual gatherings of dweeby karaoke Vinas whose numbers rivaled even the indefatigable *Star Trek* conventioneers. In point of fact Vina had once been a guest star on the *Next Generation* television series, conjured up on the holodeck to sing for an enamored Worf. He taught her Klingon and she taught him Hug-me, or another similar-sounding tongue. When the Trekkies remembered this they invited the Vina people to join forces with them, but Vina was bigger than the *Enterprise* now, she was in a continuum of her own, perhaps even the fabled Q.

There was a famous production of *Hamlet* in which Jonathan Pryce, the actor playing the Prince of Denmark, "produced" the Ghost from within himself, like a channeler or spirit medium, in an astonishing feat of body and voice control. The Vina impersonators did it the easy way, using costumes and recordings, but the idea was the same. In their own bodies they conjured up their fantasy beloved from the dead.

It's a few steps beyond Mizoguchi too, I thought. In *Ugetsu,* the poor yokel taken in by the mysterious aristocratic beauty was just in love with a ghost. But these people aren't merely under a dead woman's spell, they're actually trying to be her, wearing her kimonos, powdering their faces, walking the walk. This is a new form of auto-eroticism. Guised as Vina, these mimic women are making love to themselves.

There was some disagreement as to which Vina most merited commemoration, the firebrand Afro-Vina of her younger days, big-haired, big-voiced, big-mouthed and sexually rampant, or red-haired Mexi-Vina, older but still hot, her voice never better, her aura a little wiser, or Death-Vina, the sad-eyed lady of the broken lands. In the end, pragmatism ruled. The younger impersonators did the early Vina, the older men (yes, and women too) made the latter-day Vina their own.

This Vina, the one on Chow's arm, was unmistakably an older guy. Chinese too, which inevitably made the resemblance imperfect, but he'd put in some hard hours in front of his make-up mirror, darkening his skin, taking trouble with the shape of his eyes. He'd studied her swinging gait, the movement of her mouth, her attitude. And the red wig was very good. Tell me now if this is a bad idea, Johnny asked as they reached me, only we thought it might, oh shit, defuse something if she were in some sense here. Like Adult Children Of Alcoholics, you know that group, it can help to know you're not alone.

I so don't want to bum you out, this China-Vina said disarmingly in a fine baritone voice, and actually bowed. That's so not it. I much honored her, long time now, this is my way to give her respect.

It's fine, I told Johnny. Really. It's cool. Great job, I added to the gratified cross-dresser. Do you want to sing later, or what?

I mime, he said, breaking out in a big, proud smile. I brought my tape deck, if that's okay to do.

Go for it, I advised him, and forced myself to smile dazzlingly back. The look of relief on Chow's face told me I'd done the right thing. My friends would feel better about me now, and—with a sense of relief on all sides—they'd be more okay with leaving me alone.

For long periods, during year two after Vina, I lived alone by the sea in America. *What do you love?* I had asked her at Juhu, and she answered, *I love the sea.* That, at least, I regained, though she was gone: the ocean breezes on which I smelled her pungent, lost perfume; the beach. This long golden strand was a far cry from Cuffe Parade's urban graciousness, from Apollo Bunder's bustle, but it filled me with more than one kind of nostalgia. Cruising to the ocean past the potato fields, the cornfields, the turning banks of sunflowers, the glistened polo horses, the sweet birds of youth and the tick-bearing deer; past the exotically casual American rich in their cut-offs, their halter necks, their chinos, their polo shirts, their classic convertibles, their Range Rovers, their monied old age, their gilded childhood and their potent prime; past the Shinnecock Indians trimming the hedges and cleaning the pools and maintaining the tennis courts and mowing the grass and in general tending to the high-priced, stolen land; past the honk of the railroad and the cry of the geese and the hissing of summer lawns, I was turned back, after a long age, towards thoughts of home. Home as another lost jewel, as something else swallowed up, by time, by choice. As something else now unavailable, glowing up through the water like sunken gold, breathing painfully under the plowed earth like a lover gone down to Hell.

I did pull myself together sufficiently to assemble that show of photographs, *After Vina,* which was well and seriously received. I don't deny that this pleased me. The truth is that after all I was not immune to the disease of making Vina mean something, and what she meant to me was love, certainly, but also mystery, a woman ultimately unquantifiable and impossible to grasp, my window into the inexplicable.

The mystery at the heart of meaning. That was her.

I invited Ormus to the opening but he didn't show. I hadn't really expected it. There was one small fracas: at one point a group of New Quakers burst into the Orpheum gallery to denounce me noisily for implying that Vina was deceased, and these greasy, bikerish figures took some ejecting. When they had gone, I found myself standing next to a slender old Indian gentleman in a J. Crew check shirt and jeans, whom I did not at first recognize in this off-duty manifestation.

I want to thank you, he said in his curious, flat-accented way, for sharing my daughter with me. It surely is a positive and healing experience to be here. Yes, sirree, it surely is.

It was the Rhodopé doorman, Shetty. In the depths of my own grief I had callously forgotten that Vina's father was still alive.

MY ENCOUNTER with Doorman Shetty is like a whip of cold water across the face. It wakes me from my long unhealthy reverie, my heartsick inwardness, and renews my awareness—which is the essence of the photographer's art—of the immediacy, the presentness, of things. At the end of his shift the next day I meet up with Shetty, who is back in uniform, and we go for coffee to the Buddhist-organic place across the street from the Orpheum, that Eastern-scented room with its oddly soothing combination of great dark coffee, stripped dark wood and pale barefoot waitresses in white dresses that drag on the floor and button all the way up to the throat. Shetty seems calm, though the joviality I recall is not in evidence. He is happy, he says, that Vina found him in his old age and that the distance between them was thereby at least a little reduced. This he tells me in the new vocabulary of self-regard. *We dealt with some issues. We confronted the anger that needed to be faced and we did some good healing work. We hugged. We became comfortable with each other. We had some quality time.*

They even went into therapy together, he reveals. The therapist, an Indochinese woman named Honey and married to a successful Wall Street arbitrageur of conservative Nicaraguan origins, one day hung a giant pink piñata in the shape of a rabbit from the ceiling fan in her office and handed Vina a wooden stick. As Vina slugged the piñata she was encouraged to say whom she was really hitting out at, and why. She went for it with a vengeance, and Shetty accordingly heard many painful complaints about himself, but the spectacle of his famous daughter beating the bejesus out of a giant salmon-colored papier-mâché bunny like a retard S&M queen was so absurd that he laughed. He laughed until he cried, especially when the piñata gave way under the force of Vina's assault and the usual children's sweets and fluffy toys tumbled out, all the gifts he had failed to give his daughter when she was a child.

How did that make you feel, Honey the therapist asked him. He wiped his eyes but the chortling wouldn't stop.

Let me tell you what I think, he began, and guffawed.

Never mind what you think, she interrupted. Let's stay with what you feel.

Shetty, unable to countenance the hilarious idiocy of this remark, got up and walked out, still laughing.

The trouble was, he tells me ruefully, Vina thought the piñata was a great idea, so she felt like I was laughing at her. After that we, ah, re-experienced our previous unresolved relational negativity. We remained on friendly terms but we didn't engage any more. This was classic avoidance behavior. We didn't confront. We sidestepped. We didn't heart-to-heart.

There is a great deal more he wants to confess: how his long decline from successful butcher to down-and-out hobo began the day after he took the young Vina to dinner at the Rainbow Room and then packed her off to live with the Doodhwalas in Bombay. He wishes to speak of fate, of a self-imposed curse, of having suffered the consequences of his failures as a parent deeply enough and for long enough. He is preparing to ask me for the expiation he never fully received from his dead daughter. Doorman Shetty is pursuing a dead Vina too, like all the rest of us he needs to raise her from the dead to give him peace.

Still too shaky myself to carry his additional weight, I cut him off in mid-flow. So as not to appear too rude, I inquire after his son-in-law, Ormus. How is the rock legend dealing with his loss? To my surprise, my pro-forma inquiry occasions a savage tirade.

Listen, this was all in the *National Enquirer*! This was in *People* magazine! What, you didn't hear, you were out of town?, I'm guessing on the moon?

Almost, I reply, thinking of the sea of forgetfulness, the sea of storms, the white white sand and the sea.

Shetty snorts, and dishes.

ORMUS CAMA, the notorious recluse, has added to his list of bizarre obsessions the growing imitation-Vina industry, making a full collection of the available pornographic film and video material, and showing up unannounced and surrounded by burly Sikh bodyguards at nightclubs and strip joints, to check out the quality of the impersonations. He is believed to be a patron of certain brothels and élite "home delivery" services specializing in celebrity look-alikes. On one occasion he was actually caught *in flagrante* with a counterfeit Vina in the back of a super-stretch, but when the sharp-eyed cop who saw the hooker responding to a signal and entering the limo understood what was going on, whose surrogate was doing what to whom, he didn't have the heart to take the matter further and let the participants go without further ado. (The whore in question, Celeste Blue, subsequently tried to parlay the incident into a financially beneficial little scandal but was foiled by the absence of any charges. Clea Singh, commenting on Blue's interview in the *Enquirer,* said only: It sounds like the lady has a big mouth.)

For many years the most private of men, Ormus—eye-patched and earmuffed—is now, says the Doorman, a regular attendee at the mushrooming Vina conventions, often agreeing to adjudicate at the look-alikes' beauty contest, stipulating only that he should be the sole judge. The winning Vina, if she is thought to be of a sufficiently high standard, is sent up to his suite after the contest, and afterwards escorted out by a firm-jawed Clea Singh and compensated so handsomely that, thus far, there have been no complaints.

Ormus has also—reversing the attitudes of a lifetime—been visiting a guru. Her name is Goddess-Ma, and as the upheavals of the age have become more numerous and dramatic her popularity among the élite of New York society, who are always easily alarmed by global instability and loud noises, has increased by leaps and bounds. Goddess-Ma is from India, allegedly illiterate, made her name in Düsseldorf and arrived in the United States "by a miracle." It is rumored that there is no record of her journey to New York in the files of any airline or shipping company. Yet her immigration status has never been investigated, which would indicate to the skeptical observer that the truth is more conventional than it is being made to seem, but is treated by the Goddess-Ma people as further proof of her existence within an impregnable aura of blessing and safety. Goddess-Ma is very small, but young and beautiful enough to be a movie star, and has powerful—and anonymous—backers who have installed her right in the Rhodopé Building, three floors down from Ormus. From this splendid residence she has issued a number of "Goddess Sayings" that have reverberated in the rarefied air of the city's better locales. India-blah, Bharat-burble, the so-called Wisdom of the East, is definitely back in fashion. In fact, India in general is hotter than ever: its food, its fabrics, its doe-eyed dames, its direct line to Spirit Central, its drums, its beaches, its saints. (When India explodes a nuclear device, the notion of Holy Mother

India takes a few dents, but it is quickly agreed by *le tout* Manhattan that in this matter India's unwise political leaders have betrayed the land's true spirit. The valuable Oriental Wisdom concept suffers little lasting damage, unlike the much-shaken planet.)

Unsurprisingly, Goddess-Ma has been commenting on the Vina phenomenon. Beneath the unstable earth, she Says, there has always been a woman keeping things together, in all cultures. Our Indian earth mother parted her lips to receive pure Sita, falsely accused of having been defiled by Ravana, after Lord Ram rejected her on his spin doctors' advice. Our Greek mother Persephone sits beside Hades in his subterranean kingdom.

Now Vina, our beloved Vina, has joined these women, the greatest of women, who hold up the earth from below as mighty Atlas holds up the sky.

O dancing Earth, Says Goddess-Ma. In our Indian Puranas we learn that Lord Shiva danced You into being, He, the Lord of the Dance. Whereas the Greeks tell of Eurynome, the goddess of everything, who loved dancing and created the sea and the land so that she had someplace to groove. I Say that such also are We!, Men and Women!, dancing our world into being. I Say, Dance! And if the earth shakes, think that Vina dances, too, and see what new miracles She unveils.

As Goddess-Ma's popularity grows, as her beautiful face and her feel-good Sayings do their irresistible work on that city in which beauty and congratulation are the surest roads to success, there are dissenting noises, from the followers of older spiritual Paths and from large segments of New York's Indian community. When asked about her critics, Goddess-Ma is sharp. Mine is the true Indian way, she Says with complete assurance. These converts and long-term expatriates are happier peddling and swallowing their glamorized exotica.

(Goddess-Ma has already learned the laws of spin. Take the worst thing that is said about you, accuse your accusers of the selfsame fault, be more beautiful and media-friendly than they, and you will carry all before you, like a storm.)

Writing this, I think of Darius Cama. I think of William Methwold. I remember their attempts to build bridges between the mythologies of East and West. I remember my own hours in Darius's library, my seduction by his storehouse of ancient tales. I wonder what the old gents with their love of scholarship and uninterest in hocus-pocus would have made of Goddess-Ma and her brass-bold bid for transcultural divinity, which includes a shameless attempt to co-opt dead Vina, to hijack her popular tragedy. New York, where you go to make it big, has no problem with Goddess-Ma's hard-sell tactics, which are, in fact, admired and increase her following. Also, the city's dance venues report a significant increase in numbers. The young of Manhattan are following the pint-size seer's terpsichorean advice.

Shetty is even-handedly contemptuous both of pretty, ambitious Goddess-Ma and of those who follow her. That Ormus Cama has been going down three floors to visit her a couple of times a week only proves that he's totally lost it, in the Doorman's forcefully expressed opinion.

And there's worse to come. Ormus is apparently chasing dead Vina down every rabbit hole he can find. It is Shetty's contention that the rock god is now a heavy user of major narcotics, pursuing his dead wife along trails of powder, reading her smoke signals, feeling her needle in his veins. The Singhs manage everything, the businesses, the royalties, the women, the drugs, they have enclosed him within their fierce loyalty, it's even harder to get anywhere near him than it used to be. It is probable that his devoted retinue—determined as its members are to fulfill his every whim, to slake his every thirst, to offer him whatever partial compensations might momentarily offset his irreducible loss—is in fact killing him with love.

It's the coward's way, Shetty tells me, and I'm surprised by the sudden brutality of his words. If he wants to be with my poor girl so much, then why not be a man and shoot himself in the mouth. Yeah. Why doesn't he just blow his head off and to hell with everything. Then they'll be together until the end of time.

I liked you better when you were cheerful, I tell him. When you were rolling with the punches, I liked you fine.

And the same to you, he says, leaving. Don't think you're the only SOB who can remember when.

* * *

DOORMAN SHETTY doesn't know it, but he's echoing Plato. This is what the great philosopher has Phaedrus say in the Symposium's first speech about love: *The gods honor zeal and heroic excellence towards love. But Orpheus . . . they sent back unfulfilled from Hades, showing him a phantom of the woman . . . because he seemed to them a coward . . . [who] didn't venture to die for the sake of love, as did Alcestis, but rather devised a means of entering Hades while still alive.* Orpheus, the despised *citharode*—the singer with the lyre or, let's say, guitarist—the trickster who uses his music and wiles to cross boundaries, between Apollo and Dionysus, man and nature, truth and illusion, reality and the imagination, even between life and death, was evidently not to austere Plato's taste. Plato, who preferred martyrdom to mourning, Plato the ayatollah of love.

The pursuit of love beyond death is a harsh and joyless chase. I judge Ormus less harshly than would the Platonic Phaedrus, or that other, rather less eminent thinker, his personal gatekeeper and his dead wife's dad. I know what he's going through, because I've been down that tunnel too. I'm *there.*

Here he is, Ormus: unable to work, succumbing to Vina's weaknesses—the drink, the drugs—hoping to find her in her faults, by making them his own. And these are his chemically induced visions of her, of Vina in many guises. Here she is bearing the thousand faces of the women in whom he searched for her after she fled Bombay, also the thousand faces of all the women he gave up for her sake during the ten celibate years. They are all Vina now.

Here she is as herself. He looks on her and feels himself turn to stone.

As the Vina phenomenon swells and grows, he feels himself losing his grip on the truth of her; his Vina is slipping away for ever, dying a second time. The earthquake has already claimed her but after the earthquake comes the tidal wave, drowning Vina under the tsunami of her selves.

As she becomes all things to all people so she becomes nothing to him—nothing he knows or loves. And there is a worse thought: as she slides ever deeper into the abyss, buried beneath an avalanche of versions, as she enters the halls of the underworld to take her seat on her dark throne, is it possible that she is forgetting him?

Rilke's Eurydike, entering the nether realms, grows quickly forgetful of the light. The darkness stains her eyes, her heart. When Hermes speaks of Orpheus, this Eurydike terribly answers: *Who?*

The name Eurydice/Eurydike means "wide-ruler." The first recorded use of this name in tellings of the Orpheus story occurs in the first century B.C.E. It may therefore be a relatively recent addition to the tale. In the third century B.C.E. she was called Agriope, "savage watcher." This is also one of the names of the witch goddess Hecate; and of wide-ruling Queen Persephone herself.

Which precipitates an avalanche of questions: Did Eurydice—of whose origins we know little, although the official version is that she was a wood nymph, a dryad—actually bubble up from the Underworld to capture Orpheus's heart? Was she an avatar of the Queen of Darkness herself, hunting for love in the illuminated world above? And therefore, in being swallowed by the earth, was she merely going home?

Is the failure of Orpheus to rescue her a token of the inevitable fate of love (it dies); or of the weakness of art (it can't raise the dead); of Platonic cowardice (Orpheus won't die to be with her; no Romeo he); or of the obduracy of the so to speak gods (they harden their hearts against lovers)?

Or—most startlingly—is it a consequence of the reassertion by Eurydice of her true identity, her dark side, her citizenship of the night? And Gayomart, Ormus's dead twin, his own night self, his Other: is he her true husband, who sits beside her upon her obsidian chair?

Here's my answer. In the obsessive contemplation of death we may begin to hear, from the dead, whispers of how they lived. Hades, Persephone, all that belongs, for me, to the realm of the so-to-speak. But Vina's hidden self *during her lifetime* was no metaphor. The person she hid with was me, the self she concealed from her husband she revealed to me. Forget Gayomart; I was the flesh-and-blood Other beside her. I was her other love.

Maybe this is what Ormus can't admit to himself: that the Vina he doesn't know is not a construct of her death or afterlife. What he can't stand is the mystery of her earthly hours. Her nights above the ground.

This is a riddle I can solve but will not. *Yes, it was me,* I could say, *she was going to leave you, you crazy bastard, she was on the point of ditching you and your eye-patched visions and your whistling ears and your ten-year gestures and your famous grand passion, and making a beeline for my big brass bed.*

I am the King of her Underworld, I could tell him. *She belongs to me.*

I can't tell him this because I've lost her too, and now we're burning in the same fire. O Ormus, my brother, my self. When you scream the noise bursts from my throat. When I weep the tears seep from your eyes. I will not hurt you more.

And because I can't, I won't, he slides deeper into the bottomless pit: not Vina's abyss, but his own. He can't believe in her soiling, though she lie ever so deep in the soil. He sees her glowing up through the fog of earth and stone. He imagines her corpse as a blazing candle, phosphorescent, undimmed. His love illuminates her. He seeks her through the night.

He hopes each night to wake and see a familiar figure standing at his window, looking out at the shadowed park, the park before dawn. How often he pictures himself slipping out of bed to stand silently beside her sweet shade and watch the fingers of first light slip across the tall houses and the trees.

I know all his fears, all his hopes, all his dreams, because they are also mine.

EARTHQUAKES, SCIENTISTS say, are common phenomena. Globally speaking there are around fifteen thousand tremors a decade. Stability is what's rare. The abnormal, the extreme, the operatic, the unnatural: these rule. There is no such thing as normal life. Yet the everyday is what we need, it's the house we build to defend us against the big bad wolf of change. If, finally, the wolf is reality, the house is our best defense against the storm: call it civilization. We build our walls of straw or brick not only against the vulpine instability of the times but against our own predatory natures too; against the wolf within.

That's one view. A house can also be a jail. Big wolves (ask Mowgli, ask Romulus and Remus, ask Kevin Costner, we don't have to rely on the Three Little Pigs) are not necessarily bad. And anyhow, this new time of shocks and cracks is out of the ordinary, as even the seismologists agree. The number of tremors is up to over fifteen thousand a *year.*

Everybody reads the papers, right, so I don't have to spell out in too much detail how the world has changed in these last years, the sudden decrease in the height of the Himalayas, the crack across the Hong Kong–China frontier that turned the New Territories into an island, the sinking of Robben Island, the raising of Atlantis at Santorini-Thera in the southernmost Cyclades, the transformation of rock 'n' roll into a weapon that blasted Panama's dictator-on-the-run out of his hideout, and so forth. Everybody gets the new rolling-news stations, so we've all watched the earthquakes together, the old order falling, live, as it happens, we have seen the jails bursting open, the breaking of the so to speak seventh seal was a major breaking news story, and we're all wondering who those four horsemen are. Like Butch Cassidy and the Sundance Kid when the Pinkerton men just kept on coming after them, we turn to one another and ask, wonderingly, *Who are those guys?*

So to speak.

These frontier earthquakes are the wonder of the age, aren't they? Did you see that fault that just ripped out the whole iron curtain? "Unforgettable" doesn't even come close. And after the Chinese opened fire in Tiananmen, did you see the rift open up along *the entire length* of the Great Wall of China? So now there's nothing in China (but there's a big new airport in Japan) that can be seen from the surface of the moon, that'll teach 'em, right? Right.

Oh, man, the things these quakes are throwing up. Poets for presidents, the end of apartheid, the Nazi gold buried for fifty years deep in Swiss bank accounts, Arnold Schwarzenegger, the *Titanic,* and we guess communism just got buried in the rubble there somewhere. And those Ceauşescus? *So* not missed.

When the changes are this big, you can be sure there will be politicians lining up to take the credit. Seems that the iron curtain quakes were the result of years of covert Western activity underground. Seems we found where the pressure points were and used our best efforts to build that pressure until the whole house of cards came tumbling down. Seems that earthquakes, the ultimate weapons of mass destruction, are now at our disposal. Somebody gives us trouble, we literally pull the rug out from under his feet. This is what just happened to Saddam Hussein in what is quickly becoming known as the Shake of Araby. No, that's right, if you're being picky it hasn't been one hundred percent successful, he survived et cetera, but *did you see it?* You've gotta give our boys credit, they put on one hell of a show. Whoo-hoo! Whole lotta shakin' goin' on. And, as we hope you noted, no damage at all to the superstructures and infrastructure of that all-important Saudi oil. *Nada.* Zilcho. Zip.

What, now Mexico wants to know if United States or European Union agents were involved in their great quake? Was this some sort of dummy run, some Little Boy–Fat Man demonstration of extreme force? Jeez, there's always a killjoy. Read our lips. *Of course not.* Would we let Vina Apsara die in some sort of military-industrial megaconspiracy? That's just crazy. We loved that woman. What wouldn't we give to have her here, alive, and singing, right now. The Mexican earthquake was a natural phenomenon which we are doing our darnedest to understand. We have our best people on this. Mother Nature has her own bad moods, and we need to be in touch with those, to live well with the earth, our home. We need to build our knowledge so that we can work on setting in place systems and technologies that will minimize the risk of another such disaster. Our hearts go out to the Mexican people for their sad loss.

Okay? Are we okay on this? Okay, then. *Okay.*

The end of the Soviet Union was a good thing. The victory of the free world is a good thing. We are the good guys. The black hats lost. The new business of the world is business. Rejoice.

Peace.

ME? DON'T ask me. As I've been telling you, my head's been in a spin ever since Vina died. If you ask me (don't ask me) the Vina phenomenon inspired people and they stood up and changed their lives. If you ask me, all you need is love.

The quaking earth, don't ask. Maybe it's down to Mother Nature or NATO or the Pentagon. Me, I'm seeing ghosts. After a lifetime of refusing to accept the irrational it's here, in my work. The miracle of unreason: a woman's ghost-image in my photographs. Worlds in collision. I'm thinking wild thoughts; hypothesizing that—in spite of all the boasting and chest-beating, all the end-of-history rhetoric—the current cycle of catastrophes may have little to do with victory or defeat, the earthquakes may not be in our control, they may be little warning signs hinting at the proximity of the main event: which is, the end of the world. Or the end of one world. Ours, somebody else's, don't ask me which.

I REPEAT: Darius Cama's library of myths is as close as I have ever needed to get to fantasy. The old religions' legacy of living stories—the Ash Yggdrasil, the Cow Audumla, Ouranos-Varuna, Dionysus's Indian jaunt, the vain Olympians, the fabulous monsters, the legion of ruined, sacrificed women, the metamorphoses—continues to hold my attention; whereas Judaism, Christianity, Islam, Marxism, the Market, utterly fail to enthrall. These are faiths for the front pages, for CNN, not for me. Let them struggle over their old and new Jerusalems! It's Prometheus and the Nibelungs, Indra and Cadmus, who bring me my kind of news.

Additionally, ever since my youngest days, Ormus and Vina have added to my plate two goodly extra dollops of living myth. These have been more than enough for me.

Falling in love with Vina, I knew I was stepping out of my league. Nevertheless, I took the step and did not fall flat on my face. This is human heroism. Of this, as of little else, I am proud. Male love is a kind of self-assessment. We allow ourselves to love only those women to whom we feel we have a right to pay court, to whom we dare aspire. The young Ormus, a handsome devil, could legitimately dream of goddesses. He gave himself permission to imagine himself with them, to pursue, and (in his case) usually to attain his dreams. Then Vina, his true deity, came and went. The first time she left him he sought her in other women's bodies, her kiss on other lips. Now that won't do. It's Vina herself or no one.—But she's no longer of this world.—Then find her, wherever she is.

Which is, I confess, presently my attitude too. For, with less reason than Ormus Cama, I, too, dared to aspire to Vina; and she smiled on me also; and left me with an empty heart.

A word more about Ormus: his early gift of precognition, of hearing the future's music playing in his head, gave my anti-fantastic instincts their first severe test. In that instance I took refuge in the reasonable man's partial-knowledge defense: to admit we do not understand a phenomenon is not to admit the presence of the miraculous but merely, reasonably, to accept the limitations of human knowledge. God was invented to explain what our ancestors couldn't comprehend: the radiant mystery of being. The existence of the incomprehensible, however, is not a proof of god. . . . Listen, if I'm reheating yesterday's cold soup, it's because I'm about to set down matters strange to me; strange because they belong to the realm of the "magical," the inexplicable. I have to speak of "Maria," and her "teacher," and in my adulthood concede what is hardest for full-grown men to grant, the same truth which Hamlet, also upon seeing a ghost, obliges scholarly Horatio to accept: that there may be more things in heaven and earth than are dreamt of in his—in my—philosophy.

Returning to work after a long layoff—this is in the fall of 1991, some time after the Vina show at the Orpheum—I decide to set up a sequence of pictures about the remembered Vina, about memory and the error-strewn, partial manner of its ownership of the past. I'm back at the seaside, in Mack Schnabel's house near Montauk Point, a sprawling cliff-edge place to which the crashing ocean breakers give an air of perpetual storm, even when the skies are clear. To design the sequence I get hold of two hard, straight-backed chairs, two mirrors, a couple of life-size dolls, a few other props. Here's how it's supposed to go. A masked man—the mask is actually two eye patches, whose ties criss-cross on his forehead, making an X—is to sit on one of the chairs, against a wall on which hang oval frames containing indistinct images of women from photography's early days: Niépces, Daguerres. On the man's lap there's a circular mirror. In the first picture of the sequence, a rectangular mirror containing the reflected image of a woman's naked body will itself be seen reflected in the circular mirror, its outline proclaiming its femaleness, the body itself filled with light.

In subsequent pictures in the sequence, the circular mirror containing the reflected rectangle takes up more of the frame, and the woman's head gradually becomes distinct and takes up more of the rectangular mirror. At one point it will clearly be Vina's head. Then it will change and become the head of a woman very like Vina, but not her. (I have to find this woman somehow.) As the sequence unfolds the framing mirrors will be "lost," one at a time, and the not-Vina will be slowly pushed back into medium and then long shot. She will be seen to be sitting on a hard, straight-backed chair like the one used by the eye-patched man in the opening picture—it's similar, but it's not the same chair; she will be holding a rectangular mirror, and in it there will be the reflection of a circular mirror which in turn reflects the image of a man's naked body, its outline filled with light. The not-Vina will acquire eye patches. The man will be at first myself, then another person, less of a look-alike than the Vina double; just a not-me. Obviously the sequence is capable of infinite extension, but I plan to end it by bleaching the images into white. We change what we remember, then it changes us, and so on, until we both fade together, our memories and ourselves. Something like that.

To set up the shot, I prop a doll in a chair. Then I put together the zigzag of reflections, doll one into rectangular mirror, rectangular mirror into circular mirror held on the lap of the second seated doll, doll two into my own camera.

I'm alone at the house. When I've set up the shot I pour myself a glass of wine and sit looking at the set-up. I must be tired, because the wine sends me to sleep. Contentedly, I snooze.

I'm woken by the unmistakable noise of the camera's shutter clicking. Twice. I jerk upright, woozy with sleep and wine, and call out, but nobody replies. The set-up hasn't been touched. I check the Leica on its tripod. The first two frames of film have been exposed.

Vina, I whisper, all reason thrown to the wind. *Vina, is it you?*

But when I develop the film, Vina isn't on it. Somebody else is, though. It's the young woman who has appeared before, from time to time, as a ghost-image on various rolls of film. The photo-phantom. But this time she's sitting where the object doll should be—where, in the set-up, the object doll *still is*—and she's holding up a card with writing on it.

In the first frame this reads, *HELP*

In the second frame, the woman looks exhausted, beyond exhausted, as if the effort she has made has drained her completely. She has slumped back in the chair like a toy doll. The card dangles from her hand.

HELP OR

Who are you? I say to the photographs as they hang up to dry. What do you mean? Help how? Help or what?

But the photographs have said what they have to say.

It takes me a day to come up with the idea of the video camera, another day to drive back into the city, pick up the equipment I need and drive all the way back out to the house of perpetual storm. By the time I've got everything fixed up it's the middle of the night, and anyway, I have a notion that nothing will happen while I'm watching. I leave the camera running and go to bed.

In the morning I come into the room early, quivering with excitement, but the videotape counter reads 0000, it doesn't seem to have moved. Disappointment hits me hard. I sit down on the floor, and I'm being so sorry for myself that it's five minutes before it occurs to me that if the tape had been used until it ran out, the auto-rewind mechanism would have taken it all the way back to the beginning. I get up fast and come into a half crouch. This is what it feels like to be in one of those first-contact sci-fi movies. There are aliens on the video. Extraterrestrials who fell to earth. We come in peace, and so on. Surrender Earthlings your planet is surrounded. Don't panic. For some reason I begin to laugh.

The video camera has an internal-playback capability. I put my eye to the eyepiece and hit the Play button. The tape begins to run.

The woman sitting in the chair where the object doll should be is not the young phantom of the day before. This woman is older, in her mid-fifties, worried-looking, with a kind face and graying hair twisted into a bun. She looks and sounds Indian, but I'm sure I have never met her before in my life.

She coughs, an embarrassed little cough, and talks.

You see, one of our ancient philosophers says, consider the humble bat. You know what I'm saying, isn't it? That we should try to experience reality as a bat might. The purpose of the exercise being to explore the idea of otherness, of a radical alienness with which we can have no true contact, let alone rapport. You understand? Is it clear?

Bats live in the same space and time as we but their world is utterly unlike ours. So also: our world is as unlike yours as a bat's. And there are many such, believe me. All these bats, all of us, flapping around one another's heads. I'm not explaining this properly.

Well, we are one another's bats, that's it.

I'm sorry about Maria. The girl is brilliant but, as you see, not well. Also capricious by nature, vain, a meddler, a little bit nympho, okay?, the family has no control. I think perhaps she has been in your, what would it be, *dreams*? In your dreams, yes. Forgive her. She is, let me so express it, flimsy. I am afraid she will not survive what is to come. She does not have the strength of character. Perhaps even I do not. None of us knows how she will answer the question until it is asked. I'm talking about the great question, okay? Life or death..

You're not following me. Of course not. I'm so stupid.

(Pause.)

I don't know how to tell you so that you would get it. Suppose one day you turn a corner and there's a video store you never knew existed, and inside it there are whole walls of videos you never heard of before. Okay? Suppose a few of you find this store, quite a few, but not everybody, because many people when you send them to the street they come back saying it isn't there. The, store. The doorway to the store. It isn't really like this, but I'm doing my best.

You haven't noticed, how could you, but when we visit we don't age, okay? Like if you watch a video, a hundred years can pass in the story, but for you it's a hundred minutes, and you can skip about also. Fast-forward, freeze-frame, reverse, whatever you like. Your time is not like that of the people on the tape.

But this is wrong, because what we found, these few of us—or, not so few but not so many—is that if we, oh goodness, if we passed through the door we could be inside the video, do you see? Plainly my metaphor is not holding up, because I said the door was the door of the store, and the video was in the store, but really there is neither store nor video, just these doors, yes, these apertures, you are a photographer so you understand that word, the aperture opens and light flies in, light like a miracle, staining another reality, leaving its image behind.

I cannot explain it better. We are light from elsewhere.

I think some of the rest you have guessed. The accidentally entangled time lines, like the strings of kites. The worlds heading for collision, already it has begun, the earthquakes, you have perceived their meaning, I think. Your friend Ormus feared the worst long ago, it damaged him, I am sorry. He envisioned the end of your line. But the truth is, your line is stronger than we believed, and the damage to our line is terrible, completely terrible. Whole areas are simply devastated, torn and shredded, just no longer there. Where they were is now a non-being that drives people mad. Incomprehensible nothingness. Just think.

Can you conceive of such damage to the real? What was true yesterday—an anthrax attack by terrorists in the New York subway—is no longer true today: it seems there was no anthrax attack. Yesterday's *safe* is today's *dangerous*. There is nothing to hold on to. Nothing is any longer, with any certainty, *so*.

Do you understand? Your line is strong, like *kala manja* kite-gut. It seems you may cut us off and not we you. You will continue and we will come to an ending, to the edge, to grief. We will be your fading, what's the word, dream.

Already the damage is too great; we can't escape. The door, you see, the aperture, it is jammed. We can see through the glass, for a little while yet we can shout messages, like this, but we can no longer slip through and be there by your side. How mad we were to think that our time of free exploration, of blissful travel between universes, would not end! Perhaps we could have come to you as refugees, some of us say that now, but others say that when the line ends so do all the moments in it. All must be lost. We are lost.

This is all that will remain of us: our light in your eye. Our shadows in your images. Our floating forms, falling through nothingness, after the ground vanishes, the solid ground beneath our feet.

(The video-image begins to deteriorate. Sound and picture quality both become fuzzier. The image jumps and distorts, the audio crackles and beeps. The woman raises her voice.)

Long ago—on a plane—I spoke to your friend—I'm talking about Mr. Cama!—Ormus!—When she, Maria, approached him I at first thought maybe he was also one of us.—You can hear me? I thought he came from our side!—But he didn't—*he did not*—it was just her craziness—I'm saying she lives in a world of make-believe—fantasy! pretence!—poor girl.

Snap. Crackle. Pop.

Oh Lord!—Oh dear Lord!—It's tearing, it's shredding!—So thin, so flimsy!—It isn't strong enough.—Soon we will all be simply your make-believe world.

(It is becoming difficult to see the woman through the video "snowstorm," or to hear her through the mounting background noise. She is shouting; fading in and out and shouting as loud as she can. Her voice cuts out, returns, cuts out again, reminding me of poor cell-phone reception.)

Listen!—she fell for him!,—she truly did—she's not a bad girl, okay?—we are not bad people—our world is as beautiful as yours—but his love—Ormus's!—*for that woman, I'm saying!*—this was hard for Maria to handle.—Can you hear me?—This is what Maria wanted to say to you.—This is her last request.—My last also.—Care for him.—We are ending.—Can you hear me?—Do not let him die.

. . . HELP ORMUS . . .

Here the transmission cuts out for the last time. The snowstorm obliterates the image. I imagine that I am watching the end of a world. In the dancing video blobs I seem to see towers crash and oceans rise to swallow the alien land. In the hiss and roar of the white noise it is easy to hear the dying screams of an entire species, the death rattle of another Earth.

There is a change on the tape. The video snowstorm vanishes. In its place is the image of a doll in a chair, holding a circular mirror, in which is reflected a rectangular mirror, which in turn contains the reflection of another doll.

* * *

I STAY there most of the day, alone with my dolls and their video images, thinking about Maria and her teacher and their story and everything that has melted into air. What comes to mind, absurdly, or not so absurdly, is a scene from a movie: Superman in his private polar ice palace, fitting crystals together and conjuring up his long-dead parents, a serene doomed couple offering wisdom from a vanished world beyond the arch of time. Flighty, deranged Maria with her scribbled messages, and my other lady visitor, nameless, composed, facing oblivion with high dignity: I barely knew them—they were aliens, after all, visitors from a familiar-sounding elsewhere, slipping into our awareness by an unimaginable route—and yet I'm profoundly stirred by their loss. I'm trying to work out why that is. In the end I decide it's because although I, we, didn't really know them, they knew us, and whenever someone who knows you disappears, you lose one version of yourself. Yourself as you were seen, as you were judged to be. Lover or enemy, mother or friend, those who know us construct us, and their several knowings slant the different facets of our characters like diamond-cutter's tools. Each such loss is a step leading to the grave, where all versions blend and end.

Which notion turns my thoughts back to Vina, to whom all my mental pathways still lead. Her knowledge of me was so deep, her version so compelling, that it held together my miscellany of identities. To be sane, we choose between the diverse warring descriptions of our selves; I chose hers. I took the name she gave me, and the criticism, and the love, and I called that discourse *me*.

Since Vina's death and the loss of her incisive vision, her Rai, I have at many points felt myself separating more and more into moments, disparate, contradictory: ceasing, as I now see, to cohere. The "miracle of the videotape" has shown me what I should long ago have spotted for myself: that there are two of us mourning the loss of her redeeming judgements; and that it's time we bridged the rift that has snaked between us over the years, widening by slow degrees. Now that she's gone, we perhaps hold each other's salvation in our hands.

Help Ormus. Yes. And maybe he'll help me.

* * *

I'M LOADING up the Jeep to head back to the city and thinking about the old Bombay days with Ormus, in his dressing room or up on the Apollo Bunder roof. As a matter of fact I'm cheerful enough, feeling the return of old affection, of happier childhood times. But here's Molly Schnabel in white shirt and khakis, Mack's embattled ex and world-class all-around poor mouth, strolling hands-in-pockets up the garden path, grinning her lippy, sidelong grin.

Well if it isn't the inconsolable Indian boyo, moping over the passing of another man's wife. You great girl, Rai, will you look at you. Like Niobe, all tears.

I keep things neutral. Hey, Molly, *quelle surprise.*

She switches accents from Irish lilt to Hug-me.

O, baba, what to tell? Wehicle broke down just close by. I am thinking, can I use the phone and give mechanic a tinkle? Sorry to inconwenience.

She has spent time in India—she's a multinational conglomerate babe, her father was big in Union Carbide until the airborne toxic event, the cloud of methyl isocyanate that ate the eyes and lungs of Bhopal; old man Molony was one of the executives who took the fall for that PR disaster—and she prides herself on her mimicry of Indian idiolect. Once at some Colchis bash she drove Yul Singh to distraction with this type of goodness-gracious, until finally he snapped, For God's sake, Molly, this is America. Talk American.

If she shows up don't let her in the house under any circumstances, Mack had warned. *I don't care if she's shot and bleeding. Barricade yourself in and hunker down for a siege if necessary. I mean it. One time when Chow was out there she showed up with a U-Haul panel van and tried to clear the place out.* Now here she comes with her head cocked on one side so that her golden Veronica Lake-y hair falls in waves over one enormous eye, with her trumped-up pretext and her ingratiating Hug-me dialogue. Listen, Molly, I say, you know I can't let you do that. If you want to make a call, sure, here's my mobile.

Mobile shobile, this instrument I also have, she says, instantly dropping the cover story with a shrug, her voice rising a couple of notches. You think so you can keep me out of my own residence? What, because it is the desire of that putter of his penis into the fist of his own son?

Stop it, I tell her. Molly, just stop right now.

What, because you have received instruction from that inserter of narcotic toxins into the noses of his own kiddiwinks? That indulger within and without the marital bed in sexual perwersions both bestial and coprophile? That whited sepulchre, in whom only I have seen the worms of corruption writhe?

As well as the version that holds you together, there's also one that tears you apart. This is it for my pal Mack, this thirty-three-year-old woman shrieking in counterfeit accents on the lawn of her own past, defaming what once she loved, making accusations which carry in many people's minds an automatic guilty verdict and using the authority of her beauty and of the words "wife" and "mother" to acquire for her falsehoods the support of the law itself. This brilliant adversary who has already stripped Schnabel of his good name but wants everything he's got. It doesn't matter what Mack does for the rest of his life. This version has been branded on his forehead. It's a letter sewn on to his coat in scarlet thread.

I'll drive you to your car, I say. Or, if it really is bust, let's get the mechanic.

You'd make the perfect dogsbody courtier for some murderous third-world despot, Rai, she says, dropping the Indian voice. Or the Chairman's favorite lickspittle lackey and running dog. Or the little ratso soldier the big dons use to do their dirty work. There's a woman to abuse, to what's the argot injurize, to throw off her own land? Send for wiseguy Rai. Call him on his fucking mobile phone.

Get in, Molly, I tell her. And she does; and at once puts her hand in my lap. O, is that all, the old Adam is it, she says, feeling the movement I am unable to control. Is that where you're keepin' the keys now, why didn't you say so, poor darlin', just wait till I see you right, Molly's got the combination for your lock.

I move her hand away and start the engine.

Raincheck, okay?, I say too hotly, and drive.

When I reach the Orpheum, Clea Singh is waiting in the lobby, beneath the Latin tag about love, holding an envelope addressed to me in Ormus Cama's own—pretty unsteady—hand. Again he needs you, sir, Clea says. You must come.

The note inside the envelope is just five words long.

I've found her. She's alive.

CHAPTER SEVENTEEN

Mira on the Wall

Doorman Shetty isn't on lobby duty when we reach the Rhodopé Building. Tiny, purse-lipped Clea tells me he has finally been put out to pasture. Agelessly antique herself, she points out with some scorn and no irony that he, Shetty, was long past his superannuation date. *They only kept him on as a favor to Madam,* she says, *but now it is better he rests.* He's out in Mineola, N.Y., there's an excellent retirement home in that neighborhood, convenient for the crematorium, and he has what Clea describes as a *generous allowance, we were under no obligation but he was her Daddy after all.* There was never much love lost between Shetty and the Singhs, and once he lost Vina's protection his fate was sealed. After a suitable grace period had been allowed to elapse Clea made her endgame move. He had nothing to fight her with. Checkmate in one.

I offer up a silent valediction. Old man, you wanted to die with your boots on, but in old age our power to write our own scenarios wanes, and the shape of our last acts is decided by the rewrite merchants. Goodbye, Doorman. Enjoy the sunsets if you can.

In the matter of Doorman Shetty, Clea has acted with her habitual toughness and clarity, which makes it all the more remarkable that on our journey uptown in the limo this customarily unflappable lady has been profoundly agitated. I realize that few people outside the closed circle of the Singhs have been where I'm about to go: into the heart of the silence and shadow that now completely envelops Ormus Cama. Ormus has been invisible ever since I was last brought into his presence, in the Guadalajara Hyatt. I have Shetty's account of his activities—the visits to Goddess-Ma, etc.—but it's possible that no outsider has visited him in his heavily defended lair in all this time. Certainly Clea's acute concern is an indication of the exceptional nature of the event. No cameras, she insists before we leave. I hadn't planned on bringing any, but I am interested by the prohibition. How bad is Ormus looking these days? What is it that he, or his aides, don't want the world to see?

People in my line of work always think like this, I rebuke myself. There is no law which says that a man must agree to be photographed just because he wants to talk to a photographer. Give the guy a break.

Clea chatters without stopping all the way from the Orpheum to the Rhodopé. Mr. Rai, people have black tongues as you know, and maybe you have heard it said that we have not taken care of Sir. Probably you have read malicious comments on his physical and mental health, also cruel allegations regarding our husbandry of his assets. Mr. Rai, I beg you only to keep an open mind. If you desire I can open for you all the books, all the accounts, you will see that every cent is accounted for and all enterprises are in tip-top shape. If you require it I will present to you his personal physician who will confirm our absolute adherence to his orders. If it is your wish all things can be made plain.

He's dying, I suddenly realize. These are his last moments and Clea and her people are scared stiff.

I don't know why you're telling me all this, I say.

You see, Mr. Rai, Sir is such a lonely man. Twenty-four hours a day, seven days a week, he thinks only of dear Madam. To him, that you were Madam's good old friend makes you like his brother. It saddens him that you have been for so long absent from his side.

I decide not to challenge this remarkable statement. *Help Ormus.* That is my new resolve, and there's no time for pettiness, old grievances or ill will.

Clea in the limo has more to confess. Mr. Rai, Sir is in dire straits. He is too much reliant on wrong things to help him bear his loss. I fear for him, Mr. Rai.

Wrong things, I repeat. She looks harassed, and actually wrings her hands. Then in a low voice she speaks the names of the illegal drugs. The chauffeur today is Will Singh. He faces front and drives, stone-faced, obscure.

How much stuff is he getting through, I demand, and

when she replies I know that disaster can't be far off. I ask, How did these substances come into his hands?

Clea looks defiant. I am able to acquire whatever Sir requires, she says simply. It is my duty, as it was for Mr. Yul and Madame in the days before.

I picture tiny Clea in her sari bargaining in the back rooms of Dopeland with the likes of Harry the Horse and Candymaster C, earning their respect by her calmness, her attention to detail, her insistence on the highest standards. You see, Clea, I say, keeping my-voice friendly, many people would not understand that when you fed Ormus's habit and allowed it to grow so big, you were acting as a true friend should. Many people would question your motives.

Clea Singh in the limo draws herself up proudly; straight-backed, almost shocked. But Mr. Rai, I am not his friend, how can you think it. I am his servant. Ever since Madam and Sir rescued us, we are all his sworn subjects. I do not question or dispute his needs, Mr. Rai, I concur. I accede.

And this physician, I say. Does he have qualms about what has been going on?

He is familiar with the music business, Clea Singh replies, and the old iron is back in her voice. Mr. Rai, you are a man of the world, I am sure. Then what is the need for such innocent quizzery? The world is what it is.

EVEN AFTER these forewarnings, Ormus, waiting for me at the elevator door, is a shock. He's upright, but only just. I have the feeling that even this unconvincing display of well-being has been put on purely for my benefit. If I weren't here he'd be leaning on one of the Singhs. Strong young men dressed in white kung fu outfits wait anxiously in the corners of my eyes, looking concerned.

He was skinny in Guadalajara; now he's positively emaciated. I could probably hoist him shoulder-high with one hand. His hair has almost completely gone, and although what's left is shaved to the skull, the stubble I can see is all white. His nose looks dangerously narrow, and though he has a fine pashmina shawl pulled around his shoulders, he's shivering on a warm evening. He's walking with a stick, fifty-four going on ninety. It may be too late to help him.

There's no eye patch. I realize that he, too, knows about

the end of the otherworld. About which he was both right—because there actually were two worlds on a collision course, I know that now—and wrong, because the otherworld was in no way intrinsically superior to our own. In the end, it was that version which failed. Ours succeeded—or let's just say survived.

This was the nature of Ormus's madness: that in his thinking he privileged another version of the world over his own. Maybe now, if he can only stay alive, he has a chance to regain his mental balance, to re-enter the actually existing world. Ours.

Thanks for coming, he whispers. There's just a thing you have to see: to, ah, confirm. At which he turns and totters away through his empty white universe.

The size of the apartment is astounding, dwarfing even his Mexican Hyatt billet: the endless albino spaces, the open doorways, the emptinesses, the *room.* In the distant corner of one enormous vacant zone I spy a white futon mattress and a white reading lamp on a low white table, in another gigantic area there's only a white concert grand piano and stool. Not a speck of dust or used glass or item of dirty laundry in sight. I can't imagine how many Singhs it takes to pick up after Ormus, to create this pristine unworldliness.

He's whispering as he walks. I have to stay close to hear what he has to say.

Curtis Mayfield's paralyzed, Rai. A lighting rig fell on him. And *then* his house burned down. Yeah. Steve Marriott burned to death, you hear that. Different fire. Right. And Doc Pomus died. David Ruffin OD'd. I guess too much Temptation, huh. Will Sinott of the Shamen? Drowned. Leo Fender, Uncle Meat, Johnny Thunders, Professor Longhair, Stan Getz, RIP, baby. That little kid falling from the penthouse window too. Just terrible. And the word is Mercury doesn't have long, and Brian Jones was murdered, *Brian Jones,* they've got evidence. What's going on, Rai, I don't know what's going on. They're wiping us out.

This, I realize, is his strange, isolated, free-associative small talk. I do not judge him. I haven't forgotten my own list of the dead, which I'd reeled off at Johnny Chow not so very long ago. Different names, same obsession. These are

Vina's new companions, the first social circle of her heaven or hell.

I follow Ormus through the white hectares until we turn a corner, a softly padded white door opens and shuts, and unexpectedly I'm in what looks like a minimalist version of Mission Control, Houston: floor-to-ceiling tv monitors on all four walls of a studio covering over a thousand square feet and, at the center, a space-odyssey command complex: computer banks, audio and video mixing-and-magic desks, Yamaha, Korg, Hammond, MIDI-B and Kurzweil keyboard equipment, and two white swivel chairs.

On every screen—there must be more than three hundred—a different phoney Vina pouts and twirls. The sound's muted; three hundred dumb not-Vinas dizzily mouth and prance. If I want a model to play the almost-Vina in my unfinished photo sequence—and I guess I do—I've come to the right place.

Even after all these years, the money generated by rock music still amazes me. The resources required to own all this space and to build, at its heart, this cutting-edge audio-video facility featuring beyond-beyond PixelPixie morphotech capability and massed floating-point musicomputers that could, if reprogrammed, efficiently run a medium-range-missile guidance system; then to hire a small army of video crews to track down and tape hundreds upon hundreds of Vina surrogates: unimaginable. Unimaginable, too, is the luxury of being able to ask for anything you want, and knowing people will make it so, and you won't even notice the cost.

To be given the world as a toy.

When my head stops spinning my heart starts to hurt, not only for myself but for Ormus too. Obsession is the enactment of hidden pain. I realize that I haven't taken his note seriously until now. I interpreted it, too glibly, as the cry for help of a drowning man; it never occurred to me to make a literal reading. Now, as my eyes swim with fake Vinas, I realize he actually believes that one of these pathetic counterfeits is the real thing, poor crushed Vina whom we loved risen from her abyss-grave and singing her old hits to cowboys, militiamen, possible Unabombers and drunks in Grand Island, Nebraska, or some such humming center of the musical world.

Then Ormus sits down at a control desk, says *Look at this,* throws a bunch of switches, and there she is, three hundred times over and more, blazing from all the monitor screens. He pushes a set of audio slide controls, and her wonderful—her inimitable—voice wells up and drowns me.

Vina. It's Vina, returned from the dead.

It's not up to you, she sings. And again and again, as the old song accelerates towards its conclusion, *no, it's not up to it's not up to it's not up to you.* Her voice is doing extraordinary things—new and familiar—with the song's melodic line, stretching and bending the sound, bringing a jazzy feel to it, the way Vina used to do when she felt in the Holiday mood. She even throws in a climaxing moment of Ella-ish scat.

Be-bop! Re-bop! Rreee!
Skeedley-ooh!
Oh, mam'! Rama-lam'!
There's nothin' you can do . . .
Wo, pop! De-dop!
Mop! A-lop-a-doo!
Oh it's not, no no not, whoo whoo
Not up to you.
. . . Oh, yeah . . .

The invisible crowd goes crazy. She smiles: Vina's smile, that can light up the darkest room. Oh Vina, Vina, I think. Where did you spring from, this isn't possible, you're dead. Three hundred Vinas surround me, laugh and bow.

I don't recognize the performance, I stammer. What is it, an old bootleg, some gonzo recording from somewhere.

But I can see for myself that the tape carries a date ident. It was made less than a week ago. And I can see, too, that although this is Vina, it's her to the life, it's also an odd composite Vina, a Vina who never really was. She has the dyed red hair gathered above her head in that springy fountain I remember so well, that Woody Woodpecker crest, and she's wearing the sequin-glittered gold bustier and leather pants from Vina's last performance, but this is not a woman in her middle forties, this is not the mature solo artiste on the comeback trail. This Vina is no more than twenty years old. She is, however, wearing a moonstone ring.

When I turn to Ormus he has tears in his milky eyes.

I thought so, he whispers. I knew it wasn't just my imagination.

What's her name, I ask. I realize I'm whispering too.

He hands me a thin white file.

Mira, he says, coughing. That's what she goes by now.

MIRA CELANO, from right here in Manhattan, the file tells me. Born at Lenox Hill Hospital in January 1971, so I guessed right about her age. Nineteen seventy-one, the year of Ormus's celibacy oath, *that's* how young she is. She is an only child. Her father Tomaso was sixty-one when she was born. She remembers him (here I'm embellishing the detective agency's filed report with details gleaned from my later knowledge of her) as a short, chesty, thick-maned lion of a man, who became awkward in the presence of the adoring child of his old age, giving her quick rough embraces and handing her off, almost as quickly, to whatever female family member was closest. He was a man of honor, a high-flying corporation lawyer with an Upper East Side address, who nevertheless maintained close links with his community and prized his family roots in Assisi, Italy. He was also a decorated World War II hero with a distinguished service medal for his exploits as the oldest of the American dive-bombing aces who sank the Japanese aircraft carrier *Hiryu* at the Battle of Midway.

He is, additionally, recently deceased, at the age of eighty-one.

Mira's mother was not Italian. Surprisingly for such a conservative man, Celano, who remained single long enough to disappoint more than a generation of young Italian-American women, fell hard at the end of his sixth decade for an Indian woman doctor whom he "met-cute," as they say in the movies, when her taxi's Ibo driver deliberately rammed his cab's Hausa wheel jockey on Central Park South. The two cab drivers, passionate supporters of the opposing sides in the bloody, escalating conflict over the attempted secession of Biafra from Nigeria, initially identified one another as enemies by their prominently displayed rear- and side-window flag decals and aggressive bumper stickers. They then wound down their windows and engaged in a stop-go exchange of insults—*Tree swinger! Oil slime! Gowon goon! Ojukwu oaf!*—as their cabs inched forward through the thick rush-hour traffic; until at length the young Ibo, hot for secession, or perhaps just plain overheated on that steamy summer afternoon, swung his wheels and smashed into the taunting Hausa's vehicle in a shower of breaking glass. The drivers were unhurt, but the passengers in the two rear seats were sent flying within their confined spaces, so they took some knocks.

Tomaso Celano, always the gallant gent, insisted on ensuring that the lady in the other cab had not been injured, but then confessed to having double vision himself and sat down on the parkside curb with a bad case, as he put it, of the tweet-tweet-tweets. Fortunately the lady was a qualified doctor. Mehra Umrigar Celano was born in Bombay (still no escaping these Bombay Parsis), came West to attend medical school, stayed on, married Tommy just nine weeks after the Biafran Taxi War, named their daughter Mira because it's a name in India as well as Italy, plus it's easy to say, and in spite of becoming a consultant oncologist at New York Hospital died of a perniciously aggressive breast cancer before her fortieth birthday, when her daughter was still only four years old. Old man Celano, declaring himself too antique to care for the infant, farmed Mira out to a series of relatives whom the little girl quickly discovered to be untypical Italians: that is, resentful of their extended-family obligations towards her, deficient in the provision of love, and unwilling to have her around for very long. In spite of this uncertain, peripatetic home environment, and the difficult discontinuities of an education spread across the high schools of three boroughs, Mira became a straight-A student, a model of diligence, who was accepted by Columbia University's School of Journalism and immediately ran wild, as if all her hard work and good behavior up to that moment had been a prisoner's ruse, a way of hastening the date of her release. She had hidden her wings all her life, and now she intended to fly.

In her freshman year she unfurled a singing voice that made her an instant campus star, ran with a fast crowd and got herself pregnant, all in a single semester. She decided to keep the baby, dropped out of college, and was instantly disowned by her father, after which he thoughtlessly dropped dead playing tennis in Cape Porpoise, Maine, thus making a reconciliation impossible. He'd been crouching to receive serve when he was murdered—aced—by a huge heart seizure, and fell face first on to the hard cement court, still holding his racquet, but unfortunately defaulting the game. He died before his arms had time to come up and defend his face, which consequently suffered a broken nose that sorely impaired his gravitas, making him seem, in death, far coarser than he'd ever looked in life. With that eminent nose squashed over to the right he wasn't a big shot any more but a plug-ugly boxer who'd lost the last in a series of losing battles. It was a quick end, but it didn't come fast enough to keep Mira in his will. *Not a red cent to my daughter Mira who has been the disappointment of my old age.*

The money was divided. Some went to charitable Italian community projects in Manhattan, Brooklyn and the Bronx, the rest to the same relatives who had blighted Mira's early life. The lucky heirs made no move to assist their disinherited relation and even snubbed her at her father's funeral, as if to say, forget about it, darling, don't call, don't write, you're out on your own. Mira accepted their challenge. After failing to break into journalism, even of the lowliest sort, she started singing for her supper in dingy piano bars, taking her baby daughter along in a carry cot and hiding her behind the stage-area drapes, or under the piano, or in the women's room, or anywhere, just praying she'd sleep through the set, bribing busboys and waitresses to take care of her if she woke up.

The girl is now a little over one year old. Her name is Tara, meaning—in Hug-me—*star.*

WHILE I'M reading the file, Ormus hobbles off to the bathroom and takes his time there. I should be intervening but I don't know how to, not yet, anyway. Also, I'm reading. Also, I'm not too sure where the bathroom is.

Easy to see where this Mira Celano's interest in Vina comes from, I reflect. In spite of all the differences of community, opportunity and class, she has plenty in common with her idol: the mixed-race family, the early orphaning, the loveless childhood years, the outcast's deep-seated sense of rejection and exile. That thing about feeling out on the perimeter line and being pushed, by a powerful centripetal force, towards the heart of the game. And she's penniless now, just as Vina was when she started out.

And there's her voice, of course, the voice she kept under wraps for so long. Maybe, like Vina, she had secret places where she went to sing. Her own Jefferson Lick somewhere in the park.

I can readily imagine that when she started singing, during her solitary semester at Columbia, she was at once surrounded by admirers calling her the new Vina Apsara, or even better than that, and telling her to cut a demo, to forget journalism and reach for the stars. But then suddenly she was broke, the fair-weather college friends were gone and demos and producers and stardom seemed very far away. The repro-Vina business, however, was thriving. So, as she afterwards tells me: *If I couldn't be the new Vina, then I'd be the old one. That was the way I looked at it. I taped the picture you took—you know, Vina in the quake—on the wall of my room and decided, Okay, for now I'm her.*

ORMUS IS back from the john, looking both better and worse. I have other tapes, he says, and starts pushing buttons.

Here on three hundred screens is Mira Celano with her sleeping baby, watched by a spy camera high in a corner. She's in a tiny, unhappy dressing room, wearing a thin kimono-style dressing gown and preparing to take off her stage make-up. When she pulls off the red wig and the hairnet below it, I let out a small cry. Waist-length dark hair tumbles down her back. She shakes it loose, picks up a comb, bends forward so that the hair hangs over her face and all the way to the floor, and combs out her tangles. Then, at her mirror, she starts on her face. Once again, I'm amazed. Much of the dark skin color is coming off on the tissues. This girl has actually been blacking up to play dark Vina, crossing, in her own way, the heavily mined color line. Her own complexion—although the tape quality makes it hard to be certain—looks to be a light olive.

She's finished. Now in the mirror is a beautiful if kind of

slutty young girl, more Latin- than Indian-looking, a young single mother fighting for survival in the badness of the city, and really pretty unlike her meal ticket, barren Vina, Mrs. Ormus Cama, my dead love. To realize this is like waking from a dream.

You shouldn't have done this, I tell Ormus, trying to work out the number of people downtown who have had to be paid off to allow us our uptown voyeurism. This is wrong, I say.

Look, he whispers, ignoring my qualms. On the monitors, Mira Celano is taking off her kimono. Underneath it is Vina's naked body. Vina with lighter skin, but Vina nevertheless, in every last detail, the weight and angle of the breasts, the jaunty sling of the hips, the full, the incomparable Vina ass, the thick unshaven bush. I am standing behind Ormus and push my fist into my mouth and bite down hard. If I were to gasp, it would reveal my secret, and now, more than ever, I want to keep that secret to myself.

Now that she's back, I hear myself madly thinking. Now that she has returned from the grave.

Ormus hits more buttons. Here is Mira Celano walking home alone with little Tara in a stroller. With another leap of the heart I recognize the Bowery, Cooper Union, St. Mark's. This girl is practically my neighbor. She waves at the mooching dope peddlers, works the stroller up half a dozen steps, unlocks a door. She's calling out something as she goes inside, but the sound quality is poor, I can't hear what she's saying.

Okay, wait a minute, Ormus murmurs, and I realize I've spoken aloud. In the next thirty seconds he performs a miracle of audio engineering, isolating her voice, cleaning out the background, compensating for the distorting effects of magnifying her faint words. Okay, here we go, he whispers. This is so good.

Yo, homes, I'm in the house! Yo yo yo homie-o!

If there's a man in there, I think, if she's calling out to a lover rather than a couple of girlfriends, it's possible I may have to kill him.

You understand what she's telling us, Ormus says, freezing the frame, trapping Mira Celano on her doorstep in mid-yo. She's saying she's come back. She's saying hi, honey, I'm home.

This is insane, I say, snapping out of it once more. Ormus, you have to stop this. It's like you're stalking her. You *are* stalking her.

Mary Virgin has a stalker who actually says that, he murmurs absently. Can you believe? The guy comes up to her house every night and calls into the entry system, making like he's her little hubby back from the old nine to five. *Hi, honey, I'm home.*

Yeah, I say, wiping cold sweat from my brow, I can believe it, and this time that nut is you.

More obstinate button pushing. Here on a long telephoto lens is Mira Celano in her room, it's a third-floor walk-up at the front, she has the lights on but is leaving the shade up. She's prowling around in a cream slip worn over a nursing brassière, making phone calls, putting things in her mouth that aren't chocolates or nachos, washing them down with gulps from a bottle that isn't Evian or Pellegrino, flopping down on her bed—she's got a brass bedstead!—zapping on the tv, watching basketball or maybe just stargazing, moondancing, planetwaving, while Tara, the little star in her arms, suckles contentedly. If Mira weren't still milk-heavy, I muse, her bosom would be less ample than Vina's. She'd have to pad out her bustier to get the right effect. On the other hand, Vina also liked to watch sports, especially hoop, so they have that in common. Vina knew her Magic from her Kareem and Bird and when the new kid arrived on the block she said to me, half seriously, Let's all move to Chicago so we can go watch Mike.

I think: There's no man in that room. This inordinately pleases me.

And I think: I'm thinking about this young woman as if she were my lover.

Abruptly, Ormus shuts the system down. Mira Celano vanishes and I miss her, so help me, I do. This total stranger into whose intimacy I have pried. This nobody with—if only temporarily—the only body that I truly loved. I'm pathetic, I tell myself, and Ormus is beyond that. Ormus Cama is a graybeard loon.

Ormus, you need help, I make myself say it. Now that you've asked me over here I have to tell you. If you don't get help you'll be dead inside a year, tops.

He's still staring at the darkened monitors. If it is her, he whispers, then anything's possible. If it's her then there's hope.

It's not her, I say. The likeness is incredible, but it's someone else. It's a Mira Celano, whoever that is. A person you don't know, whose privacy you have criminally invaded. A person less than half Vina's age, and able to have a child. And you saw the make-up tape. Come *on.*

He softly says, If she chose to come back this way, low key, sub rosa, incognito, step by step, I can understand that, tell her. Tell her, I'm waiting.

My own unexpected arousal makes me snappish. You require that I go into this woman's life and say what?, I demand. What, that a dying addict in rock-star heaven has been watching her every move, that he wants her to play his dead wife not only on stage for money but in his bed for the rest of her life?, or I should say *his* life?, it's sick, Ormus, don't look to me for this.

You have to go, he whispers, openly pleading now. It has to be you. I can't go. Look at me. I can't.

Skeedley-ooh, I'm remembering. *Mop! A-lop-a-doo!*

Even if I did go, I say, and we both know I'm surrendering, we both know that Mira Celano—that's *Selayno,* by the way, Americanized from the Italian *Chelahno*—is someone I too now need to meet, even just supposing I did go over there and take this crazy meeting, what the fuck is it for? Tell me why I'd be doing it, what you want me to offer her. Tell me the deal.

Just, come home, he whispers, so softly now that I have to lean right in to his cracked, dying-junkie lips. Just, Vina, my darling, come home.

THE NEW places are Izvestia, a couple of blocks up from the Orpheum on the Bowery, which plays mostly trance music, ambient techno for the new acidheads (LSD is back), the grungy Soundgarten in the meat-packing district, and the post-CBGB's Voodoo Dollhouse at East Tenth Street and Avenue A, where bubbling-under indie bands play to an audience of sharp industry bloodhounds in search of the next big thing. None of these venues would ordinarily book a tribute act like Mira's Vina, but the spirals of postmodern irony twist tight and fast, and for five minutes that year they twist to Mira's advantage. Somebody at the Dolls decides that a "necro-themed" night—the crowd as well as the performers to arrive as their favorite dead icon—would be a fabulous one-off kitsch-camp event and perhaps even a celebration of the life of the music in what industry people are calling the year of death. So it's at the Voodoo Dollhouse, transformed for the occasion into a kind of neon graveyard, a necropolis with rhythm, and on the night of the biggest break of her musical life, that I first see Mira in person.

Waiting for her to come on, I sit through a series of—to me, at least—entirely forgettable acts, an electronica rethink of the Beach Boys doing the Monster Mash, a group of synchronized but soulless Temptations clones, a competent Mama Cass Elliot wearing a tent and drinking tea, even a no-holds-barred, utterly irony-deficient Liberace. Then Mira's up, and the moment she opens her mouth the mood of the night changes. This is no longer merely a fancy-dress ball. People are listening. She's *good.*

I haven't dressed up, but a word from Ormus's people—from Clea—has ensured my admission. I opt to listen from the bar, and as I drink my third margarita—the tequila is my own private tribute to Vina's memory—I wonder at the ease with which I've fallen back into an old routine. Once again, I'm Ormus's obedient "kid brother." Once again I'm playing Joe Cotten to his Citizen Welles, doing his dirty work. *Help Ormus.* I've come to plead his cause with this unknown woman, because I think it could save his life.

Up there on the Dollhouse stage, Mira Celano's Vina is sticking knives in my heart. I'm using the margaritas to ease the pain.

SUCCESS BREEDS excess. After the show it takes a while to get to Mira. There's a crowd of well-wishers and A&R men and would-be seducers in the way. I lean back in a narrow corridor outside the women's dressing-room door, waiting for the fan club and the other performers to leave: the Lady Day, the Bessie, the Judy, the Janis, the Patsy Cline, the Tammi Terrell, the Mamas Cass and Thornton, the upsettingly skinny Karen Carpenter, the pseudo-Icon whose "I'll be your mirror" was the only performance to come anywhere close to Mira's. By the time it's my turn Mira Celano is keen to leave. The wig and color are off, she's tired and wired—she seems fuzzy, fazed—and little Tara is beyond exhausted and cranky. So, what's your label, Abel, Mira drones, too wrecked to be polite. I'm not in the business, I answer, but you were wonderful, wonderful. (The margaritas have made me emotional.) Don't tell me, she shrugs, you were a huge Vina fan, she was the biggest thing in your life, left one hell of a heart-shaped hole, until I touched your soul. She turns her back on me and lights a cigarette with practiced, wasted cynicism, ignoring the squalling little girl, who has started throwing things on the floor, including a full glass ashtray. It smashes, there's glass and dead-cigarette detritus everywhere. Mira Celano doesn't jump. Feeling better now? Then relax, she says, and I'm interested to note that the little girl buys it, she slumps down on a cushion in a corner, sighs resignedly, calms down. Her mother rounds on me. What?, she demands, you have maybe an opinion? No opinion, I say. She nods, not really caring, then frowns. This is for an autograph, right? No, I say, it's not an autograph. It's important. I need you to come down off whatever you're on and pay attention.

I'm being intense, I've scared her a little. She puts herself between me and her daughter and says, Two minutes, then you're out. I point over her shoulder, to where Vina tottering in Tequila is taped to the wall. I'm Rai, I say, a photographer. She's a dropout journalist wannabe and a Vina student too, so she knows my name. Her eyes widen and suddenly the hardass crust cracks, she's a young girl again, just starting out and still able to be impressed.

You're *Rai*? *You're* Rai? My God, that's right. You really are Rai.

What you're acting out tonight, I tell her unnecessarily, it was my life, the love of, I loved her, I held her in my arms, she was going to, she would've, we would've, never mind, she got into a helicopter and I never, nobody ever. I just looked around and she was gone.

Gohohone. At this point, to my great discomfiture, I begin to cry. Again with the tears! What can she think of me, this man twice her age who took That Picture and who's now bawling like a baby in front of her with his hands over his face. I try to control myself. The girl and her mother are staring at me, genuinely astonished. I want to see you, I blurt out, I really need to see you again, and even I can hear how ridiculous I sound, how naked and premature. A few seconds later we're all laughing, the ice is broken, and the little girl is laughing loudest of all.

Okay, I was trying to work out if you're a serial killer or just a rapist, but I've decided you're cool, Mira Celano says, wiping her eyes. Now can we go, walk me home?, the kid needs to sleep.

An old guy followed me one day, she tells me as we walk (I'm pushing the sleeping Tara in her orange stroller), he said he was Ormus Cama, if you please. It's incredible that even someone like me gets followed around. What a town, right.

Right, I say. I'm thinking: wrong, wrong, this whole thing is off the rails, I'm supposed to be helping the big O, speaking for him. But I'm feeling the rebirth of urges which I thought had died with Vina: attraction, desire. The interesting thing is that it's not about the likeness, the impersonation, any more. It's Mira Celano herself, Mira *qua* Mira, that's responsible for these stirrings. Her long hair, as soft as Vina's was wiry, the spring in her step, the happiness bursting from her smile and giving the lie to the tough-cookie act. This is a girl permanently high on hope, with plenty of that rare commodity to spare.

I begin to feel my age, inhibiting me. If I say what I'm thinking she'll probably just laugh. Yeah right granddad in your dreams.

She's talking about herself, I haven't been paying attention, she talks fast and sometimes you get left behind, but when I do catch up with her I realize I'm being given an account of the false self she has chosen to inhabit since her disinheritance: That gig tonight, she's saying, half the performers were like upper-middle-class private-school types, you know?, slumming, I mean I don't understand those people, coming from the planet White Trash and all?, I've got tattoos, I'm subculture. Some kind of post-teen bag lady, that's me.

It's time to let her know I'm not fooled by this. Mira, I

say, that's bullshit. I know where you're from. Then I tell her the short version of what I read in Ormus Cama's file. And all the time I'm thinking, under all that armor this is one very fragile person. Don't fuck around with her, Rai. Don't try for her heart unless you're serious. She has already been hurt too much.

We're turning in to her street. She stops in her tracks and snatches the handles of the stroller away from me and puts it behind her and starts screaming. What is this, what do you want from me, you fucking peeper, you fucking spy, she yells, reaching into her shoulder bag. Okay, okay, you should be aware that I am able to handle guns.

She shouts the warning with a harsh little hiss on the end: to handle *gunss.*

People are looking. I stand my ground.

Mira, I was sent to talk to you, I say. By Ormus Cama, the real one. He likes your act, had you checked out, what can I tell you, he wants to meet you, that's all of it, that's it.

She's calming down but she's still angry. I can understand that. It is an angering thing to be fingered as the self you're struggling to shuck off. To learn at twenty that the past goes on clinging to you, it bursts out of the grave when you least expect it and grabs your ankle in a stenchy decaying claw. She's still backed away from me, adopting a high-tension stance, legs apart, her right hand in her bag, bending slightly forward at the waist, the left arm stretched straight out at me, palm up, fingers splayed. *Keep away, fucking maniac,* says her body. And she's definitely trying to convince me she's got a pistol in there.

I put my arms up like a surrendering cowpoke. Don't shoot the messenger, I say unoriginally, with a grin.

Ormus Cama? she demands, still yelling. What's his problem? I mean is this what he's doing these days, he gets turned on by the impersonation industry? He sends out for look-alikes now? A pizza, some red Vina, maybe some jalapeños on the side, so what does that make you, mister, Domino's delivery? Or his pimp.

This is New York, late at night. Nobody makes a move towards us; Mira Celano's performance has emptied the street. There's just us now, and the sleeping infant, and the audience behind the darkened windows.

Close, but no cigar, I say quietly. Mira, calm down. This isn't a sex thing. It's more that he's dying, ever since Vina passed away he's been killing himself with junk, and it's my view that he urgently requires a reason to live.

So you're asking what? she says, quietening, her body relaxing, her mood swinging rapidly away from rage. I don't really get it. You want me to do what?

He thinks you're her, I say. He truly thinks she's come back. Or, you could say, untruly thinks it. It's like he half thinks it, wholly believes it while he's half thinking it, and at other times, not. The point is he needs to deceive himself and he needs the rest of us to go along with the deception, and if we do—if you do—that just may motivate him to clean himself up, to survive. Do this for him. Go see him, in costume. Give him hope.

Sounds like a sex thing to me, she says, back in charge of herself now, intrigued. This is a woman whose internal weather is unusually quick to change.

Right now he's too weak to even jerk off, I say. You know, we haven't really been close in a long time, Ormus and me. This is a mercy mission. A favor I promised to a late mutual acquaintance. To turn Ormus's face away from the gates of death.

She moves on, until we reach the steps to her front door.

So this must be some kind of incredible selflessness, she says in a new voice: playful, almost fond. You came to that terrible show, you waited in the corridor, and then you spent all this time with me just to speak up for another man.

No, I'm no saint, I say, that's not it. I mean, helping Ormus was part of it, but I would never have come if, if.

If what, she asks, beginning to smile, but it's not a laughing-at smile, it's too happy for that, it wants me to say what I'm almost too scared to articulate.

If I hadn't wanted to, I manage lamely.

And what's your desire, your wanted-to, she says, stepping in close. Does it also come necro-themed? You want Vina, but not that old lady of forty-five: you want Vina twenty years old all over again, isn't that it? You want her back from the grave, only younger?

Maybe in the beginning, I say, hanging my head. But now it's you, it's just you.

Do you read Longfellow? she asks suddenly, completely dropping the ignorant-white-trash pretense, staying very close, so that her breath fills my nostrils. No, I guess not. But there's a poem he has about this tongue-tied soldier, Miles Standish, who begs his pal John Alden to go on his behalf to ask for Miss Priscilla's hand, not knowing that John Alden loves her too. And good John Alden, for friendship's sake, does as he is bid, but Miss Priscilla won't go for it. You remember now?

. . . And here all of a sudden, conjured up by this miraculous young woman, is the ghost of John Mullens Standish XII at my elbow, urging me on. But I'm in uncharted territory, I don't know how to move forward, where to put my foot. The sidewalk has become unreliable, yielding. I can't move. . . .

Why don't you speak for yourself, John, Mira Celano softly quotes. That was what the lady said.

Yes, I remember, I say. (What I actually remember is Vina in my bed, Vina in the midst of one of her interminable soliloquies, her Ormusiads, telling me about Ormus's very first meeting with Mull Standish on the London plane.)

Then come again tomorrow, Rai, Mira Celano says, kissing me. Come not as a messenger, but to speak for yourself.

By the time I take her to meet Ormus I know some of her secrets and she knows all of mine. She lies in my arms, or I in hers, and I run off at the mouth for long periods (their actual length is determined by Tara's constantly changing sleep patterns). I find myself telling Mira all about Vina, just as Vina would once tell me about Ormus. So we repeat in ourselves the faults of the ones we have loved. I also photograph Mira in a hundred ways, learning her through the cyclops eye, and she gives herself to the camera with an openness and freedom that shocks. In conversation, however, she expresses herself with terseness and caution. It quickly becomes plain that I'm going to have to pay attention, because she says things once and refuses to repeat. If I forget a detail of her biography she hits me with a wide-eyed, betrayed look. *You didn't care enough to listen.*

At the very outset she tells me that she is interested only in that rarest of all emotional contracts between men and women: total engagement, total fidelity, instantly. All or nothing right away, the whole heart or else forget it. That's what she is prepared to offer and if I can't reciprocate, if I'm not in it for the long haul, then so long, it's been good to know you, no hard feelings, goodbye. Her daughter, she says, deserves a little continuity in her life, not a procession of inadequate men through her mother's bedroom; and so, she adds, does she.

In this she reveals herself to be Vina's polar opposite.

The more I learn about her the more I begin to think of her absolutism as heroic. The fearless courage of the innocent—the child who extends her trusting hand towards the fire, the student prankster who places a clown's hat on a tyrant's statue, the youth in his new uniform dreaming shiny dreams of derring-do, or the Beauty at the moment of her first plunge into the pit of love—this has never impressed me. Life's raw recruits go to the edge and over it because of the blinding immensity of what they do not know. But Mira's is the courage of experience, open-eyed, bruised and fearful. Rejected by her father and family, abandoned by the father of her child, bearing the unclosed wounds of her broken loves, she is nevertheless prepared to risk her heart once more. To try for the best in spite of being terrified of the worst. *This* is brave.

Mira has lost a lover too. She, too, has a ghost in her head, though she is trying hard not to act bereaved, pretending not to mourn. Tara's father Luis Heinrich killed himself, shot himself in the head and took three days to die, he even made a mess of that, Mira snarls, the tough-bitch accents back in evidence. Luis was a musician too, a troubled spirit, fronting an East Coast grunge outfit called Wallstreet. New York influenced by Seattle: how times change. The old idea of the periphery and the center, of music as a ticket from the sticks to the bright lights, seemingly no longer applies. Luis had been a Manhattan street-and-subway musician for years, he was a late starter, but it was the beginning of success that did him in, the acclaim at Soundgarten, the first record, all of that. The closer the album's release date came the more often he talked about killing himself. I told you we liked guns, she said, he had five or six, handguns, rifles, he took good care of them. When the death talk started I got somebody to take them all away but then one of his old street compadres brought him another, go figure, okay?, and a couple of days later he did it, plugged himself right in the record company lobby, so I guess he made his point, whatever it was.

Handgunss. Rifless. Compadress.

I half remember the incident. It made the papers in a small way at the time. Then she shows me his picture and I realize I've met him. The street band was the Mall in those days, I can see why they changed it, why they turned the M upside down. I remember Luis red-eyed and shabbily goateed, playing the hybrid guisitar and abusing Doorman Shetty as he was shooed away from the Rhodopé. *One day when we're big, I mean when we're monster big, I'm gonna come back here 'n' fucking buy this fucking building.* What, Mira is asking. No, nothing, I say, it's just that I heard about his death but I didn't know about you and him, that he was Tara's, so she's called Tara Heinrich, right.

No, she snaps, her lips thin and white with anger. Tara Celano, and don't you fucking forget it, I mean fuck that snake Luis, okay?, that coward and his fucking Latino-Teuton name. He's in the stupid club now along with Del Shannon and Gram Parsons and Johnny Ace and the Singing Nun. I'm the parent that stayed.

After he died she fell apart for a while, did every drug invented, had her stomach pumped once, so I know how your Ormus feels, she tells me, I've been there; almost stayed. In the ambulance two paramedics played hard man, soft man, one going *come on honey stay awake you can make it look at you you're a great big beautiful doll so stay awake baby you can make it baby baby we need you to live do it for me baby oh yeah yeah* like a fucking dirty phone call, she says, and the other guy was snarling *fuck you trash bitch cunt you want our fucking attention you fucking got it there's people in this city getting shot and sick for real but we gotta come here and take care of you fucking self-centered bitch slit we should put you out right here in the street and let you fucking die.* He was the one who saved me, the bad guy, she confesses. I kept thinking *man, I'm gonna live to slug that bastard right in the mouth if it's the last thing I do.*

After the stomach pump she discovered she was pregnant

and then came the disinheritance et cetera, the triple whammy, but this time instead of cracking up she went to work. You never saw me when I was Pregnant Vina, she says, suddenly unleashing a wild cackle of laughter. Man, *that* was off the wall.

SHE WON'T say much about her family. I get the basic information and then the subject's permanently off-limits. I remember Vina's long silence about the bad childhood days in Chickaboom, and I want to tell Mira, honey, you don't know how like Vina you are, but I intuit that this would not go down well. Ever since we've started sleeping together it has become important for her to dissociate herself from her predecessor. She lists all the things Vina liked which she can't stand. *I hate Tolkien, you know?, and the fucking Faraway Tree, they should chop it down, and I* really *hate vegetarians, I'm a meat woman, give me meat.* As I listen to her I have to work to keep the smile off my face because she sounds exactly the way Vina did on the beach at Juhu, in the days when she was hating the hell out of India, before she discovered its good points, which included Ormus Cama and me.

One day Mira starts talking about sacred music. It seems that although her father's people were originally from Assisi they weren't all totally peace-loving St. Francis types. The original Tomaso di Celano (died *circa* 1255) was, Mira says, probably St. Francis's first biographer, but he also composed one of the great blood-and-thunder hymns of apocalypse, the *Dies Irae.* Not very love and peace and animals and birdies, is it, I reflect. Where there is discord may we bring harmony, that was the St. Francis angle, if I recall, but this Tomaso di Celano was apparently more interested in divine wrath than divine love.

She ignores my teasing. I can do the whole thing in Latin, she says proudly, and I actually let her. Such is new love.

Rex tremendae maiestatis,
qui salvandos salvas gratis,
salva me, fons pietatis.

It ends, finally, with this remarkably financial burst of praise for the king of tremendous majesty, who saves those who are fit to be saved, free of charge. Mira's eyes are shining now. There's a new worldwide appetite for a spiritual approach, she preaches, I guess it's all the earthquakes and catastrophes, the sense of an ending, people are looking for meaning, you know what I mean?

Think about it, I say sardonically, there must be higher love. (I'm thinking, I hope she isn't about to rip off her mask and turn into the early Ifredis Wing.)

That's it, she says, missing my meaning entirely—irony is what people miss—and suddenly she's any bright, super-intense twenty-year-old, that's *so it,* she repeats, and have you *heard* this stuff? Sufi music, for example, it could be Azerbaijani or Uzbek or Moroccan, I mean I'm not au courant with the belief system, okay?, but there's this incredible drumming, and amazing layered syncopation, and trumpets, and dancing like you're possessed. But it's not just Sufi, there's so much of this music crossing frontiers now, music from all over, Yoruba drumming, the old songs of the expelled Jews of Spain, Persian-Iraqi maqam concerts using mystical poems, Shinto drumming, gospel, Buddhist chants, and do you know the work of Arvo Pärt, sort of minimalist meets New Age? Have you heard Fatty Ahmed, he's played with the Ruby Goo?

Yeah, him I've heard of, I say, laughing openly now. He just died weighing three hundred and eighty pounds, which is bad news for that finagling retinue of his, they were going for every dollar they could grab while the poor man, unworldly, unaware, sat singing his devotional songs at the Hollywood Bowl like a spider trapped in his own web. That's sacred music all right.

What's funny, she wants to know. People really want this, they want the magic and the security, the idea that there's something beyond, something greater, something more. Meditation, celebration, supplication, that's . . . fuck you, Rai, why is this making you laugh?

No, it's really okay, I say. I'm sorry, it's only nostalgia. I knew someone else who talked like this once.

Oh, shit, she says. My people were doing this stuff in the fucking thirteenth century but I should have guessed she'd still have gotten in first.

* * *

HERE IS seventeen-month-old Tara Celano on my roof terrace, wearing a furry pink bomber jacket and lime-green tights, serenading the watching Chrysler Building and World Trade Center towers with a lyric-free approximation of, I'm guessing, *Da Doo Ron Ron.* Mira, meanwhile, lounges on a rug, smoking, apparently ignoring her daughter completely. Left to her own devices, Tara is growing up as a strange mixture of precocious adult and lucky survivor. On the one hand, she can now wait in the wings during her mother's performances without complaining; she can do the twist, the stomp, the mashed potato too, and the wah-watusi and the hitchhiker and the locomotion, and if you don't know how to do it, she'll show you how to walk the dog; and she knows her way around the backstage areas and women's rooms of dozens of Manhattan clubs and bars, both salubrious and unhealthy. On the other, she picks pebbles off the tops of graveled cactus pots and tries to swallow them. My apartment's electric wall sockets exert upon her a potent magnetic attraction. I have the feeling I'm saving her life a dozen times a day, but she's come this far without me, so Mira must have been keeping an eye on her while pretending to turn her loose. That's what I choose to think, anyhow, while continuing to make sure Tara doesn't succeed in mounting the wall at the edge of the roof terrace and swallow-dive to an untimely death in East Fifth Street below.

The spiritual topic, interestingly, never recurs. Mira, always quick on the uptake, has understood two things about it: one, that I do not respond well to such remarks, and two, that it's a road leading back to Vina, with whose ghost she is beginning to feel, for the first time in her short life, a tad competitive. Thus it remains unclear whether she's genuinely religious or if this is some Catholic leftover mixed up with the remains of teenage mysticism. Or, to give her her due, maybe she sees sacred music simply as something to use, there's no need to become what did she say au courant, it's just a way of getting people to listen, a storehouse to ransack for her own purposes, as Picasso once ransacked Africa's visual motherlode, as the empires of the West once ransacked the world.

This is what a generation gap feels like, I realize. In some respects I simply do not understand the workings of so young and fresh a mind.

About the *gunss,* I have formulated a private theory. I think the weapons are linked to the *tattooss* (a butterfly on her ankle and a small dragon below her left shoulder blade), the whorey clothes, the exhibitionism (in spite of my repeated requests, she won't lower the window shades when she's walking around demi-nude at home)—in brief, to her whole trash act. It's all a class rebellion, a way of defining herself against those who rejected her. The guns are pantomime. When I check inside Mira's bag, I do find a little Giuliani & Koch .09 mm persuader, but it isn't loaded, nor is she carrying ammunition clips. The city is Mira's theater and the gun is just her prop.

ON THE morning of our appointment with Ormus she's as nervous as a teenager before her first date. Tara, on the other hand, is totally cool, except for a tendency to shout at anyone within range: *Go see old guy!* Johnny Chow has come up for breakfast and she yells the news at him. Big talker, huh, Chow grins, biting into a blueberry muffin. Careful, kid, nothing gets you in trouble like your mouth. Then Mira comes out of the bedroom in her Vina get-up and he chokes. I have to thump him on the back several times and when he recovers, wiping his eyes, he turns to Tara, gasping for air: See what I mean?

To Mira he wonderingly remarks, Rai told me you were good, but I never imagined, I never fucking dreamed. Damn! And you sing like her, too. Hot damn. I've got to tell you this totally weirds me out.

He leaves, shaking his head, still clearing his throat. Gee, you can't beat a good notice for building confidence, Mira exclaims, with an uncertain smile.

In the cab uptown—Ormus offered to send Will Singh with a car, but I thought it better to arrive independently—Mira goes through her Ormus checklist. Life story, discography, influences, touchy points, e.g. the tinnitus that doomed him to perform in a glass casket. That doesn't seem to bother him too much in ordinary life, I tell her. I'm remembering how he cleaned up the sound on his spy tape so that I could hear her voice. Even with his internal crackles and tweets he can still hear well enough to work a mixing desk. Oh, Jesus, I suddenly think, he's not crazy enough to play her the surveillance tapes, is he? If she sees herself on those three hundred screens she'll walk out of both our lives and never return and I can't say I'd blame her either.

So now I'm nervous too.

His heterotopian tendencies, his forays into alternative realities, both attract and alarm her. She has grown up with Ormus's songs and pronouncements about the otherworld, but she doesn't like the idea that it wasn't a better place, just a different one, no more than a variation that didn't quite work, and she doesn't at all like the idea that it's gone, that Ormus doesn't need the eye patch any more. I've also briefed her about Gayomart, who after all was Ormus's original heterotopic discovery. Gayomart and the songs of the future. Gayomart's escape from Ormus's head in a car smash long ago. Ormus's half-belief that it's Gayo with whom Vina spent her last moments, that maybe it's Gayo she's been with in her time below. It's still difficult for me to come out with this information neutrally, without making judgements, but Mira is fascinated. I love a good twin story, she says. It's all about the different sides of the brain, I mean we really have no idea of the untapped potential, of our own powers, okay? This guy has really penetrated his dark side. It's amazing. Rai?

I think the two of you will hit it off just fine, I say. (I'm starting to feel, and therefore sound, not only edgy but more than a little sour.)

Are you jealous? she asks, extremely pleased, I thought he was old and fucked up and had terrible buzzy ears. No contest, right? You are jealous, she says, punching me on the arm, grinning from ear to ear. *Now* she's relaxed.

Buzzy ear, says Tara from her corner of the cab. Buzzy ear fucked up.

Clea's waiting in the Rhodopé lobby wearing her thick-lensed glasses, looking more than ever like a tiny old sari-clad Mrs. Mole. When she sees Mira she gasps, Oh, Madam, thank god! Then she shivers slightly, as if making an enormous effort to rein in her feelings, and turns to Tara, greeting her like they're old buddies, low- and high-fiving her, instantly stealing her young-old heart. In the elevator Tara and Clea do the swim (VTO's on the sound system) while I look at myself in the mirror. I'm not in bad shape but next to Mira I look like the essence of square. I even use words like square. Ormus, in his current decrepitude, is, I suspect, still cool. I personally would call him more hip replacement than hip but then I'm not a twenty-year-old girl being granted admission to the inner sanctum of one of the sacred monsters of rock.

He's waiting at the elevator door, looking frail but expectant, dressed in Japanese martial arts whites and leaning on Will Singh. When he lays eyes on her his fingers tighten on Will's forearm, digging in painfully. Will remains impassive; impassivity is this big man's forte.

Yes, says Ormus Cama. Just that one word. He and Mira face each other for a silent eternity: fifteen seconds, ten years, something like that. I note with some satisfaction that the look on her face is one of disguised disbelief. She's acting as if she's seen a ghost, as if Ormus, this wasted entity that used to be Ormus Cama, is the revenant, the one who's come back from the dead. Which is of course supposed to be her rôle in today's little drama.

Please, says Ormus, and leads the way, still leaning on Will, towards the white Yamaha concert grand. After a few paces Mira touches Will Singh on the shoulder. Let me do that, she says, and offers her own young arm to Ormus. He nods, twice, his eyes filled with emotion, and they move forward again. Will hovers at the rear of the group. Tara has taken Clea Singh's hand. Everyone is silenced by the moment.

When we reach the piano, Ormus sits down and starts to play a slow, haunting gospelly tune. Mira stands by him, a little behind him. The rest of us wait awkwardly, feeling like intruders. For a few minutes she just lets him play, she lets the music take her body, closes her eyes, sways. One of her hands has alighted on Ormus's shoulder and she leaves it there, she even moves it across a couple of inches and rests her fingertips against the nape of his neck. I feel my face heating up but I do not intervene.

Then Mira sings, and the room fills with her ridiculously strong voice with its great river-deep-mountain-high range. Vina's voice. Ormus Cama hears it and is forced to stop playing because his fingers have begun to shake, but she keeps going by herself, like a ray of sunlight in a ruined church.

Lead me to your light, she sings, oh sweetheart lead me to your day, I'm down at the bottom in the endless night, won't you please show me the way. If you don't lead me baby then I guess I'm down here to stay.

The song is a VTO golden oldie, a lost soul's appeal to her lover, but Mira's the one leading Ormus out of the darkness now, the one saving him from the pit. He's down in that deep dungeon and it's her voice that's setting him free.

His hands go back to the piano, the tempo rises and her voice soars in answering joy. Clea and Tara are hand-clapping now. Even Will Singh, mister stoneface himself, is joining in. Me? I'm not clapping. I'm not the musical type.

LATER, OVER dinner back at home, with Tara happily asleep in my bed, I look at Mira across the fettuccine and chianti I've set before her and I see a stranger: a tough, disenchanted young woman who is also sharp enough to seize her big opportunity, and under the eyes of her lover to flirt with another man. A woman who still isn't sure whether or not she has just had the most important encounter of her musical life. Maybe there's a future opening up for her, or maybe it's just a mad fantasy that will vanish with the dawn. I can see that she is imagining that future, she can't help picturing the rebirth of one of the legendary bands, with herself stepping into Vina's empty shoes.

Don't run away with it, I say, too roughly. You saw the shape he's in. Maybe he'll break the habit, maybe he won't. The odds are not great, you know that, you know the addictive grip of what he's on, it could be stronger even than you. Anyway it's a long way from today to a stadium show.

Damn, listen to yourself, she says, setting her jaw. I thought this whole thing was your idea anyhow. It was even you who said we shouldn't tell him about us. *Help Ormus,* yeah, right, but let's not help Mira, let's not get carried away.

I can't think of a thing to say. I just sit and eat.

You don't trust me, is that it, she asks. You don't believe what I promised you. You think I'm a whore.

No, I say after much too long a pause, it's okay, I do trust you, I really do.

In fact I am sort of confident of her love, the unlooked-for surprise of it, I want to trust her blindly, but I'm also aware that I have badly miscalculated the power of what Ormus Cama still has to offer. His music, his legendary status and, yes, also his beauty. Mira is clear about that. You're so blind, she tells me, he's the most beautiful man. Those eyes, that soft, soft voice, he's fucking irresistible. Sure, he's taken a battering, but you can't be such a *man* that you actually think that makes him less attractive.

How about his age, I say, trying to sound light-hearted. This is a fellow with childhood memories of the 1940s, of World War II, "White Christmas," the Partition Riots, the New Look, *Oklahoma*. Is this what today's youth prefers?

That's just his shell, it's just the lantern protecting his flame, okay?, she waves me away. His spirit's still young, the flame's still strong, and that's what counts. Like your spirit, she adds consolingly, coming across to my side of the table, and p.s. I also like your shell.

At night when I've moved Tara into the room next door and she and Mira are both asleep, I stare at the ceiling and reflect on fate's little table-turning ways. With Vina I was always the secret lover, the back-door man. This time it's Mira and I who are together, an item, in love, whatever, and it's my turn to fret about her secret life with Ormus. So we're rivals again, Ormus and I, and in this respect Mira has already filled Vina's boots. And even though the flow of this new triangle's energy has been reversed, some things remain the same: trust is the issue once more; and Ormus Cama still has no idea of my real importance in the story of his life.

The existence of the peekaboo videotapes is the secret Ormus and I are keeping from Mira, and must forever keep. That we have become lovers is the secret Mira and I have agreed to keep from Ormus. This is a secret I would now prefer to tell, but I am denied permission to do so by the woman I love, on pain of terrible retribution. As for Mira and Ormus, music is their secret language, in which they can commune in ways they don't trouble to explain to me.

Here is the last image in my photo-sequence about Vina.

I'm sitting in a chair with a circular mirror on my lap. Reflected in the circular mirror is a rectangular mirror containing an image of Vina Apsara. No, not Vina, but the greatest of the not-Vinas. Mira Celano, my new torment, my love.

Mira, Mira, who is the fairest one of all?

ON THE fourth anniversary of Vina's death, Mo Mallick at Colchis summons the music press wearing a smile like the elated first chord of a surefire hit to announce the imminent emergence from retirement of Ormus Cama and the relaunch of the VTO supergroup in a phase-two lineup. The place of rhythm guitarist Simone Bath will be filled by the emerging gay icon lil dagover, who insists on lower-case initials, wears men's suits and a monocle and a Louise Brooks haircut, and plays like an expressionist dream. (Bath herself, embittered by Vina's old attack on her competence, is threatening to sue Ormus for the rights to the VTO name, a move that alarms nobody and comes to nothing.) The band will be fronted as before by Ormus Cama on vocals and lead guitar, Mallick concludes, and on lead vocals we'll be introducing the new singing sensation Mira Celano, the closest thing to our beloved Vina any of you will ever see.

It's like announcing a Beatles reunion, only bigger. The VTO back catalogue still outsells most functioning bands, and the classic *Quakershaker* CD, reissued with the revised version of "Beneath Her Feet" added as a bonus track, hasn't been out of the *Billboard* top three since the day of Vina's death. The hiring of dagover is widely applauded as a recognition of the need for the band to move with the times. diamond lil brings a formidable résumé with her. At the age of seventeen she was hanging out with the mystery men of Kraftwerk and devising music for the all-female Japanese-Western crossover Takarazuka dance company, in which half the women dress as men and are worshipped by legions of female fans, and she has never looked back. She is highly rated by production gurus as diverse as the Glimmer Twins, Mutt Lange and DJ Jellybean's sidekick, Whitney and Debbie H.'s producer, Toni C. A year or two with VTO should jet-propel dagover into the major leagues, so it's a smart move for her as well as the band.

Mira Celano, however, is being kept under wraps—no interviews, no photographs, no tapes—and this is not a popular strategy. It always used to be said that VTO was Ormus and Vina and anyone, but the circumstances of Ormus's decline are well known, his recovery is uncertain, and in the absence of hard evidence to the contrary Mira is considered unlikely to be worthy of standing in the great Vina Apsara's shoes. She is the subject of intense speculation and much skepticism, and when it's learned that she started out as a lowly impersonator the mood turns ugly. As ever, the Sangria siblings lead the attack, accusing Ormus of vandalizing his own legend and turning the VTO name into a joke, a theme park version of itself. (From Rémy Auxerre no more highfalutin Francophoneries will be heard. He is dead of the Illness, just a square in the quilt now. Rémy's gone, and his sometime lover, my friend Aimé-Césaire Basquiat, is Ill.)

As for the VTO operation, we're in rehearsal, locked away in a disused aircraft hangar in Nassau County and surrounded by an army-style security blanket. This, too, is an aspect of contemporary rock music: the move up to military scale and precision for no greater reason than to shake, rattle 'n' roll. Once upon a time Jerry Apple and his guitar could arrive at the stage door five minutes before showtime, collect his ten thousand bucks in cash from the manager and head out on to the stage, barely acknowledging the house band provided to back him. If anyone in the band dared to ask about the playlist he'd reply, *sonny, tonight we're gonna be playing some Jerry Apple songs.* It's different now. Those old-time duck-walkers were itinerant tinkers. These musicians are industrialists.

Here are the sequencers, the synthesizers, the sampling devices—Fairlights, Synclaviers. Here are the musicians, working out how to lay their own playing over the swirls and twirls, the technological sound-mattresses they'll be bouncing on throughout the show. Ormus and lil dagover, in particular, are currently in deep musical communion, swapping incomprehensibilities with the techno gandalf, Eno Barber. (Yes, Eno from Radio Freddie; these days he's the undisputed king of the loop, the czar of texture, King Ear. Our lives disconnect and reconnect, we move on, and later we may again touch one another, again bounce away. This is the felt shape of a human life, neither simply linear nor wholly disjunctive nor endlessly bifurcating, but rather this bouncey-castle sequence of bumpings-into and tumblings-apart.) Ormus has brought Eno in to work on the new show and its accompanying album, and there's a lot of this huddling at present. Mira hates it. As the singer, she's largely excluded from the instrumentalists' private club. This part of Ormus is not for her; when he's with dagover, she feels the way I feel when he's with her.

Today Mira is on edge, uncertain, she can't stop moving, a few steps this way, a few steps that, smacking the palms of her hands together, snapping her fingers, talking fast, her eyes concealed behind alarming night-black goggle-like curve-around shades. Tara is off somewhere in Mira's mobile-home private zone, being cared for by Clea Singh. She's a wise enough child to know that when Mommy's in this mood it's best to keep out of her way. I'm not yet prepared to be that wise. I'm there, trying to be a reassuring presence, mostly just flak-catching when she needs someone to yell at. I'm the wife.

She's soliloquizing, and when Mira is like this you just have to hang on for the ride. The negative speculation in the media has rattled her, the decision to seal her off from premature exposure has proved more stressful than she anticipated. It isn't easy to keep your head down when half the country's press corps is on your trail, to button your lip when what they're saying is cruel and you want to fight your corner. But Mallick had said, if we expose you now we're just showing them the target before we're ready to repel their fire. On stage you'll shut their fucking mouths so wait, just wait, please. And Ormus backed Mallick and they were the pros and so she agreed, but she's full of doubts, feels she shouldn't go out in front of audiences dressed up as Vina any more, feels caged in her impersonation and wants to be herself.

Come on, it wasn't Vina who awoke him from a coma this time, she growls, it was me, Mira, me hauling him back from the dead, me firing his crooked physician with the onion breath who came on to me while I was showing him the door, me getting him into rehab along with all the other guys with pointy teeth and spiralling eyeballs, and then me making sure he stayed with the program and graduated summa cum fucking laude. When he needed someone in the night he called out for me and baby, I got up and went to him every single time, well, okay, at least until one a.m. six nights a week, I mean not right in the middle of the night when we were, when, listen, you know what I'm saying here, I left my own child in your care, okay, yours and sometimes the babysitter's, okay and sometimes Clea Singh's too, when he sent her over, but goddammit nobody went to him more than me, I played all his crazy games, I let him hold on to Vina through me until he was strong enough to stand on his own feet, and look at him now, he's a man reborn, okay, bravo, kudos to him, what I'm saying here is he owes me, I'm holding his marker, it's time he set me free. I brought him back from Hell but that doesn't mean I've got to burn in the fire instead. This Vina crap, I know it's a mistake but I can't get myself heard and when we're out there in the bright lights it's me who's going to have to take the fall.

This is what I do not bring up at this juncture: that I'm sliding into Hell too. The deeper we get into rehearsals the further from me she moves, the more she resents lil dagover the more outrageously she comes on to Ormus. I continue to discover that there are few limits to Mira's pragmatism. Whatever works, is her motto. I keep wondering about Ormus's bedroom door. Is that an inviolable borderline? Or will she go beyond that, too, to find whatever works?

(Trust me. Don't you trust me?)

(Yes, darling, I trust you, baby, I truly do. But maybe I'm an idiot to do it, just one more fool for love. One more rock 'n' roll wife.)

RUMORS REACH the world outside the aircraft hangar of dissension within it. Mira suspects dagover of being the source of the leaks. The two women are increasingly at loggerheads; they're both opinionated, strong-mindedly pushing their ideas, competing for Ormus Cama's respect. Mira tells Ormus he's letting the technology turn his head, putting the cart before the horse, you're like the generals with their smart bombs, she says, boys and their fucking toys. I'm the one who knows the clubs, she adds, I've spent more time on the scene than the rest of you put together, you're just babbling science to sound cool but you don't know shit. In the clubs this stuff is already over, it wasn't enough. People are hungry, okay?, the machines aren't feeding them, I mean it's up to us to give them something to bite on, to give their spirits food.

Ormus is listening.

But lil dagover hits back with a well-developed theory that it's technology that has taken the music back to its roots, its origins in North African atonal call-and-response rhythms. When the slaves came across the sea and were forbidden to use their drums, their talking drums, they listened to the music of the Irish slave drivers, the three-chord Celtic folk songs, and turned it into the blues. And after the end of slavery they got their drums back and that was r&b, and white kids took that from them *and added amplification* and that was the birth of rock 'n' roll. Which went back across the ocean to England and Europe and got transformed by the Beatles, the first great rock group to use stereo technology, and that stereo mutation came back to America and became VTO et cètera. But the technology goes on changing, and with the invention of sampling you can graft the oldest music on to the newest sounds and then, shazam!, in hip-hop, in scratching, you're right back to call and response, back to the future. Technology's not the enemy, lil argues, it's the means.

What is this, Mira demands of Ormus, a history seminar or a rock 'n' roll band? If she's right then the music's a closed loop, it's dead, let's go home. To go forward, to break out of the loop, we've got to go on pushing what VTO started to do, what I always thought Vina stood for. Crossing frontiers. Bringing in the rest of the fucking world.

It's an impasse, and interestingly enough Ormus doesn't seem willing or able to offer leadership, to see a way forward. The solution comes from Eno Barber, who makes it look surprisingly easy. Eno still comes across as the brother from another planet, immaculately groomed at all hours of the day and night, never seen eating or drinking or taking a leak, unflappability incarnate. He calls Mira and lil to his mixing desk and says quietly, I was thinking, we could have it both ways. And as they listen to his loops, the tabla rhythms and sitar and yes vina riffs pushed through his sequencers along with pure synthesized sound, as he fades and balances and mixes his bubbling aural brew, something starts happening, lil picks up her guitar and starts playing along, finding the rhythms or letting them find her, riding the waves, and Mira's singing scat mixed up with Ormus's lyrics and Indian *bóls,* and Ormus Cama has actually begun to smile. All over the cavernous hangar electricians and grips and roadies and record-company stiffs stop doing whatever they're doing and listen. This is the sound of a baby being born. This is the rhythm of new life.

We've got a band.

THERE IS hate mail. Well, there's always hate mail where there's attention, always the redneck *die commie perverts* messages, the religiomane *you may escape from me but you can't escape from god* fortune cookie menaces, the disappointed sexual fantasists, the fans of rival cults, the secret crazies who hold down mundane jobs and have back-yard cookouts on Sundays and fill their bedroom closets with magazine clippings over which they scrawl their epithets of existential loathing. And if the volume of the poison-pen material is greater than usual, it's partly because the band has been away so long, and the dirty water has been building up behind the dam. There's plenty of supportive fan mail too, of course, but it doesn't carry the same weight, doesn't become a part of what works on you as you go about your daily business. And this time the hostility is affecting the band more than usual, because, yes, theirs has been a long silence, and it's a new lineup, so there are uncertainties. Also, the hate mail is not just standard-issue nastiness. There's a new strain of virulence in much of it, an extra bitterness in the bile.

Vina wannabes write in to protest the choice of Mira rather than one of them, purists write to express disgust at the exhuming of the band, which should have been allowed to remain in the golden past where it belongs instead of being subjected to this zombified return, lesbian-haters send in their four-letter views of lil dagover and her Sapphic sisterhood, and that's just the polite stuff. Many correspondents send in near-illegible scrawls warning that VTO's quake songs may actually have been responsible for the current wave of seismic catastrophes and urging the band to keep away from that dangerous material. *Don't stir up yo uzual trouble again oar els, you've maid enouff money from uman mizry as it is.*

Another faction blames Ormus for the band's long silence, calling it a betrayal. Its members suggest that his envy of Vina's genius was the real reason for shutting down the band and that he must therefore be held responsible for what followed. If VTO hadn't ceased trading Vina wouldn't have needed to start building a solo career, and therefore in all probability she wouldn't have been in Mexico on that fateful Valentine's Day, so she'd still be alive, you fucking murderer, Ormus Cama, don't think we will ever forget or forgive.

Other correspondents, however, take a more positive line, praising the prophetic accuracy of Ormus's old songs, expressing the writer's belief that his music can literally change the world and begging Ormus to turn his magical powers towards the good. *Heal the breaking planet. Sing to us and soothe the aching earth.*

For everyone looking forward to Mira's début, there are five people hoping for various reasons to see her fail.

AT ONE point during the months of gestation—this is before we get to the airplane hangar—I myself get a little carried away. Mira tells me that Ormus's plan is to make the new show an exploration of the ourworld/otherworld duality with which he's wrestled most of his life. He's interested in the theme of dissolving the frontiers between the worlds, so there's a narrative he's developing about an overworld/underworld love story, perhaps a rescue. . . . When I realize he doesn't know about the music that came before him—how much, subconsciously, he must still resent his scholarly father, how much he must be suppressing!—I get excessively hot and bothered and go out and buy a stack of early operas, Jacopo Peri's *Euridice* (1600) with the Ottavio Rinuccini libretto, Monteverdi's 1607 *Orfeo,* libretto by Alessandro Striggio, and of course the Gluck, from which Vina sang her last song at Tequila. I can't find Giulio Caccini's rival setting of the Rinuccini libretto, but I don't care because it really isn't very good.

When Mira next goes over to the Rhodopé I tag along and bring Ormus the CDs. He accepts my gift and puts on the Peri and even listens patiently to what I have to say, that not only does the whole history of opera begin with these works, but it's a myth that crosses all cultural frontiers, you hear echoes of it in the Odin story, in Celtic traditions, even, I believe, in certain Native American tales, and all those versions have their own songs too, you should really have someone hunt them down. I tell him about the birth of a new style of accompanied solo song—his own art form!—in sixteenth-century Florence, at the court of Count Giovanni Bardi in the late 1570s: a song aimed at expressing the meaning of the text. This radical departure from the madrigal principle of ornamentation by division of parts made possible opera, the aria, the whole modern tradition of song right down to the three-minute Tin Pan Alley hit single with a catchy hook. This, too, is a part of his history, I tell him, and he should know it.

I try to evoke for him the first performance of Peri's opera at the Pitti Palace, on the occasion of the wedding of Maria de' Medici to Henry IV of France, and the later première of the Monteverdi at the Accademia degli Invaghiti at carnival time in Mantua, whose Gonzaga duke was patron to both Monteverdi and Striggio. . . . But before I can start in on the technicalities, strophic variation, *stile concertato,* etc., he interrupts me, very gently. I get it, it's an old tale, it's been sung before, especially in Italian, he whispers, not unkindly. I guess that's always so with any story. But what I'm trying to make here is still mine, and I'll just keep going down this stumbling path I'm on, if it's okay with you.

Okay, excuse me, I mutter, embarrassed, I just wanted to mention that the problem everybody has is with the ending, because she isn't supposed to be saved, you know. Everyone gives it a happy ending one way or another, but that's wrong, I just wanted to mention that. After all, Vina wasn't, and here I stop and bite my tongue.

Good, says Ormus, giving no sign of having heard the last few words. Unhappy ending. Got it. Thanks for stopping by.

Vina knew all this stuff, I mumble foolishly, and perhaps just a tad mutinously, and go home.

(While we're on the classics, I should say that Ormus has set the *Dies Irae* to music. Mira must have recited it to him too, and clearly he didn't pat *her* on the head and shoo her away. *O Angry Day* may be the first-ever rock lyric to be translated from a Latin original written by a *duecento* Italian monk.)

To PROCEED: the idea is to do a first, short Anglo-American tour in smaller venues, Roseland, the United Center, the Cambridge Corn Exchange, the Labatt's Apollo, no more than half a dozen gigs in total, to let the band bed down before launching, six months later, into a full, eighteen-month-long, six-continent stadium program of performances. The famous stadium rock set designer Mark McWilliam is devising a grand fantasia of an environment for this grand tour. By contrast, these first evenings will have a stripped-down, raw, back-to-basics feel. Let's get the music right, Ormus murmurs, before we get into the show.

His own singing voice is in good working order once more, though it's smaller than it used to be, needs more amplification. However, his guitar playing, according to Eno, with whose ear I do not presume to argue, is perhaps even better, more emotional, than before. He's back all right, and the band's sound is fat and hot. On our last day in the aircraft hangar there's a full as-live concert before an invited audience, with nothing held back except that nobody's in stage clothes. Even in jeans and T-shirts, however, they sound right on the money. The applause is long and sincere. VTO lives.

WE'RE AT Roseland, September 1993, just one week after the concert in the hangar, and a couple of thousand fans are in a high state of excitement, stroked by roving spotlights into an ever greater frenzy of anticipation, and then the VTO engine room starts up.

One-two-three-four!

The drummer, Patti LaBeef, the original tall Texan and one of the first women drummers to make it into the big league, is in her own monosyllabic way as much a hall-of-famer as Ormus and Vina up front. In the early days young men in the audience would yell at her, *God, you're horny,* and she'd ignore them, spit, and get on with her job. The VTO bassman, Bobby Bath, comes from Montserrat, island of earthquakes and sound studios, and plays as if his life's ambition is stability, no more. *Plenty of players got more tricks,* he says, *but it was always the basics that I loved, to be rock solid, yeah?, to lay down that bass line and let them up at the front dance all over she.* Bobby Bath was briefly married to the outcast Simone, but he has no problem about being back in the lineup. *What she's against, I'm for, baby,* is his attitude. *That's a bad-tastin' drink of rum and I drunk me all I need.*

And here's dagover, there's a big cheer for diamond lil, her personal fan club's out in force tonight, and then the dry ice clears and Ormus Cama's in his bubble with his pedal steel guitar, plunging into the intro for the first song, a souped-up version of the hard-driving oldie "Ooh Tar Baby." He takes the first verse himself and it's just like old times, only better, because lil dagover is fitting in well and filling the band's old Bath-shaped hole, and then Mira runs out and things start going badly wrong.

I'm sitting with Mo Mallick and we both see the problem at once, we see that Mira was one hundred percent right and Ormus, blinded by his need to believe in Vina Apsara's return from the dead, was very, very wrong. The audience isn't pleased. *What, you're really sending out a girl in a Vina costume and we're supposed to swallow it?* The moment we see the reaction we know the evening's a bust, and VTO could die again tonight. Here in this old ballroom it's looking like Ormus Cama's last dance.

Or not-dance, because the kids in front aren't moving, they're just standing stony-faced and staring up at the stage, pouring out their dumb hostility at Mira. How long before they start to boo? How long before they walk out?

At this point Mira Celano does an astonishing thing. She holds up her hand and the band stops playing. Then she addresses the angry crowd.

Okay, fuck you too, she says. You don't like my look, and the truth is neither do I, but for now we're both stuck with it, so why not just let's see if the music's any good, okay?, I mean if the music's no good then shoot me, fine, you're entitled, but if it's music you came for we've got some to give, and if you don't like my outfit, take my tip?, open your ears and shut your fucking eyes.

Patti LaBeef comes in here: a thunder-roll on the drums, a cymbal smash. Patti's rooting for the girl, and Patti has a lot of money in the bank with the paying public, Patti's credible. The crowd settles, grumbling, half convinced. Then it's lil, it's dagover, who fought Mira most of the way to tonight, blasting out the famous "Tar Baby" riff. That does it. *Five-six-seven-eight.* Ooh Tar Baby won't you hold me tight. We can stick together all thru the nite.

Ormus and Mira have discussed stage-diving. He can't do it—he's fifty-six years old and trapped in a soundproof cubicle—but she thinks she should. If we're talking about blurring the frontiers, she argues, then we've got to erase the line between us and them.

I'm against it, but my being protective only drives Mira further into danger, and so it's settled, she's going to do it, about halfway through the gig in the middle of the sequence of *Quakershaker* songs. But now that the show has gotten off to such a rough start, and even though the band is playing brilliantly the crowd is only about eighty percent with them, surely she won't go through with it, I think, surely she'll be smart enough to hold back.

She dives.

For an instant I think *they aren't going to catch her*, I imagine her body broken and trampled beneath the crowd's surly lethal feet, I think of Tara. But the arms do go up, they're holding her, she's swimming over the sea of hands, she's safe.

That's what I think, but I can't see what she can—the anger in many of the faces below her helpless body—I can't feel the hands that are starting to claw at her body. Only when somebody rips off her red Vina wig does it become clear. I'm on my feet now, Mallick is yelling into his walkie-talkie, it's a riot, get her out of there, but before the security guards can wade in she has somehow managed to regain the stage, and when she stands up we can all see the cuts on her midriff, her back, even her face, her long dark hair is blowing wild and ragged at her back and the bustier has gone, but she won't stop singing, she doesn't miss a beat, she stands front and center in her ripped leather pants and sings bleeding and bare-breasted right into their goddamn murderous ungrateful faces and that's when I know, when every one of us at the Roseland concert hall knows for certain that Mira Celano is going to be a big, big star.

Afterwards, backstage, I want to hold her and comfort her and to hell with Ormus and his delusions. But she's on fire and needs encircling by no man's strength. She has come off stage to lay down the law. It's not much of a green-room and we're all crowded in there and we all know what has to be said and that a woman with the guts to stage-dive into a crowd she can't trust also has the balls to face up to Ormus Cama and tear the scab off his deepest wound.

No more Vina, she says. She's standing toe-to-toe with him, she's the taller and stronger of the two and isn't planning on letting him get away. Okay, Ormus? We do it my way or let's forget the whole thing right now. Are you listening? Can you deal with this? Nobody comes back from underground. Nobody did return. Vina Apsara's gone.

But Ormus Cama is away in a Bombay record store, talking to a tall under-age beauty about the authorship of "Heartbreak Hotel."

Mira's shouting. Ormus? Did you hear what I said?

Yeah, Ormus whispers. He's actually humming the song.

Don't go crazy on me, Ormus. You're not so crazy now. I need to know your answer on this right away.

What's that? asks Ormus Cama, quietly. Vina Apsara? Oh, I'm sorry, she died.

CHAPTER EIGHTEEN

Dies Irae

O angry day, O angry day, When Time, like ash, will blow away. That's what King David and the Sibyl say.

In the West the earthquakes have stopped and the construction teams have moved in. Banks and insurance companies are building their new palaces over the faults, as if to assert the primacy of their authority, even over the misbehaving earth itself. The scars left by the quakes are being transformed into regeneration zones, gardens, office blocks, cineplexes, airports, malls. People have already started to forget and so, inevitably, resent those who remember. Ormus Cama and VTO, among others, are accused of negativity and scaremongering, because they continue to play the *Quakershaker* songs and their new gospel-influenced arrangement of Thomas of Celano's ancient minatory lines.

In the South, however, the devastation continues. It's as if the earth were discriminating against its most disadvantaged children. In India, where houses are built of mud and dreams, where the structures of life are fragile, their foundations weakened by corruption, poverty, fanaticism and neglect, the damage is immense. This is not pleasing to those who hold that India is not different from anywhere else, who deny that particularity of circumstance which makes a place itself. The fact is that the ground in America is not shaking, but some patch or other of Indian soil, one or another Indian city street, is hit by subterranean tremors almost every day.

To many third-world observers it seems self-evident that earthquakes are the new hegemonic geopolitics, the tool by which the superpower quake-makers intend to shake and break the emergent economies of the South, the Southeast, the Rim. The boastful triumphalism of the West during the revolutionary upheavals of 1989–90 has come back to haunt it. Now all earth tremors are perceived as Euro-American weapons, what were once classified by insurance brokers as acts of god are now close to being treated by entire states as acts of war, and the altruism with which ordinary Western citizens contribute to disaster relief funds, and even the indefatigable efforts of the international aid agencies, look like post-facto attempts at salving the guilty consciences of the powerful after the damage has been done. India, Pakistan, Israel, Syria, Iran, Iraq and China all announce the allocation of gigantic "plate wars" budgets. A new kind of weapons scramble has begun.

Exhaustive efforts by skeptical Western journalists and politicians to investigate and challenge the claims of responsibility made by their own military-industrial complex for the 1989–90 transglobal quakeathon are treated as disinformation by the participants in the new quake race, and interventions by international peace movements are largely ignored. Appeals from world leaders to the quake-racers to freeze their dangerously destabilizing new "rift bomb" building programs are branded arrogant and hypocritical. The U.N. Secretary-General's shuttle-diplomacy initiative to persuade all relevant parties to attend an urgently convened HARF (Hands Across the Rifts and Faults) symposium, where they might enter constructively into conflict-resolution talks, is ineffective. There are mass public demonstrations in support of the decisions taken by the leaders of all the Seismic Seven. Self-respect and national pride are invoked and people declare themselves ready to let their children starve in order to acquire the ability to shake the world, which they appear to equate with victory in such other prestigious contests as the Miss World pageant and the soccer World Cup. The very walls of Delhi, Islamabad and the other seismohawk capitals shout pro-quake-technology slogans. *No HARF measures. When we can quake land will be time to shake hand.*

As the Indian earthquakes continue, local politicos continue to blame (as well as the West) the country's traditional enemies to the north and northwest, and this creates a fevered public climate in which war is a constant possibility. Golmatol Doodhwala, widow of the assassinated Piloo, is a particular political beneficiary of this fist-shaking. In a century marked by the frequent rise to power of the widows of murdered men, the spherical, illiterate Golmatol, with her unceasing demands for revenge, is the latest in the line—perhaps the last, if she gets her warmongering way, and the world ends. Not with a bang but a shudder.

Everyone's a New Quaker now.

Much that has lain hidden for years is thrown back into view by the unceasing tremors. When it is announced that the reborn VTO rock supergroup plans to add concert dates in Bombay and Delhi to its marathon tour schedule, and that at these dates *O Angry Day* and the *Quakershaker* songs will be played as part of the band's efforts to support Western peace initiatives, the opposition to Ormus Cama's return is orchestrated by an unexpected hand. From Tihar Jail, his elder brother Cyrus Cama issues a statement that wins wide public support.

Cyrus at sixty-one is still classified as dangerously insane and has never on any occasion requested parole. It is his firmly expressed view that he should remain in "my beloved Tihar" until the day of his death, for only in prison can he be safe from the fear that the Pillowman, who may yet sleep within him, might re-emerge to commit further hideous crimes. He is a multiple murderer, that is still true, of course; yet within the jail his gentle disposition continues to win him many friends. No matter how frequently his warders are changed they leave as his disciples, for Cyrus has become a wise man, having passed the years quietly, studiously, learning the ancient languages and mastering the old books, very much in the Darius Cama tradition. His *Meditations on Kalki*—Kalki, the last manifestation of Vishnu, who will come only to announce the end of the world—have been published in learned journals and reprinted as *feuilletons* and chapbooks by various small philosophical presses, and there are numerous university professors and excited students who consider him one of the deeper thinkers in the land, a voice for our troubled and conceivably terminal times. As a published writer of polish and note, and a man whose determinedly (if somewhat inevitably) simple life and principled self-denial are striking, Cyrus has become an emblem of what a man may do with his spell on earth once he accepts his given lot. His body is in prison but his spirit, as his fans admiringly put it, his spirit is a bird's joyous song, sounding in an open sky.

To Ormus Cama, Cyrus elects to write an open letter, more in sorrow than in wrath: My brother, I regret so much to say, you have become a man who hates his own kind. This opening sentence ensures the wide publication of Cyrus's ruefully polemical text in the Indian and then the global news media. Even Ormus's recent statement opposing the quake wars is turned against him. Ormus began wryly: *As for myself, I control no weapons of mass destruction, so I hope to be excused the charge of hypocrisy when I say . . .* ah, Cyrus offers mournful rebuttal, but my brother is too modest; for who was it that penned the regrettable ditties that have become the totemic anthems of the new Quake Age? We must not take Ormus Cama at his own low estimate, as a mere troubadour or popster; for his self-hating, deracinated music has long been at the service, I would even say at very heart, of the arrogance of the West, where the world's tragedy is repackaged as youth entertainment and given an infectious, foot-tapping beat.

What Cyrus initiates, others eagerly take up. The government's favorite godmen of the moment, Ulurishi and the Aurhum Baba, announce that the former Indian and lapsed Zoroastrian "seismopropagandist" Ormus Cama must indeed bear a heavy responsibility for the West's quake-inducing "doomsday scenario"; that his songs and performances are open attacks on intercultural as well as intracultural stability; and that accordingly he and his collaborators should under no circumstances be permitted to perform on Indian soil. Within days of the Rishi and Baba's unprecedented joint communiqué, Interior Minister Golmatol Doodhwala (whose Pilooist faction has just agreed to prop up the shaky governing coalition, the Interior Ministry being the price of Golmatol's support) confirms that all VTO tour personnel, including the band members, themselves have been refused entry visas in the public interest, and also in their own, because in the present heated climate their personal safety cannot be guaranteed.

So the past reaches up its claw for Ormus, grabs his ankle and seeks to drag him down. And after the Cyrus letter is published, the hate mail from India multiplies. Violence is threatened, but that's nothing new. For years a dozen Vina wannabes a week have been threatening to kill Ormus and/or themselves for his failure to love them, for restricting himself in what they consider an unhealthy way to the starvation diet of his dead wife's memory, thus denying himself the opportunity to partake of the banquets of love that are on offer all around. Ormus has never taken such menaces seriously, and in spite of Clea Singh's concerns, this new Ormus, Ormus in his cocoon, Ormus in the strangely absent mood he's been in ever since Mira made him face the Vina facts, this vague, wafting Ormus is also immune to his angry subcontinental correspondents' new darts. The Singhs, at Clea's insistence, are nevertheless on ready alert for trouble.

When news of the Indian ban reaches the Sangrias in New York, they decide that Cyrus Cama is the hot unwritten story of the VTO phenomenon, and make arrangements to travel to Delhi on the first available flight.

O ANGRY days, O angry nights. This is how I think of the two long years of ending that followed the three deaths of Vina Apsara: as the nights and days of wrath. O final, departed times.

I think that Vina died the first time in the abyss at El Huracán, the second time very slowly, as the world turned her into its iconic Vina Divina and lost its grip on her quirky humanity until finally Clea Singh erased her voice from her own answering machine, and her third and final death occurred when my darling Mira Celano forced Ormus Cama who loved Vina best to speak the words that killed her for all time to come. After he spoke those words Ormus knew that he had severed the last tie that held him down to earth, and having lost all joy in life he began to look for death, to gaze into the faces of everyone he met as if he were asking, is it you? Please, friend, stranger, let it be you that brings me the gift I'm waiting for.

The *Into the Underworld* tour was conceived as a giant traveling memorial to Vina, whose Mira-simulacrum no longer appeared on stage but with whose silent, slo-mo image dancing across the giant Vidiwall behind the stage the show began and ended. This decision, too, was criticized in some quarters for over-commercializing the memory of a latter-day saint and was even described as a blatant attempt to cash in on a terminally rocky marriage, but Ormus continued to be impervious to criticism, to smile his quiet smile and go on down his chosen road. A man has to belong to something, even if it's just a golf club or a pet dog, and Ormus belonged to a memory now. Only the thing he had lost could hurt him; he belonged to her, and to music.

For most of 1994 and 1995 he lived exclusively in the world of the tour, an ersatz underworld environment tiered like the circles of Hell and enclosed in a giant arc by the largest Vidiwall ever built, from which the audience was nightly bombarded by incessant images of heaven and hell, both conceived of as places on earth, nuptial motels and flame-grilled-burger bars, video arcades and ballet schools, football crowds and war zones, ice deserts and political rallies, surf beaches and libraries, and it was up to each individual to decide which images were celestial, which infernal. This techno-inferno had been realized for him by the McWilliam design team but its essential concept was Ormus's own. Having created his fiction he plunged into it and did not come out for two years. The fictional universe of the show gave the impression of floating free of the real world, of being a separate reality that made contact with the earth every so often, for a night or two at a time, so that people could visit it and shake their pretty things. Voluntarily imprisoning himself within the private continuum of rock 'n' roll, Ormus Cama, too, became a floating entity, more otherworldly alien than human being, more show than O.

He moved from hotel floors stripped of superfluities, transformed into white spaces and supplied with white pianos, audiovideo editing suites and old Tuscan bread ovens, via limousines with blackened windows whose purpose was not so much to prevent people looking in as to make it impossible to see out, into that stadium environment which was always the same wherever in the world he might be, and in this illusion of continuity he found it possible for the moment to survive. When it was time to fly on the band's specially refitted 727 he took sleeping pills and did not wake up until it was time once again to enter the closed world of limousine and white hotel and underworld set which was now the only place on earth he needed to be or see.

It was as if the show were staying put while the world rushed past outside the stadium, as if the show were the permanence and human life the transient thing, as if the stadium was always the same stadium, and the limo was always the same car, always driven by Will Singh with Clea Singh by Ormus's side, and the hotel floor where he spent all his off-stage time baking and eating bread was always the same hotel floor, but the cities outside its windows came and went like the lands at the top of the Faraway Tree.

Rio, Sydney, London, Hong Kong, Los Angeles, Beijing: these places weren't real. The Indian ban wasn't important, because India wasn't real, it was just another transit zone. The changing colors and races of the faces in the crowd, the parade of celebrities who came backstage to drink with him and eat the home-baked bread he insisted on offering them, the local heroes and tour sponsors and cover girl beauties who munched away politely on his loaves and told him lies about how well he looked, none of these mattered, because they were illusions too. Only the show was real. The show, the music, was home. Outside that fiction, the cosmos was a fake.

He stood on his imagination, on what he had conjured out of nowhere, what did not, could not, would not exist without him. Now that it had been made, he existed only within it. Having created this territory, he trusted no other ground.

During the show the weight of light hitting the stage was so burdensome that in truth he could barely see the crowd, just the first few rows and beyond it a great roaring beast he had to tame, to play as if it were an instrument, but this was something he knew, this was his real life. The lion tamer in the lion's cage, putting his head into the jaws of the beast, knows that this is his true reality and the cheering, brightly colored, balloons-and-popcorn world beyond the bars is trivial, a painted backdrop, a set. So also Ormus in the bubble of the show was perfectly comfortable, perfectly at home, and by general consent his performances were extraordinary, his guitar never more achingly clear, like a desert wanderer's dream of water in a cool clean well, his singing never so subtle or so strong. The weak voice of recent times had vanished and in its place was this mighty instrument, more powerful than it had ever been in the old days when Vina herself was pouring her coloratura music over the world.

At the end of each show the other band members would murmur to each other in wonderment, almost fearful of what was coming out of him. Even LaBeef and Bath had to admit they had never seen him be so unbelievable over so long a period. *It's like he's a jet on afterburners,* Patti LaBeef said one night, *he can burn double the fuel because he knows he don't have to save none for the journey home.* Once she had said that all the band members understood that he was dying, that the fuel he was using on stage was life itself. He was burning himself up in the fire of his art, each night's show was not only a gift to Vina but a step towards the oblivion, the not-being, where she lay with his joy in her keeping; he knew that when the show was over he would no longer need to sing or speak or move or breathe or be. After that the musicians began to think of him as a creature from another world, because they could see how hard he was trying to get there, maybe some world through a gash in the air, some variant dimension where Vina was still alive. But there were no longer such gashes for him, for anyone, to see. lil dagover said to Mira, Ever since I can remember I was a fan of theirs, this is so hard to watch, but listen, at least he isn't guttering and choking like some dime-store candle, this is a fucking flameout, a supernova, a real star's way to go.

(IN REALITY the continuity of the show was maintained by doing everything in triplicate. Because the stage took a week to build, three different steel crews leapfrogged around the world, putting it up and tearing it down. There was always one stage being dismantled at the last venue, a second stage ready for action at the current stadium, and a third stage being built at the next stop down the road.

Then there was the energy requirement. Into the Underworld *pumped out four million watts of power, produced by six-thousand-horsepower generators. The three hundred and fifty cabinets in the sound system accounted for one and a half million of these watts. There were also two thousand lights, which means you could have watched the show from the moon.*

Six million people paid to watch the shows. Twenty million CDs and cassettes were sold. Hundreds of millions of dollars were made. If Ormus Cama imagined he was standing still while the world revolved around him, maybe he wasn't so very wrong. Such is the power of imagination.)

OUT ON the end of a long "finger" that ended in a great maw—intended to suggest the Gate of Hell and guarded by a three-headed animatronic Cerberus—was a small secondary stage on which Ormus was initially discovered, alone, like Orpheus at Aornum in Thesprotis, contemplating his terrible descent. On this stage Ormus played his opening solo, an acoustic version of "Beneath Her Feet," while Vina's image towered over the stadium on the Vidiwall. (As it was an acoustic solo, he could perform it unenclosed, standing in the open air, without further damaging his ears.) At the end of the song the mechanical dog lay down and slept and Ormus stepped into a clear bubble which moved forward on a track and was "swallowed" by the Maw. Now, under the catwalk linking the stages, he was transported to the main stage at high speed by the fastest-moving walkway in production, and burst into McWilliam's fantasy Hades where the other band members awaited him, as well as a zoo of flame-belching iron demons, giant inflatables and citizens of Pandemonium who were both costumed mimes and machines. Inset into the stage floor was a complex system of tracks and points, so Ormus was able to move around the great set without leaving his bubble; at one point, in a tremendous coup de théâtre, it was grasped by metal arms and became a glass elevator which rocketed Ormus high into the sky above the shrieking crowd. Thus bubbled Ormus no longer seemed separated from the action; the bubble became a metaphor of life, of his continued membership in the world of the living during his adventure in the country of the dead.

And Mira was there, of course, she was the woman he had come to rescue from the Prince of Darkness. Mira, dressed as herself now, singing her heart out, growing day by day into the stardom that was her destiny, stepping free of Vina's shadow and playing the part of Love trapped in Hell and longing to be free.

Look, it doesn't matter any more, it's not important how they behaved on stage, I understand that. I was jealous, all right?, let me admit that right up front, I was half mad with jealousy, and I was wrong. But boy, she turned out to be quite a performer, my Mira, you could see it in the way she leaned against Ormus's curving bubble, pressing her body against it, first her breasts and thighs, then her arched back and her ass, rolling across it as if she was making love to the damn thing, I couldn't watch. And at the end when she went inside it, when she was sealed in with Ormus and the bubble blazed with light and disappeared and then all of a sudden it was just Mira and Ormus back on the secondary stage, out of Hell, liberated from the bubble, and Ormus was playing his guitar as if it were sex itself and Mira was pouring herself over him like a free drink, well, hah!, I couldn't stand it!, I had to turn my back. I had to fucking leave.

I stopped going to the performances. I left the tour and went back to New York and got on with my work, I even went back to photo-journalism for the first time in years and ended up dodging bullets in places whose names I couldn't pronounce, Urgench-Turtkul on the Amu Darya, Târgul-Sačuesc in Transylvania, and the new post-Soviet hot spots of Altynaï-Asylmuratova and far-flung Nadezhda-Mandelstán; but still at night I dreamed pornographic dreams of Mira and Ormus. Sometimes my unconscious threw in lil dagover and a few Singhs to spice things up, and I'd wake up erect and sweating in some dirty murderous Cyrillic-scripted fleapit and understand that all human beings are capable of violence if they are sufficiently aroused, by the rape of their country, for example, or alternatively by the real or imagined seduction of their girl.

I know it's not the same thing, goddammit, I know the fucking difference between infidelity and genocide, but when you're out in woopwoopsky in a roachy sleeping bag in the back of a stranger's Jeep being bitten by Slavic and Asiatic insects, by Roman Catholic and Russian Orthodox and Zionist and Islamist bugs, while all around you is an exploding universe of disintegrating frontiers and crumbling realities, when you're in the midst of that kind of anarchy and mutability and you hope to make it back to East Fifth Street, New York, to read Page Six of the *Post*, just once more, while you're served a blueberry muffin and a cup of steaming organic coffee by a tall smiling barefoot Buddhist blonde, oh yes, just one more time, please, and you swear *you'll never make a single joke about designer Buddhism ever again, you want that peace-loving Buddha right now, give him to me, O Rinpoche Ginsberg, O Richard Lama, O Steven Seagal, take me, I'm yours,* and then you wake up with a head full of imaginary sex in which you were not personally involved, in which unspeakable acts are being performed on and by the body you recognize as pertaining to your beloved . . . let me assure you that at such a moment you don't think *così fan tutte,* whistle a happy tune, and turn over and go back to dreamland, you sit up ready to murder not just your little Fiordiligi, your beloved Dorabella, but whoever the rutting hog was who tempted them off the straight and narrow, just bring the bastard to me and I'll rip out his lecherous heart.

And I was wrong, all right? Wrong, wrong.

Once again I had misunderstood Ormus Cama. I'd allowed myself to forget that there was something so to speak superhuman about his love for Vina, something beyond the human capacity for loving. It was a love until the end of time, and after he failed to bring her back from the dead—after Mira made him see that Vina could not be restored to life—then women were finished for him for good. Now that Mira was just Mira he no longer wanted her to take Vina's place; even if she had come to him oiled and naked and steaming with desire, he would have simply patted her absentmindedly on the head and advised her to put some clothes on before she caught a chill.

So I admit also that Ormus's love for Vina Apsara was greater than mine, for while I had mourned Vina as I had never mourned any loss I had, after all, begun to love again. But his was a love which no other love could replace, and after Vina's three deaths he had finally entered his last celibacy, from which only the carnal embrace of death would set him free. Death was the only lover he would now accept, the only lover he would share with Vina, because that lover would reunite them forever, in the wormwood forest of the forever dead.

And lastly I admit—and I apologize to her now before the eyes of the world—that I should have trusted Mira. I was luckier than I knew: a new love had been born out of the ashes of the old. Mira wasn't interested in Ormus, or only professionally, and maybe a little bit as a way of keeping me honest. I was too stupid to believe it, but at the end of this long sad-luck saga, I was the jackpot boy.

FOUR HUNDRED years ago, Francis Bacon believed that Orpheus had to fail in his Underworld quest, that Eurydice could not be saved and that Orpheus himself had to be torn to pieces, because, for him, the Orpheus myth was the story of the failure not only of art but of civilization itself. Orpheus had to die, because culture must die. The barbarians are at the gates and cannot be resisted. Greece crumbles; Rome burns; brightness falls from the air.

ON THEIR arrival in Delhi, India's odorous high-volume importunate reality appalled Marco and Madonna Sangria, who had imagined it as being perhaps one or two steps downscale from Queens. India can be a tough country for Americans, who are seen as walking dollar signs and, what's worse, as innocents abroad: legitimate targets, easy meat. Within hours of checking in at their five-star South Delhi hotel, they had been importuned, without leaving the grounds, by money changers offering them the best black rate in town for their greenbacks, vendors of semi-precious stones which could have been polished pebbles, taxi drivers whose cousins ran a marble factory just close by, hotel-lobby palmists, young men and women of quality offering serious negotiable currency for their cameras and clothes, older men inquiring of Marco whether Madonna was, in the first place, educated and, in the second place, available, and if so, for what fee; and an elevator pickpocket who was at once incompetent and unflappable, so that when Marco pointed out that his hand was in the wrong pocket, the fellow simply extracted the offending limb, smiled broadly and said with a disarming shrug, It is an overcrowded country, what to do, we are used to treating our neighbor's pocket as our own.

Tihar Jail was, unsurprisingly, much worse. The floor alone, never mind the rooms or the prison staff and let's not even mention the inmates, just the floor was a whole horror movie, *Scream Goes East,* maybe, or *A Nightmare on Delhi Street,* the dirt, my dear, and when I say bugs, I do not refer to a famous cartoon bunny. No place, anyhow, for a high-maintenance dandy in Narciso pants to be wearing his Jimmy shoes, or for a class filly of Madonna's pedigree to risk trailing her Isaac cheesecloth skirt or her new Manolo slingbacks. And gosh, Madonna noted, people seem to talk at the tops of their *voices* all the time, and not always in English, what's *that* about?

But when Cyrus came into the interview room, shackled and manacled, Madonna suddenly started to have a very good time indeed. As she afterwards told her circle, I just felt in the presence of *wisdom,* he had this like *aura,* and I was, I don't know. Just blown *away.*

To him she said, Well, *you're* the sweetest jailbird I ever did see.

By the time they left Tihar Jail the Sangrias had sworn to launch an international campaign—celebrity fund-raisers, embassy pickets, Washington lobbyists, the works—to secure the early release of an exceptional human being. Marco returned immediately to America to set up the pressure group's HQ. Madonna remained in India, wore homespun and rope sandals, wiped the make-up off her face, pulled out her hair extensions, had henna patterns applied to the edges of her hands and the soles of her feet as if she were a bride, and visited Cyrus twice a week, which was the maximum allowable. She apologized to him for the way she looked at their first meeting—gee, I guess I looked like a *hooker, huh,* but it's my *culture,* but I so do not want to stay stuck in that like *error,* I'd like to learn your, what's the word, okay okay I remember, your *ways.*

We've been listening to the wrong Cama, she wrote to launch the Free Cyrus initiative in the first of her syndicated music columns to be filed after her arrival in India. Now let us turn from the ephemeral simplicities of Ormus's has-been rock 'n' roll to the profound contemplation of his elder brother's perennial philosophy. If we are not too old to learn, Cyrus Cama has much to teach. P.S. He's cute as a button, not that we love men for their steel buns, right? Yeah right.

During the long VTO world tour the Cyrus campaign gathered momentum. In New York, Goddess-Ma, always a trend spotter, moved out of the Rhodopé Building and denounced Ormus Cama in distinctly Cyrusian terms. *His suppression of race and skin modalities in the interests of the untenable Western dogma of universals is in reality a flight from self into the arms of the desired, admired Other.* Prominent lawyers in both New York and India took up the Cyrus case; the Indian authorities, embarrassed by the attention, indicated their willingness to be flexible; and at length Madonna Sangria proposed an attractive way forward. Hear me out, okay, she told Cyrus, all of an uncharacteristic fluster. I know this sounds like too *forward* and women in your culture just don't act this way but I guess I'm just, no, no, this is coming out all wrong, I'm saying that if I were to marry you, *okay, Cyrus?,* then you could get a *U.S. passport,* big thrill!, and we could put you on a plane and take care of you back home.

It was late in 1995, and the VTO tour was in South America, completing its last leg, when, after five months of thought, Cyrus Cama gave his reply.

Miss Madonna, when you and your brother first offered me help, I accepted, out of what I now see was weakness. You were so beautiful and persuasive and I thought, very well, if they believe in me then I am ready, I will place myself in their care and come out of my beloved Tihar. But I have also known all the time that if I came with you then soon I would feel obliged to kill you, yes, and your brother, too, and maybe also my mother who disowned me and my twin brother Ardaviraf and many other people along the way, and at the end of my journey, its only real destination and purpose, would lie the sweet murder of my younger brother Ormus, for hatred of whom I have ruined my life.

Now please see that this was most tempting. However, after due reflection, I have found it in myself to refuse. I thank you again for your interest, your declaration of love, your most generous offer of marriage, your gifts. Most particularly I thank you for providing as requested the video equipment and the tape of my brother's concert and for persuading the jail authorities to let me keep the same in my humble cell, contrary to regulations. On the video I watched my brother closely, and observed that he has already departed this life. Look in his eyes. He is dead and in Hell. So you see there is no longer any requirement for me to kill him, I am set free from the imperative of a lifetime. For me to commit other murders in this changed circumstance would be the height of bad taste, and so I will remain happily here in jail. Thanking you, Miss Madonna, and goodbye.

Now I am remembering the last things.

That winter after the end of the *Underworld* tour was the cruelest any of us could recall. Mira and I didn't see anything of Ormus, who was holed up in the Rhodopé as usual, but showed no inclination to get in touch. When I thought of him at all, I pictured him as an Indian chief who decides it's a good day to die, heads for the ground he has chosen and then just sits there waiting for the angel. But most of the time my attention was elsewhere. I had a relationship to repair. At the best of times it is hard for musicians to come home from tour. They get used to their own company, to killer schedules, nights without sleep and tearing up the floor at hot clubs around the world, to being the traveling center of the world's attention, to the coiling tension before the show, the rush of performance, the abandon and exhaustion of afterwards, the boredom with the music, the rediscovery of the music, the ups and downs with the other band members, the omnipresent sexual charge, the shipboard romances, the sense of playing hooky, of being outlaws on the run with raindrops falling on your head.

It is even harder for musicians who have taken their small children on tour. Tara Celano was old enough to go to school now, she had a place at Little Red, but while other little girls her age didn't even know the exact shape of Manhattan, Tara had circumnavigated the globe more than once and had seen more action than she was prepared to divulge, being afraid of offending her teachers' idealistic liberal sensibilities.

And the hardest return of all is the return to a steady relationship, because after the rootless years the very idea of steadiness seems like a fantasy, and in this particular case I had blotted my copybook and Mira knew it. I hadn't trusted her (hah!) with another man. In the midst of that maelstrom of infidelity I hadn't believed she could be true. There was trouble here, a problem we had to address.

I remember a Sunday in the park. It had begun to snow around Christmas and hadn't stopped. Tara loved the whiteness, space and stillness after two years of garish environments, backstage trailers and constant movement. That Sunday making snowballs she was happy being home, happy with us, and her happiness helped draw us back together, we became conscious of our joint importance in her life, of her overarching need. Such are the families of the modern epoch: elective alliances against terror or despair. This girl, this dead stranger's child, was the closest thing to a future I had found for myself anywhere in the world.

Mira took my mittened hand in hers and after that things were better between us. We went to a movie, some monsters or aliens were destroying New York as usual (this is L.A.'s way of telling Manhattan it cares), and when we got home there was a message from Clea on my voicemail.

Spenta was dead. It was cold in England too, and in a white house on a hill overlooking the Thames the octogenarian old lady had been huddling in her parlor with her "boys" around an antiquated gas fire. (Virus was sixty-three, Waldo in his mid-forties, and although they had both forgotten long ago that they weren't blood brothers, here, in truth, was another family relationship forged by circumstance rather than biology.) The heating system hadn't been serviced in years, and that night a slow leak developed under the exposed and gappy old floorboards, releasing a flow of gas which first put the three residents peacefully to sleep and then ignited, burning the great mansion to the ground and setting fire, also, to several beautiful oak trees which had stood in those grounds for over two hundred years. Ever since Spenta sequestered herself and left the details of daily life to Waldo and Virus to arrange, the house had gone into decline, and in the nearby villages after the fire people shook their heads and turned their mouths down disapprovingly. *It was an accident waiting to happen, that place,* was the general consensus. *Those sons of hers were never up to it. She should've had better sense.* The loss of the trees was, everybody agreed, a real country tragedy.

Clea's message said nothing about getting together to mourn the dead, nothing about a meeting of any kind. He just thought you'd want to know, she concluded, because of the old days. It was the last communication from Ormus I ever received.

Ormus didn't go to England for the funerals. He did send a couple of legal Singhs over for the reading of Spenta's will. When it was discovered that Spenta's only named heirs had perished with her, the assembled Methwold cousins girded themselves for battle. The house had gone, but the grounds and financial holdings were well worth a war. The Methwolds eyed the American Singh lawyers with open fear and distaste: more Indians! Will there be no end of them? Then the Singhs announced gravely that Ormus Cama wished to renounce all rights to the Methwold estate, rose to their feet, bowed courteously and left the other claimants open-mouthed, and free to fight their parochial, irrelevant, bloody, savage wars.

Although he maintained his distance from his mother's grave, her death had shaken Ormus. On the day after the reading of the will he told Clea that he was going out to walk in the frozen park alone. When she saw that it would be impossible to dissuade him she made him put on a pair of good snow boots, dressed him in his warmest coat, a navy-blue cashmere, wound his soft pashmina shawl around his neck, placed kid gloves upon his meekly extended old man's hands, and crowned him with his favorite cold-weather hat, a sixteen-dollar Chinese rabbit fur with ear flaps which Vina had bought for him in Canal Street long ago. Clea fastened the flaps with a bow knot under his chin, stood up on her tip-pytoes and kissed him on both cheeks. You're a good man, she told him. Your mother would be proud. Meaning that she thought of herself as his mother, had done so for years, but had never felt able to speak while Spenta lived. Meaning that she loved him and was as proud of him as any mother could ever be.

He smiled faintly and went down in the elevator and crossed the street and went into the park.

Of course she sent Will to follow him, but at a distance, she enjoined Will, don't you dare let him see. Which was not easy on that day of all days, the day when the snow and ice had forced all motor vehicles off the road and people were skiing down the city's empty avenues to work. New York was like the loveliest of ghost towns on that day and we were its shivering ghosts. It was a movie set and we were only actors. Reality seemed elsewhere, someplace that had not been blessed by this faery fall of snow.

He didn't walk for long. It was too cold, you could feel the air freezing the insides of your lungs. After perhaps twenty minutes he turned for home, walking briskly, and thirty-five minutes after he left he reached the high arched entrance of the Rhodopé Building. It was so cold that there was no doorman outside under the canopy. Everyone was sheltering within.

As Ormus reached the entrance, Will Singh, who was just arriving on the parkside sidewalk across from the Rhodopé, slipped and fell on the ice and sprained his right ankle. At the same moment a tall dark-skinned woman with red hair gathered above her head like a fountain stepped out of nowhere and approached Ormus. Astoundingly, given the weather conditions, she was dressed only in a sequin-glittered gold bustier, a pair of tight leather pants and stiletto heels. Her shoulders and midriff were bare.

Ormus Cama turned towards her and paused. I'm sure his eyes would have widened when he saw what she looked like, so he must have seen the small handgun that she aimed at him and emptied at point-blank range into his chest. After she had finished shooting she let go of the weapon, a .09 mm Giuliani & Koch automatic, she let it drop right there in the snow by his fallen body and walked quickly away, showing a surprising turn of speed in spite of the stilettos, turning right down a side street and vanishing from view. By the time Will Singh had hobbled slowly and painfully round the corner she was nowhere to be seen. There was a line of female footprints in the snow. Where the footprints stopped there was a red wig, a pair of leather pants, a sequinned bustier and a pair of stiletto shoes. Otherwise, nothing. No automobile tracks. Nothing, not even any witnesses, not at that time or any later date. It was as if a naked woman had flown through the air of Upper West Side Manhattan and disappeared and nobody saw a thing.

There were no prints found on the gun, either, although

Will Singh remembered (but couldn't swear) that the assassin had worn no gloves.

It was the perfect crime.

Ormus died there in the snow a few minutes later with his head in Clea's lap. Clea had been pacing up and down in the lobby, worrying, and when she heard the shots she didn't need to be told who the target was. She ran out in time to see the woman's back disappearing round the corner, and screamed at Will to get after her, but she herself stayed with her Ormus, knowing that on so brutal a day the emergency vehicles would never reach him in time, even with their snow chains they'd skid and slide on the iced surfaces if they tried to hurry, and anyhow the holes in Ormus's beautiful coat told her what she needed to know. They were clustered so close together that it was obvious nothing could be done.

Ormus, she said, sobbing, and he opened his eyes and looked at her. Oh, my Ormie, she mourned, my little shrimpy boy, what to do for you? Do you know what you want? What you need?

He looked vague and didn't reply. Then in despair she asked, Ormus, do you know who you are? You still know that, don't you? Do you know who you are?

Yes, he said. Yes, mother, I know.

BECAUSE THE murder weapon was the same make as the one known to be owned by Mira, she was briefly questioned by two embarrassed detectives. Because it was widely rumored that I had been dementedly jealous of Ormus's closeness to Mira during the *Into the Underworld* tour, I was questioned also, rather less shamefacedly. But we were each other's alibis, and Tara could vouch for both of us, and when they ran tests on Mira's gun they found it hadn't been fired in years. In the end the police decided the murderess must have been a random crazy, a loose cannon, maybe one of the many disgruntled Vina wannabes who had been sending in hate mail, in which case the use of the gun was either a coincidence or a deliberate attempt to send detectives down a false trail. When this theory was made public, several Vinas of both sexes immediately confessed to the crime, but their confessions didn't check out.

The investigators had no solution to the riddle of the

killer's disappearance. Their best guess was that she had an accomplice in one of the apartment buildings along the street where she vanished, and somehow entered the premises without leaving footprints, put on a new set of clothes and later left. Maybe the accomplice had been waiting with a broom to wipe away the traces. It was all pretty speculative, even the detectives agreed. But hey, they wound up saying, many murders are committed to which no solution is ever found. This was one such crime.

If you ask me, I think it was Vina, the real Vina, Vina Apsara herself. My Vina. No: I have to accept this too, that she was still Ormus's Vina, always and forever his. I think she came and got him because she knew how much he wanted to die. Because he couldn't bring her back from the dead she took him down with her, to be with her, where he belonged.

That's my opinion. Oh, that's right, I almost forgot to add: so to speak.

So THIS was how it came about that on an icy day in January, Mira Celano, her daughter Tara, Clea Singh and I went up from the West Side Heliport in Mo Mallick's personal helicopter with Ormus Cama's ashes in an urn on Clea's lap, to perform the last rites of a life that began on the other side of the world, a life which was in reality lived not in one place or another, but in music.

(Clea and the Singhs got generously treated in the will, by the by; they'd never go hungry again. But apart from their lump-sum payments, all Ormus's money, plus the enormous future income from his back-catalogue royalties and sheet music rights, as well as the bakeries, the winery, the real estate, the cows, in short the whole multi-million-dollar Cama estate, went to set up an Ormus and Vina memorial foundation to assist underprivileged children around the world. This will was the only indication Ormus ever gave that he regretted not having had children of his own on account of Vina's barrenness. The enormous size of the bequest was a measure of the depth of his unspoken grief.)

Tara had brought a blaster. She turned it up to top volume, because of the noise of the rotor blades, and played the last VTO CD, the one featuring her mother's stellar performance, and I didn't like to tell her that I thought it was the wrong choice, because Vina should have been with us at such a time. Below us the city stood up iced and jagged and majestic as any Himalayas. The park was empty except for a couple of skiers and a few lone walkers wrapped up like bears. The fountains and reservoir were frozen, and as I looked down on Manhattan from the sky, it still seemed to be wrapped in winter, like a gift.

The pilot insisted on doing the ash-spilling. Clea gave up the urn reluctantly, and then Ormus was flying away from us, spreading out over the city he had loved, he was a small dark cloud dispersing over the great white metropolis, losing himself in all that whiteness; he merged with it, and was gone. Let his ashes fall upon the city like kisses, I thought. Let songs spring from the sidewalks and bushes where he lies. Let music be. From Tara's music machine came the voice of Mira singing the end of the *Dies Irae,* and Mira at my side sang along.

O King of tremendous majesty
who saves the saveable for free
O fount of piety, please save me.

For no reason at all I suddenly thought of Persis Kalamanja, Persis the most beautiful girl in the world, who saved herself for Ormus and so lost herself altogether. I saw her again, still young and lovely, still standing on the roof of her long-demolished home, "Dil Kush" on Malabar Hill, Bombay, while above her the polychromatic kites of India swooped and soared, simultaneously at play and at war. Stay where you are, Persis, I thought, don't move a muscle. Don't age, don't change. Let us all become ash and scatter on the wind, but stay on your old roof, Persis, stand forever silent in the evening breeze and watch the dancers in the sky. I want to think of you this way: eternal, unchanging, immortal. Do this for me, Persis. Watch those festive kites.

I SEE in the paper today that they shot another *rai* singer. There are more and more parts of the world now where they're trying to wipe out singing altogether, where you can be murdered for carrying a tune. This particular *rai* singer had even taken the precaution of going into exile, leaving his North African home for a lightless cell in Marseilles. The killers followed him there and shot him anyway. *Pan! Pan!* Now I'm reading his obit in the *Times* and I think to myself, what a wonderful world.

Rai is music. Rai is the ungodly forbidden sound of joy.

Not long ago there was a powerful earthquake in Italy and Assisi, the town of Mira's forebears, was badly damaged. When I heard the news I didn't think of quake wars and rift bombs. I thought of Maria from the otherworld, and her teacher talking calmly to my video camera while her world crumbled around her. Maybe it's starting again, I thought. Another variant version is on a collision course with our own, and we're starting to feel the first tremors, the pre-impact vibrations. Maybe this time it's the Big Crunch and we're the ones who won't make it, however tough we've proved ourselves to be, however long we've survived. Or maybe it's not necessary to hypothesize another reality smashing into our own. Suppose the earth just got sick of our greed and cruelty and vanity and bigotry and incompetence and hate, our murders of singers and other innocents. Suppose the earth itself grew uncertain about us, or rather made up her mind just to open her jaws and swallow us down, the whole sorry lot of us. As once Zeus destroyed the human race with a flood, and only Deucalion survived to repopulate the earth's surface with beings no worse or better than the dead.

I'M UP early today, the coffee's on and I've squeezed the oranges and the muffins are warming nicely. It's the weekend. I can hear Mira and Tara in the back, arguing, laughing, fooling with Tara's mongrel, Cerberus, a grateful old stray whom we seem to have adopted. They'll be out soon. We've moved in together at the Orpheum now—after Basquiat died Mira took over his floor, so there's plenty of room—and things are good, they're good. I'm not saying there aren't problems, because there are, mainly in the traditional new baby area, but with a twist. Here I'm the one who wants a child. Mira, she's got one, and she's got a career bursting out all over, her first solo album *After* went platinum in just weeks, she's just finished work on a new movie, the offers are flooding in. This is not a good time for her to be pregnant, or so she says. But we're talking about it. It's not out of court. It's on the agenda.

There's also my past. In Mira's opinion I haven't completely got Vina out of my system. She thinks I'm still silently making comparisons, physical, psychological, vocal. I tell her that if I am, I don't mean to, and I'm doing my damnedest to stop. She's a patient woman, and she's waiting for the day.

And Tara: Tara, I love. How it is that she's growing up with Vina's wiry, springy hair, with a complexion many shades darker than her mother's, I have no idea. Perhaps Luis Heinrich had a grandmother we don't know about. Anyway, Tara and I have one important trait in common: surrounded as we have been and will always be by singers, we can't hit a note. This makes us allies, musketeers to the death in a world of non-stop mockery by the self-satisfied croony-moony élite.

"AFTER," THE title song of the album, is Mira's elegy for Ormus. You were the stranger that I needed, she sings, the wanderer who came to call. You were the changer that I heeded. Now you're just a picture on my wall. And everything is stranger after you.

In all the old stories, in different ways, the point is always reached after which the gods no longer share their lives with mortal men and women, they die or wither away or retire. They vacate the stage and leave us alone upon it, stumbling over our lines. This, the myths hint, is what a mature civilization is: a place where the gods stop jostling and shoving us and seducing our womenfolk and using our armies to lave their poxy quarrels in our children's blood; a time when they move back, still leering, still priapic, still whimsical, from the realm of the actual to the land of so to speak—Olympus, Valhalla—leaving us free to do our best or worst without their autocratic meddling.

IN MY lifetime, the love of Ormus and Vina is as close as I've come to a knowledge of the mythic, the overweening, the divine. Now that they've gone, the high drama's over. What remains is ordinary human life.

I'm looking at Mira and Tara, my islands in the storm, and I feel like arguing with the angry earth's decision to wipe us out, if indeed such a decision has been made. Here's goodness, right? The mayhem continues, I don't deny it, but we're capable also of this. Goodness drinking o.j. and munching muffins. Here's ordinary human love beneath my feet. Fall away, if you must, contemptuous earth; melt, rocks, and shiver, stones. I'll stand my ground, right here. This I've discovered and worked for and earned. This is mine.

TARA'S GOT hold of the zapper. I've never got used to having the tv on at breakfast, but this is an American kid, she's unstoppable. And today, by some fluke, wherever she travels in the cable multiverse she comes up with Ormus and Vina. Maybe it's some sort of VTO weekend and we didn't even know. I don't believe it, Tara says, zapping again and again. I don't *buh-leeve* it. Oh, *puh-leeze.* Is this what's going to happen now, for ever and *ever*? I thought they were supposed to be *dead,* but in real life they're just going to go on singing.